## GREETING

*Priest:* The Lord be with you.
*Assembly:* And with your spirit.

## PENITENTIAL ACT

I confess to almighty God
and to you, my brothers and sisters,
that I have greatly sinned,
in my thoughts and in my words,
in what I have done
    and in what I have failed to do,
    *All strike their breast as they say:*
through my fault, through my fault,
through my most grievous fault;
therefore I ask blessed Mary ever-Virgin,
all the Angels and Saints,
and you, my brothers and sisters,
to pray for me to the Lord our God.

## GLORIA

Glory to God in the highest,
and on earth peace to people of good will.

We praise you,
we bless you,
we adore you,
we glorify you,
we give you thanks for your great glory,
Lord God, heavenly King,
O God, almighty Father.

Lord Jesus Christ, Only Begotten Son,
Lord God, Lamb of God, Son of the Father,
you take away the sins of the world,
    have mercy on us;
you take away the sins of the world,
    receive our prayer;
you are seated at the right hand of the Father,
    have mercy on us.

For you alone are the Holy One,
you alone are the Lord,
you alone are the Most High,
Jesus Christ,
with the Holy Spirit,
in the glory of God the Father.
Amen.

## NICENE CREED

I believe in one God,
the Father almighty,
maker of heaven and earth
of all things visible and in

D1329357

I believe in one Lord Jesus Christ,
the Only Begotten Son of God,
born of the Father before all ages.
God from God, Light from Light,
true God from true God,
begotten, not made,
    consubstantial with the Father;
through him all things were made.
For us men and for our salvation
he came down from heaven,
    *All bow at the following words up to:*
      *and became man.*
and by the Holy Spirit was incarnate
    of the Virgin Mary,
and became man.

For our sake he was crucified under Pontius Pilate,
he suffered death and was buried,
and rose again on the third day
in accordance with the Scriptures.
He ascended into heaven
and is seated at the right hand of the Father.
He will come again in glory
to judge the living and the dead
and his kingdom will have no end.

I believe in the Holy Spirit, the Lord,
    the giver of life,
who proceeds from the Father and the Son,
who with the Father and the Son
    is adored and glorified,
who has spoken through the prophets.

I believe in one, holy, catholic and apostolic Church.
I confess one Baptism for the forgiveness of sins
and I look forward to the resurrection of the dead,
and the life of the world to come. Amen.

## PREPARATION OF THE GIFTS

*Priest:* Pray... the almighty Father.
*Assembly:* May the Lord accept the sacrifice
    at your hands
    for the praise and glory of his name,
    for our good
    and the good of all his holy Church.

## INVITATION TO HOLY COMMUNION

*Priest:* Behold... supper of the Lamb.
*Assembly:* Lord, I am not worthy
    at you should enter under my roof,
    at only say the word
    ad my soul shall be healed.

# GATHER
## THIRD EDITION

GIA PUBLICATIONS, INC.
CHICAGO

# PREFACE

In order to prepare for the implementation of the English translation of the third edition of the *Roman Missal* in Advent of 2011, it was necessary for GIA Publications, Inc. to consider the revision of several of GIA's hymnals and an updating of GIA's hymnal offerings. At this important juncture in the liturgical life of the church, and with GIA's legacy of hardbound hymnal publishing, the decision was made to create four new hymnals: a fourth edition of *Worship*, a second edition of *Lead Me, Guide Me*, a new fully bilingual Spanish-English hymnal entitled *Oramos Cantando / We Pray in Song*, and, finally, this new addition to GIA's popular *Gather* series.

The predecessor to this hymnal appeared in 2004. Normally a few more years would have passed before a new edition of *Gather* would be published. But since the new translation of the Missal is such an epic moment in the church, it was decided to review the contents of the 2004 book and offer a new edition. The 2004 edition did reflect an extensive revision of its predecessor, published in 1994. Much of the work of the editors involved in the 2004 volume was utilized in this book.

Today, we find ourselves worshiping with song in an era that has developed over the past fifty-odd years. During that time, a substantial body of repertoire has emerged and well-known favorites have surfaced. This body of musical prayer includes selections from an assortment of musical styles and historical periods, many drawn from different cultures. Chants, tunes, and hymns from centuries past have been rediscovered. Songs written in this post–Vatican II era, once thought of as particular to a certain age or ethnic group, have become "mainstream" and can be found amid the standard repertoire of most Catholic parishes. This edition of *Gather*, like its two predecessors, reflects this wonderfully diverse sacred music era in which we live. Likewise, this book tends to contain a broad selection of music in a popular style.

New to this edition are musical settings of night prayer, anointing of the sick, and marriage. The section of psalms near the beginning of the hymnal includes some of the most widely sung settings. These psalms are provided for use in various ritual celebrations, liturgy of the hours, etc. If they are used as a responsorial psalm, the norms as found in the *General Instruction of the Roman Missal* 61 apply. In keeping with the spirit of the revised *General Instruction of the Roman Missal* and the document *Liturgiam Authenticam*, all of the lectionary psalm refrains for Sundays and solemnities, set by Michel Guimont, are included near the back of this volume. The texts for the psalm verses in the Lectionary section are taken from *The Revised Grail Psalms*. Abbot Gregory Polan, OSB, and the monks of Conception Abbey, Missouri, undertook the revision of this psalm translation, which received a *recognitio* for liturgical use from the Vatican in April of 2010.

The Order of Mass includes the English chant written for the third edition of the *Roman Missal*, complete with music in place for the various dialogues. The importance of singing these brief responses, along with the various litanies and acclamations, reflects the church's desire to emphasize the significance of not just singing at liturgy but singing the liturgy itself. One can find this same musical setting in all published Roman Catholic participation aids. As time passes, this chant setting may well become one of the common settings familiar to all Roman Catholics.

Eleven more musical settings of the Order of Mass in various styles are included. Among them are a Spanish-English bilingual setting, one in an African American style, and the "Cantus Missae" in Latin. A selection of seventy-eight pieces of various service music items follows.

Many of the titles in this volume can be accompanied on either piano or organ. There are a number of selections, however, that are best experienced on the instrument for which they were written. It must be remembered that a hymnal is inherently a book for the gathered assembly. While expanded octavo versions for choir and various instruments exist for many of the titles, hymnal items have been edited to be accessible for the most commonly found resources of assembly with cantor and accompanist.

The introductions to the rites and seasons are by Gabe Huck, taken from *Worship — Third Edition*. Further acknowledgment is given to Jeffry Mickus, project director, editor, engraver, and book layout; Philip Roberts, engraver and book layout; Josh Evanovich, book layout; Clarence Reiels, proofreader; Rev. Ronald F. Krisman, text editor and indexing; and Michael Boschert, permissions editor. We gratefully acknowledge the following individuals who offered suggestions for this third edition and offered comments on the final manuscript: Tony Alonso, Michael A. Cymbala, Gary Daigle, Chris de Silva, Rob Glover, David Haas, Marty Haugen, Stephen Petrunak, and Lori True.

Soli Deo Gloria!

Alexander Harris
    Publisher
David Anderson
    Vice President
Kelly Dobbs Mickus
    Executive Editor
Kathryn R. Cuddy
Diana Macalintal
Dominic Trumfio
    Editors

# Contents

# Hymns and Songs

## Lectionary

## Indexes

# Liturgy of the Hours

When darkness gives way before the sun's light and a new day begins, people of all religions have had their rites of morning: words and songs and gestures with which to pray. It has been the same at the end of the day's light, and again in the last moments before sleep.

Christians, following the example of their Jewish ancestors, continued to pray at morning and evening and night. These moments are the hinges of daily life. As they came round each day they have been occasions to repeat what every child has learned by heart: words to praise God for a new morning, to thank the Father for Christ who is our light as evening comes, to invoke God's strong protection through the hours of night.

The daily prayers of Christians were fashioned at first from very simple things: the sign of the cross, the Lord's Prayer, a few verses and songs and short psalms, intercessions. And for most Christians morning and night remain times for such simple prayers always said by heart.

The pages of this section offer a form of daily prayer that grew from this same tradition. When Christians have gathered in the early morning, at day's end, just before retiring, the simple prayers for the individual have grown more elaborate. The daily assemblies of Christians gave shape to what became known as the divine office or "liturgy of the hours." In recent times, these prayers have been restored to some of their original simplicity and are again being prayed in parish churches and Christian households.

In using and in adapting the forms of morning, evening and night prayer given below, two things are especially important. First, these are not to be prayers which could be prayed any time. Rather, they are prayers (in word, song, gesture, silence) which are prompted by the morning itself, by the evening, by the night. Their content and pace should reflect what is unique to each of these moments. Second, the assembly's parts in these prayers should be gradually learned by heart. Simplicity, repetition and care for times of silence make it possible for these prayers to belong fully to those who assemble.

# 2 MORNING PRAISE

The Church's sense for how to pray in the morning comes from our Jewish heritage. Whatever the day, whatever the difficulties, the tradition has been to begin the day with praise for the creator. The sign of the cross, first traced on the Christian at baptism, is again made to begin the new day and its prayer. In the hymn and the psalms, in the scripture and intercessions, each one who prays and the community together finds what it is to stand at the beginning of a new day as a Christian. The morning's prayer gives the day its meaning when, through the years, these prayers become one's own.

*Stand. All make the sign of the cross.*

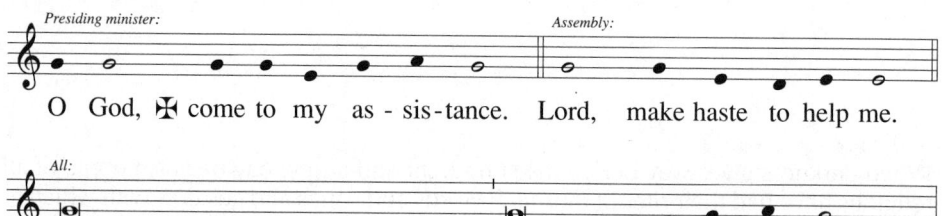

*Presiding minister:* O God, ✠ come to my as-sis-tance. *Assembly:* Lord, make haste to help me.

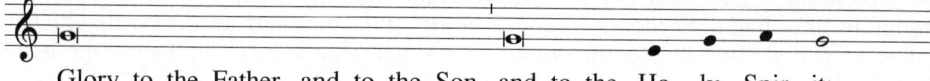

*All:* Glory to the Father, and to the Son, and to the Ho-ly Spir-it:

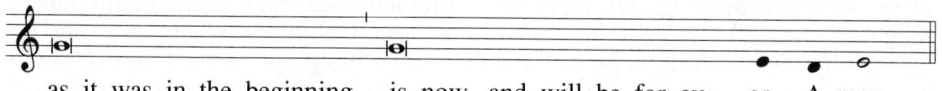

as it was in the beginning, is now, and will be for ev-er. A-men.

*Added outside Lent:*

Al - le - lu - ia.

Text: ICEL, © 1974

## MORNING HYMN

*This or another morning hymn (see nos. 854 to 856), or one related to the season or feast, may be sung.*

1. Sing your joy, pro - claim God's glo - ry!
2. All the earth is filled with re - joic - ing,
3. May we learn to be - come your King - dom.
4. Light our way, O God of the liv - ing,

Rise and sing, the morn - ing has come!
Light and life the won - der of God!
May we be your kind - ness and truth!
May we learn to see with new eyes!

Bless our God and praise all cre - a - tion;
Christ has tri - umphed! Ris - en for ev - er!
Love is our call - ing, gift of your pres - ence;
Je - sus the Lord, our pow - er and prom - ise;

Song of the earth, and light from heav - en:
Joy of our hearts, and hope of our dream - ing:
Chil - dren of God, and spir - it of Je - sus:
Light for the blind, and food for the hun - gry:

God is a - live! Al - le - lu - ia!
God is a - live! Al - le - lu - ia!
God is a - live! Al - le - lu - ia!
God is a - live! Al - le - lu - ia!

Text: David Haas, b.1957
Tune: SUMMIT HILL, Irregular; David Haas, b.1957
© 1987, GIA Publications, Inc.

## PSALMODY

*The singing of one or more psalms is a central part of morning prayer. Psalm 63, which follows, is one of the premier morning psalms. Psalm 51 is commonly substituted for Psalm 63 on Wednesday and Friday, as well as during Lent. Other appropriate psalms for morning are Psalms 5, 8, 33, 42, 47, 66, 72, 80, 85, 93, 95, 98, 100, 118, 148, 149, and 150.*

## 4   PSALM 63

*Sit*

Refrain

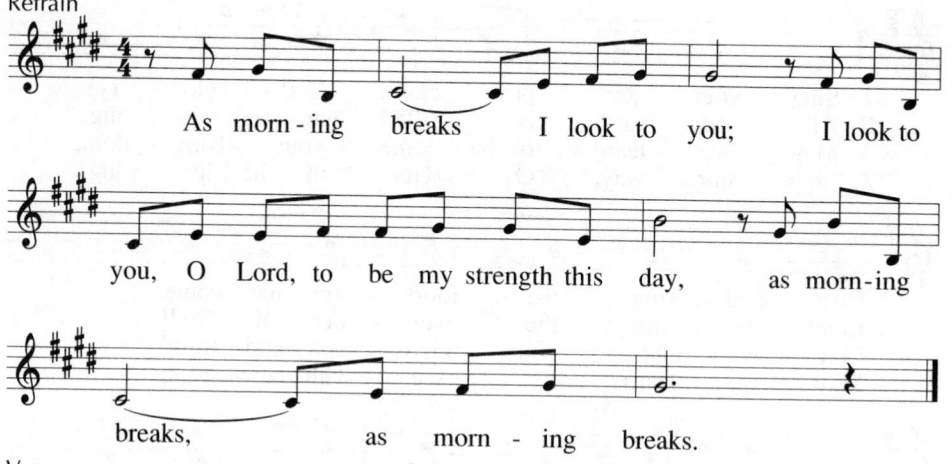

As morn-ing breaks I look to you; I look to
you, O Lord, to be my strength this day, as morn-ing
breaks, as morn - ing breaks.

Verses

1. O God, you are my God, for you I long; for you my soul is thirsting.
   My body pines for you like a dry, weary land without water.
   So I gaze on you in your holy place to see your strength and your glory.

2. For your love is better than life, my lips will speak your praise.
   So I will bless you all my life, in your name I will lift up my hands.
   My soul shall be filled as with a banquet, my mouth shall praise you with joy.

3. On my bed I remember you. On you I muse through the night
   for you have been my help; in the shadow of your wings I rejoice.
   My soul clings to you; your right hand holds me fast.

4. Glory to the Father, and to the Son, and to the Holy Spirit;
   as it was in the beginning, is now, and will be forever. Amen.

Text: Psalm 63:2–3, 4–6, 7–9; © 1963, 1986, The Grail, GIA Publications, Inc., agent; refrain trans. © 1974, ICEL
Music: Michael Joncas, © 1985, 1996, OCP

## PSALM PRAYER

*After each psalm a moment of silence is observed. This may be followed by a psalm prayer, to which all respond:* **Amen.**

## 5   WORD OF GOD

*A period of silence may follow the reading.*

## GOSPEL CANTICLE

**6**

*Stand*

Refrain

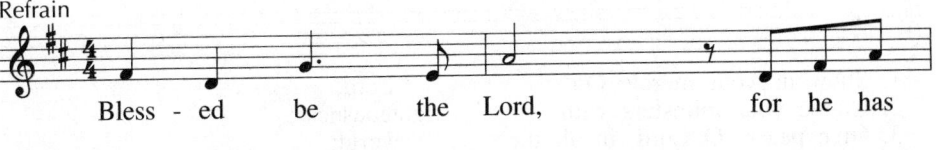

Bless - ed be the Lord, for he has

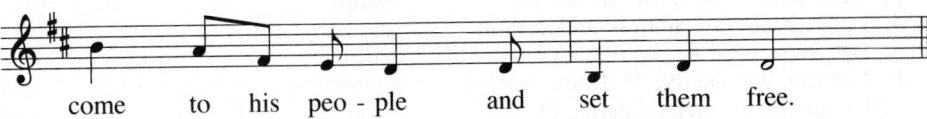

come to his peo - ple and set them free.

Verses *All make the sign of the cross.*

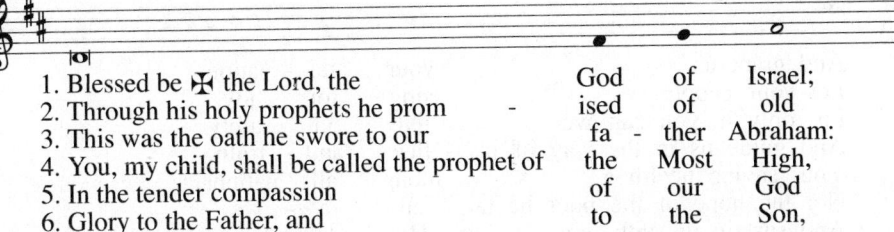

1. Blessed be ✠ the Lord, the · God of Israel;
2. Through his holy prophets he prom - ised of old
3. This was the oath he swore to our fa - ther Abraham:
4. You, my child, shall be called the prophet of the Most High,
5. In the tender compassion of our God
6. Glory to the Father, and to the Son,

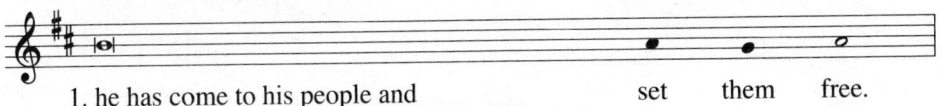

1. he has come to his people and set them free.
2. that he would save us from our enemies, from the hands of all who hate us.
3. to set us free from the hands of our enemies,
4. for you will go before the Lord to pre - pare his way,
5. the dawn from on high shall break up - on us,
6. and to the Ho - ly Spirit:

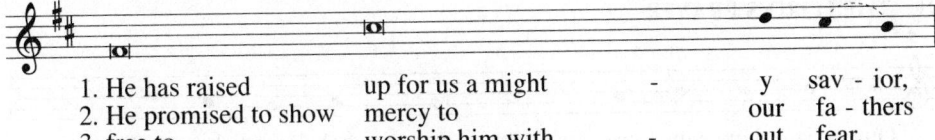

1. He has raised up for us a might - y sav - ior,
2. He promised to show mercy to our fa - thers
3. free to worship him with - out fear,
4. to give his people knowledge of sal - va - tion
5. to shine on those who dwell in darkness and the shadow of death,
6. as it was in the be - gin - ning,

**D.C.**

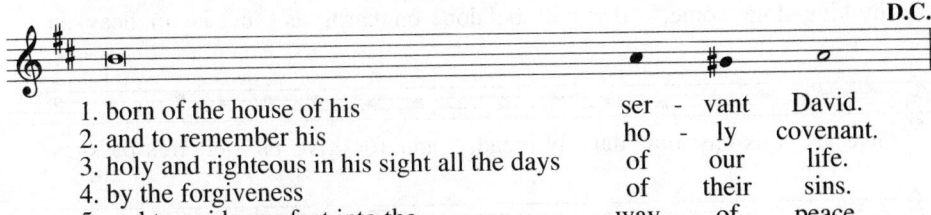

1. born of the house of his ser - vant David.
2. and to remember his ho - ly covenant.
3. holy and righteous in his sight all the days of our life.
4. by the forgiveness of their sins.
5. and to guide our feet into the way of peace.
6. is now, and will be forev - er. A - men.

Text: Luke 1:68–79; *International Consultation on English Texts*
Music: Refrain, Ronald F. Krisman, © 2011, GIA Publications, Inc.; verses, Michel Guimont, © 1994, 1998, GIA Publications, Inc.

## 7   INTERCESSIONS

*The following intercessions or similar ones may be used.*

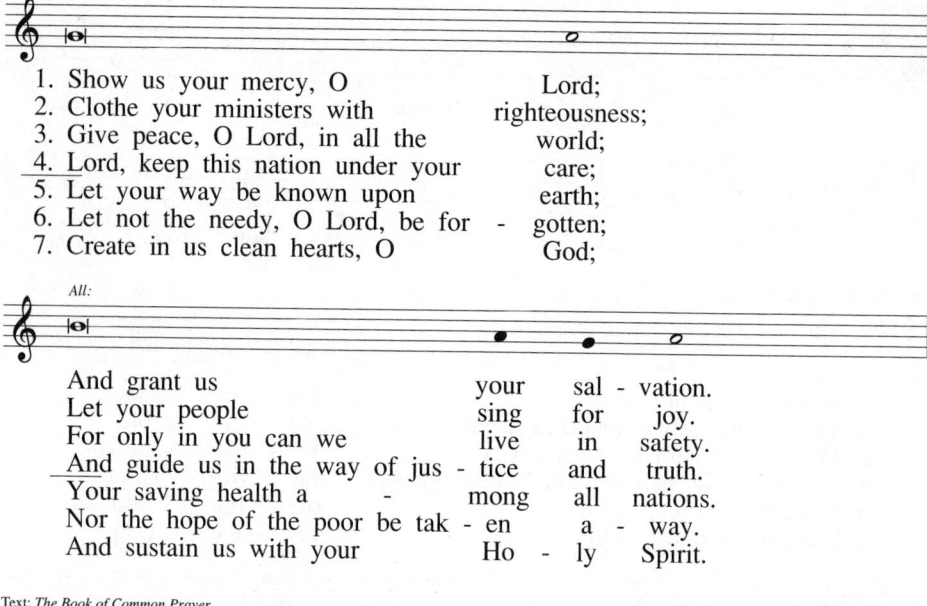

*Cantor or presiding minister:*

1. Show us your mercy, O      Lord;
2. Clothe your ministers with      righteousness;
3. Give peace, O Lord, in all the      world;
4. Lord, keep this nation under your      care;
5. Let your way be known upon      earth;
6. Let not the needy, O Lord, be for - gotten;
7. Create in us clean hearts, O      God;

*All:*

And grant us      your    sal - vation.
Let your people      sing    for    joy.
For only in you can we      live    in    safety.
And guide us in the way of jus - tice    and    truth.
Your saving health a - mong    all    nations.
Nor the hope of the poor be tak - en    a - way.
And sustain us with your      Ho - ly    Spirit.

Text: *The Book of Common Prayer*
Music: *Praise God in Song,* © 1979, GIA Publications, Inc.

## 8   THE LORD'S PRAYER

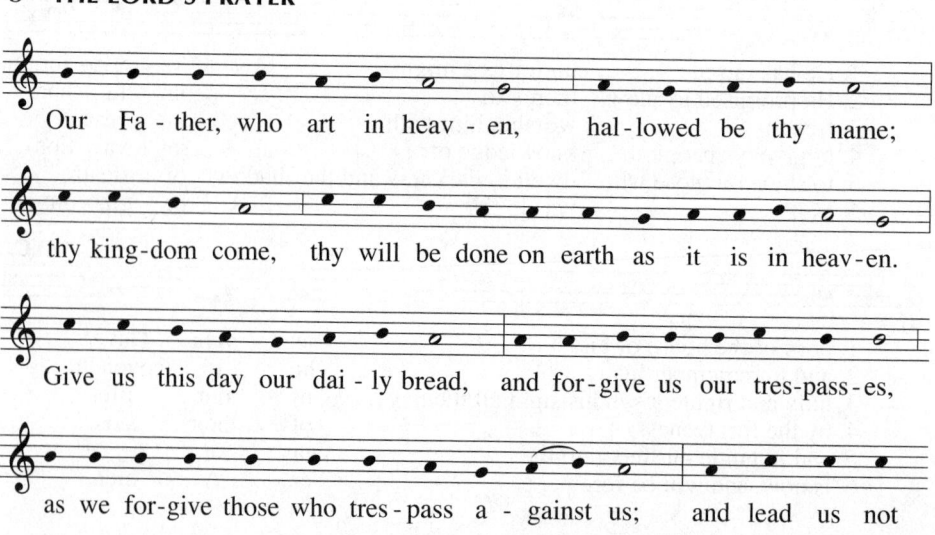

Our Fa - ther, who art in heav - en, hal - lowed be thy name;

thy king-dom come, thy will be done on earth as it is in heav - en.

Give us this day our dai - ly bread, and for - give us our tres-pass - es,

as we for - give those who tres - pass a - gainst us; and lead us not

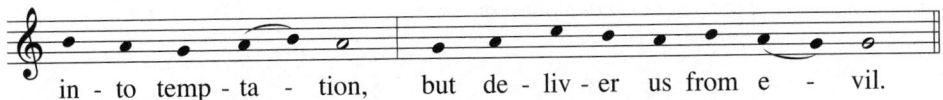

in - to temp - ta - tion, but de - liv - er us from e - vil.

Music: Traditional chant, adapt. by Robert Snow, 1964; acc. by Robert J. Batastini, © 1975, 1993, GIA Publications, Inc.

## CONCLUDING PRAYER
*All respond:* **Amen.**

## DISMISSAL

9

**A**

*Priest or deacon:*

The Lord be with you.

*Assembly:*

And with your spir - it.

*Priest or deacon:*

May almight - y God bless you, the Fa - ther,

and the Son, and the Holy Spir - it.

*All:*

A - men! A - men!

*Priest or deacon:*

Go in peace.

*Assembly:*

Thanks be to God.

Text: ICEL, © 2010
Music: Amen, Michael Joncas, © 1979, GIA Publications, Inc.

10 *Dismissal, if the leader is not a priest or deacon:*

**B**

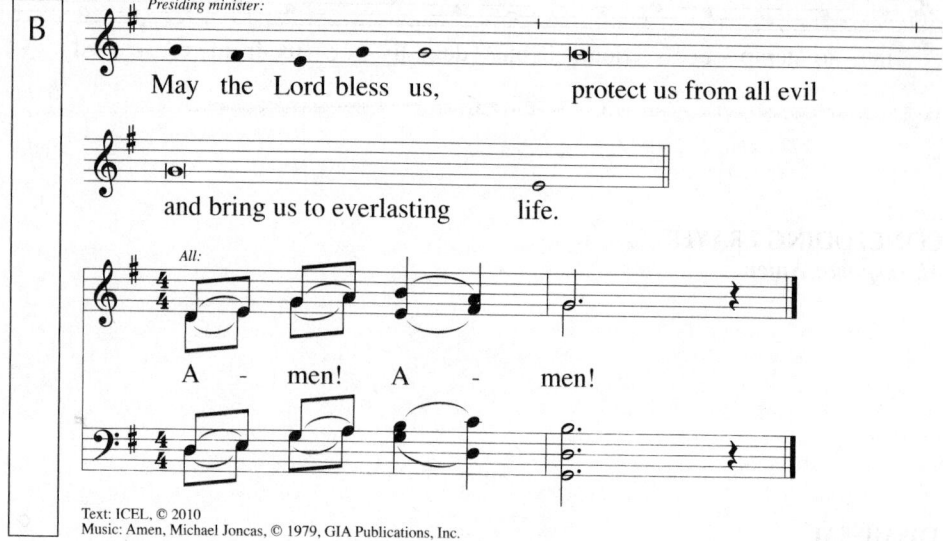

*Presiding minister:*

May the Lord bless us, protect us from all evil

and bring us to everlasting life.

*All:*

A - men! A - men!

Text: ICEL, © 2010
Music: Amen, Michael Joncas, © 1979, GIA Publications, Inc.

*All may conclude the celebration by exchanging a sign of peace.*

## 11 EVENSONG

The Church gathers in the evening to give thanks for the day that is ending. In the earliest tradition, this began with the lighting of the lamps as darkness fell and with the hymn of praise of Christ who is "radiant Light . . . of God the Father's deathless face." The evening psalms and the Magnificat bring the day just past to focus for the Christian: "God has cast down the mighty from their thrones, and has lifted up the lowly"; "God has remembered the promise of mercy, the promise made to our ancestors." Prayers of intercession are almost always part of the Church's liturgy, but those which conclude evening prayer are especially important. As day ends, the Church again and again lifts up to God the needs and sorrows and failures of all the world. Such intercession is the daily task and joy of the baptized.

*Stand. All make the sign of the cross.*

**A**

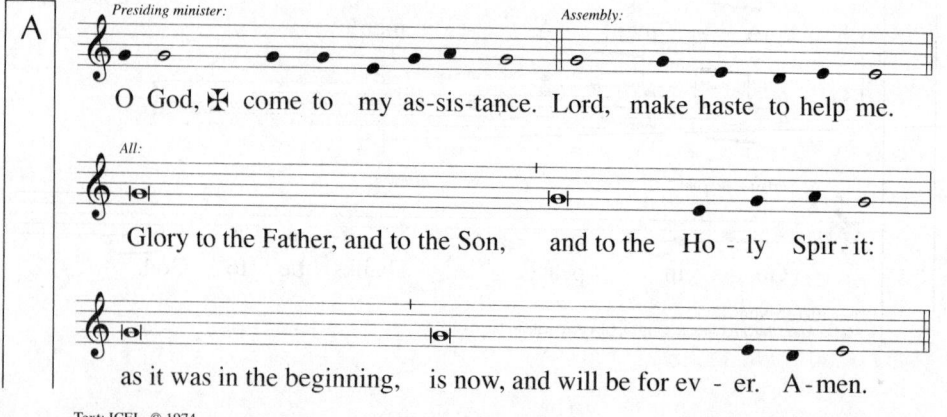

*Presiding minister:* *Assembly:*

O God, ✠ come to my as-sis-tance. Lord, make haste to help me.

*All:*

Glory to the Father, and to the Son, and to the Ho - ly Spir - it:

as it was in the beginning, is now, and will be for ev - er. A - men.

Text: ICEL, © 1974

*Added outside Lent:*

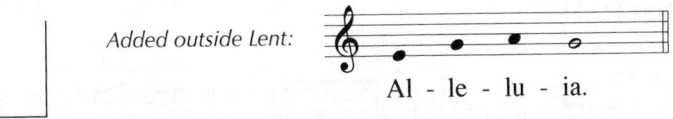

Al - le - lu - ia.

**B** *If evening prayer begins with a service of light (lucernarium), the following* 12
*greeting may be used:*

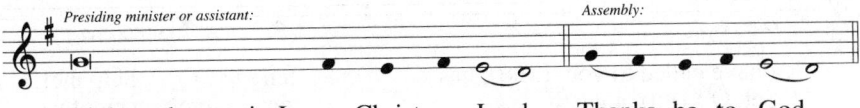

*Presiding minister or assistant:*      *Assembly:*

Light and peace in Je-sus Christ our Lord.     Thanks be to God.

## EVENING HYMN 13
*This or another evening hymn (see nos. 857 to 860), or one related to the season or feast,
may be sung.*

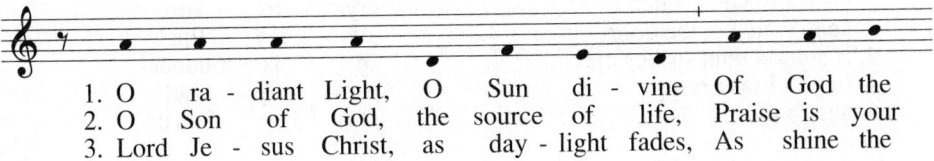

1. O   ra - diant Light,   O   Sun   di - vine   Of   God   the
2. O   Son   of   God,   the   source   of   life,   Praise   is   your
3. Lord Je - sus   Christ,   as   day - light   fades,   As   shine   the

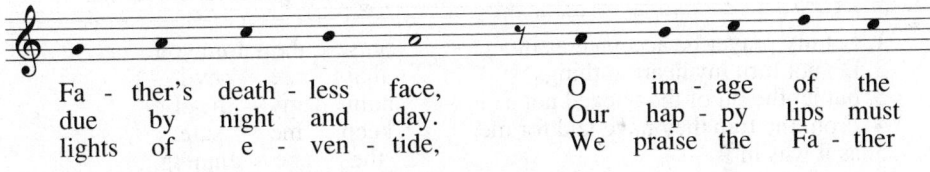

Fa - ther's   death - less   face,   O   im - age   of   the
due   by   night   and   day.   Our   hap - py   lips   must
lights   of   e - ven - tide,   We   praise   the   Fa - ther

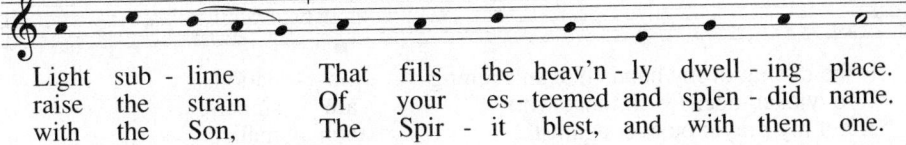

Light   sub - lime   That   fills   the   heav'n - ly   dwell - ing   place.
raise   the   strain   Of   your   es - teemed   and   splen - did   name.
with   the   Son,   The   Spir - it   blest,   and   with   them   one.

Text: *Phos Hilaron*, Greek, c.200; tr. by William G. Storey, ©
Music: JESU DULCIS MEMORIA, LM; Mode I; acc. by Richard Proulx, © 1975, GIA Publications, Inc.

*If the lucernarium is celebrated, the evening thanksgiving is now sung.*

## PSALMODY

*The singing of one or more psalms is a central part of evening prayer. Psalm 141, which
follows, is one of the premier evening psalms. It is customary to use incense as it is sung.
Other appropriate psalms for evening are Psalms 4, 19, 23, 27, 84, 91, 104, 110, 111, 112,
114, 115, 117, 118, 121, 122, 130, 136, 139, and 145.*

## 14  PSALM 141 / INCENSE PSALM

Antiphon

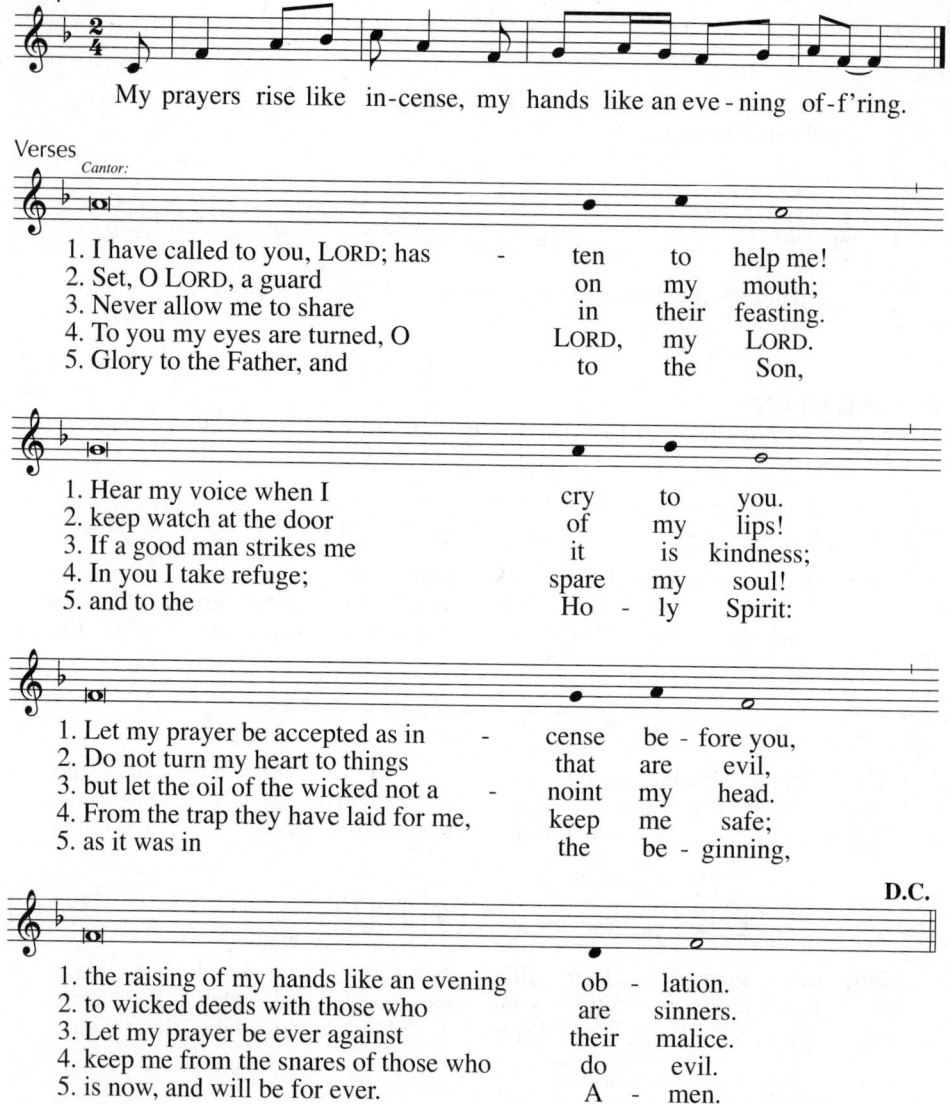

My prayers rise like in-cense, my hands like an eve-ning of-f'ring.

Verses

Cantor:

1. I have called to you, LORD; has - ten   to   help me!
2. Set, O LORD, a guard            on   my   mouth;
3. Never allow me to share         in   their feasting.
4. To you my eyes are turned, O    LORD, my   LORD.
5. Glory to the Father, and        to   the   Son,

1. Hear my voice when I            cry   to   you.
2. keep watch at the door          of   my   lips!
3. If a good man strikes me        it   is   kindness;
4. In you I take refuge;           spare my   soul!
5. and to the                      Ho - ly   Spirit:

1. Let my prayer be accepted as in - cense   be - fore you,
2. Do not turn my heart to things        that are   evil,
3. but let the oil of the wicked not a - noint my   head.
4. From the trap they have laid for me,  keep me   safe;
5. as it was in                          the  be - ginning,

D.C.

1. the raising of my hands like an evening  ob - lation.
2. to wicked deeds with those who           are   sinners.
3. Let my prayer be ever against            their malice.
4. keep me from the snares of those who     do    evil.
5. is now, and will be for ever.            A - men.

Text: Psalm 141:1–2, 3–4, 5, 8–9; *The Revised Grail Psalms*, © 2010, Conception Abbey and The Grail, admin. by GIA Publications, Inc.
Music: Howard Hughes, SM, © 1979, GIA Publications, Inc.

## PSALM PRAYER

*After each psalm a moment of silence is observed. This may be followed by a psalm prayer,
to which all respond*: **Amen.**

## 15  WORD OF GOD

*A period of silence may follow the reading.*

**GOSPEL CANTICLE** 16

*Stand*

Refrain

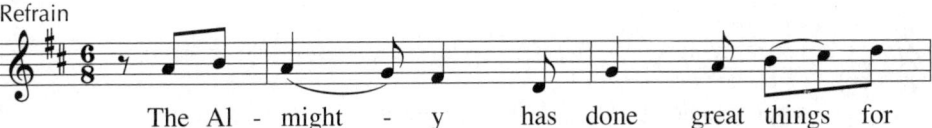

The Al - might - y has done great things for

me, and ho - ly is his Name.

Verses *All make the sign of the cross.*

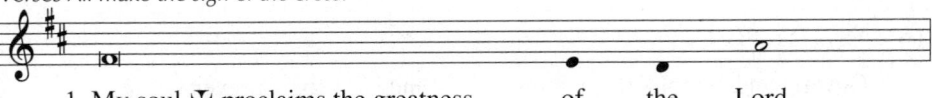

1. My soul ✠ proclaims the greatness of the Lord,
2. From this day all generations will call me blessed:
3. He has mercy on those who fear him
4. He has cast down the mighty from their thrones,
5. He has come to the help of his ser - vant Israel
6. Glory to the Father, and to the Son,

1. my spirit rejoices in God my Savior
2. the Almighty has done great things for me,
3. in every gen - er - ation.
4. and has lifted up the lowly.
5. for he has remembered his prom - ise of mercy,
6. and to the Ho - ly Spirit:

1. [ ──────────────────────────────────── ]
2. [ ──────────────────────────────────── ]
3. He has shown the strength of his arm,
4. He has filled the hungry with good things,
5. the promise he made to our fathers,
6. as it was in the be - ginning, is now,

D.C.

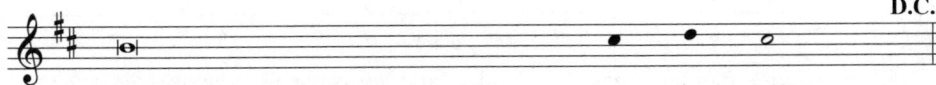

1. for he has looked with favor on his low - ly servant.
2. and holy is his Name.
3. he has scattered the proud in their con - ceit.
4. and the rich he has sent a - way empty.
5. to Abraham and his chil - dren for ever.
6. and will be for ev - er. A - men.

Text: Luke 1:46–55; *International Consultation on English Texts*
Music: Refrain, Ronald F. Krisman, © 2011, GIA Publications, Inc.; verses, Michel Guimont, © 1994, 1998, GIA Publications, Inc.

## 17  INTERCESSIONS

*The following intercessions or similar ones may be used.*

*Cantor or presiding minister:*

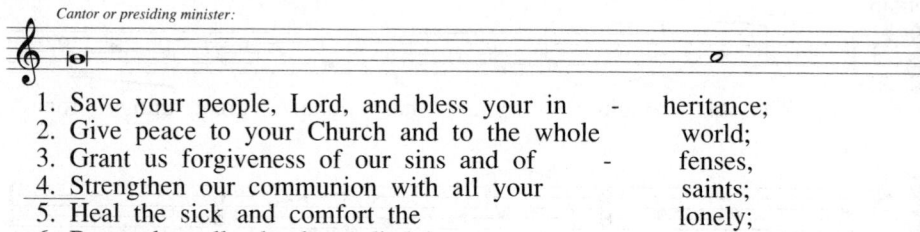

1. Save your people, Lord, and bless your in  -  heritance;
2. Give peace to your Church and to the whole      world;
3. Grant us forgiveness of our sins and of  -      fenses,
4. Strengthen our communion with all your      saints;
5. Heal the sick and comfort the      lonely;
6. Remember all who have died in your      mercy;
7. In you, Lord, is our      hope;

*All:*

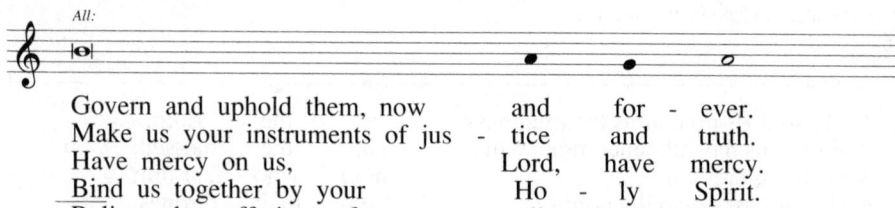

Govern and uphold them, now    and    for - ever.
Make us your instruments of jus  -  tice    and    truth.
Have mercy on us,    Lord,    have    mercy.
Bind us together by your    Ho  -  ly    Spirit.
Relieve the sufferings of    all    your    people.
Welcome them into the light    of    your    kingdom.
And we shall never    hope    in    vain.

Text: Adapted from *The Book of Common Prayer*
Music: *Praise God in Song,* © 1979, GIA Publications, Inc.

## 18  THE LORD'S PRAYER

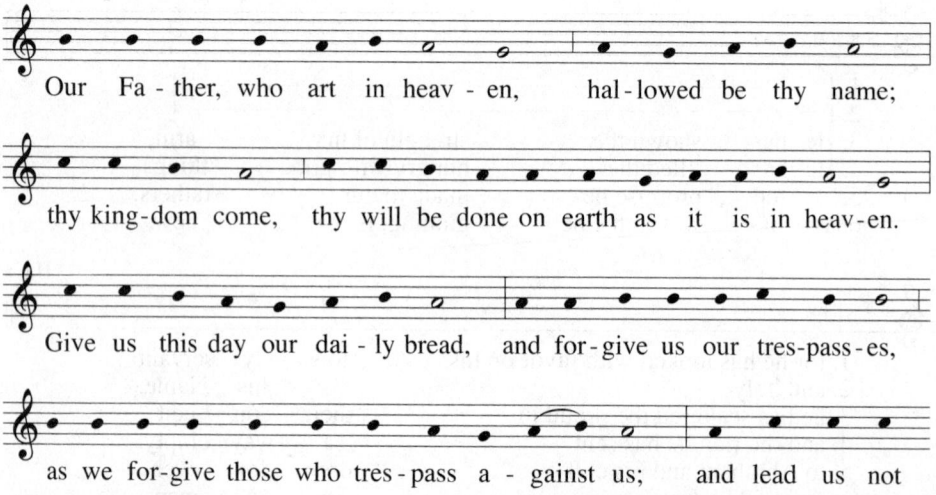

Our   Fa - ther, who   art   in   heav - en,      hal - lowed   be   thy   name;

thy   king-dom   come,   thy   will   be   done on   earth   as   it   is   in   heav-en.

Give   us   this day   our   dai - ly   bread,   and   for-give   us   our   tres-pass-es,

as   we   for-give   those   who   tres - pass   a - gainst   us;      and   lead   us   not

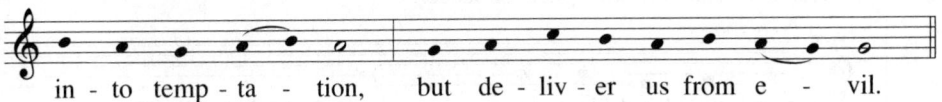

in - to temp - ta - tion, but de - liv - er us from e - vil.

Music: Traditional chant, adapt. by Robert Snow, 1964; acc. by Robert J. Batastini, © 1975, 1993, GIA Publications, Inc.

## CONCLUDING PRAYER
*All respond:* **Amen.**

## DISMISSAL

19

A

*Priest or deacon:*   *Assembly:*

The Lord be with you. And with your spir - it.

*Priest or deacon:*

May almight - y God bless you, the Fa - ther,

and the Son, and the Holy Spir - it.

*All:*

A - men! A - men!

*Priest or deacon:*   *Assembly:*

Go in peace. Thanks be to God.

Text: ICEL, © 2010
Music: Amen, Michael Joncas, © 1979, GIA Publications, Inc.

**20**  *Dismissal, if the leader is not a priest or deacon:*

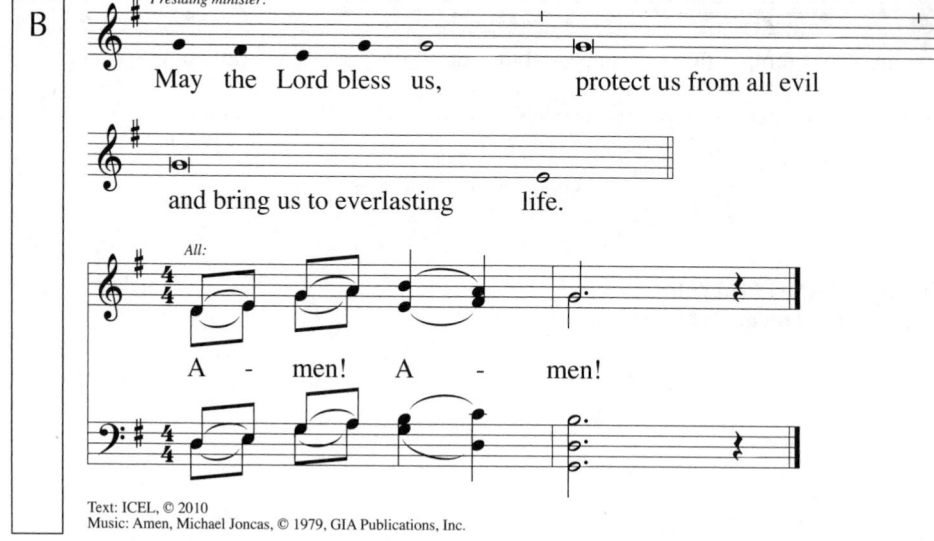

May the Lord bless us, protect us from all evil

and bring us to everlasting life.

All:

A - men! A - men!

Text: ICEL, © 2010
Music: Amen, Michael Joncas, © 1979, GIA Publications, Inc.

*All may conclude the celebration by exchanging a sign of peace.*

## 21  NIGHT PRAYER

The Church's prayers at night are direct and simple. The Christian remembers with sorrow the day's evil and failure, and places this before the mercy of God. Before surrendering to sleep, there is prayer for God's protection through the night and an expression of acceptance: "Now, Lord, you may dismiss your servant." The night prayer concludes by binding together the sleep of this night with the final falling asleep in the Lord: "May the all-powerful Lord grant us a restful night and a peaceful death." Night's last words are often a gentle invocation of our mother, "When this exile is ended, show us your womb's blessed fruit, Jesus."

*Stand. All make the sign of the cross.*

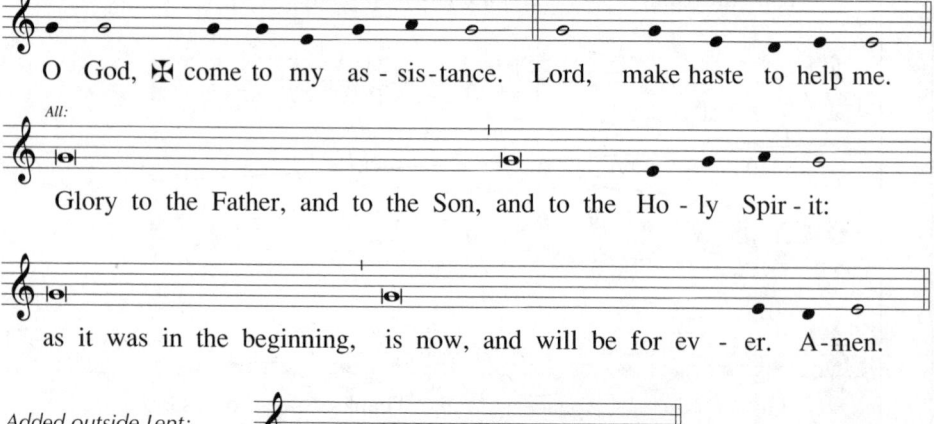

Presiding minister:

O God, ✠ come to my as - sis - tance. Lord, make haste to help me.

All:

Glory to the Father, and to the Son, and to the Ho - ly Spir - it:

as it was in the beginning, is now, and will be for ev - er. A-men.

*Added outside Lent:*

Al - le - lu - ia.

Text: ICEL, © 1974

*A brief examination of conscience may be made. At its conclusion, the following may be said:*

| Optional |
|---|

**I confess to almighty God
and to you, my brothers and sisters,
that I have greatly sinned,
in my thoughts and in my words,
in what I have done and in what I have failed to do,**

*All strike their breast as they say:*

**through my fault, through my fault,
through my most grievous fault;
therefore I ask blessed Mary ever-Virgin,
all the Angels and Saints,
and you, my brothers and sisters,
to pray for me to the Lord our God.**

# HYMN                                                        22

*This or another evening hymn (see nos. 858 to 860), or one related to the season or feast, may be sung.*

1. Be - fore the end - ing of the day, Cre - a - tor
2. Let ev - 'ry heart rest free from fear, At peace, to
3. Let peace - ful rest the strength re - new Of all who
4. Al - might - y Fa - ther, hear our cry Through Je - sus

of the world, we pray: Pro - tect us by your
feel your pres - ence near; Our souls, through night hours
place their trust in you; Let e - vil nev - er
Christ, our Lord most high, And with the Spir - it,

love and might, And keep us safe through - out the night.
veiled in sleep, In your blest light, their vig - il keep.
have its way; Pre - serve us for an - oth - er day.
Par - a - clete, Whose reign the end - less a - ges greet.

Text: *Te Lucis Ante Terminum*, 7th C.; tr. by Peter Scagnelli, ©
Music: TE LUCIS ANTE TERMINUM, LM; adapt. by Howard Hughes, SM, © 1982, GIA Publications, Inc.

# PSALMODY

*The following setting, or one of the proper psalms for night prayer, may be sung. The proper psalms are: Sunday, Psalm 91; Monday, Psalm 86; Tuesday, Psalm 143; Wednesday, Psalms 31 and 130; Thursday, Psalm 16; Friday, Psalm 88; and Saturday, Psalms 4 and 134.*

**23  PSALM 134**

Antiphon

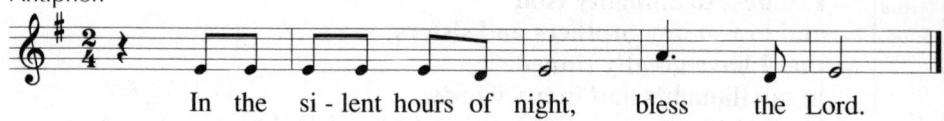

In the si - lent hours of night, bless the Lord.

Verses

1. O come, bless the LORD,
   all you servants of the LORD,
   who stand by night in the house of the LORD,
   in the courts of the house of the LORD.

2. Lift up your hands to the holy place,
   and bless the LORD.

3. May the LORD bless you from Sion,
   he who made both heaven and earth.

4. Glory to the Father, and the Son,
   and to the Holy Spirit:
   as it was in the beginning, is now,
   and will be for ever. Amen.

Text: Psalm 134; *The Revised Grail Psalms*, © 2010, Conception Abbey and The Grail, admin. by GIA Publications, Inc.; refrain text, from
  *Praise God in Song*, © 1979, GIA Publications, Inc.
Music: Howard Hughes, SM, © 1979, GIA Publications, Inc.

*After the psalm a moment of silence is observed.*

**24  WORD OF GOD**

*A period of silence may follow the reading.*

**25  RESPONSORY**

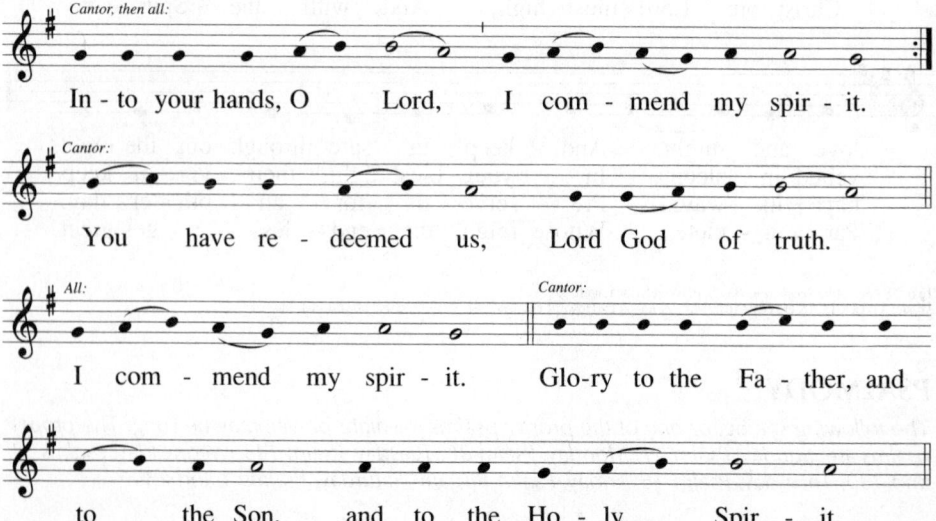

Cantor, then all:

In - to your hands, O Lord, I com - mend my spir - it.

Cantor:

You have re - deemed us, Lord God of truth.

All:

I com - mend my spir - it.

Cantor:

Glo-ry to the Fa - ther, and

to the Son, and to the Ho - ly Spir - it.

In - to your hands, O Lord, I com - mend my spir - it.

Text: *Liturgy of the Hours*, © 1974, ICEL
Music: IN MANUS TUAS; Sarum Tone, adapt. by Richard Proulx, © 1986, GIA Publications, Inc.

## GOSPEL CANTICLE 26

Refrain

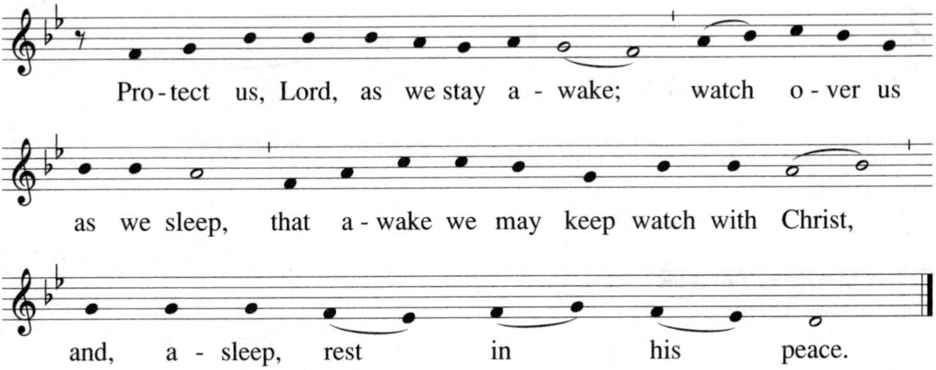

Pro - tect us, Lord, as we stay a - wake; watch o - ver us

as we sleep, that a - wake we may keep watch with Christ,

and, a - sleep, rest in his peace.

Verse 1 *All make the sign of the cross.*

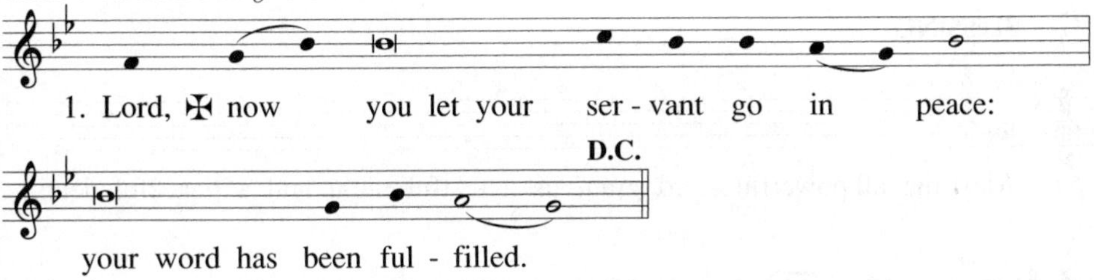

1. Lord, ✠ now you let your ser - vant go in peace:

D.C.

your word has been ful - filled.

Verse 2

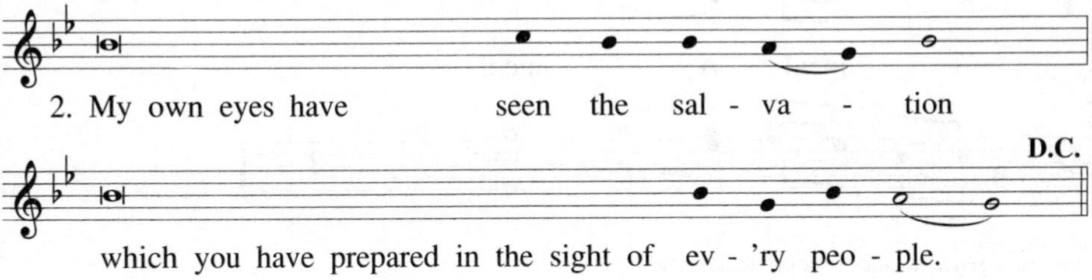

2. My own eyes have seen the sal - va - tion

D.C.

which you have prepared in the sight of ev - 'ry peo - ple.

Verse 3

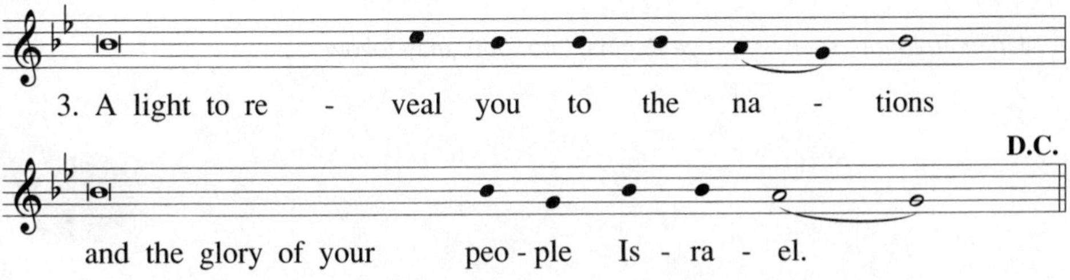

3. A light to re - veal you to the na - tions

D.C.

and the glory of your peo - ple Is - ra - el.

Verse 4

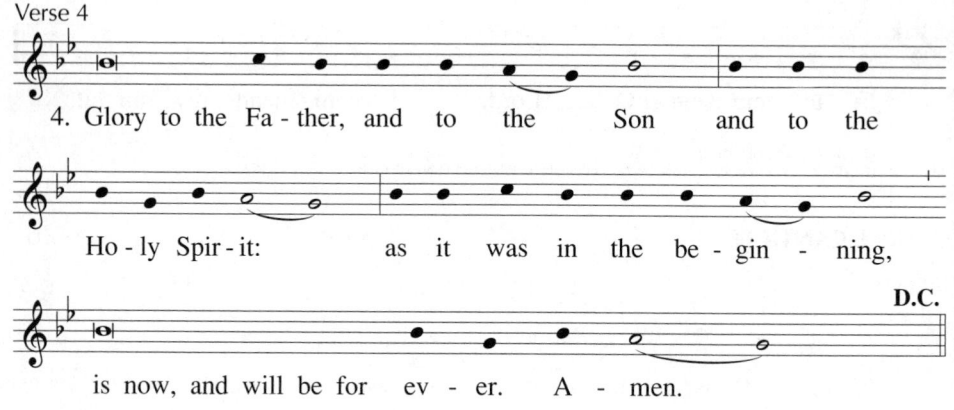

4. Glory to the Fa - ther, and to the Son and to the

Ho - ly Spir - it: as it was in the be - gin - ning,

D.C.

is now, and will be for ev - er. A - men.

Text: Antiphon from *Liturgy of the Hours*, © 1974, ICEL.; verses, Luke 2:29–32; *International Consultation on English Texts*
Music: Sarum tone, adapt. by Richard Proulx, © 1986, GIA Publications, Inc.

## CONCLUDING PRAYER
*All respond:* **Amen.**

## 27  BLESSING

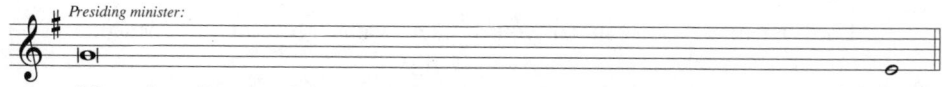

*Presiding minister:*

May the all-powerful Lord grant us a restful night and a peaceful death.

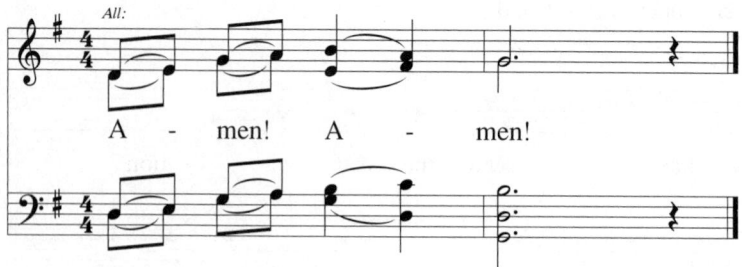

*All:*

A - men! A - men!

Text: ICEL, © 1974
Music: Amen, Michael Joncas, © 1979, GIA Publications, Inc.

*A Marian antiphon, such as "Salve Regina," no. 880, may follow.*

# Psalm 15: They Who Do Justice   28

**Refrain**

They who do jus-tice will live in the pres-ence of God!

They who do jus-tice will live in the pres-ence of God!

**Verses**

1. Those who walk blamelessly and live their lives doing justice,
   who keep the truth in their heart, and slander not with their tongue!

2. Who harm not another, nor take up reproach to their neighbor,
   who hate the sight of the wicked, but honor the people of God!

3. Who show no condition in sharing the gifts of their treasure,
   who live not off the poor: They will stand firm forever!

Text: Psalm 15:2–5; David Haas, © 1989, GIA Publications, Inc.; refrain trans. © 1969, ICEL
Music: David Haas, © 1989, GIA Publications, Inc.

# 29   Psalm 16: Keep Me Safe, O God

Refrain

Keep me safe, O God: you are my hope;

you are my hope, O God.

Verses

1. I say to God, "you are my only God, I have no good except in you."

2. I find in God always my cup of joy; and God will keep my life secure.

3. I bless my God: God who has counseled me. At night my heart gives counsel too.

4. I keep my God always before my eyes; with God beside me I'm secure.

5. And so my heart always is glad in God; my body too shall dwell secure.

6. For you will not ever abandon me, or let your servant lose the path.

7. The path of life you have revealed to me, and in your presence is my joy.

Text: Psalm 16:2, 5, 7, 8, 9, 10, 11; John Foley, SJ, © 1993, GIA Publications, Inc.; refrain trans. © 1969, ICEL
Music: John Foley, SJ, © 1993, GIA Publications, Inc.

# Psalm 16: You Will Show Me the Path of Life    30

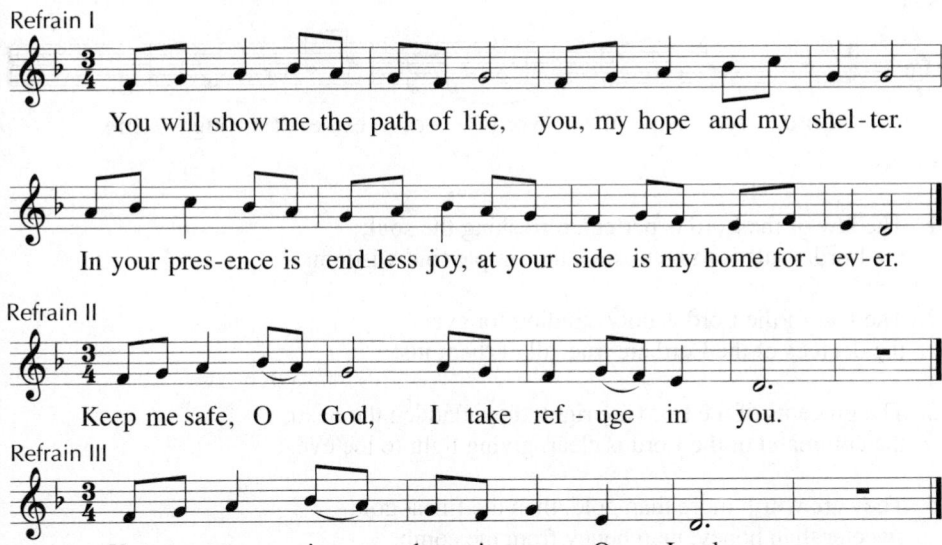

Refrain I

*You will show me the path of life, you, my hope and my shel-ter.*

*In your pres-ence is end-less joy, at your side is my home for - ev-er.*

Refrain II

*Keep me safe, O God, I take ref - uge in you.*

Refrain III

*You are my in - her - i - tance, O Lord.*

Verses

1. Faithful God, I look to you, you alone my life and fortune,
   never shall I look to other gods, you shall be my one hope.

2. From of old you are my heritage, you my wisdom and my safety,
   through the night you speak within my heart, silently you teach me.

3. So my heart shall sing for joy, in your arms I rest securely,
   you will not abandon me to death, you shall not desert me.

Text: Psalm 16:1–2, 6–8, 9–10; Marty Haugen, © 1988, GIA Publications, Inc.; refrain III trans., © 1969, ICEL
Music: Marty Haugen; refrain II and III adapt. by Diana Kodner, © 1988, 1994, GIA Publications, Inc.

# 31 Psalm 19: Lord, You Have the Words

Refrain

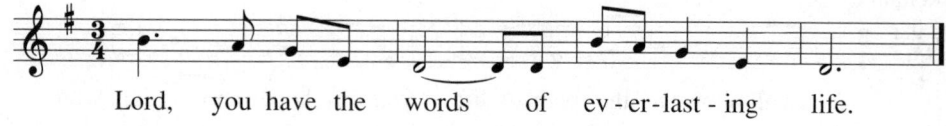

Lord, you have the words of ev-er-last-ing life.

Verses

1. The law of the Lord is perfect, refreshing the soul;
   the Lord's rule is to be trusted, the simple find wisdom.

2. The fear of the Lord is holy, abiding for ever;
   the decrees of the Lord are true, all of them just.

3. The precepts of the Lord are right, they gladden the heart,
   the command of the Lord is clear, giving light to the eye.

4. They are worth more than gold, than the finest gold,
   sweeter than honey, than honey from the comb.

Text: Psalm 19:8, 9, 10, 11; David Haas, © 1983, GIA Publications, Inc.; refrain trans. © 1969, ICEL
Music: David Haas, © 1983, GIA Publications, Inc.

# 32 Psalm 19: Words of Everlasting Life / Palabras de Vida Eterna

Bilingual Refrain

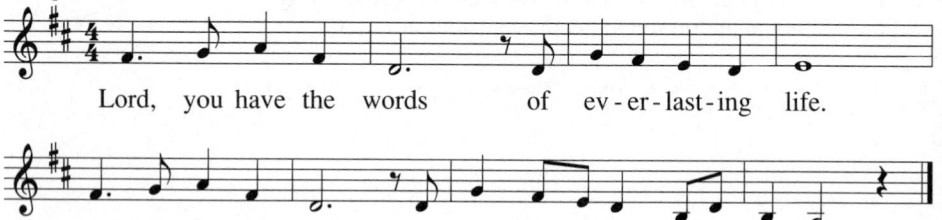

Lord, you have the words of ev-er-last-ing life.

Tú tie-nes, Se - ñor, pa - la - bras de vi - da e - ter -na.

Verses

1. The law of the LORD is perfect; it revives the soul.
   The decrees of the LORD are steadfast; they give wisdom to the simple.

2. The precepts of the LORD are right; they gladden the heart.
   The command of the LORD is clear; it gives light to the eyes.

3. The fear of the LORD is pure, abiding forever.
   The judgments of the LORD are true; they are, all of them, just.

4. They are more to be desired than gold, than quantities of gold.
   And sweeter are they than honey, than honey flowing from the comb.

1. *La ley del Señor es perfecta y es descanso del alma;*
   *fieles las palabras del Señor, instruyen al ignorante.*

2. *Los mandatos del Señor son rectos y alegran el corazón;*
   *Son luz los preceptos del Señor alumbrando el camino.*

3. *La voluntad de Dios es santa y para siempre estable;*
   *los mandatos del Señor son verdaderos y enteramente justos.*

4. *Más preciosos que el oro y las piedras más finas;*
   *y más dulces que la miel de un panal que gotea.*

Text: Psalm 19:8, 9, 10, 11; *The Revised Grail Psalms*, © 2010, Conception Abbey and The Grail, admin. by GIA Publications, Inc.; English refrain
trans. © 1969, ICEL; Spanish refrain trans. © admin. by Obra Nacional de la Buena Prensa
Music: Tony E. Alonso, © 2003, GIA Publications, Inc.

## Psalm 22: My God, My God    33

Refrain

My God,  my God,  O why have you a - ban - doned me?

Verses

1. All who see me laugh at me, they mock me and they shake their heads:
   "He relied on the Lord, let the Lord be his refuge."

2. As dogs around me, they circle me about.
   Wounded me and pierced me, I can number all my bones.

3. My clothing they divided, for my garments casting lots,
   O Lord, do not desert me, but hasten to my aid.

4. I will praise you to my people, and proclaim you in their midst,
   O fear the Lord, my people, give glory to God's name.

Text: Psalm 22:8–9, 17–18, 19–20, 23–24; Marty Haugen, © 1983, GIA Publications, Inc.; refrain trans. © 1969, ICEL
Music: Marty Haugen, © 1983, GIA Publications, Inc.

# 34  Psalm 23: My Shepherd Is the Lord

**Antiphon I**

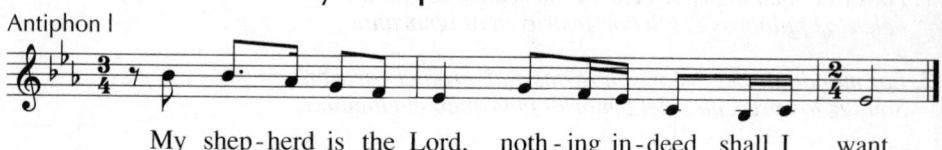

My shep-herd is the Lord, noth-ing in-deed shall I want.

Text: Psalm 23; The Grail
Music: Joseph Gelineau, SJ
© 1963, The Grail, GIA Publications, Inc., agent

**Antiphon II**

The Lord is my shep-herd, noth-ing shall I want: he

leads me by safe paths, noth - ing shall I fear.

Text: Psalm 23; The Grail
Music: A. Gregory Murray, OSB
© 1963, The Grail, GIA Publications, Inc., agent

**Psalm Tone**

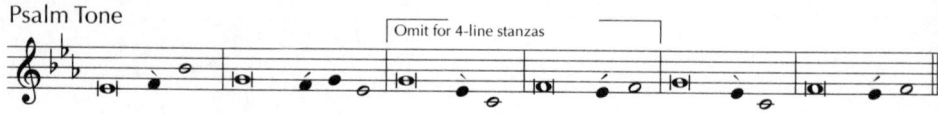

Omit for 4-line stanzas

Music: Richard Proulx, © 1975, GIA Publications, Inc.

**Gelineau Tone**

Omit for 4-line stanzas

The **LORD** is my **shep**herd;
there is **noth**ing Í shall **want**.
2 **Fresh** and **green** are thè **pastures**
where he **gives** me ré**pose**.
Near **restful wa**ters hè **leads** me;
3 **he** revives mỳ **soul**.

He **guides** me a**long** the rìght **path**,
for the **sake** óf his **name**.
4 **Though** I should **walk** in thè **valley**
of the **shad**ow óf **death**,
no **e**vil would I **fear**, for you áre
**with** me.
Your **crook** and your **staff** will give
mè **comfort**.

5 You have pre**pared** a **ta**ble bè**fore** me
in the **sight** óf my **foes**.
My **head** you have a**noint**ed wìth **oil**;
my **cup** is ové**rflow**ing.

6 Surely **good**ness and **mer**cy shàll
**fol**low me
all the **days** óf my **life**.
In the **LORD's** own **house** shall Ì **dwell**
for **length** of days ú**nend**ing.

To the **Father** and **Son** gìve **glory**,
give **glory** tó the **Spir**it.
To God who **is**, who **was**, and whò **will**
be,
for **ever** ánd **ever**.

Text: Psalm 23; *The Revised Grail Psalms*, © 2010, Conception Abbey and The Grail, admin. by GIA Publications, Inc.
Music: Joseph Gelineau, SJ, © 1963, The Grail, GIA Publications, Inc., agent

# Psalm 23: Shepherd Me, O God    35

**Refrain**

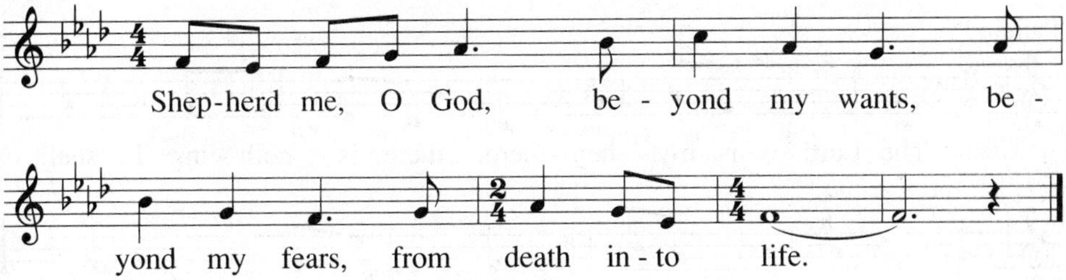

Shep-herd me, O God, be - yond my wants, be -

yond my fears, from death in - to life.

**Verses**

1. God is my shepherd, so nothing shall I want;
   I rest in the meadows of faithfulness and love;
   I walk by the quiet waters of peace.

2. Gently you raise me and heal my weary soul;
   you lead me by pathways of righteousness and truth;
   my spirit shall sing the music of your name.

3. Though I should wander the valley of death,
   I fear no evil, for you are at my side;
   your rod and your staff, my comfort and my hope.

4. You have set me a banquet of love in the face of hatred,
   crowning me with love beyond my pow'r to hold.

5. Surely your kindness and mercy follow me all the days of my life;
   I will dwell in the house of my God forevermore.

Text: Psalm 23; Marty Haugen
Music: Marty Haugen
© 1986, GIA Publications, Inc.

# 36 Psalm 23: The Lord Is My Shepherd / El Señor Es Mi Pastor

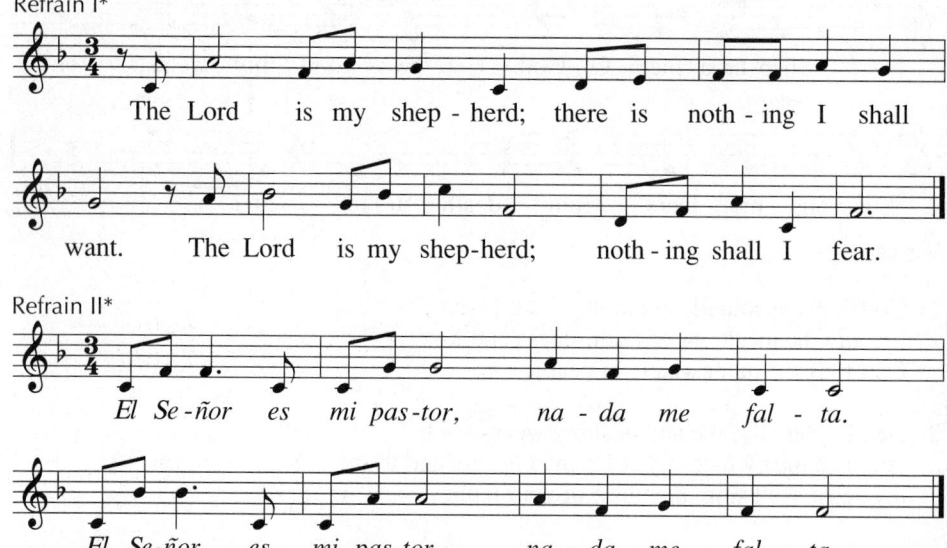

Refrain I*

The Lord is my shep-herd; there is noth-ing I shall want. The Lord is my shep-herd; noth-ing shall I fear.

Refrain II*

El Se-ñor es mi pas-tor, na-da me fal-ta.

El Se-ñor es mi pas-tor, na-da me fal-ta.

Verses

1. The LORD is my shepherd;
   there is nothing I shall want.
   Fresh and green are the pastures
   where he gives me repose.
   Near restful waters he leads me;
   he revives my soul.

2. He guides me along the right path,
   for the sake of his name.
   Though I should walk in the valley of the
      shadow of death,
   no evil would I fear, for you are with me.
   Your crook and your staff will give
      me comfort.

3. You have prepared a table before me
   in the sight of my foes.
   My head you have anointed with oil;
   my cup is overflowing.

4. Surely goodness and mercy shall
      follow me
   all the days of my life.
   In the LORD's own house shall I dwell
   for length of days unending.

1. El Señor es mi pastor, nada me falta:
   en verdes praderas me hace recostar;
   me conduce hacia fuentes tranquilas
   y repara mis fuerzas.

2. Me guía por el sendero justo,
   por el honor de su nombre.
   Aunque camine por cañadas oscuras,
   nada temo, porque tú vas conmigo:
   tu vara y tu cayado
   me sosiegan.

3. Preparas una mesa ante mí,
   enfrente de mis enemigos,
   me unges la cabeza con perfume,
   y mi copa rebosa.

4. Tu bondad y tu misericordia
   me acompañan
   todos los días de mi vida,
   y habitaré en la casa del Señor,
   por años sin término.

*Refrains I and II may be sung simultaneously.

Text: Psalm 23: *The Revised Grail Psalms*, © 2010, Conception Abbey and The Grail, admin. by GIA Publications, Inc.; refrain trans. © 1969, ICEL;
Spanish refrain, *Leccionario, Edición Hispanoamérica*, and verses, © 1970, 1972, Conferencia Episcopal Española
Music: Ronald F. Krisman; verses, Michel Guimont, © 1994, 1998, 2004, GIA Publications, Inc.

# Psalm 24: We Long to See Your Face    37

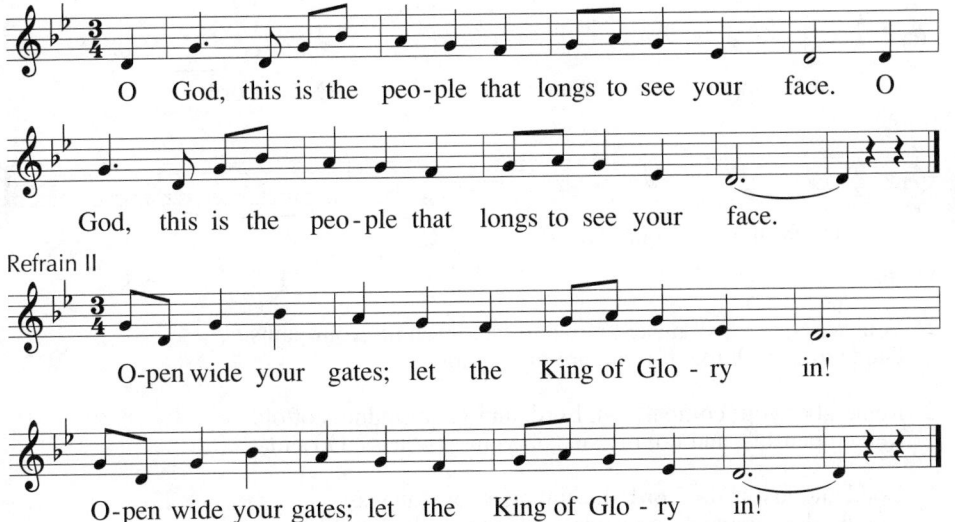

Refrain I

O God, this is the peo-ple that longs to see your face. O
God, this is the peo-ple that longs to see your face.

Refrain II

O-pen wide your gates; let the King of Glo-ry in!
O-pen wide your gates; let the King of Glo-ry in!

Verses

1. All the earth is yours, O God, the world and those who dwell on it.
   You have founded it upon the seas and established it upon the rivers.

2. Who can ascend your mountain, God? Or who may stand in this holy place?
   Those whose hands are sinless, hearts are clean, and desire not the vanity of earth.

3. They shall receive your blessing, God, their Savior shall reward them.
   Such is the face that seeks for you, that seeks your face, O God of Jacob.

Text: Psalm 24:1–2, 3–4, 5–6; Kevin Keil, © 1993, GIA Publications, Inc.; refrain 1 trans. © 1969, ICEL
Music: Kevin Keil, © 1993, GIA Publications, Inc.

# 38 Psalm 25: Remember Your Mercies

Refrain I

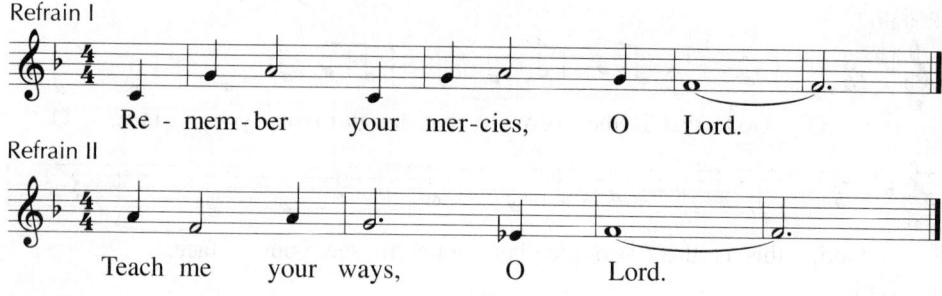

Re - mem - ber your mer-cies, O Lord.

Refrain II

Teach me your ways, O Lord.

Verses

1. Your ways, O Lord, make known to me, teach me your paths.
   Guide me, teach me, for you are my Savior.

2. Remember your compassion, Lord, and your kindness of old.
   Remember this, and not my sins, in your goodness, O Lord.

3. Good and just is the Lord, the sinners know the way.
   God guides the meek to justice, and teaches the humble.

Text: Psalm 25:4–5, 6–7, 8–9; David Haas, © 1985, GIA Publications, Inc.; refrain trans. © 1969, ICEL
Music: David Haas, © 1985, GIA Publications, Inc.

# 39 Psalm 25: To You, O Lord

Refrain

To you, O Lord, I lift my soul, to you, I lift my soul.

Verses

1. Lord, make me know your ways, teach me your paths
   and keep me in the way of your truth, for you are God, my Savior.

2. For the Lord is good and righteous, revealing the way to those who wander,
   gently leading the poor and the humble.

3. To the ones who seek the Lord, who look to God's word, who live God's love,
   God will always be near, and will show them mercy.

Text: Psalm 25:4–5, 8–9, 12–14; Marty Haugen, © 1982, GIA Publications, Inc.; refrain trans. © 1969, ICEL
Music: Marty Haugen, © 1982, GIA Publications, Inc.

# Psalm 25: To You, O Lord   40

Refrain

To you, O Lord, I lift up my soul. To
you, O Lord, I lift up my soul.

Verses

1. Lord, make me know your ways. Lord, teach me your paths.
   Make me walk in your truth, for you are God my Savior.

2. The Lord is good and upright. He shows the path to those who stray.
   God guides the humble in the right path. He teaches his way to the poor.

3. God's ways are faithfulness and love, for those who keep his covenant and will.
   The Lord's friendship is for those who revere him: to them God reveals the covenant.

Text: Psalm 25:4–5, 8–9, 10, 14; Stephen Pishner, © 2000, GIA Publications, Inc.; refrain trans. © 1969, ICEL
Music: Based on VENI EMMANUEL; Stephen Pishner, © 2000, GIA Publications, Inc.

# Psalm 27: The Lord Is My Light   41

Refrain

The Lord is my light and my sal - va - tion, of
whom should I be a - fraid, of whom should I be a - fraid?

Verses

1. The Lord is my light and my help; whom should I fear?
   The Lord is the stronghold of my life; before whom should I shrink?

2. There is one thing I ask of the Lord; for this I long:
   to live in the house of the Lord all the days of my life.

3. I believe I shall see the goodness of the Lord in the land of the living;
   hope in God, and take heart. Hope in the Lord!

Text: Psalm 27:1–2, 4, 13–14; David Haas
Music: David Haas
© 1983, GIA Publications, Inc.

# 42　Psalm 30: I Will Praise You, Lord

Refrain

I will praise you, Lord, you have res - cued me,

I will praise you, Lord, for your mer - cy. I will praise you, Lord,

you have res - cued me: I will praise you, Lord.

Verses

1. I will praise you, Lord, you have rescued me
   and have not let my enemies rejoice over me.
   O Lord, you have raised my soul from the dead,
   restored me to life from those who sink into the grave.

2. Sing psalms to the Lord, you who love him,
   give thanks to his holy name.
   His anger lasts but a moment; his favor through life.
   At night there are tears, but joy comes with dawn.

3. The Lord listened and had pity.
   The Lord came to my help.
   For me you have changed my mourning into dancing;
   O Lord my God, I will thank you for ever.

Text: Psalm 30:2, 4, 5–6, 11–13; © 1963, 1993, The Grail, GIA Publications, Inc., agent; refrain, Paul Inwood, © 1985, Paul Inwood
Music: Paul Inwood, © 1985, Paul Inwood
Published by OCP.

# Psalm 31: Father, into Your Hands / 43
# Padre, a Tus Manos

Refrain I*

Fa - ther, in - to your hands    I com - mend    my    spir - it.

Refrain II*

Pa - dre,    a tus ma - nos    en - co - mien - do    mi_es - pí - ri - tu.

Verses

1. In you, O LORD, I take refuge.
   Let me never be put to shame.
   In your justice, set me free.
   Into your hands I commend my spirit.
   You will redeem me, O LORD, O
   faithful God.

2. Because of all my foes I have become
   a reproach,
   an object of scorn to my neighbors
   and of fear to my friends.
   Those who see me in the street flee
   from me.
   I am forgotten, like someone dead,
   and have become like a broken vessel.

3. But as for me, I trust in you, O LORD;
   I say, "You are my God.
   My lot is in your hands, deliver me
   from the hands of my enemies and
   those who pursue me."

4. Let your face shine on your servant.
   Save me in your merciful love.
   Be strong, let your heart take courage,
   all who hope in the LORD.

1. A ti, Señor, me_acojo:
   no quede yo nunca defraudado;
   tú, que eres justo, ponme a salvo.
   A tus manos encomiendo mi_espíritu:
   tú, el Dios leal, me librarás.

2. Soy la burla de todos mis enemigos,
   la irrisión de mis vecinos,
   el espanto de mis conocidos:
   me ven por la calle, y escapan de mí.
   Me han olvidado como a un muerto,
   me han desechado como a un cacharro
   inútil.

3. Pero yo confío en ti, Señor,
   te digo: "Tú eres mi Dios."
   En tu mano están mis azares:
   líbrame de los enemigos que me
   persiguen.

4. Haz brillar tu rostro sobre tu siervo,
   sálvame por tu misericordia.
   Sean fuertes y valientes de corazón,
   los que esperan en el Señor.

*For a bilingual refrain, sing an entire refrain in one language, followed by the
other language.

Text: Psalm 31:2, 6, 12–13, 15–16, 17, 25; English refrain trans. © 1969, ICEL; verses, *The Revised Grail Psalms*, © 2010, Conception Abbey and
The Grail, admin. by GIA Publications, Inc.; Spanish refrain, *Leccionario, Edición Hispanoamérica*, and verses, © 1970, 1972, Conferencia
Episcopal Española
Music: Ronald F. Krisman; verses, Michel Guimont, © 1994, 1998, 2004, GIA Publications, Inc.

# 44 Psalm 33: Let Your Mercy Be on Us / Señor, Que Tu Misericordia

Refrain I

Let your mer - cy be on us, O God,
*Se - ñor, que tu mi - se - ri - cor - dia*

as we place our trust in you.
*ven - ga so - bre no - so - tros.*

Refrain II

The earth is full of the good-ness of
*La mi - se - ri - cor - dia de nues - tro*

God, the good - ness of our God.
*Dios lle - na la tie - rra.*

Refrain III

Hap - py are the peo - ple the Lord has
*Di - cho - so el pue - blo que el Se - ñor se es - co -*

cho - sen, cho - sen to be his own.
*gió co - mo he - re - dad.*

Verses

1. Your words, O God, are truth indeed, and all your works are ever faithful; you love justice and right, your compassion fills all creation.

2. See how the eye of God is watching, ever guarding all who wait in hope, to deliver them from death and sustain them in time of famine.

3. Exult, you just, in the Lord, for praise is the song of the righteous! How happy the people of God, the ones whom God has chosen!

4. Our soul is waiting for God, for God is our help and our shield. May your kindness, O God, be upon us who place our hope in you.

*1. La palabra del Señor es recta, y todas sus acciones son leales;*
   *la justicia él ama, y la tierra su gracia llena.*

*2. Los ojos de Dios ven a sus fieles, los que esperan su misericordia;*
   *los rescata de la muerte y sacia en tiempo de hambre.*

*3. Festejen, justos, al Señor, es propio de los buenos alabarlo.*
   *Dichoso el pueblo de Dios, que él se escogió como heredad.*

*4. Aguardamos al Señor: él es nuestro auxilio y escudo;*
   *que tu amor, Señor, esté con nosotros, como lo esperamos de ti.*

Text: Psalm 33:1, 4–5, 12, 18–19, 20, 22; Marty Haugen; Spanish tr. by Ronald F. Krisman, © 1987, 2011, GIA Publications, Inc.; English refrain
   tr. © 1969, ICEL
Music: Marty Haugen, © 1987, 1994, GIA Publications, Inc.

## Psalm 34: Taste and See    45

Refrain

Taste and see the good-ness of the Lord, the good - ness of the Lord.

Verses

1. I will bless the Lord at all times, God's praise ever in my mouth.
   Glory in the Lord for ever, and the lowly will hear and be glad.

2. Glory in the Lord with me, let us together extol God's name.
   I sought the Lord, who answered me and delivered me from all my fears.

3. Look to God that you might be radiant with joy,
   and your faces free from all shame.
   The Lord hears the suffering souls, and saves them from all distress.

Text: Psalm 34:2–3, 4–5, 6–7; Marty Haugen, © 1980, GIA Publications, Inc.; refrain trans. © 1969, ICEL
Music: Marty Haugen, © 1980, GIA Publications, Inc.

# 46  Psalm 34: Taste and See

Refrain I (St. 1.2.3.4 or 1.5.6.7 or 1.8.9.10.11)

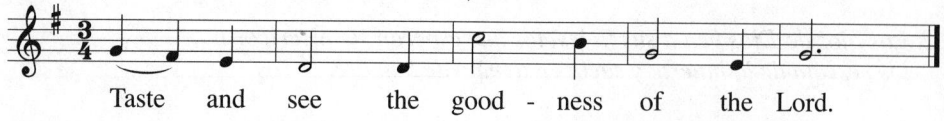

Taste and see the good - ness of the Lord.

Refrain II (St. 1.2.3.4)

I will bless the Lord at all times.

Refrain III (Vs. 2–3.17–18.19.23)

The Lord hears the cry of the poor.

Verses

1. I will bless the LORD at all times;
   praise of him is always in my mouth.
   In the LORD my soul shall make its boast;
   the humble shall hear and be glad.

2. Glorify the LORD with me;
   together let us praise his name.
   I sought the LORD, and he answered me;
   from all my terrors he set me free.

3. Look toward him and be radiant;
   let your faces not be abashed.
   This lowly one called; the LORD heard,
   and rescued him from all his distress.

4. The angel of the LORD is encamped
   around those who fear him, to rescue them.
   Taste and see that the LORD is good.
   Blessed the man who seeks refuge in him.

5. Fear the LORD, you his holy ones.
   They lack nothing, those who fear him.
   The rich suffer want and go hungry,
   but those who seek the LORD lack no blessing.

6. Come, children, and hear me,
   that I may teach you the fear of the LORD.
   Who is it that desires life
   and longs to see prosperous days?

7. Guard your tongue from evil,
    and your lips from speaking deceit.
    Turn aside from evil and do good.
    Seek after peace, and pursue it.

8. The LORD turns his eyes to the just,
    and his ears are open to their cry.
    The LORD turns his face against the wicked
    to destroy their remembrance from the earth.

9. When the just cry out, the LORD hears,
    and rescues them in all their distress.
    The LORD is close to the brokenhearted;
    those whose spirit is crushed he will save.

10. Many are the trials of the just man,
    but from them all the LORD will rescue him.
    He will keep guard over all his bones;
    not one of his bones shall be broken.

11. Evil brings death to the wicked;
    those who hate the just man are doomed.
    The LORD ransoms the souls of his servants.
    All who trust in him shall not be condemned.

Text: Psalm 34; *The Revised Grail Psalms*, © 2010, Conception Abbey and The Grail, admin. by GIA Publications, Inc.; refrain trans. © 1969, ICEL
Music: Michel Guimont, © 1995, GIA Publications, Inc.

## Psalm 34: The Cry of the Poor   47

Refrain

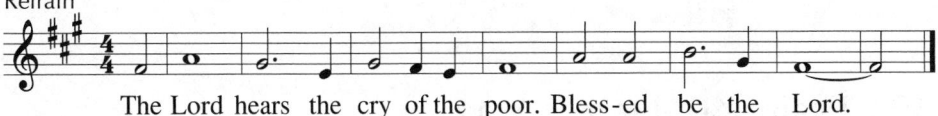

The Lord hears the cry of the poor. Bless-ed be the Lord.

Verses

1. I will bless the Lord at all times, with praise ever in my mouth.
    Let my soul glory in the Lord, who will hear the cry of the poor.

2. Let the lowly hear and be glad: the Lord listens to their pleas;
    and to hearts broken, God is near, who will hear the cry of the poor.

3. Every spirit crushed, God will save; will be ransom for their lives;
    will be safe shelter for their fears, and will hear the cry of the poor.

4. We proclaim your greatness, O God, your praise ever in our mouth;
    every face brightened in your light, for you hear the cry of the poor.

Text: Psalm 34:2–3, 6–7, 18–19, 23; John Foley, SJ
Music: John Foley, SJ
© 1978, 1991, John B. Foley, SJ, and OCP

## 48   Psalm 40: Here I Am

Refrain

Here I am, here I am, I come to do your will.

Here I am, here I am, I come to do your will.

Verses

1. I waited for God, who bent down to hear me.
   God put a new song in my mouth,
   a hymn of praise!

2. You did not seek offerings or sacrifice.
   You opened my eyes to see, my ears to hear.
   Yes, I will come to do your will!

3. I proclaim your greatness, Lord, to all those around me.
   My lips are not sealed, never holding back the story.
   You know this is true, I come to do your will!

Text: Psalm 40:2, 4, 7, 10; Tony E. Alonso
Music: Tony E. Alonso
© 2004, GIA Publications, Inc.

## 49   Psalm 40: Here I Am

Refrain

Here I am, Lord, here I am. I come to do your will.

Verses

1. Long was I waiting for God, and then he heard my cry.
   It was he who taught this song to me, a song of praise to God.

2. You asked me not for sacrifice, for slaughtered goats or lambs.
   No, my heart, you gave me ears to hear you, then I said, "Here I am."

3. You wrote it in the scrolls of law what you would have me do.
   Doing that is what has made me happy, your law is in my heart.

4. I spoke before your holy people, the good news that you save.
   Now you know that I will not be silent, I'll always sing your praise.

Text: Psalm 40:2 and 4, 7–8a, 8b–9, 10; Rory Cooney, © 1971, 1991, North American Liturgy Resources; refrain trans. © 1969, ICEL
Music: Rory Cooney, © 1971, 1991, North American Liturgy Resources
Published by OCP.

## Psalm 47: God Mounts His Throne    50

Ostinato Refrain*

God    mounts his    throne    to    shouts    of    joy,    O

sing    your    prais - es    to    the    Lord!

Verses

1. All you peoples, clap your hands, shout to God in gladness,
   the Lord we must fear, king of all the earth.

2. God goes up to shouts of joy, sound the trumpet blast.
   Sing praise to our God, praise unto our king!

3. God is king of all the earth, sing with all your skill
   to the king of all nations, God enthroned on high!

*May be sung in canon.*

Text: Psalm 47:2–3, 6–7, 8–9; Marty Haugen
Music: Marty Haugen
© 1983, GIA Publications, Inc.

# 51 Psalm 51: Be Merciful, O Lord

Refrain

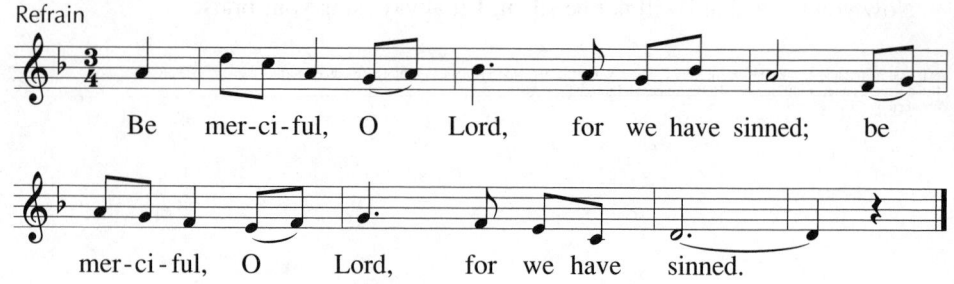

Be  mer-ci-ful,  O  Lord,  for we have sinned;  be

mer-ci-ful,  O  Lord,  for we have  sinned.

Verses

1. Have mercy on me, God, in your kindness,
   in your compassion, blot out my offense.
   O wash me more and more from my guilt and my sorrow,
   and cleanse me from all of my sin.

2. My offenses, truly I know them, and my sins are always before me;
   against you alone have I sinned, O Lord, what is evil in your sight I have done.

3. Create in me a clean heart, O God, put your steadfast spirit in my soul.
   Cast me not away from your presence, O Lord, and take not your spirit from me.

4. Give back to me the joy of your salvation, let your willing spirit bear me up
   and I shall teach your way to the ones who have wandered,
   and bring them all home to your side.

Text: Psalm 51:3–4, 5–6, 12–13, 14–15; Marty Haugen, © 1983, GIA Publications, Inc.; refrain trans. © 1969, ICEL
Music: Marty Haugen, © 1983, GIA Publications, Inc.

# Psalm 51: Be Merciful, O Lord    52

**Refrains**

I Be mer - ci - ful, O Lord, we have sinned, we have sinned.
II Cre - ate a clean heart in me, O God.

Be mer - ci - ful, O Lord for we have sinned.
Cre - ate a clean heart in me.

**Verses**

1. Have mercy on me, God, in your kindness.
   In your compassion blot out my offense.
   O wash me more and more from my guilt, from my guilt
   and cleanse me, O Lord, from my sin.

2. My offenses truly I know them;
   my sin is always before me.
   Against you, you alone, have I sinned, have I sinned;
   what is evil in your sight I have done.

3. A pure heart create for me, O God,
   put a steadfast spirit within me.
   Do not cast me away from your presence, O Lord,
   nor deprive me of your holy spirit.

4. Give me again the joy of your help, Lord;
   with a spirit of fervor sustain me.
   O Lord, open my lips, O Lord, open my lips
   and my mouth shall declare your praise.

*The refrains may be sung in canon without the accompaniment.*

Text: Psalm 51:3–4, 5–6, 12–13, 14, 17; © 1963, 1993, The Grail, GIA Publications, Inc., agent; refrain trans. © 1969, ICEL
Music: Based on WONDROUS LOVE, Stephen Pishner, © 1998, GIA Publications, Inc.

# 53  Psalm 51: Have Mercy, Lord

**Antiphon I**

Have mer - cy, Lord, cleanse me from all my sins.

Text: Psalm 51; The Grail
Music: Joseph Gelineau, SJ
© 1963, 1993, The Grail, GIA Publications, Inc., agent

**Antiphon II (Vs. 3–4.5–6ab.14–15.16.19)**

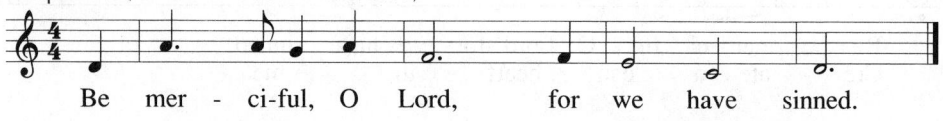

Be mer - ci - ful, O Lord, for we have sinned.

Text: *Lectionary for Mass*, © 1969, 1981, ICEL
Music: Patricia Craig, © 1975, GIA Publications, Inc.

**Antiphon III (St. 1.6.7 or 6.7.9)**

Cre - ate a clean heart, a clean heart in me, O God.

Text: *Lectionary for Mass*, © 1969, 1981, ICEL
Music: Frank Schoen, alt., © 1975, GIA Publications, Inc.

**Antiphon IV (Vs. 3–4.12–13.17.19)**

I will rise and go to my fa - ther.

Text: *Lectionary for Mass*, © 1969, 1981, ICEL
Music: James J. Chepponis, © 1986, GIA Publications, Inc.

**Antiphon V**

A sac - ri-fice you ac-cept, O God, is a hum - ble spir-it.

Text: *Praise God in Song*, 1979
Music: Michael Joncas, acc. by Robert J. Batastini
© 1979, 1995, GIA Publications, Inc.

**Psalm Tone**

Repeat for 5-line stanza
Repeat for 6-line stanza

Music: Chrysogonus Waddell, OCSO, © Gethsemani Abbey

**Gelineau Tone**

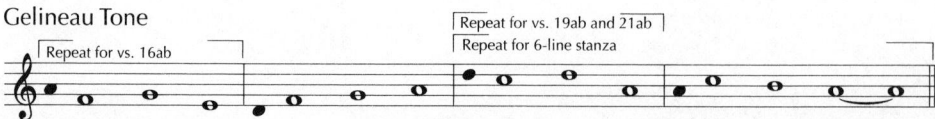

Repeat for vs. 16ab

Repeat for vs. 19ab and 21ab
Repeat for 6-line stanza

³ Have **mercy** on **mè**, O **God**,
  ac**cord**ing to your **merc**if**úl love**;
  ac**cord**ing to your **great** còm**pas**sion,
  **blot** out **my** tráns**gre**ssions.
⁴ Wash me com**plete**ly from **my** ìn**iq**uity,
  and **cleanse** me **from** mý **sin**.

⁵ My transg**res**sions, **trulỳ** I **know** them;
  my **sin** is **al**ways bé**fore** me.
⁶ Against **you**, you a**lone**, have **Ì sinned**;
  what is **e**vil in your **sight** I **háve done**.
  So **you** are **just** in yòur **sen**tence,
  with**out** re**proach** in yóur **judg**ment.

⁷ O **see**, in **guilt Ì** was **born**,
  a **sin**ner when my **moth**er cón**ceived** me.
⁸ Yes, you de**light** in sin**cer**ity òf **heart**;
  in **sec**ret you **teach** mé **wis**dom.
⁹ Cleanse me with **hys**sop, and **I** shall
  bè **pure**;
  wash me, and **I** shall be **whit**er thán **snow**.

¹⁰ Let me **hear** re**joicìng** and **glad**ness,
  that the **bones** you have **crushed** may
  é**xult**.
¹¹ **Turn** away your **face** from mỳ **sins**,
  and **blot** out **all** mý **guilt**.

¹² **Cre**ate a **pure heart** for **mè**, O **God**;
  renew a **stead**fast **spir**it wíthin me.
¹³ Do not **cast** me a**way** from yòur
  **pres**ence;
  take not your **ho**ly **spir**it fróm **me**.

¹⁴ **Re**store in me the **joy** of yòur
  sal**va**tion;
  sus**tain** in me a **will**íng **spir**it.
¹⁵ I will **teach** transg**res**sors yòur **ways**,
  that **sin**ners may re**turn** tó **you**.

¹⁶ **Res**cue me from **blood**shèd, O **God**,
  **God** of **my** sál**va**tion,
  and then my **tongue** shall ring **out**
  yòur **jus**tice.
¹⁷ O **LORD**, open mỳ **lips**
  and my **mouth** shall pro**claim** yóur
  **praise**.

¹⁸ For in **sa**crifice you **take** nò de**light**;
  burnt **off**ering from **me** would nót
  **please** you.
¹⁹ My **sa**crifice to **God**, a brokèn **spir**it:
  a **brok**en and hum**blèd heart**,
  O **God**, you **will** nót **spurn**.

²⁰ In your good **pleas**ure, show **fa**vòr to
  **Si**on;
  re**build** the **walls** of Jéru**sa**lem.
²¹ **Then** you will de**light** in rìght **sa**crifice,
  burnt **off**erings **wholl**y còn**sumed**.
  Then you will be **off**ered young **bulls**
  on yóur **al**tar.

Give **glo**ry to the **Fa**thèr Al**might**y,
to his **Son**, Jesus **Christ** thé **Lord**,
to the **Spir**it who **dwells** in òur **hearts**,
both **now** and for**ev**er. Á**men**.

Text: Psalm 51; *The Revised Grail Psalms*, © 2010, Conception Abbey and The Grail, admin. by GIA Publications, Inc.
Music: Joseph Gelineau, SJ, © 1963, 1993, The Grail, GIA Publications, Inc., agent

# 54  Psalm 51: Misericordia, Señor / Be Merciful, O Lord

Bilingual Refrain

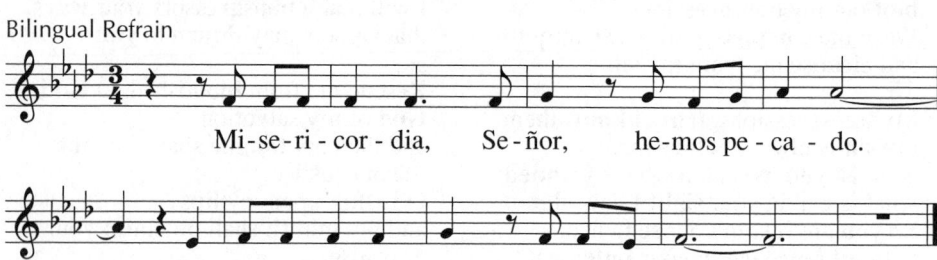

Mi-se-ri-cor-dia, Se-ñor, he-mos pe-ca-do.

Be mer-ci-ful, O Lord, for we have sinned.

Verses

1. Misericordia, Dios mío, por tu bondad; por tu inmensa compasión borra mi culpa.
   Lava del todo mi delito, todo mi delito, limpia mi pecado.

2. Pues la culpa que he hecho reconozco, tengo siempre presente mi pecado;
   contra ti sólo pequé, contra ti, Señor, contra ti, cometí la maldad que aborreces.

3. Oh Dios, crea en mí un corazón puro, renuévame con espíritu firme;
   no me arrojes lejos de tu rostro, no me quites tu santo espíritu.

4. Dame tu salvación que regocija, mantén en mí un alma generosa;
   líbrame de la muerte, mi Salvador, y mi boca cantará tu alabanza.

1. *O God, have mercy on me in your goodness;*
   *in your compassion wipe out my offense.*
   *Thoroughly wash me from my guilt,*
   *wash me from my guilt; cleanse me of all my sin.*

2. *I acknowledge my sin and my offenses for they are always before me.*
   *Against you alone have I sinned, against you alone have I sinned.*
   *I have done what is evil in your sight.*

3. *O God, create for me a clean heart, renew in me a steadfast spirit.*
   *Cast me not out from your presence, my God, do not take from me your holy spirit.*

4. *Restore my joy in your salvation; sustain a willing spirit within me!*
   *Rescue me from death, my saving God, and my mouth will proclaim your praise!*

Text: Psalm 51:3–4, 5–6, 12–13, 14, 17; vss. 2, 4 adapt. by Paul A. Tate, © 2004, GIA Publications, Inc.; vss. 1, 3 tr., © 1970, Conferencia Episcopal Española; English refrain tr. from *Lectionary for Mass*, © 1969, ICEL
Music: Paul A. Tate, © 2005, GIA Publications, Inc.

# Psalm 63: My Soul Is Thirsting 55

Refrain

My soul is thirst - ing, my soul is thirst - ing,

my soul is thirst - ing for you, O Lord my God.

Verses

1. O God, you are my God whom I seek;
   O God, you are my God whom I seek;
   for you my flesh pines, my soul thirsts like the earth,
   parched, lifeless, without water.

2. Thus have I gazed toward you in your holy place
   to see your power and your glory.
   Your kindness is a greater good than life itself;
   my lips will glorify you.

3. Thus will I bless you while I live;
   Lifting up my hands I will call upon your name.
   As with a banquet shall my soul be satisfied;
   with exultant lips my mouth shall praise you.

4. For you have been my help, you have been my help;
   in the shadow of your wings I shout for joy.
   My soul clings fast to you; your right hand holds me firm;
   in the shadow of your wings I sing for joy.

Text: Psalm 63:2, 3–4, 5–6, 8–9; verses adapt. © 1970, Confraternity of Christian Doctrine, Washington, D.C.; refrain by Michael Joncas, © 1987,
GIA Publications, Inc.
Music: Michael Joncas, © 1987, GIA Publications, Inc.

# 56 Psalm 63: My Soul Is Thirsting

Antiphon I

My soul is thirst - ing for you, O

Lord, thirst - ing for you my God.

Text: *Lectionary for Mass*, © 1969, 1981, ICEL
Music: Richard Proulx, © 1975, GIA Publications, Inc.

Antiphon II

In the morn-ing I will sing, will sing glad songs of praise to you.

Text: *Praise God in Song*
Music: David Clark Isele
© 1979, GIA Publications, Inc.

Psalm Tone

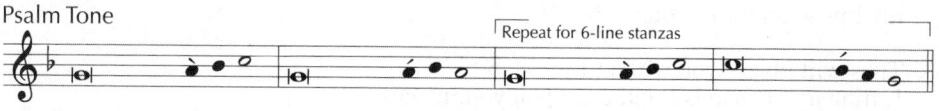

Repeat for 6-line stanzas

Music: Michel Guimont, © 1994, 1998, GIA Publications, Inc.

Gelineau Tone

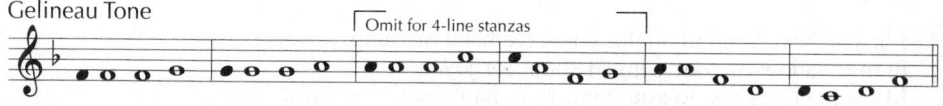

Omit for 4-line stanzas

2 O **God**, you are my **God**; at dàwn I **seek** you;
  for **you** my **sóul** is **thirst**ing.
  For **you** my **flèsh** is **pin**ing,
  like a **dry**, weary **land** wíthout **wa**ter.
3 I have **come** be**fore** you ìn the **sanc**tuary,
  to be**hold** your **strength** ánd your **glo**ry.

4 Your loving **mer**cy is **bettèr** than **life**;
  my **lips** will **spéak** your **praise**.
5 I will **bless** you àll my **life**;
  in your **name** I will **lift** úp my **hands**.
6 My **soul** shall be **filled** as wìth a **ban**quet;
  with joyful **lips**, my **móuth** shall **praise** you.

7 When I re**mem**ber **you** upòn my **bed**,
  I muse on **you** through the **watch**es óf the **night**.
8 For **you** have **bèen** my **strength**;
  in the **shad**ow of your **wings** Í re**joice**.
9 My **soul** clings **fàst** to **you**;
  **your** right **hánd** up**holds** me.

Give **praise** to the **Fà**ther Al**mighty**,
to his **Son**, Jesus **Chríst** the **Lord**,
to the **Spír**it who **dwells** ìn our **hearts**,
both **now** and forevér. **Amen**.

Text: Psalm 63:2–9; *The Revised Grail Psalms*, © 2010, Conception Abbey and The Grail, admin. by GIA Publications, Inc.
Music: Joseph Gelineau, SJ, © 1963, The Grail, GIA Publications, Inc., agent

## Psalm 63: My Soul Is Thirsting 57

Refrains

I My soul is thirst-ing for you, O Lord, thirst-
II As morn-ing breaks I look to you; be

ing for you, my God. My soul is thirst-
my strength this day. As morn-ing breaks

ing for you, O Lord, thirst-ing for you, my God,
I look to you; be my strength this day,

thirst-ing for you, my God.
be my strength this day.

Verses

1. O God, you are my God, and I will always praise you.
   In the shadow of your wings I cling to you and you hold me high.

2. Through the day you walk with me; all the night your love surrounds me.
   To the glory of your name I lift my hands, I sing your praise.

3. I will never be afraid, for I will not be abandoned.
   Even when the road grows long and weary your love will rescue me.

Text: Psalm 63:2–9, Steve Angrisano, © 1997, 1998; refrain trans. © 1969, 1981, ICEL; alt. refrain trans. from *The Liturgy of the Hours*, © 1974, ICEL
Music: Steve Angrisano, © 1997, 1998; acc. by Rick Modlin
Published by OCP.

## 58 Psalm 63: Your Love Is Finer than Life

Refrain

O God, I seek you, my soul thirsts for you, your love is fin - er than life.

Verses

1. As a dry and weary desert land, so my soul is thirsting for my God,
   and my flesh is faint for the God I seek, for your love is more to me than life.

2. I think of you when at night I rest, I reflect upon your steadfast love,
   I will cling to you, O Lord my God, in the shadow of your wings I sing.

3. I will bless your name all the days I live, I will raise my hands and call on you,
   my joyful lips shall sing your praise, you alone have filled my hungry soul.

Text: Psalm 63:2, 7–9, 5–6; Marty Haugen
Music: Marty Haugen
© 1982, GIA Publications, Inc.

## 59 Psalm 66: Let All the Earth

Refrain

Let all the earth cry out in joy to the Lord; Let all the earth cry out in joy to the

1.-3. | *To verses* | *Last time*

Lord! Lord! to the Lord!

Verses

1. Cry out in joy to the Lord, all peoples on earth,
   sing to the praise of God's name, proclaiming for ever,
   "tremendous your deeds for us."

2. Leading your people safe through fire and water,
   bringing their souls to life, we sing of your glory, your love is eternal.

3. Hearken to me as I sing my love of the Lord,
   who answers the prayer of my heart. God leads me in safety, from death unto life.

Text: Psalm 66:1–3, 12, 16; Marty Haugen
Music: Marty Haugen
© 1982, GIA Publications, Inc.

## Psalm 72: Every Nation on Earth   60

Refrain I

Ev - 'ry na - tion on earth will a - dore you, Lord;

ev - 'ry na - tion on earth will a - dore you, Lord.

Refrain II

In his days jus - tice will flou - rish;

in his days full - ness of peace for - ev - er - more.

Verses

1. O God, with your judgment endow the king;
   with your justice endow the king's son.
   With justice he will govern your people,
   your afflicted ones with right judgment.

2. Justice shall flow'r in his days,
   lasting peace 'til the moon be no more.
   May he rule from sea to sea,
   from the river to the ends of the earth.

3. The kings of Tarshish and the Isles offer gifts,
   those from Seba and Arabia bring tribute.
   All kings shall pay him their homage,
   all nations shall serve him.

4. He rescues the poor when they cry out,
   the afflicted with no one to help.
   The lowly and poor he shall pity,
   the lives of the poor he will save.

Text: Psalm 72:1–2, 7–8, 10–11, 12–13; Michael Joncas
Music: Michael Joncas
© 1987, 1994, GIA Publications, Inc.

# 61 Psalm 84: How Lovely Is Your Dwelling Place

**Antiphon**

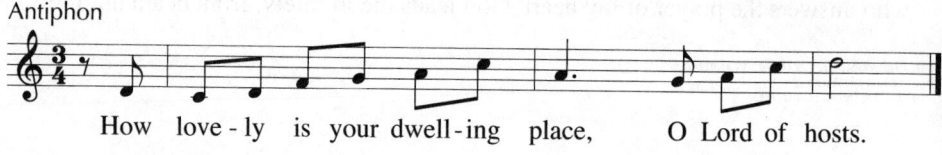

How love-ly is your dwell-ing place, O Lord of hosts.

Text: Psalm 84:2, The Grail
Music: A. Gregory Murray, OSB
© 1963, The Grail, GIA Publications, Inc., agent

**Psalm Tone**

Repeat for 5-line stanza

Omit for 2-line stanzas

Music: Chrysogonus Waddell, © Gethsemani Abbey

**Gelineau Tone**

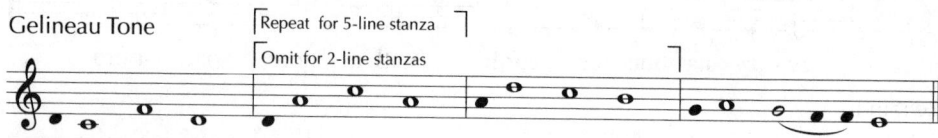

Repeat for 5-line stanza

Omit for 2-line stanzas

² How **love**ly ìs your **dwel**ling **place**,
  **O LORD** óf **hosts**.

³ My **soul** is **longì**ng and **yearn**ing
  **for** the **courts** of thé **LORD**.
  My **heart** and my **flesh** crỳ **out**
  **to** the **livíng God**.

⁴ **Even** the **spar**row finds a **home**,
  and the **swal**low a **nest** for hérself
  in which she **sets** her **young**, at yòur **altars**,
  **O LORD** of **hosts**, my **king** and mý **God**.

⁵ Blessed are **they** who **dwell** ìn your **house**,
  forever **sing**ing yóur **praise**.
⁶ Blessed the **people** whose **strength** is ìn **you**,
  whose **heart** is **set** on pilgrím **ways**.

⁷ As they **go** through the **Bàca Val**ley,
  they **make** it a **place** óf **springs**;
  the **aut**umn rain **cov**ers it wíth **pools**.
⁸ They **walk** with ever-growìng **strength**;
  the God of **gods** will apppear ín **Sion**.

⁹ O **LORD God** of **hosts**, hèar my **prayer**;
  give **ear**, O **God** óf **Ja**cob.
¹⁰ Turn your **eyes**, O **God**, òur **shield**;
   **look** on the **face** of your **ánoint**ed.

<sup>11</sup> One **day** with**ìn** your **courts**
is **bet**ter than a **thous**ánd **else**where.
The **thresh**old of the **house** òf **God**
I **prefer** to the **dwell**ings of thé **wick**ed.

<sup>12</sup> For the LORD **God** is **a sùn**, a **shield**;
the LORD will **give** us his **fa**vor ánd **glo**ry.
He will **not** with**hold** an**ỳ good**
to **those** who **walk** with**óut blame**.

<sup>13</sup> O LORD of hòsts, how blessed
is the **man** who **trusts** ín **you**!

Give **praise** to the **Fathèr Al**might**y**,
to his **Son**, Jesus **Christ** thé **Lord**,
to the **Spir**it who **dwells** in òur **hearts**,
both **now** and forever. Ámen.

Text: Psalm 84; *The Revised Grail Psalms*, © 2010, Conception Abbey and The Grail, admin. by GIA Publications, Inc.
Music: Joseph Gelineau, © 1963, 1993, The Grail, GIA Publications, Inc., agent

## Psalm 85: Lord, Let Us See Your Kindness    62

Refrain

Lord,    let us see    your    kind - ness;

Lord,    let us see    your    kind - ness.

Verses

1. Let us hear what our God proclaims: Peace to the people of God,
   salvation is near to the ones who fear God.

2. Kindness and truth, justice and peace;
   truth shall spring up as the water from the earth,
   justice shall rain from the heavens.

3. The Lord will come and you shall know his love,
   justice shall walk in his pathways, salvation the gift that he brings.

Text: Psalm 85:9–10, 11–12, 13–14; Marty Haugen, © 1983, GIA Publications, Inc.; refrain trans. © 1969, ICEL
Music: Marty Haugen, © 1983, GIA Publications, Inc.

# 63 Psalm 88: Day and Night

**Antiphon**

Day and night I cry to you, my God.

Text: *Liturgy of the Hours,* © 1974, ICEL
Music: Suzanne Toolan, SM, © 1986, GIA Publications, Inc.

**Psalm Tone**

Music: Chrysogonus Waddell, OCSO, © Gethsemani Abbey

**Gelineau Tone**

² O **LORD** and **God** of mỳ salvation,
 I **cry** be**fore** you day ánd **night**.
³ Let my **prayer come** into yòur
 **pres**ence.
 In**cline** your **ear** to mý **cry**.

⁴ For my **soul** is **filled** with **evils**;
 my **life** is on the **brink** of thé **grave**.
⁵ I am **reck**oned as **one** in thè **tomb**;
 **I** am like a **war**rior withóut **strength**,

⁶ like one **roam**ing amòng the **dead**,
 like the **slain ly**ing in théir **graves**,
 like **those** you re**mem**ber nò **more**,
 cut **off**, as they **are**, from yóur **hand**.

⁷ You have **laid** me in the **depths** òf
 the **pit**,
 in **re**gions that are **dark** ánd **deep**.
⁸ Your **anger weighs** down ùpon me;
 I am **drowned** be**neath** yóur **waves**.

⁹ You have **tak**en awày my **friends**;
 to **them** you have **made** mé **hateful**.
 Im**pris**oned, I **cannot** èscape;
¹⁰ my **eyes** are **sunk**en wíth **grief**.

 I **call** to you, **LORD**, àll day **long**;
 to **you** I **stretch** out mý **hands**.
¹¹ Will you **work** your **won**ders for thè
 **dead**?
 Will the **shades** rise **up** tó **praise** you?

¹² Will your **mer**cy be **told** ìn the **grave**,
 or your **faith**fulness in the **place** of
 **pér**dition?
¹³ Will your **won**ders be **known** in thè **dark**,
 your **justice** in the **land** of óblivion?

¹⁴ But **I**, O **LORD**, **cry** òut to **you**;
 in the **morn**ing my **prayer** comes béfore
 **you**.
¹⁵ **Why** do you re**ject** me, Ò **LORD**?
 Why do you **hide** your **face** fróm **me**?

¹⁶ I am **wretch**ed, close to **death** fròm my
 **youth**.
 I have **borne** your **trials**; I ám **numb**.
¹⁷ Your **fury** has **swept** down ùpon me;
 your **ter**rors have **utter**ly déstroyed me.

¹⁸ They sur**round** me all the **day** lìke a **flood**;
 to**geth**er they **close** in ágainst me.
¹⁹ **Friend** and **neigh**bor you have **tak**en àway:
 my **one** com**pan**ion ís **darkness**.

 Give **praise** to the **Fath**èr **Almight**y,
 to his **Son**, Jesus **Christ** thé **Lord**,
 to the **Spir**it who **dwells** in òur **hearts**,
 both **now** and forever. **Á**men.

Text: Psalm 88; *The Revised Grail Psalms,* © 2010, Conception Abbey and The Grail, admin. by GIA Publications, Inc.
Music: Joseph Gelineau, SJ, © 1963, The Grail, GIA Publications, Inc., agent

# Psalm 89: For Ever I Will Sing   64

**Refrain**

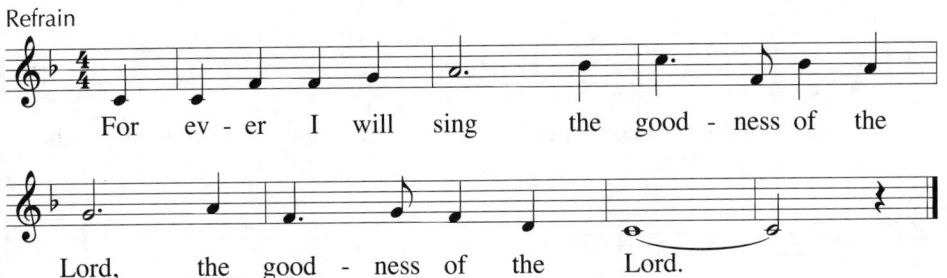

For ev - er I will sing the good - ness of the Lord, the good - ness of the Lord.

Verses

1. "With my chosen one I have made a covenant; I have sworn to David my servant:
   I will establish your dynasty forever and set up your throne through all ages."

2. Happy the people who acclaim such a God,
   who walk, O Lord, in the light of your face,
   who find their joy ev'ry day in your name,
   who make your justice the source of their bliss.

3. He will say to me: "You are my father, my God, the rock who saves me!"
   I will keep my love for him always; with him my covenant shall last.

Alternate Verses

1. I have found David my servant,
   with my holy oil I have anointed him,
   that my hand may ever be with him
   and my arm make him strong.

2. My faithfulness and love shall be with you,
   in my Name your name will be exalted.

3. He shall cry to me, "My God, my rock of salvation, my salvation."

Text: Psalm 89: 4–5, 16–17, 27–29, © 1963, 1993, The Grail, GIA Publications, Inc., agent; alt. verses 21–22, 25, 27, Marty Haugen, © 1988, 1994, GIA Publications, Inc.; refrain trans. © 1969, ICEL
Music: Marty Haugen, © 1988, 1994, GIA Publications, Inc.

## 65 Psalm 91: Be with Me

Refrain

Be with me, Lord, when I am in trou-ble, be with me, Lord, I pray.

Verses

1. You who dwell in the shelter of the Lord, Most High,
   who abide in the shadow of our God,
   say to the Lord: "My refuge and fortress, the God in whom I trust."

2. No evil shall befall you, no pain come near,
   for the angels stand close by your side,
   guarding you always and bearing you gently, watching over your life.

3. Those who cling to the Lord live secure in God's love,
   lifted high, those who trust in God's name,
   call on the Lord, who will never forsake you.
   God will bring you salvation and joy.

Text: Psalm 91:1–2, 10–11, 14–15; Marty Haugen
Music: Marty Haugen
© 1980, GIA Publications, Inc.

## 66 Psalm 95: If Today You Hear God's Voice

Refrain

If to-day you hear God's voice, hard-en not your hearts.

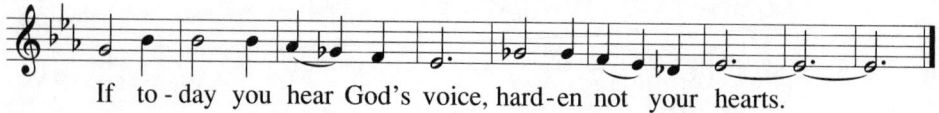

If to-day you hear God's voice, hard-en not your hearts.

Verses

1. Come, ring out our joy to the Lord, hail the rock who saves us,
   let us come now before our God, with songs let us hail the Lord.

2. Come, let us bow and bend low, let us kneel before God who made us,
   for here is our God; we the people, the flock that is led by God's hand.

3. O that today you would hear God's voice, "Harden not your hearts,
   as on that day in the desert, when your parents put me to the test."

Text: Psalm 95:1–2, 6–7, 8–9; David Haas
Music: David Haas
© 1983, 1994, GIA Publications, Inc.

## Psalm 96: Proclaim to All the Nations    67

Refrain I

Pro - claim   to   all   the   na - tions   the

mar - vel-ous deeds of the Lord! Pro - claim to all the

na - tions the mar - vel-ous deeds of the Lord!

Refrain II

Give the Lord glo - ry and hon - or.

Give the Lord glo - ry and hon - or.

Verses

1. Sing to the Lord a new song. Sing to the Lord all you lands!
   Sing to the Lord with all your heart, and bless God's name!

2. Announce salvation day by day, God's glory throughout the earth!
   Among all the people in every land, God's wondrous deeds!

3. Give to the Lord, you nations, praise to the Lord of all!
   Sing glory and praise and sing to the name, above all names!

4. Worship the Lord, and tremble, proclaim the one who reigns!
   Say to the nations: "The Lord is King;" who rules with justice!

Text: Psalm 96:1–2, 3, 7–8, 9–10; David Haas, © 1989, GIA Publications, Inc.; refrains trans. © 1969, ICEL
Music: Marty Haugen; refrain I, David Haas; refrain II adapt. by Diana Kodner; © 1989, 1994, GIA Publications, Inc.

## 68   Psalm 96: Today Is Born Our Savior

Refrain

To - day   is   born   our   Sav-ior,   Christ   the   Lord.   To-

day   is   born   our   Sav-ior,   Christ   the   Lord.

Verses

1. Sing to the Lord a new song;
   sing to the Lord, all you lands.
   Sing to the Lord; bless his name.

2. Announce his salvation, day after day.
   Tell his glory among the nations;
   Among all peoples, his wondrous deeds.

3. Let the heavens be glad and the earth rejoice;
   let the sea and what fills it resound;
   let the plains be joyful and all that is in them!
   Then shall all the trees of the forest exult.

4. They shall exult before the Lord, for he comes;
   for he comes to rule the earth.
   He shall rule the world with justice
   and the peoples with his constancy.

Text: Psalm 96:1–2a, 2b–3, 11–12, 13; verses trans. © 1970, Confraternity of Christian Doctrine, Washington, D.C.; refrain trans. © 1969, ICEL
Music: Howard Hughes, SM, © 1976, GIA Publications, Inc.

## 69   Psalm 96: Today Is Born Our Savior /
## Hoy Nos Ha Nacido un Salvador

Bilingual Refrain

To - day   is   born   our   Sav - ior,   Christ   the   Lord.

*Hoy      nos   ha   na - ci - do un Sal  -  va - dor.*      Born our

Sav - ior, Christ the Lord. *El Me - sí - as, el Se - ñor.*

Verses

1. O sing a new song to the LORD;
   sing to the LORD, all the earth.
   O sing to the LORD; bless his name.

2. Proclaim his salvation day by day.
   Tell among the nations his glory,
   and his wonders among all the peoples.

3. Let the heavens rejoice and earth be glad;
   let the sea and all within it thunder praise.
   Let the land and all it bears rejoice.
   Then will all the trees of the wood shout for joy.

4. At the presence of the LORD, for he comes,
   he comes to judge the earth.
   He will judge the world with justice;
   he will govern the peoples with his truth.

1. *Canten al Señor un cántico nuevo,*
   *canten al Señor, toda la tierra;*
   *canten al Señor, bendigan su nombre.*

2. *Proclamen día tras día su victoria.*
   *Cuenten a los pueblos su gloria,*
   *sus maravillas a todas las naciones.*

3. *Alégrese el cielo, goce la tierra,*
   *retumbe el mar y cuanto lo llena;*
   *vitoreen los campos y cuanto hay en ellos,*
   *aclamen los árboles del bosque.*

4. *Delante del Señor, que ya llega,*
   *ya llega a regir la tierra:*
   *regirá el orbe con justicia*
   *y los pueblos con fidelidad.*

Text: Psalm 96:1–2a, 2b–3, 11–12, 13, *The Revised Grail Psalms*, © 2010, Conception Abbey and The Grail, admin. by GIA Publications, Inc.;
refrain trans. © 1969, ICEL; Spanish refrain, *Leccionario, Edición Hispanoamérica*, and verses, © 1970, 1972, Conferencia Episcopal Española
Music: Ronald F. Krisman; verses, Michel Guimont, © 1995, 2004, GIA Publications, Inc.

# 70   Psalm 98: All the Ends of the Earth

Refrain I

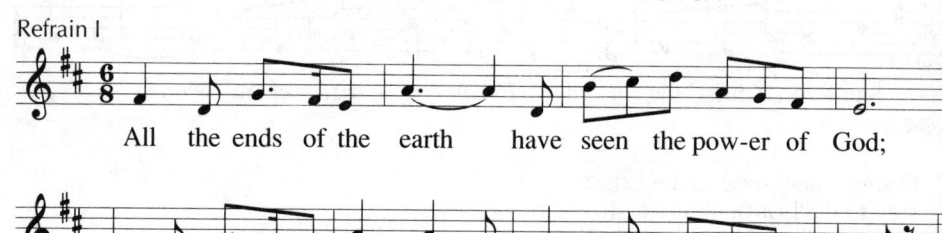

All the ends of the earth have seen the pow-er of God;

all the ends of the earth have seen the pow-er of God.

Refrain II

Sing to the Lord a new song, for God has done won-der-ful deeds.

Sing to the Lord a new song, for God has done won-der-ful deeds.

Refrain III

The Lord comes to the earth to rule the earth with jus-tice.

The Lord comes to the earth to rule the earth with jus-tice.

Verses

1. Sing to the Lord a new song, for God has done wondrous deeds;
   whose right hand has won the victory for us, God's holy arm.

2. The Lord has made salvation known, and justice revealed to all,
   remembering kindness and faithfulness to Israel.

3. All of the ends of earth have seen salvation by our God.
   Joyfully sing out all you lands, break forth in song.

4. Sing to the Lord with harp and song, with trumpet and with horn.
   Sing in your joy before the king, the king, our Lord.

Text: Psalm 98:1, 2–3, 3–4, 5–6; David Haas, Marty Haugen
Music: David Haas, Marty Haugen; refrain II, III adapt. by Diana Kodner
© 1983, 1994, GIA Publications, Inc.

# Psalm 100: We Are God's People    71

Ostinato Refrain

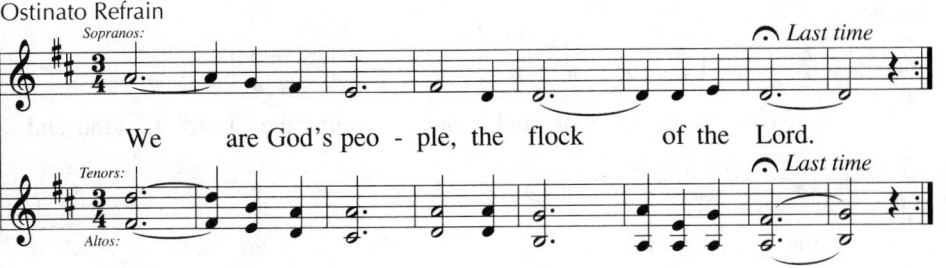

We    are God's peo - ple, the    flock    of the    Lord.

Verses

1. Cry out with joy to the Lord, all you lands, all you lands.
   Serve the Lord now with gladness, come before God singing for joy!

2. Know that the Lord is God! Know that the Lord is God,
   who made us, to God we belong, God's people, the sheep of the flock!

3. Go, now within the gates giving thanks, giving thanks.
   Enter the courts singing praise, give thanks and bless God's name!

4. Indeed, how good is the Lord, whose mercy endures for ever,
   for the Lord is faithful, is faithful from age to age!

Text: Psalm 100:1–2, 3, 4, 5; David Haas
Music: David Haas
© 1983, GIA Publications, Inc.

## 72  Psalm 103: The Lord Is Kind and Merciful

Refrain

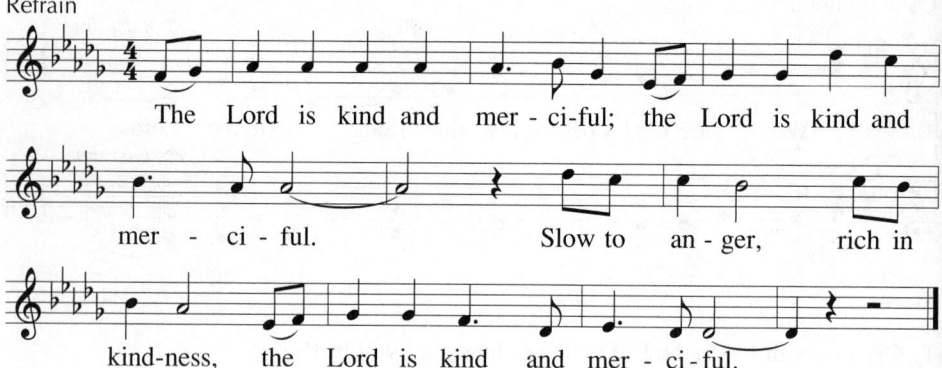

The Lord is kind and mer - ci-ful; the Lord is kind and mer - ci - ful. Slow to an - ger, rich in kind-ness, the Lord is kind and mer - ci-ful.

Verses

1. Bless the Lord, O my soul; all my being bless God's name.
   Bless the Lord, O my soul; forget not all God's blessings.

2. The Lord is gracious and merciful, slow to anger, full of kindness.
   God is good to all creation, full of compassion.

3. The goodness of God is from age to age,
   blessing those who choose to love.
   And justice toward God's children; on all who keep the covenant.

Text: Psalm 103; Jeanne Cotter
Music: Jeanne Cotter
© 1993, GIA Publications, Inc.

## 73  Psalm 103: My Soul, Give Thanks to the Lord

Antiphon

My soul, give thanks to the Lord, and bless God's Ho-ly Name.

Text: Psalm 103:1; © 1963, 1993, The Grail, GIA Publications, Inc., agent
Music: Richard Proulx, © 1986, GIA Publications, Inc.

Psalm Tone

Repeat for 5-line stanzas

Music: Michel Guimont, © 1994, 1998, GIA Publications, Inc.

Gelineau Tone

Omit for 5 lines

Omit for 4-line stanzas

Bless the LORD, Ò my soul,
and all within me, his holý name.
2 Bless the LORD, Ô my soul,
and never forget all hís benefits.

3 It is the LORD who forgives àll your sins,
who heals every one of yóur ills,
4 who redeems your life fròm the grave,
who crowns you with mercy and
cómpassion,
5 who fills your life wìth good things,
renewing your youth like án eagle's.

6 The LORD dòes just deeds,
gives full justice to all who are
óppressed.
7 He made known his wàys to Moses,
and his deeds to the children óf Israel.

8 The LORD is compassionàte and
gracious,
slow to anger and rich ín mercy.
9 He will not alwàys find fault;
nor persist in his anger fórever.
10 He does not treat us accordìng tò our
sins,
nor repay us accordìng to óur faults.

11 For as the heavens are high abòve the
earth,
so strong his mercy for those whó fear
him.
12 As far as the east is fròm the west,
so far from us does he remove our
tránsgressions.

13 As a father has compassion òn his
children,
14 the LORD's compassion is on those
whó fear him.
For he knows of what wè are made;
he remembers that we áre dust.

15 Man, his days àre like grass;
he flowers like the flower of thé field.
16 The wind blows, and it ìs no more,
and its place never sees it ágain.

17 But the mercy of the LORD is
èverlasting
upon those who hold him ín fear,
upon children's childrèn his justice,
18 for those who keep hís covenant,
and remember to fulfill his cómmands.

19 The LORD has fixed his thròne in
heaven,
and his kingdom is rulìng ovér all.
20 Bless the LORD, all yòu his angels,
mighty in power, fulfilling hís word,
who heed the voice of hís word.

21 Bless the LORD, àll his hosts,
his servants, who do hís will.
22 Bless the LORD, àll his works,
in every place where hé rules.
Bless the LORD, O mý soul!

Give praise to the Fathèr Almighty,
to his Son, Jesus Christ thé Lord,
to the Spirit who dwells ìn our hearts,
both now and forever. Ámen.

Text: Psalm 103; *The Revised Grail Psalms*, © 2010, Conception Abbey and The Grail, admin. by GIA Publications, Inc.
Music: Joseph Gelineau, SJ, © 1963, 1993, The Grail, GIA Publications, Inc., agent

# 74 Psalm 103: The Lord Is Kind and Merciful / El Señor Es Compasivo

Bilingual Refrain

The Lord is kind and mer - ci - ful, slow to an-ger and

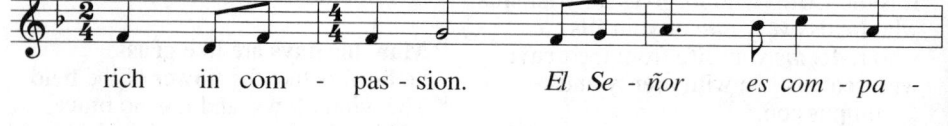

rich in com - pas - sion. *El Se - ñor es com - pa -*

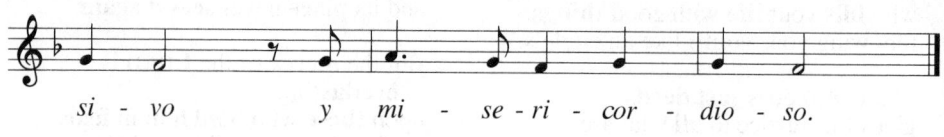

*si - vo y mi - se - ri - cor - dio - so.*

Verses

1. Bless the LORD, O my soul,
   and all within me, his holy name.
   Bless the LORD, O my soul,
   and never forget all his benefits.

2. It is the LORD who forgives
       all your sins,
   who heals every one of your ills,
   who redeems your life from
       the grave,
   who crowns you with mercy and
       compassion.

3. The LORD is compassionate and
       gracious,
   slow to anger and rich in mercy.
   He does not treat us according
       to our sins,
   nor repay us according to our faults.

4. As far as the east is from the west,
   so far from us does he remove our
       transgressions.
   As a father has compassion on his
       children,
   the LORD's compassion is on those
       who fear him.

1. *Bendice alma mía, al Señor,*
   *y todo mi ser a su santo nombre.*
   *Bendice alma mía, al Señor,*
   *y no olvides sus beneficios.*

2. *El perdona todas tus culpas*
   *y cura todas tus enfermedades;*
   *él rescata tu vida de la fosa*
   *y te colma de gracia y ternura.*

3. *El Señor es lento a la ira*
   *y rico en clemencia.*
   *No nos trata como merecen nuestros*
       *pecados*
   *ni nos paga según nuestras culpas.*

4. *Como dista el oriente del ocaso,*
   *así aleja de nosotros nuestros delitos.*
   *Como un padre siente ternura por sus*
       *hijos,*
   *siente el Señor ternura por sus fieles.*

Text: Psalm 103:1–2, 3–4, 8 and 10, 12–13; *The Revised Grail Psalms*, © 2010, Conception Abbey and The Grail, admin. by GIA Publications, Inc.;
Spanish tr. from *Leccionario, Edición Hispanoamérica*, © 1970, 1972, Conferencia Episcopal Española
Music: Tony E. Alonso, © 2010, GIA Publications, Inc.

# Psalm 103: The Lord Is Kind and Merciful  75

**Refrain**

The Lord is kind and mer-ci - ful, the
Lord is kind and mer-ci - ful.

**Verses**

1. Bless the Lord, O my soul, and all my being bless God's name;
   bless the Lord, and forget not God's benefits.

2. God pardons all your iniquities, and comforts your sorrows,
   redeems your life from destruction and crowns you with kindness.

3. Merciful, merciful, and gracious is our God;
   slow to anger, abounding in kindness.

Text: Psalm 103:1–2, 3–4, 8; para. by Marty Haugen, © 1983, GIA Publications, Inc.; refrain trans. © 1969, ICEL
Music: Marty Haugen, © 1983, GIA Publications, Inc.

# Psalm 104: Lord, Send Out Your Spirit  76

**Refrain**

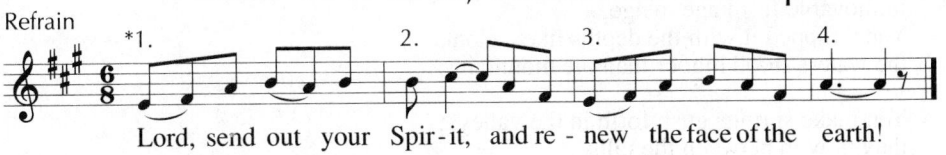

Lord, send out your Spir-it, and re - new the face of the earth!

**Verses**

1. Bless the Lord, O my soul; O Lord, my God, you are great indeed!
   How manifold are your works, O Lord! The earth is full of your creatures!

2. If you take away their breath, they die and they return to their dust.
   When you send forth your Spirit of life, they are created in your sight!

3. May his glory last for all time; may the Lord be glad in his works.
   Pleasing to him will be my theme; I will be glad in the Lord!

*May be sung as a canon.*

Text: Psalm 104:1, 24, 29–30, 31, 34; Paul Lisicky, © 1985, GIA Publications, Inc.; refrain trans. © 1969, ICEL
Music: Paul Lisicky, © 1985, GIA Publications, Inc.

# 77  Psalm 104: Lord, Send Out Your Spirit

Antiphon

Lord,       send  out  your  Spir - it,

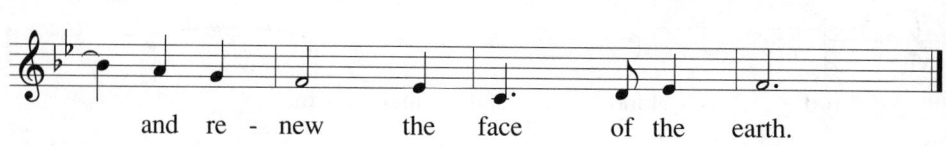

and  re - new    the    face    of the    earth.

Text: *Lectionary for Mass*, © 1969, 1981, ICEL
Music: Richard Proulx, © 1975, GIA Publications, Inc.

*Easter Vigil: Sts. 1, 3, 4, 5, 6*
*Vigil of Pentecost: Sts. 1, 6, 7, 8*
*Pentecost: Sts. 2, 8, 9*
*Confirmation: Sts. 2, 7, 8, 9*

Verses

1. Bless the LORD, O my soul!
   O LORD my God, how great you are,
   clothed in majesty and honor,
   wrapped in light as with a robe!

2. Bless the LORD, O my soul!
   O LORD my God, how great you are.
   How many are your works, O LORD!
   The earth is full of your creatures.

3. You set the earth on its foundation,
   immovable from age to age.
   You wrapped it with the depths like a cloak;
   the waters stood higher than the mountains.

4. You make springs gush forth in the valleys;
   they flow in between the hills.
   There the birds of heaven build their nests;
   from the branches they sing their song.

5. From your dwelling you water the hills;
   by your works the earth has its fill.
   You make the grass grow for the cattle
   and the plants to serve mankind's need,
   that he may bring forth bread from the earth.

6. How many are your works, O LORD!
   In wisdom you have made them all.
   The earth is full of your creatures.
   Bless the LORD, O my soul.

7. All of these look to you
    to give them their food in due season.
    You give it, they gather it up;
    you open wide your hand, they are well filled.

8. You take away their breath, they die,
    returning to the dust from which they came.
    You send forth your spirit, and they are created,
    and you renew the face of the earth.

9. May the glory of the LORD last forever!
    May the LORD rejoice in his works!
    May my thoughts be pleasing to him.
    I will rejoice in the LORD.

Text: Psalm 104:1–2, 1, 24, 5–6, 10, 12, 13–14, 24, 35, 27–28, 29–30, 31, 34; *The Revised Grail Psalms*, © 2010, Conception Abbey and The Grail, admin. by GIA Publications, Inc.

## Psalm 116: Our Blessing-Cup    78

Refrain

Our bless-ing-cup is a com-mun-ion with the Blood of the Lord.

Verses

1. How can I make a return to the Lord for all God has done for me?
    The cup of salvation I will take up, I will call on the name of the Lord.

2. Precious, indeed, in the sight of the Lord is the death of the faithful ones;
    and I am your servant, your chosen one, for you have set me free.

3. Unto your name I will offer my thanks for the debt that I owe to you.
    In the presence of all who have called on your name,
    in the courts of the house of the Lord.

Text: Psalm 116:12–13, 15–16, 17–19; Marty Haugen
Music: Marty Haugen
© 1983, GIA Publications, Inc.

# 79 Psalm 116: Our Blessing-Cup / El Cáliz que Bendecimos

Bilingual Refrain

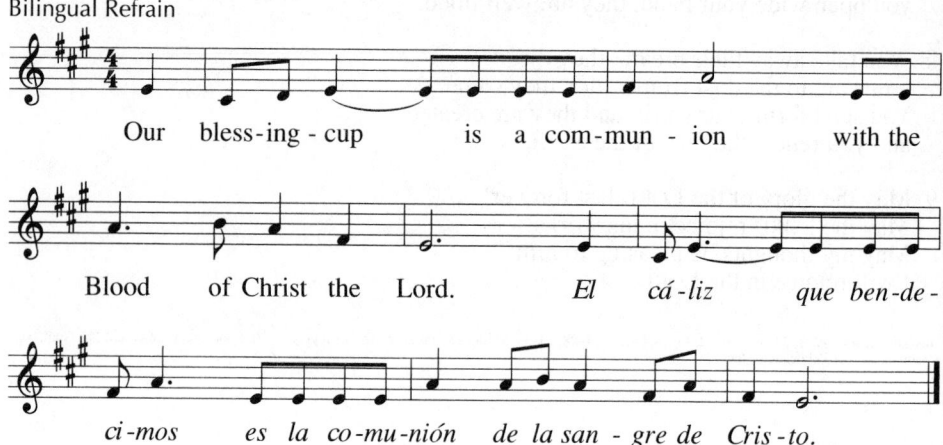

Our bless-ing-cup is a com-mun-ion with the Blood of Christ the Lord. *El cá-liz que ben-de-ci-mos es la co-mu-nión de la san-gre de Cris-to.*

Verses

1. How can I repay the Lord the goodness God has shown to me?
The cup of blessing I raise; I call upon God's name.

2. Painful to the eyes of God, the death of faithful servants.
I am your servant, your child; you rescued me from death.

3. Thanks and praise I will offer God, and call upon your name, Lord.
I will fulfill my vows to the Lord in the presence of God's people.

1. *¿Cómo le pagaré al Señor, mi Dios, todo el bien que me ha hecho?*
*Alzaré la copa de la salvación, e invocaré el nombre del Señor.*

2. *Al Señor, que penosa es la muerte de sus fieles.*
*Soy tu sirviente, tu hijo: rompiste mis cadenas.*

3. *Te ofreceré mis gracias, Dios, invocando tu nombre.*
*Cumpliré mis promesas al Señor en presencia de todo su pueblo.*

Text: Psalm 116:12–13, 15–16bc, 17–18; Tony E. Alonso, © 2003, GIA Publications, Inc.; Spanish refrain trans. © 1970, Conferencia Episcopal Española
Music: Tony E. Alonso, © 2003, GIA Publications, Inc.

# Psalm 116: The Name of God   80

**Refrain I**

I will take the cup of life,   I will call God's name   all my days.

**Refrain II**

Our bless-ing-cup is a com-mun-ion   with the Blood   of Christ.

**Refrain III**

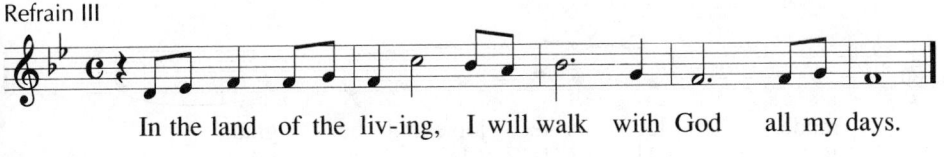

In the land  of the liv-ing,   I will walk  with God   all my days.

**Verses**

1. How can I make a return for the goodness of God?
   This saving cup I will bless and sing, and call the name of God!

2. The dying of those who keep faith is precious to our God.
   I am your servant called from your hands, you have set me free!

3. To you I will offer my thanks and call upon your name.
   You are my promise for all to see. I love your name, O God!

Text: Psalm 116:12–13, 15–16, 17–18; David Haas, © 1987, GIA Publications, Inc.; refrain II trans. © 1969, ICEL
Music: David Haas, © 1987, GIA Publications, Inc.

# 81 Psalm 118: Let Us Rejoice

Refrain

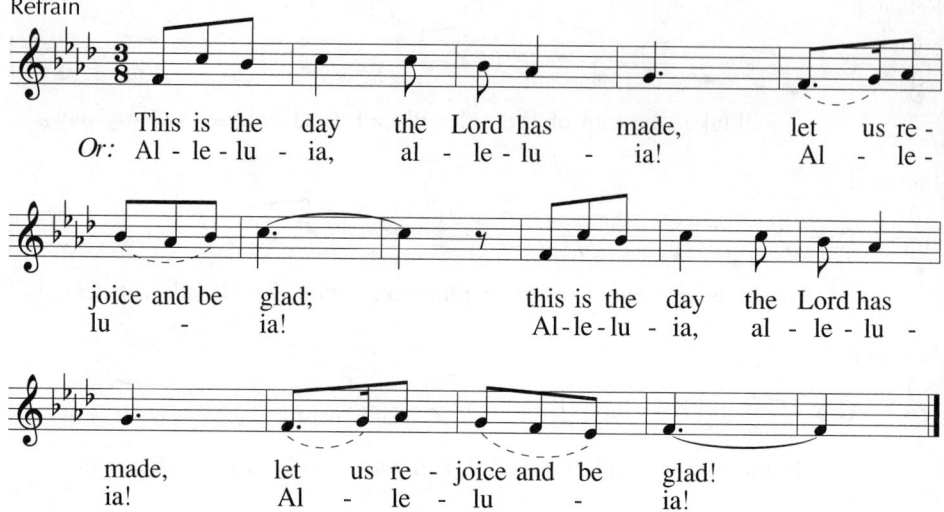

This is the day the Lord has made, let us re -
*Or:* Al - le - lu - ia, al - le - lu - ia! Al - le -

joice and be glad; this is the day the Lord has
lu - ia! Al-le-lu - ia, al - le - lu -

made, let us re - joice and be glad!
ia! Al - le - lu - ia!

Verses

1. Give thanks to the Lord, for God is good; God's mercy endures for ever;
   Let the house of Israel say: "God's mercy endures for ever."

2. The hand of the Lord has struck with power, God's right hand is exalted,
   I shall not die, but live anew, declaring the works of the Lord.

3. The stone which the builders rejected has become the cornerstone,
   the Lord of love and mercy has brought wonder to our eyes!

Text: Psalm 118:1–2, 16–17, 22–23; Marty Haugen, © 1983, GIA Publications, Inc.; refrain trans. © 1969, ICEL
Music: Marty Haugen, © 1983, GIA Publications, Inc.

# Psalm 118: This Is the Day    82

Refrain

This is the day    the    Lord  has made;    let  us  re-joice  and  be        glad.

This is the day    the    Lord   has made;    let  us  re-joice  and be        glad.

Verses

1. Give thanks to the LORD for he is good,
   his mercy endures for ever;
   let the house of Israel say:
   "His mercy endures for ever."

2. The LORD's right hand has struck with power,
   the LORD's right hand is exalted;
   I shall not die, but live
   and declare the works of the LORD.

3. The stone which the builders rejected
   has become the cornerstone.
   By the LORD has this been done;
   it is wonderful in our eyes!

# 83 Psalm 121: Our Help Comes from the Lord

Refrain

Our help comes from the Lord, the mak-er of heav-en and earth.

Verses

1. I lift up my eyes to the mountains: from where shall come my help?
   My help shall come from the Lord who made heaven and earth.

2. May God never allow you to stumble! Let God sleep not, your guard.
   Neither sleeping nor slumbering, God, Israel's guard.

3. The Lord is your guard and your shade: and at your right side stands,
   By day the sun shall not smite you nor the moon in the night.

4. The Lord will guard you from evil: God will guard your soul.
   The Lord will guard your going and coming both now and for ever.

5. Glory to the Father, and to the Son, and to the Holy Spirit:
   as it was in the beginning, is now, and will be for ever. Amen.

Text: Psalm 121; © 1963, 1993, The Grail, GIA Publications, Inc., agent; refrain by Michael Joncas, © 1979, GIA Publications, Inc.
Music: Michael Joncas, © 1979, GIA Publications, Inc.

# 84 Psalm 122: Let Us Go Rejoicing

Refrain

Let us go re - joic-ing to the house of the Lord;

Let us go re - joic-ing to the house of the Lord.

Verses

1. I rejoiced when I heard them say: "Let us go to the house of the Lord,"
   and now our feet are standing within your gates, O Jerusalem.

2. Jerusalem is a city built with unity and strength.
   It is there, it is there that the tribes go up, the tribes of the Lord.

3. For Israel's law is to praise God's name and there to give God thanks.
   There are set the judgment thrones for all of David's house.

4. Pray for the peace of Jerusalem! "May those who love you prosper;
   May peace ever reign within your walls, and wealth within your buildings!"

5. For love of my family and love of my friends, I pray that peace be yours.
   For love of the house of the Lord our God I pray for your good.

Text: Psalm 122; Michael Joncas, © 1987, GIA Publications, Inc.; refrain trans. © 1969, ICEL
Music: Michael Joncas, © 1987, GIA Publications, Inc.

## Psalm 122: Let Us Go Rejoicing  85

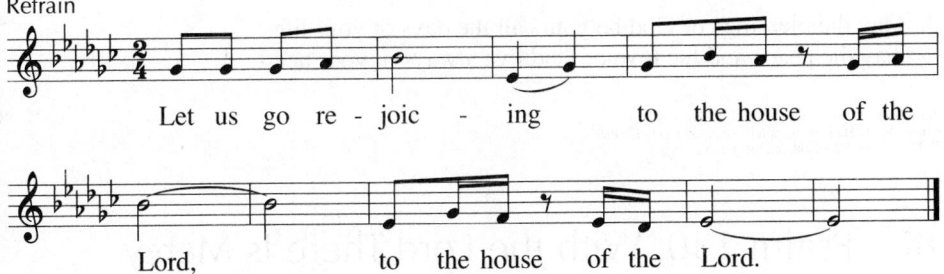

**Refrain**

Let us go re - joic - ing to the house of the Lord, to the house of the Lord.

**Verses**

1. I rejoiced because they said to me, we will go up to the house of the Lord.
   And now we have set foot within your gates, O Jerusalem.

2. We've come to praise the Lord's name as he ordered Israel.
   Here are the courts, the courts of justice, the royal courts of David.

3. For love of my brothers and sisters, I say peace, peace be with you all.
   Since God our Father, our Father lives here, we pray for your happiness.

Text: Psalm 122:1–2, 4b–5, 8–9; Leon C. Roberts, © 1981, 1997, GIA Publications, Inc.; refrain trans. © 1969, ICEL
Music: Leon C. Roberts, © 1981, 1997, GIA Publications, Inc.

# 86  Psalm 128: Blest Are Those Who Love You

Refrain I

Blest are those who love you, hap-py those who
fol-low you, blest are those who seek you, O God.

Refrain II

May the Lord bless us, may the Lord protect us, all the days, all the days of our life.

Verses

1. Happy all those who fear the Lord, and walk in God's pathway;
   you will find what you long for: the riches of our God.

2. Your spouse shall be like a fruitful vine in the midst of your home,
   your children flourish like olive plants rejoicing at your table.

3. May the blessings of God be yours all the days of your life,
   may the peace and the love of God live always in your heart.

Text: Psalm 128:1–2, 3, 5; Marty Haugen
Music: Marty Haugen; refrain II adapt. by Diana Kodner
© 1987, 1993, GIA Publications, Inc.

# 87  Psalm 130: With the Lord There Is Mercy

Refrain

With the Lord there is mer-cy, and full-ness of re-demp-tion.

Verses

1. From out of the depths, I cry unto you,
   Lord, hear my voice, come hear my prayer;
   O let your ear be open to my pleading.

2. If you, O Lord, should mark our guilt,
   then who could stand within your sight?
   But in you is found forgiveness for our failings.

3. Just as those who wait for the morning light,
   even more I long for the Lord, my God,
   whose word to me shall ever be my comfort.

Text: Psalm 130:1–2, 3–4, 5–6; Marty Haugen, © 1983, GIA Publications, Inc.; refrain trans. © 1969, ICEL
Music: Marty Haugen, © 1983, GIA Publications, Inc.

## Psalm 130: Out of the Depths   88

Refrain

Out of the depths I cry to you, O Lord.

Verses

1. Out of the depths I cry to you;
   Lord, hear my voice!
   Let your ears be attentive
   to my prayer for help.

2. If you, O Lord,
   should mark our guilt,
   Lord, who could stand?
   But with you there is mercy,
   that you may be revered.

3. I put my trust in God, the Lord,
   trusting his word.
   My soul waits for the Lord
   more than sentinels wait for the dawn.

4. More than sentinels wait for the dawn,
   Israel waits for God.
   For with God there is kindness,
   and with God, plenteous redemption.

Text: Psalm 130:1–2, 3–4, 5–6, 7; Paul Melley
Music: Paul Melley
© 2008, GIA Publications, Inc.

# 89 Psalm 131: My Soul Is Still

Refrain

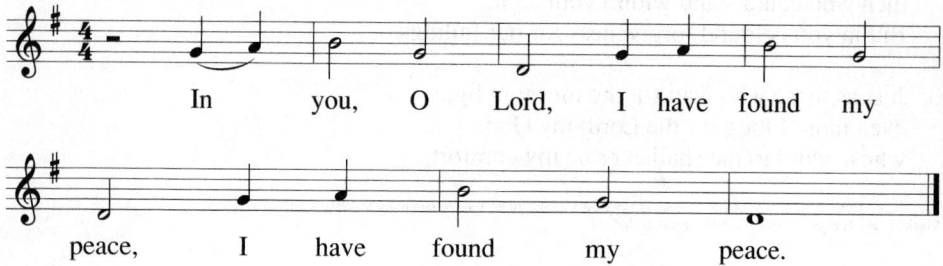

In you, O Lord, I have found my peace, I have found my peace.

Verses

1. My heart is not proud, my eyes not above you;
   You fill my soul. I am not filled with great things,
   nor with thoughts beyond me.

2. My soul is still, my soul stays quiet,
   longing for you like a weaned child
   in its mother's arms; so is my soul a child with you.

Text: Psalm 131:1, 2; David Haas, © 1985, GIA Publications, Inc.; refrain trans. © 1969, ICEL
Music: David Haas, © 1985, GIA Publications, Inc.

# Psalm 136: Love Is Never Ending    90

*Cantor:*

1. We give thanks un - to you, O God of might:
2. In your wis - dom and love you shaped the skies:
3. You have filled all the skies with glo - ry and light:
4. From of old you have led your peo - ple in faith:
5. You de - liv - ered the ones who called un - to you:
6. You have o - pened the sea and brought your peo - ple through:
7. You re - mem - ber your prom - ise age to age:
8. You give food and life to all liv - ing things:

*All:*

for your love is nev - er end - ing,

*Cantor:*

We give thanks un - to you, the God of gods:
You spread out the earth up - on the sea:
The sun for the day and moon for night:
You have shown your com - pas - sion, strength and love:
From bond - age to free - dom, you brought them forth:
Brought them in - to a land that flows with life:
You show mer - cy on those of low de - gree:
We give thanks un - to you, the God of all:

*All:*

for your love is nev - er end - ing.

Text: Psalm 136; Marty Haugen
Music: Marty Haugen
© 1987, GIA Publications, Inc.

# 91 Psalm 138: The Fragrance of Christ

Refrains

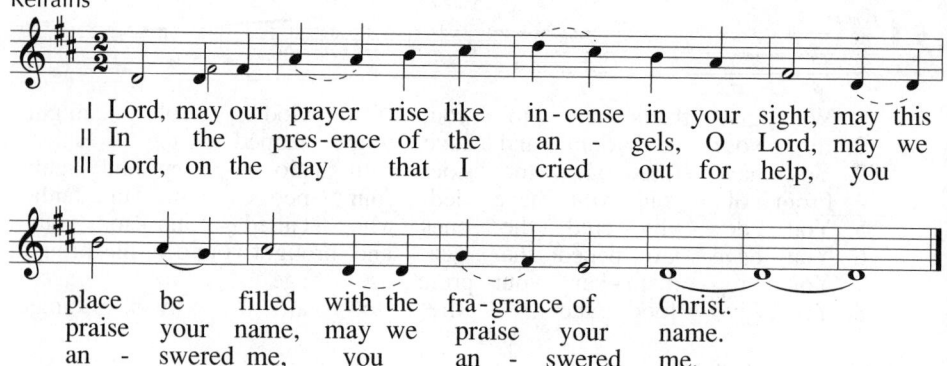

I Lord, may our prayer rise like in-cense in your sight, may this
II In the pres-ence of the an - gels, O Lord, may we
III Lord, on the day that I cried out for help, you

place be filled with the fra-grance of Christ.
praise your name, may we praise your name.
an - swered me, you an - swered me.

Verses

1. I will thank you, Lord, with all of my heart,
   you have heard the words of my mouth.
   In the presence of the angels I will bless you,
   I will adore before your holy temple.

2. I will thank you, Lord, for your faithfulness and love,
   beyond all my hopes and dreams.
   On the day that I called you answered;
   you gave life to the strength of my soul.

3. All who live on earth shall give you thanks
   when they hear the words of your voice.
   And all shall sing of your ways:
   "How great is the glory of God!"

Text: Psalm 138:1–2a, 2bc–3, 4–5; David Haas
Music: David Haas
© 1989, GIA Publications, Inc.

# 92 Psalm 145: I Will Praise Your Name

Refrain

I will praise your name, my King and my God.

I will praise your name, my King and my God.

Verses

1. I will give you glory, my God above, and I will bless your name for ever.
   Ev'ry day I will bless and praise your name for ever.

2. The Lord is full of grace and mercy, who is kind and slow to anger.
   God is good in ev'ry way, and full of compassion.

3. Let all your works give you thanks, O Lord,
   and let all the faithful bless you.
   Let them speak of your might, O Lord, the glory of your kingdom.

4. The Lord is faithful in word and deed,
   and always near, his name is holy.
   Lifting up all those who fall, God raises up the lowly.

Text: Psalm 145:1–2, 8–9, 10–11, 13b–14; David Haas
Music: David Haas
© 1983, GIA Publications, Inc.

## Psalm 146: I Will Praise the Lord　93

Refrain

I will praise the Lord all my days, make

mu - sic to my God while I live, make

mu - sic to my God while I live.

Verses

1. Put no trust in the powerful, mere mortals in whom there is no help.
   Take their breath, they return to clay, and their plans that day come to nothing.
   They are happy who are helped by Jacob's God, whose hope is in the Lord their God,
   who alone made heaven and earth, the seas and all they contain.

2. It is the Lord who keeps faith for ever, who is just to the oppressed.
   It is God who gives bread to the hungry, the Lord, who sets prisoners free.
   It is the Lord who gives sight to the blind, who raises up those who are bowed down,
   the Lord who protects the stranger, and upholds the widow and orphan.

3. It is the Lord who loves the just but thwarts the path of the wicked.
   The Lord will reign for ever, Zion's God from age to age.

Text: Psalm 146; © 1963, 1993, The Grail, GIA Publications, Inc., agent
Music: Michael Joncas, © 1990, GIA Publications, Inc.

## 94 Psalm 150: Praise God in This Holy Dwelling

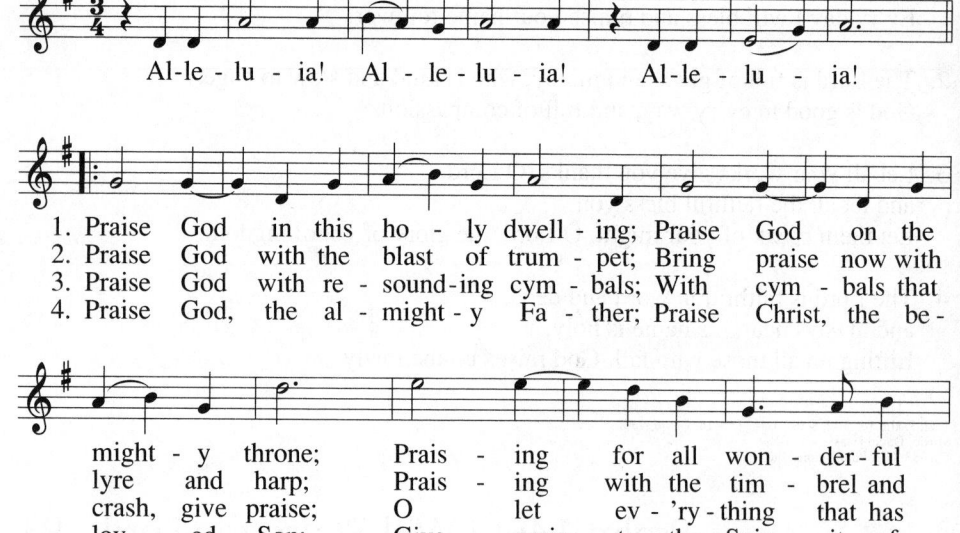

Al-le - lu - ia! Al - le - lu - ia! Al - le - lu - ia!

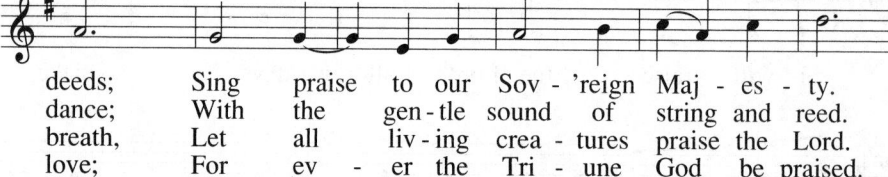

1. Praise God in this ho - ly dwell - ing; Praise God on the
2. Praise God with the blast of trum - pet; Bring praise now with
3. Praise God with re - sound-ing cym - bals; With cym - bals that
4. Praise God, the al - might - y Fa - ther; Praise Christ, the be -

might - y throne; Prais - ing for all won - der - ful
lyre and harp; Prais - ing with the tim - brel and
crash, give praise; O let ev - 'ry-thing that has
lov - ed Son; Give praise to the Spir - it of

deeds; Sing praise to our Sov - 'reign Maj - es - ty.
dance; With the gen - tle sound of string and reed.
breath, Let all liv - ing crea - tures praise the Lord.
love; For ev - er the Tri - une God be praised.

Al - le - lu - ia! Al - le - lu - ia!

1.–3.
Al - le - lu - ia!

4.
lu - ia!

Text: Psalm 150:1–2, 3–4, 5–6; adapt. by Omer Westendorf
Music: Jan M. Vermulst; arr. by Charles G. Frischmann
© 1964, World Library Publications

# Exodus 15: Song at the Sea  95

Refrain

Let us  sing    to the   Lord   who is cov-ered in    won-drous glo-ry.

Verses

1. I will sing to the Lord, in glory triumphant;
   horse and rider are thrown to the sea.
   God of strength, of song, of salvation, God of mine, hear these praises.

2. My God is a warrior whose name is "The Lord."
   Pharoah's army is thrown to the sea.
   Your right hand is magnificent in pow'r,
   your right hand has crushed the enemy.

3. In your mercy you led the people you redeemed.
   You brought them to your sacred home.
   There you will plant them on the mountain that is yours.
   The Lord shall reign for ever!

Text: Exodus 15; Niamh O'Kelly-Fischer
Music: Niamh O'Kelly-Fischer
© 1992, GIA Publications, Inc.

# 96 Exodus 15: Song of Moses

Refrain

I will sing, I will sing to the God who sets me free! I will

sing, I will sing to the God who sets me free! Phar-aoh's

ar - my and his char - i - ots God cast in - to the sea! Phar-aoh's

ar - my and his char - i - ots God cast in - to the sea!

Verses

1. The Lord is my strength, my protection and my shield;
   Pharaoh's army and his chariots God cast into the sea.
   Our God is a warrior whose name is "the Lord,"
   God of might, God of victory!

2. The brave and the mighty, the pride of Pharaoh's army,
   God plunged them to the bottom of the sea like a stone.
   The hand of the Lord is magnificent in power;
   the Lord has crushed our foes!

3. O God who redeems, who delivers us from slavery,
   you set us on the mountain of your holy place.
   Your throne and your temple shall endure for all time;
   your reign shall never end!

Text: Exodus 15; Scott Soper
Music: Scott Soper
© 1997, GIA Publications, Inc.

# Isaiah 12: With Joy You Shall Draw Water 97

**Refrain I**

With joy you shall draw wa - ter from the springs of end - less

life; With joy you shall draw wa - ter from the liv-ing well of God.

**Refrain II**

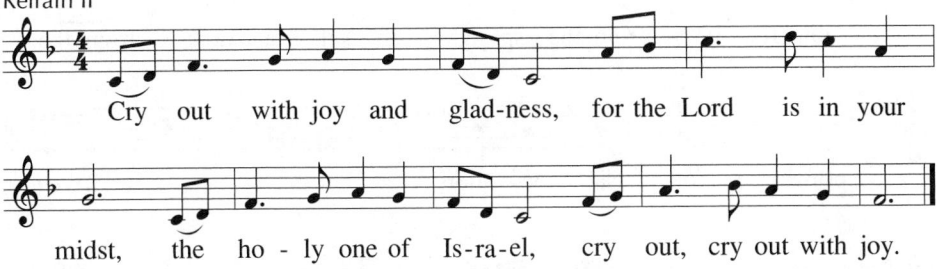

Cry out with joy and glad-ness, for the Lord is in your

midst, the ho - ly one of Is-ra-el, cry out, cry out with joy.

**Verses**

1. God indeed is my Savior, I will never be afraid,
   my strength and courage is the Lord, my Savior and my song.

2. Give thanks and praise the name of God, sing out to all the earth
   the wondrous deeds that God has done, our Savior and our song.

3. Shout with joy, O Zion, for dwelling in your midst
   is the Holy One of Israel, your Savior and your song.

Text: Isaiah 12:2–3, 4, 6; Marty Haugen
Music: Marty Haugen; refrain II adapt. by Diana Kodner
© 1988, 1994, GIA Publications, Inc.

# 98 Isaiah 12: You Will Draw Water Joyfully / Sacarán Aguas con Alegría

Bilingual Refrain

Verses

1. God indeed is my Savior; I am confident and fearless.
   My courage is the Lord, for God has been my savior!

2. Proclaim God's name to the nations, tell the world of God's works.
   Praise the Lord, all you people, how glorious is God's name!

3. Sing the wonders God works, make them known in ev'ry land.
   O people of Zion, shout: the holy one is among you.

1. *Vean al Dios que me salva, con él estoy seguro.*
   *¡Mi fuerza y protección, el Señor es mi salvación!*

2. *¡Denle las gracias a Dios, invoquen su nombre,*
   *proclamen sus hazañas, a todos proclamen su nombre!*

3. *Canten a Dios por sus proezas, anúncienlas a toda la tierra.*
   *Habitantes de Sión se alegran: "Contigo está el Dios de Israel."*

Text: Isaiah 12:2–3, 4bcd, 5–6, adapt. and tr. by Tony E. Alonso, © 2003, GIA Publications, Inc.; English refrain tr. © 1969, ICEL
Music: Tony E. Alonso, © 2003, GIA Publications, Inc.

# Daniel 3:57–88: Canticle of Daniel    99

Refrain

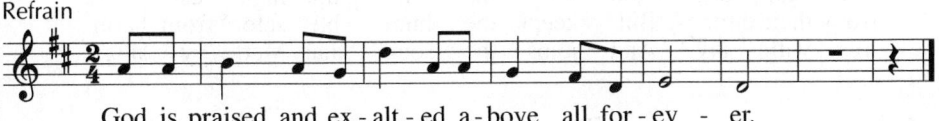

God is praised and ex-alt-ed a-bove all for-ev - er.

Verses

1. Angels of the Lord, *Response*
   you heavens, *Response*
   all waters above the heavens, *Response*
   all you hosts of the Lord, sun and moon,
   stars of heaven, bless the Lord!

Assembly Response

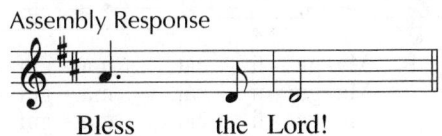

Bless        the Lord!

2. Every shower and dew, *Response*
   all wind and heat, *Response*
   cold and chill, dew and rain, *Response*
   ice and snow, nights and days,
   lights and darkness and clouds, bless the Lord!

3. Mountains and hills, *Response*
   everything growing from the earth, *Response*
   springs, seas and rivers, *Response*
   all water creatures, all you birds,
   all you beasts, sons of man, bless the Lord!

4. O Israel, *Response*
   priests and servants of the Lord, *Response*
   spirits and souls of the just, *Response*
   holy men, humble of heart,
   Hananiah, Azariah, Mishael, bless the Lord!

Text: Daniel 3:57–88; adapt. from the *New American Bible*, © 1970, Confraternity of Christian Doctrine, Inc.
Music: John Angotti; arr. by Paul A. Tate, © 2002, World Library Publications

# 100  Luke 1:46–53: My Soul Gives Glory

1. My soul gives glo - ry to my God, Who reach - es
2. God's mer - cy com - forts all who fear, Em - brac - ing
3. God's jus - tice sends the rich a - way, But feeds the

down with lov - ing grace To lift me from my
with a stead - fast arm That casts the might - y
poor with lav - ish things. Each hun - gry soul now

low es - tate And set me in the high - est place.
from their thrones, But keeps the hum - ble safe from harm.
fills with joy And joins the song that Mar - y sings:

Ma - gní - fi - cat, ma - gní - fi - cat! With all my heart, I
Ma - gní - fi - cat, ma - gní - fi - cat! The weak find strength; the
Ma - gní - fi - cat, ma - gní - fi - cat! To God, Cre - a - tor,

an - swer Yes When God an - noun - ces won - drous
wea - ry, rest. God's prom - ise sounds from age to
Christ, the Son; And Ho - ly Spir - it— tri - une

news. And ev - 'ry age shall call me blest.
age: The need - y of the world are blest.
God: All prais - es to the Three in One.

Text: Luke 1:46–53; Mary Louise Bringle, © 2004, GIA Publications, Inc.
Tune: MAGNIFICAT, LMD; Michael Joncas, © 1979, 1988, GIA Publications, Inc.

# Luke 1:46–55: Magníficat    101

Refrain

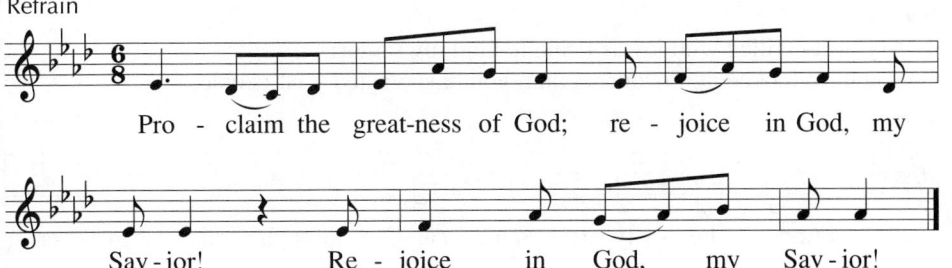

Pro - claim the great-ness of God; re - joice in God, my

Sav - ior!    Re - joice in God, my Sav - ior!

Verses

1. For he has favored his lowly one, and all shall call me blessed.
   The almighty has done great things for me, and holy is his name.

2. He favors those who fear his name, in ev'ry generation.
   He has shown the might and strength of his arm,
   and scattered the proud of heart.

3. He has cast the mighty from their thrones, and lifted up the lowly.
   He has filled the hungry with all good gifts, and sent the rich away.

4. He has helped his servant Israel, remembering his mercy.
   He promised his mercy to Abraham and his children for evermore.

Text: Luke 1:46–55; James J. Chepponis
Music: James J. Chepponis
© 1980, GIA Publications, Inc.

# 102  Luke 1:46–55: Holy Is Your Name

**Verse 1**

1. My soul is filled with joy as I sing to God my savior:
   you have looked upon your servant, you have visited your people.

Refrain

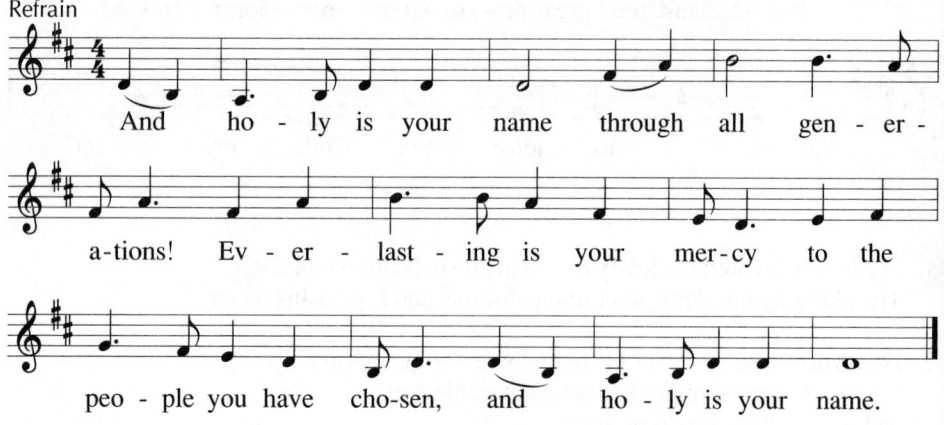

And ho - ly is your name through all gen - er - a-tions! Ev - er - last - ing is your mer-cy to the peo - ple you have cho-sen, and ho - ly is your name.

**Verses 2–5**

2. I am lowly as a child, but I know from this day forward
   that my name will be remembered, for all will call me blessed.

3. I proclaim the pow'r of God, you do marvels for your servants;
   though you scatter the proud hearted, and destroy the might of princes.

4. To the hungry you give food, send the rich away empty.
   In your mercy you are mindful of the people you have chosen.

5. In your love you now fulfill what you promised to your people.
   I will praise you Lord, my savior, everlasting is your mercy.

Text: Luke 1:46–55, David Haas
Music: WILD MOUNTAIN THYME, Irregular; Irish traditional; arr. by David Haas
© 1989, GIA Publications, Inc.

# Luke 1:68–79: Now Bless the God of Israel   103

1. Now bless the God of Is - ra - el, Who
2. Re - mem - ber - ing the cov - e - nant, God
3. In ten - der mer - cy, God will send The

comes in love and pow'r, Who rais - es from the
res - cues us from fear, That we might serve in
day - spring from on high, Our ris - ing sun, the

roy - al house De - liv - 'rance in this hour. Through
ho - li - ness And peace from year to year; And
light of life For those who sit and sigh. God

ho - ly proph - ets God has sworn To
you, my child, shall go be - fore To
comes to guide our way to peace, That

free us from a - larm, To save us from the
preach, to proph - e - sy, That all may know the
death shall reign no more. Sing prais - es to the

heav - y hand Of all who wish us harm.
ten - der love, The grace of God most high.
Ho - ly One! O wor - ship and a - dore!

Text: *Benedictus*, Luke 1:68–79; Ruth Duck, © 1992, GIA Publications, Inc.
Tune: FOREST GREEN, CMD; English; harm. by Michael Joncas, © 1987, GIA Publications, Inc.

# 104 Luke 2:29–34: Nunc Dimíttis

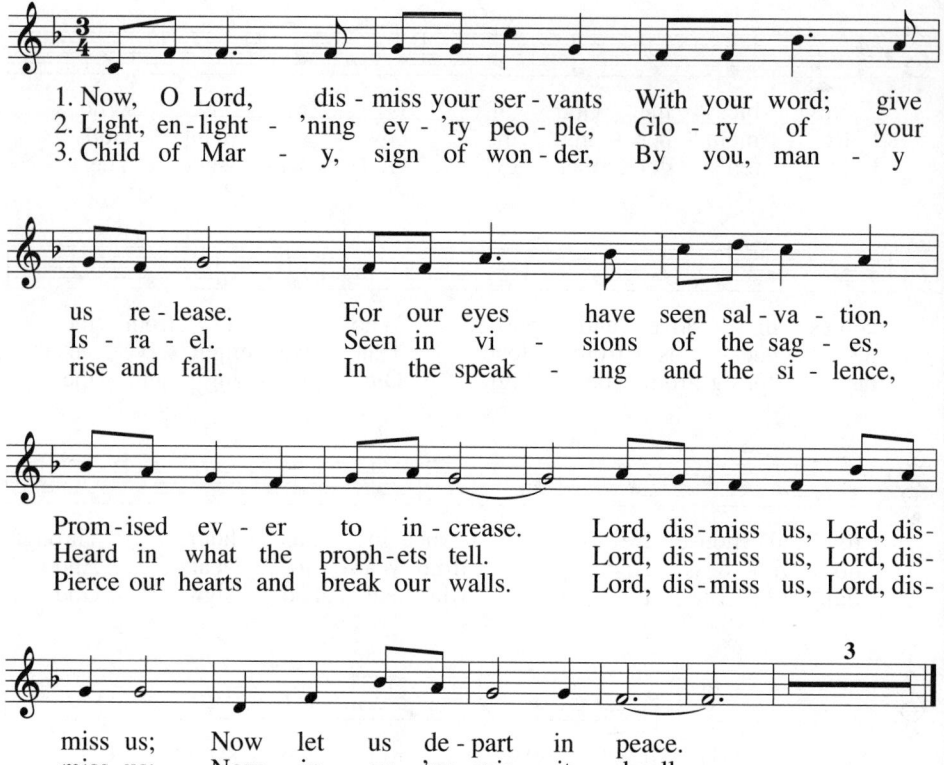

1. Now, O Lord, dis - miss your ser - vants With your word; give
2. Light, en - light - 'ning ev - 'ry peo - ple, Glo - ry of your
3. Child of Mar - y, sign of won - der, By you, man - y

us re - lease. For our eyes have seen sal - va - tion,
Is - ra - el. Seen in vi - sions of the sag - es,
rise and fall. In the speak - ing and the si - lence,

Prom - ised ev - er to in - crease. Lord, dis - miss us, Lord, dis -
Heard in what the proph - ets tell. Lord, dis - miss us, Lord, dis -
Pierce our hearts and break our walls. Lord, dis - miss us, Lord, dis -

miss us; Now let us de - part in peace.
miss us; Now in ev - 'ry spir - it dwell.
miss us; Now, our God, our life, our all.

Text: Luke 2:29–34; *Nunc Dimittis*; Sylvia Dunstan, © 1995, GIA Publications, Inc.
Music: PEACETIME, 8 7 8 7 8 7; David Haas, © 2003, GIA Publications, Inc.

# Philippians 2:6–11: Jesus Christ Is Lord!   105

Refrain

Emp-tied   and   hum-bled,   o - be-dient   to death,       Christ   em -

braced the       cross.          Je - sus   Christ   is       Lord!

Verses

1. Although he was in the form of God,
   he did not claim equality with God as something to be grasped.
   But Jesus chose to empty himself and take the form of a slave,
   human and broken like one of us, human and broken like one of us.

2. Found to be of human form, Jesus humbled himself,
   obediently accepting death, death on a cross.
   Because of this, God greatly exalted him
   and gave him the name above all names, the name above all names.

3. So that at the name of Jesus, ev'ry knee should humbly bend
   in heaven, and on earth, and under the earth,
   and ev'ry tongue proclaim and sing to the glory of God the Father:
   "Jesus Christ is Lord! Jesus Christ is Lord!"

Text: Philippians 2:6–11; David Haas, alt.
Music: David Haas
© 2010, GIA Publications, Inc.

# Christian Initiation of Adults

The passage of an adult into the Christian community takes place over an extended period of time. The members of the local Church, the catechists and sponsors, the clergy and the diocesan bishop take part in the journey from inquiry through the catechumenate to baptism, confirmation and eucharist. With their example the candidates are invited to pray, to reflect on the word of God, to fast and to join in the community's practice of charity. They are to learn the way of Jesus from the members of the Church.

This journey of the candidates and community is marked by liturgical rites; thus the community publicly acknowledges, encourages and strengthens the candidates. The first of these is the rite of becoming catechumens. It concludes the sometimes lengthy period during which those who have come to ask about the way of the Church and the life of a Christian have heard the gospel proclaimed and seen it practiced. Those who then feel called to walk in this way of Christ's Church ask to begin the journey toward baptism. If the Church judges the inquirers ready, they are accepted into the order of catechumens.

Those who have entered the catechumenate are already part of the household of Christ. During this time the catechumens are to hear and reflect on God's word, to learn the teachings and practices of the Church, to become gradually accustomed to the ways of prayer and discipline in the Church, to observe and to join in the good works of Christians. Ordinarily the catechumens are present on Sunday for the liturgy of the word and may be dismissed after the homily—to continue prayer and study with their catechists—since they cannot join in the Eucharist.

Rites of exorcism and blessing may be celebrated during the catechumenate. Through such rites the Church prays that the catechumens will be purified, strengthened against all evil and thus eagerly grow in faith and good works. The very presence of the catechumens—at the Sunday liturgy, in these special rites and in everyday life—is itself a source of strength and blessing to the faithful.

Each year as Lent begins, the bishop, with the help of the local pastor and others involved with the catechumens, is to call those catechumens who are judged ready to prepare themselves for baptism at the Easter Vigil. Thus the catechumens become the "elect," the chosen, and for the forty days of Lent they make preparations: praying, fasting, doing good works. All the faithful join them in this. On several Sundays in Lent the rites of scrutiny take place when the assembled Church prays over the elect. During Lent also the catechumens may publicly receive the words of the Church's creed and of the Lord's Prayer.

Good Friday and Holy Saturday are days of prayer, fasting and preparation for the rites of the Easter Vigil. On the night between Saturday and Sunday, the Church assembles to keep vigil and listen to many readings from Scripture. Then the catechumens are called forward for baptism and confirmation. These rites are found in the Easter Vigil.

The newly baptized, now called neophytes, take a special place in the Sunday Eucharist throughout the fifty days of Eastertime. This is a time for deepening their incorporation into the Church.

All of these stages of initiation take place in the midst of the community. In various rites, the faithful show the Christian life to the inquirers and catechumens. In turn, the faithful are strengthened and challenged in their faith by the presence of the catechumens.

Those who seek to belong to the Roman Catholic Church and who are already baptized may participate in the catechesis and in some of the rites of the catechumenate but they are not baptized again. Rather, they are received into the full communion of the Roman Catholic Church.

# ACCEPTANCE INTO THE ORDER OF CATECHUMENS 107

## INTRODUCTORY RITES

*The priest greets the assembly: candidates, sponsors, members of the parish. The candidates are asked what it is that they seek and each replies. After each candidate has responded, one of the following may be sung:*

108

We stand with you, we pray for you, O ho-ly child of God!

Text: David Haas
Music: David Haas
© 1988, GIA Publications, Inc.

109

We praise you, Lord, we praise you, Lord,

we praise you, Lord, and we bless you.

Text: ICEL, © 1985
Music: Marty Haugen, © 1995, GIA Publications, Inc.

## CANDIDATES' FIRST ACCEPTANCE OF THE GOSPEL

*The priest solemnly asks if the candidates are ready to begin walking the way of the gospel. The sponsors and all present are asked if they stand ready to assist the candidates as they strive to know and follow Christ. All respond:* **We are.**

## SIGNING OF THE CANDIDATES WITH THE CROSS

*The sign of the cross marks the candidates for their new way of life. The priest signs each on the forehead saying:*

N., receive the cross on your forehead.
It is Christ himself who now strengthens you
with this sign of his love.
Learn now to know him and follow him.

*Sponsors and others also sign the candidates. Ears and eyes and other senses may also be signed. The priest prays that the catechumens may share in the saving power of the cross.*

*One of the following musical settings with assembly acclamations may be used:*

## 110

*Priest:* Receive the sign of the cross....

Christ will be your strength! Learn to know and fol-low him.

Music: David Haas, © 1988, GIA Publications, Inc.

## 111

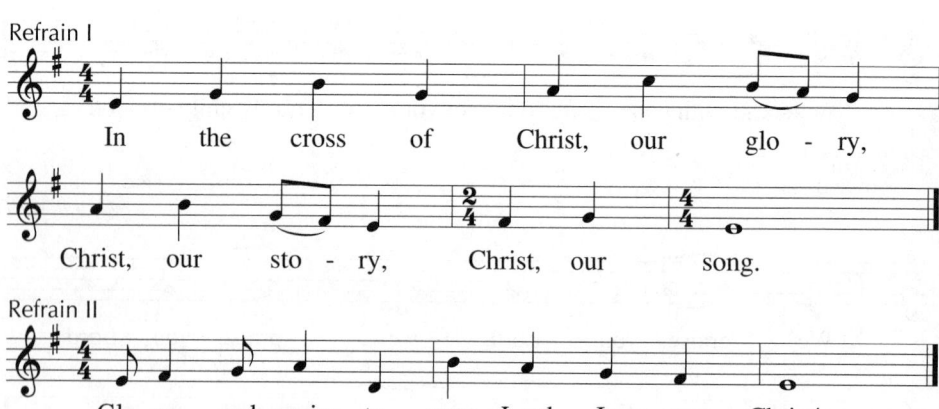

Refrain I

In the cross of Christ, our glo - ry,

Christ, our sto - ry, Christ, our song.

Refrain II

Glo - ry and praise to you, Lord Je - sus Christ!

Text: ICEL, © 1969
Music: Marty Haugen, © 1995, GIA Publications, Inc.

## 112  INVITATION TO THE CELEBRATION OF THE WORD OF GOD

*The assembly enters the church for the liturgy of the word. The following psalm may be sung:*

Come, my chil - dren, come to me, and

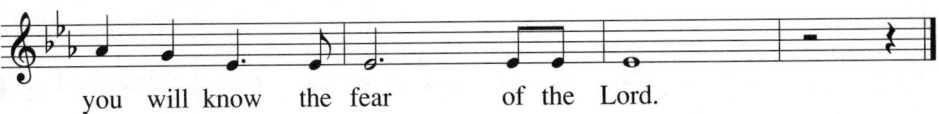

you will know the fear of the Lord.

I will bless the Lord at all times,
God's song is always on my lips.
In the Lord my soul shall make its boast,
the humble will hear and be glad. ℟.

Glory in the Lord with me,
May God's name always be our joy.

God answered me when I cried,
and freed me from my fear. ℟.

Look to God and shine with joy!
May God free your faces from all shame!
God hears the cry of all the poor,
and saves all who live in their fear. ℟.

Text: Psalm 34; adapted by David Haas
Music: David Haas
© 1988, GIA Publications, Inc.

## LITURGY OF THE WORD      113

*There may be one or more readings from Scripture, together with a responsorial psalm. After the homily, a Bible may be given to the new catechumens for their study and prayer throughout the time of the catechumenate.*

### INTERCESSIONS FOR THE CATECHUMENS
*All join in prayer for the new catechumens.*

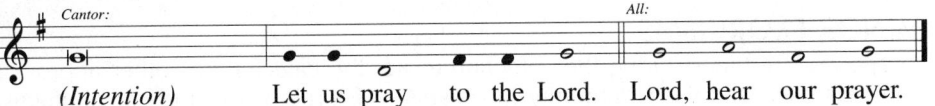

*(Intention)*     Let us pray to the Lord.    Lord, hear our prayer.

Music: Byzantine chant

*If the Eucharist is to be celebrated, the catechumens are first dismissed. For music to accompany the dismissal, see nos. 115–117.*

# RITES OF THE CATECHUMENATE      114

## DISMISSAL OF THE CATECHUMENS

When the catechumens are present at Mass, they are usually dismissed after the homily. Only when they have been baptized are they able to join the faithful in the reception of the eucharist. After their dismissal, the catechumens remain together and are joined by their catechists or others to pray and reflect on the scripture readings.

*One of the following may be sung to accompany the dismissal:*      115

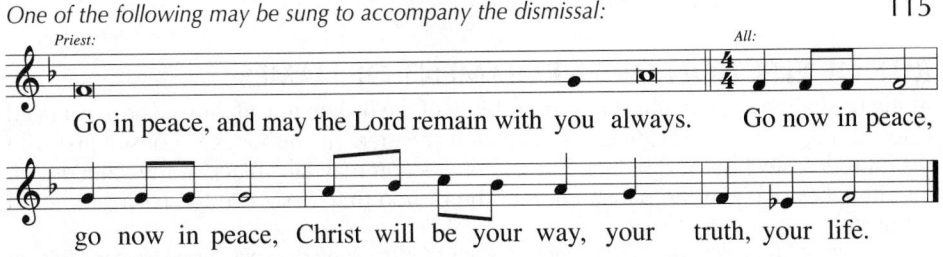

Go in peace, and may the Lord remain with you always.    Go now in peace,

go now in peace, Christ will be your way, your truth, your life.

Text: *Rite of Christian Initiation of Adults,* © 1985, ICEL
Music: Lynn Trapp, © 1991, Morning Star Music Publishers

**116**

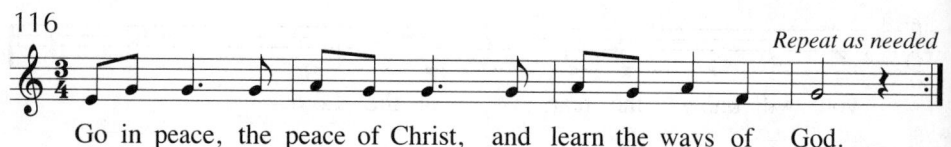

*Repeat as needed*

Go in peace, the peace of Christ, and learn the ways of God.

Text: Marty Haugen
Music: Marty Haugen
© 1997, GIA Publications, Inc.

**117**

May the Word be a lamp for our feet, and a light to guide our path!
(your)                                             (your)

Text: David Haas
Music: David Haas
© 1991, GIA Publications, Inc.

## CELEBRATIONS OF THE WORD OF GOD

On Sundays, after the catechetical sessions, before the beginning of a new liturgical season, and at other times the catechumens and others may join for liturgy: song, reading of Scripture, psalmody, prayer and silence are normally part of such a service.

## MINOR EXORCISMS

At appropriate times during the catechumenate, the catechists or other approved ministers may lead the community in prayers of exorcism over the catechumens. These prayers acknowledge the struggle against evil and ask that God strengthen the catechumens.

## BLESSINGS OF THE CATECHUMENS

Prayers of blessing and the laying on of hands may take place whenever the catechumens gather for instruction or other purposes. Catechists or other approved ministers ask these blessings over the catechumens.

## ANOINTINGS AND PRESENTATIONS

During the catechumenate or during Lent, the candidates may be anointed with the oil of catechumens as a sign of strength given for their struggle to live the gospel. At some point in this time they are publicly presented with the Church's treasury of prayer and faith, the Our Father and the Creed.

## RITE OF ELECTION OR ENROLLMENT OF NAMES

At the beginning of Lent, it is the responsibility of the bishop to call those who are judged ready to prepare for the sacraments of initiation at Easter. The bishop is to consult first with the pastors, catechists and others. The rite of election may take place at the cathedral. If the rite takes place in the parish church, the bishop may designate the pastor to act in his place.

*This rite is also called the "Enrollment of Names." Each candidate now gives his/her name, or writes it down. When all have been enrolled, the bishop says: "You have been chosen to be initiated into the sacred mysteries at the Easter Vigil." He then speaks to them and to their sponsors about their lenten preparation for baptism.*

*While or immediately after the candidates have signed their names, a hymn or acclamation (e.g., no. 900) may be sung.*

## SCRUTINIES 118

*The scrutinies occur on the Third, Fourth and Fifth Sundays of Lent. The elect are called before the community for exorcism and prayer. This rite may include the following setting:*

*1st Scrutiny* 1. We thirst for liv - ing wa - ter,
*2nd Scrutiny* 2. We search for light in dark-ness, de - liv-er us, O Lord.
*3rd Scrutiny* 3. We long to rise to new life,

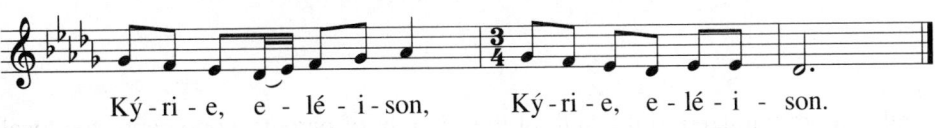

Ký - ri - e, e - lé - i - son, Ký - ri - e, e - lé - i - son.

Text: Carol Browning
Music: Carol Browning
© 2011, GIA Publications, Inc.

## PREPARATORY RITES

Various preparation rites take place during the day on Holy Saturday. These include prayer, recitation of the Creed, and the rite of Ephphetha (opening of ears and mouth).

## SACRAMENTS OF INITIATION

The sacraments of initiation take place at the Easter Vigil.

## PERIOD OF MYSTAGOGIA

"Mystagogia" refers to the fifty-day period of postbaptismal catechesis and celebration when the newly baptized are gradually drawn by the community into the fullness of Christian life and prayer. The newly baptized retain a special place in the assembly and are mentioned in the prayers of intercession. A special celebration, on Pentecost or just before, may mark the conclusion of the whole period of initiation.

# Baptism of Children

**119**
Children are baptized in the faith of the Church: of parents, godparents, the local parish, the Church throughout the world, the saints. Bringing their children for baptism, the parents profess their commitment to make a home where the gospel is lived. And the godparents and all members of the community promise to support the parents in this. Thus the children enter the waters of baptism and so are joined to this people, all baptized into the death and resurrection of Christ.

Baptism is celebrated above all at the Easter Vigil, but also on other Sundays, for Sunday is the Lord's Day, the day when the Church gathers to proclaim the paschal mystery. Baptism is always celebrated in an assembly of members of the Church and may take place at Sunday Mass.

## 120  RECEPTION OF THE CHILDREN
*The people may sing a psalm or hymn suitable for the occasion as the priest/deacon goes to meet the parents and godparents at the entrance of the church, or as all process into the church.*

*The parents and godparents are welcomed by all. The priest/deacon asks the names of the children and questions the parents about their own expectations and willingness to take on the responsibilities this baptism brings. The godparents are asked if they are ready to assist the parents in their responsibilities as Christian mothers and fathers.*

*With joy, then, the priest/deacon, the parents and godparents make the sign of the cross on the child's forehead as the priest or deacon says: "I claim you for Christ our Savior by the sign of his cross."*

*If there is to be a procession to the place where Scripture will be read, the following antiphon, or a hymn, may be sung:*

*The assembly repeats each phrase after the cantor.*

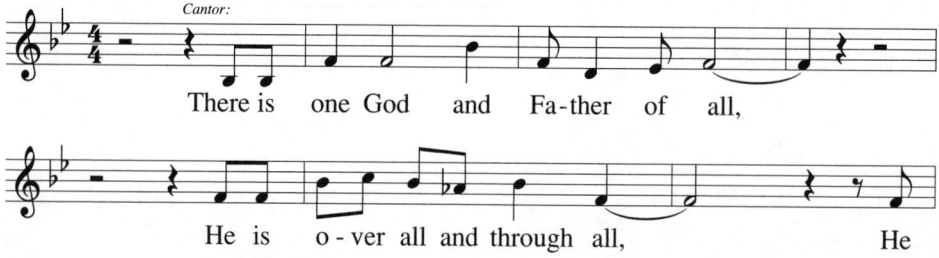

lives     in     all     of     us;          All     of     us     are     one,

u - nit - ed     in     Christ          Je - sus.

Text: ICEL, © 1969
Music: Marty Haugen, © 1995, GIA Publications, Inc.

# LITURGY OF THE WORD                                               121

## FIRST READINGS

*One or more passages from Scripture are read. At the conclusion of each:*

   *Reader:*  The word of the Lord.
*Assembly:*  **Thanks be to God.**

## RESPONSORIAL PSALM

*The following psalm, or a setting of Psalm 23 or 34, may follow the first reading:*

Refrain

The     Lord     is     my     light     and     my     sal - va - tion.

Text: *Lectionary for Mass,* © 1969, ICEL
Music: Anthony E. Jackson, © 1984

Verses

The LORD is my light and my salvation;
whom shall I fear?
The LORD is the stronghold of my life;
whom should I dread?  ℟.

There is one thing I ask of the LORD,
only this do I seek:
to live in the house of the LORD

all the days of my life,
to gaze on the beauty of the LORD,
to inquire at his temple.  ℟.

I believe I shall see the LORD's goodness
in the land of the living.
Wait for the LORD; be strong;
be stouthearted, and wait for the LORD!  ℟.

Text: Psalm 27:1, 4, 13–14, *The Revised Grail Psalms,* © 2010, Conception Abbey and The Grail, admin. by GIA Publications, Inc.
Music: Cyril Baker, © The Antilles Episcopal Conference

## GOSPEL                                                           122

*Before the gospel reading, an acclamation is sung:*

Al - le - lu - ia,          al - le - lu - ia,          al - le - lu - ia.

Music: Chant Mode VI; acc. by Richard Proulx, © 1985, GIA Publications, Inc.

*During Lent:*

Praise to you, Lord Je - sus Christ, king of end-less glo-ry!

Text: ICEL, © 1969
Music: Frank Schoen, © 1970, GIA Publications, Inc.

*Deacon (or priest):* The Lord be with you.
       *Assembly:* **And with your spirit.**
        *Deacon:* A reading from the holy Gospel according to N.
       *Assembly:* **Glory to you, O Lord.**

*After the reading:*

       *Deacon:* The Gospel of the Lord.
       *Assembly:* **Praise to you, Lord Jesus Christ.**

## 123 INTERCESSIONS

*All join in prayer for the Church, the needs of the world, the poor, the children to be baptized and their parents.*

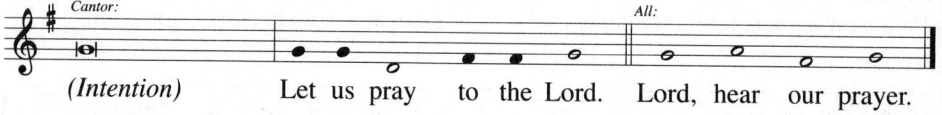

*(Intention)* Let us pray to the Lord. Lord, hear our prayer.

Music: Byzantine chant

*This prayer concludes with the litany of the saints, which may include the patron saints of the children and of the local Church.*

## 124

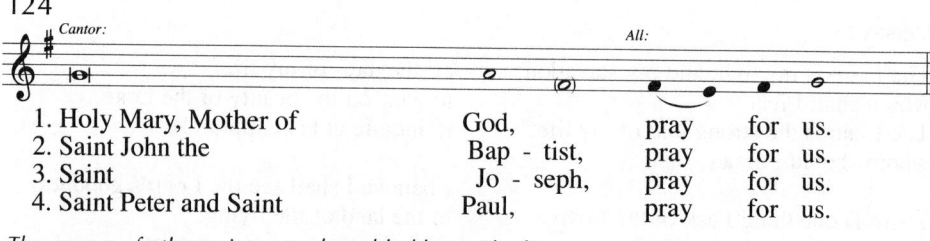

| | | | |
|---|---|---|---|
| 1. Holy Mary, Mother of | God, | pray | for us. |
| 2. Saint John the | Bap - tist, | pray | for us. |
| 3. Saint | Jo - seph, | pray | for us. |
| 4. Saint Peter and Saint | Paul, | pray | for us. |

*The names of other saints may be added here. The litany concludes:*

  5. All holy men and women, Saints of God,       pray     for us.

## 125 PRAYER OF EXORCISM AND ANOINTING

*The priest/deacon stands before the parents with their infants and prays that God deliver these children from the power of evil. The children may be anointed with the oil of catechumens, an anointing which makes them strong for their struggle against evil in their lives. Or, the priest/deacon may lay hands on each child to show the love and concern the Church has for them. If there is a procession to the baptistry, the following may be sung:*

We come to you, Lord Je - sus, fill us with your life.

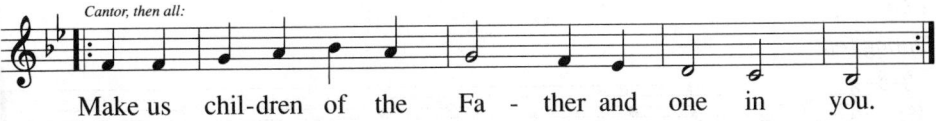

Cantor, then all:

Make us chil-dren of the Fa - ther and one in you.

Text: ICEL, © 1969
Music: Ronald Arnatt, © 1984, GIA Publications, Inc.

# SACRAMENT OF BAPTISM 126

## BLESSING AND INVOCATION OF GOD OVER BAPTISMAL WATER

*When all are gathered at the font, the priest/deacon leads a blessing of the water, unless the baptismal water has already been blessed.*

## RENUNCIATION OF SIN AND PROFESSION OF FAITH

*The priest/deacon then questions the parents and godparents, and they make a renunciation of sin and evil and profess their faith. The assembly listens to their responses. The priest/ deacon then invites all to give their assent to this profession of faith, using the following formulary, a similar one, or a suitable song by which the community expresses its faith with a single voice.*

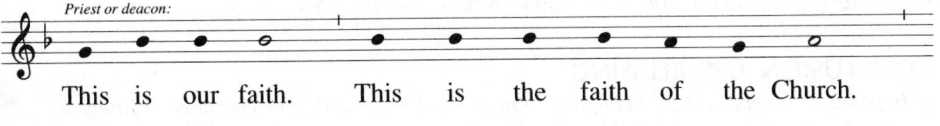

Priest or deacon:

This is our faith. This is the faith of the Church.

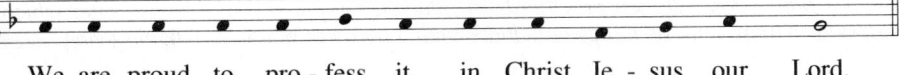

We are proud to pro - fess it, in Christ Je - sus our Lord.

All:

A - men.

Text: ICEL, © 1969

## BAPTISM 127

*One by one, the infants are brought to the font by their parents. There the parents express their desire to have their child baptized in the faith of the Church which they have professed. The infant is then immersed in the water three times (or water is poured over the infant's head three times) as the priest/deacon says: "N., I baptize you in the name of the Father, and of the Son, and of the Holy Spirit." All may respond to each baptism with an acclamation.*

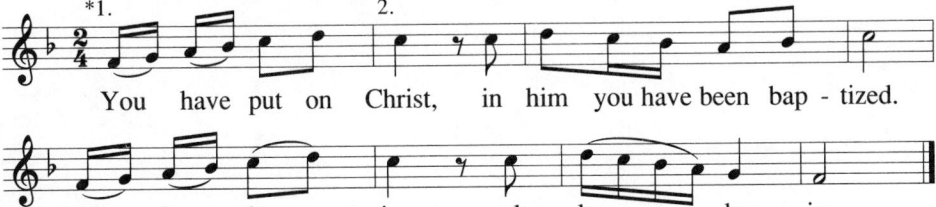

*1. 2.

You have put on Christ, in him you have been bap - tized.

Al - le - lu - ia, al - le - lu - ia.

*May be sung in canon.*

Text: ICEL, © 1969
Music: Howard Hughes, SM, © 1977, ICEL

## 128

*During Lent:*

Glo - ry    and praise    to    you, Lord    Je - sus    Christ.

Text: *Rite of Christian Initiation of Adults*, © 1985, ICEL
Music: Marty Haugen, © 1995, GIA Publications, Inc.

### 129  ANOINTING WITH CHRISM
*The priest/deacon anoints each child on the crown of the head with holy chrism, a mixture of oil and perfume. The word "Christ" means "anointed." The baptized child has been "Christ-ed" and the sweet smell of the anointing reminds all of this.*

### CLOTHING WITH THE BAPTISMAL GARMENT AND GIVING OF THE CANDLE
*The infants are then clothed in baptismal garments and a candle for each of the newly bap-tized is lighted from the paschal candle.*

### (Optional) EPHPHETHA
*The priest/deacon may touch the ears and mouth of each child: "May Jesus soon touch your ears to receive his word, and your mouth to proclaim his faith."*

### CONCLUSION AND BLESSING
*If baptism is celebrated at Mass, the liturgy continues with the Eucharist. Otherwise, all process to the altar, carrying lighted candles. The above acclamation may be sung again dur-ing this procession. All then pray the Lord's Prayer, the parents are blessed, after which all respond:* **Amen***, and the liturgy concludes with a hymn of praise and thanksgiving.*

# Holy Communion outside Mass

When for good reason Communion cannot be received at Mass, the faithful may share in the paschal mystery through the liturgy of the word and the reception of Holy Communion.

## INTRODUCTORY RITES
*An appropriate hymn or psalm may be sung.*

### GREETING
*If the minister is a priest or deacon, the usual form of greeting is used:*

*Assembly:* **And with your spirit.**

*If the minister is not a priest or deacon, another form of greeting may be used:*

*Assembly:* **Blessed be God for ever.**

### PENITENTIAL RITE
*The minister invites silent reflection and repentance. After some silence:*

*Assembly:* **I confess to almighty God**
**and to you, my brothers and sisters,**
**that I have greatly sinned,**
**in my thoughts and in my words,**
**in what I have done and in what I have failed to do,**
*All strike their breast as they say:*
**through my fault, through my fault,**
**through my most grievous fault;**
**therefore I ask blessed Mary ever-Virgin,**
**all the Angels and Saints,**
**and you, my brothers and sisters,**
**to pray for me to the Lord our God.**

*The forms found at nos. 168 and 169 may also be used.*

## 132 CELEBRATION OF THE WORD OF GOD

### FIRST READINGS

*One or more passages from Scripture are read. At the conclusion of each:*

*Reader:* The word of the Lord.

*Assembly:* **Thanks be to God.**

### RESPONSORIAL PSALM

*An appropriate psalm may follow the first reading.*

### 133 GOSPEL

*Before the gospel reading, an alleluia or Lenten acclamation is sung.*

[ *Deacon (or priest):* The Lord be with you. ]
[        *Assembly:* **And with your spirit.** ]
        *Reader:* A reading from the holy Gospel according to N.
       *Assembly:* **Glory to you, O Lord.**

*After the reading:*

       *Reader:* The Gospel of the Lord.
       *Assembly:* **Praise to you, Lord Jesus Christ.**

### 134 INTERCESSIONS

*The assembly joins in prayer for the needs of the world, of the poor, and of the Church.*

## 135 HOLY COMMUNION

*The minister invites all to join in the Lord's Prayer, then to exchange a sign of peace. The minister then raises the eucharistic bread and all respond to the invitation.*

*Assembly:* **Lord, I am not worthy**
         **that you should enter under my roof,**
         **but only say the word**
         **and my soul shall be healed.**

*A psalm or hymn may be sung during Communion. Afterwards, there may be a period of silence or the singing of a psalm or hymn. The minister then recites a concluding prayer.*

### CONCLUDING RITE

*All are blessed and dismissed.*

*Presiding minister:* Go in the peace of Christ.

       *Assembly:* **Thanks be to God.**

# Eucharistic Exposition and Benediction

"Exposition of the holy eucharist . . . is intended to acknowledge Christ's marvelous presence in the sacrament. Exposition invites us to the spiritual union with him that culminates in sacramental communion. Thus it fosters very well the worship which is due to Christ in spirit and in truth.

This kind of exposition must clearly express the cult of the blessed sacrament in its relationship to the Mass. The plan of the exposition should carefully avoid anything which might somehow obscure the principal desire of Christ in instituting the eucharist, namely, to be with us as food, medicine, and comfort" (Holy Communion and Worship of the Eucharist outside of Mass, #82).

## EXPOSITION                                                137

*As the priest or deacon prepares the holy eucharist for adoration, the following or another suitable song is sung:*

1. O Sav - ing Vic - tim, o - p'ning wide The
2. To your great name be end - less praise, Im -
1. *O sa - lu - tá - ris hó - sti - a, Quae*
2. *U - ni tri - nó - que Dó - mi - no Sit*

gate of heav'n to us be - low! Our foes press on from
mor - tal God - head, One in Three; O grant us end - less
*cae - li pan - dis ó - sti - um: Bel - la pre - munt ho -*
*sem - pi - tér - na gló - ri - a: Qui vi - tam si - ne*

ev - 'ry side: Your aid sup - ply, your strength be - stow.
length of days When our true na - tive land we see.
*stí - li - a, Da ro - bur fer au - xí - li - um.*
*tér - mi - no No - bis do - net in pá - tri - a.*

Text: Thomas Aquinas, c.1225–1274; tr. by Edward Caswall, 1814–1878 and John Mason Neale, 1818–1866, alt.
Tune: DUGUET, LM; Dieudonné Duguet, 1794–1849

## 138  ADORATION

*During the adoration there are prayers, songs, scripture readings, and possibly a homily to develop a better understanding of the eucharistic mystery. Silent prayer is also encouraged. If time allows, the Liturgy of the Hours may be celebrated here.*

## 139  BENEDICTION

*As the priest or deacon incenses the Blessed Sacrament, the following or another appropriate hymn or song may be sung:*

1. Come a - dore this won - drous pres - ence; Bow to Christ, the
2. Glo - ry be to God the Fa - ther, Praise to his co -
1. Tan - tum er - go Sa - cra - mén - tum Ve - ne - ré - mur
2. Ge - ni - tó - ri, Ge - ni - tó - que Laus et ju - bi -

source of grace! Here is kept the an - cient prom - ise
e - qual Son, Ad - o - ra - tion to the Spir - it,
cér - nu - i: Et an - tí - quum do - cu - mén - tum
lá - ti - o, Sa - lus, ho - nor, vir - tus quo - que

Of God's earth - ly dwell - ing - place. Sight is blind be -
Bond of love, in God - head one. Blest be God by
No - vo ce - dat rí - tu - i: Prae - stet fi - des
Sit et be - ne - dí - cti - o: Pro - ce - dén - ti

fore God's glo - ry. Faith a - lone may see his face.
all cre - a - tion Joy - ous - ly while a - ges run!
sup - ple - mén - tum Sén - su - um de - fé - ctu - i.
ab u - tró - que Com - par sit lau - dá - ti - o.

Text: Thomas Aquinas, c.1225–1274; tr. by James Quinn, SJ, 1919–2010, © 1969. Used by permission of Selah Publishing Co., Inc.
Tune: ST. THOMAS, 8 7 8 7 8 7; John F. Wade, 1711–1786

*After a prayer, the priest or deacon blesses the assembly with the Blessed Sacrament.*

# REPOSITION                                    140

*As the priest or deacon replaces the Sacrament in the tabernacle, the assembly sings or says the following acclamations:*

**Blessed be God.**
**Blessed be his holy name.**
**Blessed be Jesus Christ, true God and true man.**
**Blessed be the name of Jesus.**
**Blessed be his most sacred heart.**
**Blessed be his most precious blood.**
**Blessed be Jesus in the most holy sacrament of the altar.**
**Blessed be the Holy Spirit, the Paraclete.**
**Blessed be the great Mother of God, Mary most holy.**
**Blessed be her holy and immaculate conception.**
**Blessed be her glorious assumption.**
**Blessed be the name of Mary, virgin and mother.**
**Blessed be Saint Joseph, her most chaste spouse.**
**Blessed be God in his angels and in his saints.**

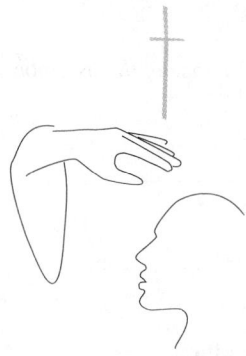

# Reconciliation of Several Penitents

**141**
The sacrament of penance, also called the sacrament of reconciliation, may be celebrated with one penitent or with many. The latter form, the communal penance service, is a gathering of a few or a large number of Christians. Together they listen to Scripture, sing psalms and hymns, pray, individually confess their sins and receive absolution, then praise God whose mercy and love are greater than our evil. In the rite of penance, the members of the Church confront the struggle that was entered at baptism. There has been failure, evil done and good undone, but the penitent Church comes again and again to name and renounce its sins and to return to the way of the Lord.

## 142 INTRODUCTORY RITES
*An appropriate hymn or psalm may be sung.*

### GREETING
*The priest greets the assembly, using these or other words:*

> *Priest:* Grace to you and peace from God our Father
> and the Lord Jesus Christ.
> *Assembly:* **And with your spirit.**

### OPENING PRAYER
*After silent prayer, the priest concludes the gathering rite with a solemn prayer.*

## 143 CELEBRATION OF THE WORD OF GOD

### FIRST READINGS
*One or more passages from Scripture are read. At the conclusion of each:*

> *Reader:* The word of the Lord.
> *Assembly:* **Thanks be to God.**

## RESPONSORIAL PSALM

*The following psalm, or a setting of Psalm 13, 25, 31, 51, 90, 123, or 143, may follow the first reading:*

With the Lord there is mer-cy, and full-ness of re-demp-tion.

Out of the depths I cry to you, O LORD;
Lord, hear my voice!
O let your ears be attentive
to the sound of my pleadings. ℟.

If you, O LORD, should mark iniquities,
Lord, who could stand?
But with you is found forgiveness,
that you may be revered. ℟.

I long for you, O LORD,
my soul longs for his word.
My soul hopes in the Lord
more than watchmen for daybreak. ℟.

For with the LORD there is mercy,
in him is plentiful redemption.
It is he who will redeem Israel
from all its iniquities. ℟.

Text: Psalm 130:1–2, 3–4, 5–6, 7–8; *The Revised Grail Psalms*, © 2010, Conception Abbey and The Grail, admin. by GIA Publications, Inc.;
refrain trans. © 1969, ICEL
Music: Michel Guimont, © 1995, GIA Publications, Inc.

## GOSPEL

144

*Before the gospel reading, an acclamation is sung:*

Al-le-lu-ia, al - le-lu-ia, al-le - lu - ia.

Music: Chant Mode VI; acc. by Richard Proulx, © 1985, GIA Publications, Inc.

*During Lent:*

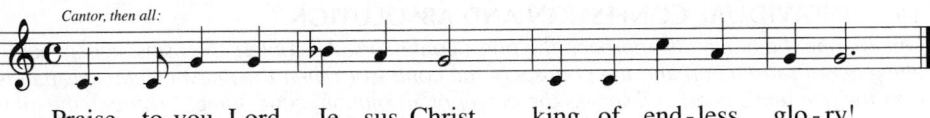

Praise to you, Lord Je-sus Christ, king of end-less glo-ry!

Text: ICEL, © 1969
Music: Frank Schoen, © 1970, GIA Publications, Inc.

*Deacon (or priest):* The Lord be with you.
    *Assembly:* **And with your spirit.**
        *Deacon:* A reading from the holy Gospel according to N.
    *Assembly:* **Glory to you, O Lord.**

*After the reading:*

        *Deacon:* The Gospel of the Lord.
    *Assembly:* **Praise to you, Lord Jesus Christ.**

## HOMILY

## EXAMINATION OF CONSCIENCE
*In silence or through some other manner all reflect on their lives with sorrow for their sins.*

## 145 SACRAMENT OF PENANCE

### GENERAL CONFESSION OF SINS
*Kneeling (or with another posture that expresses sorrow,) all join in confession. This form may be used:*

*Assembly:* **I confess to almighty God
and to you, my brothers and sisters,
that I have greatly sinned,
in my thoughts and in my words,
in what I have done and in what I have failed to do,**
*All strike their breast as they say:*
**through my fault, through my fault,
through my most grievous fault;
therefore I ask blessed Mary ever-Virgin,
all the Angels and Saints,
and you, my brothers and sisters,
to pray for me to the Lord our God.**

## 146
*Standing, all join in a litany using one of the following responses, or a song asking God's mercy. The Lord's Prayer is then recited or sung.*

A | **We pray you, hear us.**

B | **Lord, be merciful to me, a sinner.**

C | **Lord, have mercy.**

## 147 INDIVIDUAL CONFESSION AND ABSOLUTION
*One by one the penitents approach the priest confessors. All confess their sins, accept some fitting act of satisfaction and the counsel of the confessor. Then the priest extends his hands over the penitent's head and speaks the prayer of absolution, concluding: "Through the ministry of the Church may God give you pardon and peace, and I absolve you from your sins in the name of the Father, and of the Son, and of the Holy Spirit." The penitent responds, "Amen." (Note: On those occasions when general absolution is permitted, the rest of the rite remains the same.)*

### PROCLAMATION OF PRAISE FOR GOD'S MERCY
*The priest invites all to give thanks and to show by their lives—and in the life of the whole community—the grace of repentance. A psalm, canticle or hymn may be sung to proclaim God's mercy.*

### CONCLUDING PRAYER OF THANKSGIVING
*This prayer is spoken by the priest.*

### BLESSING AND DISMISSAL
*The priest blesses all present and the deacon or other minister dismisses the assembly.*
*All respond:* **Thanks be to God.**

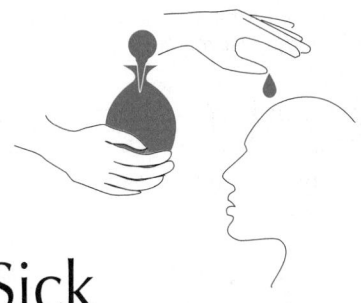

# Anointing of the Sick

The sacrament of the anointing of the sick is celebrated when a Christian's health is seriously impaired by sickness or old age. Through the anointing with the blessed oil of the sick, the Church supports those who struggle against illness or injury and continues the healing work of Christ. The anointing is intended to bring hope and comfort to those anointed and, to the gathered assembly of family and friends, a spirit of support and sharing in the sufferings of their brothers and sisters.

The anointing may be celebrated within Mass or outside Mass. In either case a liturgy of the word precedes the anointing. Following is the rite of anointing within Mass.

## INTRODUCTORY RITES                                                        149

*An appropriate hymn or psalm may be sung (see nos. 952–955).*

### GREETING

*After all make the sign of the cross, the priest greets the assembly, using these or other words.*

> *Priest:* The grace of our Lord Jesus Christ,
> and the love of God,
> and the communion of the Holy Spirit
> be with you all.
>
> *Assembly:* **And with your spirit.**

*The priest introduces the celebration, and the penitential act may follow (see Order of Mass, nos. 168 and 169). Then, after a period of silence, he says the opening prayer, to which all respond:* **Amen**.

## LITURGY OF THE WORD                                                      150

### FIRST READINGS

*One or more passages from Scripture are read. At the conclusion of each:*

> *Reader:* The word of the Lord.
> *Assembly:* **Thanks be to God.**

## RESPONSORIAL PSALM

*The following psalm, or a setting of Psalm 6, 15, 27, 34, 42, 63, 86, 90, 102, 103, 123, or 143, may follow the first reading:*

Refrain

My God, my God, come quick-ly to help me.

Verses

In you, O LORD, I take refuge;
let me never be put to shame.
In your justice, rescue me, free me;
incline your ear to me and save me. ℟.

My mouth is filled with your praise,
with your glory, all the day long.
Do not reject me now that I am old;
when my strength fails do not forsake me. ℟.

It is you, O Lord, who are my hope,
my trust, O LORD, from my youth.
On you I have leaned from my birth;
from my mother's womb, you have
been my help. ℟.

But as for me, I will always hope,
and praise you more and more.
My mouth will tell of your justice,
and all the day long of your salvation. ℟.

Text: Psalm 71:1–2, 5–6, 8–9, 14–15, *The Revised Grail Psalms*, © 2010, Conception Abbey and The Grail, admin. by GIA Publications, Inc.;
    refrain from *Pastoral Care of the Sick: Rites of Anointing and Viaticum*, © 1982, ICEL
Music: Paul M. French, © 2011, GIA Publications, Inc.

## 151 GOSPEL

*Before the gospel reading, an acclamation is sung:*

Cantor, then all:

Al - le - lu - ia, al - le - lu - ia, al - le - lu - ia.

Music: Chant Mode VI; acc. by Richard Proulx, © 1985, GIA Publications, Inc.

*During Lent:*

Cantor, then all:

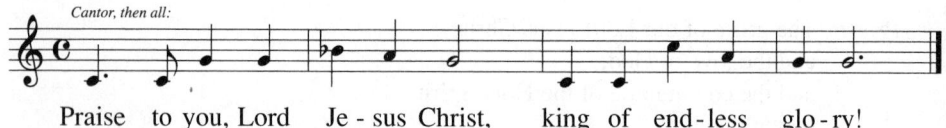

Praise to you, Lord Je - sus Christ, king of end - less glo - ry!

Text: ICEL, © 1969
Music: Frank Schoen, © 1970, GIA Publications, Inc.

*Deacon (or priest):* The Lord be with you.
    *Assembly:* **And with your spirit.**
      *Deacon:* A reading from the holy Gospel according to N.
    *Assembly:* **Glory to you, O Lord.**

*After the reading:*

      *Deacon:* The Gospel of the Lord.
    *Assembly:* **Praise to you, Lord Jesus Christ.**

## HOMILY

# LITURGY OF ANOINTING                            152

## LITANY
*The assembly joins in prayers for the sick and for those who care for them. Each petition concludes with "Lord, have mercy," and all repeat:*

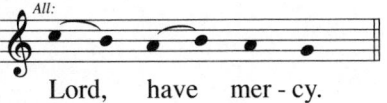

Lord,   have   mer - cy.

## LAYING ON OF HANDS
*The priest silently lays hands on the head of each sick person in a gesture of prayer, healing and solidarity.*

## PRAYER OVER THE OIL
*If the oil is already blessed, the priest leads a prayer of thanksgiving over it. After each invocation:*

Bless - ed   be   God   who   heals   us   in   Christ.

Text: *Pastoral Care of the Sick: Rites of Anointing and Viaticum,* © 1982, ICEL
Music: Paul M. French, © 2011, GIA Publications, Inc.

*If the oil is not blessed, the priest says the prayer of blessing.*

## ANOINTING
*The priest anoints each sick person on the forehead, saying:*

Through this holy anointing may the Lord in his love and mercy help you with the grace of the Holy Spirit.

*Assembly:* **Amen.**

*The priest anoints the hands of each sick person, saying:*

May the Lord who frees you from sin save you and raise you up.

*Assembly:* **Amen.**

*The priest may anoint other parts of the body.*

## PRAYER AFTER ANOINTING                            153
*The priest prays for those who have been anointed. Then the liturgy of the eucharist is celebrated with special prayers for the sick (see Order of Mass, no. 177).*

*[If the rite of anointing is celebrated outside Mass, the liturgy begins with the greeting, introduction, and penitential rite (or sacrament of penance). After the scripture readings a period of silence is observed, or the priest gives a brief homily. The liturgy of anointing is celebrated as above. Then the Lord's Prayer is recited or sung, the liturgy of Holy Communion may follow, and a final blessing is given.]*

# Marriage

## 154

The mutual and lifelong commitment of a man and a woman in marriage is viewed by the Church as a sacred covenant. When two Christians marry, it is also a sacrament, an effective sign of the presence of God in the world and a symbol of Christ's love for his Church. In the sacrament of matrimony God's special graces are given to the couple to live out "in mutual and lasting fidelity" the vows they make to each other and to God in the presence of the Christian community.

At their wedding the bride and groom themselves are the ministers of the sacrament to each other; the priest or deacon who presides over the wedding serves as the authorized witness of the Church and prays the nuptial blessing of the Church over the spouses.

The rite of marriage may be celebrated at Mass or outside of Mass. In either case the rite begins with a liturgy of the word: the proclamation of God's faithful love by means of readings from Scripture and a reflection on them (the homily). The following elements are included in all celebrations.

## 155  INTRODUCTORY RITES

*An appropriate hymn or psalm may be sung during the procession or immediately after it (see nos. 966–971).*

### GREETING

*After all make the sign of the cross, the priest or deacon greets the assembly, using these or other words.*

> *Priest:*  The grace of our Lord Jesus Christ,
> and the love of God,
> and the communion of the Holy Spirit
> be with you all.
>
> *Assembly:*  **And with your spirit.**

### OPENING PRAYER

*The priest or deacon introduces the celebration and, after a period of silence, says the opening prayer, to which all respond:* **Amen***. All then sit.*

# LITURGY OF THE WORD 156

## FIRST READINGS

*One or more passages from Scripture are read. At the conclusion of each:*

*Reader:* The word of the Lord.
*Assembly:* **Thanks be to God.**

## RESPONSORIAL PSALM

*The following psalm, or a setting of Psalm 103, 112, 128, 145, or 148, may follow the first reading:*

Refrain

Taste and see the good - ness of the Lord.

Verses

I will bless the Lord at all times;
praise of him is always in my mouth.
In the Lord my soul shall make its boast;
the humble shall hear and be glad. ℟.

Glorify the Lord with me;
together let us praise his name.
I sought the Lord, and he answered me;
from all my terrors he set me free. ℟.

Look toward him and be radiant;
let your faces not be abashed.
This lowly one called; the Lord heard,
and rescued him from all his distress. ℟.

The angel of the Lord is encamped
around those who fear him, to rescue them.
Taste and see that the Lord is good.
Blessed the man who seeks refuge in
him. ℟.

Text: Psalm 34:2–9, *The Revised Grail Psalms*, © 2010, Conception Abbey and The Grail, admin. by GIA Publications, Inc.; refrain trans. © 1969, ICEL
Music: Michel Guimont, © 2004, GIA Publications, Inc.

## GOSPEL 157

*Before the gospel reading, all stand as an acclamation is sung:*

Cantor, then all:

Al - le - lu - ia, al - le - lu - ia, al - le - lu - ia.

Music: Chant Mode VI; acc. by Richard Proulx, © 1985, GIA Publications, Inc.

*During Lent:*

Cantor, then all:

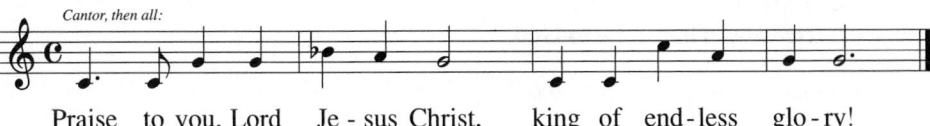

Praise to you, Lord Je - sus Christ, king of end-less glo-ry!

Text: ICEL, © 1969
Music: Frank Schoen, © 1970, GIA Publications, Inc.

*Deacon (or priest):* The Lord be with you.
    *Assembly:* **And with your spirit.**
      *Deacon:* A reading from the holy Gospel according to N.
    *Assembly:* **Glory to you, O Lord.**

*After the reading:*

> *Deacon:* The Gospel of the Lord.
> *Assembly:* **Praise to you, Lord Jesus Christ.**

**HOMILY** *(All sit)*

## 158  RITE OF MARRIAGE

*After the homily all stand. The priest or deacon invites the couple to declare to each other their consent to enter into marriage, and receives the couple's vows in the name of the Church. Wedding rings, a sign of love and fidelity, may be blessed and exchanged and, according to particular customs, other rituals expressing the couple's union may be added.*

*In the prayer of the faithful the Church prays for the needs of the world, the local community, and the newly married couple. A common response to each petition is:* **Lord, hear our prayer.**

*If the liturgy of the eucharist does not follow the rite of marriage, the priest or deacon prays the nuptial blessing at the end of the prayer of the faithful. The celebration concludes with the Lord's Prayer and a final blessing.*

*[When the liturgy of the eucharist follows the rite of marriage, the nuptial blessing is given after the Lord's Prayer before Holy Communion. Everything else follows the Order of Mass, beginning with the presentation and preparation of the gifts. The bride and groom may bring the bread and wine to the altar. See Order of Mass, no. 177.]*

### 159  THE LORD'S PRAYER

*Assembly:* **Our Father, who art in heaven,**
**hallowed be thy name;**
**thy kingdom come,**
**thy will be done**
**on earth as it is in heaven.**
**Give us this day our daily bread,**
**and forgive us our trespasses,**
**as we forgive those who trespass against us;**
**and lead us not into temptation,**
**but deliver us from evil.**

### BLESSING AND DISMISSAL

*All respond to each part of the blessing:* **Amen.**

> *Deacon or priest:* Go in peace.
> *Assembly:* **Thanks be to God.**

*A hymn or instrumental music may follow.*

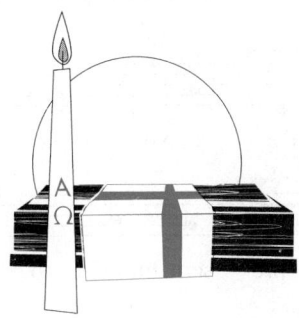

# Funerals

160
The rites which surround the death of a Christian extend from Viaticum (the last Holy Communion) and final prayers before death through the wake service and funeral liturgy to the burial of the body or cremated remains. In all of this the community affirms its faith in the communion of saints and the resurrection of the dead. The family and friends are helped in their time of sorrow with prayer and song. Thus they express present grief even as they hold to the Church's lasting hope.

The funeral liturgy may be celebrated within Mass or outside Mass. In either case the rite begins with a liturgy of the word. The following elements are included in all celebrations.

## INTRODUCTORY RITES
### GREETING 161
*All stand as the priest (or deacon) greets the assembly at the door, using these or other words.*

*Priest:*  Grace to you and peace from God our Father
and the Lord Jesus Christ.

*Assembly:*  **And with your spirit.**

*The body is sprinkled with holy water, a reminder of baptism. The family or pall bearers spread the pall, a garment like that which the Christian received at baptism, over the body. The funeral procession then moves into the church accompanied by an appropriate hymn or psalm.*

*The liturgy continues as usual with the Collect prayer and the liturgy of the word (see Order of Mass, no. 171).*

## FINAL COMMENDATION 162
*If the funeral liturgy is celebrated within Mass, the final commendation follows the prayer after communion. When the funeral liturgy is celebrated outside Mass, the final commendation follows the prayer of the faithful. The commendation begins with an invitation to silent prayer.*

## 163  SONG OF FAREWELL

*The following or another appropriate responsory or song may be sung.*

Refrain

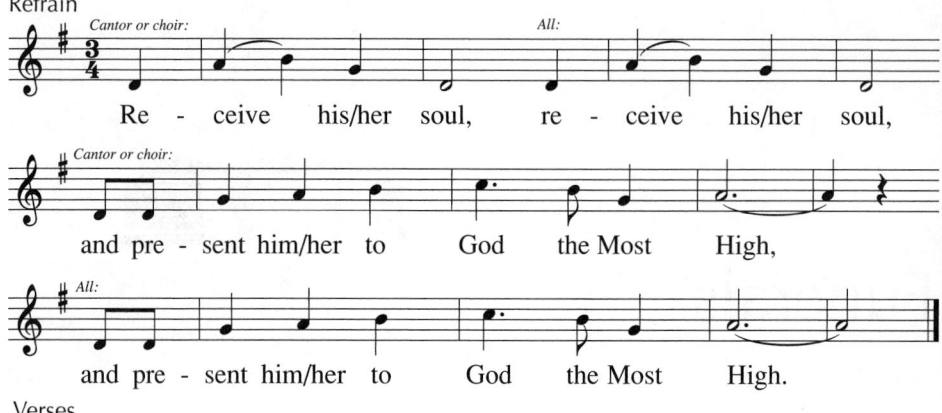

Re - ceive his/her soul, re - ceive his/her soul,

and pre - sent him/her to God the Most High,

and pre - sent him/her to God the Most High.

Verses

1. Saints of God, come to his/her aid!
   Hasten to meet him/her, angels of the Lord!

2. May Christ, who called you, take you to himself;
   may angels lead you to the bosom of Abraham.

3. Eternal rest grant unto him/her, O Lord,
   and let perpetual light shine upon him/her.

Text: *Order of Christian Funerals,* © 1985, ICEL
Music: Steven R. Janco, © 1990, GIA Publications, Inc.

## 164  PRAYER OF COMMENDATION

*At the conclusion of the prayer all respond:* **Amen.**

# PROCESSION TO THE PLACE OF COMMITTAL

*The deacon or priest says:* In peace let us take our brother/sister to his/her place of rest.

## 165  SONG

*As the assembly leaves the church, the following or another appropriate responsory or song may be sung.*

May the an - gels lead you in - to par - a - dise; may the

mar - tyrs come to wel-come you and take you to the ho - ly

cit - y, the new and e - ter - nal Je - ru - sa - lem.

Text: *Order of Christian Funerals,* © 1985, ICEL
Music: Steven R. Janco, © 1990, GIA Publications, Inc.

# Order of Mass

The Church gathers on the Lord's Day to listen to Scripture, to offer prayers, to give thanks and praise to God while recalling God's gifts in creation and saving deeds in Jesus, and to share in Holy Communion.

In these rites of word and eucharist, the Church keeps Sunday as the Lord's Day, the day of creation and resurrection, the "eighth day" when the fullness of God's kingdom is anticipated. The Mass or eucharistic celebration of the Christian community has rites of gathering, of word, of eucharist, of dismissal. All those who gather constitute the assembly. One member of this assembly who has been ordained to the presbyterate or episcopate, the priesthood, leads the opening and closing prayers and the eucharistic prayer, and presides over the whole assembly. A member ordained to the diaconate may assist, read the gospel, and preach. Other members of the assembly are chosen and trained for various ministries: These are the readers, servers, ushers, musicians, communion ministers. All of these assist the assembly. It is the assembly itself, all those present, that does the liturgy.

The Order of Mass which follows is familiar to all who regularly join in this assembly. It is learned through repetition. This Order of Mass leaves many decisions to the local community, and others are determined by the various seasons of the liturgical year.

## INTRODUCTORY RITES

*The rites which precede the liturgy of the word assist the assembly to gather as a community. They prepare that community to listen to Scripture and to celebrate the Eucharist together. The procession and entrance song are ways of expressing the unity and spirit of the assembly.*

### GREETING

*All make the sign of the cross.*

*Priest:* In the name of the Father, and of the Son, and of the Holy Spirit.

A - men.

*After the sign of the cross one of the greetings is given.*

A      *Priest:*   The grace of our Lord Jesus Christ,
                            and the love of God,
                            and the communion of the Holy Spirit
                            be with you all.

B      *Priest:*   Grace to you and peace from God our Father
                            and the Lord Jesus Christ.

C      *Priest:*   The Lord be with you. (*Bishop:* Peace be with you.)

And with your spir - it.

## 167   BLESSING AND SPRINKLING OF HOLY WATER

*On Sundays, especially during the season of Easter, instead of the penitential act below, the blessing and sprinkling of holy water may take place.*

## 168   PENITENTIAL ACT

*The priest invites all to be mindful of their sins and of the great mercy of God. After a time of silence, one of the following forms is used.*

A    *Assembly:*   **I confess to almighty God**
                       **and to you, my brothers and sisters,**
                       **that I have greatly sinned,**
                       **in my thoughts and in my words,**
                       **in what I have done and in what I have failed to do,**
                       *All strike their breast as they say:*
                       **through my fault, through my fault,**
                       **through my most grievous fault;**
                       **therefore I ask blessed Mary ever-Virgin,**
                       **all the Angels and Saints,**
                       **and you, my brothers and sisters,**
                       **to pray for me to the Lord our God.**

B

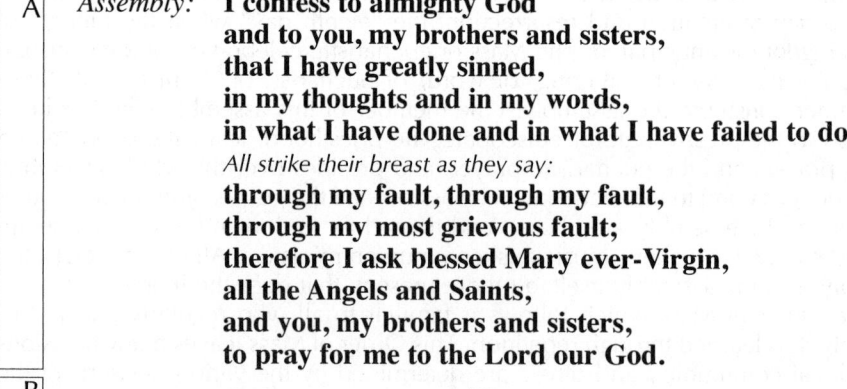

*Priest:* Have mercy on us, O Lord.     *Assembly:* For we have sinned against you.

*Priest:* Show us, O Lord, your mer-cy.     *Assembly:* And grant us your sal-va-tion.

C

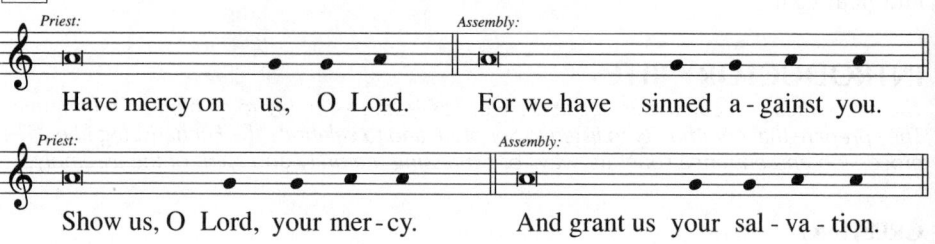

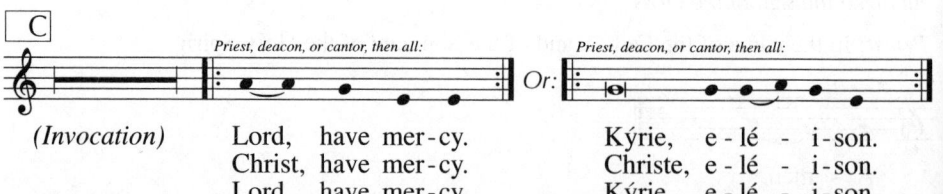

*(Invocation)*     *Priest, deacon, or cantor, then all:*
Lord, have mer-cy.
Christ, have mer-cy.
Lord, have mer-cy.

*Or:*     *Priest, deacon, or cantor, then all:*
Kýrie, e - lé - i-son.
Christe, e - lé - i-son.
Kýrie, e - lé - i-son.

*Priest:* May almighty God…everlasting life.

A - men.

## KÝRIE                                                                                   169
*Unless form C of the penitential act has been used, the Kyrie follows.*

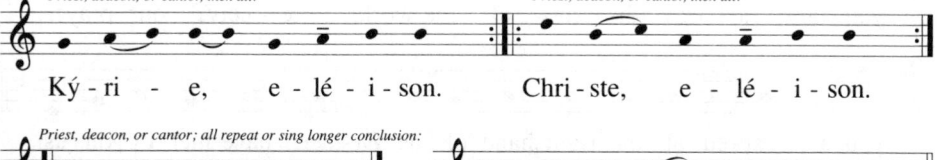

Ký - ri - e, e - lé - i - son.     Chri - ste, e - lé - i - son.

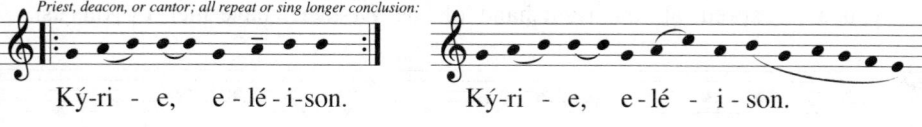

Ký - ri - e, e - lé - i - son.     Ký - ri - e, e - lé - i - son.

*Or:*

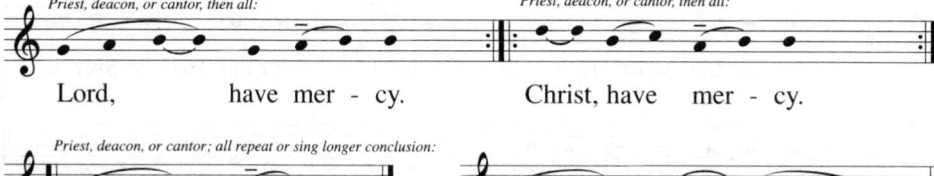

Lord, have mer - cy.     Christ, have mer - cy.

Lord, have mer - cy.     Lord, have mer - cy.

## GLÓRIA                                                                                  170
*The Gloria is omitted during Advent, Lent, and most weekdays.*

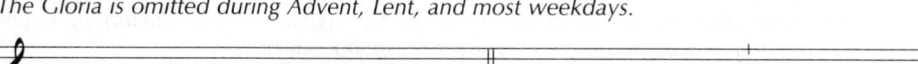

Glo - ry to God in the high-est,     and on earth peace to peo - ple

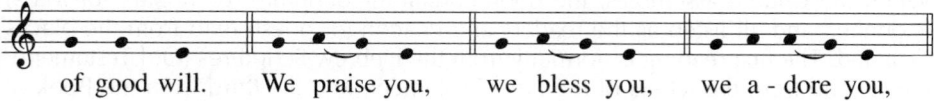

of good will.     We praise you,     we bless you,     we a - dore you,

we glo - ri - fy you,     we give you thanks for your great glo - ry,

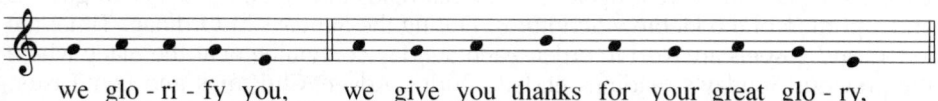

Lord God, heav - en - ly King, O God, al - might - y Fa - ther.

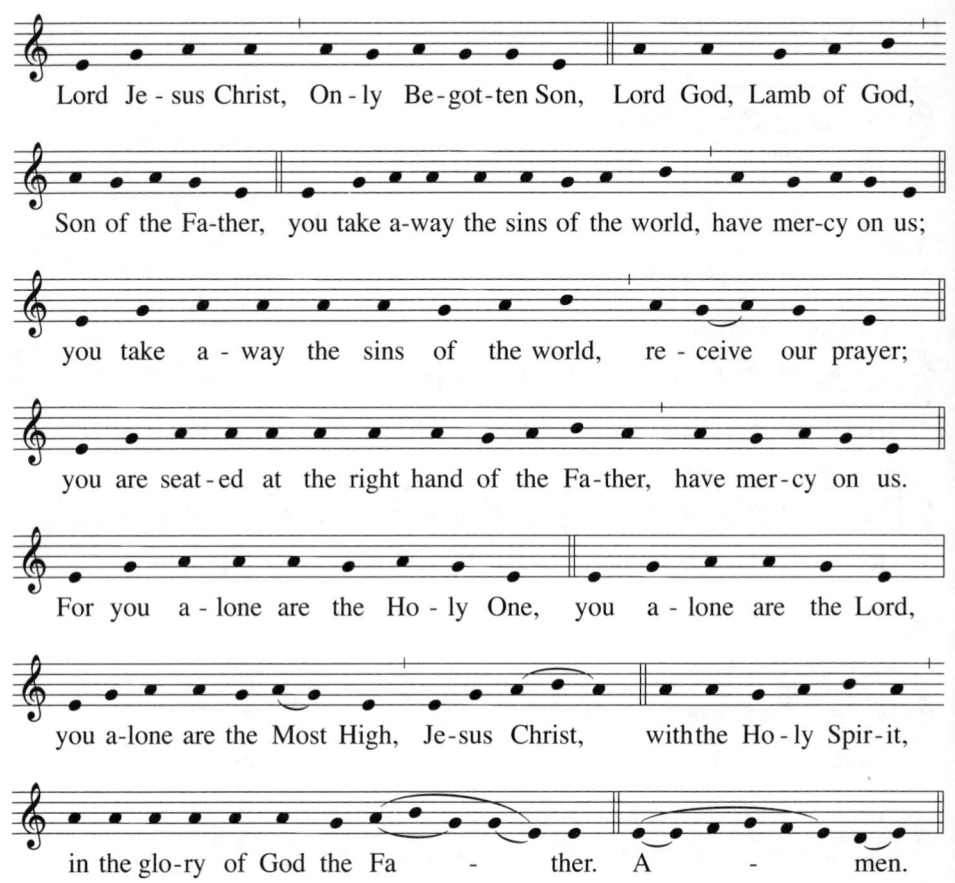

Lord Je - sus Christ, On - ly Be - got-ten Son, Lord God, Lamb of God,

Son of the Fa-ther, you take a-way the sins of the world, have mer-cy on us;

you take a - way the sins of the world, re - ceive our prayer;

you are seat - ed at the right hand of the Fa-ther, have mer-cy on us.

For you a - lone are the Ho - ly One, you a - lone are the Lord,

you a-lone are the Most High, Je-sus Christ, with the Ho - ly Spir-it,

in the glo-ry of God the Fa - ther. A - men.

## 171 COLLECT

*After the invitation from the priest, all pray in silence for a while. The introductory rites conclude with the proper opening prayer to which all respond:* **Amen.**

## 172 LITURGY OF THE WORD

When the Church assembles, the book containing Scripture (*Lectionary for Mass*) is opened and all listen as the readers and deacon (or priest) read from the places assigned. The first reading is normally from the Hebrew Scriptures (Old Testament), the second from the letters of the New Testament, and the third from the Book of Gospels. Over a three-year cycle, the Church reads through the letters and gospels and a portion of the Hebrew Scriptures. During the Sundays of Ordinary Time, the letters and gospels are read in order, each Sunday continuing near the place where the previous Sunday's readings ended. During Advent/Christmas and Lent/Easter, the readings are those which are traditional and appropriate to these seasons.

The Church listens to and—through the weeks and years—is shaped by the word of God. Those who have gathered for the Sunday liturgy are to give their full attention to the words of the reader. A time of silence and reflection follows each of the first two readings. After the first reading, this reflection continues in the singing of the psalm. A homily, bringing together the scripture readings and the life of the community, follows the gospel. The liturgy of the word concludes with the creed, the dismissal of the catechumens and the prayers of intercession. In the latter, the assembly continues its constant work of recalling and praying for the universal Church and all those in need.

This reading and hearing of the word—simple things that they are—are the foundation of the liturgical celebration. The public reading of Scripture and the rituals which surround this—silence and psalm and acclamation, posture and gesture, preaching and litany of intercession—gather the Church generation after generation. They gather and sustain and gradually make of us the image of Christ.

## FIRST READING

*After the reading:*

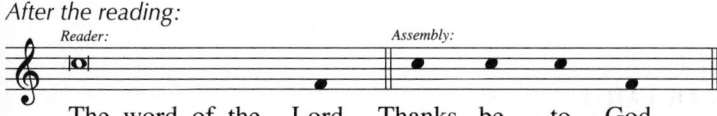

After a period of silence, the responsorial psalm is sung.

## SECOND READING

*After the reading:*

*A time of silence follows the reading.*

## GOSPEL 173

*Before the gospel, an acclamation is sung.*

*During Lent:*

*Before the gospel:*

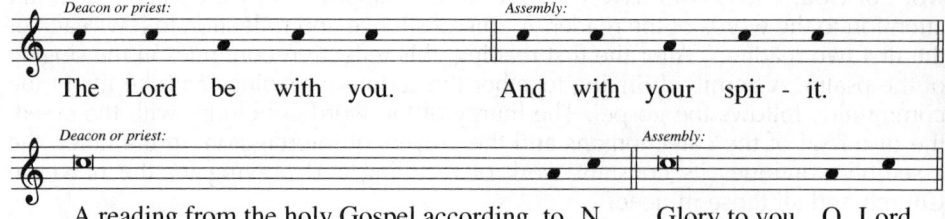

*Deacon or priest:*

The Lord be with you.

*Assembly:*

And with your spir - it.

*Deacon or priest:*

A reading from the holy Gospel according to N.

*Assembly:*

Glory to you, O Lord.

*After the reading:*

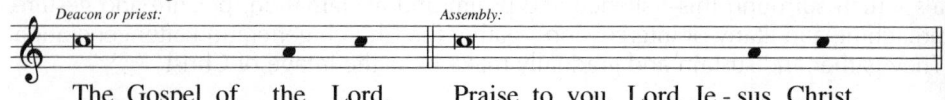

*Deacon or priest:*

The Gospel of the Lord.

*Assembly:*

Praise to you, Lord Je - sus Christ.

## HOMILY

## 174 PROFESSION OF FAITH
*A musical setting can be found at no. 191.*

**I believe in one God,**
**the Father almighty,**
**maker of heaven and earth,**
**of all things visible and invisible.**

**I believe in one Lord Jesus Christ,**
**the Only Begotten Son of God,**
**born of the Father before all ages.**
**God from God, Light from Light,**
**true God from true God,**
**begotten, not made, consubstantial with the Father;**
**through him all things were made.**
**For us men and for our salvation**
**he came down from heaven,**
*All bow at the following words up to: and became man.*
**and by the Holy Spirit was incarnate**
**of the Virgin Mary,**
**and became man.**

**For our sake he was crucified under Pontius Pilate,**
**he suffered death and was buried,**
**and rose again on the third day**
**in accordance with the Scriptures.**
**He ascended into heaven**
**and is seated at the right hand of the Father.**
**He will come again in glory**
**to judge the living and the dead**
**and his kingdom will have no end.**

I believe in the Holy Spirit, the Lord, the giver of life,
who proceeds from the Father and the Son,
who with the Father and the Son is adored and glorified,
who has spoken through the prophets.

I believe in one, holy, catholic and apostolic Church.
I confess one Baptism for the forgiveness of sins
and I look forward to the resurrection of the dead
and the life of the world to come. Amen.

*Instead of the Nicene Creed, especially during Lent and the Easter season,*    175
*the Apostles' Creed may be used:*

I believe in God,
the Father almighty,
Creator of heaven and earth,
and in Jesus Christ, his only Son, our Lord,
*All bow at the following words up to: the Virgin Mary.*
who was conceived by the Holy Spirit,
born of the Virgin Mary,
suffered under Pontius Pilate,
was crucified, died and was buried;
he descended into hell;
on the third day he rose again from the dead;
he ascended into heaven,
and is seated at the right hand of God the Father almighty;
from there he will come to judge the living and the dead.

I believe in the Holy Spirit,
the holy catholic Church,
the communion of saints,
the forgiveness of sins,
the resurrection of the body,
and life everlasting. Amen.

## PRAYER OF THE FAITHFUL    176
*The people respond to each petition as follows, or according to local practice.*

*Deacon or cantor:* Let us pray to the Lord.

Lord, hear our prayer.

*Or:*

Lord, have mer - cy.

## 177 LITURGY OF THE EUCHARIST

To celebrate the Eucharist means to give God thanks and praise. When the altar has been prepared with the bread and wine, the assembly joins the priest in remembering the gracious gifts of God in creation and God's saving deeds. The center of this is the paschal mystery, the death of our Lord Jesus Christ which destroyed the power of death and his rising which brings us life. That mystery into which we were baptized we proclaim each Sunday at the Eucharist. It is the very shape of Christian life. We find this in the simple bread and wine which stir our remembering and draw forth our prayer of thanksgiving. "Fruit of the earth and work of human hands," the bread and wine become our Holy Communion in the Body and Blood of the Lord. We eat and drink and so proclaim that we belong to one another and to the Lord.

The members of the assembly quietly prepare themselves even as the table is prepared. The priest then invites all to lift up their hearts and join in the eucharistic prayer. All do this by giving their full attention and by singing the acclamations from the "Holy, Holy, Holy" to the great "Amen." Then the assembly joins in the Lord's Prayer, the sign of peace and the "Lamb of God" litany which accompanies the breaking of bread. Ministers of communion assist the assembly to share the Body and Blood of Christ. A time of silence and prayer concludes the liturgy of the eucharist.

### PRESENTATION AND PREPARATION OF THE GIFTS

*Bread and wine are brought to the altar and the deacon or priest prepares these gifts. If there is no music, the prayers may be said aloud, and all may respond:* **Blessed be God for ever.** *The priest then invites all to pray.*

*Priest:* Pray, brethren (brothers and sisters),
    that my sacrifice and yours
    may be acceptable to God, the almighty Father.

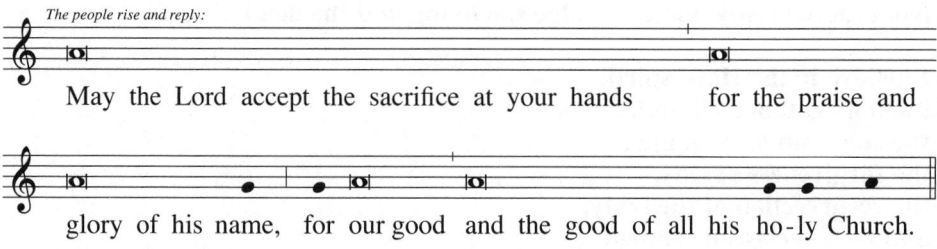

*The people rise and reply:*

May the Lord accept the sacrifice at your hands    for the praise and glory of his name, for our good and the good of all his ho-ly Church.

*The priest says the prayer over the offerings and all respond:* **Amen.**

## 178 EUCHARISTIC PRAYER

*The central prayer of the Mass begins with this dialogue between priest and assembly.*

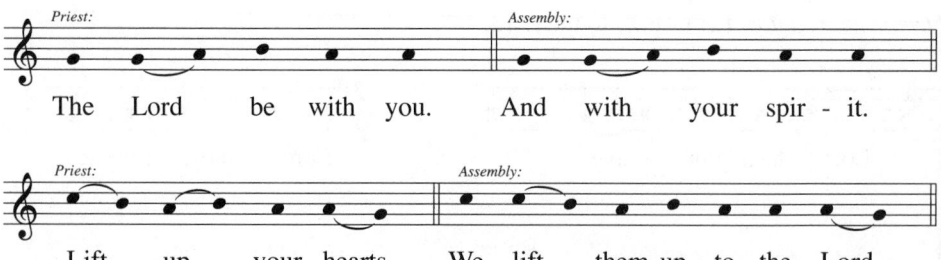

Priest: The Lord be with you. Assembly: And with your spir - it.

Priest: Lift up your hearts. Assembly: We lift them up to the Lord.

*Priest:* Let us give thanks to the Lord our God. *Assembly:* It is right and just.

*The Holy, Holy, Holy acclamation is sung to conclude the introduction to the eucharistic prayer.* 179

Ho-ly, Ho-ly, Ho-ly Lord God of hosts. Heav-en and earth are full of your glo-ry. Ho-san-na in the high-est. Bless-ed is he who comes in the name of the Lord. Ho-san-na in the high-est.

*One of the following acclamations follows the priest's invitation: "The mystery of faith."* 180

A

We pro-claim your Death, O Lord, and pro-fess your Res-ur-rec-tion un-til you come a-gain.

B 181

When we eat this Bread and drink this Cup, we pro-claim your Death, O Lord, un-til you come a-gain.

C 182

Save us, Sav-ior of the world, for by your Cross and Res-ur-rec-tion you have set us free.

**183**  *The eucharistic prayer concludes:*
*Priest:* Through him, and with him, and in him,
       O God, almighty Father,
       in the unity of the Holy Spirit,
       all glory and honor is yours,
       for ever and ever.

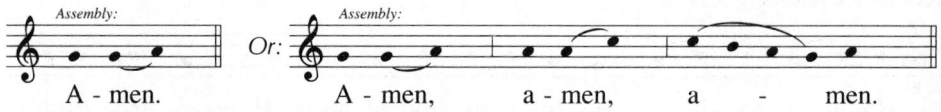

*Assembly:* A - men.    Or:    *Assembly:* A - men, a - men, a - men.

## 184 COMMUNION RITE

*The priest invites all to join in the Lord's Prayer.*

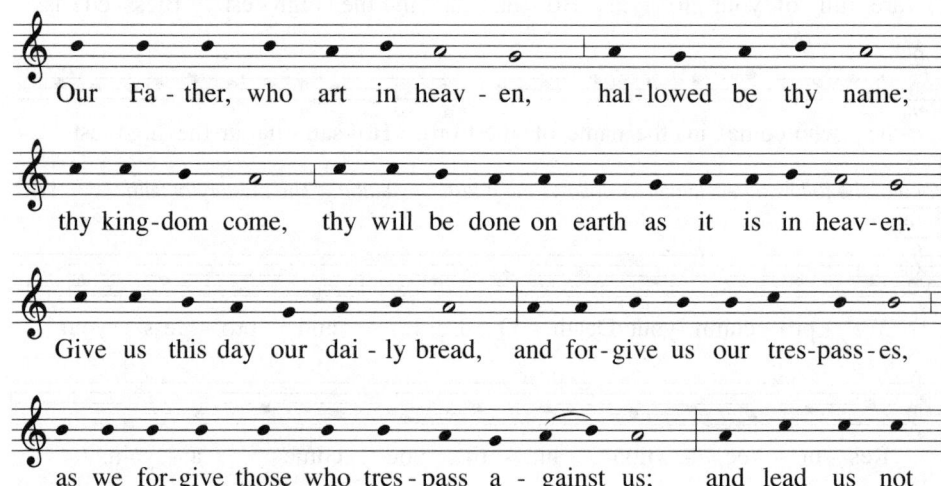

Our Fa - ther, who art in heav - en, hal - lowed be thy name;

thy king-dom come, thy will be done on earth as it is in heav-en.

Give us this day our dai - ly bread, and for-give us our tres-pass-es,

as we for-give those who tres - pass a - gainst us; and lead us not

in - to temp - ta - tion, but de - liv - er us from e - vil.

*Priest:* Deliver us, Lord…and the coming of our Savior, Jesus Christ.

*All:* For the king-dom, the pow'r, and the glo-ry are yours now and for ev - er.

### SIGN OF PEACE

*Priest:* Lord Jesus Christ, who said…for ever and ever.

*Assembly:* A - men.

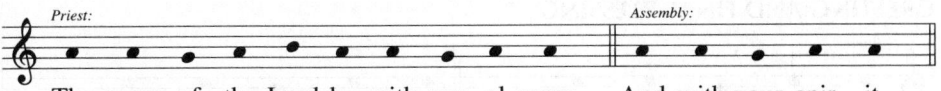

The peace of the Lord be with you al-ways.   And with your spir - it.

*Deacon or priest:* Let us offer each other the sign of peace.

*All exchange a sign of peace.*

*Then the eucharistic bread is solemnly broken and the consecrated bread and wine*   185
*are prepared for Holy Communion. The litany "Lamb of God" is sung during the*
*breaking of the bread.*

Lamb of God,   you take a-way the sins of the world, have mer - cy on us.

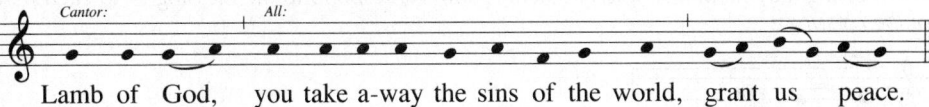

Lamb of God,   you take a-way the sins of the world,   grant us   peace.

*The priest then invites all to share in Holy Communion.*   186

*Priest:* Behold the Lamb of God,
     behold him who takes away the sins of the world.
     Blessed are those called to the supper of the Lamb.

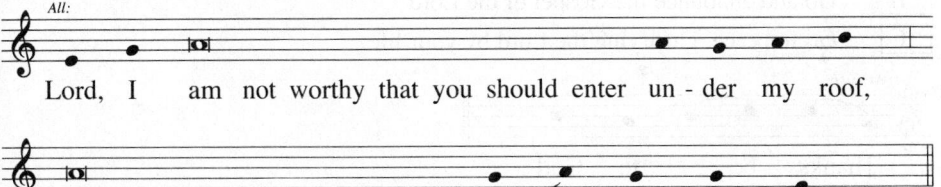

Lord, I   am not worthy that you should enter un - der my roof,

but only say the word and my   soul   shall   be   healed.

*Minister of communion:* The Body (Blood) of Christ.
     *Communicant:* **Amen.**

*While the priest is receiving the Body of Christ, the communion song or psalm begins. After*
*communion, a time of silence is observed or a song of thanksgiving is sung. The rite concludes*
*with the prayer after communion to which all respond:* **Amen.**

# CONCLUDING RITES   187
*The liturgy of the eucharist ends very simply. There may be announcements of events and*
*concerns for the community, then the priest gives a blessing and the assembly is dismissed.*

## GREETING AND FINAL BLESSING

*Priest:* The Lord be with you. *Assembly:* And with your spir - it.

*When a bishop blesses the people, he adds the following:*

*Bishop:* Blessed be the name of the Lord. *Assembly:* Now and for ev - er.

*Bishop:* Our help is in the name of the Lord. *Assembly:* Who made heaven and earth.

*The blessing may be in a simple or solemn form. All respond to the blessing or to each part of the blessing:*

*Assembly:* A - men.

## DISMISSAL

*The deacon or priest then dismisses the assembly:*

A   Go forth, the Mass is ended.
B   Go and announce the Gospel of the Lord.
C   Go in peace, glorifying the Lord by your life.

*Assembly:* Thanks be to God.

D

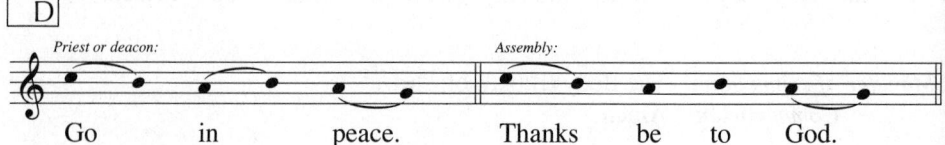

*Priest or deacon:* Go in peace. *Assembly:* Thanks be to God.

## EASTER DISMISSAL

*The deacon or priest then dismisses the assembly:*

A   Go forth, the Mass is ended, alleluia, alleluia.
B   Go in peace, alleluia, alleluia.

*Assembly:* Thanks be to God, al - le - lú - ia, al - le - lú - ia.

# Additional Chants

## SIMPLE CHANTS

### GREETING

*Priest:* In the name of the Father, and of the Son, and of the Holy Spirit.

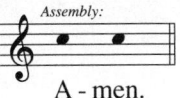

A - men.

| | |
|---|---|
| A | *Priest:* The grace of our Lord Jesus Christ, and the love of God, and the communion of the Holy Spirit be with you all. |
| B | *Priest:* Grace to you and peace from God our Father and the Lord Jesus Christ. |
| C | *Priest:* The Lord be with you. (*Bishop:* Peace be with you.) |

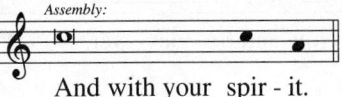

And with your spir - it.

## 189 PENITENTIAL ACT

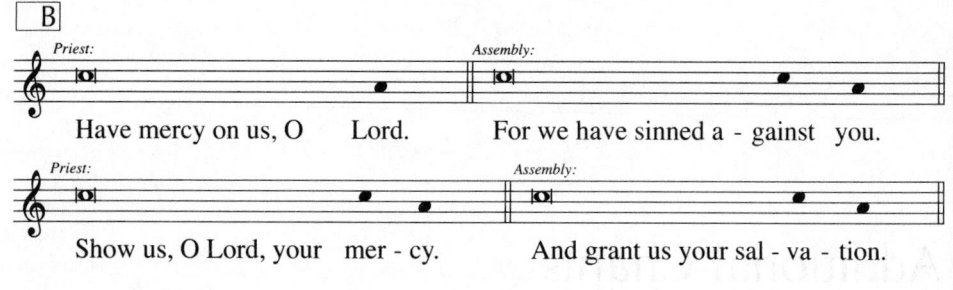

B

*Priest:*                         *Assembly:*

Have mercy on us, O     Lord.        For we have sinned a - gainst  you.

*Priest:*                         *Assembly:*

Show us, O Lord, your   mer - cy.       And grant us your sal - va - tion.

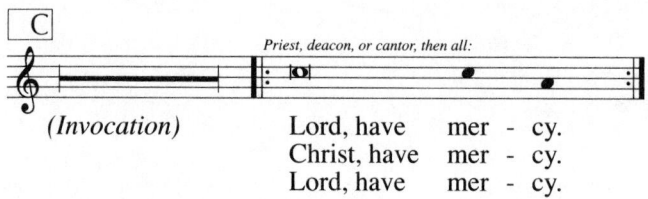

C

*Priest, deacon, or cantor, then all:*

*(Invocation)*       Lord, have    mer - cy.
                      Christ, have  mer - cy.
                      Lord, have    mer - cy.

*Priest:* May almighty God...everlasting life.

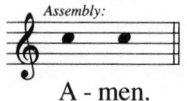

*Assembly:*

A - men.

## 190 GREETING AND FINAL BLESSING

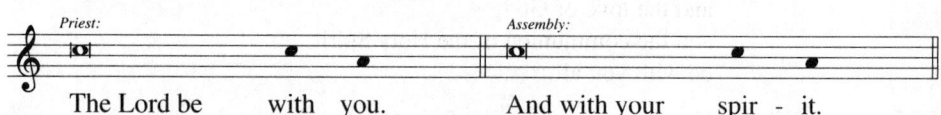

*Priest:*                         *Assembly:*

The Lord be     with  you.        And with your    spir - it.

*When a bishop blesses the people, he adds the following:*

*Bishop:*                         *Assembly:*

Blessed be the name of the    Lord.     Now and for   ev - er.

*Bishop:*                         *Assembly:*

Our help is in the name of the   Lord.   Who made heaven and   earth.

*The blessing may be in a simple or solemn form. All respond to the blessing or to each part of the blessing:*

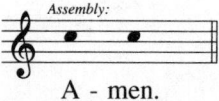

*Assembly:*

A - men.

# CREDO I

I be - lieve in one God, the Fa-ther al-might-y, mak-er of

heav-en and earth, of all things vis - i - ble and in - vis - i - ble.

I be-lieve in one Lord Je - sus Christ, the Only Be - got-ten

Son of God, born of the Father be - fore all a - ges.

God from God, Light from Light, true God from true God,

be - got-ten, not made, con - sub - stan - tial with the Fa - ther;

through him all things were made. For us men and for our sal-va-tion

All bow

he came down from heav-en, and by the Ho-ly Spir-it was in-car-nate

of the Vir - gin Mar - y, and be - came man.

For our sake he was cru - ci - fied un - der Pon-tius Pi - late,

he suffered death and was bur-ied, and rose a-gain on the third day

# Setting One

## MASS OF CREATION

**PENITENTIAL ACT**<space count="51" />192

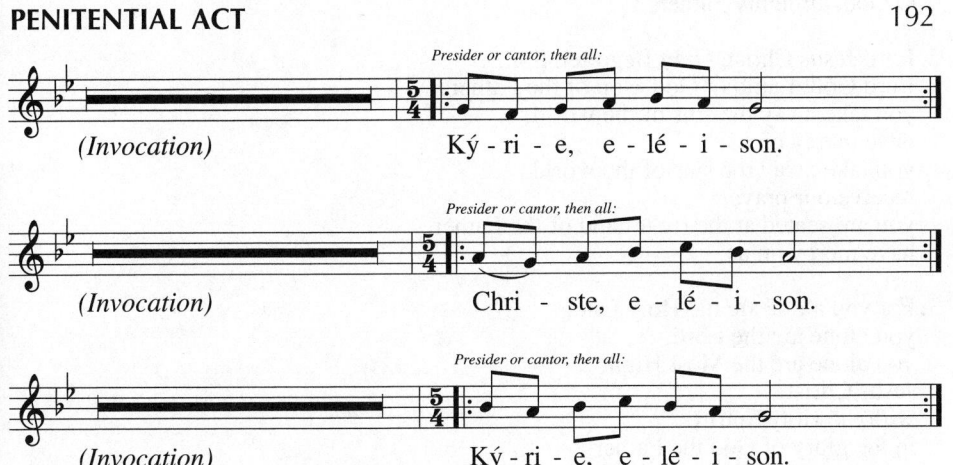

*(Invocation)*<space count="20" />Ký - ri - e, e - lé - i - son.

*(Invocation)*<space count="20" />Chri - ste, e - lé - i - son.

*(Invocation)*<space count="20" />Ký - ri - e, e - lé - i - son.

*Priest:* May almighty God...everlasting life.

A - men.

Music: *Mass of Creation*, Marty Haugen, © 2010, GIA Publications, Inc.

## 193  GLÓRIA

Refrain

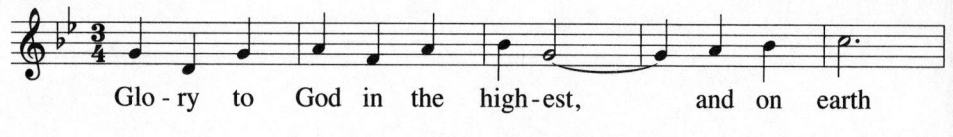

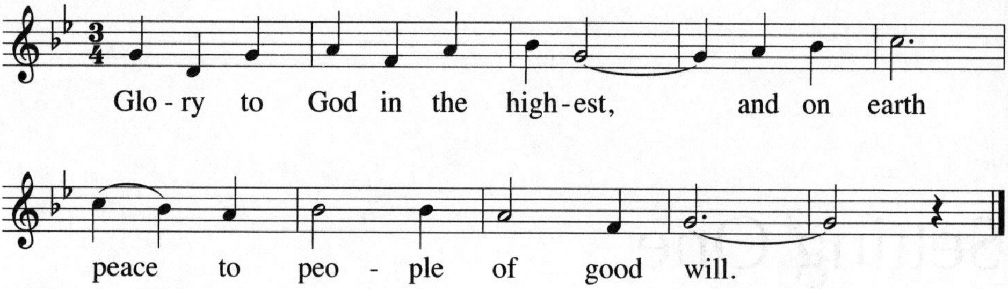

Glo - ry to God in the high-est, and on earth peace to peo - ple of good will.

Verses

1. We praise you,
   we bless you,
   we adore you,
   we glorify you,
   we give you thanks for your great glory,
   Lord God, heavenly King,
   O God, almighty Father.

2. Lord Jesus Christ, Only Begotten Son,
   Lord God, Lamb of God, Son of the Father,
   you take away the sins of the world,
   have mercy on us;
   you take away the sins of the world,
   receive our prayer;
   you are seated at the right hand of the Father,
   have mercy on us.

3. For you alone are the Holy One,
   you alone are the Lord,
   you alone are the Most High,
   Jesus Christ,
   with the Holy Spirit,
   in the glory of God the Father.
   Amen.

Text: ICEL, © 2010
Music: *Mass of Creation*, Marty Haugen, © 1984, 1985, 2010, GIA Publications, Inc.

## 194  GOSPEL ACCLAMATION

Refrain

Al-le - lu - ia, al-le - lu - ia, al-le - lu-ia, al - le - lu - ia. Al-le-

lu - ia, al - le - lu - ia, al - le - lu - ia, al - le - lu - ia.

Music: *Mass of Creation*, Marty Haugen, © 1984, 1985, 2010, GIA Publications, Inc.

## LENTEN GOSPEL ACCLAMATION 195

Refrain

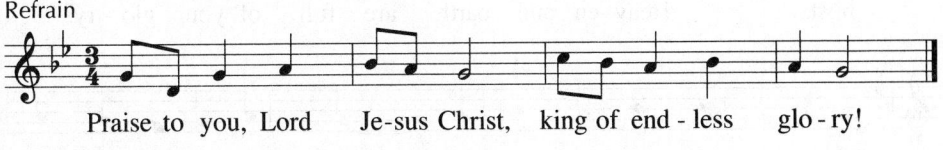

Praise to you, Lord Je-sus Christ, king of end - less glo - ry!

Text: ICEL, © 1969
Music: *Mass of Creation*, Marty Haugen, © 1984, 1985, GIA Publications, Inc.

## PRAYER OF THE FAITHFUL 196

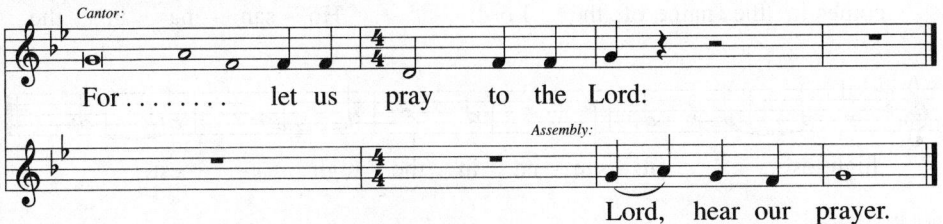

For . . . . . . . let us pray to the Lord:

Lord, hear our prayer.

Music: *Mass of Creation*, Marty Haugen, © 1984, 1985, GIA Publications, Inc.

## PREFACE DIALOGUE 197

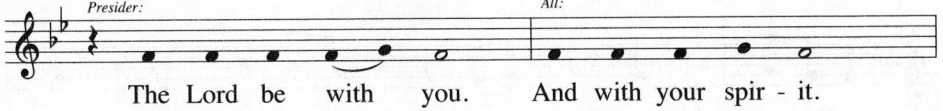

The Lord be with you. And with your spir - it.

Lift up your hearts. We lift them up to the Lord.

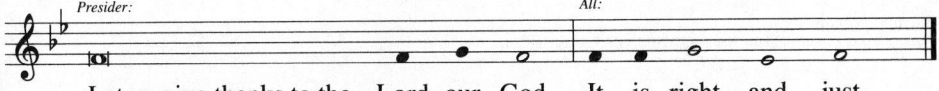

Let us give thanks to the Lord our God. It is right and just.

Text: ICEL, © 2010
Music: *Mass of Creation*, Marty Haugen, © 1984, 1985, 2010, GIA Publications, Inc.

## 198  HOLY, HOLY, HOLY

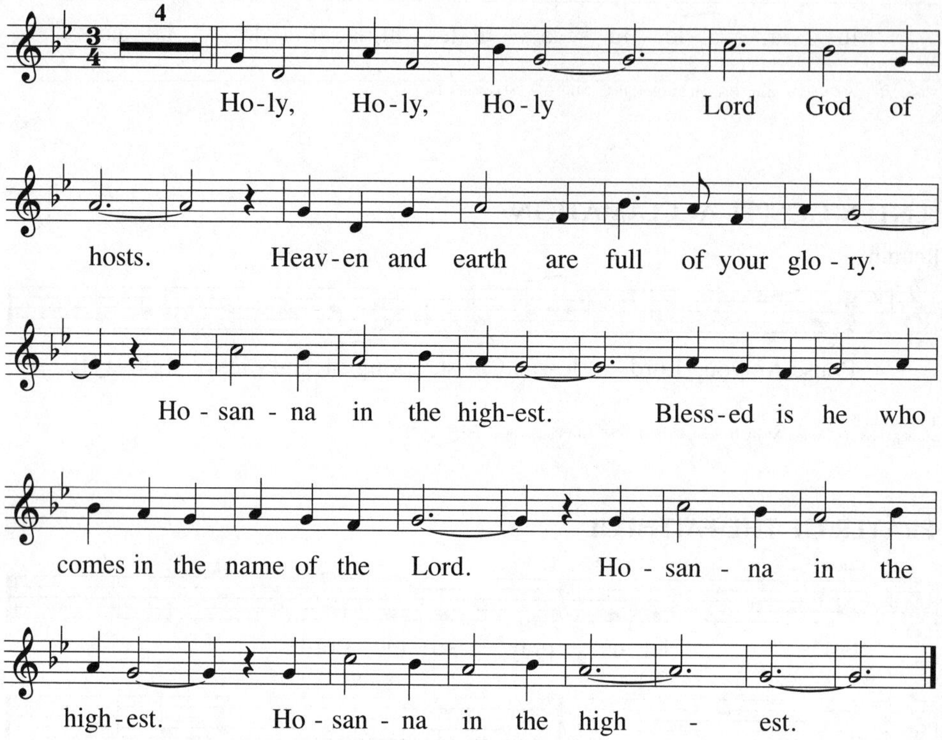

Ho-ly,    Ho-ly,    Ho-ly    Lord    God    of

hosts.    Heav-en and earth    are    full    of your glo-ry.

Ho - san - na    in    the    high-est.    Bless-ed is he who

comes in    the    name of the    Lord.    Ho - san - na    in    the

high-est.    Ho - san - na    in    the    high - est.

Text: ICEL, © 2010
Music: *Mass of Creation,* Marty Haugen, © 1984, 1985, 2010, GIA Publications, Inc.

## 199  MEMORIAL ACCLAMATION A

We pro - claim your Death, O    Lord,    and pro - fess    your Res - ur -

rec - tion un - til    you come a - gain,    un - til    you come a - gain.

Text: ICEL, © 2010
Music: *Mass of Creation,* Marty Haugen, © 2010, GIA Publications, Inc.

## MEMORIAL ACCLAMATION B 200

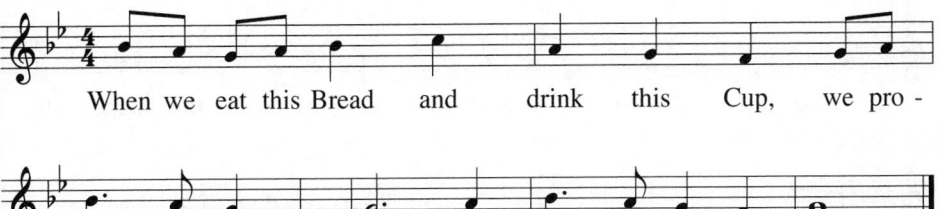

When we eat this Bread and drink this Cup, we proclaim your Death, O Lord, un - til you come a - gain.

Text: ICEL, © 2010
Music: *Mass of Creation,* Marty Haugen, © 2010, GIA Publications, Inc.

## MEMORIAL ACCLAMATION C 201

Save us, Sav - ior of the world, for by your Cross and Res - ur -
rec - tion you have set us free, you have set us free.

Text: ICEL, © 2010
Music: *Mass of Creation,* Marty Haugen, © 2010, GIA Publications, Inc.

## AMEN 202

A - men, a - men, a - men.
A - men, a - men, a - men.

Music: *Mass of Creation,* Marty Haugen, © 1984, 1985, GIA Publications, Inc.

## 203   THE LORD'S PRAYER

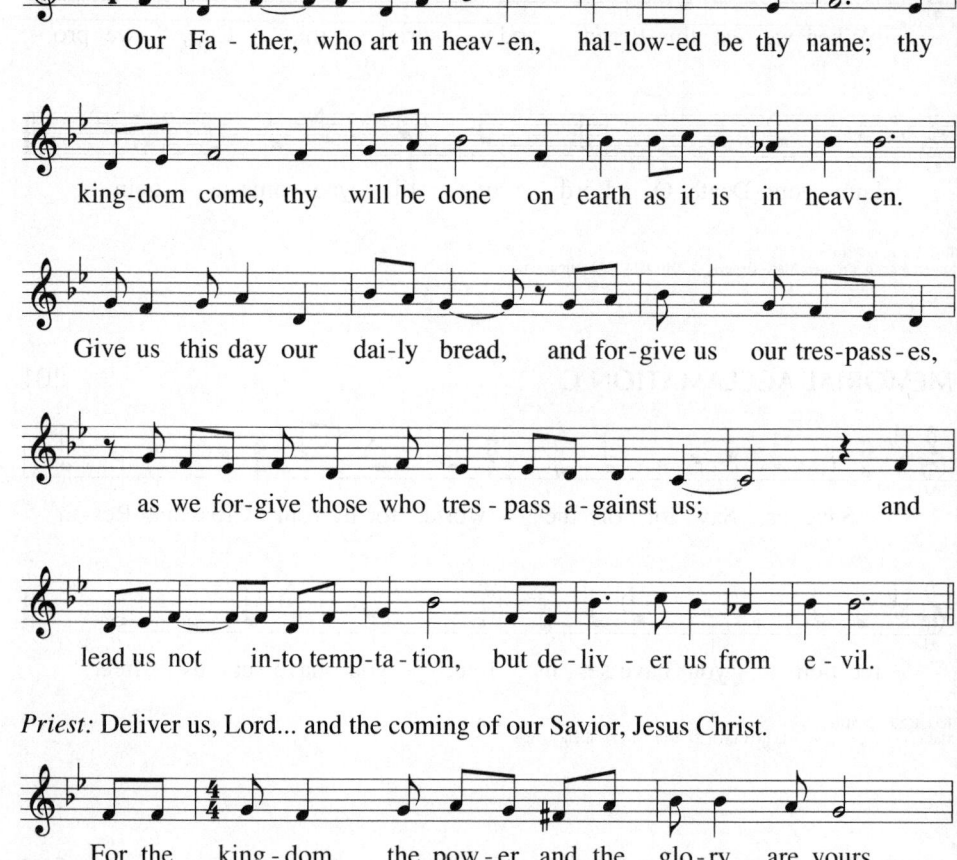

Our Fa - ther, who art in heav-en, hal-low-ed be thy name; thy

king-dom come, thy will be done on earth as it is in heav-en.

Give us this day our dai-ly bread, and for-give us our tres-pass-es,

as we for-give those who tres - pass a-gainst us; and

lead us not in-to temp-ta-tion, but de-liv - er us from e - vil.

*Priest:* Deliver us, Lord... and the coming of our Savior, Jesus Christ.

For the king - dom, the pow - er and the glo-ry are yours

now and for ev - er. A - men.

Music: *Mass of Creation*, Marty Haugen, © 1984, 1985, GIA Publications, Inc.

# LAMB OF GOD

Lamb of God, you take a-way the sins of the

To repeat

world, have mer - cy on us.

Last time

world, grant us peace.

Music: *Mass of Creation*, Marty Haugen, © 1984, 1985, GIA Publications, Inc.

# Setting Two

## MASS OF JOY AND PEACE

### 205 SPRINKLING SONG

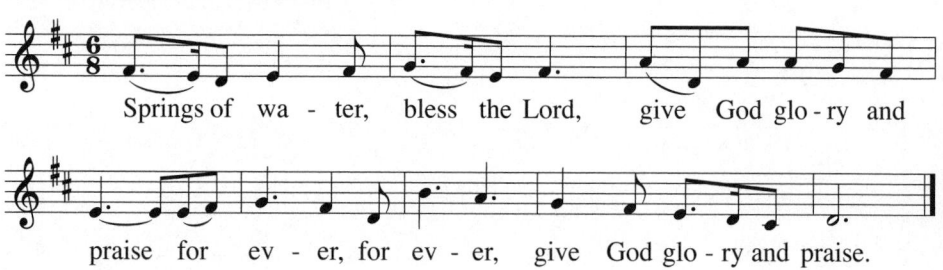

Springs of wa - ter, bless the Lord, give God glo - ry and
praise for ev - er, for ev - er, give God glo - ry and praise.

Music: *Mass of Joy and Peace*, Tony E. Alonso, © 2010, GIA Publications, Inc.

### 206 PENITENTIAL ACT

*Cantor or presider, then all:*

*(Invocation)* Ký - ri - e, e - lé - i - son.

*Cantor or presider, then all:*

*(Invocation)* Chri - ste, e - lé - i - son.

*Cantor or presider, then all:*

*(Invocation)* Ký - ri - e, e - lé - i - son.

Music: *Mass of Joy and Peace*, Tony E. Alonso, © 2010, GIA Publications, Inc.

# GLÓRIA

207

**Refrain**

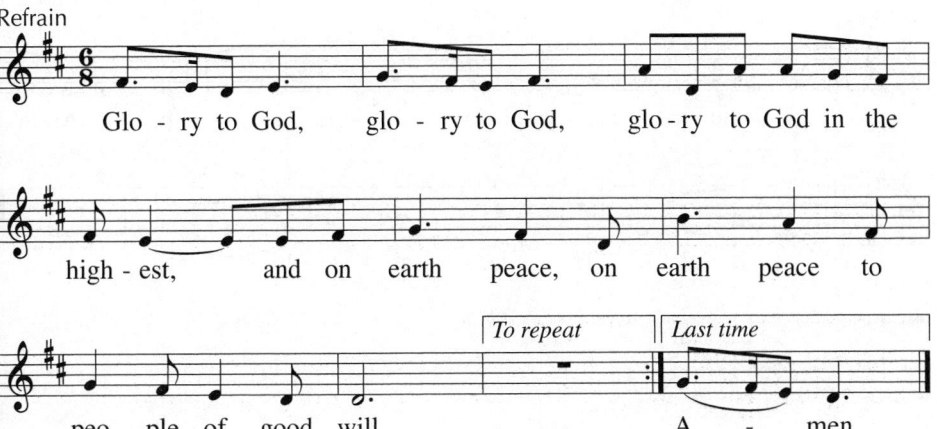

Glo - ry to God, glo - ry to God, glo - ry to God in the

high - est, and on earth peace, on earth peace to

*To repeat*   *Last time*

peo - ple of good will.   A - men.

**Verses**

1. We praise you,
   we bless you,
   we adore you,
   we glorify you,
   we give you thanks for your great glory,
   Lord God, heavenly King,
   O God, almighty Father.

2. Lord Jesus Christ, Only Begotten Son,
   Lord God, Lamb of God, Son of the Father,
   you take away the sins of the world,
   have mercy on us;
   you take away the sins of the world,
   receive our prayer;
   you are seated at the right hand of the Father,
   have mercy on us.

3. For you alone are the Holy One,
   you alone are the Lord,
   you alone are the Most High,
   Jesus Christ,
   with the Holy Spirit,
   in the glory of God the Father.
   Amen.

Text: ICEL, © 2010
Music: *Mass of Joy and Peace,* Tony E. Alonso, © 2010, GIA Publications, Inc.

## 208  GOSPEL ACCLAMATION

Refrain

Al - le-lu - ia,    al - le-lu - ia,    al - le - lu - ia.    Al-le-

lu - ia, al - le - lu - ia,    al - le - lu - ia.

Music: *Mass of Joy and Peace,* Tony E. Alonso, © 2010, GIA Publications, Inc.

## 209  LENTEN GOSPEL ACCLAMATION

Refrain

Glo - ry to you,    Word of God,    Lord    Je - sus Christ!

Glo - ry to you,    Word of God,    Lord    Je-sus    Christ!

Text: ICEL, © 1969
Music: *Mass of Joy and Peace,* Tony E. Alonso, © 2010, GIA Publications, Inc.

## 210  PRAYER OF THE FAITHFUL

Introduction
*Cantor, then all:*

God of mer - cy, hear    our    prayer.    *(Invocation)*

Response
*Cantor:*    *Assembly:*

We pray to the Lord:    God of mer-cy, hear our prayer.

Music: *Mass of Joy and Peace,* Tony E. Alonso, © 2010, GIA Publications, Inc.

# HOLY, HOLY, HOLY                                            211

Ho - ly, Ho - ly, Ho - ly Lord God of hosts.

Heav-en and earth are full of your glo - ry. Ho -

san - na in the high - est, ho - san - na in the

high - est. Bless-ed is he, bless-ed is he who

comes in the name of the Lord. Ho - san - na in the

high-est, ho - san - na in the high-est. Ho - san - na in the

high - est, ho - san - na in the high - est.

Text: ICEL, © 2010
Music: *Mass of Joy and Peace,* Tony E. Alonso, © 2010, GIA Publications, Inc.

# MEMORIAL ACCLAMATION A                                     212

We pro - claim your Death, O Lord, and pro -

fess your Res - ur - rec-tion un - til you come a - gain.

Text: ICEL, © 2010
Music: *Mass of Joy and Peace,* Tony E. Alonso, © 2010, GIA Publications, Inc.

## 213 MEMORIAL ACCLAMATION B

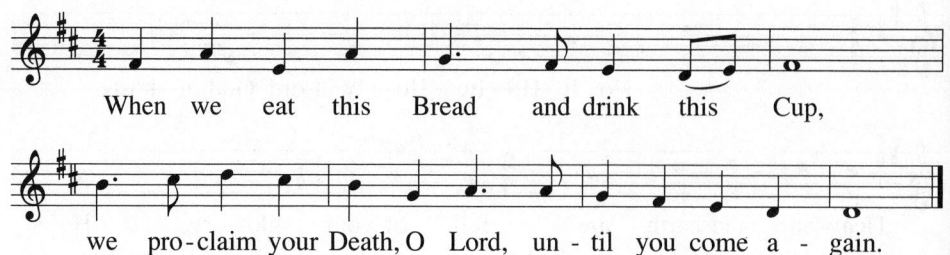

When we eat this Bread and drink this Cup, we pro-claim your Death, O Lord, un - til you come a - gain.

Text: ICEL, © 2010
Music: *Mass of Joy and Peace,* Tony E. Alonso, © 2010, GIA Publications, Inc.

## 214 MEMORIAL ACCLAMATION C

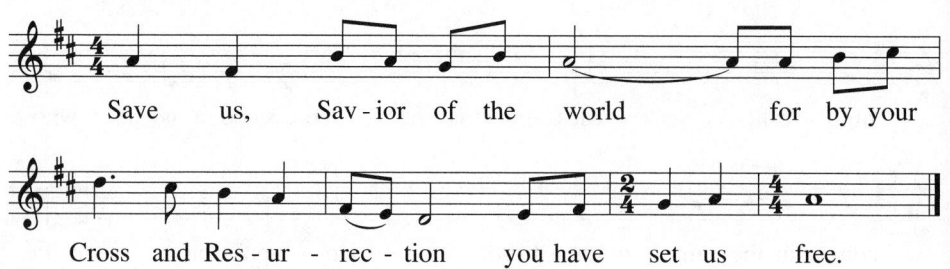

Save us, Sav - ior of the world for by your Cross and Res - ur - rec - tion you have set us free.

Text: ICEL, © 2010
Music: *Mass of Joy and Peace,* Tony E. Alonso, © 2010, GIA Publications, Inc.

## 215 AMEN

A - men, a - men, a - men, a - men. A - men, a - men, a - men, a - men.

Music: *Mass of Joy and Peace,* Tony E. Alonso, © 2010, GIA Publications, Inc.

## 216 LAMB OF GOD

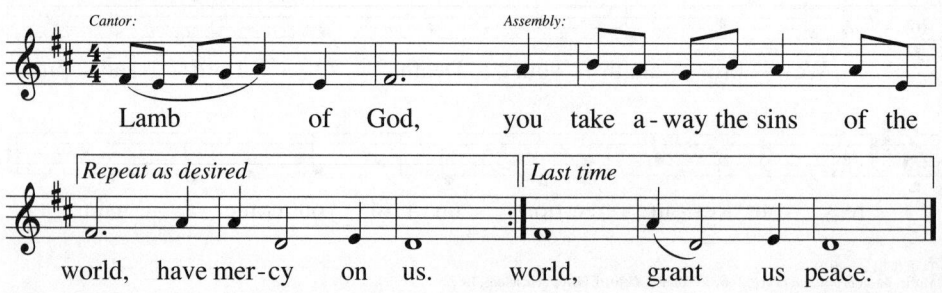

*Cantor:*    *Assembly:*

Lamb of God, you take a - way the sins of the

*Repeat as desired*    *Last time*

world, have mer - cy on us. world, grant us peace.

Music: *Mass of Joy and Peace,* Tony E. Alonso, © 2010, GIA Publications, Inc.

# Setting Three

## MASS FOR A NEW WORLD

### PENITENTIAL ACT

217

*Cantor, then assembly:*

1. Ký-ri - e,    Ký-ri - e,    Ký-ri - e,    e - lé - i - son.
2. Chri - ste,    Chri - ste,    Chri - ste,    e - lé - i - son.
3. Ký-ri - e,    Ký-ri - e,    Ký-ri - e,    e - lé - i - son.

## 218 **GLÓRIA**

world, have mer - cy on us; you take a -

way the sins of the world, re - ceive our prayer;

you are seat - ed at the right hand of the

**D.C.**

Fa - ther, have mer - cy on us.

Verse 3

3. For you a - lone are the Ho - ly One, you a - lone

are the Lord, you a - lone are the

Most High, Je - sus Christ, with the

Ho - ly Spir - it, in the glo - ry of God the

**D.C.**

Fa - ther. A - men. A - men.

Text: ICEL, © 2010
Music: *Mass for a New World,* David Haas, © 2010, GIA Publications, Inc.

## 219 GOSPEL ACCLAMATION

Al-le-lu-ia, al - le-lu - ia! Al-le-lu-ia, al - le-lu - ia!

Al-le-lu-ia, al - le-lu - ia! Al-le-lu-ia, al - le-lu - ia!

Al - le - lu - ia, al - le - lu - ia!

Music: *Mass for a New World,* David Haas, © 2010, GIA Publications, Inc.

## 220 LENTEN GOSPEL ACCLAMATION

Refrain

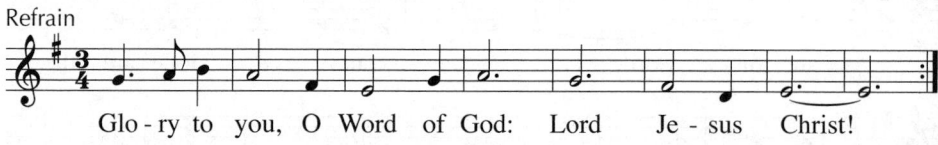

Glo - ry to you, O Word of God: Lord Je - sus Christ!

Text: ICEL, © 1969
Music: *Mass for a New World,* David Haas, © 2010, GIA Publications, Inc.

## 221 PRAYER OF THE FAITHFUL

Refrain

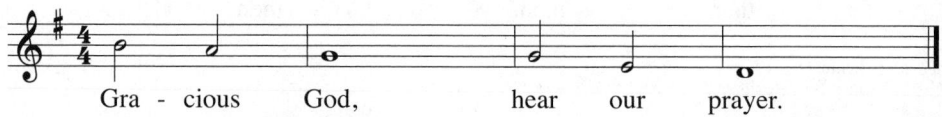

Gra - cious God, hear our prayer.

Music: *Mass for a New World,* David Haas, © 2010, GIA Publications, Inc.

# HOLY, HOLY, HOLY

222

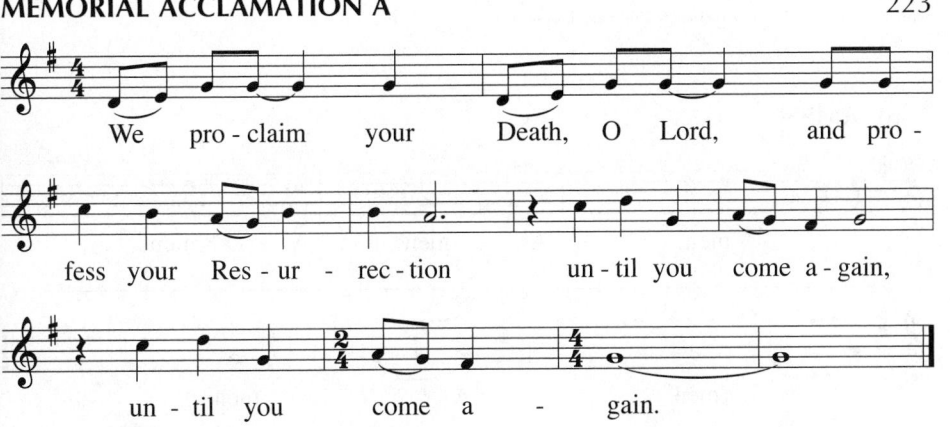

Ho - ly, Ho - ly,
Ho - ly Lord God of hosts. Heav-en and earth are
full of your glo - ry. Ho - san - na in the
high - est. Bless-ed is he, bless-ed is he who
comes in the name of the Lord. Ho - san - na in the
high - est, ho - san - na in the high - est.

Text: ICEL, © 2010
Music: *Mass for a New World,* David Haas, © 2010, GIA Publications, Inc.

# MEMORIAL ACCLAMATION A

223

We pro - claim your Death, O Lord, and pro -
fess your Res - ur - rec - tion un - til you come a - gain,
un - til you come a - gain.

Text: ICEL, © 2010
Music: *Mass for a New World,* David Haas, © 2010, GIA Publications, Inc.

## 224 MEMORIAL ACCLAMATION B

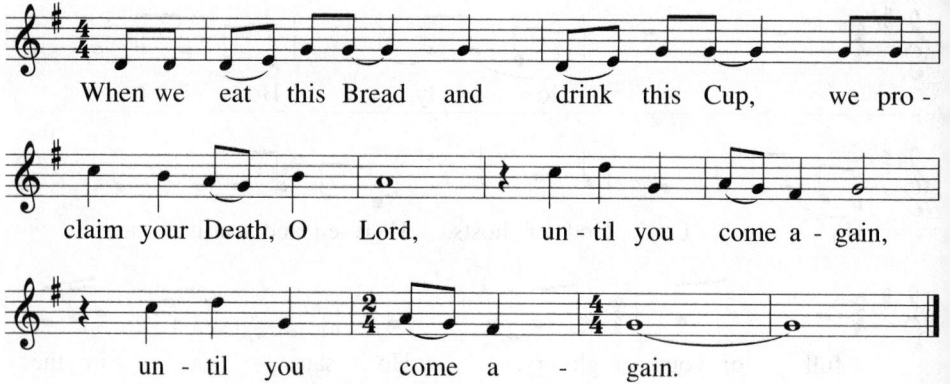

When we eat this Bread and drink this Cup, we proclaim your Death, O Lord, un - til you come a - gain,
un - til you come a - gain.

Text: ICEL, © 2010
Music: *Mass for a New World*, David Haas, © 2010, GIA Publications, Inc.

## 225 MEMORIAL ACCLAMATION C

Save us, Sav - ior of the world, for by your
Cross and Res - ur - rec - tion you have set us free,
you have set us free.

Text: ICEL, © 2010
Music: *Mass for a New World*, David Haas, © 2010, GIA Publications, Inc.

## 226 AMEN

A - men. A - men. A - men.
1. A - men. 2. A - men.

Music: *Mass for a New World*, David Haas, © 2010, GIA Publications, Inc.

# THE LORD'S PRAYER

227

Our Fa-ther, who art in heav-en, hal-low-ed be thy

name; thy king-dom come, thy will be done on earth as it is in

heav-en. Give us this day our dai-ly bread, and for-

give us our tres-pass-es, as we for-give those who

tres-pass a-gainst us; and lead us not in-to temp-

ta-tion, but de-liv-er us from e-vil.

*Priest:* Deliver us, Lord... and the coming of our Savior, Jesus Christ.

For the king-dom, the pow'r and the glo-ry are yours

now and for ev-er. A-men.

Music: *Mass for a New World,* David Haas, © 2010, GIA Publications, Inc.

## 228  LAMB OF GOD

Cantor: Lamb of God, you take a-way the

All: (us.) Lamb of God, you take a-way

**To repeat**

sins of the world, have mer-cy on us.

the sins of the world, have mer-cy on

**Last time**

world, grant us peace.

sins of the world, grant us peace.

Music: *Mass for a New World*, David Haas, © 2010, GIA Publications, Inc.

# Setting Four

## STORRINGTON MASS

### PENITENTIAL ACT

*(Invocation)* Ký - ri - e, e - lé - i - son.

*(Invocation)* Chri - ste, e - lé - i - son.

*(Invocation)* Ký - ri - e, e - lé - i - son.

*Priest:* May almighty God...everlasting life.

A - men.

Music: *Storrington Mass*, Marty Haugen, © 2010, GIA Publications, Inc.

## 230  GLÓRIA

Refrain

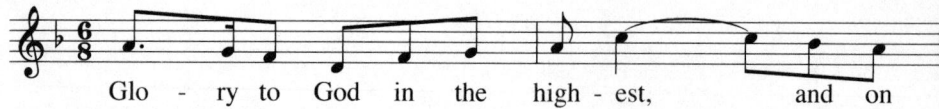

Glo - ry to God in the high - est, and on

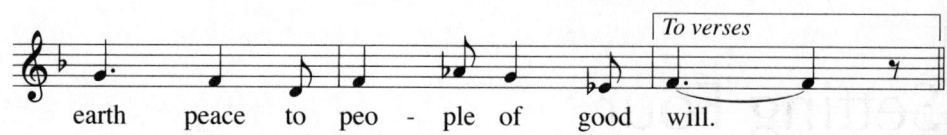

earth peace to peo - ple of good will.

*To verses*

*Last time*

will.          A - men, a - men, a - men.

Verses

1. We praise you,
   we bless you,
   we adore you,
   we glorify you,
   we give you thanks for your great glory,
   Lord God, heavenly King,
   O God, almighty Father.

2. Lord Jesus Christ, Only Begotten Son,
   Lord God, Lamb of God, Son of the Father,
   you take away the sins of the world,
   have mercy on us;
   you take away the sins of the world,
   receive our prayer;
   you are seated at the right hand of the Father,
   have mercy on us.

3. For you alone are the Holy One,
   you alone are the Lord,
   you alone are the Most High,
   Jesus Christ,
   with the Holy Spirit,
   in the glory of God the Father.
   Amen.

Text: ICEL, © 2010
Music: *Storrington Mass,* Marty Haugen, © 2010, GIA Publications, Inc.

## 231  GOSPEL ACCLAMATION

Refrain

Al - le - lu - ia, al - le - lu - ia, al - le - lu - ia.

Al - le - lu - ia, al - le - lu - ia, al - le - lu - ia.

Music: *Storrington Mass*, Marty Haugen, © 2010, GIA Publications, Inc.

## LENTEN GOSPEL ACCLAMATION 232

Refrain

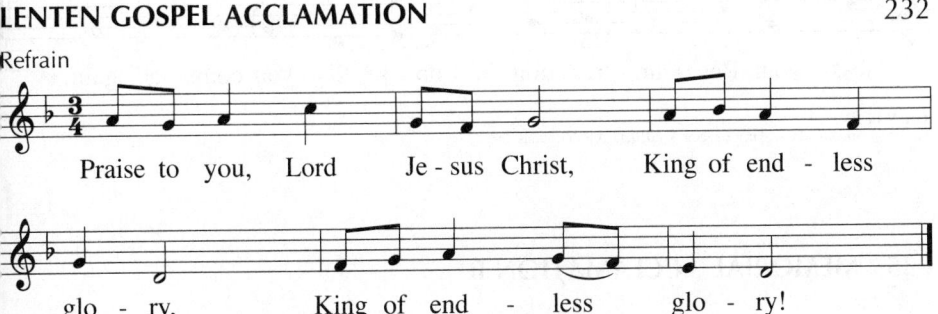

Praise to you, Lord Je - sus Christ, King of end - less glo - ry, King of end - less glo - ry!

Text: ICEL, © 1969
Music: *Storrington Mass*, Marty Haugen, © 2010, GIA Publications, Inc.

## HOLY, HOLY, HOLY 233

Ho - ly, Ho - ly, Ho - ly

Lord God of hosts. Heav - en and earth are full of your

glo - ry. Ho - san - na in the high - est. Bless - ed is he who

comes in the name of the Lord. Ho - san - na, ho -

san - na, ho - san - na in the high - est.

Text: ICEL, © 2010
Music: *Storrington Mass,* Marty Haugen, © 2010, GIA Publications, Inc.

## 234 MEMORIAL ACCLAMATION A

We pro - claim your Death, O Lord, and pro-
fess your Res - ur - rec - tion un - til you come a - gain.

Text: ICEL, © 2010
Music: *Storrington Mass,* Marty Haugen, © 2010, GIA Publications, Inc.

## 235 MEMORIAL ACCLAMATION B

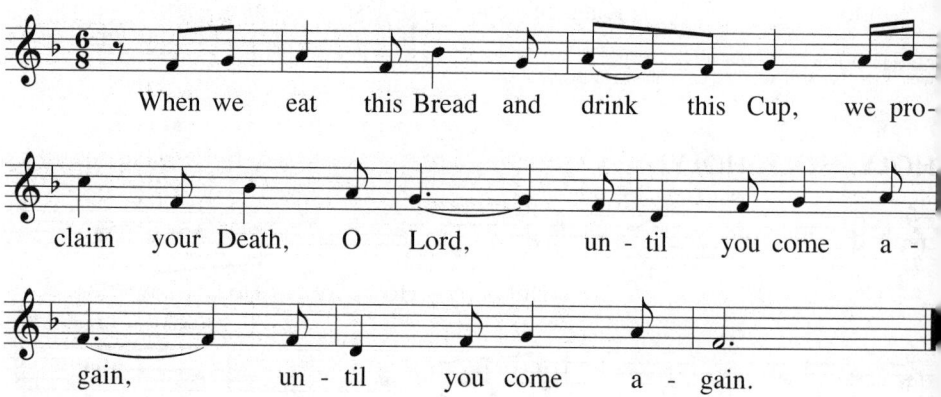

When we eat this Bread and drink this Cup, we proclaim your Death, O Lord, un - til you come a -
gain, un - til you come a - gain.

Text: ICEL, © 2010
Music: *Storrington Mass,* Marty Haugen, © 2010, GIA Publications, Inc.

## 236 MEMORIAL ACCLAMATION C

Save us, Sav - ior of the world, for by your
Cross and Res - ur - rec - tion you have set us free.

Text: ICEL, © 2010
Music: *Storrington Mass,* Marty Haugen, © 2010, GIA Publications, Inc.

# AMEN 237

A - men, a - men, a - men.

A - men, a - men, a - men.

Music: *Storrington Mass,* Marty Haugen, © 2010, GIA Publications, Inc.

# LAMB OF GOD 238

Cantor:          + Assembly:

Lamb of God,    you take a-way the sins    of the

To repeat

world,    have mer-cy    on us.

Last time

Lamb of God,    you take a-way the sins    of the

world,    grant    us peace,    grant    us peace.

Music: *Storrington Mass,* Marty Haugen, © 2010, GIA Publications, Inc.

# Setting Five

## BLACK MOUNTAIN LITURGY

### 239 KÝRIE

Lord, have mer - cy. Christ, have mer - cy. Lord, have mer - cy.

Music: *Black Mountain Liturgy,* Sally Ann Morris, © 2003, GIA Publications, Inc.

### 240 GLÓRIA

Refrain

Glo-ry to God in the high - est, and on earth peace to peo - ple of good will.

*To verses*

1. We
2. ˀ
3. For

**Verse 1**

praise you, we bless you, we a - dore you, we glo - ri - fy you, we give you thanks for your great glo - ry,

*opt. D.C.

Lord God, heav-en-ly King, O God, al-might-y Fa - ther.

**Verse 2**

2. Lord Je - sus Christ, On - ly Be - got - ten Son, Lord God, Lamb of God, Son of the Fa - ther, you take a - way the sins of the world, have mer - cy on us; you take a - way the sins of the world, re - ceive our prayer; you are seat-ed at the right hand of the Fa -

opt. **D.C.**

ther, have mer - cy on us. 3. For

*May be sung with or without refrains.

Verse 3

you a-lone are the Ho-ly One, you a-lone are the

Lord, you a-lone are the Most High, Je - sus

Christ, with the Ho - ly Spir-it, in the

*opt.* **D.C.**

glo-ry of God the Fa - ther. A - men.

Text: ICEL, © 2010
Music: *Black Mountain Liturgy,* Sally Ann Morris, © 2003, 2010, GIA Publications, Inc.

## 241 GOSPEL ACCLAMATION

Al - le-lu - ia, al - le - lu - ia.
*Lent:* Praise and hon-or to you, Lord Je - sus Christ!

Al - le-lu - ia, al - le - lu - ia.
Praise and hon-or to you, Lord Je - sus Christ!

Text: ICEL, © 1969
Music: *Black Mountain Liturgy,* Sally Ann Morris, © 2003, GIA Publications, Inc.

## 242 HOLY, HOLY, HOLY

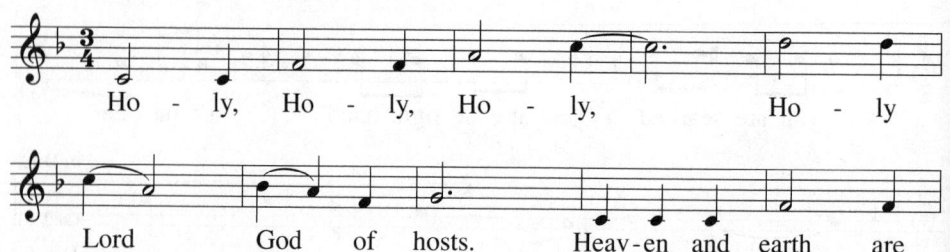

Ho - ly, Ho - ly, Ho - ly, Ho - ly

Lord God of hosts. Heav-en and earth are

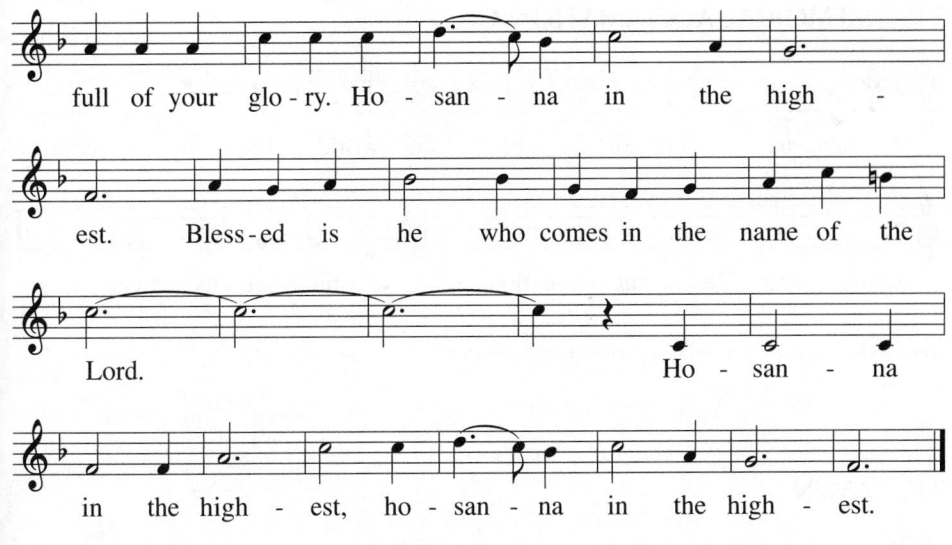

full of your glo - ry. Ho - san - na in the high -
est. Bless-ed is he who comes in the name of the
Lord. Ho - san - na
in the high - est, ho - san - na in the high - est.

Text: ICEL, © 2010
Music: *Black Mountain Liturgy,* Sally Ann Morris, © 2003, 2010, GIA Publications, Inc.

## MEMORIAL ACCLAMATION A 243

We pro - claim your Death, O Lord, and pro - fess your
Res - ur - rec - tion un - til you come a - gain.

Text: ICEL, © 2010
Music: *Black Mountain Liturgy,* Sally Ann Morris, © 2010, GIA Publications, Inc.

## MEMORIAL ACCLAMATION B 244

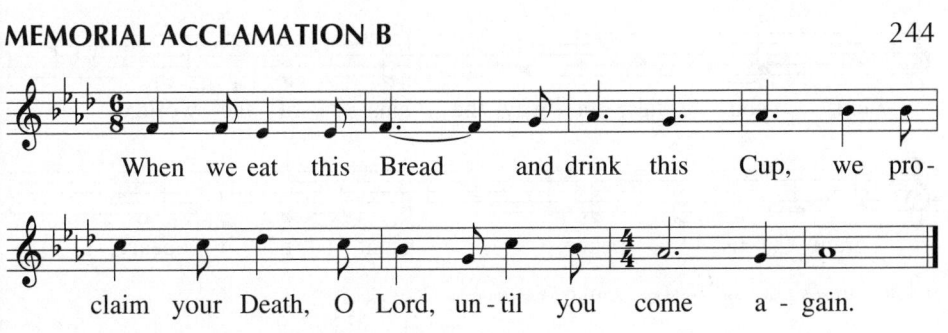

When we eat this Bread and drink this Cup, we proclaim your Death, O Lord, un - til you come a - gain.

Text: ICEL, © 2010
Music: *Black Mountain Liturgy,* Sally Ann Morris, © 2010, GIA Publications, Inc.

## 245 MEMORIAL ACCLAMATION C

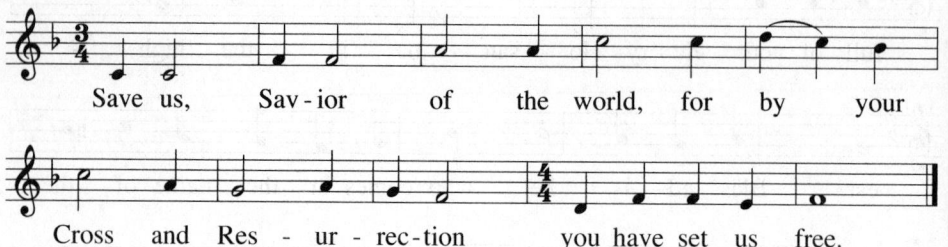

Save us, Sav-ior of the world, for by your
Cross and Res - ur - rec-tion you have set us free.

Text: ICEL, © 2010
Music: *Black Mountain Liturgy,* Sally Ann Morris, © 2010, GIA Publications, Inc.

## 246 AMEN

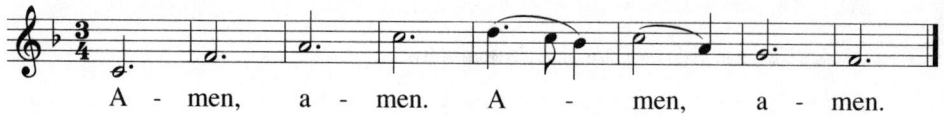

A - men, a - men. A - men, a - men.

Music: *Black Mountain Liturgy,* Sally Ann Morris, © 2003, GIA Publications, Inc.

## 247 LAMB OF GOD

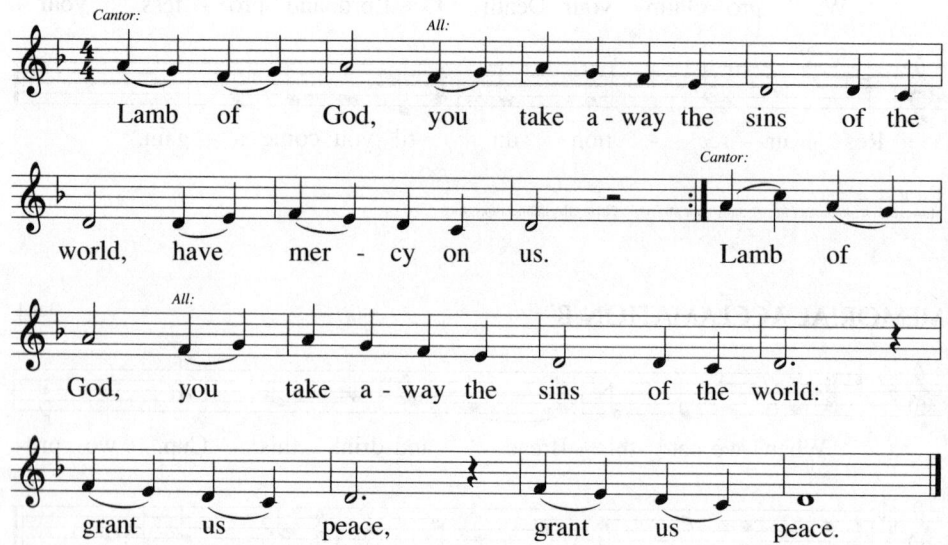

*Cantor:* *All:*

Lamb of God, you take a - way the sins of the

*Cantor:*

world, have mer - cy on us. Lamb of

*All:*

God, you take a - way the sins of the world:

grant us peace, grant us peace.

Music: *Black Mountain Liturgy,* Sally Ann Morris, © 2003, GIA Publications, Inc.

# Setting Six

## MASS FROM AGE TO AGE

### KÝRIE 248

Music: *Mass from Age to Age*, Chris de Silva, © 2010, GIA Publications, Inc.

## 249 GLÓRIA

Refrain

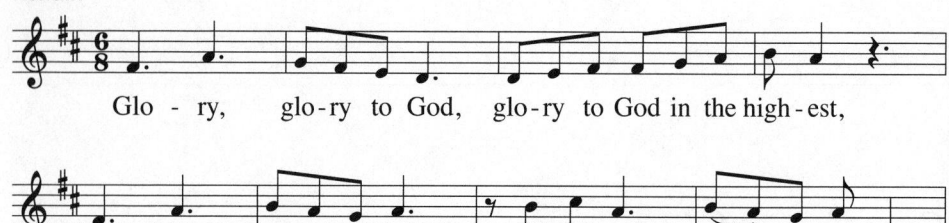

Glo - ry, glo-ry to God, glo-ry to God in the high-est,

glo - ry, glo-ry to God, and on earth peace to peo-ple,

*To verses* | *Last time*

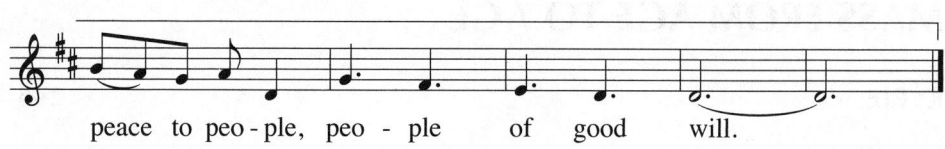

peo - ple of good will. and on earth

peace to peo-ple, peo - ple of good will.

Verse 1

1. We praise you,
   we bless you,
   we adore you,
   we glorify you,
   we give you thanks for your great glory,
   Lord God, heavenly King,
   O God, almighty Father.

Verse 2

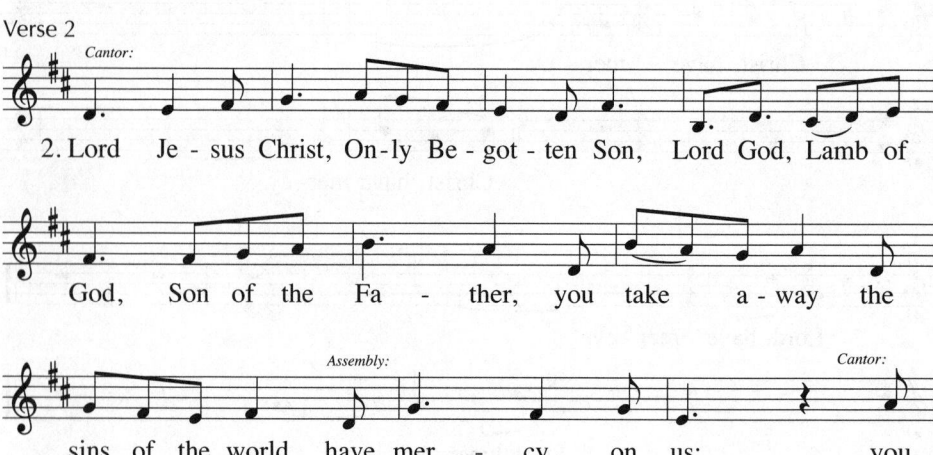

*Cantor:*

2. Lord Je - sus Christ, On-ly Be - got - ten Son, Lord God, Lamb of

God, Son of the Fa - ther, you take a - way the

*Assembly:*      *Cantor:*

sins of the world, have mer - cy on us; you

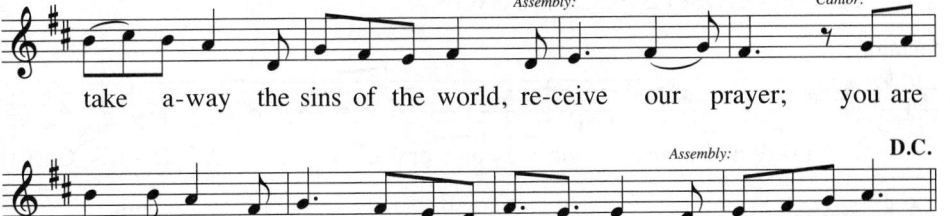

take a-way the sins of the world, re-ceive our prayer; you are

*Assembly:*     *Cantor:*

seat - ed at the right hand of the Fa - ther, have mer-cy on us.

*Assembly:*     **D.C.**

Verse 3

3. For you alone are the Holy One,
   you alone are the Lord,
   you alone are the Most High,
   Jesus Christ,
   with the Holy Spirit,
   in the glory of God the Father.
   Amen.

Text: ICEL, © 2010
Music: *Mass from Age to Age,* Chris de Silva, © 2010, GIA Publications, Inc.

## GOSPEL ACCLAMATION     250

Refrain

Al - le-lu - ia, al - le - lu - ia, al - le-lu - ia.

Al - le-lu - ia, al - le - lu - ia, al - le-lu - ia.

*Repeat first time only* | *Last time*

al - le - lu - ia.

Verse Response (2x)

**D.C.**

Al - le - lu - ia.

Music: *Mass from Age to Age,* Chris de Silva, © 2010, GIA Publications, Inc.

## 251 LENTEN GOSPEL ACCLAMATION

Refrain

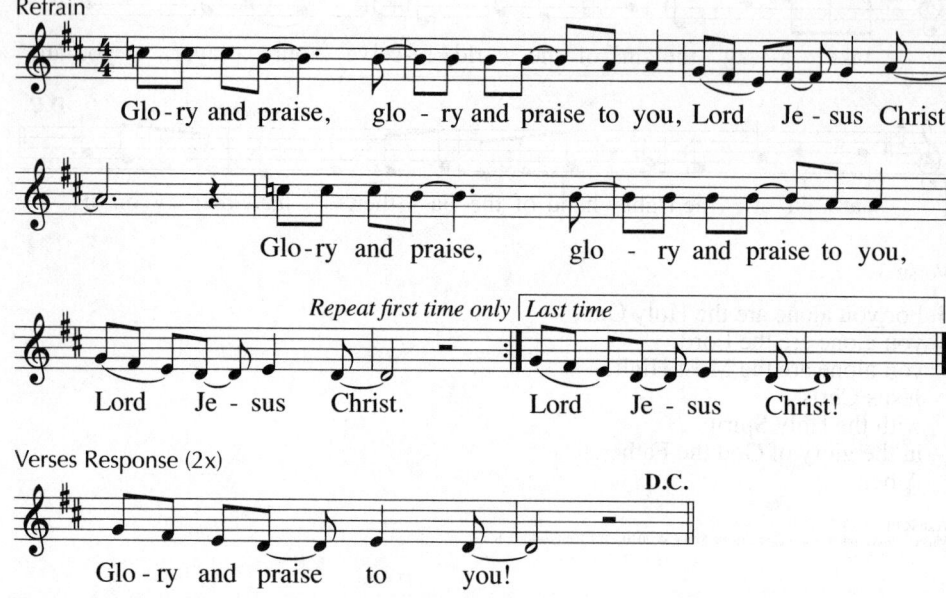

Glo-ry and praise, glo - ry and praise to you, Lord Je - sus Christ!

Glo-ry and praise, glo - ry and praise to you,

*Repeat first time only* | *Last time*

Lord Je - sus Christ. Lord Je - sus Christ!

Verses Response (2x)

D.C.

Glo - ry and praise to you!

Text: ICEL, © 1969
Music: *Mass from Age to Age*, Chris de Silva, © 2010, GIA Publications, Inc.

## 252 PRAYER OF THE FAITHFUL

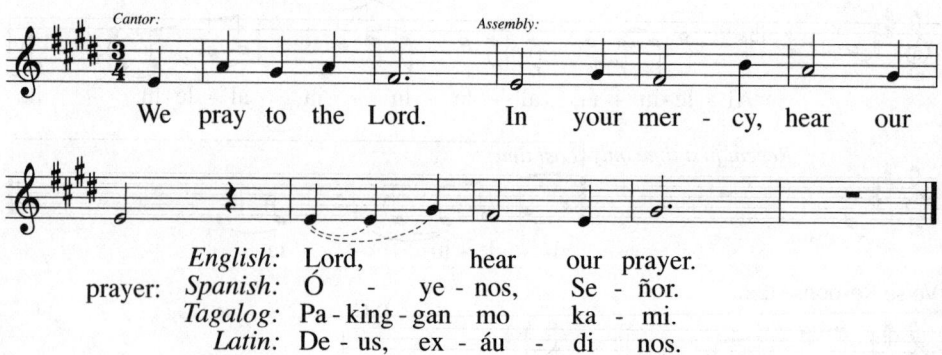

*Cantor:*

We pray to the Lord.

*Assembly:*

In your mer - cy, hear our

prayer: 

| | |
|---|---|
| *English:* | Lord, hear our prayer. |
| *Spanish:* | Ó - ye - nos, Se - ñor. |
| *Tagalog:* | Pa - king - gan mo ka - mi. |
| *Latin:* | De - us, ex - áu - di nos. |

Music: *Mass from Age to Age*, Chris de Silva, © 2010, GIA Publications, Inc.

# HOLY, HOLY, HOLY 253

Ho - ly, Ho - ly, Ho - ly Lord God of hosts. Heav - en and earth are full of your glo-ry. Ho - san - na in the high - est. Ho - san - na, ho - san - na, ho - san - na in the high - est. Bless-ed is he who comes in the name of the Lord. Ho - san - na, ho - san - na, ho - san - na in the high - est. Ho - san - na, ho - san - na, ho - san - na in the high - est.

Text: ICEL, © 2010
Music: *Mass from Age to Age*, Chris de Silva, © 2010, GIA Publications, Inc.

# MEMORIAL ACCLAMATION A 254

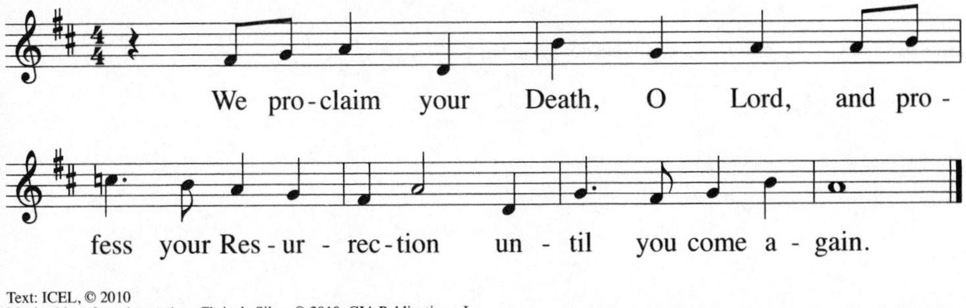

We pro-claim your Death, O Lord, and pro - fess your Res - ur - rec - tion un - til you come a - gain.

Text: ICEL, © 2010
Music: *Mass from Age to Age*, Chris de Silva, © 2010, GIA Publications, Inc.

## 255 MEMORIAL ACCLAMATION B

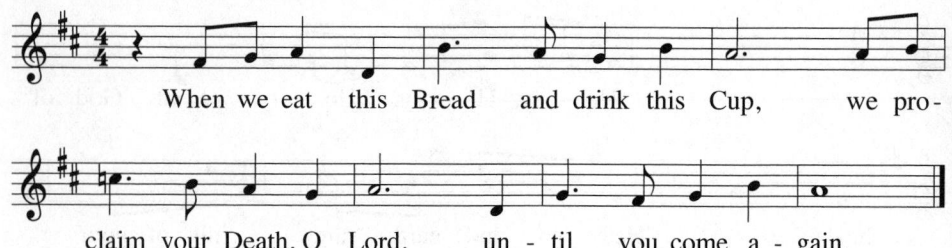

When we eat this Bread and drink this Cup, we pro-

claim your Death, O Lord, un - til you come a - gain.

Text: ICEL, © 2010
Music: *Mass from Age to Age*, Chris de Silva, © 2010, GIA Publications, Inc.

## 256 MEMORIAL ACCLAMATION C

Save us, Sav - ior of the world, for by your Cross and Res - ur -

rec - tion you have set us free.

Text: ICEL, © 2010
Music: *Mass from Age to Age*, Chris de Silva, © 2010, GIA Publications, Inc.

## 257 AMEN

A - men, a - men, a - men.

A - men, a - men, a - men.

Music: *Mass from Age to Age*, Chris de Silva, © 2010, GIA Publications, Inc.

SETTING SIX

# THE LORD'S PRAYER

258

*Priest:* Deliver us, Lord... and the coming of our Savior, Jesus Christ.

Music: *Mass from Age to Age,* Chris de Silva, © 2010, GIA Publications, Inc.

## 259 LAMB OF GOD

Cantor:

Lamb of God,

Assembly:

you take a-way the sins of the

world, have mer-cy on us, Lamb of God.

Cantor:

Lamb of

Assembly:

God, you take a-way the sins of the world, have

1.

mer-cy on us, Lamb of God.

Cantor:

Lamb of world,

2.

grant us peace, grant us peace, grant us peace.

Music: *Mass from Age to Age*, Chris de Silva, © 2010, GIA Publications, Inc.

# Setting Seven

## THE GLENDALOUGH MASS

**KÝRIE** 260

Ký - ri - e, e - lé - i - son.

Chri - ste, e - lé - i - son.

Ký - ri - e, e, e - léi - son. Ký - ri - e, e, e - léi - son.

Ký - ri - e, e - lé - i - son.

Music: *The Glendalough Mass*, Liam Lawton; arr. by Paul A. Tate, © 2010, GIA Publications, Inc.

## 261 GLÓRIA

Refrain

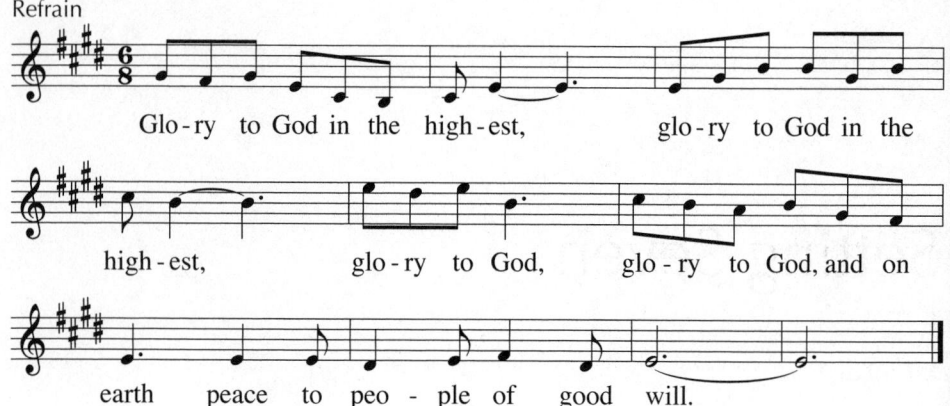

Glo-ry to God in the high-est, glo-ry to God in the

high-est, glo-ry to God, glo-ry to God, and on

earth peace to peo - ple of good will.

Verses

1. We praise you,
   we bless you,
   we adore you,
   we glorify you,
   we give you thanks for your great glory,
   Lord God, heavenly King,
   O God, almighty Father.

2. Lord Jesus Christ, Only Begotten Son,
   Lord God, Lamb of God, Son of the Father,
   you take away the sins of the world,
   have mercy on us;
   you take away the sins of the world,
   receive our prayer;
   you are seated at the right hand of the Father,
   have mercy on us.

3. For you alone are the Holy One,
   you alone are the Lord,
   you alone are the Most High,
   Jesus Christ,
   with the Holy Spirit,
   in the glory of God the Father.
   Amen.

Text: ICEL, © 2010
Music: *The Glendalough Mass*, Liam Lawton; arr. by Paul A. Tate, © 2010, GIA Publications, Inc.

## 262 GOSPEL ACCLAMATION

Refrain

Al - le-lu - ia, al - le-lu-ia, al - le-lu - ia.

Al - le-lu - ia,    al - le-lu - ia,    al - le - lu - ia.

Music: *The Glendalough Mass,* Liam Lawton; arr. by Paul A. Tate, © 2010, GIA Publications, Inc.

## HOLY, HOLY, HOLY          263

Ho - ly, Ho - ly, Ho - ly Lord, Lord God of

hosts.    Heav - en and earth are full of your glo - ry.    Ho -

san - na, ho - san - na, ho - san - na in the high - est.    Ho -

san - na, ho - san - na, ho - san - na in the

high - est.    Bless - ed is he who comes in the name of the

Lord.    Ho - san - na, ho - san - na, ho -

san - na in the high - est.    Ho - san - na, ho -

san - na, ho - san - na in the high - est.

Text: ICEL, © 2010
Music: *The Glendalough Mass,* Liam Lawton; arr. by Paul A. Tate, © 2010, GIA Publications, Inc.

## 264 MEMORIAL ACCLAMATION A

We pro-claim your Death, O Lord, and pro-
fess your Res - ur - rec-tion un - til you come a - gain.

Text: ICEL, © 2010
Music: *The Glendalough Mass,* Liam Lawton; arr. by Paul A. Tate, © 2010, GIA Publications, Inc.

## 265 MEMORIAL ACCLAMATION B

When we eat this Bread and drink this Cup, we proclaim your Death, O Lord, un - til you come a - gain.

Text: ICEL, © 2010
Music: *The Glendalough Mass,* Liam Lawton; arr. by Paul A. Tate, © 2010, GIA Publications, Inc.

## 266 MEMORIAL ACCLAMATION C

Save us, Sav-ior of the world, save us, Sav-ior of the
world, for by your Cross and Res - ur - rec-tion
you have set us free, you have set us free.

Text: ICEL, © 2010
Music: *The Glendalough Mass,* Liam Lawton; arr. by Paul A. Tate, © 2010, GIA Publications, Inc.

## 267 AMEN

A - men, a - men, a - men, a - men.

Music: *The Glendalough Mass,* Liam Lawton; arr. by Paul A. Tate, © 2010, GIA Publications, Inc.

## THE LORD'S PRAYER 268

Our Fa-ther, who art in heav-en, hal-lowed be thy name; thy king-dom come, thy will be done on earth as it is in heav - en. Give us this day our dai - ly bread, and for - give us our tres-pass-es, as we for - give those who tres - pass a - gainst us; and lead us not in - to temp-ta - tion, but de - liv - er us from e - vil.

Music: *The Glendalough Mass*, Liam Lawton; arr. by Paul A. Tate, © 2010, GIA Publications, Inc.

## LAMB OF GOD 269

Lamb of God, you take a - way the sins of the world, have mer-cy on us. Lamb of Lamb of God, you take a - way the sins of the world, grant us peace, grant us peace.

Music: *The Glendalough Mass*, Liam Lawton; arr. by Paul A. Tate, © 2010, GIA Publications, Inc.

# Setting Eight

## MISSA PACEM

### 270 PENITENTIAL ACT

*Cantor, then all:*

(*Invocation*)

Lord, have mer - cy.
Christ, have mer - cy.
Lord, have mer - cy.

Music: *Missa Pacem*, L. Randolph Babin, © 2004, 2010, GIA Publications, Inc.

### 271 GLÓRIA

Refrain

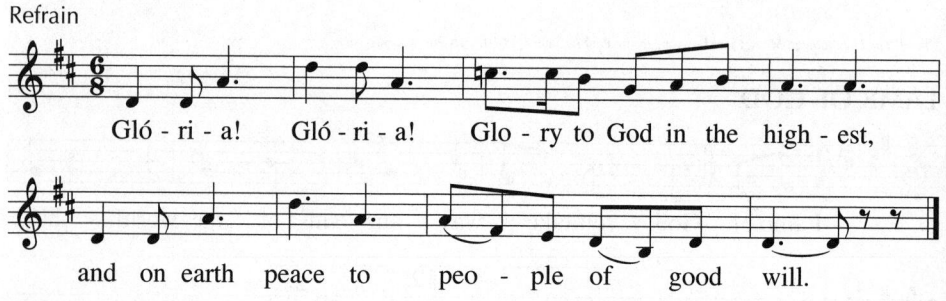

Gló - ri - a! Gló - ri - a! Glo - ry to God in the high - est,

and on earth peace to peo - ple of good will.

Verses

1. We praise you,
   we bless you,
   we adore you,
   we glorify you,
   we give you thanks for your great glory,
   Lord God, heavenly King,
   O God, almighty Father.

2. Lord Jesus Christ, Only Begotten Son,
   Lord God, Lamb of God, Son of the Father,
   you take away the sins of the world,
   have mercy on us;
   you take away the sins of the world,
   receive our prayer;
   you are seated at the right hand of the Father,
   have mercy on us.

3. For you alone are the Holy One,
   you alone are the Lord,
   you alone are the Most High,
   Jesus Christ,
   with the Holy Spirit,
   in the glory of God the Father.
   Amen.

Text: ICEL, © 2010
Music: *Missa Pacem,* L. Randolph Babin, © 2004, 2010, GIA Publications, Inc.

## GOSPEL ACCLAMATION
272

Refrain

Al - le - lu - ia, al - le - lu - ia, al - le - lu - ia.

Music: *Missa Pacem,* L. Randolph Babin, © 2004, GIA Publications, Inc.

## HOLY, HOLY, HOLY
273

Ho - ly, Ho - ly, Ho - ly Lord God of

hosts. Heav'n and earth are full of your glo - ry. Ho -

san - na in the high - est. Ho - san - na in the

high - est. Bless - ed is he who comes in the name, who

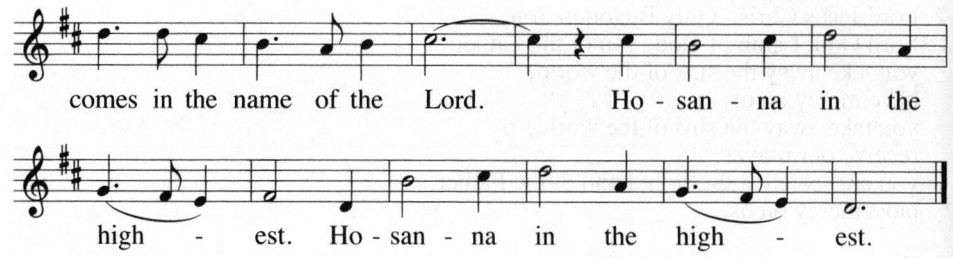

comes in the name of the Lord. Ho - san - na in the

high - est. Ho - san - na in the high - est.

Text: ICEL, © 2010
Music: *Missa Pacem*, L. Randolph Babin, © 2004, 2010, GIA Publications, Inc.

## 274 MEMORIAL ACCLAMATION A

We pro - claim your Death, O Lord, and pro -

fess your Res - ur - rec-tion un - til you come a - gain.

Text: ICEL, © 2010
Music: *Missa Pacem*, L. Randolph Babin, © 2010, GIA Publications, Inc.

## 275 MEMORIAL ACCLAMATION B

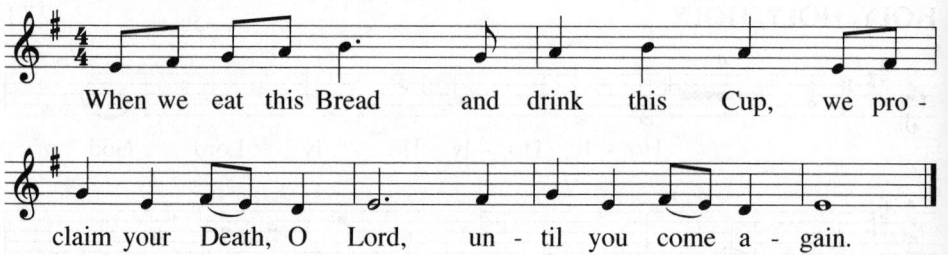

When we eat this Bread and drink this Cup, we pro -

claim your Death, O Lord, un - til you come a - gain.

Text: ICEL, © 2010
Music: *Missa Pacem*, L. Randolph Babin, © 2010, GIA Publications, Inc.

## 276 MEMORIAL ACCLAMATION C

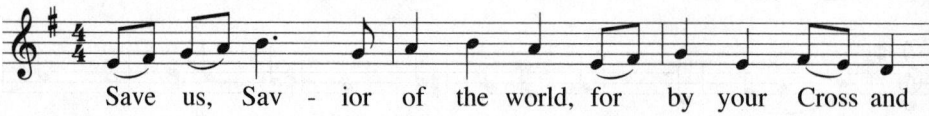

Save us, Sav - ior of the world, for by your Cross and

Res - ur - rec - tion you have set us free.

Text: ICEL, © 2010
Music: *Missa Pacem,* L. Randolph Babin, © 2010, GIA Publications, Inc.

## AMEN 277

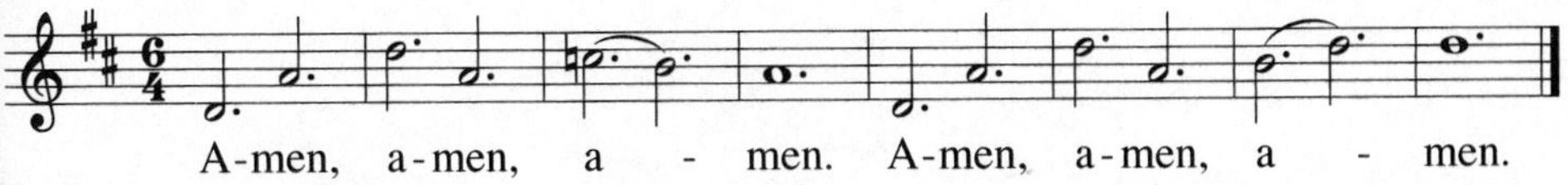

A-men, a-men, a - men. A-men, a-men, a - men.

Music: *Missa Pacem,* L. Randolph Babin, © 2004, GIA Publications, Inc.

## LAMB OF GOD 278

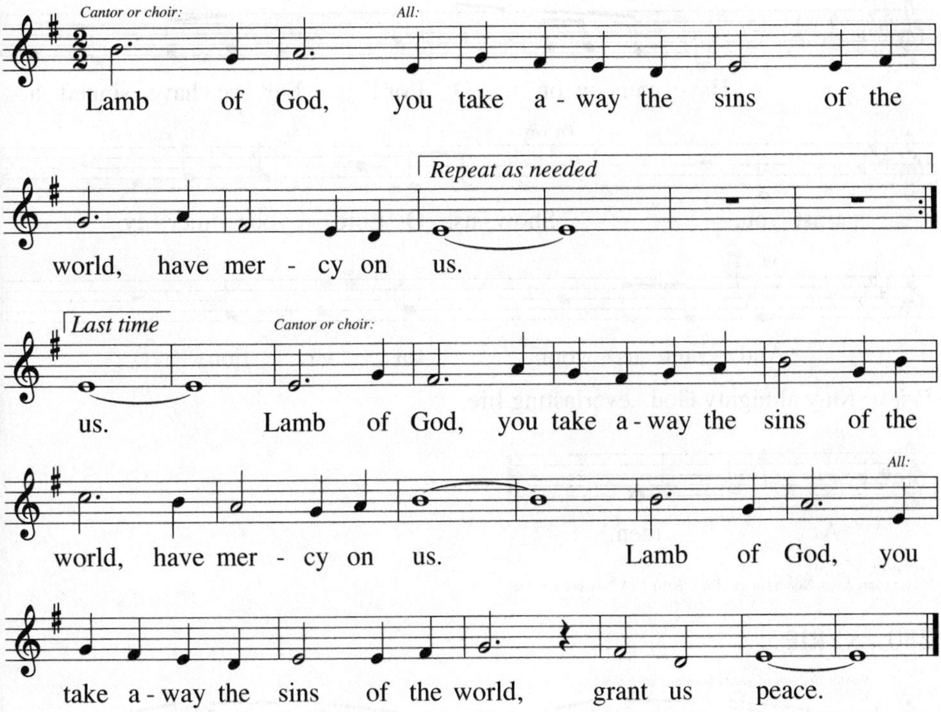

*Cantor or choir:*     *All:*

Lamb of God, you take a - way the sins of the

*Repeat as needed*

world, have mer - cy on us.

*Last time*     *Cantor or choir:*

us. Lamb of God, you take a - way the sins of the

*All:*

world, have mer - cy on us. Lamb of God, you

take a - way the sins of the world, grant us peace.

Music: *Missa Pacem,* L. Randolph Babin, © 2004, GIA Publications, Inc.

# Setting Nine

## UNITY MASS

### 279 PENITENTIAL ACT

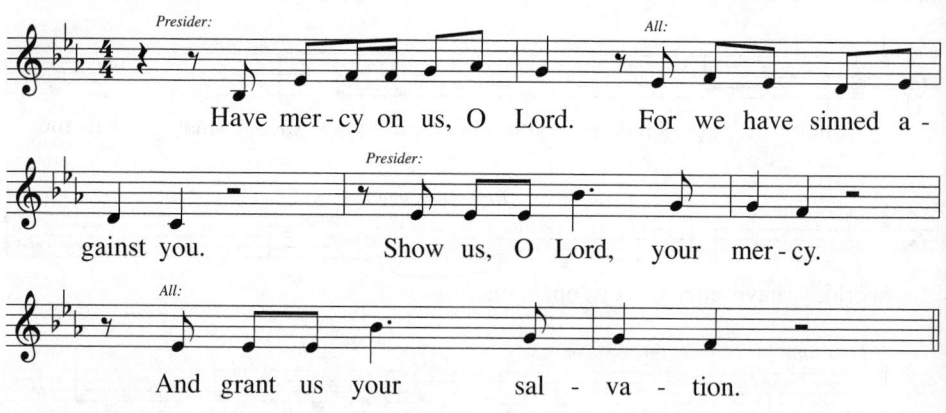

*Presider:*
Have mer - cy on us, O Lord. *All:* For we have sinned a -

*Presider:*
gainst you. Show us, O Lord, your mer - cy.

*All:*
And grant us your sal - va - tion.

*Priest:* May almighty God...everlasting life.

*All:*
A - men.

Text: ICEL, © 2010
Music: *Unity Mass,* Norah Duncan IV, © 2010, GIA Publications, Inc.

### 280 KÝRIE

*Cantor first, all repeat in harmony each time:*

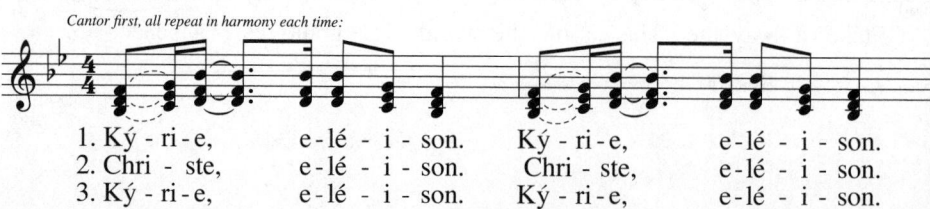

1. Ký - ri - e,    e - lé - i - son.    Ký - ri - e,    e - lé - i - son.
2. Chri - ste,    e - lé - i - son.    Chri - ste,    e - lé - i - son.
3. Ký - ri - e,    e - lé - i - son.    Ký - ri - e,    e - lé - i - son.

Ký - ri - e, e - lé - i son.
Chri - ste, e - lé - i - son.
Ký - ri - e, e - lé - i son.

Music: *Unity Mass,* Norah Duncan IV, © 2010, GIA Publications, Inc.

# GLÓRIA

281

Refrain

Glo - ry to God in the high - est, and on

*To verses*

earth peace to peo - ple, peo-ple of good will.

Last time

A - men, a - men, a - men. A - men, a - men, a - men.

Verses

1. We praise you,
   we bless you,
   we adore you,
   we glorify you,
   we give you thanks for your great glory,
   Lord God, heavenly King,
   O God, almighty Father.

2. Lord Jesus Christ, Only Begotten Son,
   Lord God, Lamb of God, Son of the Father,
   you take away the sins of the world,
   have mercy on us;
   you take away the sins of the world,
   receive our prayer;
   you are seated at the right hand of the Father,
   have mercy on us.

3. For you alone are the Holy One,
   you alone are the Lord,
   you alone are the Most High,
   Jesus Christ,
   with the Holy Spirit,
   in the glory of God the Father.
   Amen.

Text: ICEL, © 2010
Music: *Unity Mass,* Norah Duncan IV, © 2010, GIA Publications, Inc.

## 282 GOSPEL ACCLAMATION

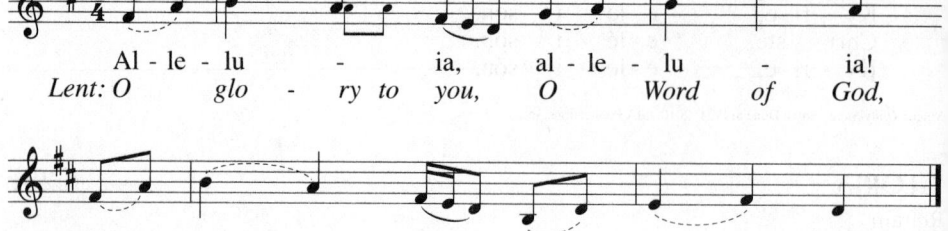

Al - le - lu - ia, al - le - lu - ia!
*Lent: O glo - ry to you, O Word of God,*

Al - le - lu - ia, al - le - lu - ia!
*Lord Je - sus Christ, Lord Je - sus Christ.*

Text: ICEL, © 1969
Music: *Unity Mass*, Norah Duncan IV, © 2010, GIA Publications, Inc.

## 283 HOLY, HOLY, HOLY

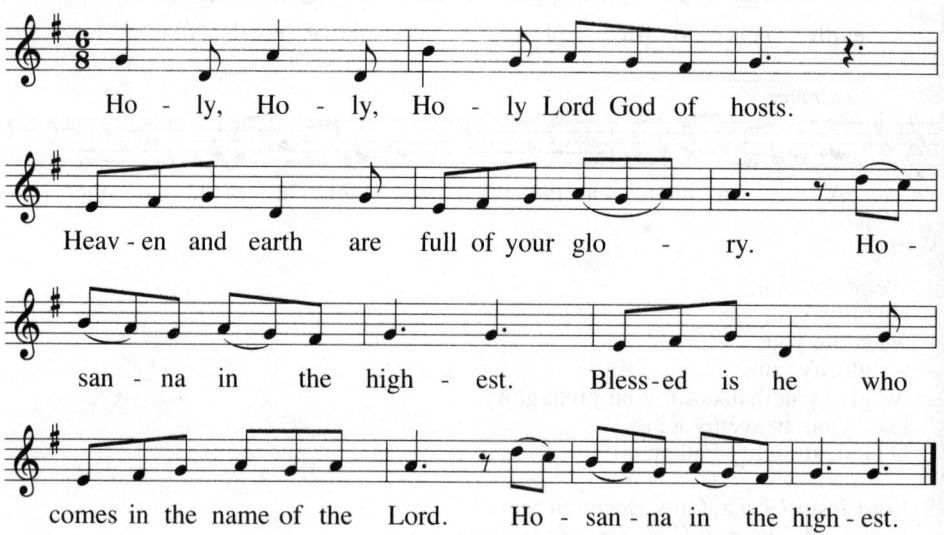

Ho - ly, Ho - ly, Ho - ly Lord God of hosts.

Heav - en and earth are full of your glo - ry. Ho -

san - na in the high - est. Bless-ed is he who

comes in the name of the Lord. Ho - san - na in the high - est.

Text: ICEL, © 2010
Music: *Unity Mass*, Norah Duncan IV, © 2010, GIA Publications, Inc.

## 284 MEMORIAL ACCLAMATION A

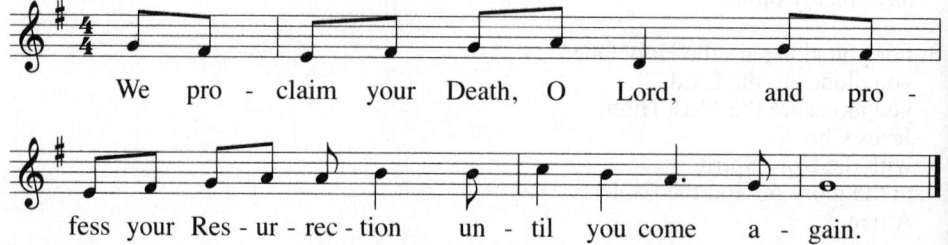

We pro - claim your Death, O Lord, and pro -

fess your Res - ur - rec - tion un - til you come a - gain.

Text: ICEL, © 2010
Music: *Unity Mass*, Norah Duncan IV, © 2010, GIA Publications, Inc.

## MEMORIAL ACCLAMATION B 285

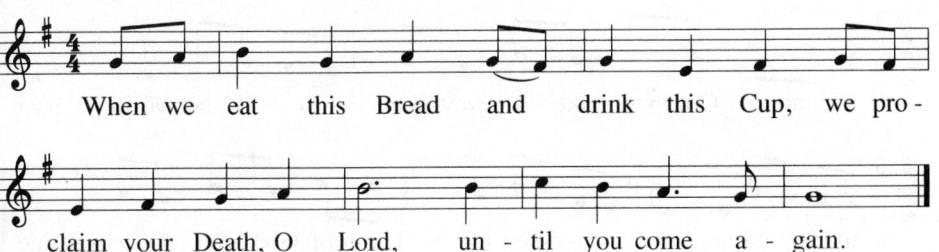

When we eat this Bread and drink this Cup, we pro -
claim your Death, O Lord, un - til you come a - gain.

Text: ICEL, © 2010
Music: *Unity Mass*, Norah Duncan IV, © 2010, GIA Publications, Inc.

## MEMORIAL ACCLAMATION C 286

Save us, Sav - ior of the world, for by your
Cross and Res - ur - rec - tion you have set us free.

Text: ICEL, © 2010
Music: *Unity Mass*, Norah Duncan IV, © 2010, GIA Publications, Inc.

## AMEN 287

A - men, a - men, a - men, a - men, a - men.

Music: *Unity Mass*, Norah Duncan IV, © 2010, GIA Publications, Inc.

## 288 LAMB OF GOD

Lamb of God, you take a - way the sins of the world, have
mer-cy on us, have mer-cy on us. Lamb of God, you take a-way the
sins of the world, grant us peace, grant us peace.

Music: *Unity Mass,* Norah Duncan IV, © 2010, GIA Publications, Inc.

# Setting Ten

## MISA UNA SANTA FE / ONE HOLY FAITH MASS

**PENITENTIAL ACT / ACTO PENITENCIAL**

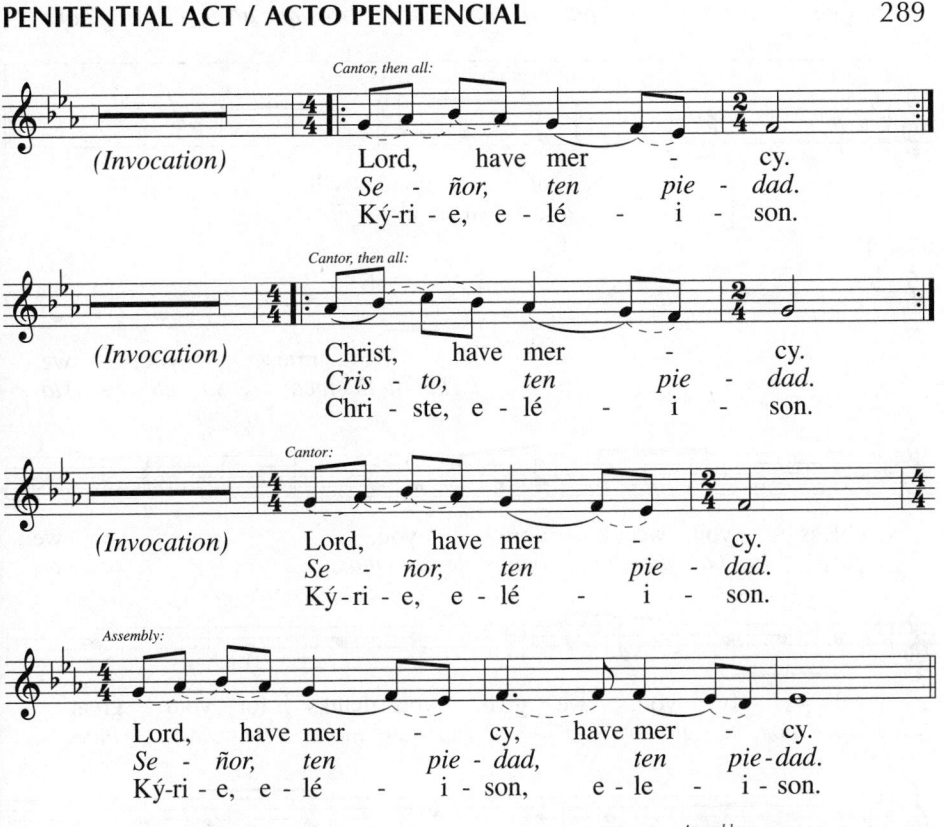

Cantor, then all:

(Invocation)
Lord, have mer - cy.
Se - ñor, ten pie - dad.
Ký-ri - e, e - lé - i - son.

Cantor, then all:

(Invocation)
Christ, have mer - cy.
Cris - to, ten pie - dad.
Chri - ste, e - lé - i - son.

Cantor:

(Invocation)
Lord, have mer - cy.
Se - ñor, ten pie - dad.
Ký-ri - e, e - lé - i - son.

Assembly:

Lord, have mer - cy, have mer - cy.
Se - ñor, ten pie - dad, ten pie-dad.
Ký-ri - e, e - lé - i - son, e - le - i - son.

*Priest:* May almighty God...everlasting life.
*Dios todopoderoso...vida eterna.*

Assembly:

A - men.
A - mén.

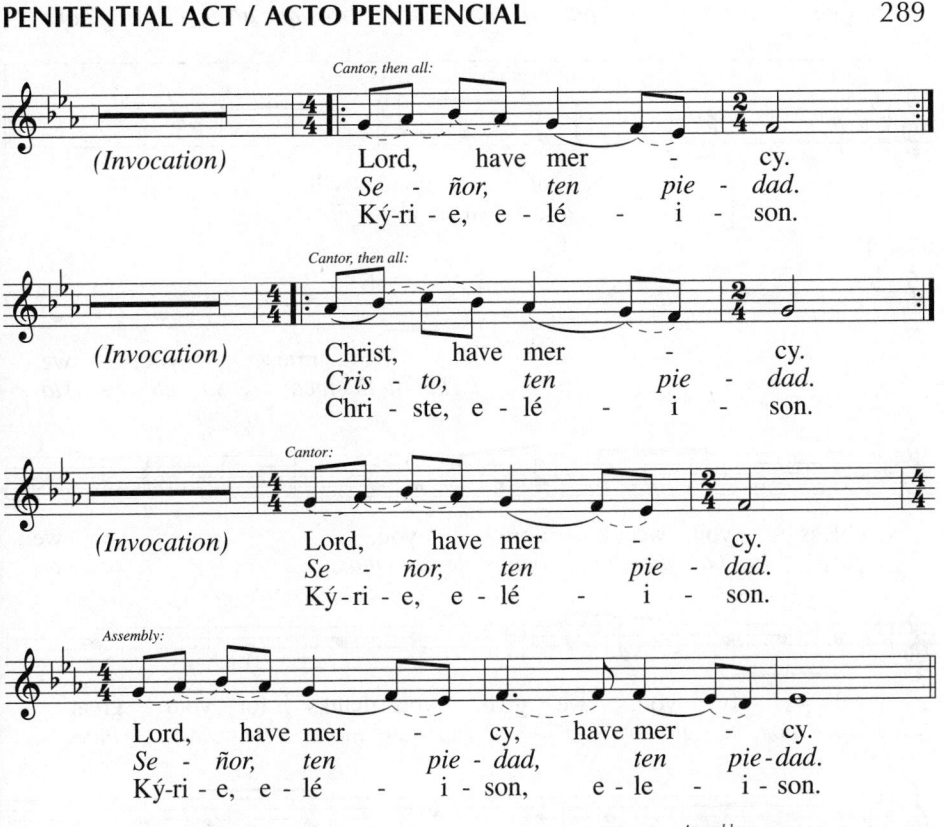

Music: *Misa Una Santa Fe,* Ronald F. Krisman, © 2010, GIA Publications, Inc.

289

## 290 GLÓRIA

Refrain

Glo - ry to God in the high - est,
*Glo - ria_a Dios en el cie - lo,*

glo - ry to God in the high - est,
*glo - ria_a Dios en el cie - lo,*

Optional repeat

and on earth peace to peo - ple of good will.
*y_en la tie - rra paz a los hom - bres que_a - ma_el Se - ñor.*

To verses

of good will.
*que_a - ma_el Se - ñor.*

Verse 1

1. We praise you, we
*1. Por tu_in - men - sa glo - ria*

bless you, we a - dore you, we
*te_a - la - ba - mos, te ben - de - ci - mos, te_a - do -*

glo - ri - fy you, we give you thanks for your great
*ra - mos, te glo - ri - fi - ca - mos, te da - mos*

glo - ry, Lord God, heav - en - ly King,
*gra - cias, Se - ñor Dios, Rey ce - les - tial,*

**D.C.**

O God, al - might - y Fa - ther.
*Dios Pa - dre to - do - po - de - ro - so.*

**Verse 2**

2. Lord Je - sus Christ, On - ly Be -
*2. Se - ñor, Hi - jo ú - ni - co, Je - su -*

got - ten Son, Lord God, Lamb of God,
*cris - to, Se - ñor Dios, Cor - de - ro de Dios,*

Son of the Fa - ther, you take a - way the
*Hi - jo del Pa - dre; tú que qui - tas el pe -*

sins of the world, have mer - cy on us; you
*ca - do del mun - do, ten pie - dad de no - so - tros; tú que*

take a - way the sins of the world, re - ceive our
*qui - tas el pe - ca - do del mun - do, a - tien - de nues - tra*

prayer; you are seat - ed at the
*sú - pli - ca; tú que es - tás sen - ta - do a la de -*

right hand of the Fa - ther, have mer - cy on
*re - cha del Pa - dre, ten pie - dad de no -*

**D.C.**

us, have mer - cy on us.
*so - tros, ten pie - dad de no - so - tros.*

Verse 3

3. For you  a - lone are the  Ho - ly One,
*3. Por -que só - lo  tú  e -res  San  -  to,*

you    a - lone are the  Lord,    you    a - lone are the
*só  -  lo  tú   Se - ñor,    só  -  lo  tú    Al -*

Most    High,    Je - sus    Christ,    with  the  Ho - ly
*tí  - si -mo,    Je - su - cris -to,    con  el  Es -pí - ri - tu*

Spir - it,    in the glo-ry of  God    the  Fa - ther.
*San - to    en la  glo  - ria  de   Dios  Pa - dre.*

Final Refrain

Glo - ry  to  God in the high-est,    glo - ry  to  God in the
*Glo  - ria a Dios en el  cie - lo,    glo - ria a Dios en el*

high-est,    and    on   earth    peace    to  peo  -  ple
*cie - lo,    y en    la  tie - rra  paz  a   los hom  - bres*

of    good   will.    A - men, a - men,
*que a-ma el  Se - ñor.    A - mén, a - mén,*

a - men.    A - men, a - men,    a - men.
*a - mén.    A - mén, a - mén,    a - mén.*

A - men,    a - men, a - men, a - men.
*A - mén,    a - mén, a - mén, a - mén.*

Text: English, © 2010, ICEL
Music: *Misa Una Santa Fe,* Ronald F. Krisman, © 2010, GIA Publications, Inc.

## GOSPEL ACCLAMATION / ACLAMACIÓN ANTES DEL EVANGELIO

291

Refrain

Al - le-lu - ia, al - le-lu - ia, al - le-lu - ia.
*A - le-lu - ya, a - le-lu - ya, a - le-lu - ya.*

Al - le-lu - ia, al - le-lu - ia, al - le-lu - ia.
*A - le-lu - ya, a - le-lu - ya, a - le-lu - ya.*

Music: *Misa Una Santa Fe*, Ronald F. Krisman, © 2010, GIA Publications, Inc.

## LENTEN GOSPEL ACCLAMATION / ACLAMACIÓN ANTES DEL EVANGELIO DURANTE LA CUARESMA

292

Refrain

*Praise to you, Lord Je-sus Christ, king of end-less glo-ry.*
*A - la-ban - za a ti, oh Cris - to, rey de e-ter - na glo-ria.*

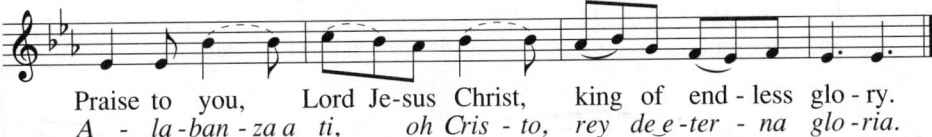

Praise to you, Lord Je-sus Christ, king of end-less glo-ry.
*A - la-ban - za a ti, oh Cris - to, rey de e-ter - na glo-ria.*

*For a bilingual refrain, sing the italicized text.

Text: English, © 2010, ICEL
Music: *Misa Una Santa Fe*, Ronald F. Krisman, © 2010, GIA Publications, Inc.

## PRAYER OF THE FAITHFUL / ORACIÓN DE LOS FIELES

293

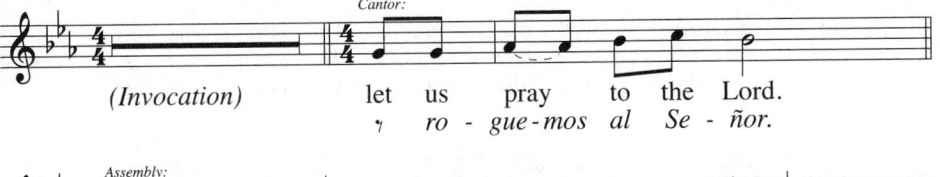

Cantor:

(*Invocation*) let us pray to the Lord.
*ro - gue-mos al Se - ñor.*

Assembly:

In your lov - ing - kind - ness, Lord, hear our prayer.
*Ó - ye - nos en tu bon - dad, Dios del a - mor.*
Bilingual: *Ó - ye - nos en tu bon - dad. Lord, hear our prayer.*

Music: *Misa Una Santa Fe*, Ronald F. Krisman, © 2010, GIA Publications, Inc.

## 294  SANTO, SANTO, SANTO / HOLY, HOLY, HOLY

San - to, san - to, san - to_es el Se -
*Ho - ly, Ho - ly, Ho - ly*
*Bilingual:* Ho - ly, Ho - ly, Ho - ly

ñor, Dios del u - ni - ver - so. Lle - nos es - tán el
*Lord       God       of   hosts.       Heav - en  and  earth   are*
Lord       God       of   hosts.       Heav - en  and  earth   are

cie - lo       y la  tie - rra de       tu   glo - ria.
*full,       are       full       of       your  glo - ry.*
full,       are       full       of       your  glo - ry.

San - to, san - to, san - to_es el Se - ñor, Dios del u - ni -
*Ho - ly, Ho - ly, Ho - ly       Lord       God       of*
San - to, san - to, san - to_es el Se - ñor, Dios del u - ni -

ver - so. Lle - nos es - tán       el cie - lo       y la
*hosts.       Heav - en and earth       are   full,       are*
ver - so. Lle - nos es - tán       el cie - lo       y la

tie - rra de       tu   glo - ria.       Ho - san - na en       el
*full       of       your  glo - ry.       Ho - san - na in       the*
tie - rra de       tu   glo - ria.       Ho - san - na in       the

cie - lo.       Ho - san - na en       el cie - lo.       Ho -
*high - est.       Ho - san - na in       the high - est.       Ho -*
high - est.       Ho - san - na in       the high - est.       Ho -

san - na en el cie - lo. Ho - san - na en el
*san - na in the high - est. Ho - san - na in the*
san - na in the high - est. Ho - san - na in the

cie - lo. Ben - di - to el que
*high - est. ⁊ Bless - ed is he who*
high - est. Ben - di - to el que

vie - ne en nom - bre del Se - ñor. Ho -
*comes in the name of the Lord. Ho -*
vie - ne en nom - bre del Se - ñor. Ho -

san - na en el cie - lo. Ho - san - na en el
*san - na in the high - est. Ho - san - na in the*
san - na en el cie - lo. Ho - san - na en el

cie - lo. Ho - san - na en el cie - lo. Ho -
*high - est. Ho - san - na in the high - est. Ho -*
cie - lo. Ho - san - na en el cie - lo. Ho -

san - na en el cie - lo.
*san - na in the high - est.*
san - na en el cie - lo.

Text: English, © 2010, ICEL
Music: *Misa Una Santa Fe,* Ronald F. Krisman, © 2010, GIA Publications, Inc.

## 295 ACLAMACIÓN AL MEMORIAL A / MEMORIAL ACCLAMATION A

A - nun - cia-mos tu muer - te, pro - cla -
*We pro - claim your Death, O Lord, and pro -*

ma-mos tu re - su - rrec - ción. ¡Ven, Se - ñor Je -
*fess your Res - ur - rec-tion un - til you come a -*

sús! ¡Ven, Se - ñor Je - sús!
*gain, un - til you come a - gain.*

Text: English, © 2010, ICEL
Music: *Misa Una Santa Fe,* Ronald F. Krisman, © 2010, GIA Publications, Inc.

## 296 ACLAMACIÓN AL MEMORIAL B / MEMORIAL ACCLAMATION B

Ca - da vez que co - me - mos de es - te pan
*When we eat this Bread and drink this Cup,*

y be - be - mos de es - te cá - liz, a-nun - cia-mos tu
*we pro-claim your Death, O Lord, un - til you*

muer-te, Se - ñor, has - ta que vuel-vas.
*come a - gain, un - til you come a - gain.*

Text: English, © 2010, ICEL
Music: *Misa Una Santa Fe,* Ronald F. Krisman, © 2010, GIA Publications, Inc.

## ACLAMACIÓN AL MEMORIAL C / MEMORIAL ACCLAMATION C

297

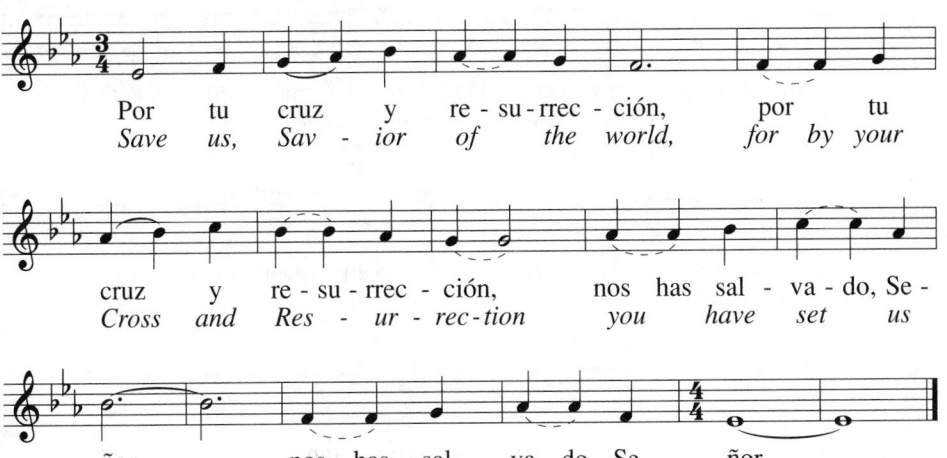

Por tu cruz y re - su - rrec - ción, por tu
*Save us, Sav - ior of the world, for by your*

cruz y re - su - rrec - ción, nos has sal - va - do, Se -
*Cross and Res - ur - rec - tion you have set us*

ñor, nos has sal - va - do, Se - ñor.
*free, you have set us free.*

Text: English, © 2010, ICEL
Music: *Misa Una Santa Fe*, Ronald F. Krisman, © 2010, GIA Publications, Inc.

## AMÉN / AMEN

298

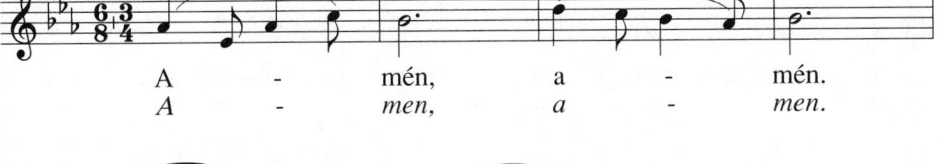

A - mén, a - mén.
*A - men, a - men.*

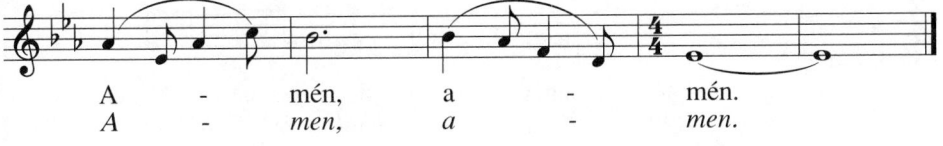

A - mén, a - mén.
*A - men, a - men.*

Music: *Misa Una Santa Fe*, Ronald F. Krisman, © 2010, GIA Publications, Inc.

## 299 EL PADRENUESTRO / THE LORD'S PRAYER

Pa - dre nues - tro, que es - tás en el cie - lo, san - ti - fi -
*Our Fa - ther, who art in heav - en,*

ca - do se - a tu Nom - bre; ven - ga a no - so - tros tu
*hal -lowed be thy name; thy king - dom*

rei - no; há - ga - se tu vo - lun - tad en la
*come, thy will be done on*

tie - rra co - mo en el cie - lo. Da - nos hoy nues-tro
*earth as it is in heav - en. Give us this day our*

pan de ca - da dí - a; per - do - na nues - tras o - fen - sas,
*dai - ly bread, and for - give us our tres -pass -es,*

co - mo tam - bién no - so - tros per - do - na - mos a
*as we for - give those who*

los que nos o - fen - den; no nos de - jes ca - er en la
*tres - pass a - gainst us; and lead us not in - to temp -*

ten - ta - ción, y lí - bra - nos del mal.
*ta - tion, but de - liv - er us from e - vil.*

*Priest:* Líbranos de todos los males...nuestro Salvador, Jesucristo.
*Deliver us, Lord...and the coming of our Savior, Jesus Christ.*

Tu - yo_es el rei - no, tu - yo_el po - der y la
*For* *the king - dom, the pow'r* *and the glo - ry are*

glo - ria, por siem - pre, Se - ñor, la
*yours* *now* *and for* *ev - er,* *are*

glo - ria, por siem - pre, Se - ñor.
*yours* *now* *and for* *ev - er.*

Music: *Misa Una Santa Fe,* Ronald F. Krisman, © 2010, GIA Publications, Inc.

## 300 LAMB OF GOD / CORDERO DE DIOS

Lamb of God, you take a-way the
*Cor - de - ro de Dios, que qui - tas el pe-*

sins of the world, have mer - cy, have
*ca - do del mun - do, ten pie - dad,*

mer - cy, have mer - cy on us.
*ten pie - dad, ten pie - dad de no - so - tros.*

Lamb of God, you take a - way the
*Cor - de - ro de Dios, que qui - tas el pe -*

sins of the world, have mer - cy, have
*ca - do del mun - do, ten pie - dad,*

mer - cy, have mer - cy on us.
*ten pie-dad, ten pie - dad de no - so - tros.*

Lamb of God, you take a - way the sins of the
*Cor - de - ro de Dios, que qui - tas el pe - ca - do del*

world, grant us, grant us, grant us peace.
*mun - do, da - nos, da - nos, da - nos la paz.*

Music: *Misa Una Santa Fe*, Ronald F. Krisman, © 2010, GIA Publications, Inc.

# Setting Eleven

## CANTUS MISSAE

### KÝRIE

Ký-ri - e,    * e - lé - i-son.

Chri - ste,    e - lé - i - son.

Ký-ri - e,    e - lé - i - son.

Ký-ri-e,    *    ** e - lé-i-son.

Music: Vatican Edition VIII; acc. by Richard Proulx, © 1995, GIA Publications, Inc.

302  **GLÓRIA**

Tu so-lus Dó - mi - nus.    Tu so-lus Al - tís - si - mus,

Je - su Chri - ste.    Cum San - cto    Spí - ri - tu:

in gló-ri - a De - i Pa - tris.    A - men.

Music: Vatican Edition VIII, acc. by Richard Proulx, © 1995, GIA Publications, Inc.

# LITURGY OF THE WORD

## FIRST READINGS                                        303

*After the first reading:*

*Reader:*                    *Assembly:*

Ver - bum Dó - mi - ni.    De - o grá - ti - as.

*After the second reading or if there is only one reading before the gospel:*

*Reader:*                    *Assembly:*

Ver - bum Dó - mi - ni.    De - o grá - ti - as.

## GOSPEL                                                304

*Before the gospel:*

*Deacon or priest:*                    *Assembly:*

Dó - mi - nus vo - bís-cum.    Et cum spí - ri - tu tu - o.

*Deacon or priest:*

Lé - cti - o san - cti E - van - gé - li - i se - cún - dum

*Assembly:*

N...    Gló - ri - a ti - bi, Dó - mi - ne.

*After the reading:*

*Deacon or priest:*                    *Assembly:*

Ver-bum Dó - mi-ni.    Laus ti - bi, Chri-ste.

305   **CREDO**

Cre-do in u-num De - um,   Pa - trem o - mni - po - tén - tem, fa-

ctó-rem cae - li   et  ter-rae,   vi - si - bí - li - um  ó  -  mni-um

et in - vi - si - bí - li-um.   Et in  u - num Dó - mi - num

Je - sum Chri-stum,   Fí - li - um De - i   U - ni - gé - ni - tum.

Et ex Pa-tre na - tum an-te ó - mni - a  sáe - cu - la.

De - um de De - o,   lu - men de lú - mi - ne,   De - um ve - rum

de De - o ve-ro.   Gé - ni-tum,   non fa - ctum, con-sub-stan - ti -

á - lem Pa - tri:   per quem ó - mni - a   fa - cta sunt.

Qui pro-pter nos hó - mi - nes   et pro-pter no-stram sa - lú - tem de-

scén-dit de   cae-lis.   Et in-car-ná-tus est   de Spí - ri - tu

San - cto   ex Ma - rí - a  Vír-gi - ne,   et ho - mo fa-ctus est.

Cru - ci - fí - xus é - ti - am pro no - bis sub

Pón - ti - o Pi - lá - to; pas - sus et se - púl - tus est.

Et re - sur - ré - xit tér - ti - a di - e, se - cún-dum Scri -ptú - ras.

Et a - scén - dit in cae - lum, se - det ad déx-te-ram Pa - tris.

Et í - te -rum ven - tú - rus est cum gló - ri - a, ju - di - cá - re

vi - vos et mór - tu - os, cu - ius re - gni non e - rit fi - nis.

Et in Spí - ri-tum San-ctum, Dó - mi-num et vi - vi - fi - cán-tem:

qui ex Pa - tre Fi - li - ó - que pro - cé - dit.

Qui cum Pa - tre et Fí - li - o si - mul a - do - rá - tur et con-glo -

ri - fi - cá-tur: qui lo - cú-tus est per pro - phé-tas. Et u-nam,

san-ctam, ca - thó - li-cam et a - po-stó - li-cam Ec-clé - si - am.

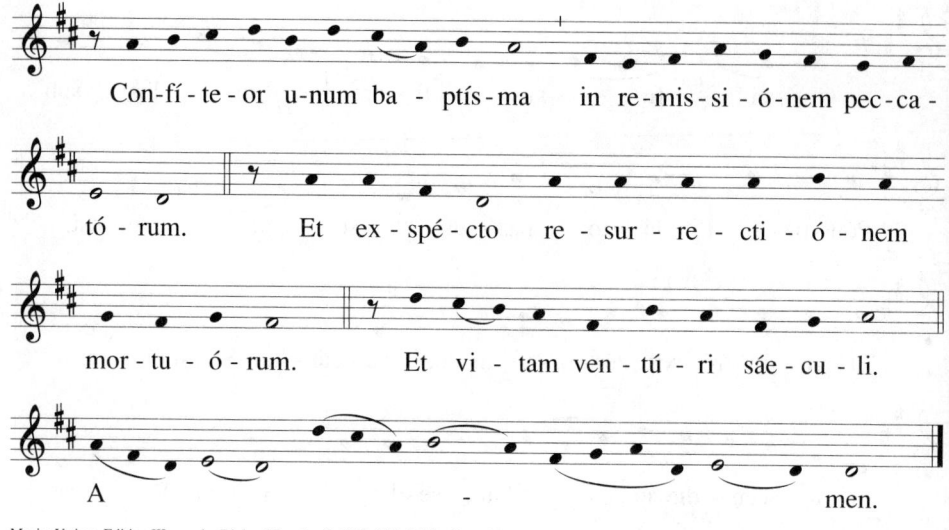

Con-fí - te - or u-num ba - ptís-ma in re-mis-si - ó-nem pec-ca-

tó - rum. Et ex - spé - cto re - sur - re - cti - ó - nem

mor-tu - ó - rum. Et vi - tam ven - tú - ri sáe - cu - li.

A - men.

Music: Vatican Edition III; acc. by Richard Proulx, © 1995, GIA Publications, Inc.

## 306 PRAYER OF THE FAITHFUL

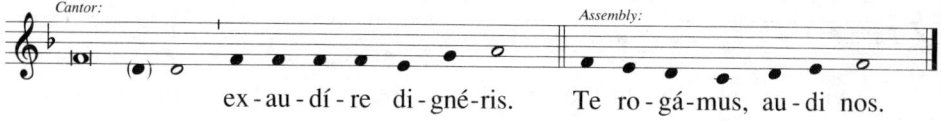

*Cantor:* ex - au - dí - re di - gné-ris. *Assembly:* Te ro - gá-mus, au - di nos.

# LITURGY OF THE WORD

## 307 PREFACE DIALOGUE

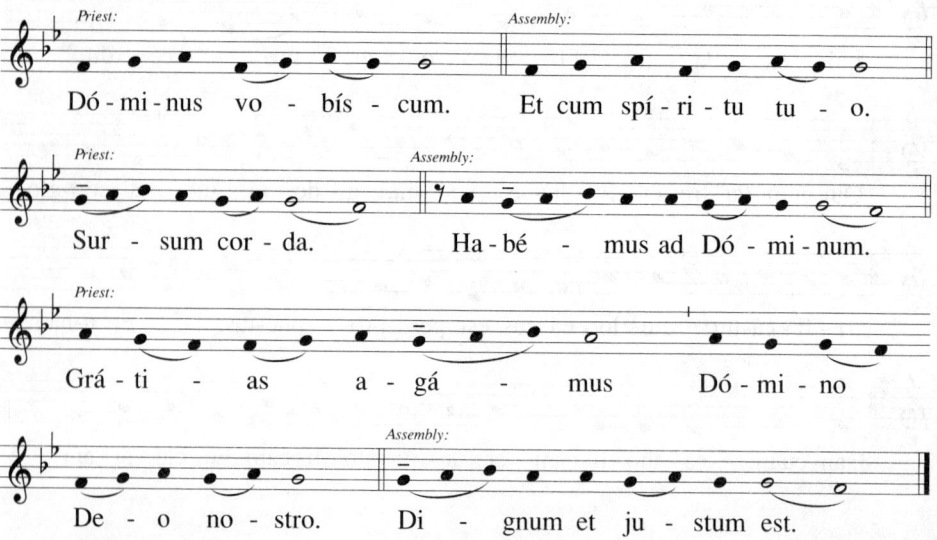

*Priest:* Dó - mi - nus vo - bís - cum. *Assembly:* Et cum spí - ri - tu tu - o.

*Priest:* Sur - sum cor - da. *Assembly:* Ha - bé - mus ad Dó - mi - num.

*Priest:* Grá - ti - as a - gá - mus Dó - mi - no

De - o no - stro. *Assembly:* Di - gnum et ju - stum est.

# SANCTUS

A

San - ctus, * San - ctus, San -

ctus Dó - mi - nus De - us Sá -

ba - oth. Ple - ni sunt cae - li et

ter - ra gló - ri - a tu - a. Ho - sán -

na in ex - cél - sis. Be - ne - dí - ctus qui

ve - nit in nó - mi - ne Dó - mi - ni. Ho - sán -

na in ex - cél - sis.

Music: Vatican Edition VIII; acc. by Richard Proulx, © 1995, GIA Publications, Inc.

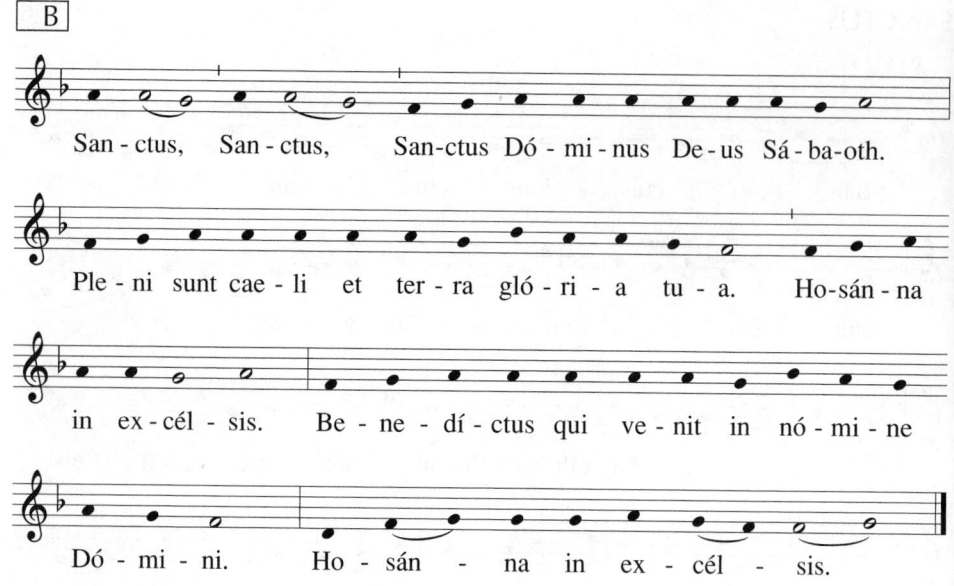

B

San - ctus, San - ctus, San-ctus Dó - mi - nus De - us Sá - ba-oth.

Ple - ni sunt cae - li et ter - ra gló - ri - a tu - a. Ho-sán - na

in ex - cél - sis. Be - ne - dí - ctus qui ve - nit in nó - mi - ne

Dó - mi - ni. Ho - sán - na in ex - cél - sis.

Music: Vatican Edition XVIII; acc. by Richard Proulx, © 1995, GIA Publications, Inc.

## 309 MEMORIAL ACCLAMATION

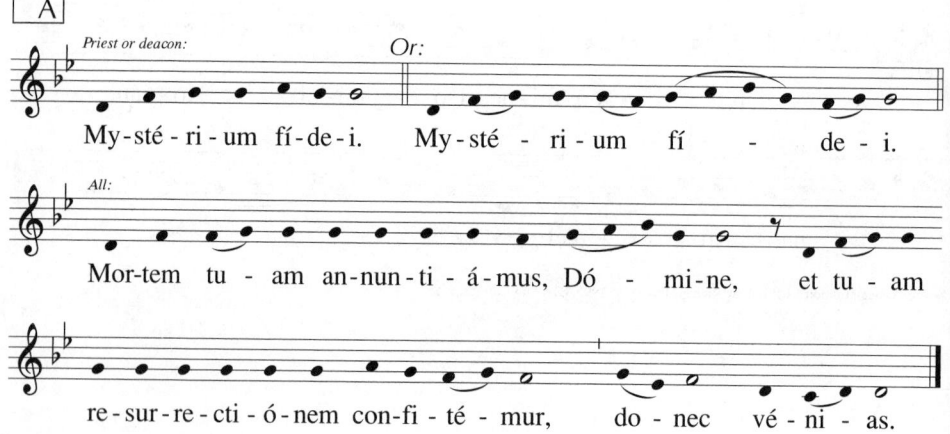

A

*Priest or deacon:*  *Or:*

My - sté - ri - um fí - de - i. My - sté - ri - um fí - de - i.

*All:*

Mor-tem tu - am an-nun-ti - á - mus, Dó - mi-ne, et tu - am

re - sur - re - cti - ó - nem con - fi - té - mur, do - nec vé - ni - as.

Music: Vatican Edition; acc. by Richard Proulx, © 1995, GIA Publications, Inc.

B

*Priest or deacon:*

My - sté - ri - um fí - de - i.

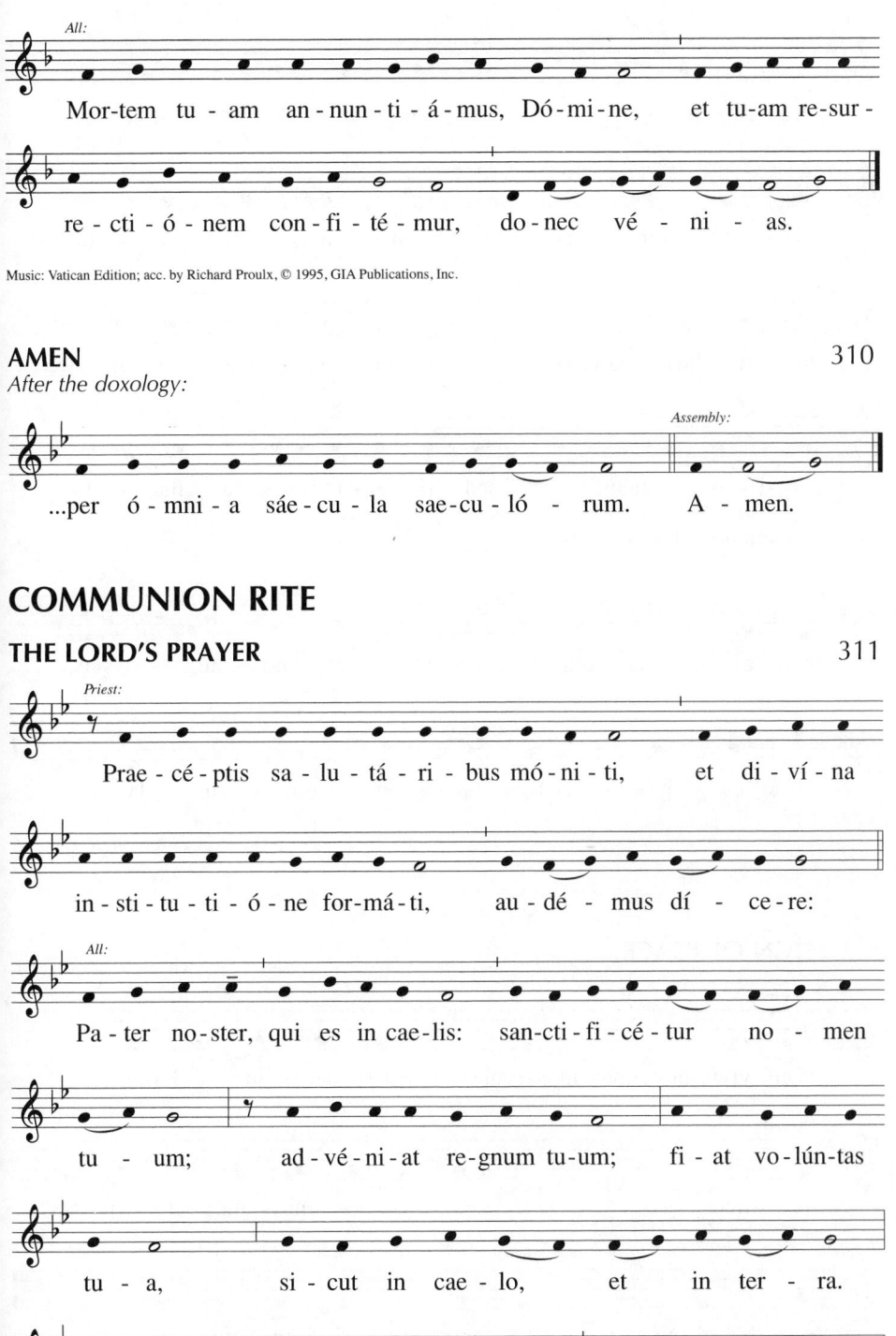

Mor-tem tu - am an - nun - ti - á - mus, Dó-mi-ne, et tu-am re-sur -

re - cti - ó - nem con - fi - té - mur, do - nec vé - ni - as.

Music: Vatican Edition; acc. by Richard Proulx, © 1995, GIA Publications, Inc.

## AMEN 310
*After the doxology:*

Assembly:

...per ó - mni - a sáe - cu - la sae-cu - ló - rum. A - men.

# COMMUNION RITE

## THE LORD'S PRAYER 311

Priest:

Prae - cé - ptis sa - lu - tá - ri - bus mó - ni - ti, et di - ví - na

in - sti - tu - ti - ó - ne for-má - ti, au - dé - mus dí - ce - re:

All:

Pa - ter no-ster, qui es in cae-lis: san-cti - fi - cé - tur no - men

tu - um; ad - vé - ni - at re-gnum tu-um; fi - at vo-lún-tas

tu - a, si - cut in cae - lo, et in ter - ra.

Pa - nem no-strum co - ti - di - á - num da no - bis hó - di - e;

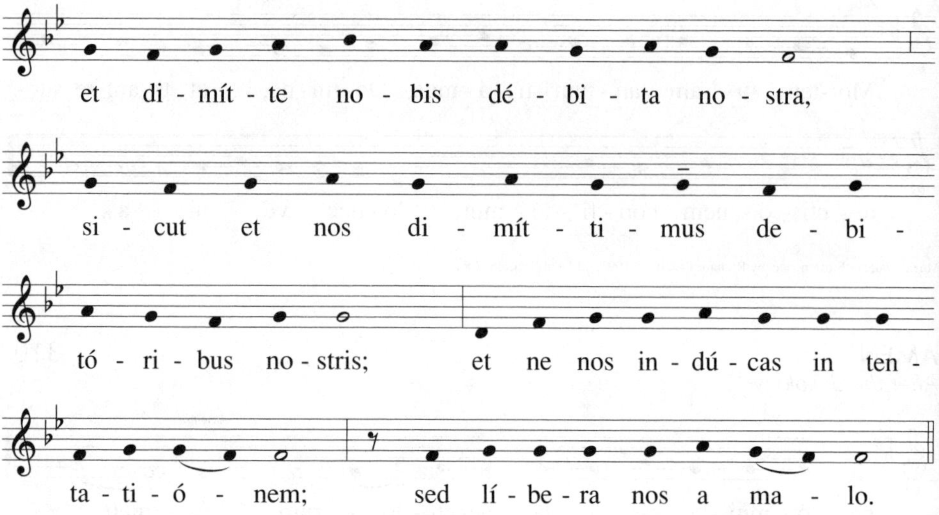

et di - mít - te no - bis dé - bi - ta no - stra,

si - cut et nos di - mít - ti - mus de - bi -

tó - ri - bus no - stris; et ne nos in - dú - cas in ten -

ta - ti - ó - nem; sed lí - be - ra nos a ma - lo.

*Priest:* Líbera nos...Jesu Christi.

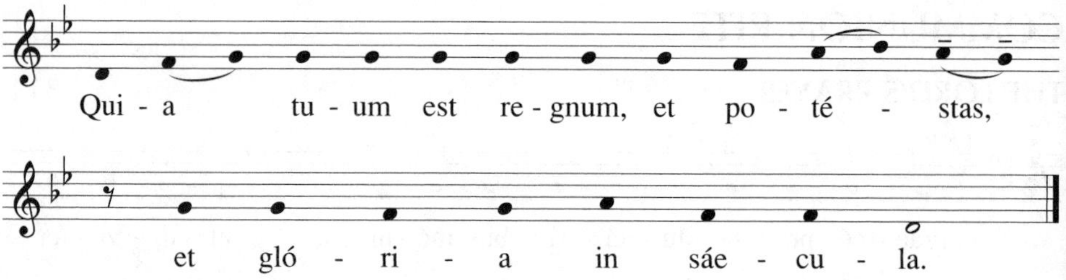

Qui - a tu - um est re - gnum, et po - té - stas,

et gló - ri - a in sáe - cu - la.

## 312 SIGN OF PEACE

*Priest:*

Qui vivis et regnas in sáecula sae - cu - ló - rum.

*Assembly:*

A - men.

*Priest:*

Pax Dó - mi - ni sit sem - per

vo - bís - cum.

*Assembly:*

Et cum spí - ri - tu tu - o.

# AGNUS DEI

A

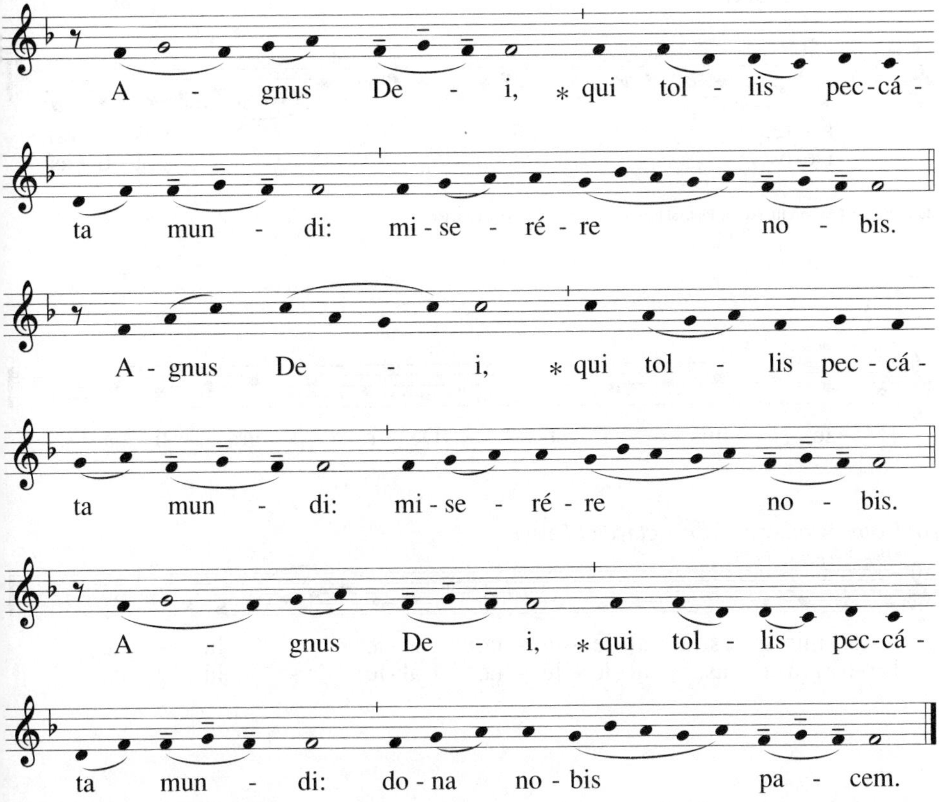

A - gnus De - i, * qui tol - lis pec-cá -

ta mun - di: mi - se - ré - re no - bis.

A - gnus De - i, * qui tol - lis pec - cá -

ta mun - di: mi - se - ré - re no - bis.

A - gnus De - i, * qui tol - lis pec-cá -

ta mun - di: do - na no - bis pa - cem.

Music: Vatican Edition VIII; acc. by Richard Proulx, © 1995, GIA Publications, Inc.

B

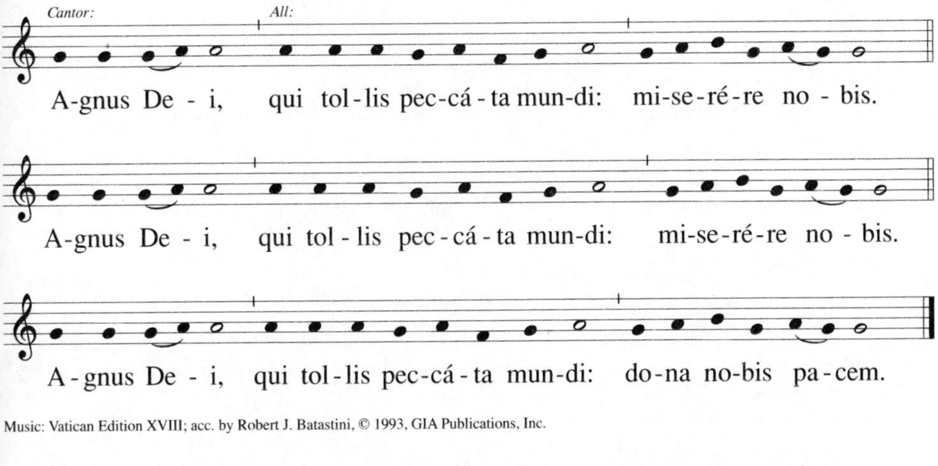

*Cantor:*   *All:*

A-gnus De - i, qui tol-lis pec-cá-ta mun-di: mi-se-ré-re no - bis.

A-gnus De - i, qui tol-lis pec-cá-ta mun-di: mi-se-ré-re no - bis.

A-gnus De - i, qui tol-lis pec-cá-ta mun-di: do-na no-bis pa-cem.

Music: Vatican Edition XVIII; acc. by Robert J. Batastini, © 1993, GIA Publications, Inc.

# CONCLUDING RITES

## 314  DISMISSAL

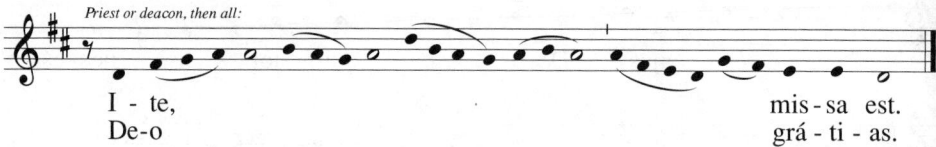

*Priest or deacon, then all:*

I - te,                                    mis - sa  est.
De-o                                    grá - ti - as.

Music: Vatican Edition VIII; acc. by Richard Proulx, © 1995, GIA Publications, Inc.

*Or:*

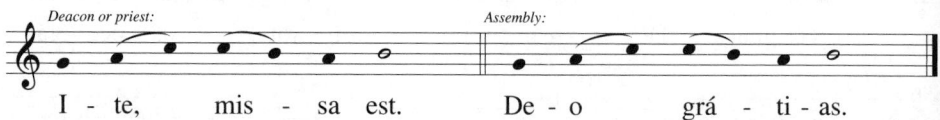

*Deacon or priest:*                          *Assembly:*

I - te,     mis - sa  est.     De - o     grá - ti - as.

*For Easter Sunday and the octave of Easter:*

*Deacon or priest, then all:*

I - te, mis-sa  est,    al - le - lú - ia,    al - le  -  lú  -  ia.
De-o  grá - ti - as,    al - le - lú - ia,    al - le  -  lú  -  ia.

# Service Music

## SPRINKLING SONG

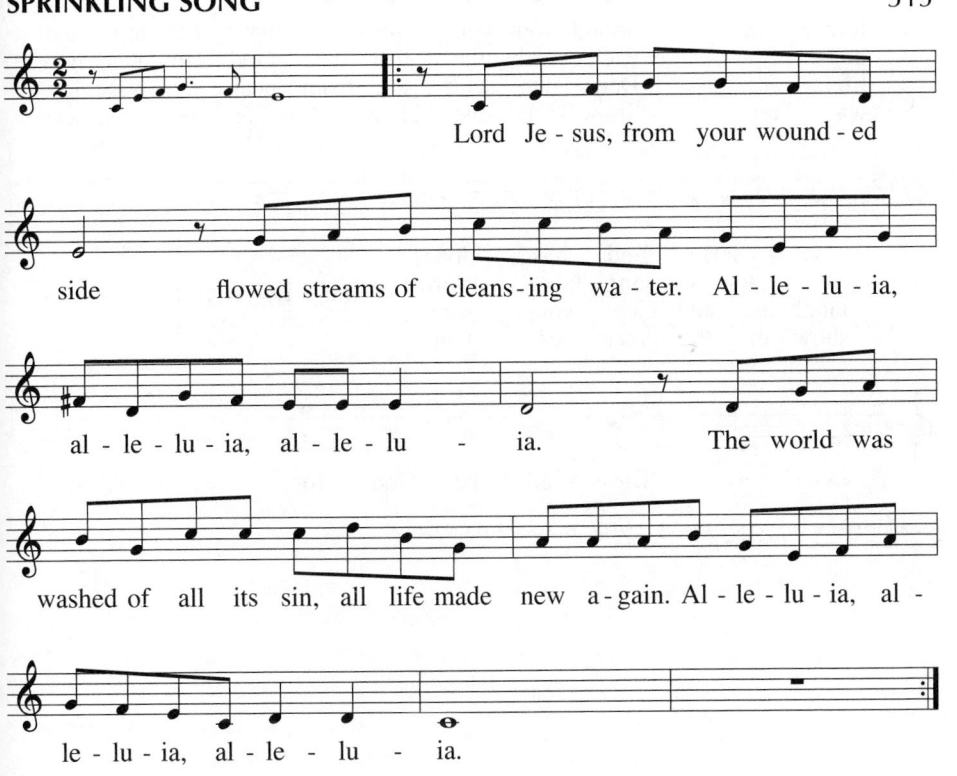

Lord Je - sus, from your wound - ed side flowed streams of cleans - ing wa - ter. Al - le - lu - ia, al - le - lu - ia, al - le - lu - ia. The world was washed of all its sin, all life made new a - gain. Al - le - lu - ia, al - le - lu - ia, al - le - lu - ia.

Text: ICEL, © 1973
Music: *Festival Liturgy*, Richard Hillert, © 1983, GIA Publications, Inc.

## 316  SPRINKLING SONG

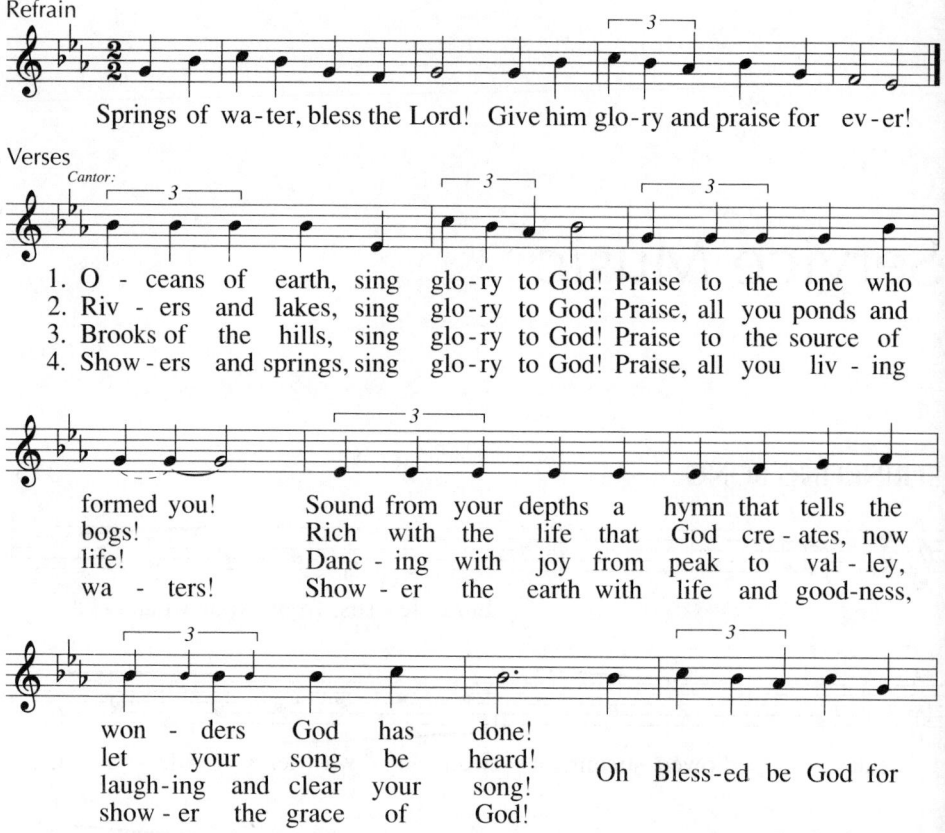

Refrain

Springs of wa-ter, bless the Lord! Give him glo-ry and praise for ev-er!

Verses

Cantor:

1. O - ceans of   earth, sing   glo-ry to God! Praise to the   one who
2. Riv - ers   and   lakes, sing   glo-ry to God! Praise, all you ponds and
3. Brooks of   the   hills, sing   glo-ry to God! Praise to the source of
4. Show - ers and springs, sing   glo-ry to God! Praise, all you   liv - ing

formed you!   Sound from your depths a   hymn that tells the
bogs!   Rich with the   life that God cre - ates, now
life!   Danc - ing with   joy from peak to   val - ley,
wa - ters!   Show - er   the   earth with   life and good-ness,

won - ders   God   has   done!
let   your   song   be   heard!   Oh   Bless-ed be God for
laugh-ing and clear   your   song!
show - er   the grace   of   God!

All:   D.C.

ev - er!   Bless - ed   be   God   for   ev - er!

# KÝRIE

*Cantor, then all:*  
Lord, have mer - cy.  
*Cantor, then all:*  
Christ, have mer - cy.

*Cantor, then all:*  
Lord, have mer - cy.

Music: *Litany of the Saints;* adapt. by Richard Proulx, © 1971, GIA Publications, Inc.

*Or:*

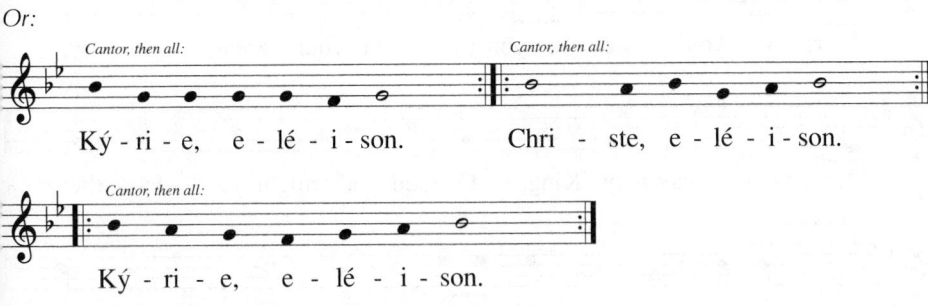

*Cantor, then all:*  
Ký - ri - e, e - lé - i - son.  
*Cantor, then all:*  
Chri - ste, e - lé - i - son.

*Cantor, then all:*  
Ký - ri - e, e - lé - i - son.

Music: *Litany of the Saints;* adapt. by Richard Proulx, © 1971, GIA Publications, Inc.

# KÝRIE

Ký - ri - e, e - léi - son.   Ký - ri - e, e - léi - son.  
Chri - ste, e - léi - son.   Chri - ste, e - léi - son.  
Ký - ri - e, e - léi - son.   Ký - ri - e, e - léi - son.

Ký - ri - e, e - léi - son.  
Chri - ste, e - léi - son.  
Ký - ri - e, e - léi - son.

Music: Russian Orthodox; arr. by John L. Bell, © 1990, Iona Community, GIA Publications, Inc., agent

## 319  GLÓRIA

*All:*
Glo-ry to God in the high-est, and on earth peace to peo-ple of good

will. We praise you, we bless you, we a-dore you, we

glo-ri-fy you, we give you thanks for your great glo-ry,

Lord God, heav'n-ly King, O God, al-might-y Fa-ther.

*Choir (Congr. ad lib):*
Lord Je-sus Christ, On-ly Be-got-ten Son, Lord God,

Lamb of God, Son of the Fa-ther, you take a-way the

sins of the world, have mer-cy on us; you

take a-way the sins of the world, re-ceive our

prayer; you are seat-ed at the right hand of the

Fa-ther, have mer-cy on us.

*All:*
For you a-lone are the Ho-ly One, you a-lone are the Lord,

you a - lone are the Most High, Je - sus Christ, with the Ho-ly Spir-it,

in the glo - ry of God the Fa - ther. A - men.

ext: ICEL, © 2010
Music: *A New Mass for Congregations,* Carroll T. Andrews, revised by Ronald F. Krisman © 1970, 2011, GIA Publications, Inc.

# GLÓRIA 320

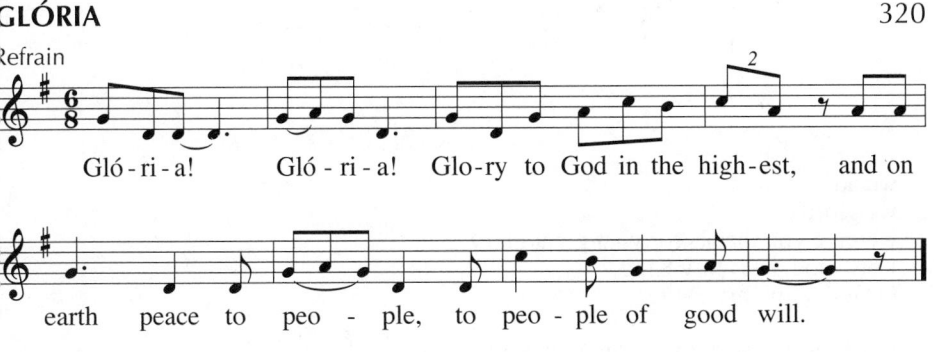

Refrain

Gló - ri - a! Gló - ri - a! Glo-ry to God in the high-est, and on

earth peace to peo - ple, to peo - ple of good will.

Verses

1. We praise you,
   we bless you,
   we adore you,
   we glorify you,
   we give you thanks for your great glory,
   Lord God, heavenly King,
   O God, almighty Father.

2. Lord Jesus Christ, Only Begotten Son,
   Lord God, Lamb of God, Son of the Father,
   you take away the sins of the world,
   have mercy on us;
   you take away the sins of the world,
   receive our prayer;
   you are seated at the right hand of the Father,
   have mercy on us.

3. For you alone are the Holy One,
   you alone are the Lord,
   you alone are the Most High,
   Jesus Christ,
   with the Holy Spirit,
   in the glory of God the Father.
   Amen.

Text: ICEL, © 2010
Music: *Jubilation Mass,* James Chepponis, © 1999, 2010, GIA Publications, Inc.

## 321 GLÓRIA

Refrain

Glo - ry to God in the high - est, glo - ry to God, and on earth peace to peo - ple, to peo - ple of good will.

Verses

1. We praise you,
   we bless you,
   we adore you,
   we glorify you,
   we give you thanks for your great glory,
   Lord God, heavenly King,
   O God, almighty Father.

2. Lord Jesus Christ, Only Begotten Son,
   Lord God, Lamb of God, Son of the Father,
   you take away the sins of the world,
   have mercy on us;
   you take away the sins of the world,
   receive our prayer;
   you are seated at the right hand of the Father,
   have mercy on us.

3. For you alone are the Holy One,
   you alone are the Lord,
   you alone are the Most High,
   Jesus Christ,

with the Ho - ly Spir - it, in the glo - ry of God the Fa - ther. A - men.

Text: ICEL, © 2010
Music: *Mass of Light*, David Haas, © 1988, 2010, GIA Publications, Inc.

# GLÓRIA

**I** *(Cantor or choir)*
Glo-ry to God in the high-est, and on earth peace to peo-ple of good will.

**II** *(Assembly)* **I**
We praise you, we bless you, we a-dore you, we glo-ri-fy you,

**II**
we give you thanks for your great glo-ry, Lord God, heav'n-ly King,

**I**
O God, al-might-y Fa - ther. Lord Je - sus Christ,

On-ly Be-got-ten Son, Lord God, Lamb of God, Son of the Fa-ther,

**II**
you take a-way the sins of the world, have mer-cy on us;

**I**
you take a-way the sins of the world, re - ceive our prayer;

**II**
you are seat-ed at the right hand of the Fa - ther,

**I**
have mer-cy on us. For you a-lone are the Ho-ly One,

you a-lone are the Lord, you a-lone are the Most High, Je-sus Christ,

**II** *Slower*
with the Ho-ly Spir-it, in the glo-ry of God the Fa-ther. A - men.

Text: ICEL., © 2010
Music: *Congregational Mass;* John Lee, revised by Ronald F. Krisman, © 1970, 2011, GIA Publications, Inc.

## 323 GLÓRIA

All:
Glo - ry to God in the high - est, and on earth peace to peo - ple of good will. We praise you, we bless you, we a - dore you, we glo - ri - fy you, we give you thanks for your great glo - ry, Lord God, heav - en - ly King, O God, al - might - y Fa - ther.

Choir (Cong. ad lib.):
Lord Je - sus Christ, On - ly Be - got - ten Son, Lord God, Lamb of God, Son of the Fa - ther, you take a - way the sins of the world, have mer - cy on us; you take a - way the sins of the world, re - ceive our prayer; you are seat - ed at the right hand of the Fa - ther, have mer - cy on us.

*All:*

For you a-lone are the Ho-ly One, you a-lone are the

Lord, you a-lone are the Most High, Je - sus

Christ, with the Ho-ly Spir-it, in the glo-ry of God the

Fa - ther. A - men.

Text: ICEL, © 2010
Music: *Holy Name of Jesus Gloria,* Norah Duncan IV, © 2011, GIA Publications, Inc.

## CHILDREN'S DISMISSAL FOR LITURGY OF THE WORD 324

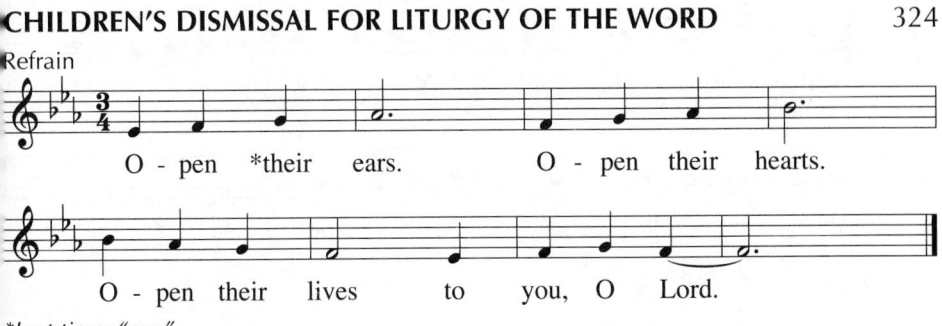

Refrain

O - pen *their ears. O - pen their hearts.

O - pen their lives to you, O Lord.

*Last time: "our"*

Text: Francis Patrick O'Brien
Music: Francis Patrick O'Brien
© 2003, 2011, GIA Publications, Inc.

## CHILDREN'S DISMISSAL FOR LITURGY OF THE WORD 325

*Cantor:* *All:*

Go and lis-ten to the Word of God. Go and lis-ten to the

*Cantor:*

Word of God. God has the words of ev-er - last - ing life.

*All:*

God has the words of ev - er - last - ing life.

Text: Robert J. Batastini
Music: Robert J. Batastini
© 2003, GIA Publications, Inc.

## 326 GOSPEL ACCLAMATION

Al - le - lu - ia,    al - le - lu - ia,    al - le - lu - ia.

Music: Chant Mode VI; acc. by Richard Proulx, © 1985, GIA Publications, Inc.

## 327 GOSPEL ACCLAMATION

Al - le - lu - ia,    al - le - lu - ia,    al - le - lu - ia!

Music: *Mass of Remembrance*, Marty Haugen, © 1987, GIA Publications, Inc.

## 328 GOSPEL ACCLAMATION

Al - le - lu - ia!    Al - le - lu - ia!

Al - le - lu - ia!    Al - le - lu - ia!

Music: Norah Duncan IV, © 1987, GIA Publications, Inc.

## 329 GOSPEL ACCLAMATION

Hal - le, hal - le, hal - le - lu - jah!    Hal - le, hal - le, hal -

le - lu - jah!    Hal - le, hal - le, hal - le -

lu - jah!    Hal - le - lu - jah!    Hal - le - lu - jah!

Music: Traditional Caribbean, arr. by John L. Bell, © 1990, Iona Community, GIA Publications, Inc., agent; verses and acc. by Marty Haugen, © 1993, GIA Publications, Inc.

## GOSPEL ACCLAMATION 330

Al - le - lu - ia! Al - le - lu - ia! Al - le - lu - ia!

Al - le - lu - ia! Al - le - lu - ia! Al - le - lu - ia!

Al - le - lu - ia! Al - le - lu - ia!

Music: David Haas, © 1986, 1997, GIA Publications, Inc.

## GOSPEL ACCLAMATION 331

Al - le - lu - ia, al - le - lu - ia, al - le - lu - ia.

Al - le - lu - ia, al - le - lu - ia, al - le - lu - ia!

Music: Alleluia 7; Jacques Berthier, © 1984, Les Presses de Taizé, GIA Publications, Inc., agent

## GOSPEL ACCLAMATION 332

Al-le-lu - ia, al-le - lu-ia, al - le - lu-ia, al-le - lu - ia!

Music: Alleluia 17; Jacques Berthier, © 1998, Les Presses de Taizé, GIA Publications, Inc., agent

## GOSPEL ACCLAMATION 333

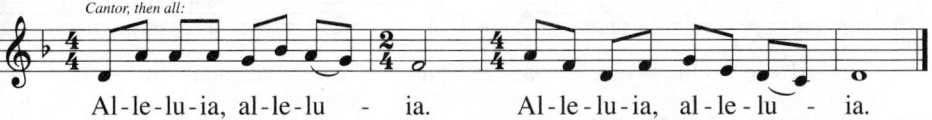

Al - le - lu - ia, al - le - lu - ia. Al - le - lu - ia, al - le - lu - ia.

Music: Based on VENI EMMANUEL, Stephen Pishner, © 2000, GIA Publications, Inc.

## 334 GOSPEL ACCLAMATION

Al - le - lu - ia, al - le - lu - ia!

Al - le - lu - ia, al - le - lu - ia!

Text: Fintan O'Carroll and Christopher Walker
Music: Fintan O'Carroll and Christopher Walker
© 1985, Fintan O'Carroll and Christopher Walker. Published by OCP.

## 335 GOSPEL ACCLAMATION

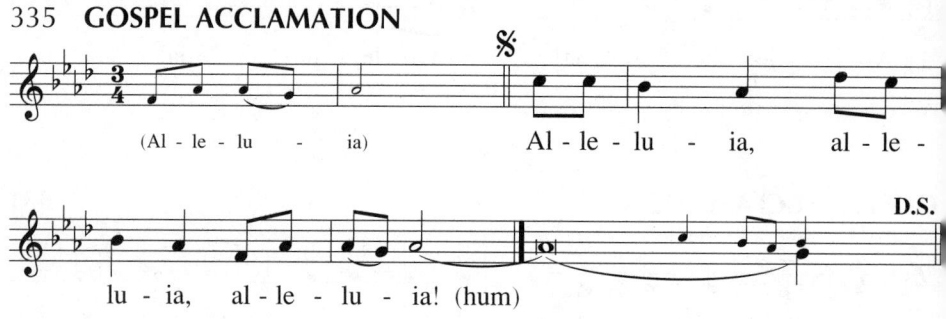

(Al - le - lu - ia)    Al - le - lu - ia, al - le -

lu - ia, al - le - lu - ia! (hum)

Music: *Alleluia II*, Jacques Berthier, © 1984, Les Presses de Taizé, GIA Publications, Inc., agent

## 336 GOSPEL ACCLAMATION

*Cantor:* Al - le - lu - ia.    *Assembly:* Al - le - lu - ia.    *Cantor:* Al - le - lu - ia.

*Assembly:* Al - le - lu - ia.    *Cantor:* Al - le - lu - ia.    *Assembly:* Al - le - lu - ia.

Music: *Alleluia in C*, Howard Hughes, SM, © 1973, 1982, GIA Publications, Inc.

## 337 GOSPEL ACCLAMATION

Al - le - lu - ia, al - le - lu - ia, al - le - lu - ia.

Music: A. Gregory Murray, OSB, © 1958, The Grail, GIA Publications, Inc., agent

## GOSPEL ACCLAMATION 338

*Cantor, then all:*

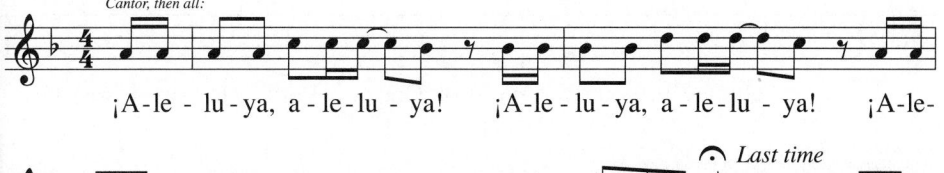

¡A - le - lu - ya, a - le - lu - ya! ¡A - le - lu - ya, a - le - lu - ya! ¡A - le -

*Last time*

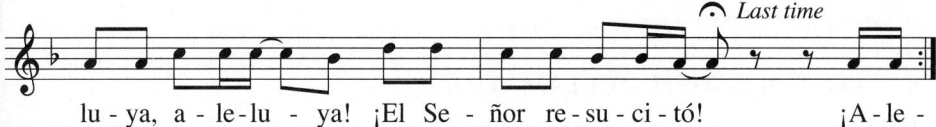

lu - ya, a - le - lu - ya! ¡El Se - ñor re - su - ci - tó! ¡A - le -

Music: *The Honduras Alleluia,* arr. by Rob Glover, © 1997, GIA Publications, Inc.

## GOSPEL ACCLAMATION 339

Refrain

*Cantor:*      *Assembly:*      *Cantor:*      *Assembly:*

Al - le - lu - ia, al - le - lu - ia, al - le - lu - ia, al - le - lu - ia,

*Cantor:*      *Assembly:*

al - le - lu - ia, al - le - lu - ia, al - le - lu - ia, al - le - lu - ia.

Verse Responses

I, II            III            D.C.

Al - le - lu - ia,      al - le - lu - ia, al - le - lu - ia.

Text: Tony E. Alonso
Music: Based on LAMBILLOTTE, Louis Lambillotte, SJ, 1796–1855; adapt. by Tony E. Alonso
© 2007, GIA Publications, Inc.

## GOSPEL ACCLAMATION 340

Refrain

Al - le - lu - ia, al - le - lu - ia, al - le - lu - ia!
*Lent:* Glo-ry to you, O Word of God, Lord Je - sus Christ.

Text: ICEL, © 1969
Music: *Mass of Light,* David Haas, © 1988, GIA Publications, Inc.

## LENTEN GOSPEL ACCLAMATION 341

*Cantor, then all:*

Praise to you, Lord Je - sus Christ, king of end - less glo - ry!

Text: ICEL, © 1969
Music: Frank Schoen, © 1970, GIA Publications, Inc.

## 342  LENTEN GOSPEL ACCLAMATION

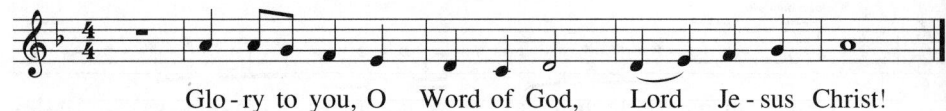

Glo-ry to you, O  Word of God,  Lord  Je-sus  Christ!

Text: ICEL, © 1969
Music: Richard Proulx, © 1975, GIA Publications, Inc.

## 343  LENTEN GOSPEL ACCLAMATION

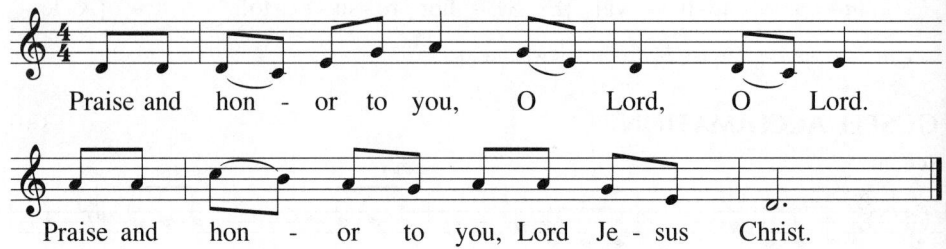

Praise and  hon - or to you,  O  Lord,  O  Lord.

Praise and  hon - or  to  you, Lord Je - sus  Christ.

Text: ICEL, © 1969
Music: Based on WONDROUS LOVE, Stephen Pishner, © 1998, GIA Publications, Inc.

## 344  PRAYER OF THE FAITHFUL

God  ev - er - faith - ful,  God  ev - er - mer - ci - ful,

God  of your peo - ple,  hear  our  prayer.

Text: Michael Joncas
Music: Michael Joncas
© 1990, GIA Publications, Inc.

## 345  PRAYER OF THE FAITHFUL

Ký-ri-e, e - lé-i-son, Ký-ri-e, e - lé-i-son.

Music: Jacques Berthier, © 1998, Les Presses de Taizé, GIA Publications, Inc., agent

## 346  PRAYER OF THE FAITHFUL

Ký-ri-e, Ký-ri-e, Ký-ri-e, e - léi-son. léi - son.

Music: Jacques Berthier, © 1998, Les Presses de Taizé, GIA Publications, Inc., agent

## PRAYER OF THE FAITHFUL 347

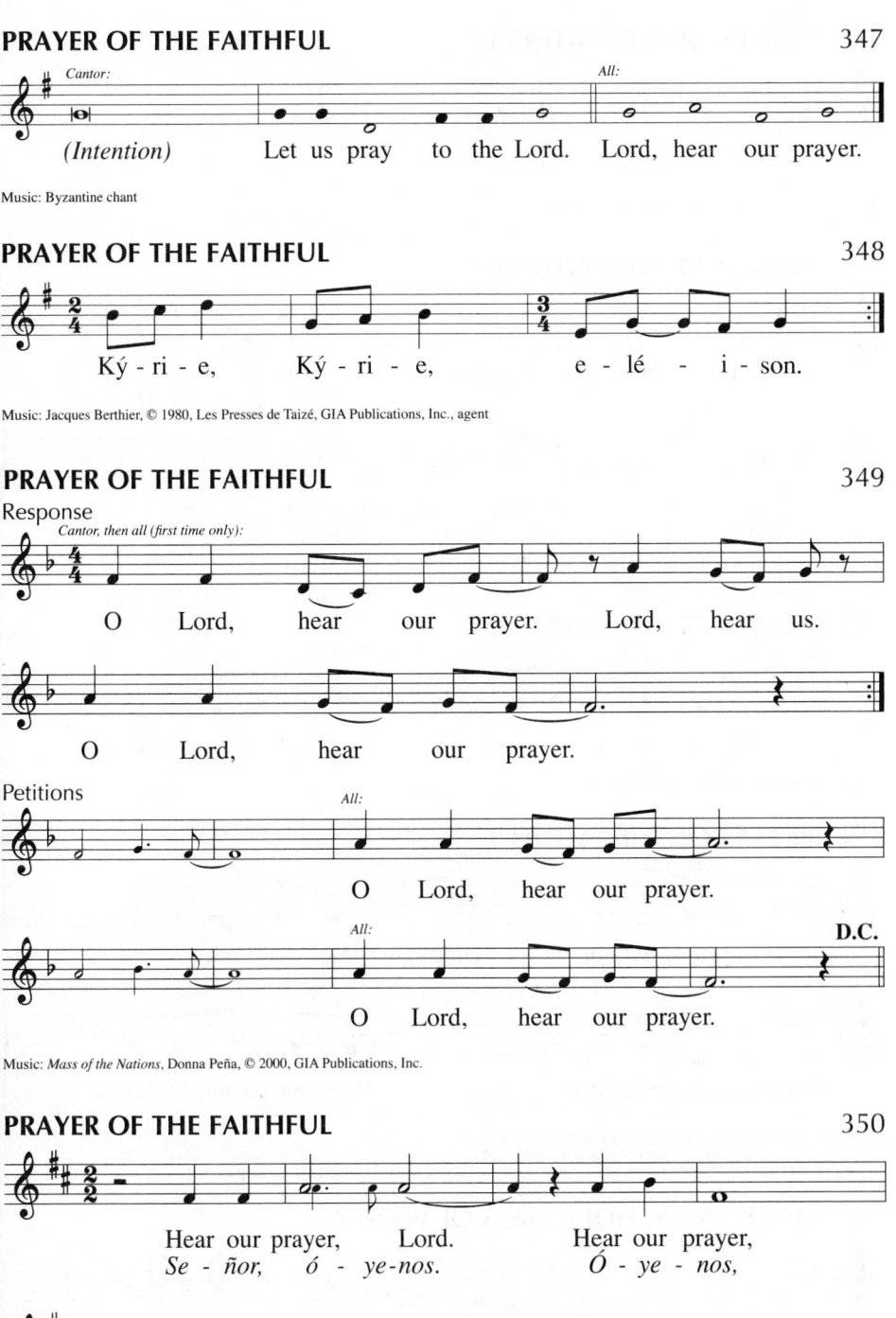

*(Intention)* Let us pray to the Lord. Lord, hear our prayer.

Music: Byzantine chant

## PRAYER OF THE FAITHFUL 348

Ký - ri - e, Ký - ri - e, e - lé - i - son.

Music: Jacques Berthier, © 1980, Les Presses de Taizé, GIA Publications, Inc., agent

## PRAYER OF THE FAITHFUL 349

Response

*Cantor, then all (first time only):*

O Lord, hear our prayer. Lord, hear us.

O Lord, hear our prayer.

Petitions  *All:*

O Lord, hear our prayer.

*All:*  **D.C.**

O Lord, hear our prayer.

Music: *Mass of the Nations*, Donna Peña, © 2000, GIA Publications, Inc.

## PRAYER OF THE FAITHFUL 350

Hear our prayer, Lord. Hear our prayer,
*Se - ñor, ó - ye-nos.* *Ó - ye - nos,*

Lord, hear our prayer.
*Se - ñor, ó - ye - nos.*

Music: Tony E. Alonso, © 2001, GIA Publications, Inc.

## 351 PRAYER OF THE FAITHFUL

Gra-cious Lord, hear us we pray.

Music: Ronald F. Krisman, © 1977, GIA Publications, Inc.

## 352 PRAYER OF THE FAITHFUL

Lord, hear our prayer; De-us, ex - áu - di
*Pa-nie, wy - słu - chaj*

nos; Se - ñor, es - cú - cha - nos.
*nas;*

Music: Michael Hay, © 1994, World Library Publications

## 353 PRAYER OF THE FAITHFUL

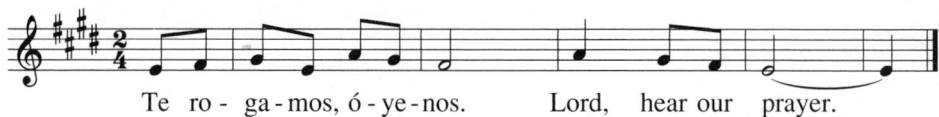

Te ro - ga - mos, ó - ye - nos. Lord, hear our prayer.

Music: Peter M. Kolar, © 2001, World Library Publications

## 354 PRAYER OF THE FAITHFUL

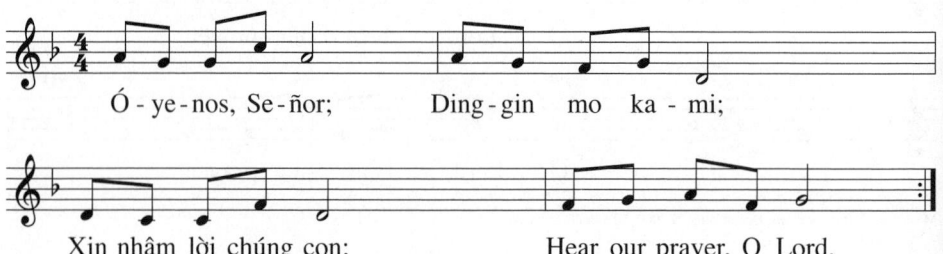

Ó - ye - nos, Se - ñor; Ding - gin mo ka - mi;

Xin nhậm lời chúng con; Hear our prayer, O Lord.

Text: *Misa San Quentin*, DaoKim Nguyen and Rufino Zaragoza, OFM
Music: *Misa San Quentin*, DaoKim Nguyen and Rufino Zaragoza, OFM
© 2004, Rufino Zaragoza, OFM. Published by OCP.

## 355 HOLY, HOLY, HOLY–MASS OF PLENTY

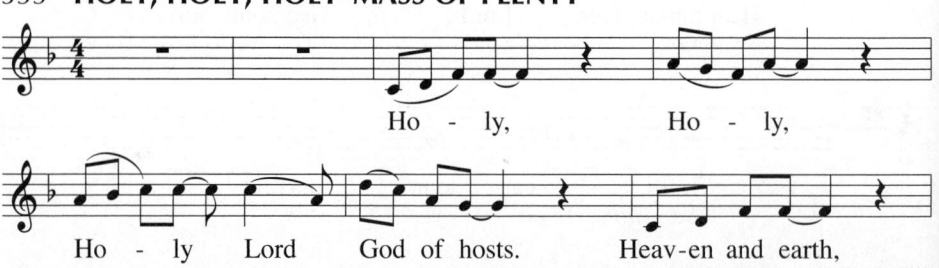

Ho - ly, Ho - ly,

Ho - ly Lord God of hosts. Heav-en and earth,

heav-en and earth are full of your glo - ry.

Ho - san - na in the high - est, ho -

san - na in the high - est. Bless-ed is he,

bless-ed is he who comes in the name of the Lord.

Ho - san - na in the high - est, ho -

san - na in the high - est. Ho - san - na in the

high - est, ho - san - na in the high - est.

Text: ICEL, © 2010
Music: *Mass of Plenty*, Rob Glover, © 2000, 2010, GIA Publications, Inc.

## MEMORIAL ACCLAMATION A 356

We pro - claim your Death, O Lord, and pro -

fess your Res - ur - rec - tion un - til you come a - gain,

un - til you come a - gain.

Text: ICEL, © 2010
Music: *Mass of Plenty*, Rob Glover, © 2010, GIA Publications, Inc.

## 357 AMEN

A - men, a - men, a -

men, a - men, a - men, a -

men, a - men, a - men.

Music: *Mass of Plenty*, Rob Glover, © 2000, GIA Publications, Inc.

## 358 HOLY, HOLY, HOLY–MISSA EMMANUEL

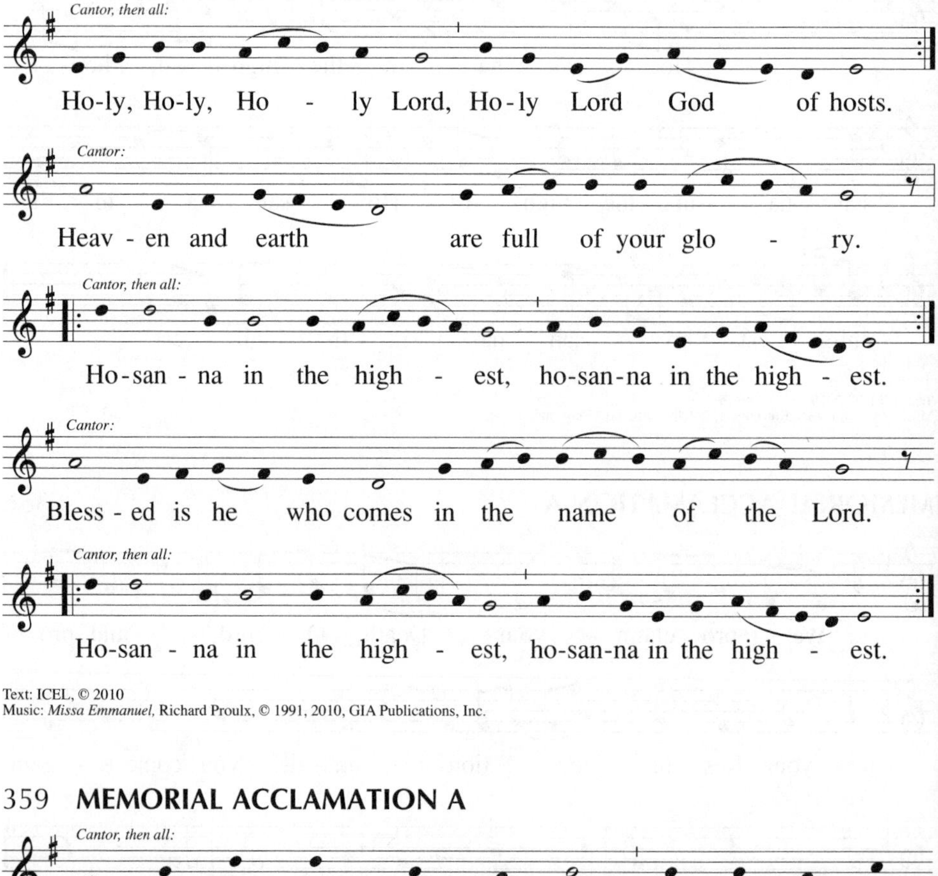

*Cantor, then all:*

Ho-ly, Ho-ly, Ho - ly Lord, Ho-ly Lord God of hosts.

*Cantor:*

Heav - en and earth are full of your glo - ry.

*Cantor, then all:*

Ho-san - na in the high - est, ho-san-na in the high - est.

*Cantor:*

Bless - ed is he who comes in the name of the Lord.

*Cantor, then all:*

Ho-san - na in the high - est, ho-san-na in the high - est.

Text: ICEL, © 2010
Music: *Missa Emmanuel*, Richard Proulx, © 1991, 2010, GIA Publications, Inc.

## 359 MEMORIAL ACCLAMATION A

*Cantor, then all:*

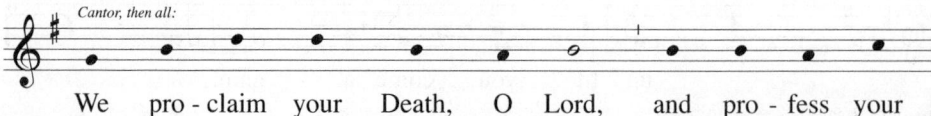

We pro - claim your Death, O Lord, and pro - fess your

Res - ur - rec - tion    un - til    you    come    a - gain.

Text: ICEL, © 2010
Music: *Missa Emmanuel*, adapt. by Robert J. Batastini, © 2011, GIA Publications, Inc.

## AMEN                                                                 360

*Cantor, then all:*

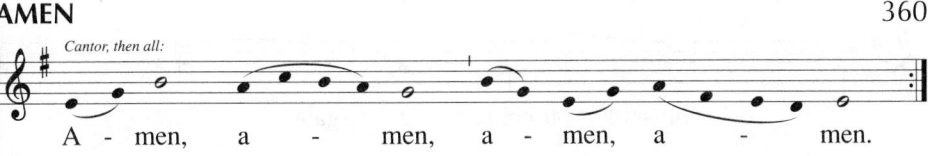

A - men,   a   -   men,   a - men,   a   -   men.

Music: *Missa Emmanuel*, Richard Proulx, © 1991, 2002, GIA Publications, Inc.

## HOLY, HOLY, HOLY–MASS OF LIGHT                                        361

Ho - ly,    Ho - ly,    Ho - ly Lord

God    of hosts.    Heav - en and earth    are    full    of your

glo - ry.    Ho - san - na in    the    high - est.

Bless - ed   is   he   who comes in   the name of   the   Lord.   Ho -

san - na in    the    high - est.                    Ho -

san - na in    the    high - est.

Text: ICEL, © 2010
Music: *Mass of Light,* David Haas, © 1988, 2010, GIA Publications, Inc.

## 362 MEMORIAL ACCLAMATION B

When we eat this Bread and drink this Cup,
we pro-claim your Death, O Lord, un-til you come,
un - til you come a - gain.

Text: ICEL, © 2010
Music: *Mass of Light,* David Haas, © 1988, 2010, GIA Publications, Inc.

## 363 AMEN

A - men, a - men, a - men, a - men.

Music: *Mass of Light,* David Haas, © 1988, GIA Publications, Inc.

## 364 HOLY, HOLY, HOLY–DEUTSCHE MESSE

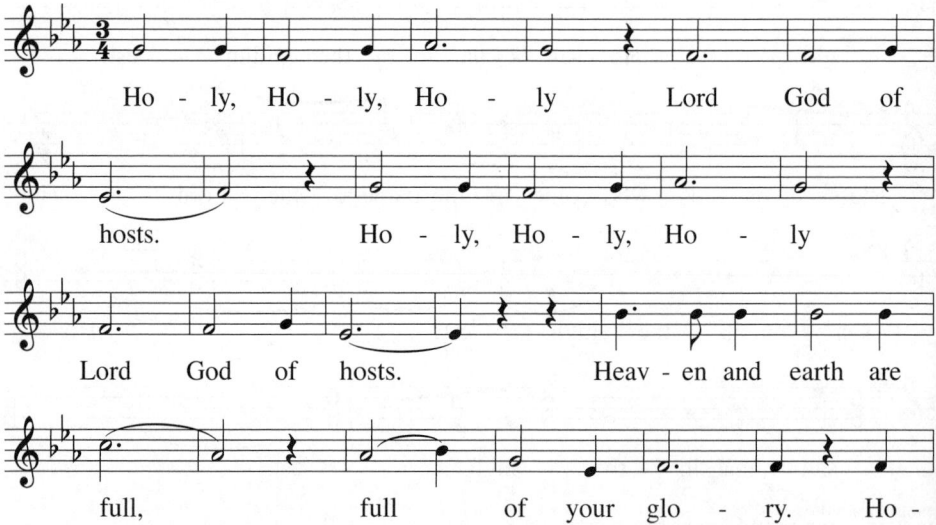

Ho - ly, Ho - ly, Ho - ly Lord God of
hosts. Ho - ly, Ho - ly, Ho - ly
Lord God of hosts. Heav - en and earth are
full, full of your glo - ry. Ho -

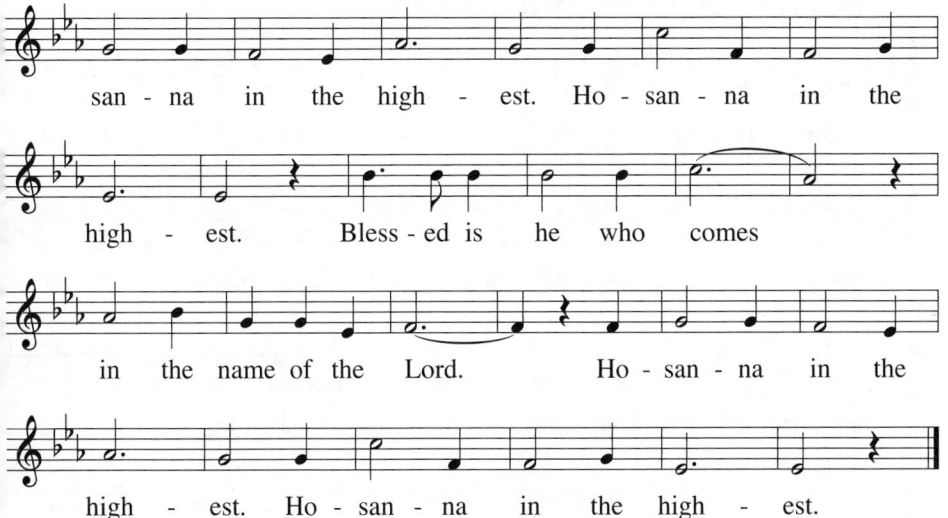

san - na in the high - est. Ho - san - na in the

high - est. Bless - ed is he who comes

in the name of the Lord. Ho - san - na in the

high - est. Ho - san - na in the high - est.

Text: ICEL, © 2010
Music: *Deutsche Messe*, Franz Schubert, 1797–1828, adapt. by Richard Proulx, © 1985, 1989, 2010, GIA Publications, Inc.

## MEMORIAL ACCLAMATION C                                                      365

Save us, Sav - ior of the world, Sav - ior of the

world, for by your Cross and Res - ur - rec - tion

you have set us free, you have set us free.

Text: ICEL, © 2010
Music: *Deutsche Messe*, Franz Schubert, 1797–1828, adapt. by Richard Proulx, © 1985, 1989, 2010, GIA Publications, Inc.

## AMEN                                                                        366

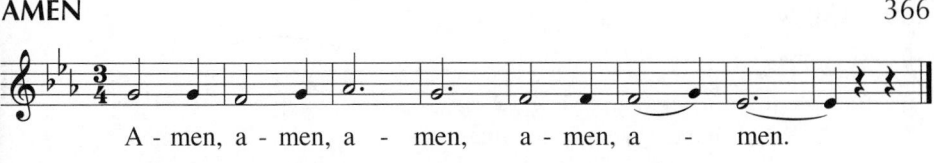

A - men, a - men, a - men, a - men, a - men.

Music: *Deutsche Messe*, Franz Schubert, 1797–1828, adapt. by Richard Proulx, © 1985, 1989, GIA Publications, Inc.

## 367 HOLY, HOLY, HOLY–LAND OF REST

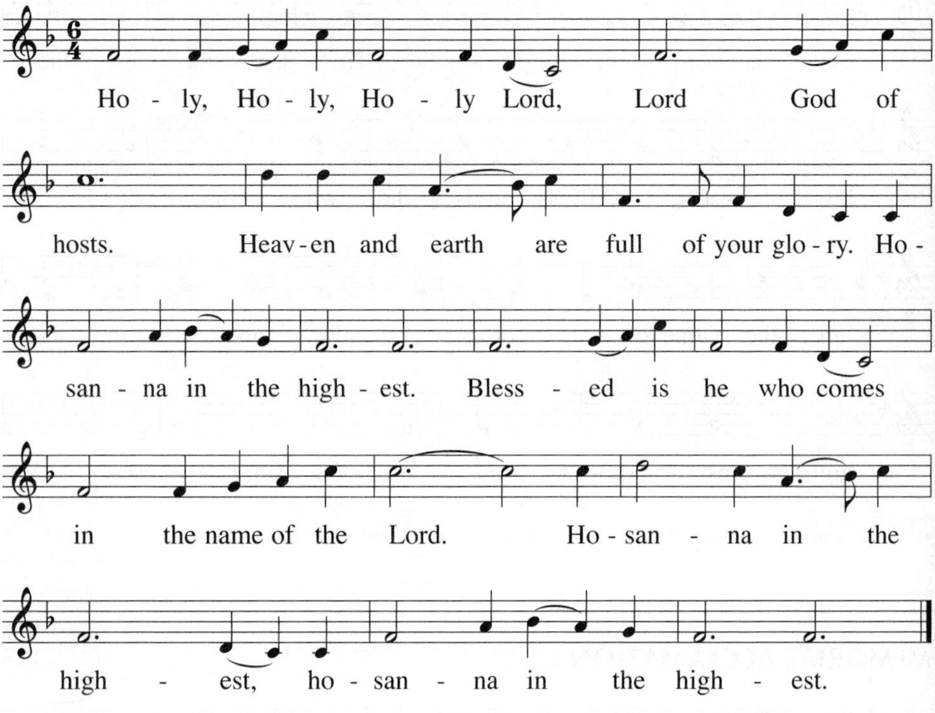

Ho - ly, Ho - ly, Ho - ly Lord, Lord God of

hosts. Heav - en and earth are full of your glo - ry. Ho -

san - na in the high - est. Bless - ed is he who comes

in the name of the Lord. Ho - san - na in the

high - est, ho - san - na in the high - est.

Text: ICEL, © 2010
Music: *Land of Rest*, adapt. by Marcia Pruner, © 1980, alt., Church Pension Fund; acc. by Richard Proulx, © 1986, 2011, GIA Publications, Inc.;
  choral arr. by Kelly Dobbs-Mickus, © 2004, GIA Publications, Inc.

## 368 MEMORIAL ACCLAMATION B

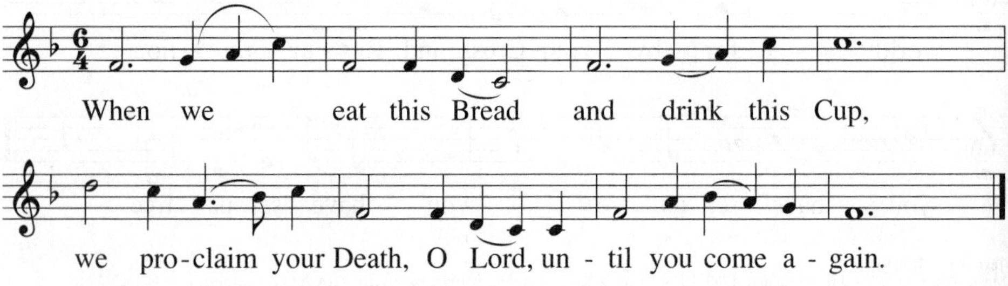

When we eat this Bread and drink this Cup,

we pro - claim your Death, O Lord, un - til you come a - gain.

Text: ICEL, © 2010
Music: *Land of Rest*, acc. by Richard Proulx, © 1986, GIA Publications, Inc.; choral arr. and adapt. by Kelly Dobbs-Mickus, © 2004, 2011,
  GIA Publications, Inc.

## 369 AMEN

A - men, a - men, a - men.

Music: *Land of Rest*, adapt. by Richard Proulx, © 1986, GIA Publications, Inc.; choral acc. by Kelly Dobbs-Mickus, © 2004, GIA Publications, Inc.

## HOLY, HOLY, HOLY–A COMMUNITY MASS 370

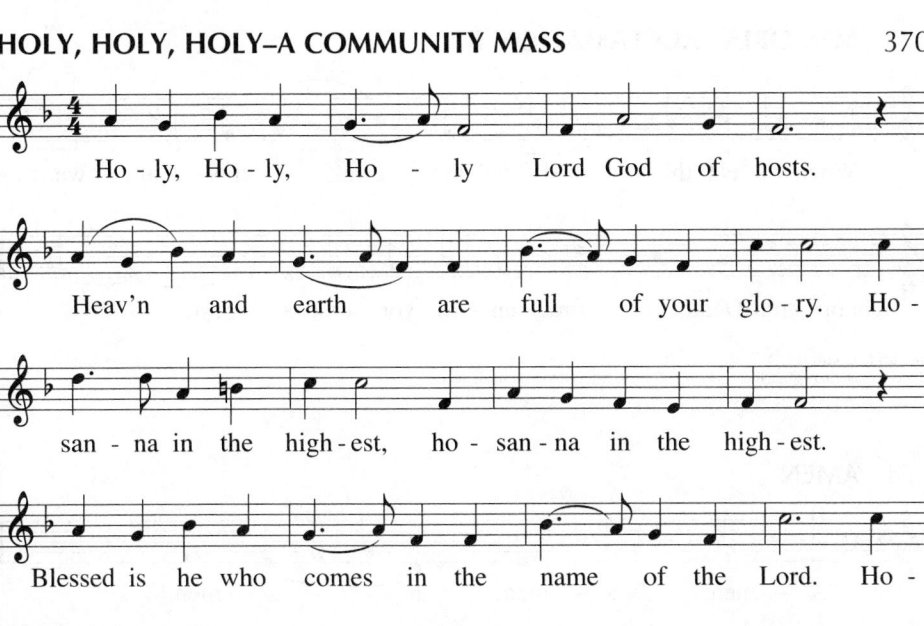

Ho - ly, Ho - ly, Ho - ly Lord God of hosts.

Heav'n and earth are full of your glo - ry. Ho -

san - na in the high - est, ho - san - na in the high - est.

Blessed is he who comes in the name of the Lord. Ho -

san - na in the high - est, ho - san-na in the high-est.

Text: ICEL, © 2010
Music: *A Community Mass*, Richard Proulx, © 1971, 1977, 2006, GIA Publications, Inc.

## MEMORIAL ACCLAMATION A 371

We pro-claim your Death, O Lord, and pro-fess your

Res - ur - rec - tion un - til you come a - gain.

Text: ICEL, © 2010
Music: *A Community Mass*, Richard Proulx, © 1985, 2010, GIA Publications, Inc.

## AMEN 372

A - men, a - men, a - men.

Music: *A Community Mass*, Richard Proulx, © 1971, 1977, 2006, GIA Publications, Inc.

## 373 MEMORIAL ACCLAMATION B

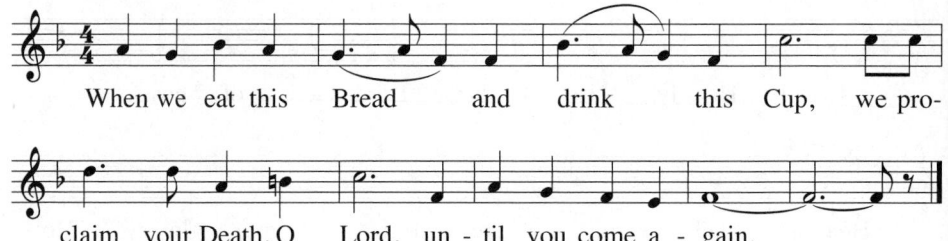

When we eat this Bread and drink this Cup, we proclaim your Death, O Lord, un - til you come a - gain.

Text: ICEL, © 2010
Music: *A Community Mass*, Richard Proulx, © 1988, 2010, GIA Publications, Inc.

## 374 AMEN

A - men, a - men, a - men.

Music: Danish Amen

## 375 HOLY, HOLY, HOLY–MASS OF THE ANGELS AND SAINTS

Ho - ly, Ho - ly, Ho - ly Lord God of hosts.

Heav'n and earth are full of your glo - ry. Ho -

san - na, ho - san - na, ho - san - na in the

high - est, ho - san - na, ho - san - na, ho -

san - na in the high - est. Bless - ed is he who comes in the

name of the Lord. Ho - san - na, ho -

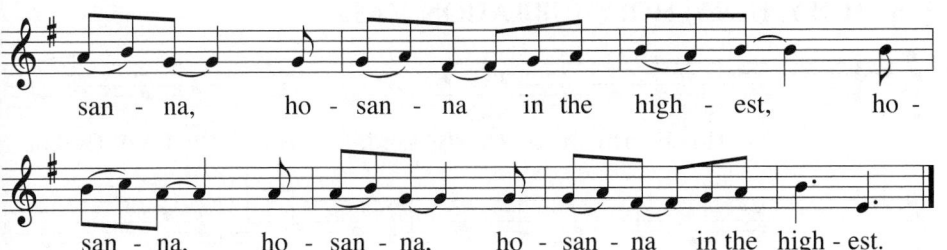

san - na, ho - san - na in the high - est, ho -

san - na, ho - san - na, ho - san - na in the high - est.

## MEMORIAL ACCLAMATION C 376

Save us, Sav - ior of the world, for by your

Cross and Res - ur - rec - tion you have set us free.

## AMEN 377

A - men, a - men, a - men.

A - men, a - men, a - men.

## 378 HOLY, HOLY, HOLY–JUBILATION MASS

Ho - ly, Ho - ly, Ho - ly Lord, Ho - ly Lord God of

hosts. Heav-en and earth are full of your glo - ry. Ho -

san - na, ho - san - na, ho - san - na in the high - est.

Bless - ed is he who comes in the name of the Lord. Ho -

san - na, ho - san - na, ho - san - na in the high-est. Ho -

san - na, ho - san - na, ho - san - na in the high - est.

Text: ICEL, © 2010
Music: *Jubilation Mass*, James Chepponis, © 1999, 2010, GIA Publications, Inc.

## 379 MEMORIAL ACCLAMATION B

When we eat this Bread and drink this Cup, we pro-claim your Death, O

Lord, un - til you come a - gain, un - til you come a - gain.

Text: ICEL, © 2010
Music: *Jubilation Mass*, James Chepponis, © 1999, 2010, GIA Publications, Inc.

## 380 AMEN

A - men, a - men, a - men.

A - men, a - men, a - men.

Music: *Jubilation Mass,* James Chepponis, © 1999, GIA Publications, Inc.

## HOLY, HOLY, HOLY–PEOPLE'S MASS 381

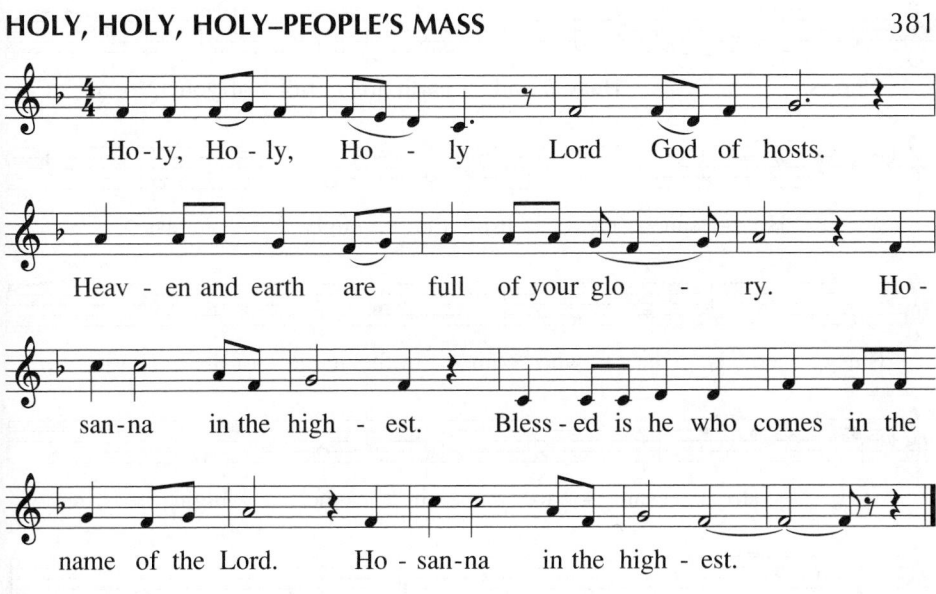

Ho-ly, Ho-ly, Ho - ly Lord God of hosts.

Heav - en and earth are full of your glo - ry. Ho -

san-na in the high - est. Bless - ed is he who comes in the

name of the Lord. Ho - san-na in the high - est.

Text: ICEL, © 2010
Music: *People's Mass,* Jan Vermulst; acc. by Richard Proulx, © 1970, 1987, 2010, World Library Publications

## MEMORIAL ACCLAMATION B 382

When we eat this Bread and drink this Cup, we pro-claim your

Death, O Lord, un - til you come a - gain.

Text: ICEL, © 2010
Music: David Kraehenbuehl; acc. by Charles G. Frischmann, © 1970, 1973, 2011, World Library Publications

## AMEN 383

A - men, a - men, a - men.

Music: Danish Amen

## 384 HOLY, HOLY, HOLY–MASS OF REMEMBRANCE

Ho - ly, Ho - ly, Ho - ly Lord God of

hosts. Heav'n and earth are full of your glo-ry.

Ho - san - na in the high - est.

Bless - ed is he who comes in the name of the Lord.

Ho - san - na in the high -

est. Ho - san - na in the high - est.

Text: ICEL, © 2010
Music: *Mass of Remembrance*, Marty Haugen, © 1987, 2010, GIA Publications, Inc.

## 385 MEMORIAL ACCLAMATION C

Save us, Sav-ior of the world, for by your Cross and

Res - ur - rec - tion you have set us free.

Text: ICEL, © 2010
Music: *Mass of Remembrance*, Marty Haugen, © 1987, 2010, GIA Publications, Inc.

## 386 AMEN

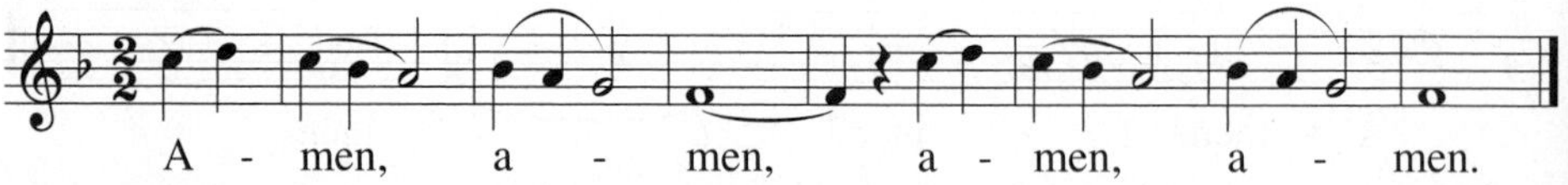

A - men, a - men, a - men, a - men.

Music: *Mass of Remembrance*, Marty Haugen, © 1987, 2010, GIA Publications, Inc.

# THE LORD'S PRAYER

Our Fa - ther, who art in heav - en, hal - low-ed

be thy name. Thy king-dom come, thy will be done

on earth as it is in heav - en. Give us this day

our dai - ly bread; and for - give us our tres - pass -

es as we for - give those who tres-pass a - gainst us;

and lead us not in - to temp - ta - tion,

but de - liv - er us from e - vil.

*Priest:* Deliver us, Lord... and the coming of our Savior, Jesus Christ.

For the king-dom, the pow'r, and the glo - ry are yours

now and for ev - er, now and for ev - er.

Music: Steven C. Warner; acc. by Karen Schneider Kirner, © 1980, 2004, World Library Publications

## 388 LAMB OF GOD

Have mer - cy on us.

Grant us peace. Grant us peace.

Music: *Mass of the Angels and Saints*, Steven R. Janco, © 1996, GIA Publications, Inc.

## 389 LAMB OF GOD

Lamb of God, you take a-way the sins of the

world: have mer-cy on us. Lamb of God, you

take a-way the sins of the world: grant us peace.

Music: *A Community Mass*, Richard Proulx, © 1971, 1977, GIA Publications, Inc.

## 390 LAMB OF GOD

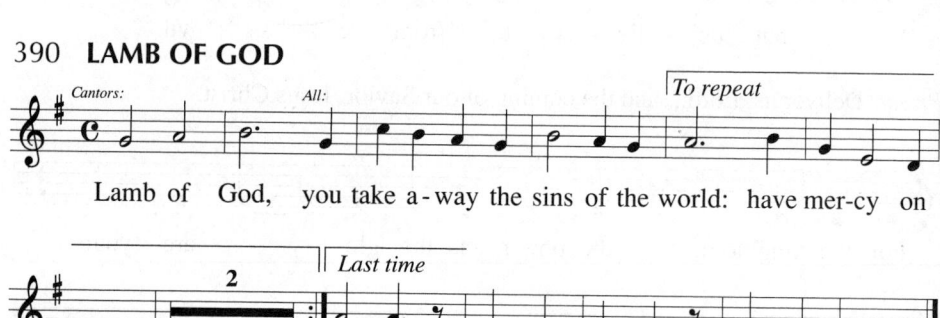

Lamb of God, you take a-way the sins of the world: have mer-cy on

us. world: grant us peace, grant us peace.

Music: *Mass of Remembrance*, Marty Haugen, © 1987, GIA Publications, Inc.

# LAMB OF GOD

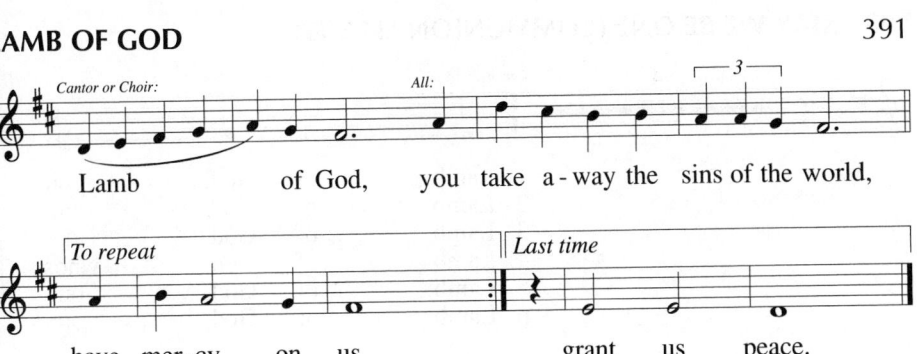

*Cantor or Choir:* ... *All:*

Lamb of God, you take a-way the sins of the world,

*To repeat* ... *Last time*

have mer-cy on us. grant us peace.

Music: *Holy Cross Mass,* David Clark Isele, © 1979, GIA Publications, Inc.

# LAMB OF GOD

*Cantor:\**

O Lamb of God, you take a - way

*Repeat as needed*

the sins of the world: have mer - cy on us.

*Last time*

Grant us peace, grant us peace.

*\*The assembly echoes each phrase of the cantor at the interval of one measure.*

Music: Ralph R. Stewart, © 1999, GIA Publications, Inc.; acc. by Robert J. Batastini, © 2003, GIA Publications, Inc.

## 393 MAY WE BE ONE (COMMUNION LITANY)

*Cantor(s):*

1. Lamb of God, you
2. Lamb of God, un -
3. Lamb of God, de -
4. Lamb of God, whose
5. Lamb of God, our
6. Lamb of God, our

take a - way the sins of the world:
blem - ished of - f'ring made for our sin:
stroyed that all who eat might be healed:
blood will save your peo - ple from death:
com - mon mem - 'ry, cov - e - nant feast:
free - dom won, re - mem - bered for ev - er:

*All:*

have mer - cy on us, have mer - cy on us.

*Last time*

*Cantor(s):*

Lamb of God, you take a-way the sins of the world,

*All:*

grant us peace, grant us peace.

*Additional invocations:*

Lamb of God, the shepherd of all who hunger and thirst…
Lamb of God, joy of the martyrs, song of the saints…
Lamb of God, all peoples will sing your victory song…
Lamb of God, unconquered light of the city of God…
Lamb of God, how blessed are those who are called to your feast…

Text: *Agnus Dei;* additional text by Rory Cooney
Music: Gary Daigle
© 1993, GIA Publications, Inc.

# MAY WE BE ONE (COMMUNION HYMN)

Refrain

When we eat this Bread and drink this Cup,

we pro-claim your death, Lord Je - sus. So as we

share this feast may we be - come, heal-ing and

To verses | Last time

light and peace. May we be one. one.

Verses

2

A - men, a - men.

A - men, a - men. A - men, a -

4 D.C.

men. A - men, a - men.

Text: Rory Cooney, b.1952
Tune: Gary Daigle, b.1957
© 1993, GIA Publications, Inc.

# 395 O Come, O Come, Emmanuel

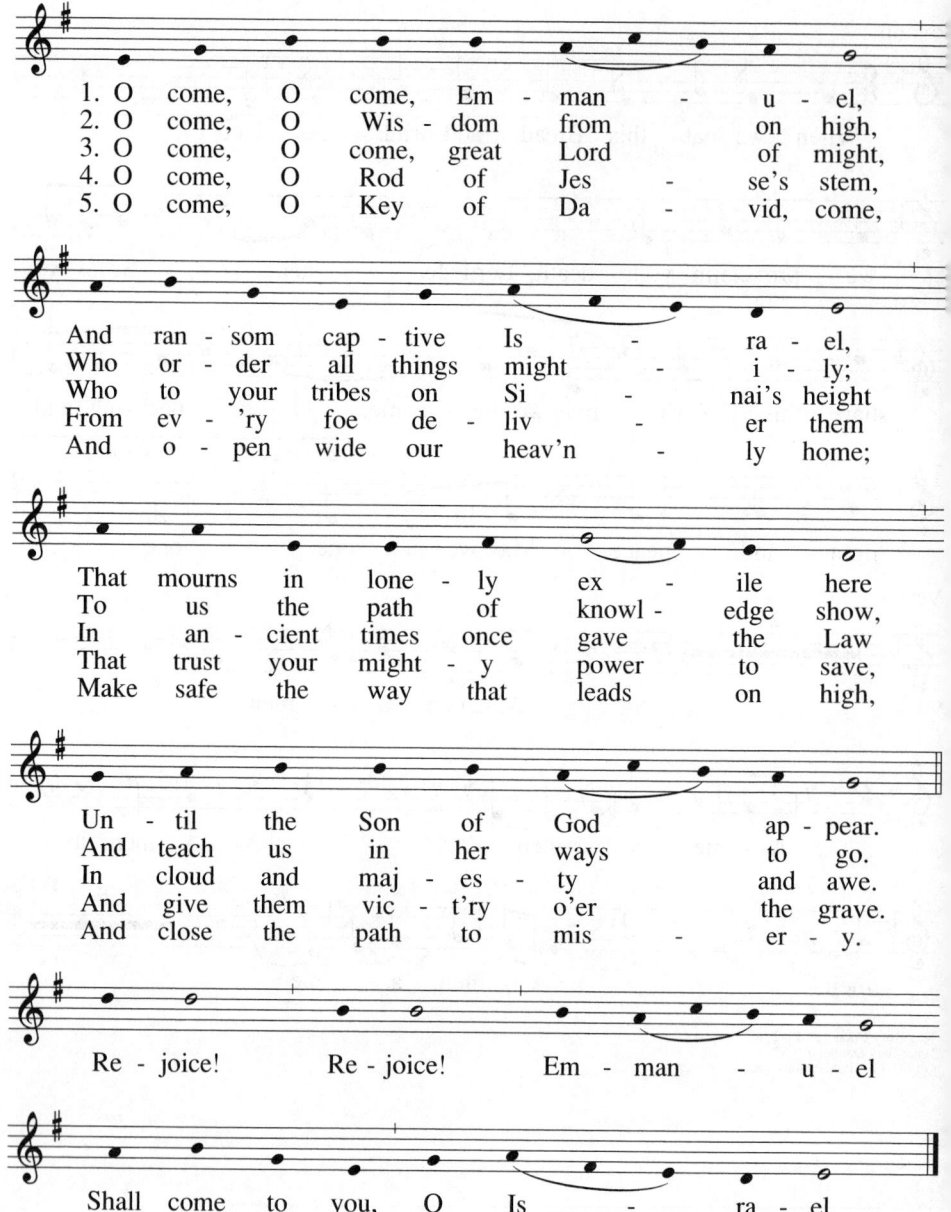

1. O come, O come, Em - man - u - el,
2. O come, O Wis - dom from on high,
3. O come, O come, great Lord of might,
4. O come, O Rod of Jes - se's stem,
5. O come, O Key of Da - vid, come,

And ran - som cap - tive Is - ra - el,
Who or - der all things might - i - ly;
Who to your tribes on Si - nai's height
From ev - 'ry foe de - liv - er them
And o - pen wide our heav'n - ly home;

That mourns in lone - ly ex - ile here
To us the path of knowl - edge show,
In an - cient times once gave the Law
That trust your might - y power to save,
Make safe the way that leads on high,

Un - til the Son of God ap - pear.
And teach us in her ways to go.
In cloud and maj - es - ty and awe.
And give them vic - t'ry o'er the grave.
And close the path to mis - er - y.

Re - joice! Re - joice! Em - man - u - el

Shall come to you, O Is - ra - el.

6. O come, O Dayspring from on high,
And cheer us by your drawing nigh;
Disperse the gloomy clouds of night,
And death's dark shadow put to flight.

7. O come, Desire of nations, bind
In one the hearts of humankind;
O bid our sad divisions cease,
And be for us our King of Peace.

Text: *Veni, veni Emmanuel*; Latin 9th C.; tr. by John M. Neale, 1818–1866, alt.
Tune: VENI EMMANUEL, LM with refrain; Mode I; adapt. by Thomas Helmore, 1811–1890; acc. by Richard Proulx, 1937–2010, © 1975, GIA Publications, Inc.

# Comfort, My People  396

1. Com - fort, my peo - ple, and calm all your fear; the day of sal - va - tion is quick-ly draw - ing near. The One you long to see will soon set you free.

2. Si - lence the thun - der, si - lence sounds of war. End all de - struc - tion and com - fort those who mourn. Your dream draws near; your vi - sion is here.

(3.) light in the dark - ness; be truth for our lives. Be strength for the help - less, the poor and lost who cry. O sav - ing voice, O liv - ing choice,

O come, Lord Je - sus, come.

O come, Lord Je - sus, come.

1., 2.  D.C.  3.

3. Be

Text: Ian Callanan, b.1971
Tune: Ian Callanan, b.1971
© 2006, GIA Publications, Inc.

# 397   Maranatha, Lord Messiah

Verses

1. Gra - cious God of Wis-dom, who hear your peo-ple's
2. Might - y Voice on Si - nai, whom Mos - es heard in
3. Fra - grant Bud of Jes - se, whose bloom - ing kings re -
4. Da - vid's Key of Heav - en, re - lease us from our
5. Blaz - ing Sun of Jus - tice, the flame of east - ern
6. Sov - ereign of all na - tions, our cor - ner-stone of
7. Je - sus, be God with us, Em - man - u - el fore -

cry,                 teach us ways of pru - dence,   O
awe,                 Ad - o - nai, now lead us        with
vere,                root your words with - in us,    God's
sins.                Freed from er - ror's pris - on, our
dawn,                scat - ter cling - ing shad - ows, that
trust,     de - liv - er, in your mer - cy,           your
told.      Like a shep - herd feed us,                in

Breath of God Most High.
ho - ly arm and law.
Word for all to hear.
life in you be - gins.
gloom of death be gone.
crea - tures made from dust.
safe - ly gath - ered fold.

Ma-ra-

Refrain

na - tha, Lord Mes - si - ah, long a - wait - ed from a -

far.        Come and make your home a-mong us.        Let us

| 1.-6. | To verses | Last time |

see your birth - ing star.                              star.

Text: Based on the "O" Antiphons; Kathy Powell, b.1942
Tune: Kathy Powell, b.1942
© 1999, GIA Publications, Inc.

# Prepare! Prepare! 398

Ostinato Refrain

Pre-pare! Pre - pare the way of the Lord.

Pre - pare! Pre - pare the way of the Lord, oh,

Pre - pare! Pre-pare the way of the Lord. The Lord our God is

*To repeat*      *To verses*      *Last time*

com - ing     soon.    Oh,     com - ing     soon.

Verses   *Cantor:*

1. Pre - pare the way,      the
2. Make straight the path,
3. Jus - tice and peace,
4. Sing and re - joice!      The
5. A vir - gin will bear a son,      Em -

way of the Lord.     Read - y your hearts.
lev - el the hills,     lift up the gates.
kind - ness and truth     shall come to the earth.
Lord is near,     I say re - joice!
man - u - el:     God with us!

D.C.

Oh, the Lord our God is com-ing soon!

Text: Stephen Pishner
Tune: Stephen Pishner
© 2007, GIA Publications, Inc.

# 399  Awake to the Day

Refrain

A - wake to the day of the com-ing of the Lord. Sing

out! Re-joice in this land. Make straight the way for the

*Last time to Coda*

King-dom of God is at hand.

Verse 1

*Cantor:*

*Choir:*

1. Signs in the sun and the moon and the stars, We pre-pare for you,

*Cantor:*

Lord. Then all shall sing of the pow - er of God.

*Choir:*

*All:*

We pre-pare for you, Lord. As long as the sun shall re -

**D.S.**

main so the name of the Lord God will reign. A -

Verse 2

*Cantor:*

*Choir:*

2. Wrapped in the cloak of jus-tice from God, We pre-pare for you,

Cantor:

Lord.     Gath-ered   at the word    of the   Ho - ly One,

Choir:                                    All:

We    pre-pare for you,   Lord.      Ev-'ry moun-tain and hill   be made

**D.S.**

low      that the glo - ry   of God we may    know.        A -

✿ Coda

hand.       A - wake to the day      of the com-ing of the Lord.   Sing

out!    Re - joice  in  this    land.      Make straight the way      for the

*First time only*

King-dom of God is    at      hand.        Make the  way!

Text: Ed Bolduc, b.1969, and John Barker
Tune: Ed Bolduc, b.1969, and John Barker
© 2003, World Library Publications

# Prepare the Way of the Lord   400

Canon         (A)                    (B)

Pre - pare  the way of the Lord.   Pre-pare  the way of the Lord,    and

(C)                           (D)

all     peo-ple will see     the  sal - va - tion of   our   God.      Pre -

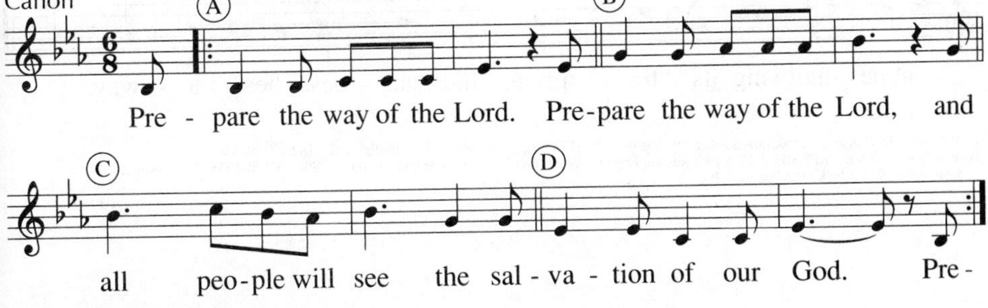

Text: Luke 3:4, 6; Taizé Community, 1984
Tune: Jacques Berthier, 1923–1994
© 1984, Les Presses de Taizé, GIA Publications, Inc., agent

# 401 O Come, Divine Messiah!

1. O come, Divine Messiah! The world in silence waits the day When hope shall sing its triumph, And sadness flee away.
2. O come, Desired of nations, Whom priest and prophet long foretold. Come break the captive fetters, Redeem the long-lost fold.
3. O come in peace and meekness, For lowly will your cradle be: Though clothed in human weakness We shall your Godhead see.

Dear Savior, haste! Come, come to earth. Dispel the night and show your face, And bid us hail the dawn of grace. O come, Divine Messiah! The world in silence waits the day When hope shall sing its triumph, And sadness flee away.

Text: *Venez, divin Messie;* Abbé Simon-Joseph Pellegrin, 1663–1745; tr. by Sr. Mary of St. Philip, SND, 1825–1904, alt.
Tune: VENEZ, DIVIN MESSIE, 7 8 7 6 with refrain; French Noël, 16th C.; harm. by Healey Willan, 1880–1968, © 1958, The Basilian Fathers, assigned to Ralph Jusko Publications, Inc.

# Like a Shepherd  402

**Refrain**

Like a shep-herd he feeds his flock and gath-ers the
lambs in his arms, hold-ing them care-ful-ly
close to his heart, lead-ing them home.

**Verses 1, 2**

1. Say to the cit-ies of Ju - dah: Pre - pare the
2. I my - self will shep-herd them, for oth - ers have

way of the Lord. Go to the moun-tain top,
led them a - stray. The lost I will res - cue and

**D.C.**

lift your voice; Je - ru - sa - lem, here is your God.
heal their wounds and pas - ture them, giv-ing them rest.

**Verse 3**

3. Come un - to me if you are

heav - i - ly bur - dened, and take my yoke up -

**D.C.**

on your shoul - ders, I will give you rest.

Text: Isaiah 40:9ff, Ezekiel 34:11, Matthew 11:28ff; Bob Dufford, SJ, b.1943
Tune: Bob Dufford, SJ, b.1943; acc. by Sr. Theophane Hytrek, OSF, 1915–1992, alt.
© 1976, Robert J. Dufford, SJ, and OCP

# 403 Come, O Long-Expected Jesus

1. Come, O long - ex - pect - ed Je - sus, Born to set your
2. Born your peo - ple to de - liv - er, Born a child, and

peo - ple free; From our fears and sins re - lease us:
yet a king; Born to reign in us for - ev - er,

Christ, in you our rest shall be. Is - rael's strength and
Now your grac - ious king - dom bring. By your own e -

con - so - la - tion, Hope to all the earth im - part;
ter - nal Spir - it Rule in all our hearts a - lone;

Dear de - sire of ev - 'ry na - tion,
By your all - suf - fi - cient mer - it

En - ter ev - 'ry long - ing heart.
Raise us to your glo - rious throne.

Text: Haggai 2:7; Charles Wesley, 1707–1788, alt.
Tune: JEFFERSON, 8 7 8 7 D; William Walker's *Southern Harmony,* 1855; acc. by Theophane Hytrek, OSF, 1915–1992, © 1981, ICEL

*Alternate tune:* STUTTGART, *4 Stanzas*

# When the King Shall Come Again   404

1. When     the   King   shall     come    a - gain,       All      his    pow'r re -
2. In         the   des - ert        trees   take    root      Fresh   from   his    cre -
3. Strength-en   fee - ble     hands  and   knees,    Faint - ing   hearts, be
4. There   God's  high - way    shall   be      seen      Where  no      roar - ing

veal - ing,        Splen - dor      shall     an - nounce  his    reign,
a - tion;           Plants   and     flow'rs   and    sweet - est    fruit
cheer - ful!       God,    who      comes    for    such    as     these,
li - on,            Noth - ing        e - vil    or       un - clean,

Life      and       joy     and      heal - ing:        Earth    no
Join      the       cel - e - bra - tion;        Riv - ers
Seeks    and       saves   the       fear - ful.        Deaf     ears
Walks    the       road    to        Zi - on.          Ran - somed

long - er     in     de - cay,      Hope    no    more   frus - trat - ed;
spring up    from   the   earth,    Bar - ren   lands   a - dorn - ing;
hear the      si - lent tongues    Sing    a - way   their weep - ing;
peo - ple  home - ward bound,    All     your  prais - es   voic - ing,

This     is     God's    re - demp - tion   day
Val - leys,     this     is     your   new    birth,
Blind    eyes   see     the     life - less   ones
See      your   Lord    with    glo - ry   crowned,

Long - ing - ly    a - wait - ed.
Moun - tains,      greet   the   morn - ing!
Walk - ing,        run - ning,   leap - ing.
Share    in        his    re - joic - ing!

Text: Isaiah 35; Christopher M. Idle, b.1938, alt., © 1982, The Jubilate Group (admin. by Hope Publishing Company)
Tune: GAUDEAMUS PARITER, 7 6 7 6 D; Johann Horn, c. 1495–1547

# 405  Advent Gathering Song

Refrain

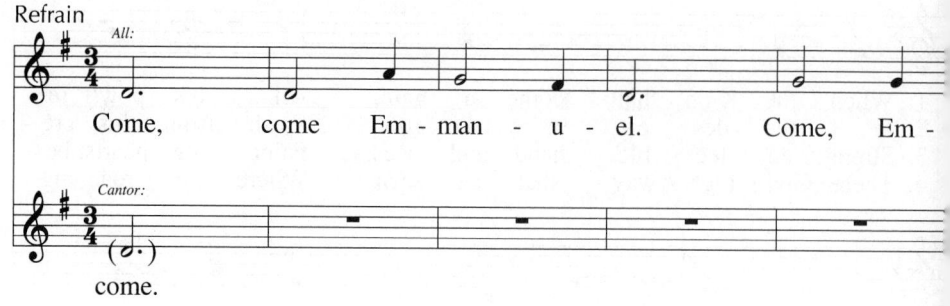

Come,  come  Em - man - u - el.  Come,  Em -

come.

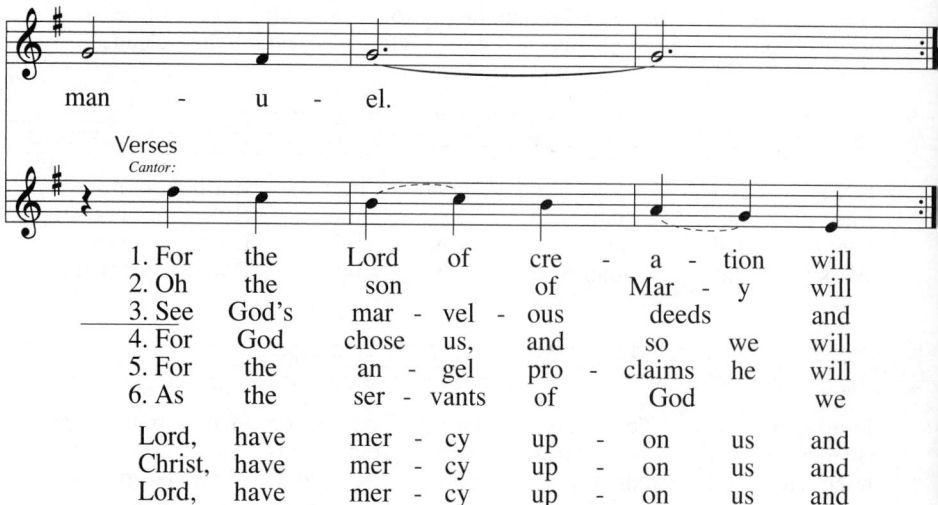

man - u - el.

Verses
Cantor:

| | | | | | | | | |
|---|---|---|---|---|---|---|---|---|
| 1. For | the | Lord | of | cre - | a - | tion | will | |
| 2. Oh | the | son | of | Mar - | y | | will | |
| 3. See | God's | mar - vel - | ous | deeds | | | and | |
| 4. For | God | chose | us, | and | so | we | will | |
| 5. For | the | an - gel | pro - | claims | he | | will | |
| 6. As | the | ser - vants | of | God | | | we | |

| | | | | | | |
|---|---|---|---|---|---|---|
| Lord, | have | mer - cy | up - | on | us | and |
| Christ, | have | mer - cy | up - | on | us | and |
| Lord, | have | mer - cy | up - | on | us | and |

Text: James J. Chepponis, b.1956
Tune: James J. Chepponis, b.1956
© 1995, GIA Publications, Inc.

# 406  Wait for the Lord

Ostinato Refrain

| | | | | | |
|---|---|---|---|---|---|
| Wait | for the Lord, | whose day | is | near. | |
| *Spanish:* Con - tem - pla - ré | tu | vi - da_en | mi. | | |
| *Polish:* Pan | blis - ko jest, | o - cze - kuj | Go. | | |
| *Italian:* Cri - sto Ge - sù | io | spe - ro_in | Te. | | |

Wait for the Lord: be strong, take heart!
*Con - tem - pla - ré, Se - ñor, tu_a - mor.*
Pan blis - ko jest, w Nim ser - ca moc!
*Sei tu Si - gnor la pa - ce del cuor.*

Text: Isaiah 40, Philippians 4, Matthew 6–7; Taizé Community, 1984
Tune: Jacques Berthier, 1923–1994
© 1984, Les Presses de Taizé, GIA Publications, Inc., agent

## People of the Night 407

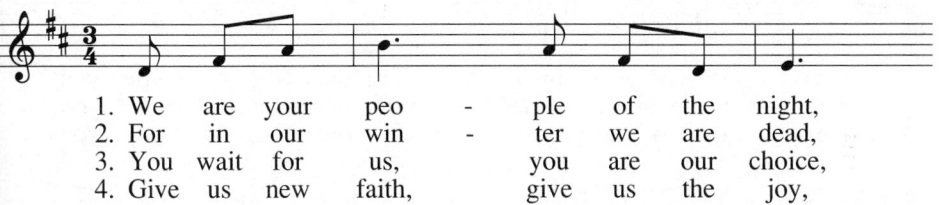

1. We are your peo - ple of the night,
2. For in our win - ter we are dead,
3. You wait for us, you are our choice,
4. Give us new faith, give us the joy,

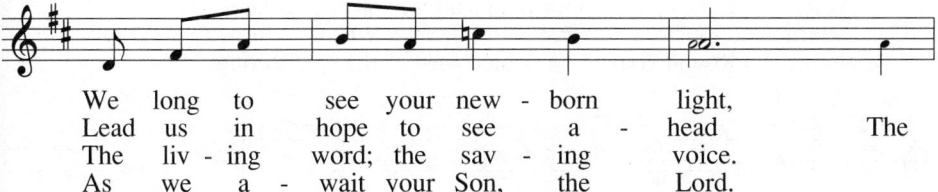

We long to see your new - born light,
Lead us in hope to see a - head The
The liv - ing word; the sav - ing voice.
As we a - wait your Son, the Lord.

Dis - tant glim - mer; ris - ing from a - far.
spring-time and the gift that is to come.
Break the si - lence, lis - ten to our call.
In our pres - ence, child born of your breath,

We a - wait you, ho - ly morn - ing star.
Come and save us, be God's on - ly Son.
Be our an - swer, new life for us all.
Sav - ior broth - er; life that shat - ters death.

Text: David Haas, b.1957
Tune: SHEPHERD'S SONG, 88 99; David Haas, b.1957
© 1983, GIA Publications, Inc.

# 408  Like a Bird

1. Like a bird that spreads her wings to gath er in her
2. From the ends of earth you call your sons and daugh-ters
3. For the na-tions you pre - pare and spread a splen-did

young,    So you o - pen wide your arms to
home,    Say - ing, "Gath - er now from far and
feast,    Gath - er ev - 'ry tribe and race, the

gath - er in your own.    For our free re-sponse you
near,    my peo-ple, come."    For our sim-ple trust you
great - est to the least.    For one fam-'ly, how you

wait,    Ear - ly morn-ing, noon, and late.
yearn    Till, at last in love, we turn.    Come and
long;    'Round your ta - ble, vast the throng.

wake us, come and wake us, come and wake us to your

wel-come.    Ma-ra-na - tha, come.

Text: Delores Dufner, OSB, b.1939
Tune: WAKE US, 13 13 77 with refrain; Michael Joncas, b.1951
© 2011, GIA Publications, Inc.

# People, Look East   409

1. Peo - ple,  look  East.   The  time   is  near
2. Fur - rows,  be  glad.   Though  earth  is  bare,
3. Birds, though  you  long   have  ceased  to  build,
4. Stars,  keep  the  watch.   When  night  is  dim,
5. An - gels  an - nounce   with  shouts  of  mirth

Of  the  crown - ing  of  the  year.
One  more  seed  is  plant - ed  there.
Guard  the  nest  that  must  be  filled.
One  more  light  the  bowl  shall  brim,
Him  who  brings  new  life  to  earth.

Make  your  house  fair  as  you  are  a - ble,
Give  up  your  strength  the  seed  to  nour - ish,
E - ven  the  hour  when  wings  are  fro - zen
Shin - ing  be - yond  the  frost - y  weath - er,
Set  ev - 'ry  peak  and  val - ley  hum - ming

Trim  the  hearth  and  set  the  ta - ble.
That  in  course  the  flow'r  may  flour - ish.
God  for  fledg - ing - time  has  cho - sen.
Bright  as  sun  and  moon  to - geth - er.
With  the  word,  the  Lord  is  com - ing.

Peo - ple  look  East  and  sing  to - day—

Love,  the  Guest,  is  on  the  way.
Love,  the  Rose,  is  on  the  way.
Love,  the  Bird,  is  on  the  way.
Love,  the  Star,  is  on  the  way.
Love,  the  Lord,  is  on  the  way.

Text: Eleanor Farjeon, 1881–1965, © David Higham Assoc. Ltd.
Tune: BESANÇON, 87 98 87; French traditional; harm. by Martin Shaw, 1875–1958, © Oxford University Press

# 410 Maranatha, Come

Refrain

Ma-ra-na-tha, come, come, Lord Je-sus.

Ma-ra-na-tha, come, come, O God.

Verses

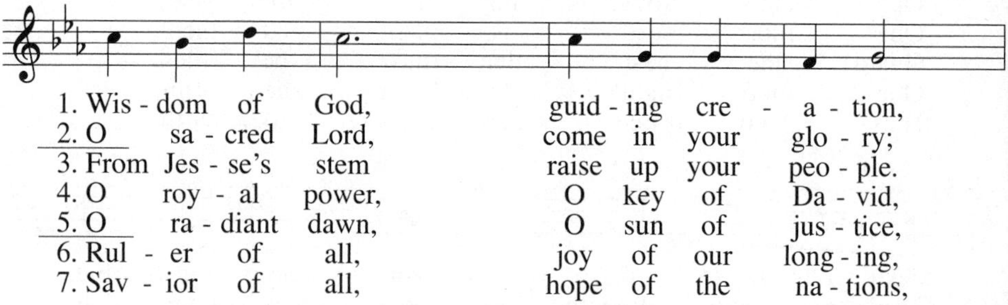

1. Wis-dom of God, guid-ing cre - a - tion,
2. O sa-cred Lord, come in your glo - ry;
3. From Jes-se's stem raise up your peo - ple.
4. O roy-al power, O key of Da - vid,
5. O ra-diant dawn, O sun of jus - tice,
6. Rul-er of all, joy of our long - ing,
7. Sav-ior of all, hope of the na - tions,

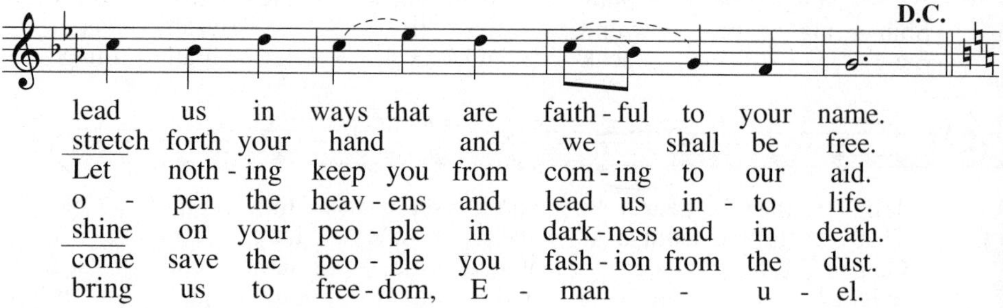

D.C.

lead us in ways that are faith-ful to your name.
stretch forth your hand and we shall be free.
Let noth-ing keep you from com-ing to our aid.
o - pen the heav-ens and lead us in - to life.
shine on your peo-ple in dark-ness and in death.
come save the peo-ple you fash-ion from the dust.
bring us to free-dom, E - man - u - el.

Text: Based on the "O" Antiphons; Francis Patrick O'Brien, b.1958
Tune: Francis Patrick O'Brien, b.1958
© 1996, GIA Publications, Inc.

# 411 Advent Alleluia

Refrain

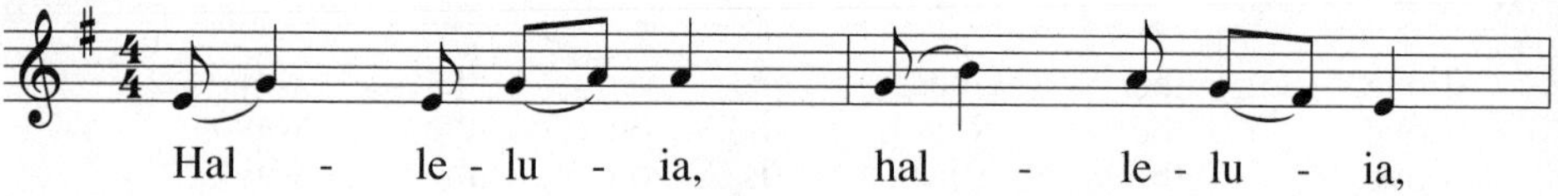

Hal - le - lu - ia, hal - le - lu - ia,

hal - le - lu - ia, hal - le - lu - ia!

Verses

1. Lord, show us your mercy and love,
   and grant us your salvation.

2. Prepare the way of the Lord, make straight his paths:
   all people shall see the salvation of God.

3. The Spirit of the Lord is upon me,
   he sent me to bring good news to the poor.

4. A virgin will give birth to a Son; a virgin will give birth to a Son;
   his name will be Emmanuel: God is with us.

5. I am the servant of the Lord:
   may his will for me be done.

Text: *Lectionary for Mass*, © 1969, 1981, ICEL
Tune: Michael Joncas, b.1951, © 1988, GIA Publications, Inc.

## God of All People 412

1. God of all plac-es: pres-ent, un-seen;
2. God of all dream-ing, near and yet far.
3. God of all peo-ple, dust and the clay.

Voice in our si-lence, song in our midst.
Vi-sion un-heard of, wake us to rest.
Breath of a new wind, fire in our hearts.

We are your peo-ple, know-ing, un-sure.
We are your pres-ence, sent forth a-fraid.
Light born of heav-en, peace on the earth.

Come, Lord Je-sus, come!
Come, Lord Je-sus, come!
Come, Lord Je-sus, come!

Text: David Haas, b.1957
Tune: KINGDOM, 9 9 9 5; David Haas, b.1957
© 1988, GIA Publications, Inc.

# 413 Comfort, Comfort, O My People

1. Com - fort, com - fort, O my peo - ple,
2. Hark, the voice of one who's cry - ing
3. O make straight what long was crook - ed,

Speak of peace, now says our God.
In the des - ert far and near,
Make the rough - er plac - es plain.

Com - fort those who sit in dark - ness,
Bid - ding all to full re - pent - ance
Let your hearts be true and hum - ble,

Mourn - ing un - der sor - rows' load.
Since the king - dom now is here.
As be - fits his ho - ly reign.

Speak un - to Je - ru - sa - lem
Oh, that warn - ing cry o - bey!
For the glo - ry of the Lord

Of the peace that waits for them.
Now pre - pare for God a way!
Now o'er earth is shed a - broad.

Tell of all the sins I cov - er,
Let the val - leys rise to meet him
And all flesh shall see the to - ken

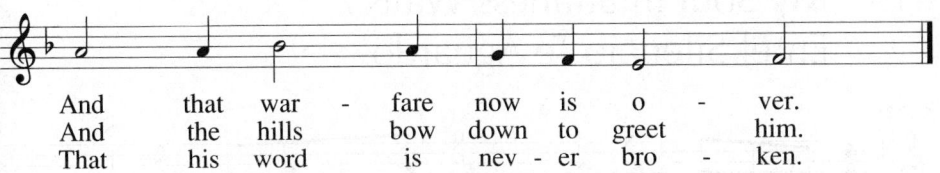

| And | that | war | - | fare | now | is | o | - | ver. |
| And | the | hills | | bow | down | to | greet | | him. |
| That | his | word | | is | nev | - er | bro | - | ken. |

Text: Isaiah 40:1–8; *Tröstet, tröstet, meine Lieben;* Johann Olearius, 1611–1684; tr. by Catherine Winkworth, 1827–1878, alt.
Tune: GENEVA 42, 8 7 8 7 77 88; *Genevan Psalter,* 1551; harm. adapt. from Claude Goudimel, 1505–1572

# The King Shall Come When Morning Dawns 414

1. The King shall come when morn - ing dawns And
2. Not, as of old, a lit - tle child, To
3. The King shall come when morn - ing dawns And
4. And let the end - less bliss be - gin, By
5. The King shall come when morn - ing dawns And

light tri - um - phant breaks, When beau - ty gilds the
suf - fer and to die, But crowned with glo - ry
earth's dark night is past; O haste the ris - ing
wea - ry saints fore - told, When right shall tri - umph
light and beau - ty brings. Hail, Christ, the Lord! Your

east - ern hills And life to joy a - wakes.
like the sun That lights the morn - ing sky.
of that morn Whose day shall ev - er last.
o - ver wrong, And truth shall be ex - tolled.
peo - ple pray: Come quick - ly, King of kings.

Text: John Brownlie, 1857–1925, alt.
Tune: MORNING SONG, CM; John Wyeth, 1770–1858; arr. by Robert J. Batastini, b.1942, © 1994, GIA Publications, Inc.

# 415 My Soul in Stillness Waits / En el Silencio Te Aguardo

**Refrain**

For you, O Lord, my soul in still-ness waits;
*En el si - len - cio te_a-guar-do_a ti, Se - ñor.*

| To verses | Last time |

tru - ly my hope is in you. you.
*Tú_e -res mi luz y mi_a - mor. mor.*

**Verses**

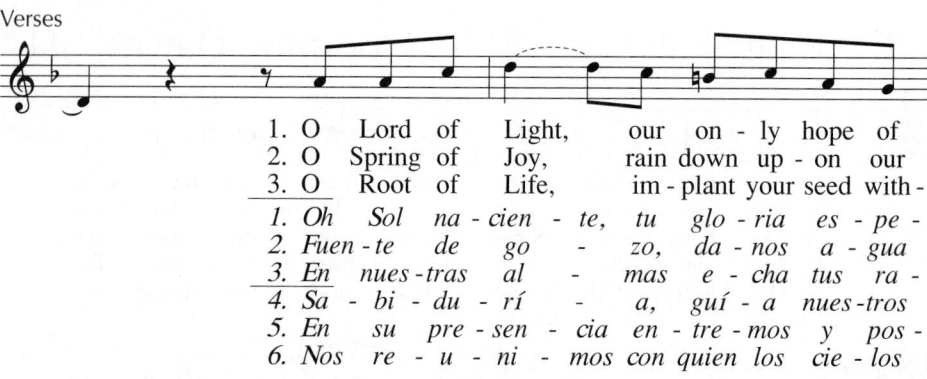

1. O Lord of Light, our on - ly hope of
2. O Spring of Joy, rain down up - on our
3. O Root of Life, im - plant your seed with -
1. *Oh Sol na - cien - te, tu glo - ria es - pe -*
2. *Fuen - te de go - zo, da - nos a - gua*
3. *En nues -tras al - mas e - cha tus ra -*
4. *Sa - bi - du - rí - a, guí - a nues -tros*
5. *En su pre - sen - cia en - tre - mos y pos -*
6. *Nos re - u - ni - mos con quien los cie - los*

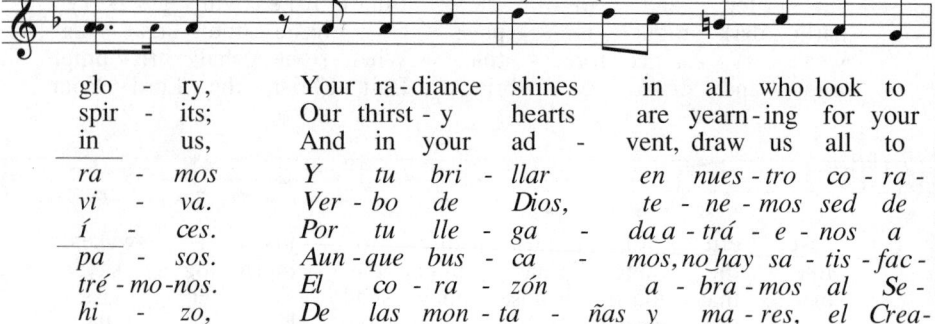

glo - ry, Your ra - diance shines in all who look to
spir - its; Our thirst - y hearts are yearn - ing for your
in us, And in your ad - vent, draw us all to
*ra - mos Y tu bri - llar en nues - tro co - ra -*
*vi - va. Ver - bo de Dios, te - ne - mos sed de*
*í - ces. Por tu lle - ga - da_a - trá - e - nos a*
*pa - sos. Aun -que bus - ca - mos, no_hay sa - tis - fac -*
*tré - mo -nos. El co - ra - zón a - bra - mos al Se -*
*hi - zo, De las mon - ta - ñas y ma - res, el Crea-*

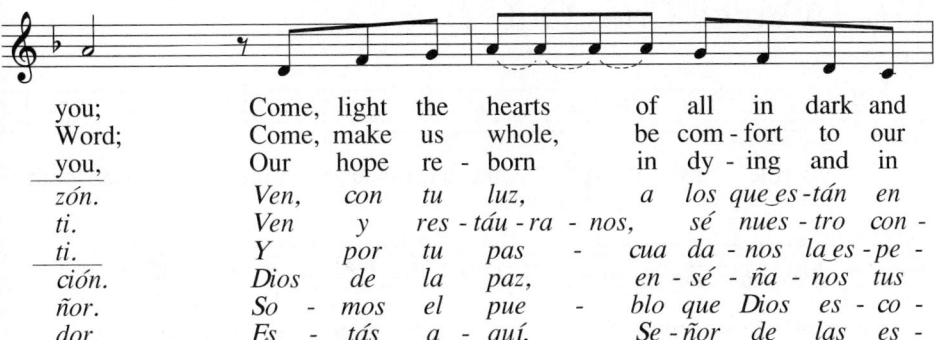

|  | Come, | light | the | hearts | of | all | in | dark | and |
|---|---|---|---|---|---|---|---|---|---|
| you; | Come, | make | us | whole, | be | com - fort | to | our |  |
| Word; | Our | hope | re - born | in | dy - ing | and | in |  |  |
| you, | Ven, | con | tu | luz, | a | los | que_es -tán | en |  |
| zón. | Ven | y | res - táu - ra - nos, | sé | nues - tro | con - |  |  |  |
| ti. | Y | por | tu | pas - | cua | da - nos | la_es - pe - |  |  |
| ti. | Dios | de | la | paz, | en - sé - ña - nos | tus |  |  |  |
| ción. | So - mos | el | pue - | blo | que | Dios | es - co - |  |  |
| ñor. | Es - tás | a - quí, | Se - ñor | de | las | es - |  |  |  |
| dor. |  |  |  |  |  |  |  |  |  |

**D.C.**

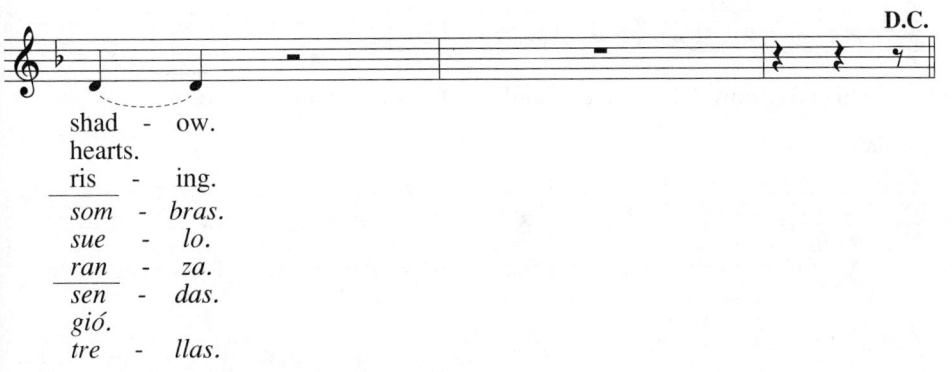

shad - ow.
hearts.
ris - ing.
*som - bras.*
*sue - lo.*
*ran - za.*
*sen - das.*
*gió.*
*tre - llas.*

4. O Key of Knowledge, guide us in our pilgrimage;
we ever seek, yet unfulfilled remain;
open to us the pathway of your peace.

5. Come, let us bow before the God who made us;
let ev'ry heart be opened to the Lord,
for we are all the people of his hand.

6. Here we shall meet the Maker of the heavens,
Creator of the mountains and the seas,
Lord of the stars, and present to us now.

Text: Psalm 95 and "O" Antiphons; Marty Haugen, b.1950; tr. by Ronald F. Krisman, b.1946
Tune: Marty Haugen, b.1950
© 1982, 2005, GIA Publications, Inc.

# 416  A Voice Cries Out

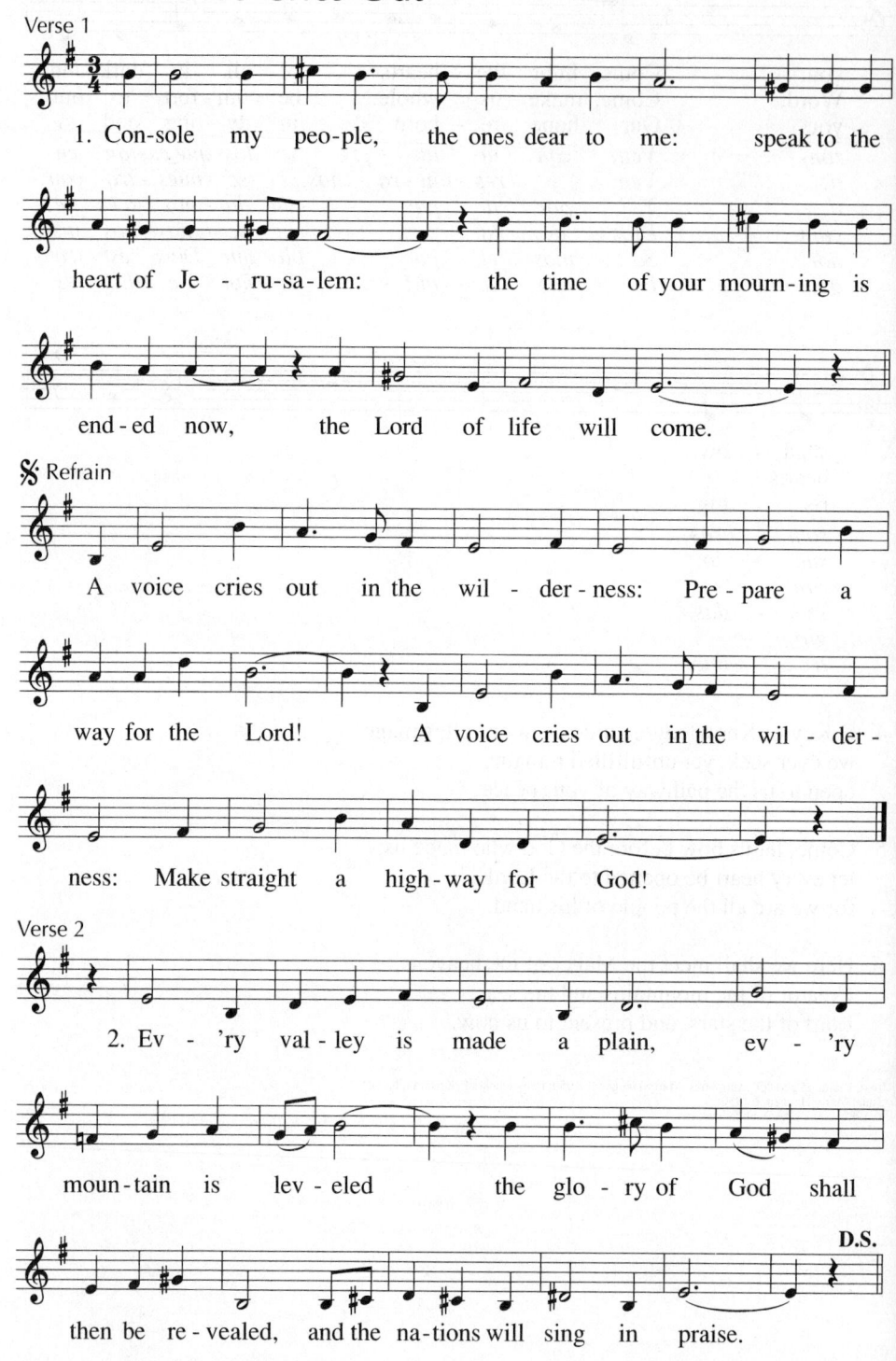

Verse 1

1. Con-sole my peo-ple, the ones dear to me: speak to the heart of Je - ru-sa-lem: the time of your mourn-ing is end - ed now, the Lord of life will come.

𝄋 Refrain

A voice cries out in the wil - der - ness: Pre - pare a way for the Lord! A voice cries out in the wil - der - ness: Make straight a high - way for God!

Verse 2

2. Ev - 'ry val - ley is made a plain, ev - 'ry moun-tain is lev - eled the glo - ry of God shall then be re - vealed, and the na-tions will sing in praise.

D.S.

Verse 3

3. A voice shouts: "Cry!" O what shall I cry? All flesh is like

grass and its flow - ers: the grass may with-er, the

**D.S.**

flow-er may fade, but the Word of the Lord is for - ev-er.

Verse 4

4. Zi - on, shout from the moun - tain top, lift up your

voice O Je - ru-sa-lem, and say to the peo-ple of

**D.S.**

God's own land, "Be-hold, be - hold your God!"

Verse 5

5. The Lord will ap - pear as a shep-herd, hold-ing his

lambs in his arms, keep-ing his flock so

**D.S.**

close to his heart lead-ing them all, old and young.

Text: Isaiah 40:1–11; Michael Joncas, b.1951
Tune: Michael Joncas, b.1951
© 1981, 1982, Jan Michael Joncas Trust. Published by OCP.

# 417 Warm the Time of Winter

Verses

1. When the wind of win-ter blows, bring-ing times of
2. When we shiv-er in des-pair, when the chill of
3. When in days of fall-en snow, change con-founds or

sol - i - tude, fill the si - lent, ic - y night;
death comes near, hold us, Spir - it, calm our fear,
love burns low, from the ash - es may there rise

Refrain

be our hearts' com - pas - sion.
while the eve - ning deep - ens. Ho - ly Light,
phoe - nix of our grow - ing.

warm our night; warm the time of win-ter. Ho-ly Light,

warm our night; warm the time of win - ter.

Text: Ruth Duck, b.1947, © 1992, GIA Publications, Inc.
Tune: Lori True, b.1961, © 2000, GIA Publications, Inc.

# 418 On Jordan's Bank

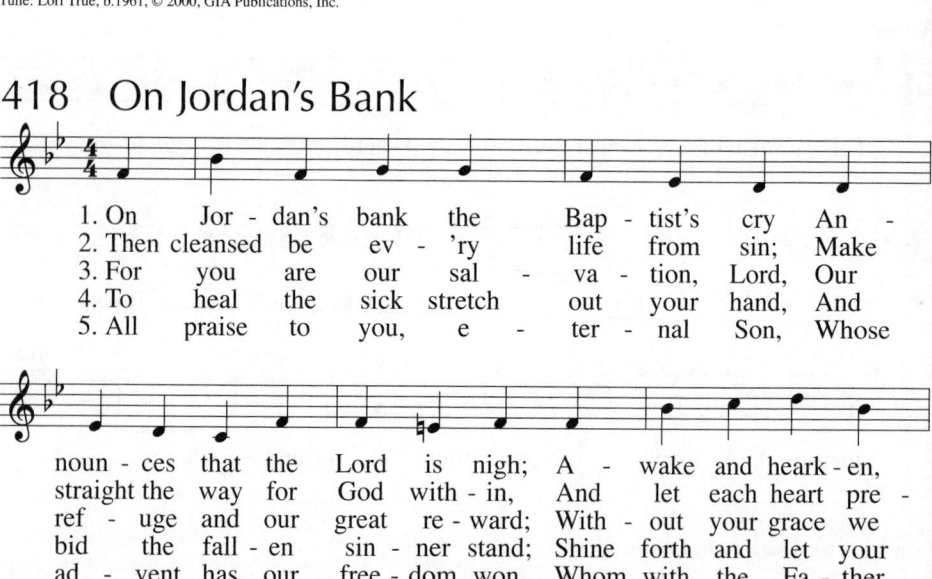

1. On Jor - dan's bank the Bap - tist's cry An -
2. Then cleansed be ev - 'ry life from sin; Make
3. For you are our sal - va - tion, Lord, Our
4. To heal the sick stretch out your hand, And
5. All praise to you, e - ter - nal Son, Whose

noun - ces that the Lord is nigh; A - wake and heark - en,
straight the way for God with - in, And let each heart pre -
ref - uge and our great re - ward; With - out your grace we
bid the fall - en sin - ner stand; Shine forth and let your
ad - vent has our free - dom won, Whom with the Fa - ther

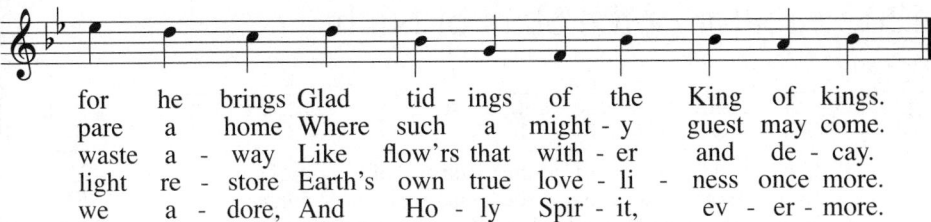

| for | he | brings Glad | tid - ings | of | the | King | of | kings. |
| pare | a | home Where | such | a | might - y | guest | may | come. |
| waste | a - way | Like | flow'rs that | with - er | and | de - cay. |
| light | re - store | Earth's | own true | love - li - ness | once | more. |
| we | a - dore, And | Ho - ly | Spir - it, | ev - er - more. |

Text: *Jordanis oras praevia*; Charles Coffin, 1676–1749; tr. by John Chandler, 1806–1876, alt.
Tune: WINCHESTER NEW, LM; adapt. from *Musikalisches Handbuch*, Hamburg, 1690

## Each Winter As the Year Grows Older  419

1. Each win - ter as the year grows old - er, We
2. When race and class cry out for trea - son, When
3. Yet I be - lieve be - yond be - liev - ing, That
4. So e - ven as the sun is turn - ing, To
5. O Child of ec - sta - sy and sor - rows, O

each grow old - er too. The chill sets in a
si - rens call for war, They o - ver - shout the
life can spring from death; That growth can flow - er
jour - ney to the north, The liv - ing flame, in
Prince of peace and pain, Bright - en to - day's world

lit - tle cold - er; The ver - i - ties we
voice of rea - son, And scream till we ig -
from our griev - ing; That we can catch our
se - cret burn - ing, Can kin - dle on the
by to - mor - row's, Re - new our lives a -

knew Seem shak - en and un - true.
nore All we held dear be - fore.
breath And turn trans - fixed by faith.
earth, And bring God's love to birth.
gain; Lord Je - sus, come and reign!

Text: William Gay, fl. 1969, © 1971, United Church Press
Tune: CAROL OF HOPE, 9 6 9 66; Annabeth Gay, b.1925, © 1971, United Church Press; acc. by Marty Haugen, b.1950, alt.,
© 1987, GIA Publications, Inc.

# 420 Creator of the Stars of Night

Verses

1. Cre - a - tor of the stars of night, Your
2. In sor - row that the an - cient curse Should
3. When this old world drew on toward night, You
4. At your great Name, O Je - sus, now All
5. Come in your ho - ly might, we pray, Re -
6. To God the Fa - ther, God the Son, And

peo - ple's ev - er - last - ing light, O
doom to death a u - ni - verse, You
came; but not in splen - dor bright, Not
knees must bend, all hearts must bow: All
deem us for e - ter - nal day; De -
God the Spir - it, Three in One, Praise,

Christ, Re - deem - er of us all, We
came, O Sav - ior, to set free Your
as a mon - arch, but the child Of
things on earth with one ac - cord, Like
fend us while we dwell be - low From
hon - or, might, and glo - ry be From

*To next verse**

pray you hear us when we call.
own in glo - rious lib - er - ty.
Mar - y, blame - less moth - er mild.
those in heav'n, shall call you Lord.
all as - saults of our dread foe.
age to age e - ter - nal - ly.

*To refrain*   Refrain

Come, O Lord, and bring your light, O ra - diant

*Hymn may be sung without refrain.*

star,     our hearts' de - light.          O  God - with - us, Em - man - u -

*Last time*

el,     with your love, the dark dis - pel.

Text: *Creator alme siderum*, Latin 9th. C.; tr. *The Hymnal 1982*, © 1985, The Church Pension Fund; refrain, Carol E. Browning, b.1956,
 © 2004, GIA Publications, Inc.
Tune: CONDITOR ALME SIDERUM, LM; Mode IV; acc. and refrain music by Carol E. Browning, b.1956, © 2004, GIA Publications, Inc.

## Savior of the Nations, Come     421

1. Sav - ior    of    the     na - tions, come;    Vir - gin's Son,   make
2. Not    by    hu - man    flesh  and  blood,    But    the   Spir - it
3. Won - drous birth!    O    won - drous child    Of    the   Vir - gin
4. From God's heart    the    Sav - ior speeds,    Back   to    God   his
5. Bright - ly    does Christ's    man - ger  shine,    Glo - rious  is    its

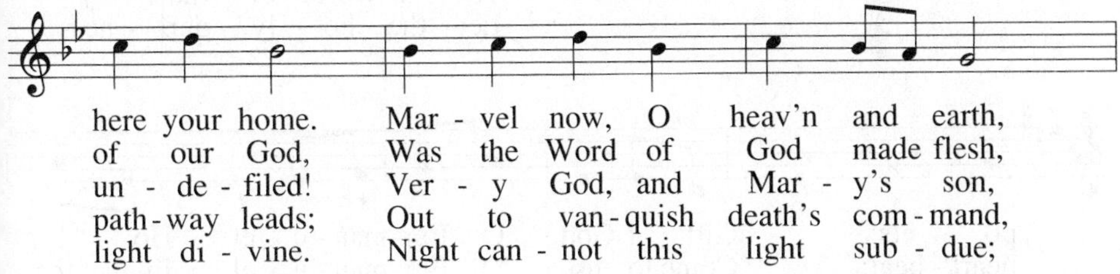

here  your  home.    Mar - vel   now,   O    heav'n   and  earth,
of   our  God,    Was   the  Word  of    God    made flesh,
un - de - filed!    Ver - y    God,  and    Mar - y's    son,
path - way  leads;    Out   to   van - quish    death's   com - mand,
light  di - vine.    Night can - not  this    light    sub - due;

That    the    Lord    chose    such    a    birth.
Wom - an's    off - spring,    pure    and    fresh.
Ea - ger    now    his    race    to    run!
Back    to    reign    at    God's    right   hand.
Let    our    faith    shine    ev - er    new.

Text: *Veni, Redemptor gentium*; ascr. to St. Ambrose, 340–397; German tr. by Martin Luther, 1483–1546; English tr. sts. 1–3, 5 by William M. Reynolds,
 1812–1876; st. 4 by Martin L. Seltz, 1909–1967, alt. © 2006, Augsburg Fortress
Tune: NUN KOMM DER HEIDEN HEILAND, 77 77; *Geystliche gesangk Buchleyn*, Wittenberg, 1524

# 422   Gift of God

**Refrain**

| Christmas: | Gift | of | God, | O | Em - man - u - el. | Gift | of | God, | O | Em - |
| Advent: | Come to | us, | | O | Em - man-u - el. | Come to | us, | | O | Em - |

*Last time*   **Christmas Verses**
Cantor:

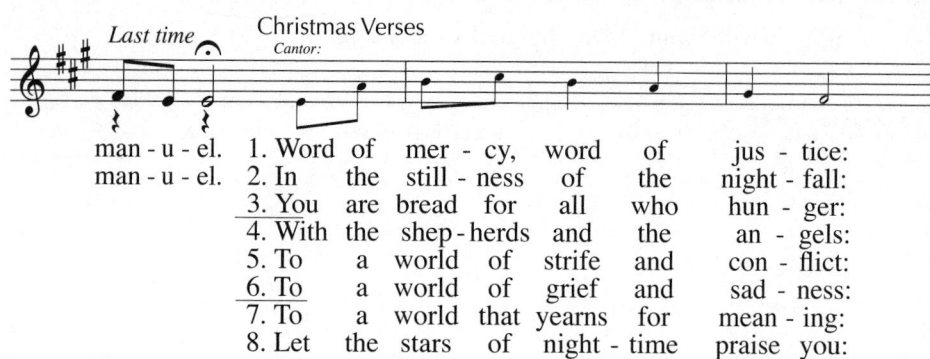

man - u - el.
man - u - el.

1. Word of mer - cy, word of jus - tice:
2. In the still - ness of the night - fall:
3. You are bread for all who hun - ger:
4. With the shep - herds and the an - gels:
5. To a world of strife and con - flict:
6. To a world of grief and sad - ness:
7. To a world that yearns for mean - ing:
8. Let the stars of night - time praise you:

All:                                                      Cantor:

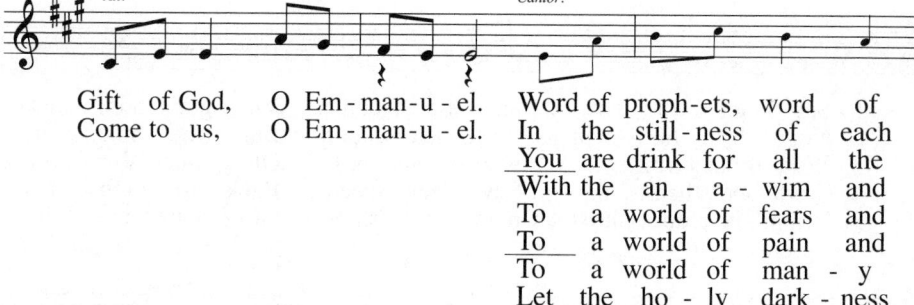

Gift of God, O Em - man-u - el.     Word of proph-ets, word of
Come to us, O Em - man-u - el.      In the still - ness of each
                                    You are drink for all the
                                    With the an - a - wim and
                                    To a world of fears and
                                    To a world of pain and
                                    To a world of man - y
                                    Let the ho - ly dark - ness

All:                                                      Cantor:

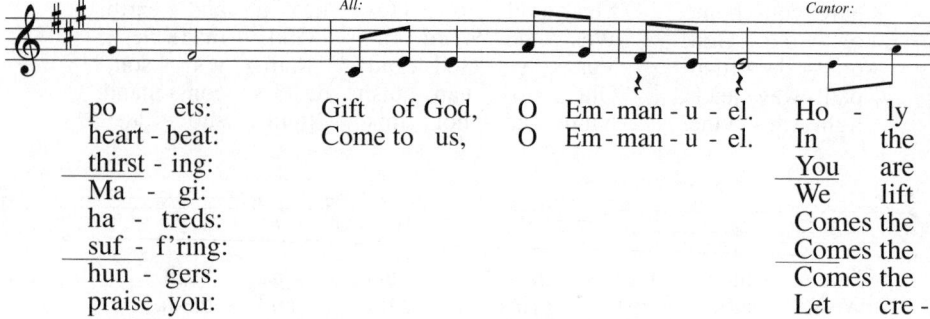

po - ets:     Gift of God, O Em - man - u - el.   Ho - ly
heart - beat:  Come to us, O Em - man - u - el.    In the
thirst - ing:                                      You are
Ma - gi:                                            We lift
ha - treds:                                         Comes the
suf - f'ring:                                       Comes the
hun - gers:                                         Comes the
praise you:                                         Let cre -

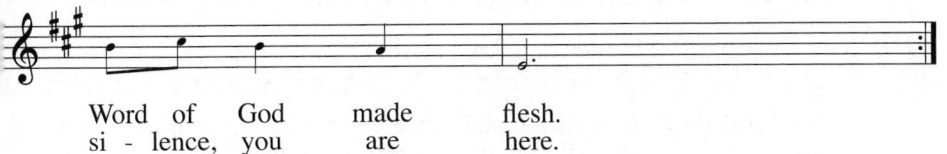

| | | | |
|---|---|---|---|
| Word of God | made | flesh. |
| si - lence, you | are | here. |
| sac - ri - fice | and | feast. |
| up our prayers | to | you. |
| gen - tle Prince | of | Peace. |
| hope of joy | re - | newed. |
| Liv - ing Bread | of | Life. |
| a - tion join | in | song. |

**Advent Verses**

1. Come, O Wisdom, breathe within us:
   Come, O mighty, tender Teacher:
   Come, and show us how to live.

2. Come, O Lord, of ancient Israel:
   You who lead us through the desert:
   Come, and set your people free.

3. Come, O Root of Jesse's lineage:
   Come, O ruler of all nations:
   Come, and be our Savior sure.

4. Come, O Holy Key of David:
   Come, and open hearts to knowledge:
   Come, and break the chains of death.

5. Come, O Radiant Sun of Justice:
   Come, and shine on those in darkness:
   All who dwell in shades of death.

6. Come, O Light of all the nations:
   Come, bright Morning Star of new hope:
   Come, and shine among us here.

7. Come, O Living Flame of Freedom:
   Living hope of our redemption:
   Come, and lead us to new life.

Text: Advent verses based on "O" Antiphons; Marty Haugen, b.1950
Tune: Marty Haugen, b.1950
© 2000, GIA Publications, Inc.

# 423 Awake! Awake, and Greet the New Morn

1. A - wake! A - wake, and greet the new morn, For
2. To us, to all in sor - row and fear, Em -
3. In dark - est night his com - ing shall be, When
4. Re - joice, re - joice, take heart in the night, Though

an - gels her - ald its dawn - ing. Sing out your joy, for
man - u - el comes a - sing - ing; His hum - ble song is
all the world is de - spair - ing, As morn - ing light so
dark the win - ter and cheer - less, The ris - ing sun shall

soon* he is born, Be - hold the Child of our long - ing!
qui - et and near, Yet fills the earth with its ring - ing.
qui - et and free, So warm and gen - tle and car - ing.
crown you with light; Be strong and lov - ing and fear - less.

Come as a ba - by weak and poor, To bring all hearts to -
Mu - sic to heal the bro - ken soul And hymns of lov - ing -
Then shall the mute break forth in song, The lame shall leap in
Love be our song and love our prayer And love our end - less

geth - er, He o - pens wide the heav'n - ly door And
kind - ness, The thun - der of his an - thems roll To
won - der, The weak be raised a - bove the strong, And
sto - ry. May God fill ev - 'ry day we share And

lives now in - side us for ev - er.
shat - ter all ha - tred and blind - ness.
weap - ons be bro - ken a - sun - der.
bring us at last in - to glo - ry.

*During the Christmas season: "now"

Text: Marty Haugen, b.1950
Tune: REJOICE, REJOICE, 9 8 9 8 8 7 8 9; Marty Haugen, b.1950
© 1983, GIA Publications, Inc.

# Hark! The Herald Angels Sing  424

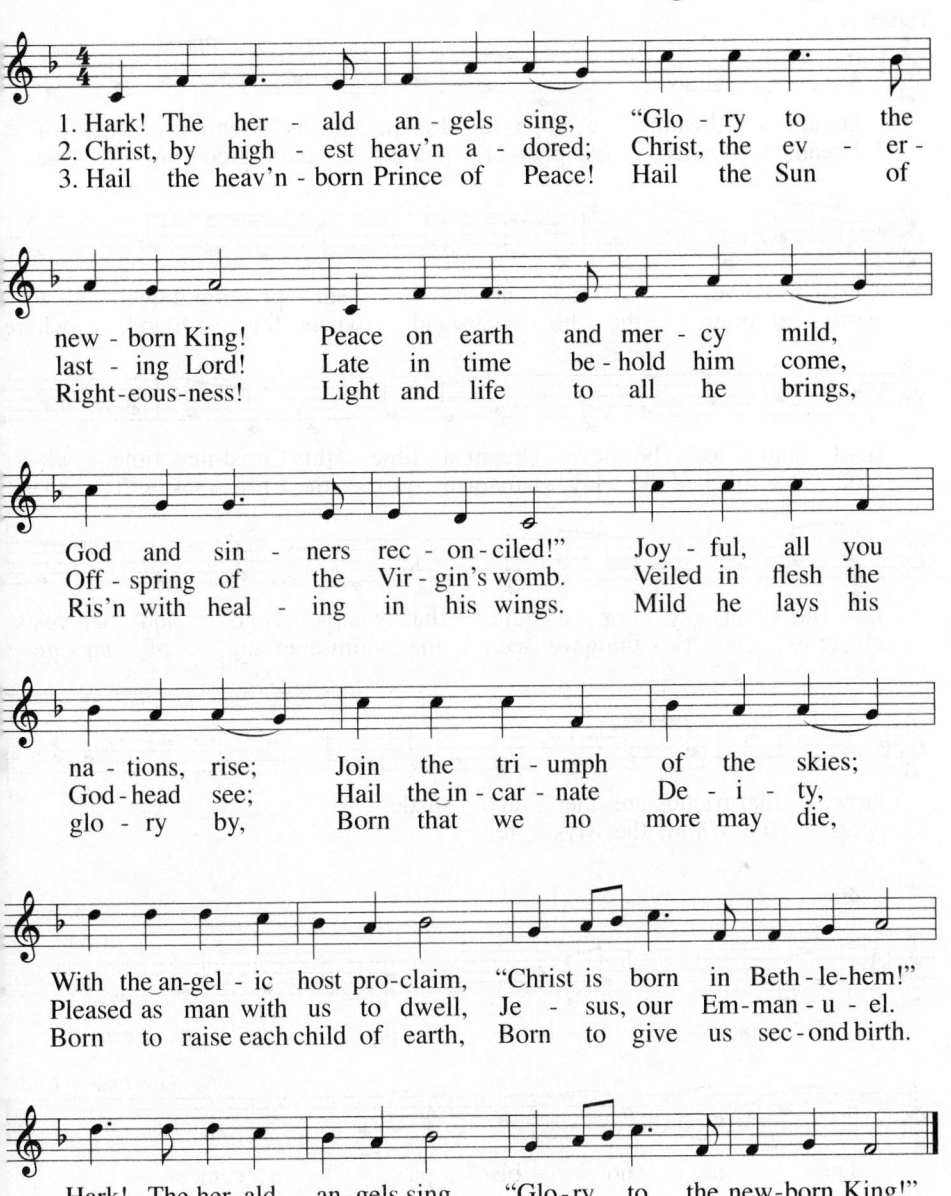

1. Hark! The her - ald an - gels sing, "Glo - ry to the
2. Christ, by high - est heav'n a - dored; Christ, the ev - er -
3. Hail the heav'n - born Prince of Peace! Hail the Sun of

new - born King! Peace on earth and mer - cy mild,
last - ing Lord! Late in time be - hold him come,
Right - eous - ness! Light and life to all he brings,

God and sin - ners rec - on - ciled!" Joy - ful, all you
Off - spring of the Vir - gin's womb. Veiled in flesh the
Ris'n with heal - ing in his wings. Mild he lays his

na - tions, rise; Join the tri - umph of the skies;
God - head see; Hail the in - car - nate De - i - ty,
glo - ry by, Born that we no more may die,

With the an - gel - ic host pro - claim, "Christ is born in Beth - le - hem!"
Pleased as man with us to dwell, Je - sus, our Em - man - u - el.
Born to raise each child of earth, Born to give us sec - ond birth.

Hark! The her - ald an - gels sing, "Glo - ry to the new - born King!"

Text: Charles Wesley, 1707–1788, alt.
Tune: MENDELSSOHN, 77 77 D with refrain; Felix Mendelssohn, 1809–1847

# 425 Dream a Dream

Verses 1, 2

1. Dream a dream, a hope-ful dream, as chil-dren do on
2. Dream a peace, our plan-et's peace, the green-ing of the

Christ-mas Eve, i - mag - in - ings, sur - pris-ing things to
earth at play, the ho - ly ground where life is found, where

hold and to be - lieve. Dream a time, this Christ-mas time, when
God has touched the clay. Dream a gift, the Christ-mas gift that

no one's hun - gry or a - fraid; that weap - ons go and har - vests
chang-es ev - 'ry - thing we see: the shim - mer - ing of an - gel

grow, that friends are met and made.
wing, the Child, the Mys - ter -

Canon

(y.) Do - na no - bis pa - cem, pa - cem.

*Last time to Coda*

Do - na no - bis pa - cem.

Do - na no - bis pa - cem.

*Last time to Coda*

Do - na no - bis pa - cem.

3.

Do - na no - bis pa - cem.

*Last time to Coda*

Do - na no - bis pa - cem.

Coda

3. Dream a gift, the Christ - mas gift that

chang-es ev - 'ry - thing we see: the shim-mer - ing of

an - gel wing, the Child, the Mys - ter - y.

Text: Shirley Erena Murray, b.1931, © 1998, Hope Publishing Company; *Dona Nobis Pacem*, traditional
Tune: Lori True, b.1961, © 2005, GIA Publications, Inc.; *Dona Nobis Pacem*, traditional

# Glória, Glória   426

Canon–*4 voices*

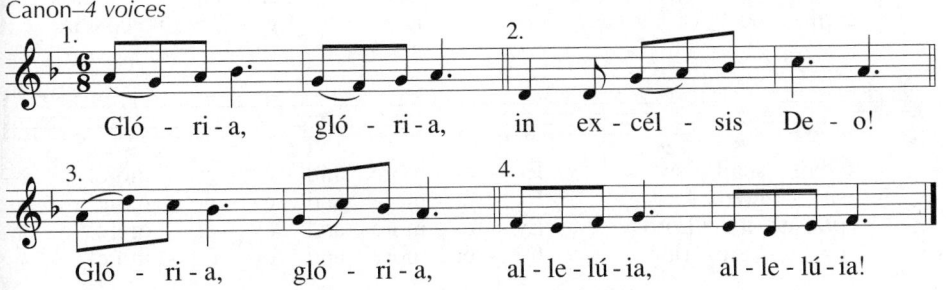

1.
2.

Gló - ri - a, gló - ri - a, in ex - cél - sis De - o!

3.
4.

Gló - ri - a, gló - ri - a, al - le - lú - ia, al - le - lú - ia!

Tune: Jacques Berthier, 1923–1994, © 1979, 1988, Les Presses de Taizé, GIA Publications, Inc., agent

# 427  Of the Father's Love Begotten

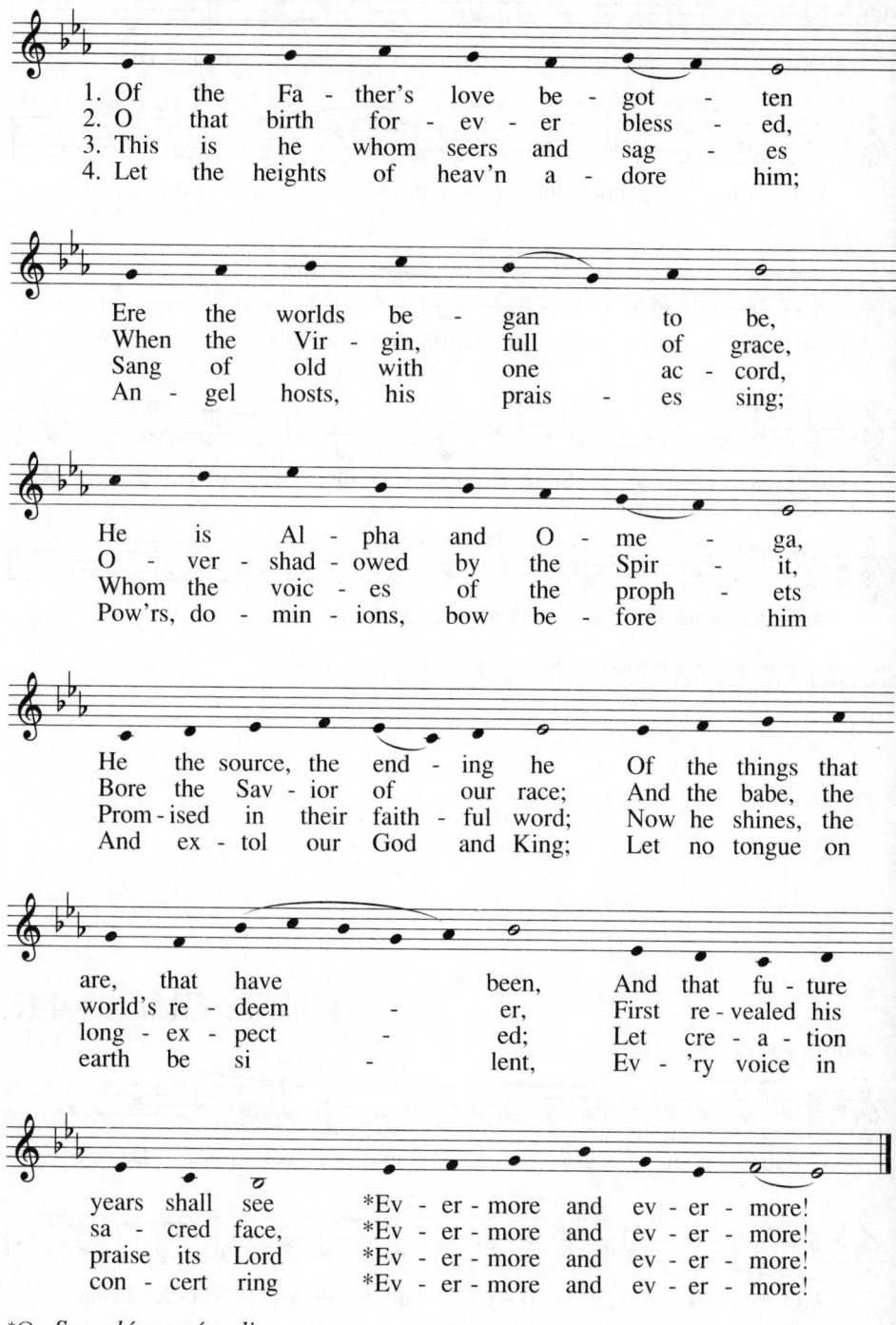

1. Of the Fa - ther's love be - got - ten
2. O that birth for - ev - er bless - ed,
3. This is he whom seers and sag - es
4. Let the heights of heav'n a - dore him;

Ere the worlds be - gan to be,
When the Vir - gin, full of grace,
Sang of old with one ac - cord,
An - gel hosts, his prais - es sing;

He is Al - pha and O - me - ga,
O - ver - shad - owed by the Spir - it,
Whom the voic - es of the proph - ets
Pow'rs, do - min - ions, bow be - fore him

He the source, the end - ing he Of the things that
Bore the Sav - ior of our race; And the babe, the
Prom - ised in their faith - ful word; Now he shines, the
And ex - tol our God and King; Let no tongue on

are, that have been, And that fu - ture
world's re - deem - er, First re - vealed his
long - ex - pect - ed; Let cre - a - tion
earth be si - lent, Ev - 'ry voice in

years shall see *Ev - er - more and ev - er - more!
sa - cred face, *Ev - er - more and ev - er - more!
praise its Lord *Ev - er - more and ev - er - more!
con - cert ring *Ev - er - more and ev - er - more!

*Or: Saeculórum sáeculis.

5. Christ, to you, with God the Father,
And the Spirit, One in Three,
Hymn and chant and high thanksgiving
And unwearied praises be:
Honor, glory, and dominion,
And eternal victory
Evermore and evermore! *Or: Saeculórum sáeculis.*

Text: *Corde natus ex Parentis;* Aurelius Prudentius, 348–413; tr. by John M. Neale, 1818–1866 and Henry W. Baker, 1821–1877, alt.
Tune: DIVINUM MYSTERIUM, 8 7 8 7 8 7 7; 12th C.; Mode V; acc. by Richard Proulx, 1937–2010, © 1985, GIA Publications, Inc.

# Go Tell It on the Mountain  428

**Refrain**

Go tell it on the moun-tain, O-ver the hills and ev - 'ry-where;

Go tell it on the moun - tain That Je - sus Christ is born!

**Verses**

1. While shep - herds kept their watch - ing O'er
2. The shep - herds feared and trem - bled When,
3. Down in a low - ly man - ger The

si - lent flocks by night, Be - hold through - out the
lo, a - bove the earth Rang out the an - gel
hum - ble Christ was born, And God sent us sal -

**D.C.**

heav - ens There shone a ho - ly light.
cho - rus That hailed our Sav - ior's birth.
va - tion That bless - ed Christ - mas morn.

Text: African American spiritual; verses by John W. Work, Jr., 1872–1925
Tune: GO TELL IT ON THE MOUNTAIN, 7 6 7 6 with refrain; African American spiritual; harm. by Robert J. Batastini, b.1942, © 1995, GIA
Publications, Inc.

# 429 He Came Down

He came down that we may have *love; He came down that we may have love; He came down that we may have love, Hal-le-lu-jah for ev-er-more.

Cantor: Why did he come?

*Substitute* peace, joy, hope, life, *etc.*

Text: Cameroon traditional
Tune: Cameroon traditional; transcribed and arr. by John L. Bell, b.1949, © 1990, Iona Community, GIA Publications, Inc., agent

# Angels We Have Heard on High    430

1. An - gels  we  have  heard  on high  Sweet - ly  sing - ing
2. Shep - herds, why  this  ju - bi - lee?  Why  your  joy - ous
3. Come  to  Beth - le - hem  and see  Him  whose birth  the
4. See  him  in  a  man - ger laid  Whom  the  choirs  of

o'er  the plains,  And  the  moun - tains  in  re - ply
strains  pro - long?  Say  what may  the  tid - ings  be
an - gels sing;  Come, a - dore  on  bend - ed  knee
an - gels praise;  Mar - y,  Jo - seph,  lend  your aid,

Ech - o  back  their  joy - ous strains.
Which  in - spire  your  heav'n - ly  song.
Christ  the  Lord,  the  new - born King.
While  our  hearts  in  love  we  raise.

Gló - - - ri - a

in ex - cél - sis De - o.    Gló - -

- - ri - a  in ex - cél - sis  De - o.

Text: *Les anges dans nos campagnes;* French, c. 18th C.; tr. from *Crown of Jesus Music,* London, 1862
Tune: GLORIA, 7 7 7 7 with refrain; French traditional

# 431 Child of Mercy

**Refrain**

Child of mer-cy, child of peace, Je-sus, Bread of life,

food to fill our long-ing. Child of jus-tice, child of light,

Je-sus, sav-ing cup, Em-man-u-el, God with us.

**Verses**

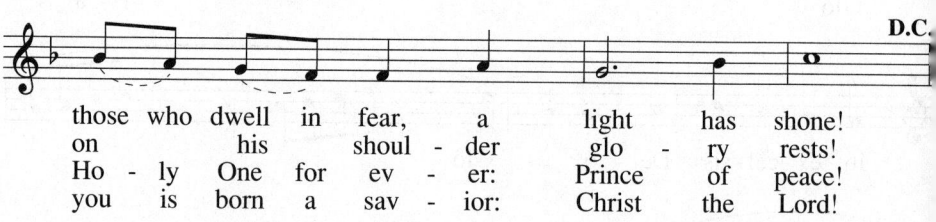

1. All who walk in dark - ness have seen a great light, to
2. ⁷ A child is born to us, a son is giv - en us, up-
3. ⁷ We name him: "Won-der, coun-s'lor, he - ro, might-y God," The
4. We pro-claim good news to you, great tid - ings of joy: To

**D.C.**

those who dwell in fear, a light has shone!
on his shoul - der glo - ry rests!
Ho - ly One for ev - er: Prince of peace!
you is born a sav - ior: Christ the Lord!

Text: Isaiah 9:1, 5; David Haas, b.1957
Tune: David Haas, b.1957
© 1991, GIA Publications, Inc.

# Nativity Carol 432

**Verses**

1. Si - lent,     in the chill of mid - night,
2. "Fear not,"     said an - gel - ic voic - es;
3. Je - sus,     Lord of all cre - a - tion,

star - light     shines up - on a low - ly man - ger.
"tid - ings     of a won - drous love we bring you.
sleep now     close be - side your moth - er, Mar - y.

Won - der,     won - der of the a - ges;
Go now,     find him in a man - ger;
Bring us     light a - mid the dark - ness,

heav - en breaks forth on the earth.
vis - it God's home on the earth."
prom - ise of life with - out end.

**Refrain**

For a child is born, the world re - joic - es! Shep-herds and

an-gels pro - claim his birth. This is Je - sus the Lord, our

Sav - ior and broth-er, bear - ing God's peace to the earth.

Text: Francis Patrick O'Brien, b.1958
Tune: Francis Patrick O'Brien, b.1958
© 1992, GIA Publications, Inc.

# 433 It Came upon the Midnight Clear

1. It came up - on the mid - night clear, That
2. Still through the clo - ven skies they come With
3. Yet with the woes of sin and strife The
4. For lo! The days are has - t'ning on, By

glo - rious song of old, From an - gels bend - ing
peace - ful wings un - furled, And still their heav'n-ly
world has suf - fered long; Be - neath the heav'n-ly
proph - ets seen of old, When with the ev - er -

near the earth To touch their harps of gold: "Peace
mu - sic floats O'er all the wea - ry world. A -
hymn have rolled Two thou - sand years of wrong; And
cir - cling years Shall come the time fore - told, When

on the earth, good will to all, From
bove its sad and low - ly plains They
war - ring hu - man - kind hears not The
peace shall o - ver all the earth Its

heav'n's all - gra - cious King." The world in sol - emn
bend on hov - 'ring wing, And ev - er o'er its
tid - ings which they bring; O hush the noise and
an - cient splen - dors fling, And all the world give

still - ness lay, To hear the an - gels sing.
Ba - bel sounds The bless - ed an - gels sing.
cease your strife And hear the an - gels sing.
back the song Which now the an - gels sing.

Text: Edmund H. Sears, 1810–1876, alt.
Tune: CAROL, CMD; Richard S. Willis, 1819–1900

# Sing Alleluia 434

Verses

1. Dark is the night and deep are the shad - ows;
2. Who would be - lieve that here in a man - ger
3. Great is the joy of Mar - y, his moth - er.
4. Hope for the poor, re - lease for the cap - tive,

Qui - et the ba - by bathed in lan - tern light.
God comes a - mong us as a ti - ny child?
Great is the joy of Jo - seph by her side.
Love for the out - cast, light for wea - ry eyes;

Hushed are the sounds of cat - tle and shep - herds;
See in his eyes the glo - ry of heav - en;
Great is the joy of all those in dark - ness.
Word that brings life, em - brac - ing hu - man - i - ty,

Sweet is the mu - sic the an - gels bring this night.
Hear in his laugh-ter the joy of God on high.
Here lies the Sav - ior so soon to die and rise.
Je - sus, com-pan - ion, be born in - to our lives.

Refrain

Sing al - le - lu - ia, sing al - le - lu - ia.

Wel - come the Sav - ior, the prom-ise of new life.

Sing al - le - lu - ia, sing al - le - lu - ia.

All of cre - a - tion, sing this night.

Text: Francis Patrick O'Brien, b.1958
Tune: Francis Patrick O'Brien, b.1958
© 1996, GIA Publications, Inc.

## 435 God Rest You Merry, Gentlemen

1. God rest you mer - ry, gen - tle - men, Let noth - ing you dis -
2. In Beth - le - hem in Ju - dah This bless - ed babe was
3. From God our heav'n - ly Fa - ther A bless - ed an - gel
4. The shep - herds at those tid - ings Re - joic - ed much in
5. Now to the Lord sing prais - es, All you with - in this

may; Re - mem - ber Christ our Sav - ior Was
born, And laid with - in a man - ger Up -
came, And un - to cer - tain shep - herds Brought
mind, And left their flocks a - feed - ing In
place, And with true love and char - i - ty Each

born on Christ - mas day To save us all from
on this bless - ed morn, For which his moth - er
tid - ings of the same, How that in Beth - le -
tem - pest, storm, and wind, And went to Beth - le -
oth - er now em - brace; This ho - ly tide of

Sa - tan's pow'r When we were gone a - stray.
Mar - y Did noth - ing take in scorn.
hem was born The Son of God by name.
hem straight - way, This bless - ed babe to find.
Christ - mas All oth - ers shall re - place.

O tid - ings of com - fort and joy, com - fort and

joy; O tid - ings of com - fort and joy!

Text: English carol, 18th C.
Tune: GOD REST YOU MERRY, 8 6 8 6 8 6 with refrain; English 18th C.; harm. by John Stainer, 1840–1901

# Wood of the Cradle  436

Verses

1. Wood of the cra - dle, wood of the cross,
2. Shep - herds lie sleep - ing, deep in their dreams;
3. Star in the heav - ens bear - ing new light,
4. Come, all who hun - ger, come, all who thirst;

bear - ing a life - time of joy and of loss,
an - gels a - wak - en them. "What could this mean?
guid - ing the sag - es and a - ges this night:
come, all who seek him, God's joy on the earth.

who is your loved one? Who could he be,
Whom do you her - ald? Whom must we find? A
Where will you lead us? Where can he be, the
Find him a shel - ter, bright, safe, and warm;

born in a man - ger to die on a tree?
child in a man - ger? Our God born in time?"
child born of mys - t'ry who died on a tree?
see in all peo - ple his love be - ing born.

Refrain

This, this is Je - sus the Lord, here in the bod - y and

blood out-poured. Come, come, walk in his ways. Kneel at the

man - ger and rise from the grave.

Text: Francis Patrick O'Brien, b.1958
Tune: Francis Patrick O'Brien, b.1958
© 2002, GIA Publications, Inc.

# 437 Joy to the World

1. Joy to the world, the Lord is come! Let
2. Joy to the earth, the Sav - ior reigns! Let
3. No more let sin and sor - row grow, Nor
4. He rules the world with truth and grace, And

[⌢]

earth re - ceive her king; Let ev - 'ry
us our songs em - ploy; While fields and
thorns in - fest the ground; He comes to
makes the na - tions prove The glo - ries

heart pre - pare him room And heav'n and na - ture
floods, rocks, hills and plains Re - peat the sound - ing
make his bless - ings flow Far as the curse is
of his right - eous - ness, And won - ders of his

sing, And heav'n and na - ture sing, And
joy, Re - peat the sound - ing joy, Re -
found, Far as the curse is found, Far
love, And won - ders of his love, And

heav'n, and heav'n and na - ture sing.
peat, re - peat the sound - ing joy.
as, far as the curse is found.
won - ders, won - ders of his love.

Text: Psalm 98; Isaac Watts, 1674–1748
Tune: ANTIOCH, CM; arr. from George F. Handel, 1685–1759, in T. Hawkes' *Collection of Tunes*, 1833

# Angels, from the Realms of Glory 438

1. An - gels, from the realms of glo - ry,
2. Shep - herds, in the field a - bid - ing,
3. Sag - es, leave your con - tem - pla - tions,
4. Though an in - fant now we view him,

Wing your flight o'er all the earth; You who sang cre -
Watch - ing o'er your flocks by night, God on earth is
Bright - er vi - sions beam a - far; Seek the great De -
He shall fill his heav'n - ly throne, Gath - er all the

a - tion's sto - ry, Now pro - claim Mes - si - ah's birth:
now re - sid - ing, Yon - der shines the in - fant light.
sire of na - tions; You have seen his morn - ing star.
na - tions to him; Ev - 'ry knee shall then bow down.

Come and wor - ship, come and wor - ship,

Wor - ship Christ, the new - born King.

Text: Sts. 1–3, James Montgomery, 1771–1854; st. 4, *Christmas Box,* 1825
Tune: REGENT SQUARE, 8 7 8 7 8 7; Henry Smart, 1813–1879

# 439 O Come, All Ye Faithful / Venid, Fieles Todos / Adéste Fidéles

1. O come, all ye faith-ful, joy-ful and tri - um - phant, O
2. God of God, Light of Light,
1. *Ve - nid, fie - les to - dos, a Be - lén mar - che - mos De*
2. *El que_es Hi - jo_e - ter - no del e - ter - no Pa - dre, Y*
1. *Ad - é - ste fi - dé - les, laé - ti, tri - um - phán - tes, Ve -*
2. *De - um de De - o, Lu - men de Lú - mi-ne*

come ye, O come ye to Beth - le - hem;
Lo! He comes forth from the Vir - gin's womb.
*go - zo triun - fan - tes, y lle - nos de_a -mor; Y_al*
*Dios ver - da - de - ro que_al mun - do cre - ó, Al*
ní - te, ve - ní - te in Béth - le - hem.
Ge - stant pu - él - lae ví - sce - ra.

Come and be - hold him, born the King of an - gels;
Our ver - y God, be - got - ten not cre - a - ted,
*Rey de los cie - los con - tem - plar po - dre - mos;*
*se - no vir - gí - neo vi - no de_u - na ma - dre;*
Na - tum vi - dé - te, Re - gem an - ge - ló - rum.
De - um ve - rum, Gé - ni - tum, non fa - ctum.

O come, let us a - dore him, O come, let us a -
*Ve - nid, a - do - re - mos, ve - nid, a - do -*
Ve - ní - te a - do - ré - mus, ve - ní - te a - do -

dore him, O come, let us a - dore him, Christ, the Lord!
*re - mos, ve - nid, a - do - re - mos a Cris - to_el Se - ñor.*
ré - mus, ve - ní - te a - do - ré - mus Dó - mi - num.

3. Sing, choirs of angels,
   sing in exultation,
   Sing, all ye citizens of heav'n above!
   Glory to God, all
   glory in the highest;

4. Yea, Lord, we greet thee,
   born this happy morning,
   Jesus, to thee be all glory giv'n;
   Word of the Father,
   now in flesh appearing;

3. *Cantad jubilosas,*
   *célicas criaturas:*
   *Resuenen los cielos con vuestra canción;*
   *¡Al Dios bondadoso,*
   *gloria_en las alturas;*

4. *Jesús, celebramos*
   *tu bendito nombre*
   *Con himnos solemnes de grato loor;*
   *Por siglos eternos*
   *todo ser te_adore;*

3. Cantet nunc io,
   chorus angelórum,
   Cantet nunc aula caeléstium.
   Glória, glória in excélsis Deo.

4. Ergo qui natus
   Die hodiérna,
   Jesu tibi sit glória.
   Patris aetérnae verbum caro factum.

Text: *Adeste fideles;* John F. Wade, c.1711–1786; English tr. by Frederick Oakeley, 1802–1880, alt.; Spanish tr. by Juan Bautista Cabrera, 1837–1916
Tune: ADESTE FIDELES, Irregular with refrain; John F. Wade, c.1711–1786

## Good Christian Friends, Rejoice 440

Text: *In dulci jubilo;* Latin and German, 14th C.; tr. by John M. Neal, 1818–1866
Tune: IN DULCI JUBILO, 66 77 78 55; Klug's *Geistliche Lieder,* Wittenberg, 1535; harm. by Robert L. Pearsall, 1795–1856

# 441 Silent Night / Noche de Paz

1. Si - lent night, ho - ly night! All is calm,
2. Si - lent night, ho - ly night! Shep - herds quake
3. Si - lent night, ho - ly night! Son of God,

1. ¡No-che de paz, no - che de_a - mor! To - do duer - me_en
2. ¡No-che de paz, no - che de_a - mor! O - ye_hu -mil - de_el
3. ¡No-che de paz, no - che de_a - mor! Mi - ra qué gran

all is bright Round yon vir - gin
at the sight; Glo - ries stream from
love's pure light Ra - diant beams from

de - rre - dor, En - tre los as - tros que_es -
fiel pas - tor, Co - ros ce - les - tes que_a -
res - plan - dor Lu - ce_en el ros - tro del

moth - er and child. Ho - ly In - fant so
heav - en a - far; Heav'n - ly hosts sing
thy ho - ly face, With the dawn of re -

par - cen su luz, Be - lla,_a -nun - cian - do_al ni -
nun - cian sa - lud, Gra - cias y glo - rias en
ni - ño Je - sús, En el pe - se - bre, del

ten - der and mild, Sleep in heav - en - ly
al - le - lu - ia! Christ, the Sav - ior, is
deem - ing grace, Je - sus, Lord, at thy

ñi - to Je - sús, Bri - lla la_es - tre - lla de
gran ple - ni - tud, Por nues - tro buen Re - den -
mun - do la luz, As - tro de_e - ter - no ful -

peace, Sleep in heav - en - ly peace.
born! Christ, the Sav - ior, is born!
birth, Je - sus, Lord, at thy birth.

paz, Bri - lla la_es - tre - lla de paz.
tor, Por nues - tro buen Re - den - tor.
gor, As - tro de_e - ter - no ful - gor.

Text: *Stille Nacht, heilige Nacht;* Joseph Mohr, 1792–1848; English tr. by John F. Young, 1820–1885; Spanish tr. by Federico Fliedner, 1845–1901
Tune: STILLE NACHT, 66 89 66; Franz X. Gruber, 1787–1863

# Night of Silence  442

1. Cold are the peo - ple, win - ter of life, We
2. Voice in the dis - tance, call in the night, On
3. Spir - it a - mong us, shine like the star, Your

trem - ble in shad - ows this cold end - less night.
wind you en - fold us, you speak of the light.
light that guides shep - herds and kings from a - far.

Fro - zen in the snow lie ros - es sleep - ing,
Gen - tle on the ear you whis-per, soft - ly,
Shim-mer in the sky so emp - ty, lone - ly,

Flow - ers that will ech - o the sun - rise.
Ru - mors of a dawn so em - brac - ing.
Ris - ing in the warmth of the Son's love.

Fire of hope is our on - ly warmth;
Breath-less love a - waits dark - ened souls.
Star un - know - ing of night and day,

3

Wea - ry, its flame will be dy - ing soon.
Soon will we know of the morn - ing.
Spir - it, we wait for the lov - ing Son.

Text: Daniel Kantor, b.1960
Tune: Daniel Kantor, b.1960
© 1984, GIA Publications, Inc.

# 443  Carol at the Manger

1. Ho - ly Child with - in the man - ger, Long a -
2. Once a - gain we tell the sto - ry— How your
3. Ho - ly Child with - in the man - ger, Lead us

go yet ev - er near; Come as friend to ev - 'ry
love for us was shown, When the Im - age of your
ev - er in your way, So we see in ev - 'ry

stran - ger, Come as hope for ev - 'ry fear. As you
glo - ry Wore an im - age like our own. Come, en -
stran - ger How you come to us to - day. In our

lived to heal the bro - ken, Greet the
light - en with your wis - dom, Come, and
lives and in our liv - ing Give us

out - cast, free the bound, As you taught us love un -
fill us with your grace, May the fire of your com -
strength to live as you, That our hearts might be for -

spo - ken, Teach us now where you are found.
pas - sion Kin - dle ev - 'ry land and race.
giv - ing And our spir - its strong and true.

Text: Marty Haugen, b.1950
Tune: JOYOUS LIGHT, 8 7 8 7 D; Marty Haugen, b.1950
© 1987, GIA Publications, Inc.

# The People Who Walked in Darkness  444

**Verses**

1. The peo-ple who walked in dark-ness A - wak - en to
2. For God has en-larged the na - tion, And pros-pered the
3. The yoke of de - spair and bond-age, The chains and the
4. For us now a child is giv-en, For all the de -
5. How vast is our God's do - min-ion! How far truth and

see a great light. The peo-ple who dwelt in the land of the
fruit of its land. God's peo-ple are blest with the har-vest of
slave-mas-ter's rod Are shat-tered and scat-tered like dust in a
spised and for - lorn. The rule of com-pas-sion shall rest on his
mer - cy ex - tend. The zeal of the Lord will ac - com-plish its

**Refrain**

shad - ow Rise to a Star shin - ing bright.
vic - t'ry, Gift from a boun - ti - ful hand.
wind-storm Loosed by the jus - tice of God. His name is
shoul - der. God's own Mes - si - ah is born!
pur - pose: Jus - tice shall reign with-out end.

Won - der-ful, Coun-sel-or, Al-might-y God, Fa - ther for - ev - er,

Prince of Peace. Won - der-ful, Coun-sel-or, Al-might-y God,

**To verses** / **Last time** / **D.C.**

Fa - ther for-ev-er, Prince of Peace. Peace.

Text: Isaiah 9:1–6; Mary Louise Bringle, b.1953
Tune: ISAIAH 9, 8 8 12 7 with refrain; Sally Ann Morris, b.1952
© 2009, GIA Publications, Inc.

# 445 Infant Holy, Infant Lowly

1. In - fant ho - ly, In - fant low - ly, For his bed a
2. Flocks were sleep - ing; Shep-herds, keep - ing Vig - il till the

cat - tle stall; Ox - en low - ing, Lit - tle know - ing
morn-ing new, Saw the glo - ry, Heard the sto - ry,

Christ the babe is Lord of all. Swift are wing - ing
Tid - ings of a gos - pel true. Thus re - joic - ing,

An - gels sing - ing, No - els ring - ing, Tid - ings bring - ing:
Free from sor - row, Prais-es voic - ing, Greet the mor - row:

Christ the babe is Lord of all!
Christ the babe was born for you!

Text: Polish carol; para. by Edith M. G. Reed, 1885–1933
Tune: W ŻŁOBIE LEŻY, 44 7 44 7 4444 7; Polish carol; harm. by A. E. Rusbridge, 1917–1969, © Bristol Churches Housing Assoc. Ltd.

# O Little Town of Bethlehem 446

1. O lit - tle town of Beth - le - hem, How
2. For Christ is born of Mar - y And,
3. How si - lent - ly, how si - lent - ly The
4. O ho - ly Child of Beth - le - hem, De -

still we see thee lie! A - bove thy deep and
gath - ered all a - bove While mor - tals sleep, the
won - drous gift is giv'n! So God im - parts to
scend to us, we pray; Cast out our sin and

dream - less sleep The si - lent stars go by;
an - gels keep Their watch of won - d'ring love.
hu - man hearts The bless - ings of his heav'n.
en - ter in, Be born in us to - day.

Yet in the dark streets shin - eth The
O morn - ing stars, to - geth - er Pro -
No ear may hear his com - ing, But
We hear the Christ - mas an - gels The

ev - er - last - ing Light. The hopes and fears of
claim the ho - ly birth, And prais - es sing to
in this world of sin, Where meek souls will re -
great glad tid - ings tell; O come to us, a -

all the years Are met in thee to - night.
God the King, And peace to all on earth!
ceive him, still The dear Christ en - ters in.
bide with us, Our Lord Em - man - u - el!

Text: Phillips Brooks, 1835–1893
Tune: ST. LOUIS, 8 6 8 6 7 6 8 6; Lewis H. Redner, 1831–1908

## 447 Jesus Comes

1. In a far - off place, Je - sus comes to earth.
2. For the poor in heart, Je - sus comes to earth.
3. In our deep - est night, Je - sus comes to earth:

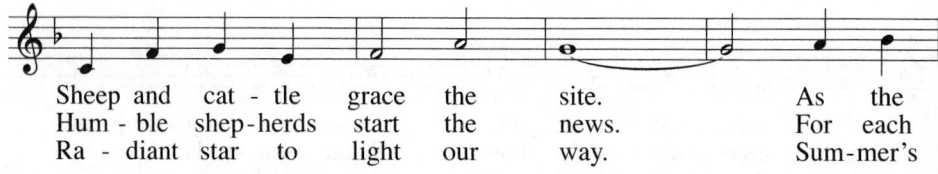

Sheep and cat - tle grace the site. As the
Hum - ble shep - herds start the news. For each
Ra - diant star to light our way. Sum-mer's

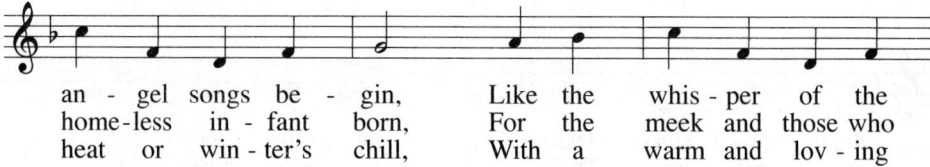

an - gel songs be - gin, Like the whis - per of the
home-less in - fant born, For the meek and those who
heat or win - ter's chill, With a warm and lov - ing

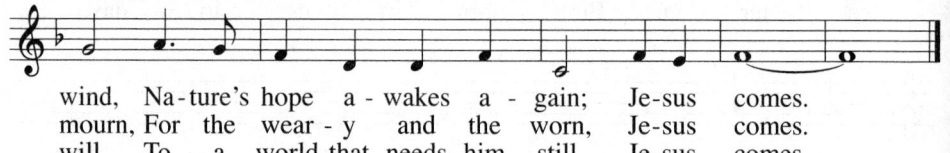

wind, Na - ture's hope a - wakes a - gain; Je-sus comes.
mourn, For the wear - y and the worn, Je-sus comes.
will, To a world that needs him still, Je-sus comes.

Text: Mary Louise Bringle, b.1953
Tune: TENTH NIGHT, 5 5 7 7 7 7 3; Sally Ann Morris, b.1952
© 2009, GIA Publications, Inc.

## 448 Away in a Manger

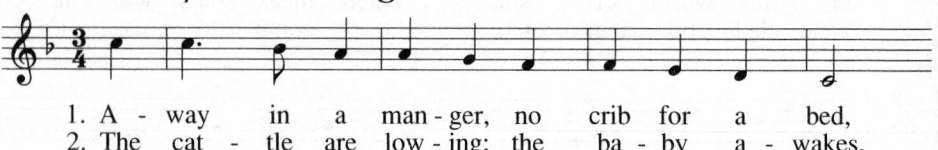

1. A - way in a man - ger, no crib for a bed,
2. The cat - tle are low - ing; the ba - by a - wakes,
3. Be near me, Lord Je - sus; I ask you to stay

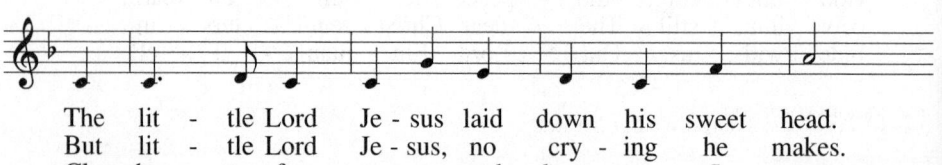

The lit - tle Lord Je - sus laid down his sweet head.
But lit - tle Lord Je - sus, no cry - ing he makes.
Close by me for - ev - er, and love me, I pray.

The stars in the bright sky looked down where he lay,
I love you, Lord Je - sus! Look down from the sky
Bless all the dear chil - dren in your ten - der care,

The lit - tle Lord Je - sus, a - sleep on the hay.
And stay by my cra - dle till morn - ing is nigh.
And fit us for heav - en, to live with you there.

Text: St. 1–2, anonymous, st. 3, John T. McFarland, 1851–1913
Tune: MUELLER, 11 11 11 11; James R. Murray, 1841–1905; harm. by Robert J. Batastini, b.1942, © 1994, GIA Publications, Inc.

# Star-Child 449

Verses

1. Star - Child, earth - Child, go - be - tween of God,
2. Street child, beat child, no place left to go,
3. Grown child, old child, mem - 'ry full of years,
4. Spared child, spoiled child, hav - ing, want - ing more,
5. Hope - for - peace Child, God's stu - pen - dous sign,

love Child, Christ Child, heav - en's light - ning rod:
hurt child, used child, no one wants to know:
sad child, lost child, sto - ry told in tears:
wise child, faith child, know - ing joy in store:
down - to - earth Child, Star of stars that shine:

Refrain

This year, this year let the day ar - rive when

Christ-mas comes for ev-'ry-one, ev - 'ry-one a - live.

Text: Shirley Erena Murray, b.1931, © 1994, Hope Publishing Company
Tune: NOAH'S SONG, 4 5 4 5 with refrain; Ronald F. Krisman, b.1946, © 2003, GIA Publications, Inc.

# 450 Where the Promise Shines

1. When a star is shin-ing o-ver east-ern
2. Where the world is wait-ing for an un-known
3. Lead us on, O Day-star, in the qui-et

hills, When the air is si-lent,
day, Where a voice for-got-ten
night; Guide us through the shad-ow

and the clam-or stills, When the night is
cries, "Pre-pare the way!" Where an earth-ly
with your gen-tle light; Show us in a

wait-ing, and the old hopes rise,
pow-er makes the heart turn cold,
man-ger our re-demp-tion's sign;

Then the time has rip-ened and the heart grows
There the gifts are of-fered— in-cense, myrrh, and
Bring us to a morn-ing where the prom-ise

wise.
gold. Lead us on, lead us on,
shines.

to a morn-ing where the prom-ise shines.

Lead us on, lead us on, to a

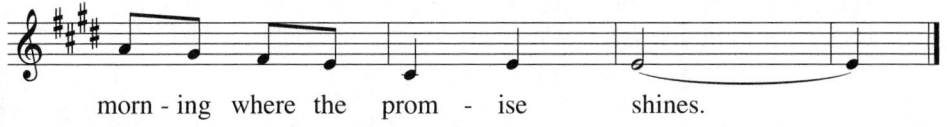

morn - ing where the prom - ise shines.

Text: Sylvia G. Dunstan, 1955–1993, © 1995, GIA Publications, Inc.
Tune: Bob Moore, b.1962, © 2003, GIA Publications, Inc.

## Lo, How a Rose E'er Blooming   451

1. Lo, how a Rose e'er bloom-ing From ten - der stem hath
2. I - sa - iah 'twas for - told it, The Rose I have in
3. This Flow'r, whose fra - grance ten - der With sweet-ness fills the

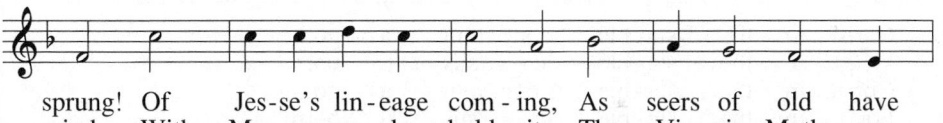

sprung! Of Jes-se's lin-eage com - ing, As seers of old have
mind; With Mar - y we be - hold it, The Vir - gin Moth - er
air, Dis - pels with glo-rious splen - dor The dark-ness ev - 'ry -

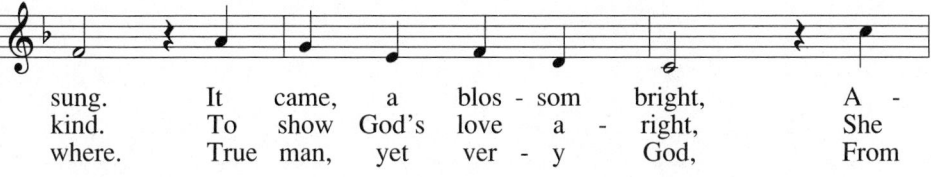

sung. It came, a blos - som bright, A -
kind. To show God's love a - right, She
where. True man, yet ver - y God, From

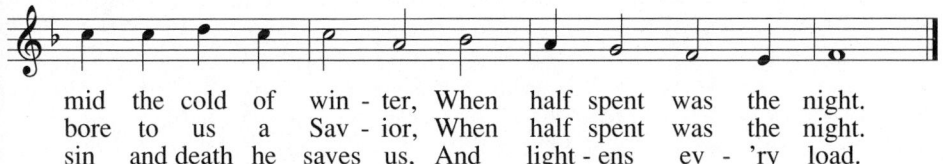

mid the cold of win - ter, When half spent was the night.
bore to us a Sav - ior, When half spent was the night.
sin and death he saves us, And light - ens ev - 'ry load.

Text: Isaiah 11:1; *Es ist ein' Ros' entsprungen; Speier Gesangbuch,* 1599; tr. sts. 1–2 by Theodore Baker, 1851–1934, alt.; st. 3, Friedrich Layritz,
    1808–1859; tr. by Harriet Reynolds Krauth, 1845–1925, alt.
Tune: ES IST EIN' ROS' ENSTSPRUNGEN, 7 6 7 6 6 7 6; *Geistliche Kirchengesang,* Cologne, 1599; harm. by Michael Praetorius, 1571–1621

# 452 Song of the Stable

1. Chill of the night - fall, Lamps in the win-dows,
2. Si - lence of mid - night, Voic - es of an - gels,
3. Splen - dor of star - light High on the hill - side,
4. Glo - ry of day - break! Sor - rows and shad - ows,

Let - ting their light fall Clear on the snow;
Sing - ing to bid night Yield to the dawn;
Faint is the far light Burn - ing be - low;
Sud - den - ly they break Forth in - to morn;

Bit - ter De - cem - ber Bids us re - mem - ber
Dark - ness is end - ed, Sin - ners be - friend - ed,
Kneel-ing be - fore him Shep - herds a - dore him,
Sing out and tell now All shall be well now,

Christ in the sta - ble Long, long a - go.
Where in the sta - ble Je - sus is born.
Christ in the sta - ble Long, long a - go.
For in the sta - ble Je - sus is born!

Text: *Chill of the Nightfall*, Timothy Dudley-Smith, b.1926, © 1980, Hope Publishing Company
Tune: PRIOR LAKE, 5 5 5 4 D; David Haas, b.1957, © 1985, GIA Publications, Inc.

# Rise Up, Shepherd, and Follow    453

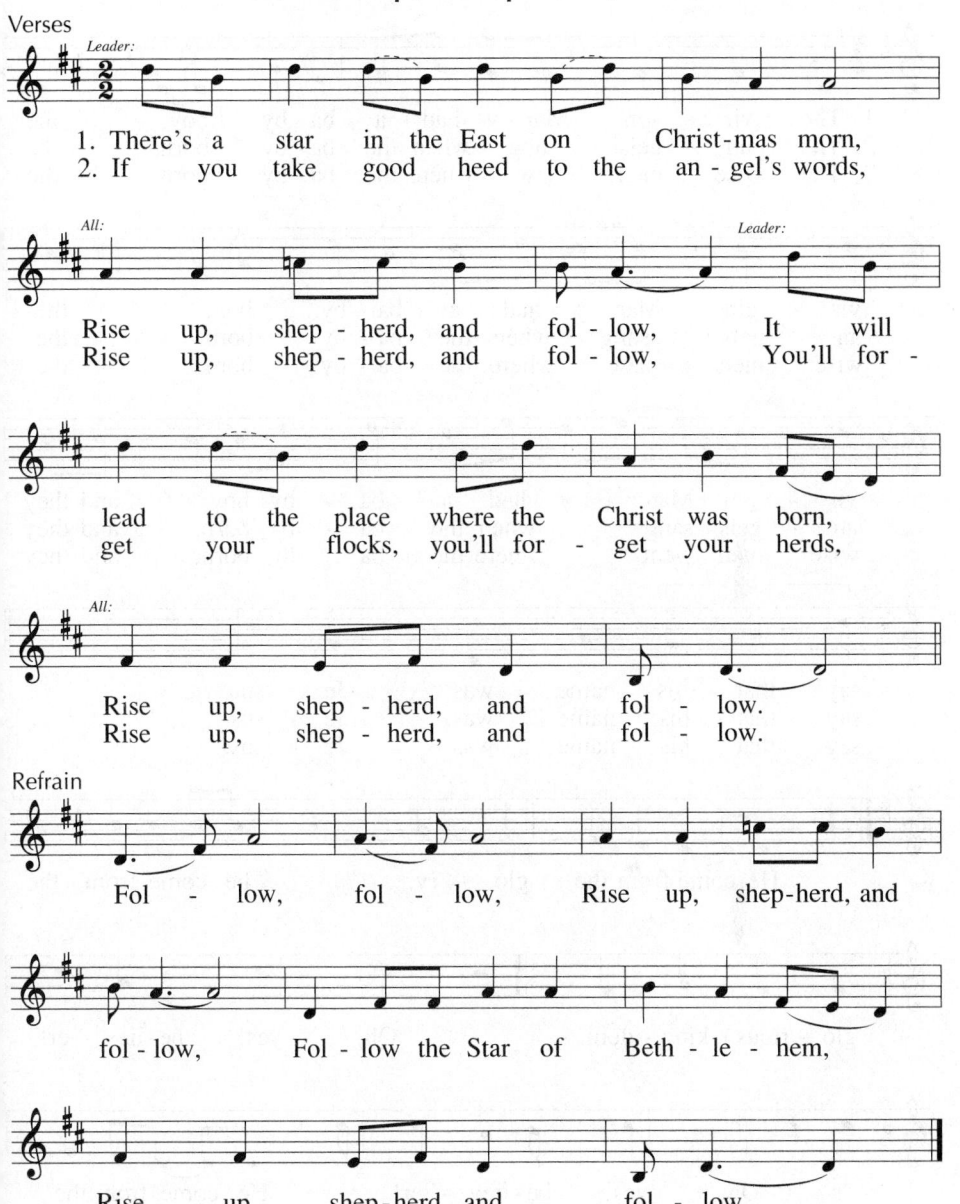

**Verses**

*Leader:*

1. There's a star in the East on Christ-mas morn,
2. If you take good heed to the an - gel's words,

*All:*

Rise up, shep - herd, and fol - low,

*Leader:*

It will
You'll for -

lead to the place where the Christ was born,
get your flocks, you'll for - get your herds,

*All:*

Rise up, shep - herd, and fol - low.
Rise up, shep - herd, and fol - low.

**Refrain**

Fol - low, fol - low, Rise up, shep-herd, and

fol - low, Fol - low the Star of Beth - le - hem,

Rise up, shep-herd, and fol - low.

Text: Traditional
Tune: African American spiritual

# 454 The Virgin Mary Had a Baby Boy

1. The vir - gin Mar - y had a ba - by boy, the
2. The an - gels sang when the ba - by born, the
3. The wise men saw where the ba - by born, the

vir - gin Mar - y had a ba - by boy, the
an - gels sang when the ba - by born, the
wise men saw where the ba - by born, the

vir - gin Mar - y had a ba - by boy, and they
an - gels sang when the ba - by born, and they
wise men went where the ba - by born, and they

say that his name was Je - sus.
say that his name was Je - sus.
say that his name was Je - sus.

He come from the glo - ry, he come from the

glo - rious king - dom. Oh, yes! be - liev - er!

Oh, yes! be - liev - er! He come from the

glo - ry, he come from the glo - rious king - dom.

# Once in Royal David's City   455

1. Once in roy - al Da - vid's cit - y Stood a
2. He came down to earth from heav - en Who is
3. And, through all his won - drous child - hood, He would
4. For he is our child - hood's pat - tern, Day by
5. And our eyes at last shall see him, Through his

low - ly cat - tle shed, Where a moth - er laid her
God and Lord of all, And his shel - ter was a
hon - or and o - bey, Love and watch the low - ly
day like us he grew; He was lit - tle, weak, and
own re - deem - ing love; For that child so dear and

ba - by In a man - ger for his bed. Mar - y
sta - ble, And his cra - dle was a stall. With the
maid - en In whose gen - tle arms he lay. Chris - tian
help - less, Tears and smiles like us he knew. And he
gen - tle Is our Lord in heav'n a - bove. And he

was that moth - er mild; Je - sus
poor and meek and low - ly Lived on
chil - dren all should be Kind, o -
feels for all our sad - ness, And he
leads his chil - dren on To the

Christ, her lit - tle child.
earth our Sav - ior ho - ly.
be - dient, good as he.
shares in all our glad - ness.
place where he is gone.

Text: Cecil Frances Alexander, 1818–1895, alt.
Tune: IRBY, 8 7 8 7 77; Henry J. Gauntlett, 1805–1876; harm. by Arthur H. Mann, 1850–1929, © 1957, Novello & Company Limited

## 456 The Aye Carol

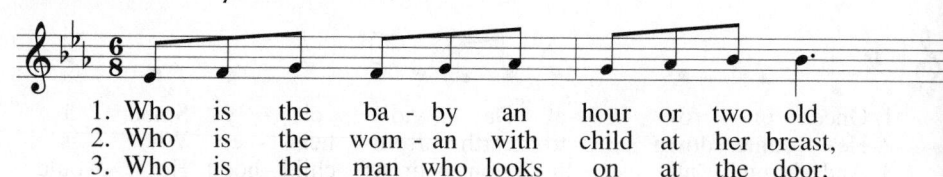

1. Who is the ba - by an hour or two old
2. Who is the wom - an with child at her breast,
3. Who is the man who looks on at the door,
4. Who are the peo - ple come in from the street,
5. Will you come with me, ev'n though I feel shy,

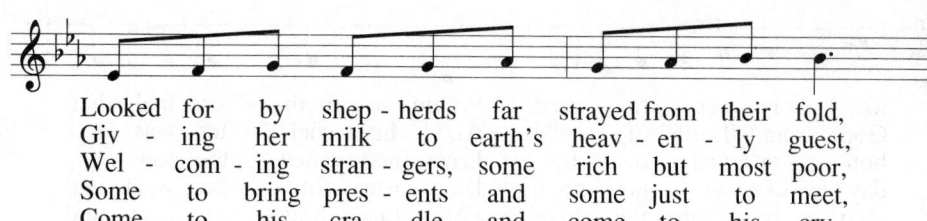

Looked for by shep - herds far strayed from their fold,
Giv - ing her milk to earth's heav - en - ly guest,
Wel - com - ing stran - gers, some rich but most poor,
Some to bring pres - ents and some just to meet,
Come to his cra - dle and come to his cry,

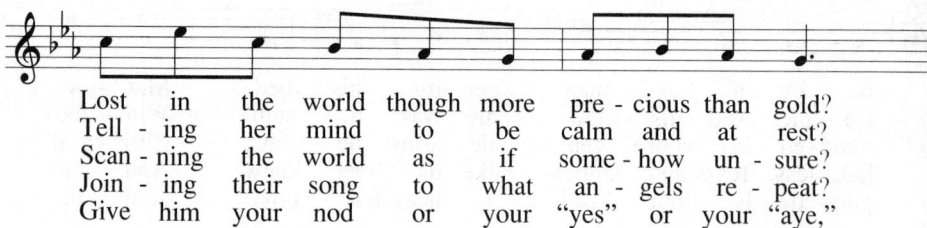

Lost in the world though more pre - cious than gold?
Tell - ing her mind to be calm and at rest?
Scan - ning the world as if some - how un - sure?
Join - ing their song to what an - gels re - peat?
Give him your nod or your "yes" or your "aye,"

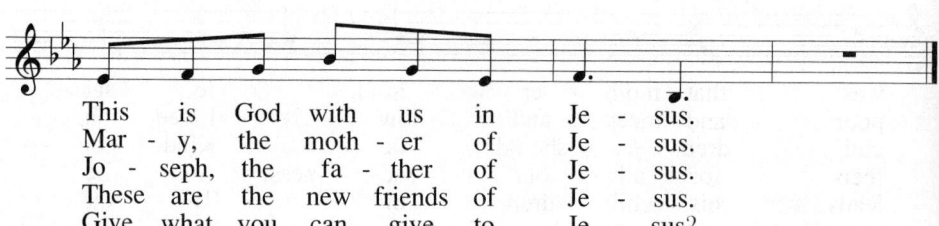

This is God with us in Je - sus.
Mar - y, the moth - er of Je - sus.
Jo - seph, the fa - ther of Je - sus.
These are the new friends of Je - sus.
Give what you can give to Je - sus?

Text: John L. Bell, b.1949
Tune: AYE CAROL, 10 10 10 8; John L. Bell, b.1949
© 1987, Iona Community, GIA Publications, Inc., agent

# Sing of Mary, Pure and Lowly   457

1. Sing of Mar - y, pure and low - ly, Vir - gin Moth - er
2. Sing of Je - sus, son of Mar - y, In the home at
3. Glo - ry be to God the Fa - ther; Glo - ry be to

un - de - filed. Sing of God's own Son most ho - ly,
Naz - a - reth. Toil and la - bor can - not wea - ry
God the Son; Glo - ry be to God the Spir - it;

Who be - came her lit - tle child. Fair - est Child of
Love en - dur - ing un - to death. Con - stant was the
Glo - ry to the Three in One. From the heart of

fair - est Moth - er, God the Lord who came to earth,
love he gave her, Though he went forth from her side,
bless - ed Mar - y, From all saints the song as - cends,

Word - made - flesh, our ver - y broth - er,
Forth to preach, and heal, and suf - fer,
And the Church the strain re - ech - oes

Takes our na - ture by his birth.
Till on Cal - va - ry he died.
Un - to earth's re - mot - est ends.

Text: Roland F. Palmer, 1891–1985, © Estate of Roland Palmer
Tune: PLEADING SAVIOR, 8 7 8 7 D; *Christian Lyre*, 1830; harm. by Richard Proulx, 1937–2010, © 1986, GIA Publications, Inc.

# 458 I Sing a Maid

1. I sing a maid of ten - der years To
2. She watched him grow to man - hood's strength To
3. And if the song had end - ed then, Our

whom an an - gel came, And knelt, as to a
meet his des - ti - ny. And when the dan - ger
eyes would fill with tears, But ah! the song had

might - y queen, And bowed bright wings of
of his truth Brought him to Cal - va -
just be - gun To ech - o down the

flame: A na - tion's hope in her re - ply, This
ry, She stood by him all pow - er - less To
years! Now lift your voic - es, hearts and souls, To

maid of match - less grace; For God's own son be -
ease his dy - ing pain, 'Til in the dark - est
sing with one ac - cord To hon - or Mar - y,

came her child, And she his rest - ing place.
hour of all, She held her son a - gain.
Moth - er of The Christ, the Ris - en Lord!

Text: M. D. Ridge, b.1938, © 1987, GIA Publications, Inc.
Tune: THE FLIGHT OF THE EARLS, CMD; traditional Celtic melody; harm. by Michael Joncas, b.1951, © 1987, GIA Publications, Inc.

# Songs of Thankfulness and Praise   459

1. Songs of thank - ful - ness and praise,   Je - sus, Lord, to
2. Man - i - fest at   Jor - dan's stream,   Proph-et, Priest, and
3. Man - i - fest in   mak - ing whole   Pal - sied limbs and
4. Grant us grace to   see you, Lord,   Pres - ent in your

you we raise,   Man - i - fest - ed   by the star
King su - preme;   And at Ca - na,   wed - ding guest,
faint - ing soul;   Man - i - fest in   val - iant fight,
ho - ly word.   By that grace which   you en - dow,

To the sag - es   from a - far;   Branch of roy - al
In your God - head   man - i - fest;   Man - i - fest in
Quell-ing all the   dev - il's might;   Man - i - fest in
Help us im - i - tate you now,   That we, pure like

Da - vid's stem   In your birth at   Beth - le - hem;
pow'r di - vine,   Chang - ing wa - ter   in - to wine;
gra - cious will,   Ev - er bring - ing   good from ill;
you, may be   At your great e - piph - a - ny;

An - thems be to you ad-dressed, God in flesh made man - i - fest.
An - thems be to you ad-dressed, God in flesh made man - i - fest.
An - thems be to you ad-dressed, God in flesh made man - i - fest.
And may praise you, ev - er blest, God in flesh made man - i - fest.

Text: Christopher Wordsworth, 1807–1885, alt.
Tune: SALZBURG, 77 77 D; Jakob Hintze, 1622–1702, alt; harm. by J. S. Bach, 1685–1750

## 460  The First Nowell

1. The first No - well the an - gel did say Was to
2. They look - ed up and saw a star Shin-ing
3. And by the light of that same star Three
4. This star drew nigh to the north - west, O'er
5. Then en - tered in those wise men three, Full
6. Then let us all with one ac - cord Sing

cer - tain poor shep - herds in fields as they lay; In
in the east be - yond them far; And
wise men came from coun - try far; To
Beth - le - hem it took its rest; And
rev - 'rent - ly up - on their knee, And
prais - es to our heav - 'nly Lord, Who

fields where they lay keep - ing their sheep, On a
to the earth it gave great light, And
seek for a king was their in - tent, And to
there it did both stop and stay Right
of - fered there in his pres - ence Their
made the heav'ns and earth of naught, And

cold win - ter's night that was so deep.
so it con - tin - ued both day and night.
fol - low the star where - ev - er it went.
o - ver the place where Je - sus lay.
gold and myrrh and frank - in - cense.
with his blood our life has bought.

No - well, No - well, No - well, No - well!

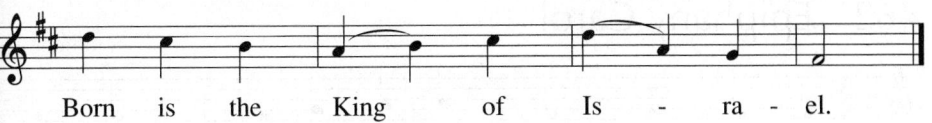

Born    is    the    King    of    Is  -  ra  -  el.

Text: English Carol, 17th C.
Tune: THE FIRST NOWELL, Irregular; English Melody; harm. from *Christmas Carols New and Old*, 1871

## What Star Is This    461

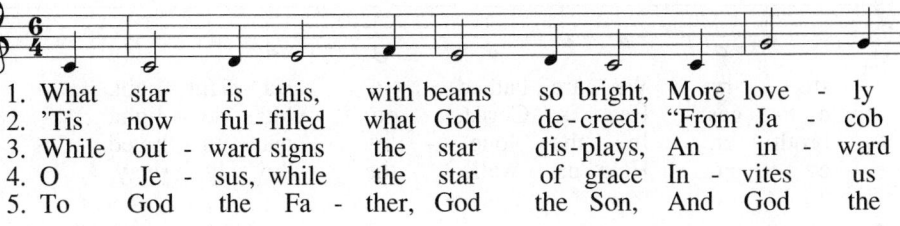

1. What   star   is   this,   with beams   so bright,   More love  -  ly
2. 'Tis   now   ful - filled   what God   de - creed:   "From Ja  -  cob
3. While   out - ward signs   the   star   dis - plays,   An   in  -  ward
4. O   Je - sus, while   the   star   of grace   In - vites   us
5. To   God   the   Fa  -  ther, God   the   Son,   And   God   the

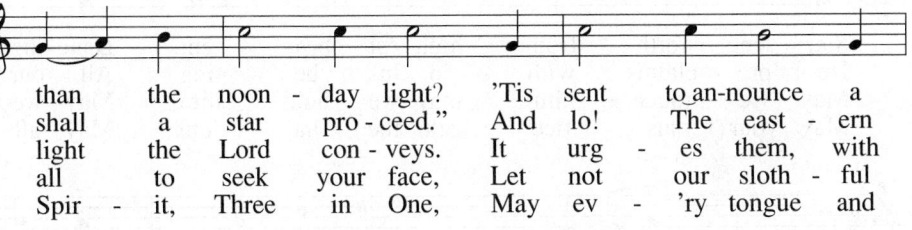

than   the   noon - day light?   'Tis   sent   to an-nounce   a
shall   a   star   pro - ceed."   And   lo!   The   east - ern
light   the   Lord   con - veys.   It   urg  -  es   them,   with
all   to   seek   your face,   Let   not   our   sloth - ful
Spir  -  it,   Three   in   One,   May   ev  -  'ry   tongue   and

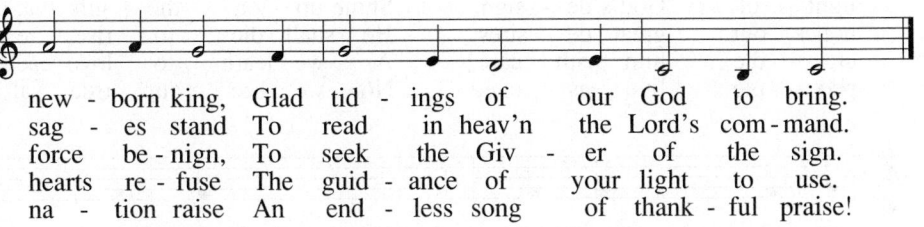

new - born king,   Glad   tid - ings   of   our   God   to   bring.
sag  -  es stand   To   read   in heav'n   the   Lord's   com - mand.
force   be - nign,   To   seek   the   Giv  -  er   of   the   sign.
hearts   re - fuse   The   guid - ance   of   your   light   to   use.
na  -  tion raise   An   end - less song   of   thank - ful   praise!

Text: *Quem stella sole pulchrior*, Charles Coffin, 1676–1749; tr. by John Chandler, 1806–1876, alt.
Tune: PUER NOBIS, LM; adapt. by Michael Praetorius, 1571–1621

# 462 Epiphany Carol

1. Ev - 'ry na - tion sees the glo - ry Of a
2. Ev - 'ry tongue shall sing the prais - es Of his
3. Once a - gain may we dis - cov - er Word made
4. Gath-er, God, the world to - geth - er In the

star that pierced the night. As we tell the won-drous
birth in deep-est night. He is heal - ing for the
flesh sent from a - bove. In our neigh - bor, sis - ter,
bright - ness of your day. Fill our hearts with joy for -

sto - ry We are bathed in ra - diant light.
a - ges; He is Christ, our God's de - light.
broth - er, In the lone - ly and un - loved.
ev - er; Help us walk the ho - ly way.

Star sent forth from high-est heav - en, Danc-ing
He pro - claims with - in his be - ing All our
May we touch him, may we hold him, May we
May your jus - tice rule the na - tions; May all

light of God's de - sign, Shine up - on the gift that's
hopes, our great de - sires. He shall die to rise, re -
cra - dle him with care As we learn to love each
peo - ple live as one. Now we see our true sal -

giv - en: Word made flesh now born in time.
deem - ing All who fol - low with their lives.
oth - er, Bring-ing hope from out de - spair.
va - tion In the glo - ry of your Son.

Text: Francis Patrick O'Brien, b.1958, © 2002, GIA Publications, Inc.
Tune: BEACH SPRING, 8 7 8 7 D; *The Sacred Harp*, 1844; harm. by Ronald A. Nelson, b.1927, © 1978, *Lutheran Book of Worship*

# We Three Kings of Orient Are  463

1. We three kings of O - ri - ent are; Bear - ing
2. Born a King on Beth - le - hem's plain, Gold I
3. Frank - in - cense to of - fer have I; In - cense
4. Myrrh is mine: its bit - ter per - fume Breathes a
5. Glo - rious now be - hold him a - rise, King and

gifts, we trav - erse a - far Field and foun - tain,
bring to crown him a - gain; King for - ev - er,
owns a De - i - ty nigh; Prayer and prais - ing,
life of gath - er - ing gloom; Sor - rowing, sigh - ing,
God and Sac - ri - fice; "Al - le - lu - ia,

Moor and moun - tain, Fol - low - ing yon - der star.
Ceas - ing nev - er, O - ver us all to reign.
Glad - ly rais - ing, Wor - ship - ing God on high.
Bleed - ing, dy - ing, Sealed in the stone - cold tomb.
Al - le - lu - ia!" Sounds through the earth and skies.

O star of won - der, star of night, Star with

roy - al beau - ty bright, West - ward lead - ing,

still pro - ceed - ing, Guide us to the per - fect Light.

Text: Matthew 2:1–11; John H. Hopkins, Jr., 1820–1891, alt.
Tune: KINGS OF ORIENT, 88 44 6 with refrain; John H. Hopkins, Jr., 1820–1891

# 464 Lord, Today

**Refrain**

Lord, to-day we have seen your glo-ry, dawn fol-lows the night. We, your peo-ple who walked in dark-ness now have seen a great light.

**Verses**

1. A child is born, a Son giv-en us, on him do-min-ion shall rest.
2. The Lord is king, the na-tions re-joice, let all God's peo-ple be glad.
3. O Beth-le-hem, you are from of old, too small a-mong Ju-dah's clans.
4. The days will come, the Lord prom-ised us, when God would raise up a shoot
5. New light has dawned up-on all the just, glad-ness for up-right of heart.

1. His name shall be Won-der-ful God, Coun-sel-or, Prince of Peace.
2. The heav-ens pro-claim jus-tice for all. Glo-ry has filled the land.
3. From you shall come a rul-er this day, shep-herd to guide the land.
4. to rule the land, reign as a king, whose name is Lord the Just.
5. Re-joice in the Lord, you faith-ful ones. Give thanks to God's great name.

**D.C.**

Text: Mike Balhoff, b.1946
Tune: Darryl Ducote, b.1945, Gary Daigle, b.1957
© 1978, Damean Music. Distributed by GIA Publications, Inc.

# As with Gladness Men of Old   465

1. As with glad - ness men of old Did the guid - ing
2. As with joy - ful steps they sped To that low - ly
3. As they of - fered gifts most rare At that man - ger
4. Ho - ly Je - sus, ev - 'ry day Keep us in the
5. In the heav'n - ly cit - y bright None shall need cre -

star be - hold; As with joy they hailed its light,
man - ger - bed, There to bend the knee be - fore
crude and bare; So may we this ho - ly day,
nar - row way; And when earth - ly things are past,
at - ed light; You, its light, its joy, its crown,

Lead - ing on - ward, beam - ing bright; So, most gra - cious
Him, whom heav'n and earth a - dore; So may we with
Drawn to you with - out de - lay, All our cost - liest
Bring our ran - somed souls at last Where they need no
You, its sun which goes not down; There for - ev - er

Lord, may we Ev - er - more your splen - dor see.
hur - ried pace Run to seek your throne of grace.
treas - ures bring, Christ, to you, our heav'n - ly King.
star to guide, Where no clouds your glo - ry hide.
may we sing Al - le - lu - ias to our King.

Text: William C. Dix, 1837–1898, alt.
Tune: DIX, 77 77 77; arr. from Conrad Kocher, 1786–1872, by William H. Monk, 1823–1889

# 466 What Child Is This

1. What child is this, who, laid to rest, On
2. Why lies he in such mean es - tate Where
3. So bring him in - cense, gold, and myrrh; Come,

Mar - y's lap is sleep - ing, Whom an - gels greet with
ox and ass are feed - ing? Good Chris - tian, fear; for
peas - ant, king, to own him. The King of kings sal -

an - thems sweet While shep - herds watch are keep - ing?
sin - ners here The si - lent Word is plead - ing.
va - tion brings; Let lov - ing hearts en - throne him.

This, this is Christ the King, Whom shep - herds guard and an-gels sing;

Haste, haste to bring him laud, The babe, the son of Mar - y.

Text: William C. Dix, 1837–1898
Tune: GREENSLEEVES, 8 7 8 7 with refrain; English melody, 16th C.; harm. by John Stainer, 1840–1901

# When John Baptized by Jordan's River  467

1. When    John    bap - tized    by    Jor - dan's    riv - er
2. There    as    the    Lord,    bap - tized    and    pray - ing,
3. O    Son    of    Man,    our    na - ture    shar - ing,

In    faith    and    hope    the    peo - ple    came,    That    John and
Rose    from    the    stream,    the    sin - less    one,    A    voice was
In    whose    o - be - dience    all    are    blest,    Sav - ior,    our

Jor - dan    might    de - liv - er    Their    trou - bled
heard from    heav - en    say - ing,    "This    is    my
sins    and    sor - rows    bear - ing,    Hear    us    and

souls from    sin    and    shame.    They    came    to    seek    a
own    be - lov - ed    Son."    There    as    the    Fa - ther's
grant    us    this    re - quest:    Dai - ly    to    grow,    by

new    be - gin - ning,    The    hu - man    spir - it's    age - less
word was    spo - ken,    Not    in    the    pow'r of    wind    and
grace    de - fend - ed,    Filled    with    the    Spir - it    from    a -

quest,    Re - pent - ance,    and    an    end    of
flame,    But    of    his    love    and    peace    the
bove;    In    Christ    bap - tized,    be - loved,    be -

sin - ning,    Re - nounc - ing    ev - 'ry    wrong    con - fessed.
to - ken,    Seen    as    a    dove,    the    Spir - it    came.
friend - ed,    Chil - dren    of    God    in    peace    and    love.

Text: Timothy Dudley-Smith, b.1926, © 1984, Hope Publishing Company
Tune: RENDEZ À DIEU, 9 8 9 8 D; *Genevan Psalter*, 1551; attr. to Louis Bourgeois, c.1510–1561

# 468 Dust and Ashes

Verses

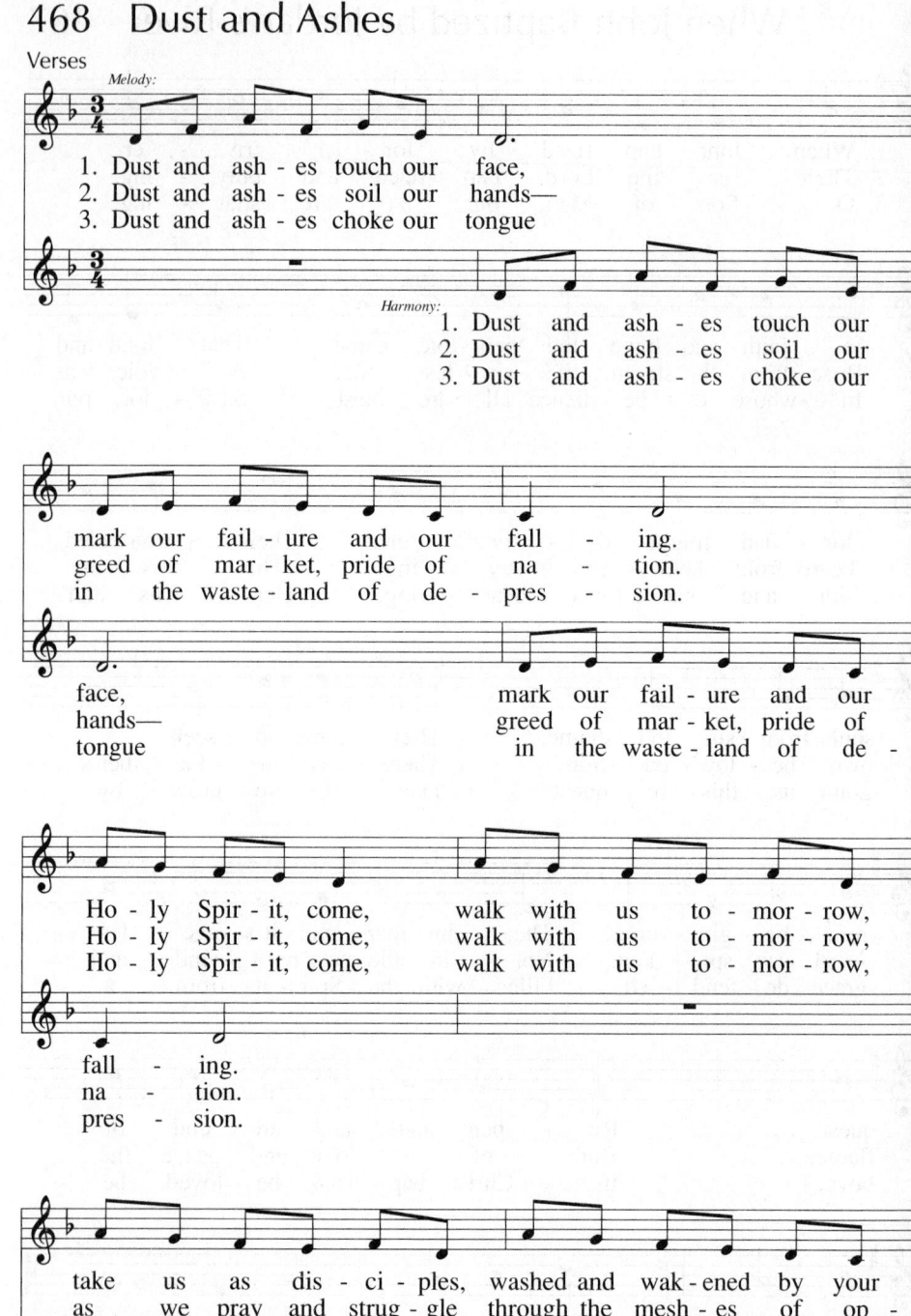

*Melody:*

1. Dust and ash - es touch our face,
2. Dust and ash - es soil our hands—
3. Dust and ash - es choke our tongue

*Harmony:*

1. Dust and ash - es touch our
2. Dust and ash - es soil our
3. Dust and ash - es choke our

mark our fail - ure and our fall - ing.
greed of mar - ket, pride of na - tion.
in the waste - land of de - pres - sion.

face,
hands—
tongue

mark our fail - ure and our
greed of mar - ket, pride of
in the waste - land of de -

Ho - ly Spir - it, come, walk with us to - mor - row,
Ho - ly Spir - it, come, walk with us to - mor - row,
Ho - ly Spir - it, come, walk with us to - mor - row,

fall - ing.
na - tion.
pres - sion.

take us as dis - ci - ples, washed and wak - ened by your
as we pray and strug - gle through the mesh - es of op -
through all gloom and griev - ing to the paths of res - ur -

call - ing.
pres - sion.
rec - tion.

efrain

Take us by the hand and lead us,

Take us by the hand and

lead us through the des - ert sands,

lead us, lead us through the des - ert

bring us liv - ing wa - ter,

sands, bring us liv - ing

Ho - ly Spir - it, come.

wa - ter, Ho - ly Spir - it, come.

xt: Brian Wren, b.1936, © 1989, Hope Publishing Co.
ne: David Haas, b.1957, © 1991, GIA Publications, Inc.

# 469 Remember You Are Dust

**Refrain**

Turn a-way from sin and be faith - ful to the Gos-pel. Re-

mem-ber you are dust, and to dust you will re - turn.

**Verses**

*Cantor:*

*All:*

1.-4. Re - pent, the king-dom is at hand. Re -

pent, the king-dom is at hand.

*\*Cantor:*

1. Rend your
2. Blow the
3. For -
4. Now, the

hearts, not your gar-ments.
trum - pet in Zi - on.
give one an - oth - er.
day of sal - va - tion.

Now, the ac - cept - a - ble

*All:*

D.C.

time. Now, the ac-cept-a-ble time.

*\*Additional verses for the season of Lent:*

Seek the God of compassion…
Live in kindness and mercy…
Trust in God and be faithful…
Praise the God of salvation…
Let us bow down in worship…

Text: Joel 2:12–18, 2 Corinthians 5:20—6:2; Paul A. Tate, b.1968, © 2003, GIA Publications, Inc.; refrain from the *Sacramentary,* © 1973, ICEL
Tune: Paul A. Tate, b.1968, © 2003, GIA Publications, Inc.

# Somebody's Knockin' at Your Door  470

Some-bod - y's knock-in' at your door. Some-bod - y's

knock-in' at your door. O sin - ner, why don't you

an - swer? Some-bod - y's knock-in' at your door.

*Solo:*                          *All:*

1. Knocks like Je - sus,
2. Can't you hear him?
3. Je - sus calls you,  Some-bod - y's knock-in' at your door.
4. Can't you trust him?

*Solo:*                          *All:*

Knocks like Je - sus,
Can't you hear him?
Je - sus calls you,  Some-bod - y's knock-in' at your door.
Can't you trust him?

O sin - ner, why don't you an - swer?

Some-bod - y's knock-in' at your door.

Text: African American spiritual
Tune: SOMEBODY'S KNOCKIN', Irregular; African American spiritual; harm. by Richard Proulx, 1937–2010, © 1986, GIA Publications, Inc.

# 471 Return to the Lord

Refrain

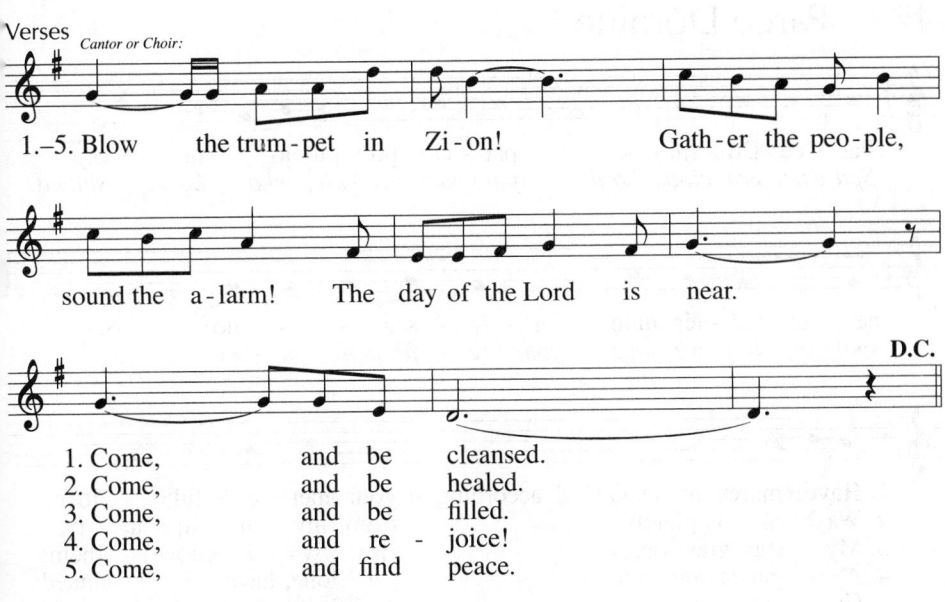

**Verses** *Cantor or Choir:*

1.–5. Blow the trum-pet in Zi-on! Gath-er the peo-ple,

sound the a-larm! The day of the Lord is near.

**D.C.**

1. Come, and be cleansed.
2. Come, and be healed.
3. Come, and be filled.
4. Come, and re - joice!
5. Come, and find peace.

Text: Based on Joel 2:1, 12–18, 26
Tune: Paul A. Tate, b.1968, © 2005, GIA Publications, Inc.

## Kýrie  472

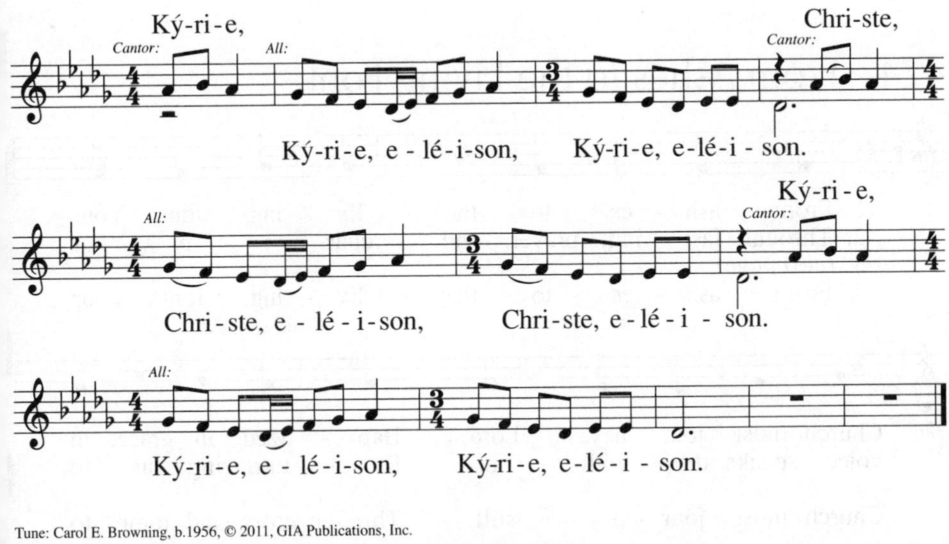

*Cantor:* Ký-ri-e,   *All:*   Ký-ri-e, e - lé-i-son,   *Cantor:* Chri-ste,   Ký-ri-e, e-lé-i - son.

*All:* Chri-ste, e - lé - i - son,   Chri-ste, e - lé - i - son.   *Cantor:* Ký-ri - e,

*All:* Ký-ri-e, e - lé-i-son,   Ký-ri-e, e-lé-i - son.

Tune: Carol E. Browning, b.1956, © 2011, GIA Publications, Inc.

## 473  Parce Dómine

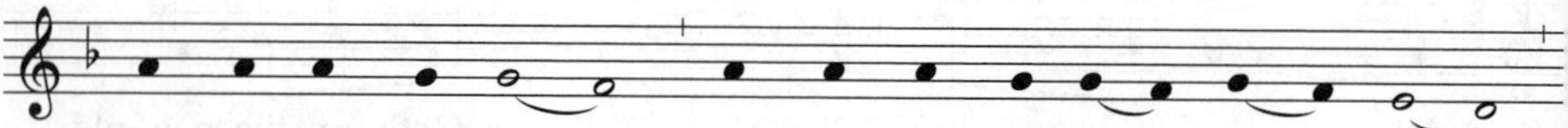

Par - ce Dó - mi - ne, par - ce pó - pu - lo tu - o:
*Spare us, gra-cious Lord,* *spare your peo-ple, who* *have* *sinned:*

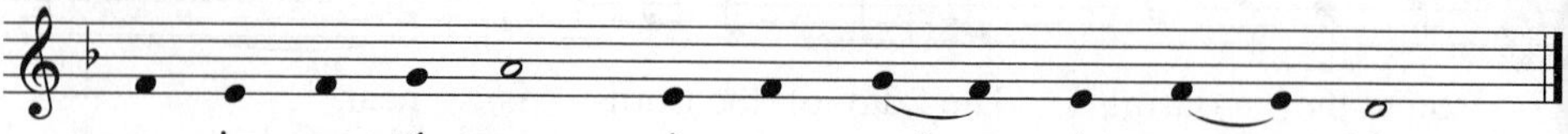

ne in ae - tér - num i - ra - scá - ris no - bis.
*spare us, lest we face* *your re - proach for - ev - er.*

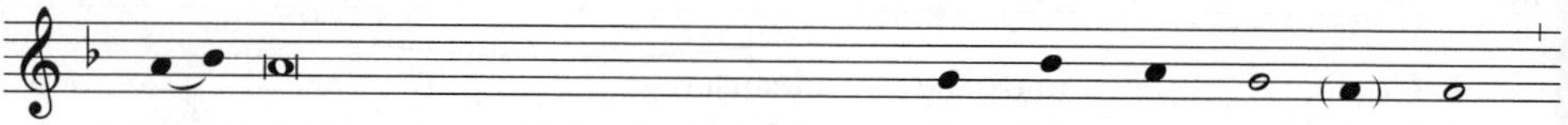

1. Have mercy on me, O God, according to your mer - ci - ful love;
2. Wash me completely from my in - iq - ui - ty,
3. My transgressions, tru - ly I know them;
4. A - gainst you, you a - lone, have I sinned;
5. Cre - ate a pure heart for me, O God;

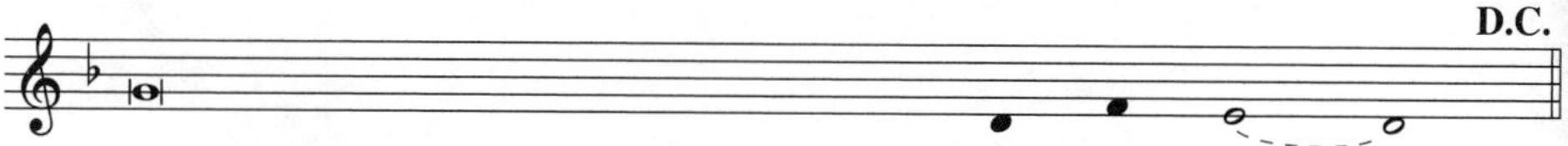

**D.C.**

according to your great compassion, blot out my trans - gress - ions.
and cleanse me from my sin.
my sin is always be - fore me.
what is evil in your sight I have done.
renew a steadfast spirit with - in me.

Text: Joel 2:17; tr. by Ronald F. Krisman, b.1946, © 2011, GIA Publications, Inc.; verses, Psalm 51:3–6, 12, *The Revised Grail Psalms*, © 2010, Conception Abbey and The Grail, admin. by GIA Publications, Inc.
Tune: PARCE DOMINE, Irregular; Mode I with Tonus Peregrinus; acc. by Robert LeBlanc, b.1948, © 1986, GIA Publications, Inc.

## 474  From Ashes to the Living Font

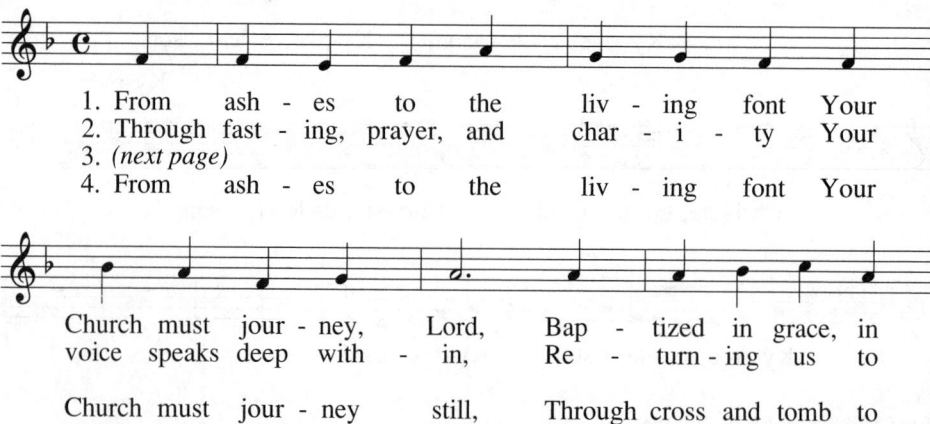

1. From ash - es to the liv - ing font Your
2. Through fast - ing, prayer, and char - i - ty Your
3. *(next page)*
4. From ash - es to the liv - ing font Your

Church must jour - ney, Lord, Bap - tized in grace, in
voice speaks deep with - in, Re - turn - ing us to

Church must jour - ney still, Through cross and tomb to

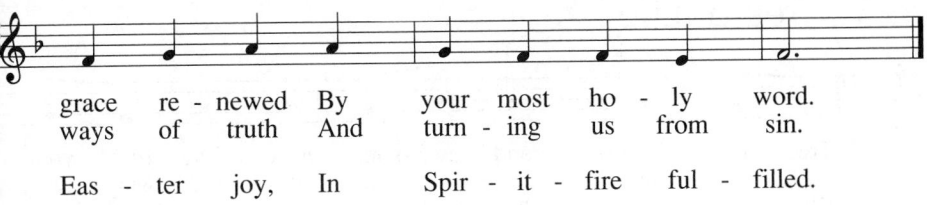

| grace | re - newed | By | your | most | ho - ly | word. |
| ways | of truth | And | turn - ing | us | from | sin. |

| Eas - ter | joy, | In | Spir - it - fire | ful - filled. |

## Year A

**Sundays I & II**
3. From desert to the mountaintop
   In Christ our way we see,
   So, tempered by temptation's might
   We might transfigured be.

**Sunday III**
3. For thirsting hearts let waters flow,
   Our fainting souls revive;
   And at the well your waters give
   Our everlasting life.

**Sunday IV**
3. We sit beside the road and plead,
   "Come, save us, David's son!"
   Now with your vision heal our eyes,
   The world's true Light alone.

**Sunday V**
3. Our graves split open, bring us back,
   Your promise to proclaim;
   To darkened tombs call out, "Arise!"
   And glorify your name.

## Year B

**Sundays I & II**
3. From desert to the mountaintop
   In Christ our way we see,
   So, tempered by temptation's might
   We might transfigured be.

**Sunday III**
3. Come, purify our hearts and lives,
   Cast out our sinful ways;
   As temples of the Spirit, cleansed,
   Restore us for your praise.

**Sunday IV**
3. The Son of Man is lifted up,
   Our eyes behold the sign:
   You are God's own beloved Son,
   The source of life divine.

**Sunday V**
3. Unless, like grains of wheat, we fall
   Upon the ground to die,
   We cannot share the gift of life,
   Raised up, like you, on high.

## Year C

**Sundays I & II**
3. From desert to the mountaintop
   In Christ our way we see,
   So, tempered by temptation's might
   We might transfigured be.

**Sunday III**
3. You call us to be penitent,
   You tend us patiently,
   Preserving us from perishing,
   So fruitful we might be.

**Sunday IV**
3. When we repent, you run to us,
   Forgiving arms spread wide;
   You celebrate when we return,
   And come home to your side.

**Sunday V**
3. When we self-righteously condemn,
   You ask: "Who has no sin?"
   We hear you say "Go, sin no more."
   New life in you begins.

Text: Alan J. Hommerding, b.1956, © 1994, 2011, World Library Publications
Tune: ST. FLAVIAN, CM; *John's Day Psalter,* 1562; harm. based on the original *faux-bourdon* setting

# 475 Tree of Life

1. Tree of Life and awe-some mys - t'ry, In your
2. Seed that dies to rise in glo - ry, May we
3. We re - mem - ber truth once spo - ken, Love passed
4. Gen - tle Je - sus, might - y Spir - it, Come in -
5. Christ, you lead and we shall fol - low, Stum - bling

death we are re - born, Though you die in all of
see our - selves in you, If we learn to live your
on through act and word, Ev - 'ry per - son lost and
flame our hearts a - new, We may all your joy in -
though our steps may be, One with you in joy and

his - t'ry, Still you rise with ev - 'ry morn, Still you
sto - ry We may die to rise a - new, We may
bro - ken Wears the bod - y of our Lord, Wears the
her - it If we bear the cross with you, If we
sor - row, We the riv - er, you the sea, We the

rise with ev - 'ry morn.
die to rise a - new.
bod - y of our Lord.
bear the cross with you.
riv - er, you the sea.

**Lenten Verses**

*General:*  Light of life beyond conceiving, Mighty Spirit of our Lord;
Give new strength to our believing, Give us faith to live your word.

*1st Sunday:*  From the dawning of creation, You have loved us as your own;
Stay with us through all temptation, Make us turn to you alone.

*2nd Sunday:*  In our call to be a blessing, May we be a blessing true;
May we live and die confessing Christ as Lord of all we do.

*3rd Sunday:*  Living Water of salvation, Be the fountain of each soul;
Springing up in new creation, Flow in us and make us whole.

*4th Sunday:*  Give us eyes to see you clearly, Make us children of your light;
Give us hearts to live more nearly As your gospel shining bright.

*5th Sunday:*  God of all our fear and sorrow, God who lives beyond our death;
Hold us close through each tomorrow, Love as near as every breath.

Text: Marty Haugen, b.1950
Tune: THOMAS, 8 7 8 77; Marty Haugen, b.1950
© 1984, GIA Publications, Inc.

# Adorámus Te Christe  476

Text: Antiphon from Good Friday Liturgy; *We adore you, O Christ, and we bless you, because by your holy cross you have redeemed the world.*
Tune: Marty Haugen, b.1950, © 1984, GIA Publications, Inc.

# 477 Lord Jesus Christ

Ostinato Refrain

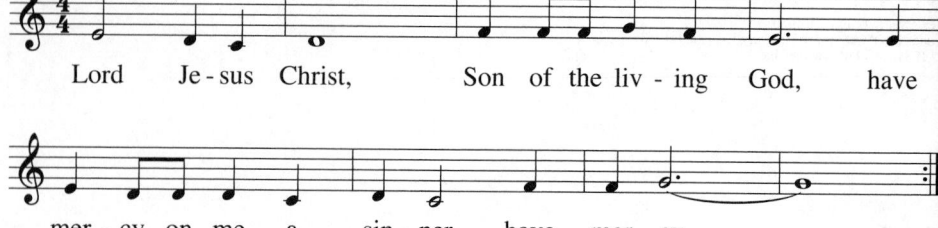

Lord Je - sus Christ, Son of the liv - ing God, have

mer - cy on me, a sin - ner, have mer - cy.

Text: *The Jesus Prayer*; verses, Psalm 51 and Agnus Dei, adapt. by Carol E. Browning, b.1956
Tune: Carol E. Browning, b.1956; acc. by Kathy McGrath
© 2003, GIA Publications, Inc.

# 478 Return to God / Volvamos Hoy a Nuestro Dios

Refrain

Re - turn to God with all your heart, the source of grace and
*Vol - va - mos hoy a nues - tro Dios, Se - ñor de to - da*

mer - cy; come seek the ten - der faith - ful - ness of God.
*gra - cia, bus - can - do su per - dón y le - al - tad.*

Verses

1. Now the time of grace has come,
the day of salvation;
come and learn now the way of our God.

1. *Día de la salvación,*
*y tiempo favorable;*
*caminemos por las sendas de Dios.*

2. I will take your heart of stone
and place a heart within you,
a heart of compassion and love.

2. *Quitaré tu corazón de piedra;*
*te daré un corazón*
*de amor y compassión.*

3. If you break the chains of oppression,
   if you set the pris'ner free;
   if you share your bread with the hungry,
   give protection to the lost;
   give a shelter to the homeless,
   clothe the naked in your midst,
   then your light shall break forth
      like the dawn.

*3. Si tú rompes vínculos injustos,*
   *y_a los presos das libertad;*
   *ofreciendo pan al hambriento,*
   *protección al extraviado;*
   *dando_abrigo_a quien está*
      *sin techo,*
   *y vestido al desnudo;*
   *surgirá tu luz como la_aurora.*

Text: Marty Haugen, b.1950; tr. by Ronald F. Krisman, b.1946
Tune: Marty Haugen, b.1950
© 1990, 1991, 2005, GIA Publications, Inc.

# Lord, Who throughout These Forty Days 479

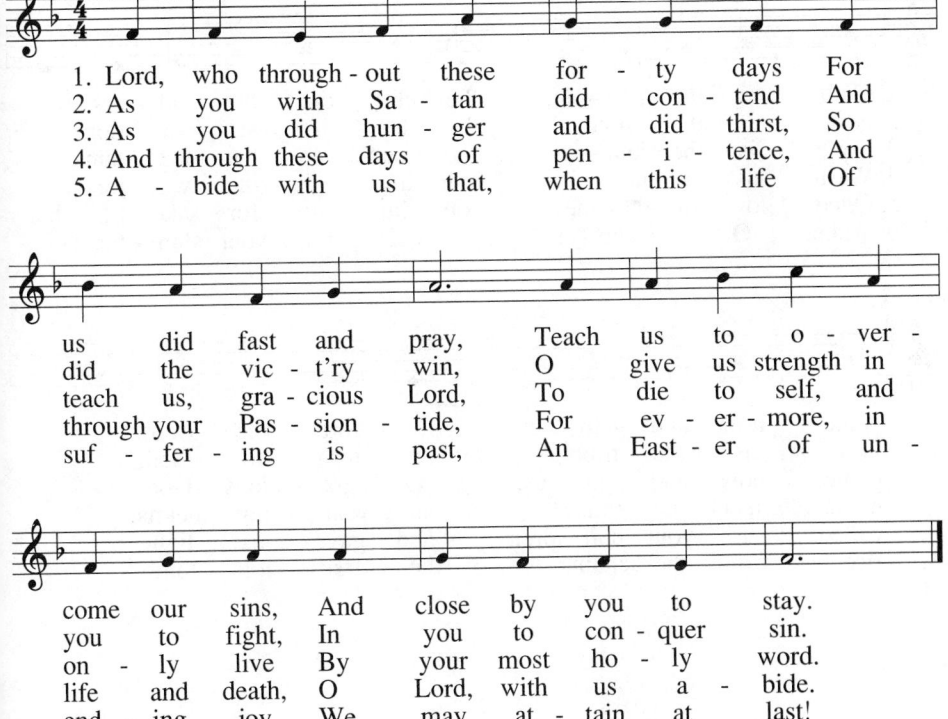

1. Lord, who through-out these for - ty days For us did fast and pray, Teach us to o - ver - come our sins, And close by you to stay.
2. As you with Sa - tan did con - tend And did the vic - t'ry win, O give us strength in you to fight, In you to con - quer sin.
3. As you did hun - ger and did thirst, So teach us, gra - cious Lord, To die to self, and on - ly live By your most ho - ly word.
4. And through these days of pen - i - tence, And through your Pas - sion - tide, For ev - er - more, in life and death, O Lord, with us a - bide.
5. A - bide with us, that, when this life Of suf - fer - ing is past, An East - er of un - end - ing joy We may at - tain at last!

Text: Claudia F. Hernaman, 1838–1898, alt.
Tune: ST. FLAVIAN, CM; *John's Day Psalter,* 1562; harm. based on the original *faux-bourdon* setting

# 480 Mercy, O God

**Refrain**

Mer-cy, O God, have mer-cy on us.

Send down your mer-cy to set us free.

Mer-cy, O God, have mer-cy on us.

Send down your mer-cy to set us free.

**Verses**

1. Gath - er the peo - ple, the chil - dren, the eld - ers;
2. Now is the hour, the day of sal - va - tion;
3. Long is the jour - ney and steep are the moun - tains,
4. Wash us a - new in your life - giv - ing wa - ter;
5. Once lost in dark-ness you did not for - sake us, but
6. Wake, O sleep - er, a - wake from your slum - ber;

come now and gath - er be - fore the Lord.
now is the time to re - turn to God.
come now and guide us, O gra - cious God.
come quench the thirst of our yearn - ing hearts.
called us your chil - dren and gave us light.
rise from the chains of the dark, cold tomb.

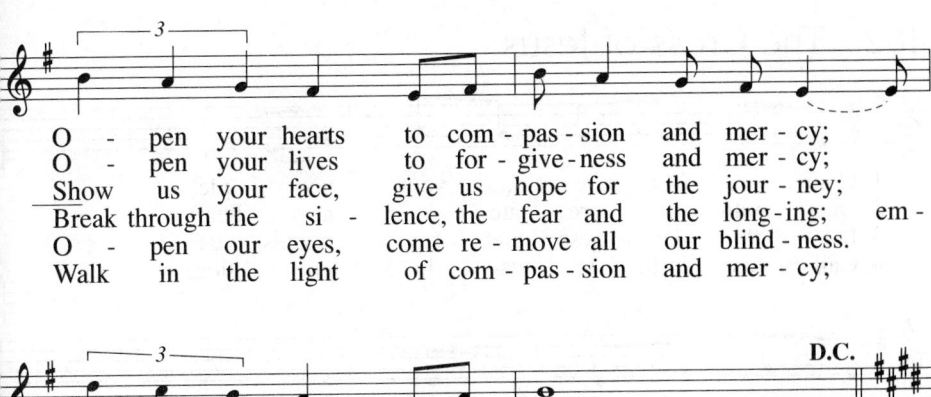

O - pen your hearts to com - pas - sion and mer - cy;
O - pen your lives to for - give - ness and mer - cy;
Show us your face, give us hope for the jour - ney;
Break through the si - lence, the fear and the long-ing; em -
O - pen our eyes, come re - move all our blind - ness.
Walk in the light of com - pas - sion and mer - cy;

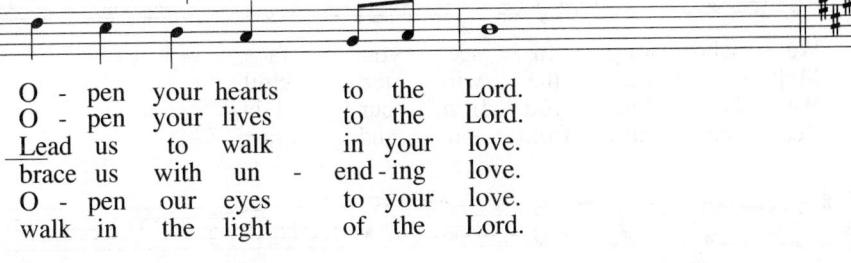

D.C.

O - pen your hearts to the Lord.
O - pen your lives to the Lord.
Lead us to walk in your love.
brace us with un - end - ing love.
O - pen our eyes to your love.
walk in the light of the Lord.

Text: Francis Patrick O'Brien, b.1958
Tune: Francis Patrick O'Brien, b.1958
© 2001, GIA Publications, Inc.

## The Glory of These Forty Days 481

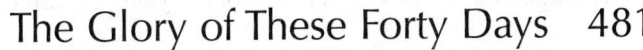

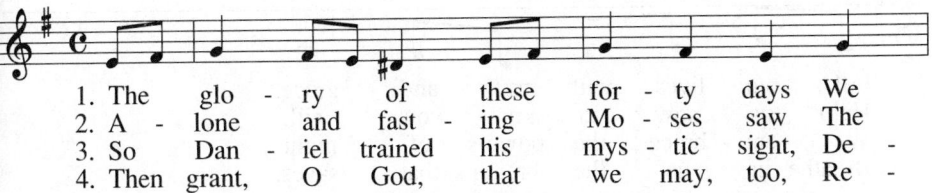

1. The glo - ry of these for - ty days We
2. A - lone and fast - ing Mo - ses saw The
3. So Dan - iel trained his mys - tic sight, De -
4. Then grant, O God, that we may, too, Re -

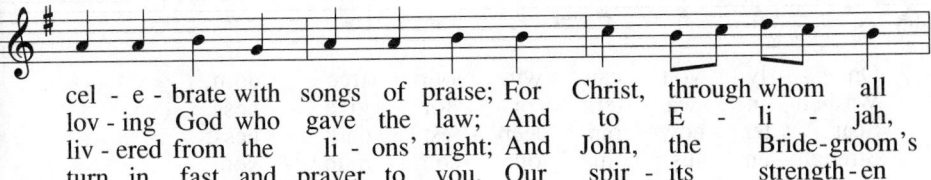

cel - e - brate with songs of praise; For Christ, through whom all
lov - ing God who gave the law; And to E - li - jah,
liv - ered from the li - ons' might; And John, the Bride-groom's
turn in fast and prayer to you. Our spir - its strength - en

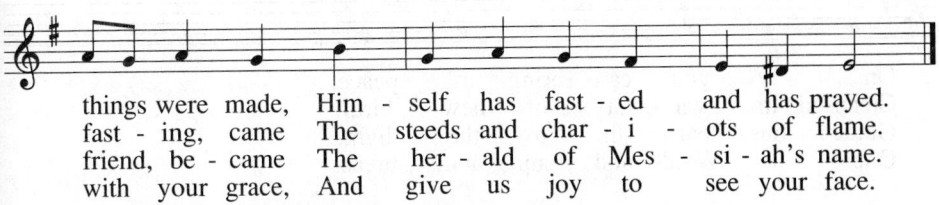

things were made, Him - self has fast - ed and has prayed.
fast - ing, came The steeds and char - i - ots of flame.
friend, be - came The her - ald of Mes - si - ah's name.
with your grace, And give us joy to see your face.

Text: *Clarum decus jejunii*; ascr. to Gregory the Great, c.540–604; tr. by Maurice F. Bell, 1862–1947, alt.
Tune: ERHALT UNS HERR, LM; Klug's *Geistliche Lieder*, 1543; harm. by J. S. Bach, 1685–1750

*Alternate tune:* OLD HUNDREDTH

# 482 The Cross of Jesus

1. Come, O God, re - new your peo - ple,
2. Deep with - in cre - ate a new heart;
3. In the dark - ness that sur - rounds us
4. Call us forth to walk in jus - tice;

We who long to see your face.
Melt a - way the win - ter chill.
We have lost you from our sight.
Res - cue us from sin and grave.

Strength - en hearts that have grown fee - ble;
Help us now to make a new start;
E - ven though your love has found us,
Through the pow - er of your Spir - it,

Fill our lives with truth and grace.
Help us now to know your will.
We em - brace the powers of night.
Breathe in us the breath that saves.

On - ly you can win our free - dom;
Washed in wa - ters of for - give - ness,
Scat - ter now our deep - est dark - ness;
Strength - en us in our com - mun - ion,

On - ly you can bring us peace.
Cleansed in wa - ters of new birth,
Guide our hearts in - to the light.
One in Word and cup and bread.

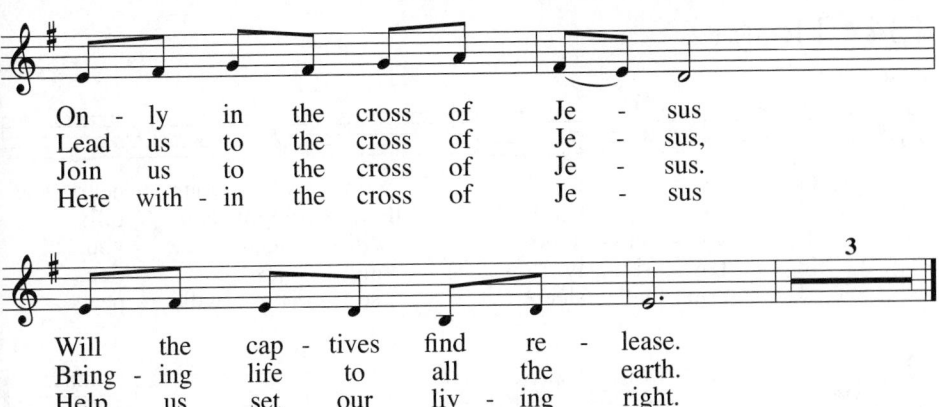

On - ly in the cross of Je - sus
Lead us to the cross of Je - sus,
Join us to the cross of Je - sus.
Here with - in the cross of Je - sus

3

Will the cap - tives find re - lease.
Bring - ing life to all the earth.
Help us set our liv - ing right.
All who hun - ger will be fed.

Text: Francis Patrick O'Brien, b.1958
Tune: Francis Patrick O'Brien, b.1958
© 1996, GIA Publications, Inc.

## Forty Days and Forty Nights  483

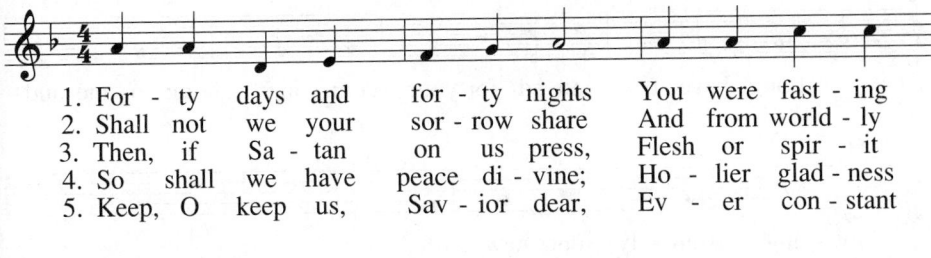

1. For - ty days and for - ty nights You were fast - ing
2. Shall not we your sor - row share And from world - ly
3. Then, if Sa - tan on us press, Flesh or spir - it
4. So shall we have peace di - vine; Ho - lier glad - ness
5. Keep, O keep us, Sav - ior dear, Ev - er con - stant

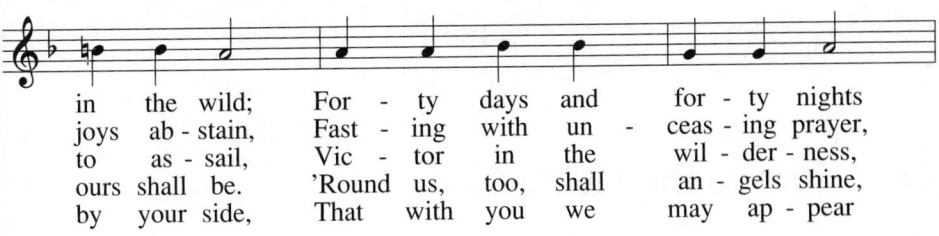

in the wild; For - ty days and for - ty nights
joys ab - stain, Fast - ing with un - ceas - ing prayer,
to as - sail, Vic - tor in the wil - der - ness,
ours shall be. 'Round us, too, shall an - gels shine,
by your side, That with you we may ap - pear

Tempt - ed, and yet un - de - filed.
Strong with you to suf - fer pain?
Grant we may not faint nor fail!
Such as served you faith - ful - ly.
At the e - ter - nal East - er - tide.

Text: George H. Smyttan, 1822–1870, alt.
Tune: HEINLEIN, 7 7 7 7; attr. to Martin Herbst, 1654–1681, *Nürnbergisches Gesangbuch*, 1676

# 484 Hosea

Verses

1. Come back to me with all your heart.
   Trees do bend, 'though straight and tall;
2. The wil - der - ness will lead you
   In - teg - ri - ty and jus - tice,
3. You shall sleep se - cure with peace;

Don't let fear keep us a - part.
so must we to oth - ers' call. *(To refrain)*
to your heart where I will speak.
With ten - der - ness, you shall know. *(To refrain)*
faith - ful - ness will be your joy. *(To refrain)*

Refrain

Long have I wait-ed for your com - ing home to me and

liv - ing deep - ly our new life.

Text: Hosea 6:1, 3:3, 2:16, 21; Joel 2:12; Weston Priory, Gregory Norbet, OSB, b.1940
Tune: Gregory Norbet, OSB, b.1940; arr. by Mary David Callahan, OSB, b.1923
© 1972, 1980, The Benedictine Foundation of the State of Vermont, Inc.

# 485 Turn to the Living God

Refrain

Turn, turn to the liv - ing God, the God of heal-ing and

com-fort, and with de-light, God will turn to

you. With de - light, God will turn to you.

Verses

1. For now is the time of fulfillment. The reign of our God is at hand.
   Reform your life, turn from sin and believe this glorious news.

2. Come, and return to the Lord. All you weary, bring your grieving hearts.
   With kindness and mercy God's compassion will fill your hearts with love.

3. Have mercy, O Lord, on your people. In your goodness wipe away our guilt.
   Wash us clean, free us to become your living song of praise.

4. Come, sing with joy to the Lord. Listen with an open heart.
   Hear God's voice and follow; our good shepherd is guiding the way.

Text: Lori True, b.1961
Tune: Lori True, b.1961
© 2003, GIA Publications, Inc.

# Deep Within   486

Refrain

Deep with - in     I will plant my law,
not on stone,     but in your heart.
Fol - low me,     I will bring you back,     you will
be my own, and I     will be your God.

Verses

1. I will give you a     new heart,     a new spir - it with -
2. Seek     my face,     and see     your
3. Re - turn     to me,     with     all     your

D.C.

in you,     for I will     be your     strength.
God,     for I will     be your     hope.
heart,     and I will     bring you     back.

Text: Jeremiah 31:33, Ezekiel 36:26, Joel 2:12; David Haas, b.1957
Tune: David Haas, b.1957; acc. by Jeanne Cotter, b.1964
© 1987, GIA Publications, Inc.

# 487  Again We Keep This Solemn Fast

1. A - gain we keep this sol - emn fast,
2. The law and proph - ets from of old
3. More spar - ing, there - fore, let us make
4. Let us a - void each harm - ful way
5. We pray, O bless - ed Three in One,

A gift of faith from a - ges past,
In fig - ured ways this Lent fore - told,
The words we speak, the food we take,
That lures the care - less mind a - stray;
Our God while end - less a - ges run,

This Lent which binds us lov - ing - ly
Which Christ, all a - ges' Lord and Guide,
Our sleep, our laugh - ter, ev - 'ry sense;
By watch - ful prayer our spir - its free
That this, our Lent of for - ty days,

To faith and hope and char - i - ty.
In these last days has sanc - ti - fied.
Learn peace through ho - ly pen - i - tence.
From schem - ing of the En - e - my.
May bring us growth and give you praise.

Text: *Ex more docti mystico;* ascr. to Gregory the Great, c.540–604; tr. by Peter J. Scagnelli, b.1949, ©
Tune: OLD HUNDREDTH, LM; Louis Bourgeois, c.1510–1561

## At the Cross Her Station Keeping    488

1. At the cross her sta - tion keep-ing, Mar - y stood in
2. While she wait - ed in her an-guish, See - ing Christ in
3. With what pain and des - o - la - tion, With what no - ble
4. Ev - er pa - tient in her yearn-ing, Though her tear - filled

sor - row, weep - ing, When her Son was cru - ci - fied.
tor - ment lan - guish, Bit - ter sor - row pierced her heart.
res - ig - na - tion, Mar - y watched her dy - ing Son.
eyes were burn - ing, Mar - y gazed up - on her Son.

5. Who, that sorrow contemplating,
   On that passion meditating,
   Would not share the Virgin's grief?

6. Christ she saw, for our salvation,
   Scourged with cruel acclamation,
   Bruised and beaten by the rod.

7. Christ she saw with life-blood failing,
   All her anguish unavailing,
   Saw him breathe his very last.

8. Mary, fount of love's devotion,
   Let me share with true emotion
   All the sorrow you endured.

9. Virgin, ever interceding,
   Hear me in my fervent pleading:
   Fire me with your love of Christ.

10. Mother, may this prayer be granted:
    That Christ's love may be implanted
    In the depths of my poor soul.

11. At the cross, your sorrow sharing,
    All your grief and torment bearing,
    Let me stand and mourn with you.

12. Fairest maid of all creation,
    Queen of hope and consolation,
    Let me feel your grief sublime.

13. Virgin, in your love befriend me,
    At the Judgment Day defend me.
    Help me by your constant prayer.

14. Savior, when my life shall leave me,
    Through your mother's prayers receive me
    With the fruits of victory.

15. Let me to your love be taken,
    Let my soul in death awaken
    To the joys of Paradise.

Text: *Stabat mater dolorosa;* Jacopone da Todi, 1230–1306; trans. by Anthony G. Petti, 1932–1985, © 1971, Faber Music, Ltd.
Tune: STABAT MATER, 88 7; *Mainz Gesangbuch,* 1661; harm. by Richard Proulx, 1937–2010, © 1986, GIA Publications, Inc.

# 489 Merciful God

Refrain

*Ash Wednesday:* Sign us with ash - es, mer - ci - ful God,
*Lent Gathering:* Gath - er your peo - ple, mer - ci - ful God,
*Lent Communion:* Feed us and guide us, mer - ci - ful God:

Chil - dren of dust, as to dust we re - turn. Sign us with
Gath - er the long - ing, the lost, and un - sure. Gath - er your
Light, when the shad - ows of life cloud our view. Feed us and

ash - es, mer - ci - ful God; Mark us and make us your
peo - ple, mer - ci - ful God, Name us and claim us as
guide us, mer - ci - ful God, Peo - ple who hun - ger for

*To verses* / *Last time*

own. own, mark us and make us your own.
yours. yours, name us and claim us as yours.
you. you, peo - ple who hun - ger for you.

Verses

1. Sure - ly, you a - lone can save us. You pay our price with
2. Sure - ly, you a - lone up - hold us. You give us strength for
3. Sure - ly, you a - lone can heal us. Yours is the will to
4. Sure - ly, you a - lone can free us. You break the bonds of
5. Sure - ly, you a - lone re - fine us. You give us grace for
6. Sure - ly, you a - lone re - deem us. You fill our dust with

pre - cious blood. Reach - ing through your great com -
all our needs. Shield - ing with a fa - ther's
make us whole. Sooth - ing with a moth - er's
guilt and sin. Brac - ing, till we walk up -
lives made new, Forg - ing, through your fire and
ho - ly breath. Burst - ing from the grave in

D.C.

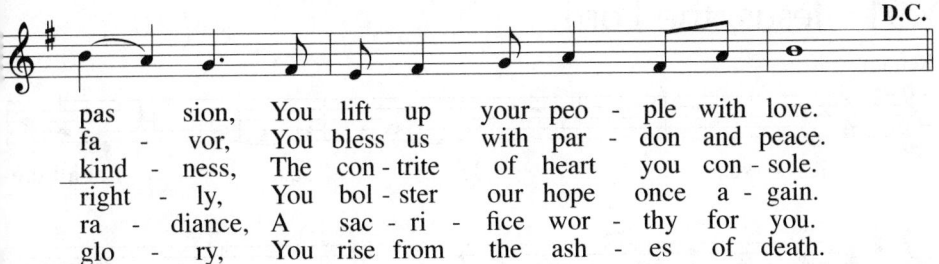

| pas - sion, | You lift up | your peo - ple with love. |
| fa - vor, | You bless us | with par - don and peace. |
| kind - ness, | The con - trite | of heart you con - sole. |
| right - ly, | You bol - ster | our hope once a - gain. |
| ra - diance, | A sac - ri - | fice wor - thy for you. |
| glo - ry, | You rise from | the ash - es of death. |

Text: Mary Louise Bringle, b.1953, © 2006, 2009, GIA Publications, Inc.
Tune: Tony E. Alonso, b.1980, © 2009, GIA Publications, Inc.

## Kýrie 490

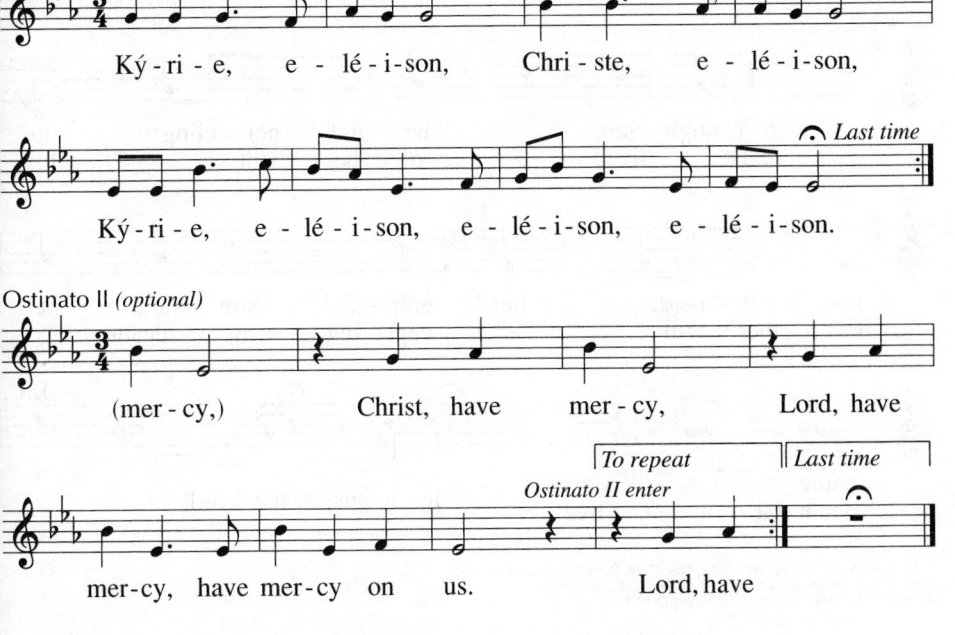

Ostinato I

Ký - ri - e, e - lé - i - son, Chri - ste, e - lé - i - son,

Last time

Ký - ri - e, e - lé - i - son, e - lé - i - son, e - lé - i - son.

Ostinato II *(optional)*

(mer - cy,) Christ, have mer - cy, Lord, have

To repeat | Last time
Ostinato II enter

mer - cy, have mer - cy on us. Lord, have

Text: Marty Haugen, b.1950
Tune: Marty Haugen, b.1950
© 2001, GIA Publications, Inc.

# 491 Jesus, the Lord

Refrain

Je - sus. Je - sus. Let all cre-a-tion bend the knee to the Lord.

Verse 1

1. In him we live, we move and have our be - ing; in him the Christ, in him the King! Je - sus, the Lord.

D.C.

Verses 2, 3

2. Though Son, he did not cling to god - li - ness; but emp - tied him - self, be - came a slave!
3. He lived o - be - dient - ly his Fa - ther's will ac - cept - ing his death, death on a tree!

Je - sus, the Lord.

D.C.

Text: *Jesus Prayer,* Philippians 2:5–11; Acts 17:28; Roc O'Connor, SJ, b.1949
Tune: Roc O'Connor, SJ, b.1949; arr. by Rick Modlin, b.1966
© 1981, 1994, Robert F. O'Connor, SJ, and OCP

# Jerusalem, My Destiny  492

**Refrain**

I have fixed my eyes on your hills, Je - ru - sa-lem, my
des - ti-ny! Though I can - not see the end for me, I
can - not turn a - way. We have set our hearts for the
way; this jour - ney is our des - ti-ny. Let
no-one walk a - lone. The jour - ney makes us one.

**Verses**

1. Oth - er spir - its, less - er gods, have court-ed me with lies.
2. See, I leave the past be-hind; a new land calls to me.
3. In my thirst, you let me drink the wa - ters of your life.
4. All the worlds I have not seen you o - pen to my view.
5. To the tombs I went to mourn the hope I thought was gone.

**D.C.**

Here a - mong you I have found a truth which bids me rise.
Here a - mong you now I find a glimpse of what might be.
Here a - mong you I have met the sav - ior, Je - sus Christ.
Here a - mong you I have found a vi - sion, bright and new.
Here a - mong you I a - woke to un - ex - pect - ed dawn.

Text: Rory Cooney, b.1952
Tune: Rory Cooney, b.1952
© 1990, GIA Publications, Inc.

# 493 Change Our Hearts

Refrain

Change our hearts this time, Your word says it can
be. Change our minds, this time, Your life could make us
free. We are the peo - ple Your call set a - part,
Lord, this time change our hearts.

Verses

1. Brought by your hand to the edge of our dreams.
2. Now as we watch you stretch out your hands,
3. Show us the way that leads to your side,

One foot in par - a - dise, one in the waste.
of - 'fring a - bun - dan - ces, full - ness of joy.
o - ver the moun - tains and sands of the soul.

Drawn by your prom - is - es, still we are
Your milk and hon - ey seem dis - tant, un -
Be for us man - na, wa - ter from

D.C.

lured by the shad - ows and the chains we leave be - hind. But
real, when we have bread and wa - ter in our hands. But
stone, light which says we nev - er walk a - lone. And

Text: Rory Cooney, b.1952
Tune: Rory Cooney, b.1952
© 1984, North American Liturgy Resources. Published by OCP.

# Hold Us in Your Mercy: Penitential Litany   494

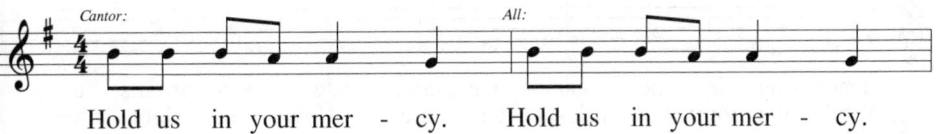

*Cantor:* Hold us   in  your mer - cy.   *All:* Hold us   in  your mer - cy.

*Cantor:* Hold us   in  your mer - cy.   *All:* Hold us   in  your mer - cy.

*Cantor:* *(Invocation)*   *All:* Hold us   in  your mer - cy.

*Cantor:* *(Invocation)*   *All:* Hold us   in  your mer - cy.

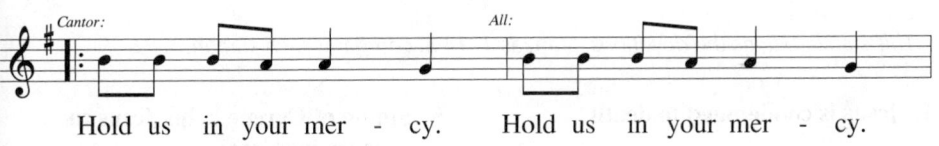

*Cantor:* Hold us   in  your mer - cy.   *All:* Hold us   in  your mer - cy.

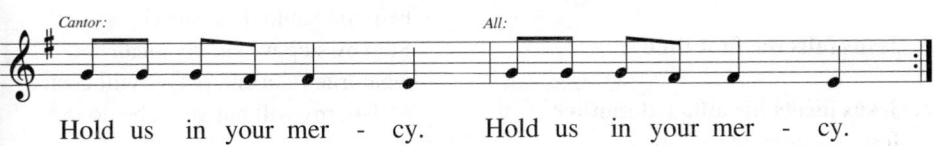

*Cantor:* Hold us   in  your mer - cy.   *All:* Hold us   in  your mer - cy.

*Cantor:* Hold us   in  your mer - cy.   *All:* Hold us   in  your mer - cy.

Text: Rory Cooney, b.1952
Tune: Based on PARCE DOMINE; Gary Daigle, b.1957
© 1993, GIA Publications, Inc.

# 495  Stations of the Cross

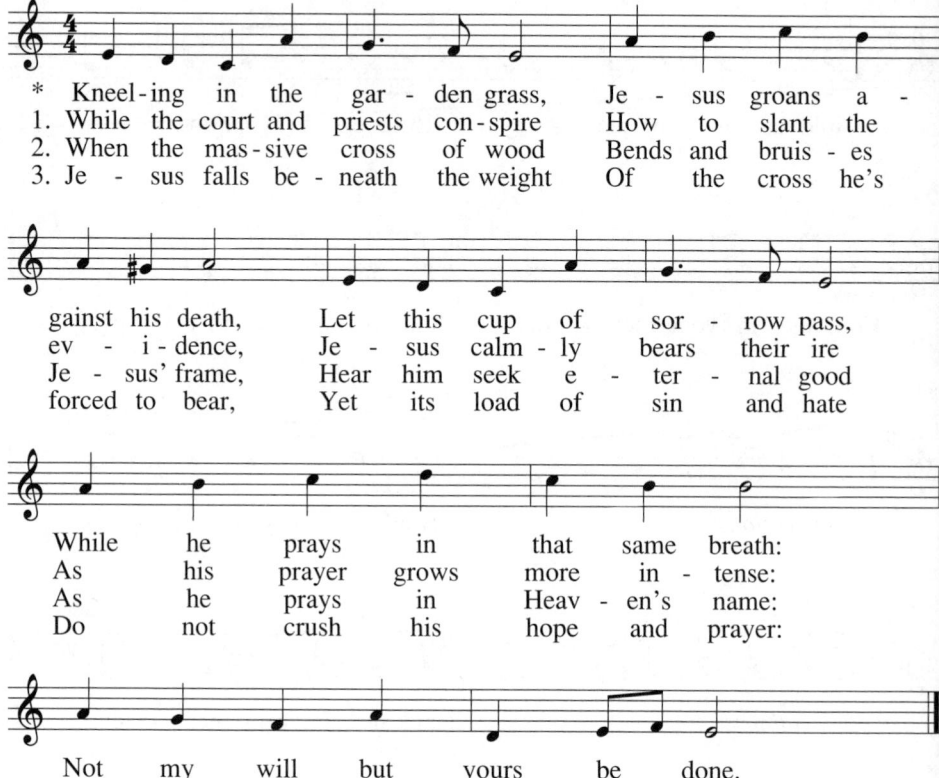

```
*  Kneel-ing   in   the   gar - den grass,   Je - sus  groans   a -
1. While  the  court and  priests  con-spire  How   to   slant   the
2. When  the  mas-sive  cross   of  wood   Bends and  bruis - es
3. Je - sus  falls  be - neath  the weight   Of   the   cross  he's
```

```
gainst  his  death,   Let   this   cup   of   sor - row  pass,
ev - i - dence,   Je - sus  calm - ly   bears   their  ire
Je - sus'  frame,   Hear  him   seek   e - ter - nal  good
forced  to  bear,   Yet   its   load   of   sin   and  hate
```

```
While   he   prays   in   that   same  breath:
As   his   prayer  grows  more   in - tense:
As   he   prays   in   Heav - en's  name:
Do   not   crush  his   hope  and  prayer:
```

```
Not   my   will   but   yours   be   done.
```

*This stanza begins the devotions. Stanzas 1–14 accompany each station.*

**1. Jesus is condemned to death**

**2. Jesus carries his Cross**

**3. Jesus falls the first time**

**4. Jesus meets his afflicted mother**
Jesus reads in Mary's eyes
all the sorrow mothers bear,
and he prays his friend supplies
grace to strengthen her own prayer:
Not my will but yours be done.

**5. Simon of Cyrene helps Jesus to carry his Cross**
We with Simon of Cyrene
help the Savior bear the cross.
Step by step we slowly glean
what true faith and prayer will cost:
Not my will but yours be done.

6. **Veronica wipes the face of Jesus**
Seek the courage and the grace
that Veronica displays
when she wipes the bleeding face
of the one who bravely prays:
Not my will but yours be done.

7. **Jesus falls the second time**
Jesus trips and falls again
as he struggles through the street
where the mob's unceasing din
mocks the prayer his lips repeat:
Not my will but yours be done.

8. **Jesus meets the women of Jerusalem**
Christ directs the women's tears
toward the coming judgment day
when God weighs our faithless years
with our willingness to pray:
Not my will but yours be done.

9. **Jesus falls a third time**
Jesus stumbles one last time,
nearly broken by the load,
yet by prayer finds strength to climb
Calvary's final stretch of road:
Not my will but yours be done.

10. **Jesus is stripped of his clothes**
Naked to the sun and clouds
and the jeers and gawking stare
of the soldiers and the crowds,
Christ continues with his prayer:
Not my will but yours be done.

11. **Jesus is nailed to the Cross**
While the soldiers throw their dice,
they ignore their victim's groans,
lost to them the sacrifice
and the prayer that Jesus moans:
Not my will but yours be done.

12. **Jesus dies on the Cross**
Jesus gives one loud last cry
at the moment of his death
while his prayer moves heaven's sky
with his final, parting breath:
Not my will but yours be done.

13. **The body of Jesus is taken
    down from the Cross**
As they take the body down
and they wrap it in a sheet,
in their hearts they hear the sound
that his lips no more repeat:
Not my will but yours be done.

14. **Jesus is laid in the tomb**
Quiet is the hollowed cave.
Peace and tears and grief descend.
Mourners offer at the grave
what they learned from Christ their
friend:
Not my will but yours be done.

Text: Thomas Troeger, b.1945, © 1994, Oxford University Press
Tune: VIA CRUCIS, 7 7 7 7 with refrain; William P. Rowan, b.1951, © 1995, GIA Publications, Inc.

# 496 Palm Sunday Processional

*Cantor:*

1. When they heard that Je - sus was com - ing,
2. Spread their cloaks and branch - es be - fore him,
3. Blest is he, like Da - vid be - fore him.
4. Guid - ing cloud and pil - lar of fire,
5. Vi - sion blest, and hope for the fu - ture,
6. Won - drous bread and stream in the des - ert,
7. Eye of God, who sees to the heart of us,
8. Ris - ing sun, the light of the world,
9. Friend in death, who weeps for our dy - ing,
10. Friend in death, who wakes us to new life,

*Assembly:*

Sing ho - san - na to the cho - sen one!

*Cantor:*

All the peo - ple went out to meet him.
Chil - dren sang, with palm branch - es wav - ing.
Blest is he, God's bless - ing up - on him.
Sa - tan's foe and friend of the sin - ner.
God's be - lov - ed, ra - diant with glo - ry.
Heav'n - ly food and God's liv - ing wa - ter.
Heal - ing touch and sight for our blind - ness.
Word of life, who gives us the Spir - it.
Friend in death, who rolls back the stone for us.
Friend in life: we sing glad ho - san - nas.

*Assembly:*

Sing ho - san - na to the cho - sen one!

Sing ho - san - na, sing ho - san - na,

sing ho - san - na to the cho - sen one!

Text: Rory Cooney, b.1952
Tune: Rory Cooney, b.1952
© 1999, GIA Publications, Inc.

# Ride On, Jesus, Ride    497

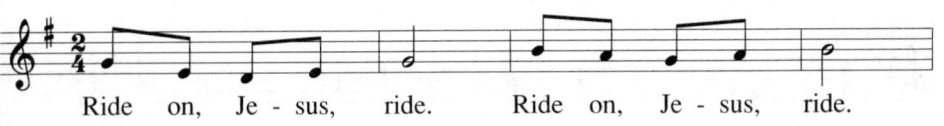

Ride on, Je - sus, ride.    Ride on, Je - sus, ride.

Ride on, Je - sus, con - quering King,    Ride on, Je - sus ride.

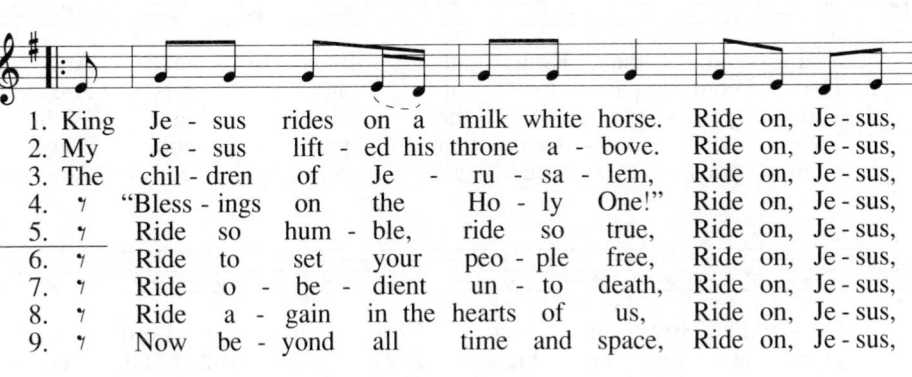

1. King    Je - sus    rides    on    a    milk white horse.    Ride on, Je - sus,
2. My    Je - sus    lift - ed his throne    a - bove.    Ride on, Je - sus,
3. The    chil - dren    of    Je - ru - sa - lem,    Ride on, Je - sus,
4. ⸜    "Bless - ings    on    the    Ho - ly    One!"    Ride on, Je - sus,
5. ⸜    Ride    so    hum - ble,    ride    so    true,    Ride on, Je - sus,
6. ⸜    Ride    to    set    your    peo - ple    free,    Ride on, Je - sus,
7. ⸜    Ride    o - be - dient    un - to    death,    Ride on, Je - sus,
8. ⸜    Ride    a - gain    in the hearts    of    us,    Ride on, Je - sus,
9. ⸜    Now    be - yond    all    time    and    space,    Ride on, Je - sus,

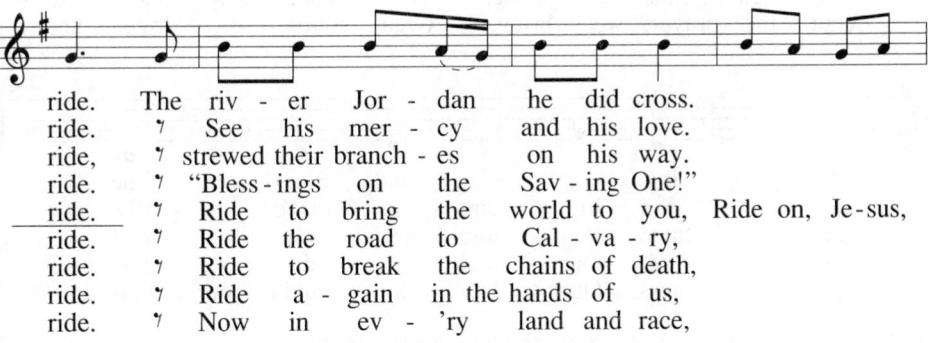

ride.    The    riv - er    Jor - dan    he    did cross.
ride.    ⸜ See    his    mer - cy    and    his love.
ride,    ⸜ strewed their branch - es    on    his way.
ride.    ⸜ "Bless - ings    on    the    Sav - ing One!"
ride.    ⸜ Ride    to    bring    the    world to    you,    Ride on, Je - sus,
ride.    ⸜ Ride    the    road    to    Cal - va - ry,
ride.    ⸜ Ride    to    break    the    chains of death,
ride.    ⸜ Ride    a - gain    in the hands of    us,
ride.    ⸜ Now    in    ev - 'ry    land and race,

ride.    Ride on, Je - sus, con - quering King. Ride on, Je - sus ride.

Text: African American spiritual; verses 3–9, Marty Haugen, b.1950, © 1991, GIA Publications, Inc.
Tune: African American spiritual; harm. by Barbara Jackson Martin, b.1947, © 1987, GIA Publications, Inc.

## 498 All Glory, Laud, and Honor

Refrain

All glo - ry, laud, and hon - or To you, Re - deem - er, King!

To whom the lips of chil - dren Made sweet ho - san - nas ring.

Verses

1. You are the King of Is - ra - el And
2. The com - pa - ny of an - gels Are
3. The peo - ple of the He - brews With
4. To you, be - fore your pas - sion, They
5. Their prais - es you ac - cept - ed; Ac -

Da - vid's roy - al Son, Now in the Lord's Name
prais - ing you on high; And we, with all cre -
palms be - fore you went; Our praise and prayers and
sang their hymns of praise. To you, now high ex -
cept the prayers we bring, Great source of love and

D.C.

com - ing, Our King and Bless - ed One.
a - tion, In cho - rus make re - ply.
an - thems Be - fore you we pre - sent.
alt - ed, Our mel - o - dy we raise.
good - ness, Our Sav - ior and our King.

Text: *Gloria, laus et honor;* Theodulph of Orleans, c.760–821; tr. by John M. Neale, 1818–1866, alt.
Tune: ST. THEODULPH, 7 6 7 6 D; Melchior Teschner, 1584–1635

# Hosanna 499

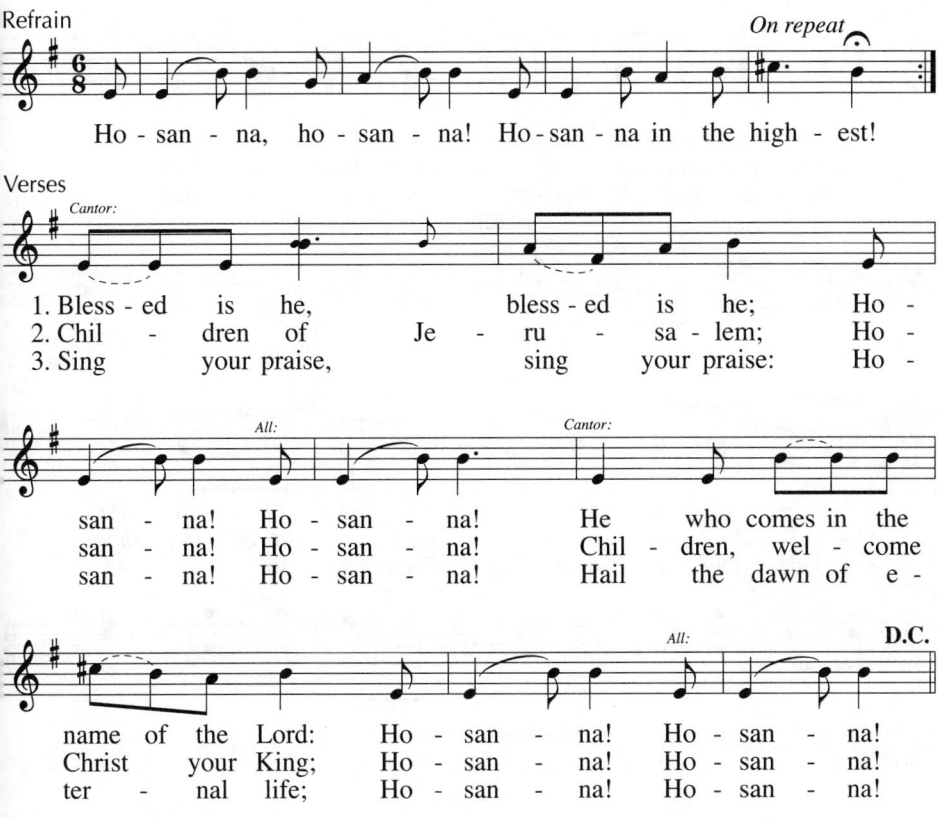

Refrain

*On repeat*

Ho - san - na, ho - san - na! Ho - san - na in the high - est!

Verses

*Cantor:*

1. Bless - ed    is    he,         bless - ed    is    he;         Ho -
2. Chil  -  dren    of    Je  -  ru  -  sa - lem;         Ho -
3. Sing         your praise,         sing    your praise:         Ho -

*All:*    *Cantor:*

san - na!    Ho - san - na!    He         who comes in    the
san - na!    Ho - san - na!    Chil - dren,    wel - come
san - na!    Ho - san - na!    Hail    the    dawn of    e -

*All:*    **D.C.**

name    of    the    Lord:    Ho - san - na!    Ho - san - na!
Christ    your    King;    Ho - san - na!    Ho - san - na!
ter  -  nal    life;    Ho - san - na!    Ho - san - na!

Text: Scott Soper, b.1961
Tune: Scott Soper, b.1961
© 1997, GIA Publications, Inc.

# 500 Ubi Cáritas

Refrain

U - bi cá - ri - tas · et a - mor,
*Where true char - i - ty · and love a - bide,*
Don - de hay a - mor · y ca - ri - dad,

u - bi cá - ri - tas · De - us i - bi est.
*God is dwell - ing there; · God is dwell - ing there.*
don - de hay a - mor · Dios a - llí es - tá.

Text: 1 Corinthians 13:2–8, 13; *Where charity and love are found*, God is there; Taizé Community, 1978
Tune: Jacques Berthier, 1923–1994
© 1979, 2009, 2011, Les Presses de Taizé, GIA Publications, Inc., agent

# 501 Glory in the Cross

Refrain

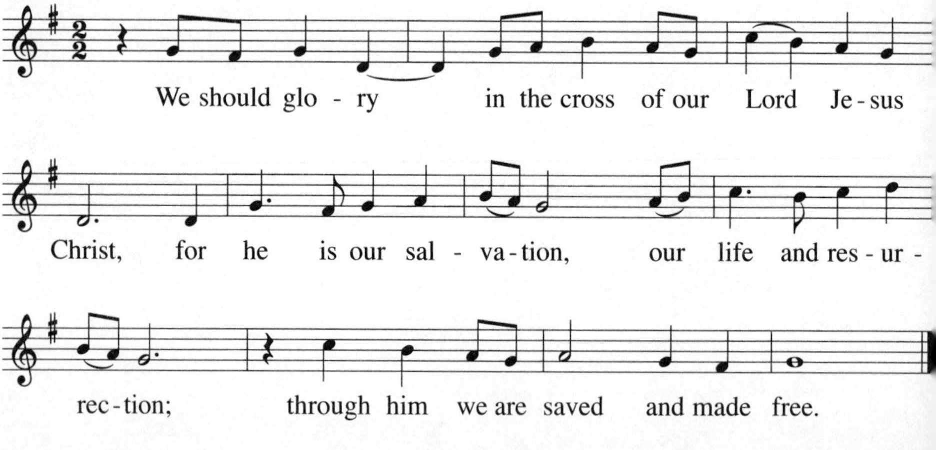

We should glo - ry · in the cross of our Lord Je - sus

Christ, for he is our sal - va - tion, our life and res - ur -

rec - tion; through him we are saved and made free.

1. Sing, my tongue, the hymn of glo - ry;
2. Tell how, when at length the full - ness
3. With the thir - ty years now end - ed,
4. Faith - ful Cross, true sign of tri - umph,

Of the fi - nal con - flict sing. Shout the tri - umph
Of the ho - ly time had come, Christ was sent, the
Which on earth he willed to see, Will - ing - ly he
Be for all the no - blest tree; None in fol - iage,

of the vic - tim; Far and wide the
world's Cre - a - tor, From the Fa - ther's
meets his pas - sion, Born to set his
none in blos - som, None in fruit your

ech - oes ring: Je - sus Christ, the world's sal - va - tion,
heav'n - ly home, And was found a - mong us dwell - ing,
peo - ple free; On the cross the Lamb is lift - ed,
peer may be; Sym - bol of the world's re - demp - tion,

D.C.

From the cross now reigns as King.
Off - spring of the Vir - gin's womb.
There the sac - ri - fice to be.
For your bur - den makes us free.

Text: Refrain, from *Rite of Holy Week*, © 1972, ICEL; verses by Venantius Fortunatus, c.530–609; verses 1–3 tr. by Steven R. Janco, b.1961, alt.,
© 1997, GIA Publications, Inc.; verse 4 tr. by John Mason Neale, 1818–1866, alt.
Tune: GLORY IN THE CROSS, 8 7 8 7 8 7 with refrain; Steven R. Janco, b.1961, © 1997, GIA Publications, Inc.

# 502 Stay Here and Keep Watch

Ostinato Refrain

Stay here and keep watch with me. The hour has come.
*Es - tén des-pier-tos, qué - den - se a - quí con - mi-go.*

Stay here and keep watch with me. Watch and pray.
*Es - tén des-pier-tos, qué - den - se. O - ren y ve - len.*

Text: Matthew 26:38–40; Taizé Community
Tune: Jacques Berthier, 1923–1994
© 1984, 2011, Les Presses de Taizé, GIA Publications, Inc., agent

# 503 This Is My Example

Refrain

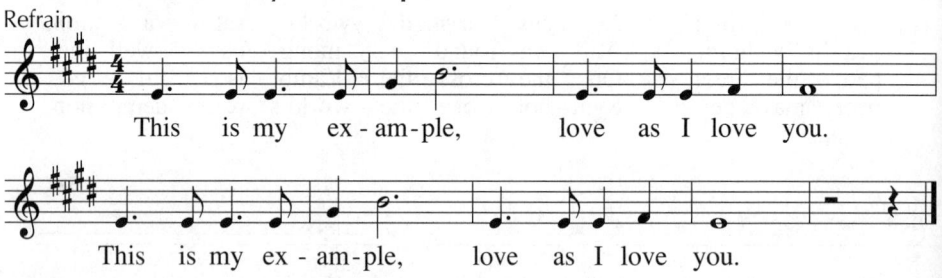

This is my ex - am - ple, love as I love you.

This is my ex - am - ple, love as I love you.

Verses

1. Breaking bread with friends as his life was at an end,
   Jesus knelt to wash their their feet.

2. In a time to come you will know what I have done;
   let me wash you, let me serve.

3. Simon Peter said, "Wash my hands, my feet, my head!"
   Jesus looked on him with love.

4. Make my love complete, go and wash each other's feet;
   what I have done so you must must do.

5. To the poor and weak, be the comfort that they seek;
   let my example be your guide.

6. May your lives be one in this work I have begun;
come and follow where I lead.

7. Go forth and care for all people ev'rywhere.
Find your strength within my love.

8. Speak my words of peace. To the captives bring release.
Go embrace them in my name.

9. If my love you bear to the people ev'rywhere,
all will know that you are mine.

10. In your faith is pow'r to embrace the darkest hour;
go without fear to heal and serve.

11. This my life I give; I must die that you may live.
All this I do for love of you.

12. When your lives are through, I will come to welcome you.
We will be forever one.

Text: Francis Patrick O'Brien, b.1958
Tune: Francis Patrick O'Brien, b.1958
© 2001, GIA Publications, Inc.

# Prepare a Room for Me    504

*To be sung in alternating verses by cantor and congregation.*

1. "Pre - pare a room for me, Your Sav - ior, Host and Priest, Where I may gath - er you, my friends, To cel - e - brate the feast."
2. This room we have pre - pared; The Ta - ble now is set. We wait your prom - ised pres - ence, Lord, Where we once more are met.
3. "Where e - ven two or three Have come the Meal to share, Un - seen, but liv - ing, lov - ing still, I sure - ly will be there!"
4. Lord Christ, we seek the food Your grace a - lone can give. We come with emp - ty, hun - g'ring hearts That we may eat and live.
5. "My prom - ise I will keep; Your hun - ger will be fed, For in this Meal I Sav - ior, Lord, and Friend, That through this Loaf and Cup you share Your love that has no end!"
6. All thanks and praise to you, Our Sav - ior, Lord, and Friend, That through this Loaf and Cup you share Your love that has no end!

Text: Herman G. Stuempfle, Jr., 1923–2007, © 2000, GIA Publications, Inc.
Tune: SOUTHWELL, SM; Damon's *Psalmes*, alt.

# 505  Jesu, Jesu

**Refrain**

Je - su,   Je - su,   fill  us  with your love,   show

us how to serve   the  neigh - bors  we have   from  you.

**Verses**

1. Kneels   at   the   feet   of   his   friends,
2. Neigh - bors   are   wealth - y   and   poor,
3. These   are   the   ones   we   should   serve,
4. Kneel   at   the   feet   of   our   friends,

Si - lent - ly   wash - es   their   feet,
Var - ied   in   col - or   and   race,
These   are   the   ones   we   should   love:
Si - lent - ly   wash - ing   their   feet:

**D.C.**

Mas - ter   who pours   out   him - self   for   them.
Neigh - bors   are   near - by   and   far   a - way.
All   these   are neigh - bors   to   us   and   you.
This   is   the   way   we should   live   with   you.

Text: Tom Colvin, 1925–2000, alt.
Tune: CHEREPONI, Irregular; Ghana folk song; adapt. by Tom Colvin, 1925–2000; acc. by Jane M. Marshall, b.1924
© 1969, and arr. © 1982, Hope Publishing Company

# Song of the Lord's Command  506

Refrain

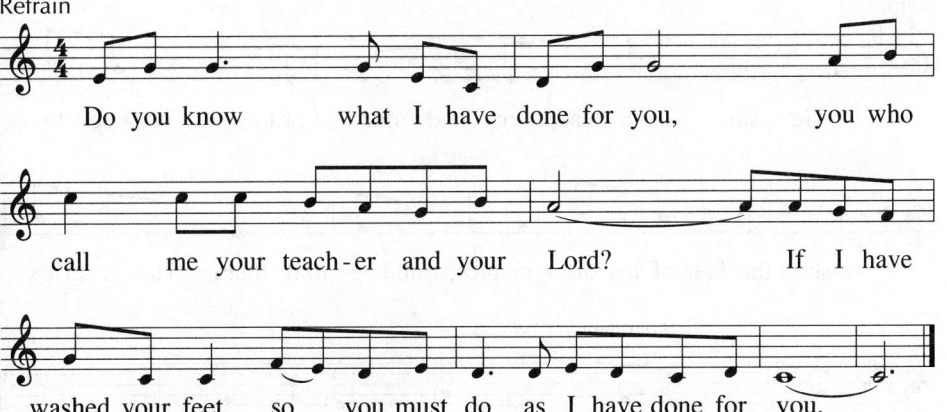

Do you know what I have done for you, you who call me your teach-er and your Lord? If I have washed your feet, so you must do as I have done for you.

Verses

1. What I am doing now you do not know,
   but after a time has gone by, you will understand.

2. Don't you understand what I must do?
   If you would be mine, then I must bend to wash your feet.

3. I have given to you an example;
   what I have done for you, you must do for one another.

4. There is no greater love than this:
   than to lay down your life for a friend.

5. Go, and live in my love.
   You will live in my love if you keep my commands.

6. Go, and love as I have shown you.
   Love one another as I have loved you.

7. You did not choose me, I chose you;
   I chose you to go forth and bear fruit that will endure.

Text: John 13:1–15, 15:12–14, 16; David Haas, b.1957
Tune: David Haas, b.1957
© 1997, GIA Publications, Inc.

# 507 So You Must Do

**Refrain**

Je - sus, our teach - er and our Lord, stooped to

wash the feet of his dis - ci - ples, and he told them, "This is an ex -

*Last time to Coda*

am - ple; just as I have done, so you must do."

**Verses**

1. When Je - sus had gath - ered with those he loved, as a
2. With tow - el and ba - sin he washed their feet, so that
3. He asked, "Do you know what I have done? I give
4. "As I, your teach - er, have washed your feet, so must
5. "A new com - mand - ment I give to you, that you

**D.C.**

hum - ble ser - vant he knelt at their feet.
they might share in his pas - sion and death.
you a wit - ness of what you must do."
you be will - ing to serve in my name."
love each oth - er as I have loved you."

**Coda**

done, so you must do." And he told them, "This is an ex -

am - ple; just as I have done, so you must do."

Text: John 13:1–15, adapt. by Marty Haugen, b.1950
Tune: Marty Haugen, b.1950
© 1998, GIA Publications, Inc.

# Song of the Lord's Supper 508

1. We re - mem - ber one who loved us well,
2. We re - mem - ber how he spoke of you,
3. On the night be - fore he suf - fered death,
4. As they sat at ta - ble he took bread,
5. Now we take these gifts of field and vine,

Shared our life, its joy and sor - row, Walked a - mong us as the
Taught us to be - lieve your prom-ise, Showed us all what you are
Je - sus gath-ered his dis - ci - ples, Knelt be - fore them as a
Blest it, broke it, gave it free - ly: "Take this bread and eat it,
Bless and share them in his mem-'ry: Bread of life and cup of

least of all, Gave him - self in - to our keep - ing.
real - ly like— Faith - ful, ten - der, God of peo - ple:
ser-vant might, Washed their feet and bid them wel-come:
all of you; Take and eat, this is my bod - y."
cov - e - nant, King - dom - feast in pledge and prom - ise.

He is light that dawns for blind - ed eyes,
Not a God to break the wound - ed heart,
"Do you know what I have done for you,
Then he took the cup and passed it round:
When we eat this bread and drink this cup

He is hope for the de - spair - ing; All on earth can find a
Not the thun - der of the might - y, But a God that wel - comes
I who am your Lord and Mas - ter? If I bend to you and
"Take and drink, this is my life - blood, Shed for you and for all
We pro-claim the death of Je - sus, Taste his pres-ence, liv - ing

place with him, Saint and sin - ner at his ta - ble.
sin - ners home, Meets the low - ly with com - pas-sion.
wash your feet, So must you for one an - oth - er."
hu - man-kind, Shed that sins may be for - giv - en."
in our midst, Look for him to come in glo - ry.

Text: Michael Joncas, b.1951
Tune: Michael Joncas, b.1951
© 1988, GIA Publications, Inc.

# 509 Hail Our Savior's Glorious Body / Pange Lingua

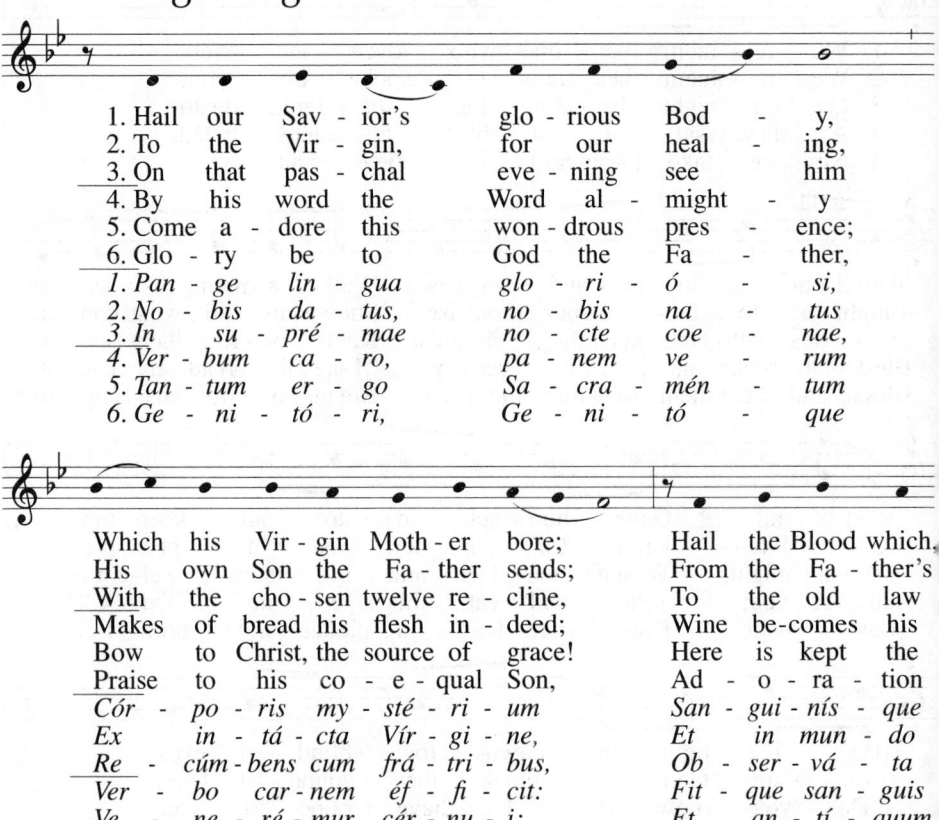

1. Hail our Sav - ior's glo - rious Bod - y,
2. To the Vir - gin, for our heal - ing,
3. On that pas - chal eve - ning see him
4. By his word the Word al - might - y
5. Come a - dore this won - drous pres - ence;
6. Glo - ry be to God the Fa - ther,

1. Pan - ge lin - gua glo - ri - ó - si,
2. No - bis da - tus, no - bis na - tus
3. In su - pré - mae no - cte coe - nae,
4. Ver - bum ca - ro, pa - nem ve - rum
5. Tan - tum er - go Sa - cra - mén - tum
6. Ge - ni - tó - ri, Ge - ni - tó - que

Which his Vir - gin Moth - er bore; Hail the Blood which,
His own Son the Fa - ther sends; From the Fa - ther's
With the cho - sen twelve re - cline, To the old law
Makes of bread his flesh in - deed; Wine be-comes his
Bow to Christ, the source of grace! Here is kept the
Praise to his co - e - qual Son, Ad - o - ra - tion

Cór - po - ris my - sté - ri - um San - gui - nís - que
Ex in - tá - cta Vír - gi - ne, Et in mun - do
Re - cúm - bens cum frá - tri - bus, Ob - ser - vá - ta
Ver - bo car - nem éf - fi - cit: Fit - que san - guis
Ve - ne - ré - mur cér - nu - i: Et an - tí - quum
Laus et ju - bi - lá - ti - o, Sa - lus, ho - nor,

shed for sin - ners, Did a bro - ken world re - store;
love pro - ceed - ing Sow - er, seed, and word de - scends;
still o - be - dient In its feast of love di - vine;
ver - y life - blood; Faith God's liv - ing Word must heed!
an - cient prom - ise Of God's earth - ly dwell - ing - place!
to the Spir - it, Bond of love, in God - head one!

pre - ti - ó - si, Quem in mun - di pré - ti - um
con - ver - sá - tus, Spar - so ver - bi sé - mi - ne,
le - ge ple - ne Ci - bis in le - gá - li - bus,
Chri - sti me - rum, Et si sen - sus dé - fi - cit,
do - cu - mén - tum No - vo ce - dat rí - tu - i;
vir - tus quo - que Sit et be - ne - dí - cti - o:

Hail the sac - ra - ment most ho - ly,   Flesh and Blood of
Won - drous life of Word in - car - nate   With his great - est
Love di - vine, the new law giv - ing,   Gives him - self as
Faith a - lone may safe - ly guide us   Where the sens - es
Sight is blind be - fore God's glo - ry.   Faith a - lone may
Blest be God by all cre - a - tion   Joy - ous - ly while
*Fru - ctus ven - tris ge - ne - ró - si*   *Rex ef - fú - dit*
*Su - i mo - ras in - co - lá - tus*   *Mi - ro clau - sit*
*Ci - bum tur - bae du - o - dé - nae*   *Se dat su - is*
*Ad fir - mán - dum cor sin - cé - rum*   *So - la fi - des*
*Prae - stet fi - des sup - ple - mén - tum*   *Sén - su - um de -*
*Pro - ce - dén - ti ab u - tró - que*   *Com - par sit lau -*

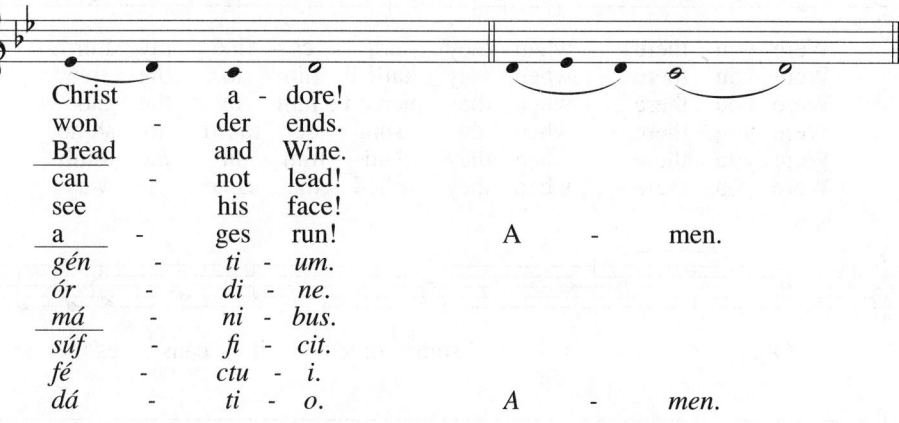

Christ a - dore!
won - der ends.
Bread and Wine.
can - not lead!
see his face!
a - ges run!    A - men.
*gén - ti - um.*
*ór - di - ne.*
*má - ni - bus.*
*súf - fi - cit.*
*fé - ctu - i.*
*dá - ti - o.*    *A - men.*

Text: *Pange lingua*, Thomas Aquinas, 1227–1274; tr. by James Quinn, SJ, 1919–2010, © 1969; Used by permission of Selah Publishing Co., Inc.
Tune: Mode III; acc. by Eugene Lapierre, 1899–1970, © 1964, GIA Publications, Inc.

## Jesus, Remember Me   510

Ostinato Refrain

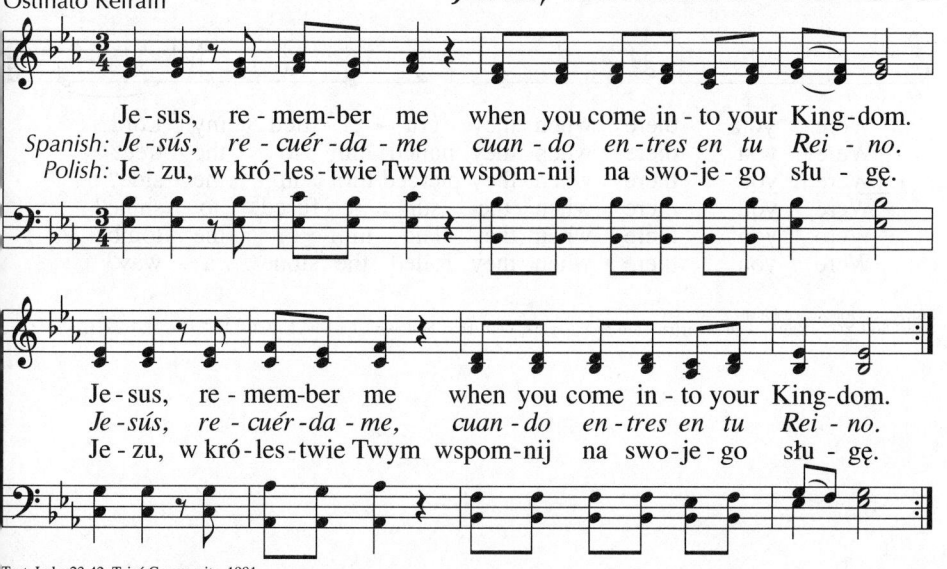

Je - sus, re - mem - ber me when you come in - to your King - dom.
*Spanish:* Je - sús, re - cuér - da - me cuan - do en - tres en tu Rei - no.
*Polish:* Je - zu, w kró - les - twie Twym wspom - nij na swo - je - go słu - gę.

Je - sus, re - mem - ber me when you come in - to your King - dom.
Je - sús, re - cuér - da - me, cuan - do en - tres en tu Rei - no.
Je - zu, w kró - les - twie Twym wspom - nij na swo - je - go słu - gę.

Text: Luke 23:42; Taizé Community, 1981
Tune: Jacques Berthier, 1923–1994
© 1981, 2005, Les Presses de Taizé, GIA Publications, Inc., agent

# 511 Were You There

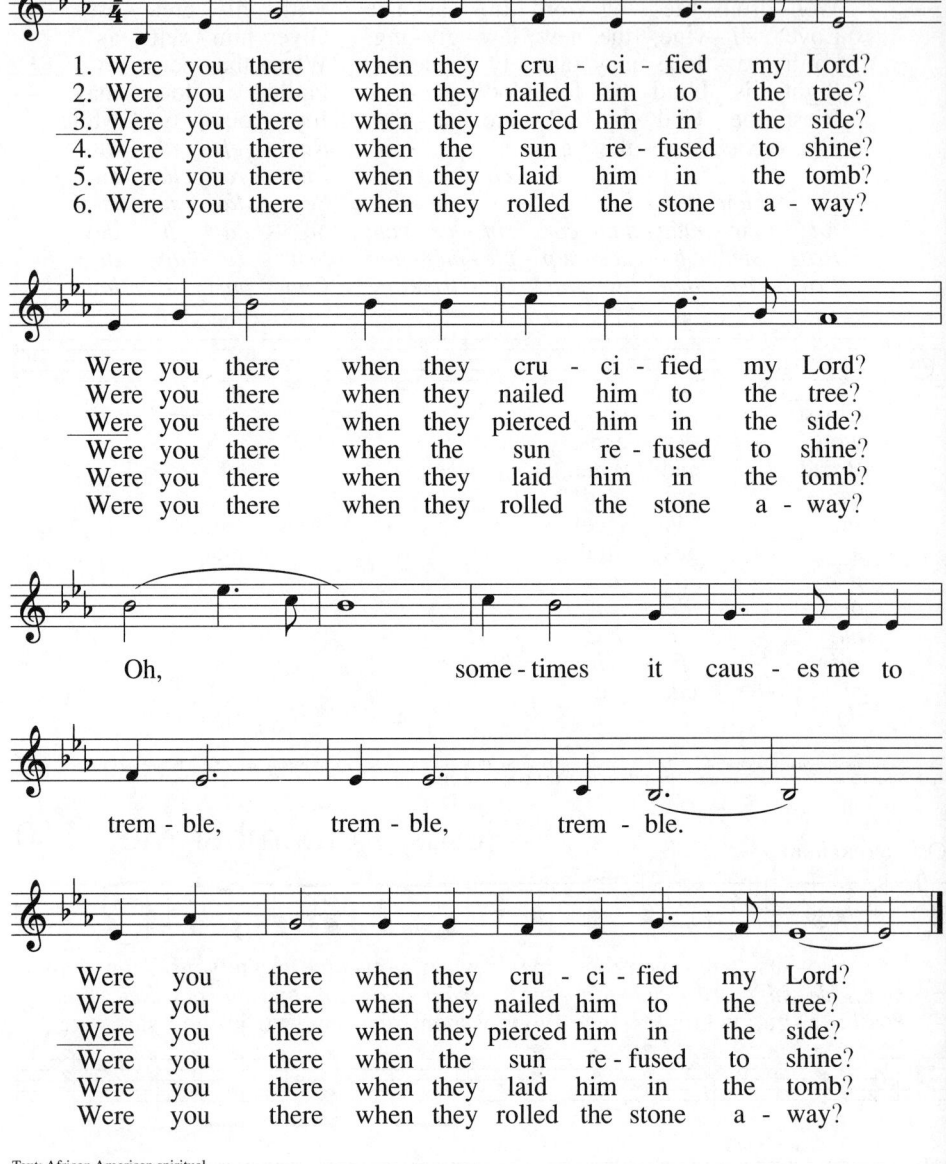

1. Were you there when they cru - ci - fied my Lord?
2. Were you there when they nailed him to the tree?
3. Were you there when they pierced him in the side?
4. Were you there when the sun re - fused to shine?
5. Were you there when they laid him in the tomb?
6. Were you there when they rolled the stone a - way?

Were you there when they cru - ci - fied my Lord?
Were you there when they nailed him to the tree?
Were you there when they pierced him in the side?
Were you there when the sun re - fused to shine?
Were you there when they laid him in the tomb?
Were you there when they rolled the stone a - way?

Oh, some - times it caus - es me to

trem - ble, trem - ble, trem - ble.

Were you there when they cru - ci - fied my Lord?
Were you there when they nailed him to the tree?
Were you there when they pierced him in the side?
Were you there when the sun re - fused to shine?
Were you there when they laid him in the tomb?
Were you there when they rolled the stone a - way?

Text: African American spiritual
Tune: WERE YOU THERE, 10 10 with refrain; African American spiritual; harm. by Robert J. Batastini, b.1942, © 1987, GIA Publications, Inc.

# O Sacred Head Surrounded / 512
# Oh Rostro Ensangrentado

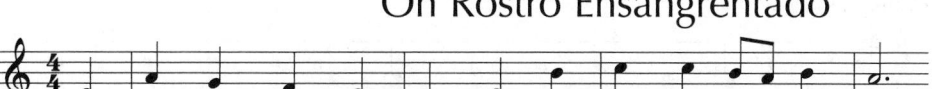

1. O Sa - cred Head, sur - round - ed By crown of pierc-ing thorn!
2. I see your strength and vig - or All fad - ing in the strife,
3. In this, your bit - ter pas - sion, Good Shep-herd, think of me

1. ¡Oh ros -tro_en - san - gren - ta - do, I - ma - gen del do - lor,
2. Cu - brió tu no - ble fren - te La pa - li - dez mor - tal,
3. Se - ñor, tu_has so - por - ta - do Lo que yo me - re - cí;

O bleed - ing Head, so wound - ed, Re - viled and put to scorn!
And death with cru - el rig - or, Be - reav-ing you of life;
With your most sweet com - pas - sion, Un - worth - y though I be:

Que su - fres re - sig - na - do La bur - la y_el fu - ror!
Cual ve - lo trans - pa - ren - te De tu su - frir, se - ñal.
La cul - pa que_has car - ga - do, Car - gar - la yo de - bí.

The pow'r of death comes o'er you, The glow of life de - cays,
O ag - o - ny and dy - ing! O love to sin - ners free!
Be - neath your cross a - bid - ing For ev - er would I rest,

So - por - tas la tor - tu - ra, La sa - ña, la mal - dad;
Ce - rró - se_a - que - lla bo - ca, La len-gua_en-mu - de - ció,
Mas mí - ra - me, con - fí - o En tu cruz y pa - sión.

Yet an - gel hosts a - dore you And trem - ble as they gaze.
Je - sus, all grace sup - ply - ing, O turn your face on me.
In your dear love con - fid - ing, And with your pres-ence blest.

En tan cruel a - mar - gu - ra, ¡Qué gran-de_es tu bon - dad!
La frí - a muer - te to - ca Al que la vi - da dio.
O - tór - ga - me, Dios mí - o, La gra - cia del per - dón.

Text: *Salve caput cruentatum*; ascr. to Bernard of Clairvaux, 1091–1153; tr. by Henry Baker, 1821–1877; Spanish tr. by Federico Fliedner, 1845–1901
Tune: PASSION CHORALE, 7 6 7 6 D; Hans Leo Hassler, 1564–1612; harm. by J. S. Bach, 1685–1750

## 513 In Manus Tuas, Pater

Ostinato Refrain

(spí - ri-tum)

In      ma - nus   tu - as,   Pa - ter, com-mén - do   spí - ri-tum
In - to   your hands, O   Fa - ther,   I   now com - mend   my
Oh   Pa-dre, en - tre   tus   ma - nos mi es-pí - ri - tu   en -

me  -  um.   In   ma - nus   tu - as,   Pa  -  ter,   com-
spir  -  it.   In - to   your hands, O   Fa  -  ther,   I
tre  -  go.   Oh   Pa-dre, en - tre   tus   ma - nos   mi es-

*Last time* 𝆌

mén  -  do   spí - ri - tum   me  -  um.   In
now   com - mend   my   spir  -  it.   In -
pí  -  ri - tu   en  -  tre  -  go.   Oh

*Last time* 𝆌

Text: Psalm 31:6, Luke 23:46; Taizé Community
Tune: Taizé Community
© 2007, 2011, Les Presses de Taizé, GIA Publications, Inc., agent

# Behold the Wood   514

**Refrain**

Be - hold, be - hold the wood of the

cross, on which is hung our sal - va - tion.

O come, let us a - dore.

**Verses**

1. Un - less a grain of wheat shall fall up -
2. And when my hour of glo - ry comes as
3. For there can be no great - er love
4. My Fa - ther, if it be your plan, this
5. For sure - ly he has borne our tears, is
6. My bod - y now is torn with pain, my

on the ground and die, it shall re - main but a
all was meant to be, you shall see me
shown up - on this land than in the one who
cup might pass me by, yet let it hap - pen
wound - ed by our sin, and yet he o - pens
friends have left and gone. O lov - ing Fa - ther,

**D.C.**

sin - gle grain and not give life.
lift - ed up up - on a tree.
came to die that we might live.
as you will if I must die.
not his mouth that we might live.
take my life in - to your hands.

Text: John 12; Dan Schutte, b.1947
Tune: Dan Schutte, b.1947

## 515 In the Cross of Christ

**Refrain**

In the cross of Christ, our glo-ry, Christ, our sto-ry,
Christ, our song, Christ, our song.

**Verses 1, 2**

1. Let your mind and heart be one with Christ who
2. He was pierced for our in-iq-ui-ties, and

emp-tied him-self, for us be-came a slave, ac-
crushed for our sins. He died to make us whole, and

**D.C.**

cept - ing death up - on the cross.
by his suf - f'ring we are healed.

**Verses 3–5**

3. Come, be-hold the cross of sac-ri-fice on which
4. May we nev-er boast of an-y-thing save the
5. Now in Christ, we who were a-li-ens have been

Je - sus died— the Sav-ior of us all— to
cross of Christ, by which we die to sin and
rec - on - ciled; as mem-bers of God's house, we

**D.C.**

save a lost and bro-ken world.
rise to life in Je - sus Christ.
live as God's own dwell-ing place.

Text: Philippians 2:5–8, Ephesians 2:12–13, Galatians 6:14; adapt. by Marty Haugen, b.1950
Tune: Marty Haugen, b.1950
© 1997, GIA Publications, Inc.

# Be Not Afraid   516

Ostinato Refrain

Be not a-fraid, sing out for joy! Christ is ris-en, al-le-
*Czech:* Ne-boj - te se, ra - duj - te se! Kris - tus slav-ný ví - těz
*Polish:* Nie bój - cie się, ra - duj-cie się! Chry - stus rze-czy-wi-ście
*Croatian:* O - dag-naj strah i ra-duj se! Krist je do - is - ta us -

lu - ia! Be not a-fraid, sing out for joy!
z hro-bu vstal. Ne - boj - te se, ra - duj - te se!
z gro-bu wstał. Nie bój - cie się, ra - duj - cie się!
krs - nu - o! O - dag-naj strah i ra - duj se!

Christ is ris - en, al - le - lu - ia!
Kris - tus slav - ný ví - těz z hro - bu vstal.
Chry - stus rze - czy - wi - ście z gro - bu wstał.
Krist je do - is - ta us - krs - nu - o!

Text: Taizé Community
Tune: Taizé Community

# 517 We Walk His Way / Ewe, Thina

Refrain

We walk his way. We walk
E - we, thi - na. E - we,

We walk his way. We walk his way.
E - we, thi - na. E - we, thi - na.

1.

his way. We walk
thi - na. E - we,

We walk his way. We walk his way.
E - we, thi - na. E - we, thi - na.

2. To verses | Last time

1. Un - armed, he
2. He breaks the
3. The tree of
1. Si - zo - wa

We walk his way. We walk his way.
E - we, thi - na. E - we, thi - na.

Verses

(1.) fac - es   forc - es   of   de - mons and death.   We   walk
(2.) bonds   of   hell,   dy - ing   on   the   cross.   E - we,
(3.) free - dom   blooms   by   his   emp - ty   grave.
(1.) nya - the - la   a - ma - di - mo - ni.

(1.) fac - es   forc - es   of   de - mons and   death.
(2.) bonds   of   hell,   dy - ing   on   the   cross.
(3.) free - dom   blooms   by   his   emp - ty   grave.
(1.) nya - the - la   a - ma - di - mo - ni.

We walk   his way.   We walk   his way.
E - we,   thi - na.   E - we,   thi - na.

his   way.   Un - armed, he
thi - na.   He breaks the
The tree of
Si - zo - wa

We walk   his way.   We walk   his way.
E - we,   thi - na.   E - we,   thi - na.

We walk   his way.   We walk   his way.
E - we,   thi - na.   E - we,   thi - na.

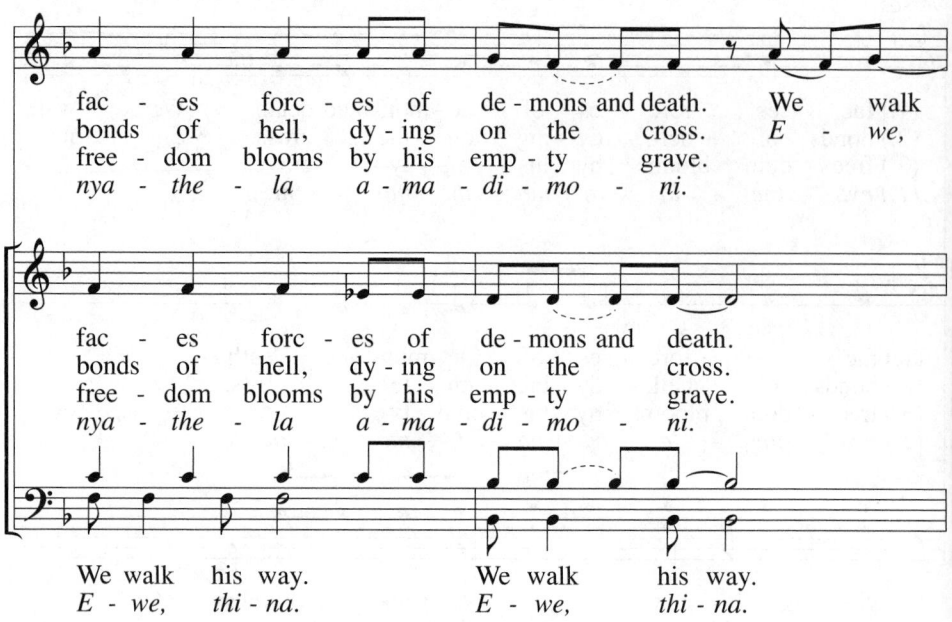

fac - es  forc - es  of  de - mons and death.  We  walk
bonds  of  hell,  dy - ing  on  the  cross.  E - we,
free - dom  blooms  by his  emp - ty  grave.
*nya - the - la  a - ma - di - mo - ni.*

fac - es  forc - es  of  de - mons and  death.
bonds  of  hell,  dy - ing  on  the  cross.
free - dom  blooms  by his  emp - ty  grave.
*nya - the - la  a - ma - di - mo - ni.*

We walk  his way.
*E - we,  thi - na.*
We walk  his way.
*E - we,  thi - na.*

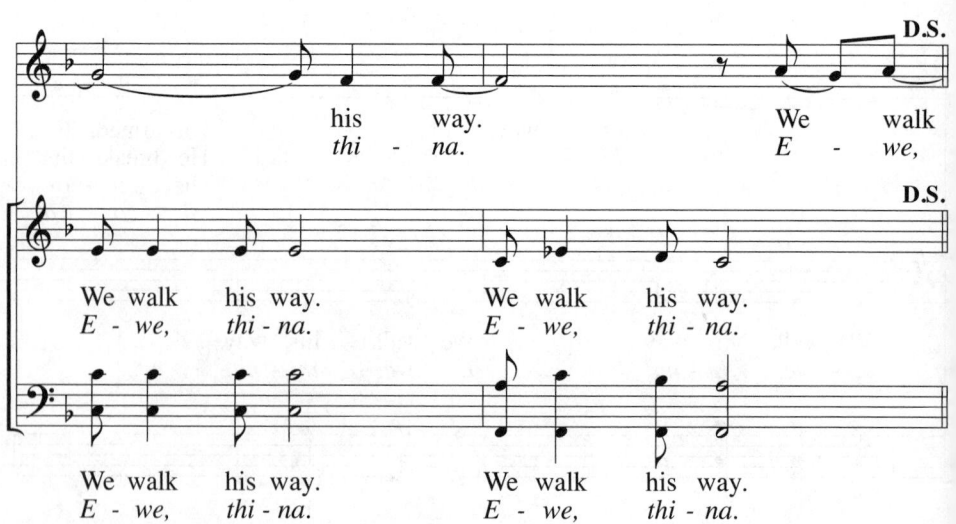

his  way.
*thi - na.*
We  walk
*E - we,*

We walk  his way.
*E - we,  thi - na.*
We walk  his way.
*E - we,  thi - na.*

We walk  his way.
*E - we,  thi - na.*
We walk  his way.
*E - we,  thi - na.*

Text: South African; tr. by Anders Nyberg, b.1955, and Sven-Bernhard Fast
Tune: South African; arr. by Anders Nyberg, b.1955
© 1984, Utryck, Walton Music Corp., agent

# Alleluia, Christ Is Risen 518

1. Al - le - lu - ia, Christ is ris - en, now the
2. Al - le - lu - ia, Christ is ris - en from his
3. Al - le - lu - ia, Christ is ris - en, truth and

stone is cast a - way! Dark - ness gone and
death up - on a cross. Now all share a
jus - tice from the grave, and brought forth for

sin for - giv - en, on this joy - ful day of
com - mon vi - sion, love now reigns and hate is
all who lis - ten: new life from the life he

days. Songs of hope and love e - ter - nal
lost. In this feast we share the sto - ry:
gave. Now with joy - ful hearts and voic - es

from our hearts to you we raise.
love's new birth for all to see.
joined as one we share your love.

In your death and life's re - new - al
From our God's al - might - y glo - ry,
Here in Christ the world re - joic - es,

we pour forth our joy - ful praise!
sign of things to ev - er be.
sight now turned to God a - bove.

Text: Tony E. Alonso, b.1980
Tune: Tony E. Alonso, b.1980
© 2002, GIA Publications, Inc.

# 519  Sing to the Mountains

**Refrain**

Sing to the moun-tains, sing to the sea. Raise your
voic - es, lift your hearts. This is the day the
Lord has made. Let all the earth re - joice.

**Verse 1**

1. I will give thanks to you, my Lord. You have
an - swered my plea. You have saved my
soul from death. You are my strength and my song.

D.C.

**Verse 2**

2. Ho - ly, ho - ly, ho - ly Lord,
heav - en and earth are full of your glo - ry.

D.C.

**Verse 3**

3. This is the day that the Lord has made. Let us be
glad and re - joice. Death has lost and

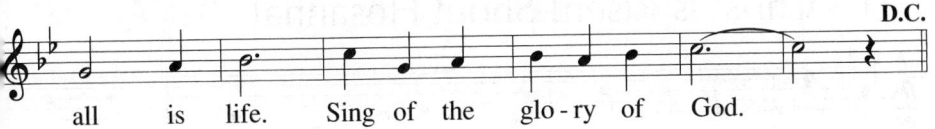

**D.C.**

all    is    life.    Sing of the    glo-ry  of    God.

Text: Psalm 118; Bob Dufford, SJ, b.1943
Tune: Bob Dufford, SJ, b.1943; acc. by Randall DeBruyn
© 1975, Robert J. Dufford, SJ, and OCP

## This Is the Feast of Victory    520

This is the    feast    of    vic-to-ry  for  our  God.    Al-le-

*To verses*    *Last time*

lu - ia, al-le-lu - ia,  al - le - lu - ia.    lu - ia.

1.    Wor-thy    is    Christ, the Lamb    who was    slain,    whose
2. Pow    -    er,    rich - es,    wis - dom, and strength,    and
3. Sing    with    all    the    peo - ple of    God,    and
4. Bless    -    ing,    hon - or,    glo - ry, and might    be  to
5. For    the    Lamb    who was    slain    has  be -

**D.C.**

blood    set  us    free    to    be    peo - ple of    God.
hon    -    or,    bless -  ing,    and    glo - ry  are  his.
join    in  the  hymn  of    all    cre - a    -    tion.
God    and the  Lamb  for - ev - er.    A    -    men.
gun    his    reign.    Al - le - lu    -    ia.

Text: Based on Revelation 5, © 1978, *Lutheran Book of Worship*
Tune: FESTIVAL CANTICLE, Irregular; Richard Hillert, 1923–2010, © 1975, 1988, Richard Hillert

## 521 Christ Is Risen! Shout Hosanna!

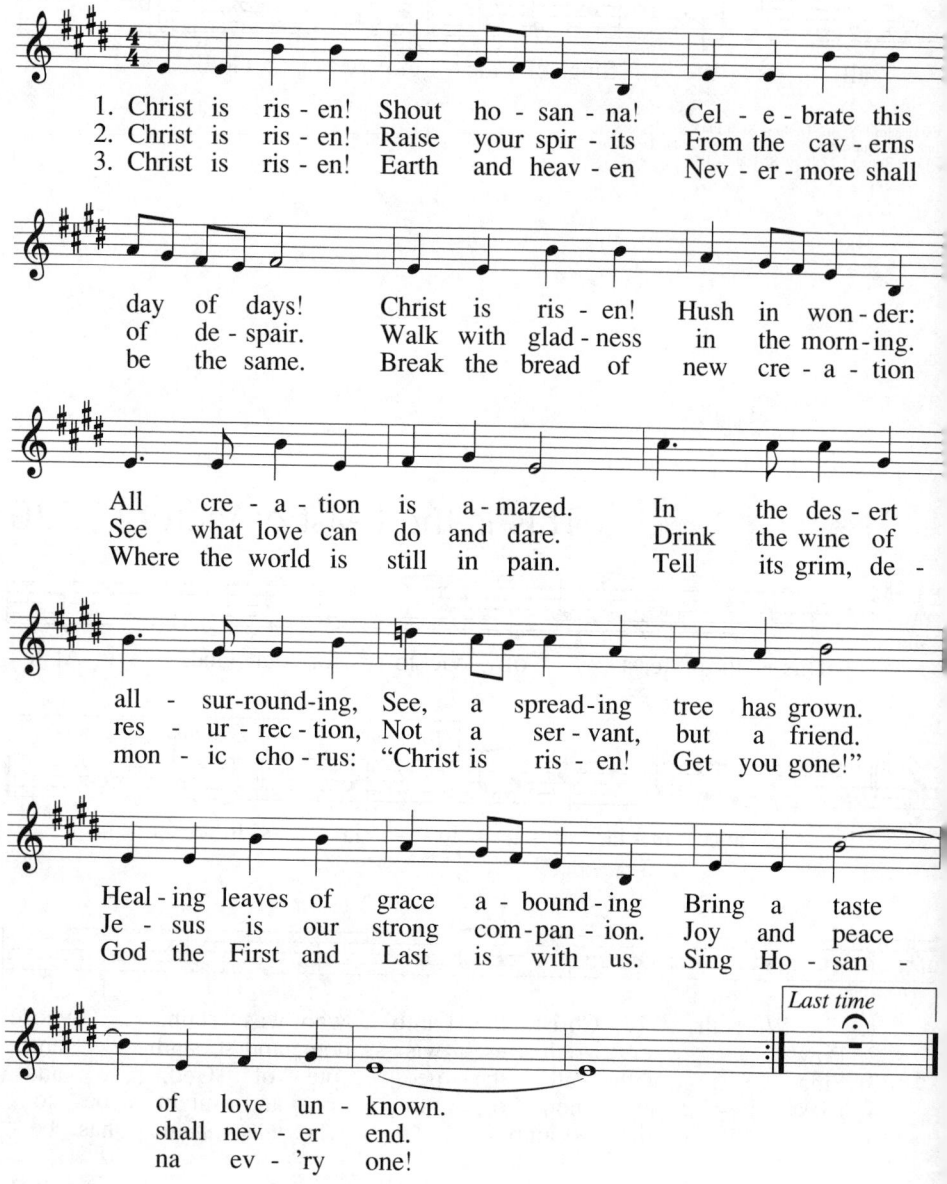

1. Christ is ris - en! Shout ho - san - na! Cel - e - brate this
2. Christ is ris - en! Raise your spir - its From the cav - erns
3. Christ is ris - en! Earth and heav - en Nev - er - more shall

day of days! Christ is ris - en! Hush in won - der:
of de - spair. Walk with glad - ness in the morn - ing.
be the same. Break the bread of new cre - a - tion

All cre - a - tion is a - mazed. In the des - ert
See what love can do and dare. Drink the wine of
Where the world is still in pain. Tell its grim, de -

all - sur-round-ing, See, a spread-ing tree has grown.
res - ur - rec - tion, Not a ser - vant, but a friend.
mon - ic cho - rus: "Christ is ris - en! Get you gone!"

Heal - ing leaves of grace a - bound - ing Bring a taste
Je - sus is our strong com - pan - ion. Joy and peace
God the First and Last is with us. Sing Ho - san -

*Last time*

of love un - known.
shall nev - er end.
na ev - 'ry one!

Text: Brian Wren, b.1936, © 1986, Hope Publishing Company
Tune: HOSANNA, 8 7 8 7 D; David Haas, b.1957, © 1991, GIA Publications, Inc.

# This Is a Day of New Beginnings 522

Refrain

Christ is a-live, and goes be-fore us to show and share what love can do. This is a day of new be-gin-nings; our God is mak-ing all things new, our God is mak - ing all things new.

Verses

1. This is a day of new be - gin-nings, time to re-mem - ber,
2. For by the life and death of Je - sus, love's might-y Spir - it,
3. Then let us, with the Spir - it's dar - ing, step from the past, and

and move on, time to be-lieve what love is bring-ing,
now as then, can make for us a world of dif - f'rence
leave be - hind our dis - a-point - ment, guilt, and griev-ing,

D.C.

lay - ing to rest the pain that's gone.
as faith and hope are born a - gain.
seek-ing new paths, and sure to find.

Text: Brian Wren, b.1936, © 1975, 1995, Hope Publishing Co.
Tune: Lori True, b.1961, © 2003, GIA Publications, Inc.

# 523 Christ the Lord Is Risen Today

1. Christ the Lord is ris'n to - day, Al - le -
2. Lives a - gain our glo - rious king, Al - le -
3. Love's re - deem - ing work is done, Al - le -
4. Soar we now where Christ has led, Al - le -

lu - ia! All on earth with an - gels say:
lu - ia! Where, O death, is now your sting?
lu - ia! Fought the fight, the bat - tle won,
lu - ia! Fol - l'wing our ex - alt - ed Head,

Al - le - lu - ia! Raise your joys and
Al - le - lu - ia! Once he died our
Al - le - lu - ia! Death in vain for -
Al - le - lu - ia! Made like him, like

tri - umphs high, Al - le - lu - ia!
souls to save, Al - le - lu - ia!
bids him rise, Al - le - lu - ia!
him we rise, Al - le - lu - ia!

Sing, O heav'ns; and, earth, re - ply,
Where your vic - to - ry, O grave?
Christ has o - pened par - a - dise.
Ours the cross, the grave, the skies.

Al - le - lu - ia!

Text: Charles Wesley, 1707–1788, alt.
Tune: LLANFAIR, 77 77 with alleluias; Robert Williams, 1781–1821

# Alleluia No. 1  524

**Refrain**

Al - le - lu - ia, al - le - lu - ia, give

thanks to the ris - en Lord. Al - le - lu - ia, al - le -

lu - ia, give praise to his Name.

**Verses**

1. Je - sus is Lord of all the earth.
2. Spread the good news o'er all the earth:
3. We have been cru - ci - fied with Christ.
4. God has pro - claimed his gra - cious gift:
5. Come, let us praise the liv - ing God,

**D.C.**

He is the King of cre - a - tion.
Je - sus has died and has ris - en.
Now we shall live for ev - er.
Life e - ter - nal for all who be - lieve.
Joy - ful - ly sing to our Sav - ior.

Text: Donald Fishel, b.1950,
Tune: ALLELUIA NO. 1, 8 8 with refrain; Donald Fishel, b.1950; descant harm. by Betty Pulkingham, b.1929, Charles Mallory, b.1953, and
  George Mims, b.1938,
© 1973, and descant 1979, International Liturgy Publications

## 525 The Strife Is O'er

Refrain

Al-le - lu - ia, al - le - lu - ia, al - le - lu - ia!

Verses

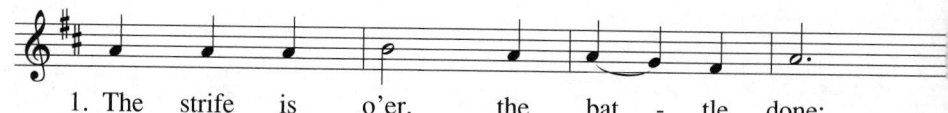

1. The strife is o'er, the bat - tle done;
2. The pow'rs of death have done their worst;
3. On the third day Christ rose a - gain,
4. He closed the yawn - ing gates of hell;
5. Lord, by the stripes which wound - ed you,

Now is the Vic - tor's tri - umph won! Songs of re -
But Christ their le - gions has dis - persed. Let shouts of
Glo - rious in maj - es - ty to reign. O let us
The bars from heav'n's high por - tals fell. Let hymns of
Free from death's sting your ser - vants too, That we may

D.C.

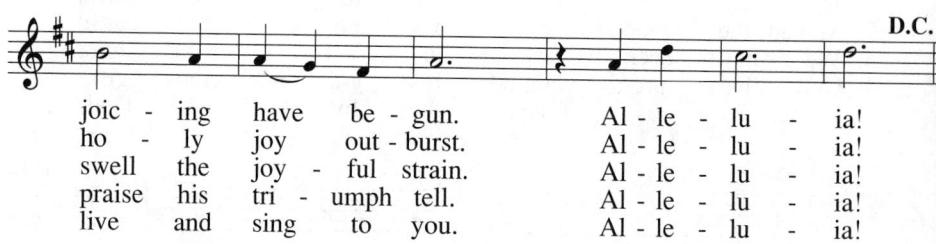

joic - ing have be - gun. Al - le - lu - ia!
ho - ly joy out - burst. Al - le - lu - ia!
swell the joy - ful strain. Al - le - lu - ia!
praise his tri - umph tell. Al - le - lu - ia!
live and sing to you. Al - le - lu - ia!

Text: *Finita jam sunt praelia;* Latin, 12th C.; tr. by Francis Pott, 1832–1909, alt.
Tune: VICTORY, 888 with alleluias; Giovanni da Palestrina, 1525–1594; adapt. by William H. Monk, 1823–1889

## 526 Be Joyful, Mary

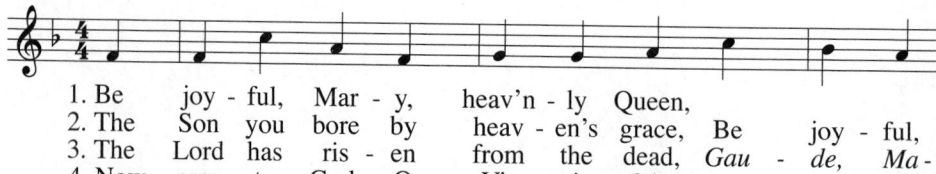

1. Be joy - ful, Mar - y, heav'n - ly Queen,
2. The Son you bore by heav - en's grace, Be joy - ful,
3. The Lord has ris - en from the dead, *Gau - de, Ma* -
4. Now pray to God, O Vir - gin fair,

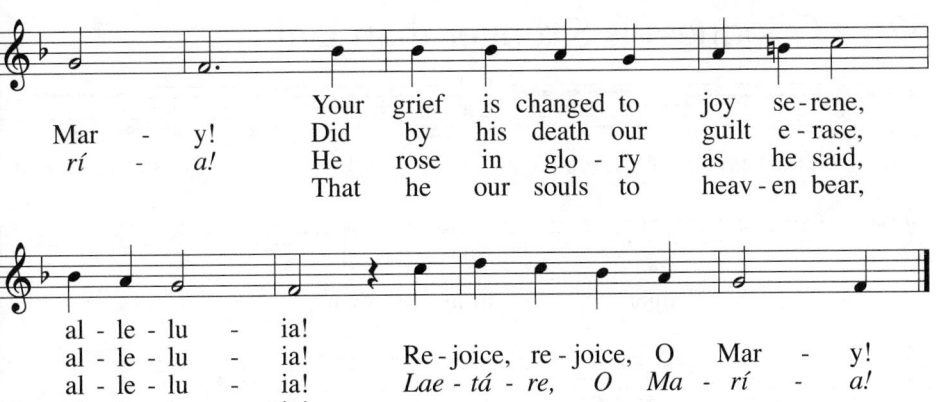

Mar - y!
rí - a!

Your grief is changed to joy se-rene,
Did by his death our guilt e-rase,
He rose in glo - ry as he said,
That he our souls to heav-en bear,

al - le - lu - ia!
al - le - lu - ia!
al - le - lu - ia!
al - le - lu - ia!

Re-joice, re-joice, O Mar - y!
*Lae - tá - re, O Ma - rí - a!*

Text: *Regina caeli, jubila*; Latin, 17th C.; tr. anon. in *Psallite*, 1901
Tune: REGINA CAELI, 8 5 8 4 7; Leisentritt's *Gesangbuch*, 1584, alt.

# I Know That My Redeemer Lives! 527

1. I know that my Re - deem - er lives!
2. He lives to bless me with his love;
3. He lives and grants me dai - ly breath;
4. He lives, all glo - ry to his name;

What joy this blest as - sur - ance gives!
He lives to plead for me a - bove;
He lives, and I shall con - quer death;
He lives, my Sav - ior, still the same;

He lives, he lives who once was dead;
He lives my hun - gry soul to feed;
He lives my man - sion to pre - pare;
What joy this blest as - sur - ance gives:

He lives, my ev - er - last - ing Head!
He lives to help in time of need.
He lives to bring me safe - ly there.
I know that my Re - deem - er lives!

Text: Samuel Medley, 1738–1799
Tune: DUKE STREET, LM; John Hatton, c.1710–1793

# 528 Goodness Is Stronger than Evil

Good-ness is strong-er than e - vil; love is strong-er than

hate; light is strong-er than dark - ness;

life is strong-er than death. Vic-'try is ours, vic-t'ry is

ours through him who loved us. Vic-'try is

ours, vic-t'ry is ours through him who loved us.

Text: Desmond Tutu, b.1931, ©; adapt. by John L. Bell, b.1949
Tune: GOODNESS IS STRONGER, Irregular; John L. Bell, b.1949, © 1996, Iona Community, GIA Publications, Inc., agent

# 529 Surréxit Christus

Ostinato Refrain

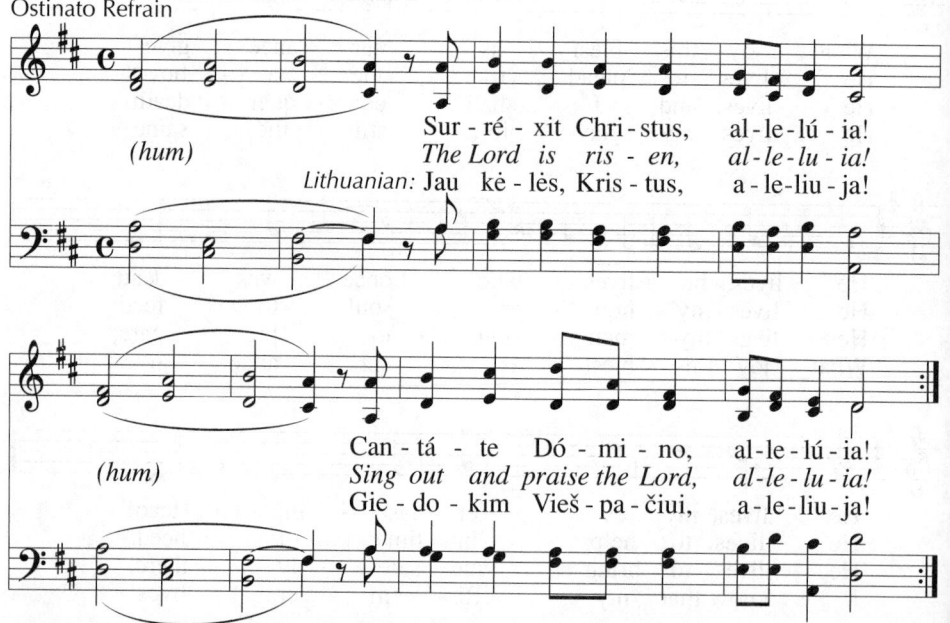

Sur - ré - xit Chri - stus, al - le - lú - ia!
*(hum)*   *The Lord is ris - en,*   *al - le - lu - ia!*
Lithuanian: Jau kė - lės, Kris - tus, a - le-liu - ja!

Can - tá - te Dó - mi - no, al - le - lú - ia!
*(hum)*   *Sing out and praise the Lord,*   *al - le - lu - ia!*
Gie - do - kim Vieš - pa - čiui, a - le-liu - ja!

Text: *Christ is risen, sing to the Lord;* Daniel 3; Taizé Community, 1984
Tune: Jacques Berthier, 1923–1994
© 1984, Les Presses de Taizé, GIA Publications, Inc., agent

# Christ Has Risen  530

Text: John L. Bell, b.1949
Tune: TRANSFORMATION, 8 7 8 7 D; John L. Bell, b.1949
© 1988, Iona Community, GIA Publications, Inc., agent

*Alternate tune:* HOLY MANNA

## 531 Earth, Earth, Awake!

1. Earth, earth, a - wake! Your prais - es sing! Al - le - lu - ia!
2. All na - ture sings of hope re - born! Al - le - lu - ia!
3. Win - ter is past; the night is gone! Al - le - lu - ia!
4. Praise we the Fa - ther, Spir - it, Son! Al - le - lu - ia!

Greet with the dawn your ris - en King! Al - le - lu - ia!
Christ lives to com - fort those who mourn! Al - le - lu - ia!
Christ's light, tri - um - phant, brings the dawn! Al - le - lu - ia!
Praise we the vic - t'ry God has won! Al - le - lu - ia!

Bright suns and stars, your hom - age pay! Al - le - lu - ia!
First fruit of all the dead who sleep! Al - le - lu - ia!
Cre - a - tion spreads its spring - time bloom! Al - le - lu - ia!
Praise we the Lamb who reigns a - bove! Al - le - lu - ia!

Life reigns a - gain this East - er day! Al - le - lu - ia!
Prom - ise of joy for all who weep! Al - le - lu - ia!
Life bursts like flame from death's cold tomb! Al - le - lu - ia!
Praise we the King whose rule is love! Al - le - lu - ia!

Text: Herman G. Stuempfle, Jr., 1923–2007
Tune: STUEMPFLE, LM with alleluias; Sally Ann Morris, b.1952
© 1996, GIA Publications, Inc.

# O Sons and Daughters 532

Al - le - lu - ia,    al - le - lu - ia,    al - le - lu - ia.

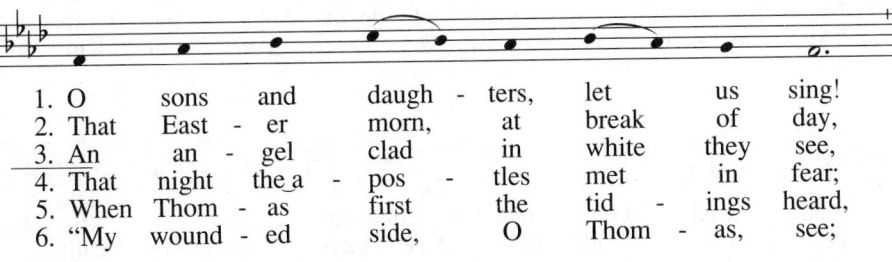

| 1. O | sons | and | daugh - ters, | let | us | sing! |
|------|------|-----|---------------|-----|-----|-------|
| 2. That | East - er | morn, | at | break | of | day, |
| 3. An | an - gel | clad | in | white | they | see, |
| 4. That | night the a - pos - tles | met | in | fear; |
| 5. When | Thom - as | first | the | tid - ings | heard, |
| 6. "My | wound - ed | side, | O | Thom - as, | see; |

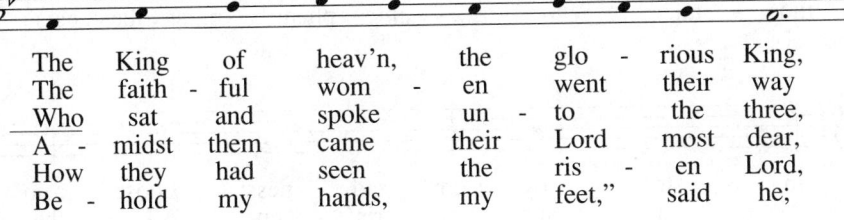

| The | King | of | heav'n, | the | glo - rious | King, |
|-----|------|-----|---------|-----|-------------|------|
| The | faith - ful | wom - en | went | their | way |
| Who | sat | and | spoke | un - to | the | three, |
| A - midst | them | came | their | Lord | most | dear, |
| How | they | had | seen | the | ris - en | Lord, |
| Be - hold | my | hands, | my | feet," | said | he; |

**D.C.**

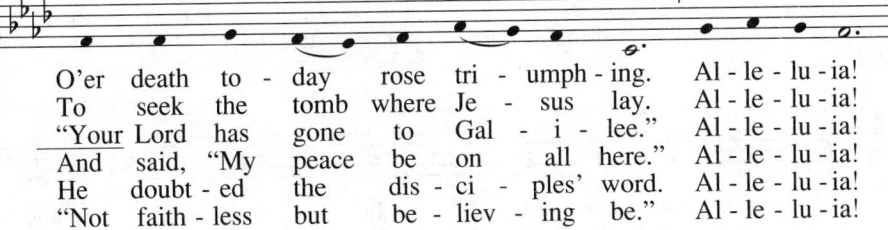

| O'er | death | to - day | rose | tri - umph - ing. | Al - le - lu - ia! |
|------|-------|---------|------|-------------------|--------------------|
| To | seek | the | tomb | where Je - sus | lay. | Al - le - lu - ia! |
| "Your | Lord | has | gone | to | Gal - i - lee." | Al - le - lu - ia! |
| And | said, "My | peace | be | on | all | here." | Al - le - lu - ia! |
| He | doubt - ed | the | dis - ci - ples' | word. | Al - le - lu - ia! |
| "Not | faith - less | but | be - liev - ing | be." | Al - le - lu - ia! |

7. No longer Thomas then denied;
   He saw the feet, the hands, the side;
   "You are my Lord and God," he cried. Alleluia!

8. How blest are they who have not seen,
   And yet whose faith has constant been,
   For they eternal life shall win. Alleluia!

9. On this most holy day of days,
   To God your hearts and voices raise,
   In laud and jubilee and praise. Alleluia!

Text: *O filii et filiae;* Jean Tisserand, d.1494; tr. by John M. Neale, 1818–1866, alt.
Tune: O FILII ET FILIAE, 888 with alleluias; Mode II; acc. by Richard Proulx, 1937–2010, © 1975, GIA Publications, Inc.

# 533 Come, You Faithful, Raise the Strain

1. Come, you faith - ful, raise the strain Of tri - um - phant
2. 'Tis the spring of souls to - day: Christ has burst his
3. Now the queen of sea - sons, bright With the day of
4. Nei - ther could the gates of death, Nor the tomb's dark
5. "Al - le - lu - ia!" now we cry To our King im -

glad - ness! God has brought his Is - ra - el
pris - on, And from three days' sleep in death
splen - dor, With the roy - al feast of feasts,
por - tal, Nor the watch - ers, nor the seal
mor - tal, Who tri - um - phant burst the bars

In - to joy from sad - ness; Loosed from
As a sun has ris - en. All the
Comes its joy to ren - der; Comes to
Hold him as a mor - tal: For to -
Of the tomb's dark por - tal; "Al - le -

Phar - aoh's bit - ter yoke Ja - cob's sons and
win - ter of our sins, Long and dark, is
glad Je - ru - sa - lem, Who with true af -
day a - mong his own Christ ap - pears, be -
lu - ia!" with the Son, God the Fa - ther

daugh - ters; Led them with un - moist - ened foot
fly - ing From the Light, to whom we give
fec - tion Wel - comes in un - wea - ried strains
stow - ing Last - ing peace which ev - er - more
prais - ing; "Al - le - lu - ia!" yet a - gain

| | | | | | | |
|---|---|---|---|---|---|---|
| Through | the | Red | Sea | wa | - | ters. |
| Laud | and | praise | un | - | dy | - | ing. |
| Je | - | sus' | res | - | ur | - | rec | - | tion. |
| Pass | - | es | hu | - | man | know | - | ing. |
| To | the | Spir | - | it | rais | - | ing. |

Text: Exodus 15; Ασωμεν παντες λαοι; John of Damascus, c.675–c.749; tr. by John M. Neale, 1818–1886, alt.
Tune: GAUDEAMUS PARITER, 7 6 7 6 D; Johann Horn, c.1495–1547

# Now the Green Blade Rises   534

1. Now   the   green blade   ris - es   from   the   bur - ied   grain,
2. In   the   grave they   laid   him,   Love   by   ha - tred   slain,
3. Forth   he   came   at   East - er,   like   the   ris - en   grain,
4. When our   hearts   are   win - try,   griev - ing,   or   in   pain,

Wheat that   in   the   dark earth   man - y   days   has   lain;
Think - ing   he would   nev - er   wake   to   life   a - gain,
Spring - ing   from   the   grave where   three   days   he   had   lain;
By   your   touch you   call   us   back   to   life   a - gain,

Love   lives   a - gain,   that with   the   dead   has   been;
Laid   in   the   earth   like   grain that   sleeps   un - seen;
Raised   from   the   dead,   my   liv - ing   Lord   is   seen;
Fields   of   our   hearts   that dead   and   bare   have   been;

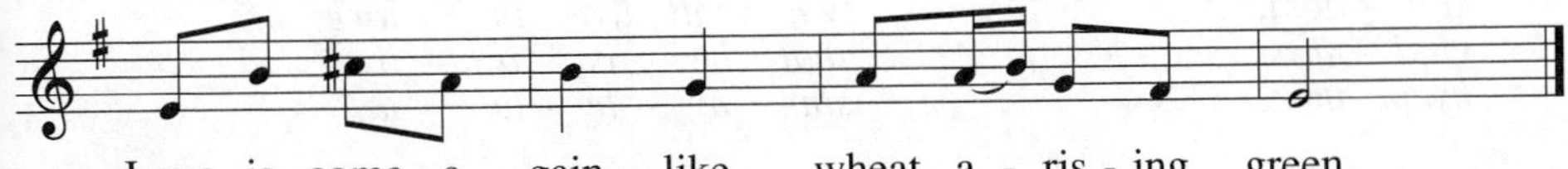

Love   is   come   a - gain,   like   wheat   a - ris - ing   green.

Text: John M. C. Crum, 1872–1958, *Oxford Book of Carols*, alt., © Oxford University Press
Tune: NOËL NOUVELET, 11 11 10 11; French carol; harm. by Thomas Foster, b.1938, © 1986, GIA Publications, Inc.

# 535 Resucitó

**Refrain**

Re - su - ci - tó, re - su - ci - tó, re - su - ci -
A - le - lu - ya, a - le - lu - ya, a - le - lu -

*To verses* | *Final ending*

tó, a - le - lu - ya. A - le - lu - ya.
ya, re - su - ci - tó.

**Verses**

1. La muer - te ¿dón - de es - tá la
2. Gra - cias se - an da - das al
3. A - le - grí - a, a - le - grí - a her -
4. Si con Él mo - ri - mos, y con Él vi -
1. And death now, van - ished is the
2. The king - dom, praise to God, the
3. Our glad - ness, bliss - ful in our
4. With him then, die and live with

muer - te? ¿Dón - de es - tá mi
Pa - dre que nos pa - só a su
ma - nos, que si hoy nos que -
vi - mos, y con Él can -
fear now, ban - ished are my
king - dom! Raised up to the
glad - ness, this will be our
him then, rise and sing our

**D.C.**

muer - te? ¿Dón - de su vic - to - ria?
rei - no dón - de se vi - ve de a - mor.
re - mos es que re - su - ci - tó.
ta - mos. y ¡A - le - lu - ya!
tears now, death has passed a - way.
king - dom, we shall live in love.
glad - ness, that he is a - live.
hymn then, sing al - le - lu - ia.

Text: Kiko Argüello, © 1972, Ediciones Musical PAX, U.S. agent: OCP; tr. © 1988, OCP
Tune: Kiko Argüello, © 1972, Ediciones Musical PAX, U.S. agent: OCP; acc. by Diana Kodner, b.1957

# At the Lamb's High Feast We Sing  536

1. At the Lamb's high feast we sing Praise to our vic -
2. Where the Pas - chal blood is poured, Death's dark an - gel
3. Might - y vic - tim from on high, Hell's fierce pow'rs be -
4. East - er tri - umph, East - er joy, This a - lone can

to - rious King, Who has washed us in the tide
sheathes his sword; Is - rael's hosts tri - umph - ant go
neath you lie; You have con - quered in the fight,
sin de - stroy; From sin's pow'r, Lord, set us free,

Flow - ing from his pierc - ed side. Praise we him, whose
Through the wave that drowns the foe. Praise we Christ, whose
You have brought us life and light. Now no more can
New - born souls in you to be. Fa - ther, who the

love di - vine Gives his sa - cred Blood for wine,
blood was shed, Pas - chal vic - tim, Pas - chal bread;
death ap - pall, Now no more the grave en - thrall;
crown shall give, Sav - ior, by whose death we live,

Gives his Bod - y for the feast:
With sin - cer - i - ty and love
You have o - pened par - a - dise,
Spir - it, guide through all our days:

Christ the vic - tim, Christ the priest.
Eat we man - na from a - bove.
And in you your saints shall rise.
Three in One, your name we praise.

Text: *Ad regias agni dapes;* Latin, 4th C.; tr. by Robert Campbell, 1814–1868, alt.
Tune: SALZBURG, 77 77 D; Jakob Hintze, 1622–1702; harm. by J. S. Bach, 1685–1750

## 537 Easter Alleluia

**Refrain**

Al-le-lu-ia, al - le - lu-ia, al-le-lu - ia!

**Verses**

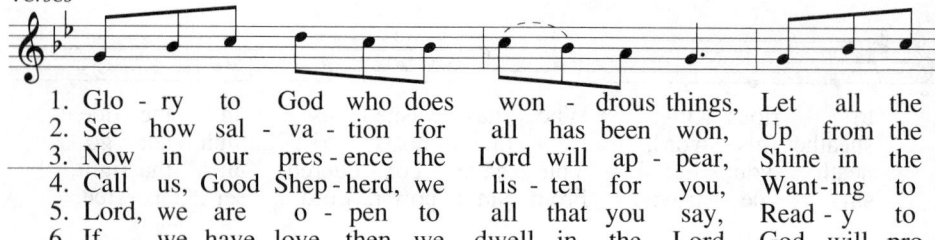

1. Glo - ry    to    God who does    won - drous things, Let    all    the
2. See    how sal - va - tion for    all    has been    won,    Up from the
3. Now    in    our    pres - ence the    Lord will ap - pear, Shine    in    the
4. Call    us, Good Shep - herd, we    lis - ten    for    you,    Want - ing    to
5. Lord, we    are    o - pen    to    all    that you    say,    Read - y    to
6. If    we have love, then we    dwell    in    the    Lord,    God will pro -

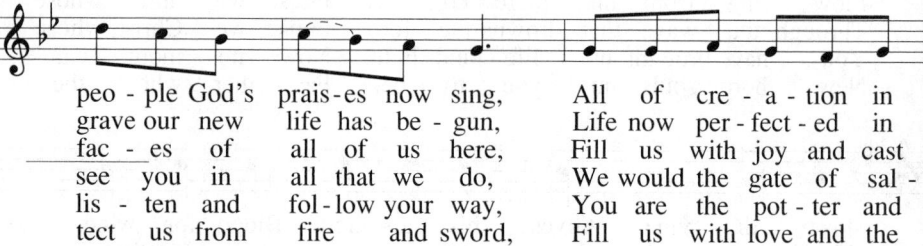

peo - ple God's    prais - es now sing,    All    of    cre - a - tion    in
grave our    new    life has be - gun,    Life now per - fect - ed    in
fac - es    of    all    of    us here,    Fill    us    with joy and cast
see    you    in    all that we    do,    We would the gate    of    sal -
lis - ten    and    fol - low your way,    You    are    the    pot - ter and
tect    us from    fire    and sword,    Fill    us    with love and the

**D.C.**

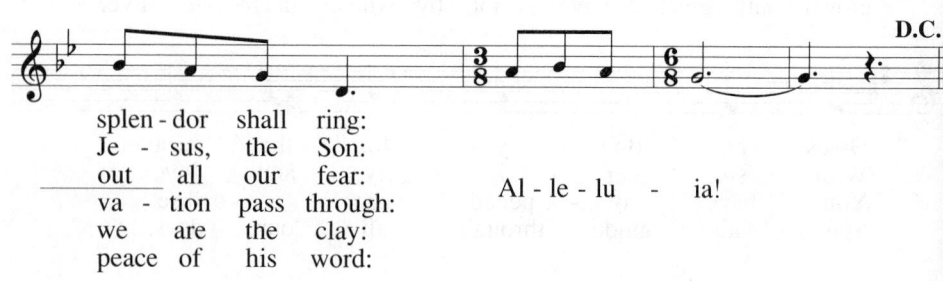

splen - dor shall    ring:
Je - sus,    the    Son:
out    all    our    fear:                    Al - le - lu - ia!
va - tion    pass through:
we    are    the    clay:
peace of    his    word:

Text: Marty Haugen, b.1950
Tune: O FILII ET FILIAE, 10 10 10 with alleluias; adapt. by Marty Haugen, b.1950
© 1986, GIA Publications, Inc.

# On the Journey to Emmaus 538

1. On the jour - ney to Em - ma - us with our
2. And our hearts burned with - in us as we
3. And that eve - ning at the ta - ble as he
4. On our jour - ney to Em - ma - us, in our

hearts cold as stone— The One who would
talked on the way, How all that was
blessed and broke bread, We saw it was
stor - ies and feast, With Je - sus we

save us had left us a - lone. Then a
prom - ised was ours on that day. So we
Je - sus a - ris'n from the dead; Though he
claim that the great - est is least: And his

stran - ger walks with us and, to our sur - prise, He
begged him, "Stay with us and grant us your word." We
van - ished be - fore us we knew he was near— The
words burn with - in us— let none be ig - nored— Who

o - pens our stor - ies and he o - pens our eyes.
wel - comed the stran - ger and we wel - comed the Lord.
life in our dy - ing and the hope in our fear.
wel - comes the stran - ger shall wel - come the Lord.

Text: Luke 24:13–35; Marty Haugen, b.1950
Tune: COLUMCILLE, Irregular; Gaelic, arr. by Marty Haugen, b.1950
© 1995, GIA Publications, Inc.

# 539 Sing with All the Saints in Glory / Canten con Gloriosos Fieles

1. Sing with all the saints in glo - ry, Sing the res - ur -
2. O what glo - ry, far ex - ceed - ing All that eye has
3. Life e - ter - nal! heav'n re - joic - es: Je - sus lives who

1. *Can - ten con glo - rio - sos fie - les Him - nos de re -*
2. *¡Oh! qué glo - ria tan ex - cel - sa, Im - po - si - ble*
3. *Vi - da_e - ter - na_ex - cla - ma_el cie - lo; Vi - ve Cris - to*

rec - tion song! Death and sor - row, earth's dark sto - ry,
yet per-ceived! Ho - liest hearts, for a - ges plead - ing,
once was dead. Shout with joy, O death - less voic - es!

*su - rrec - ción. Muer - te_y due - lo, tris - te_his - to - ria,*
*con - ce - bir. Los más pu - ros co - ra - zo - nes*
*que mu - rió. ¡Gri - ten, vo - ces in - mor - ta - les!*

To the for - mer days be - long. All a - round the
Nev - er that full joy con-ceived. God has prom-ised,
Child of God, lift up your head! Pa - tri - archs from

*Pe - nas del pa - sa - do son. Nu - bes ne - gras*
*No_es - pe - ra - ron re - ci - bir. Dios pro - me - te,*
*Al - cen ros - tros ha - cia Dios. Los pa - triar - cas*

clouds are break-ing, Soon the storms of time shall cease; In God's
Christ pre - pares it, There on high our wel-come waits. Ev - 'ry
dis - tant a - ges, Saints all long-ing for their heav'n, Proph-ets,

*se di - si - pan, La tor - men - ta ce - sa ya. Des - per -*
*Cris - to_o - fre - ce El ban - que - te ce - les - tial. Pa - ra*
*del pa - sa - do, Los que_es-pe - ran ce - le - brar, To - dos*

like - ness we a - wak-en, Know-ing ev - er - last-ing peace.
hum - ble spir - it shares it; Christ has passed the_e - ter - nal gates.
psalm-ists, seers, and sag - es, All a - wait the glo - ry giv'n.

*tan - do en su_i - ma - gen, Dios la_e - ter - na paz nos da.*
*to - dos los hu - mil - des, Vi - da_en Cris-to_es e - ter - nal.*
*sa - bios y pro - fe - tas Glo - ria_an - he - lan sin ce - sar.*

4. Life eternal! O what wonders
Crowd on faith; what joy unknown,
When, amid earth's closing thunders,
Saints shall stand before the throne!
Oh, to enter that bright portal,
See that glowing firmament,
Know, with you, O God immortal,
Jesus Christ whom you have sent!

4. *¡Vida_eterna! ¡Gozo_eterno!*
*Fieles cantan a_una voz.*
*Cesan truenos y nos vemos*
*Frente_al trono tuyo, Dios.*
*Y_al pasar por tus portales,*
*Brilla_el cielo con fulgor.*
*Celebramos tu venida*
*En tu Hijo,_el Salvador.*

Text: 1 Corinthians 15:20; William J. Irons, 1812–1883, alt.; tr. by Alberto Merubia, b.1919, © 2010, GIA Publications, Inc.
Tune: HYMN TO JOY, 8 7 8 7 D; arr. from Ludwig van Beethoven, 1770–1827, by Edward Hodges, 1796–1867

# Jesus Christ Is Risen Today    540

1. Je - sus Christ is ris'n to - day, Al - le - lu - ia!
2. Hymns of praise then let us sing, Al - le - lu - ia!
3. But the pains which he en - dured, Al - le - lu - ia!
4. Sing we to our God a - bove, Al - le - lu - ia!

Our tri - um-phant ho - ly day, Al - le - lu - ia!
Un - to Christ, our heav'n-ly King, Al - le - lu - ia!
Our sal - va - tion have pro - cured; Al - le - lu - ia!
Praise e - ter - nal, as his love; Al - le - lu - ia!

Who did once up - on the cross, Al - le - lu - ia!
Who en - dured the cross and grave, Al - le - lu - ia!
Now a - bove the sky he's King, Al - le - lu - ia!
Praise him, now his might con - fess, Al - le - lu - ia!

Suf - fer to re - deem our loss. Al - le - lu - ia!
Sin - ners to re - deem and save. Al - le - lu - ia!
Where the an - gels ev - er sing. Al - le - lu - ia!
Fa - ther, Son, and Spir - it blest. Al - le - lu - ia!

Text: St. 1, *Surrexit Christus hodie*, Latin, 14th C.; para. in *Lyra Davidica*, 1708, alt.; st. 2, 3, *The Compleat Psalmodist*, c.1750, alt.; st. 4, Charles
Wesley, 1707–1788, alt.
Tune: EASTER HYMN, 77 77 with alleluias; *Lyra Davidica*, 1708

## 541 All Things New

wa - ter and the sand, brought us out of
daugh - ters and as sons, fam - 'ly to the
us like tongues of flame? Who is ten - der

**D.C.**

slav - er - y and fed us from the sky?
First - born who is ris - en from the grave?
mer - cy? On - ly God and God a - lone.

Text: Rory Cooney, b.1952
Tune: Rory Cooney, b.1952
© 1993, GIA Publications, Inc.

## That Easter Day with Joy Was Bright 542

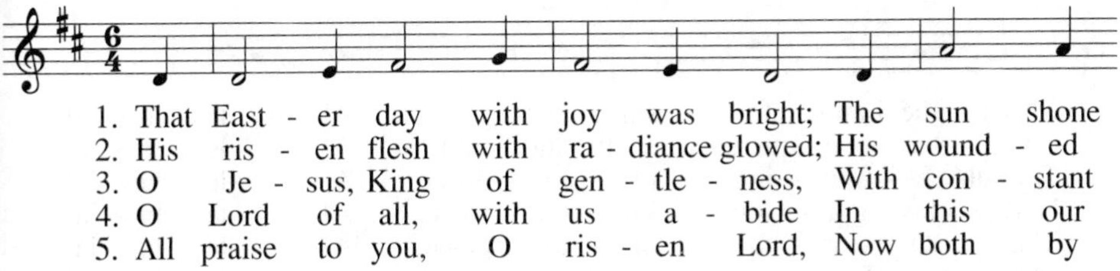

1. That East - er day with joy was bright; The sun shone
2. His ris - en flesh with ra - diance glowed; His wound - ed
3. O Je - sus, King of gen - tle - ness, With con - stant
4. O Lord of all, with us a - bide In this our
5. All praise to you, O ris - en Lord, Now both by

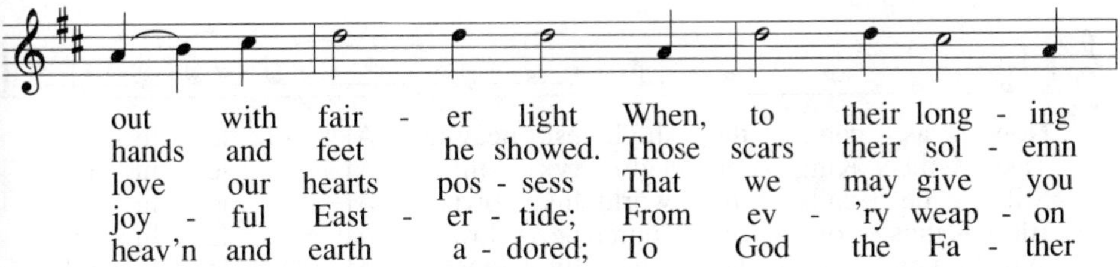

out with fair - er light When, to their long - ing
hands and feet he showed. Those scars their sol - emn
love our hearts pos - sess That we may give you
joy - ful East - er - tide; From ev - 'ry weap - on
heav'n and earth a - dored; To God the Fa - ther

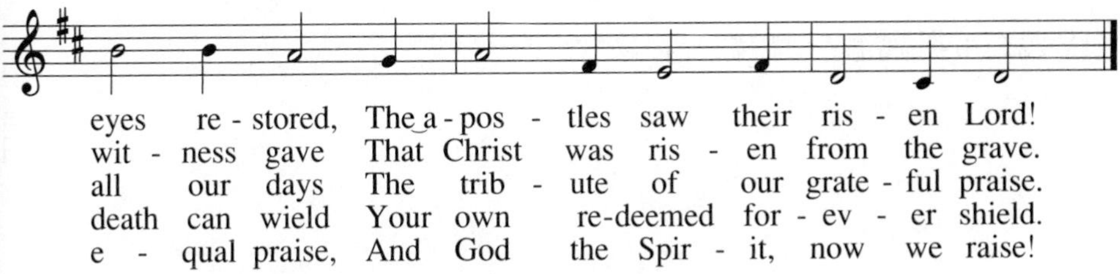

eyes re - stored, The a - pos - tles saw their ris - en Lord!
wit - ness gave That Christ was ris - en from the grave.
all our days The trib - ute of our grate - ful praise.
death can wield Your own re - deemed for - ev - er shield.
e - qual praise, And God the Spir - it, now we raise!

Text: *Claro paschali gaudio*; Latin 5th C.; tr. by John M. Neale, 1818–1866, alt.
Tune: PUER NOBIS, LM; adapt. by Michael Praetorius, 1571–1621

# 543   Hail the Day That Sees Him Rise

1. Hail the day that sees him rise, Al - le - lu - ia!
2. There the glo - rious tri - umph waits; Al - le - lu - ia!
3. High - est heav'n its Lord re - ceives, Al - le - lu - ia!
4. See, he lifts his hands a - bove; Al - le - lu - ia!
5. Christ, for us still in - ter - cede, Al - le - lu - ia!
6. There we shall with you re - main, Al - le - lu - ia!

To his throne a - bove the skies; Al - le - lu - ia!
Lift your heads, e - ter - nal gates; Al - le - lu - ia!
Yet he loves the earth he leaves; Al - le - lu - ia!
See, he shows the wounds of love; Al - le - lu - ia!
By your suf - f'ring for us plead; Al - le - lu - ia!
Part - ners of your end - less reign; Al - le - lu - ia!

Christ, the Lamb for sin - ners giv'n, Al - le - lu - ia!
Christ has con - quered death and sin; Al - le - lu - ia!
Though re - turn - ing to his throne, Al - le - lu - ia!
Hark, his gra - cious lips be - stow, Al - le - lu - ia!
Make us wor - thy of the place, Al - le - lu - ia!
There your face un - cloud-ed see, Al - le - lu - ia!

Now as - cends the high - est heav'n. Al - le - lu - ia!
Take the King of glo - ry in! Al - le - lu - ia!
Still he calls the world his own. Al - le - lu - ia!
Bless - ings on his Church be - low. Al - le - lu - ia!
Which you of - fer us by grace. Al - le - lu - ia!
Live with you e - ter - nal - ly. Al - le - lu - ia!

Text: Charles Wesley, 1707–1788, alt.; st. 5 from *The New Century Hymnal*, © 1992, The Pilgrim Press
Tune: LLANFAIR, 77 77 with alleluias; Robert Williams, 1781–1821

# Lord, You Give the Great Commission 544

1. Lord, you give the great com - mis - sion: "Heal the
2. Lord, you call us to your serv - ice: "In my
3. Lord, you make the com - mon ho - ly: "This my
4. Lord, you show us love's true meas - ure: "Fa - ther,
5. Lord, you bless with words as - sur - ing: "I am

sick and preach the word." Lest the Church ne -
name bap - tize and teach." That the world may
bod - y, this my blood." Let us all, for
what they do, for - give." Yet we hoard as
with you to the end." Faith and hope and

glect its mis - sion And the Gos - pel go un - heard,
trust your prom - ise, Life a - bun - dant meant for each,
earth's true glo - ry, Dai - ly lift life heav - en - ward,
pri - vate treas - ure All that you so free - ly give.
love re - stor - ing, May we serve as you in - tend,

Help us wit - ness to your pur - pose With re -
Give us all new fer - vor, draw us Clos - er
Ask - ing that the world a - round us Share your
May your care and mer - cy lead us To a
And, a - mid the cares that claim us, Hold in

newed in - teg - ri - ty;
in com - mun - i - ty;
chil - dren's lib - er - ty; With the Spir - it's gifts em -
just so - ci - e - ty;
mind e - ter - ni - ty;

pow'r us For the work of min - is - try.

Text: Jeffery Rowthorn, b.1934, © 1978, Hope Publishing Company
Tune: ABBOT'S LEIGH, 8 7 8 7 D; Cyril V. Taylor, 1907–1991, © 1942, ren. 1970, Hope Publishing Company

# 545  A Hymn of Glory Let Us Sing!

1. A hymn of glo - ry let us sing! New
2. The ho - ly ap - os - tol - ic band Up -
3. To whom the shin - ing an - gels cry, "Why
4. "You see him now, as - cend - ing high Up
5. O Lord, our home - ward path - way bend, That

songs through - out the world shall ring: Al - le - lu - ia! Al - le -
on the Mount of Ol - ives stand. Al - le - lu - ia! Al - le -
stand and gaze up - on the sky?" Al - le - lu - ia! Al - le -
to the por - tals of the sky." Al - le - lu - ia! Al - le -
our un - wea - ried hearts as - cend, Al - le - lu - ia! Al - le -

lu - ia! Christ, by a road be - fore un - trod, As -
lu - ia! And with his faith - ful fol - l'wers see Their
lu - ia! "This is the Sav - ior," thus they say. "This
lu - ia! "Here - af - ter Je - sus you shall see Re -
lu - ia! Where, seat - ed on your Fa - ther's throne, You

cends un - to the throne of God.
Lord as - cend in maj - es - ty.
is his glo - rious tri - umph day." Al - le - lu - ia! Al - le -
turn - ing in great maj - es - ty."
reign as King of kings a - lone.

lu - ia! Al - le - lu - ia! Al - le - lu - ia! Al - le - lu - ia!

Text: *Hymnum canamus gloriae;* Venerable Bede, 673–735; tr. by Benjamin Webb, 1819–1885, *The Hymnal Noted,* 1854, alt.
Tune: LASST UNS ERFREUEN, LM with alleluias; *Geistliche Kirchengesange,* Cologne, 1623; harm. by Ralph Vaughan Williams, 1872–1958

# Go to the World!  546

1. Go to the world! Go in-to all the earth. Go preach the cross where Christ re-news life's worth, bap-tiz-ing as the sign of our re-birth.
2. Go to the world! Go in-to ev-'ry place. Go live the Word of God's re-deem-ing grace. Go seek God's pres-ence in each time and space.
3. Go to the world! Go strug-gle, bless and pray. The nights of tears give way to joy-ous day. As ser-vant Church, you fol-low Christ's own way.
4. Go to the world! Go as the ones I send, For I am with you till the age shall end, When all the hosts of glo-ry cry "A-men!"

Al - le - lu - ia! Al - le - lu - ia!

Text: Sylvia G. Dunstan, 1955–1993, © 1991, GIA Publications, Inc.
Tune: SINE NOMINE, 10 10 10 with alleluias; Ralph Vaughan Williams, 1872–1958

# 547 Holy Spirit, Come to Us

Ostinato Refrain

Ho - ly Spir-it, come to us, kin-dle in us the fire of your love.
*Ven, Es - pí - ri - tu de Dios, y de tu a-mor en-cien-de la lla-ma.*
Ve - ni San-cte Spí - ri - tus, tu - i a - mó-ris i-gnem ac-cén-de.

Ho - ly Spir-it, come to us, Ho - ly Spir-it, come to us.
*Ven, Es - pí - ri - tu de a-mor, ven, Es - pí - ri - tu de a-mor.*
Ve - ni San-cte Spí - ri - tus, ve - ni San-cte Spí - ri - tus

Text: John 13:35, 15:12–13, 1 John 3:16, 4:10, 16
Tune: Jacques Berthier, 1923–1994
© 1998, Les Presses de Taizé, GIA Publications, Inc., agent

# 548 We Are One

We are one, we are one. We are one in the
Spir - it, we are one. Hal - le - lu - jah, Hal - le -
lu - jah, we are one in the Spir-it, we are one.

Text: Timothy Wright, 1947–2009, ©
Tune: Congregational Praise Song, arr. Valeria A. Foster, © 2000, GIA Publications, Inc.

# Living Spirit, Holy Fire 549

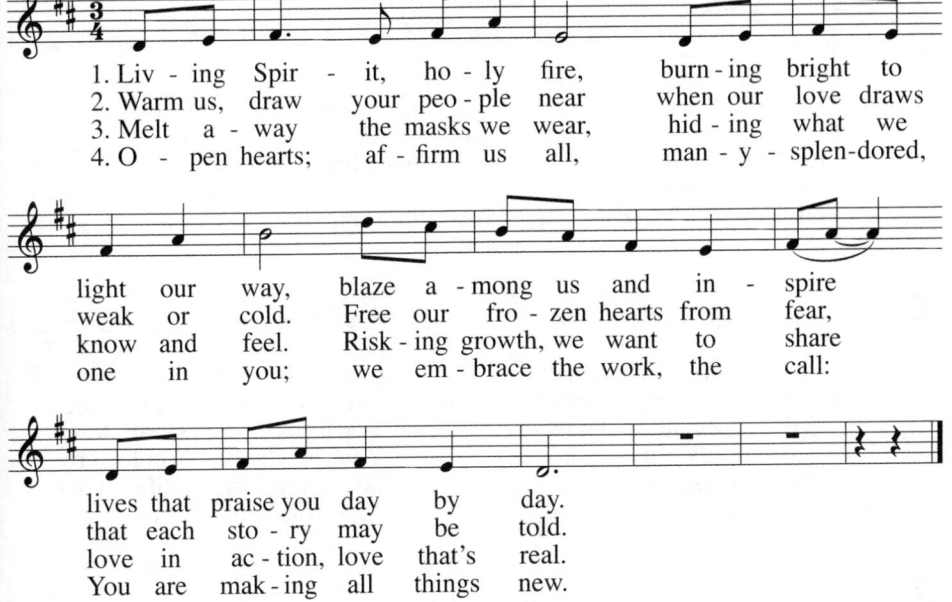

1. Liv - ing Spir - it, ho - ly fire, burn - ing bright to
2. Warm us, draw your peo - ple near when our love draws
3. Melt a - way the masks we wear, hid - ing what we
4. O - pen hearts; af - firm us all, man - y - splen-dored,

light our way, blaze a - mong us and in - spire
weak or cold. Free our fro - zen hearts from fear,
know and feel. Risk - ing growth, we want to share
one in you; we em - brace the work, the call:

lives that praise you day by day.
that each sto - ry may be told.
love in ac - tion, love that's real.
You are mak - ing all things new.

Text: Ruth Duck, b.1947, © 2005, GIA Publications, Inc.
Tune: Lori True, b.1961, © 2007, GIA Publications, Inc.

# Veni Sancte Spíritus 550

Ostinato Refrain

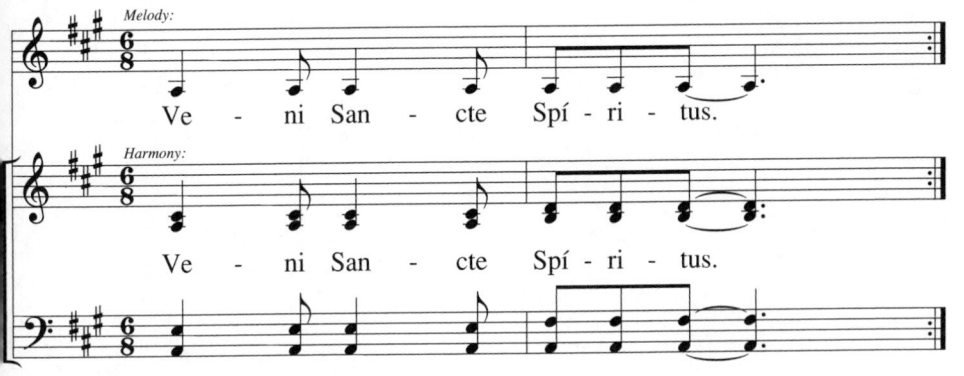

Melody:

Ve - ni San - cte Spí - ri - tus.

Harmony:

Ve - ni San - cte Spí - ri - tus.

Text: *Come Holy Spirit;* Verses drawn from the Pentecost Sequence; Taizé Community, 1978
Tune: Jacques Berthier, 1923–1994
© 1979, Les Presses de Taizé, GIA Publications, Inc., agent

# 551  O Holy Spirit, by Whose Breath

1. O      Ho - ly   Spir - it,     by whose breath    Life   ris - es
2. You    are   the   seek - er's   sure  re - source,   Of   burn - ing
3. In     you God's en - er - gy   is   shown,    To   us   your
4. Flood  our   dull  sens - es    with your light;   In   mu - tual
5. From   in - ner  strife grant   us   re - lease;   Turn  na - tions
6. Praise to   the   Fa - ther, Christ the Word,   And   to   the

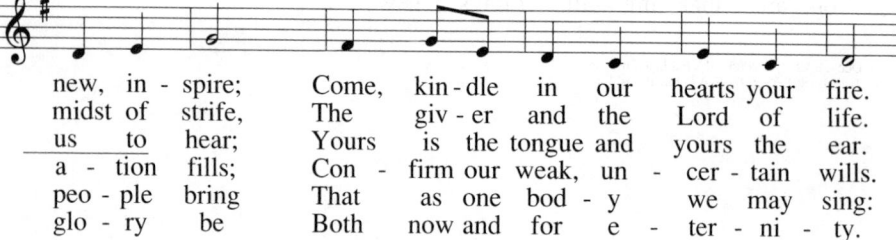

vi - brant    out   of   death:      Come to   cre - ate,   re -
love the     liv - ing  source,    Pro - tec - tor  in   the
var - ied    gifts make known.    Teach us   to   speak, teach
love our     hearts u - nite.     Your pow'r the  whole cre -
to   the     ways of   peace.     To   full - er  life  your
Spir - it:   God   the   Lord,     To   whom all  hon - or,

new, in - spire;    Come,  kin - dle  in   our   hearts your  fire.
midst of   strife,   The   giv - er  and  the  Lord of   life.
us   to   hear;     Yours  is   the tongue and yours the  ear.
a - tion  fills;     Con -  firm our weak, un - cer - tain  wills.
peo - ple  bring    That   as   one  bod - y   we  may  sing:
glo - ry  be       Both   now and for  e - ter - ni - ty.

Text: *Veni, Creator Spiritus;* attr. to Rabanus Maurus, 776–865; tr. by John W. Grant, 1919–2006, © 1971
Tune: VENI CREATOR SPIRITUS, LM; Mode VIII; setting by Richard J. Wojcik, b.1923, © 1975, GIA Publications, Inc.

# Send Us Your Spirit 552

**Refrain**

*1.                    2.

Come   Lord   Je - sus,      send   us   your   Spir - it,   re -

new   the   face   of   the   earth.      Come   Lord

Je - sus,   send   us   your   Spir-it,   re - new   the   face   of   the

earth.

**Verses**

1. Come           to   us,      Spir - it   of   God,   breathe   in   us
2. Fill   us   with      the      fire   of   your   love,   burn   in   us
3. Send      us         the      wings   of   new   birth,   fill   all   the

now,            we   sing   to - geth - er.      Spir - it   of
now,            bring   us   to - geth - er.      Come   to   us,
earth   with   the   love   you   have   taught   us.   Let   all   cre -

hope   and   of   light,      fill      our   lives,
dwell   in   us,   change   our   lives,      O   Lord,
a   -   tion   now   be   shak - en   with   love,

**D.C.**

come   to   us,   Spir - it   of   God.
come   to   us,   Spir - it   of   God.
come   to   us,   Spir - it   of   God.

*May be sung in canon.*

Text: David Haas, b.1957
Tune: David Haas, b.1957; acc. by Jeanne Cotter, b.1964
© 1981, 1982, 1987, GIA Publications, Inc.

# 553 O Spirit All-Embracing

1. O Spir - it all - em - brac - ing and coun-sel - or all - wise,
2. O Beau - ty ev - er blaz - ing in flow-er, field, and face,
3. Come, pas - sion's pow - er ho - ly, your in-sight here im - part,

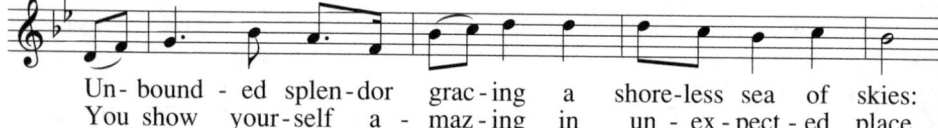

Un- bound - ed splen-dor grac - ing a shore-less sea of skies:
You show your-self a - maz - ing in un - ex - pect - ed place.
And give your ser - vants low - ly an un - der-stand-ing heart

Un - fail - ing is your treas-ure, un - fad - ing your re - ward;
We see you and re - mem - ber what once our dreams had been;
To know your care more clear - ly when faith and love are tried,

Sur - pass - ing world - ly pleas-ure, the rich -es you af - ford.
You fan the glow - ing em - ber and kin-dle hope with - in.
To seek you more sin - cere - ly when false i - deals have died:

Come, stream of end - less flow - ing, and res - cue us from death;
Come, fire of glo - ry gra - cious, bless all who trust in you;
For vi - sion we im - plore you, for wis-dom's pure de - light;

Come, wind of spring-time blow-ing, and warm us by your breath.
Un - dy - ing flame te - na - cious, burn in your Church a - new.
In prayer we come be - fore you to wait up - on your light.

Text: Delores Dufner, OSB, b.1939, © 1995, 2003, GIA Publications, Inc.
Tune: THAXTED, 13 13 13 13 13 13; Gustav Holst, 1874–1934

# Spirit of God  554

**Refrain**

Spir - it of God, who dwells in me, O - pen my
eyes that I may see. Come fill my heart
and make me whole. Spir - it of God, I am yours.

**Verses**

1. This is the Spir-it of the liv-ing God,
2. Come, Ho - ly Spir-it, and set me free

Who hears your ev - 'ry sin - gle prayer. O
To do the best I can. O

this is the Spir - it of the liv - ing God,
come, Ho - ly Spir - it, and set me free

**D.C.**

Who is al - ways right there.
To be all that I am.

Text: James E. Moore, Jr., b.1951
Tune: James E. Moore, Jr., b.1951
© 2002, GIA Publications, Inc.

# 555 Spirit Blowing through Creation

Verses

1. Spir - it blow - ing through cre - a - tion,
2. As you moved up - on the wa - ters,
3. Love that sends the riv - ers danc - ing,
4. All the crea - tures you have fash - ioned,

Spir - it burn - ing in the skies,
As you ride up - on the wind,
Love that wa - ters all that lives,
All that live and breathe in you,

Let the hope of your sal - va - tion fill our eyes;
Move us all, your sons and daugh - ters deep with - in;
Love that heals and holds and rous - es and for - gives;
Find their hope in your com - pas - sion, strong and true;

God of splen - dor, God of glo - ry,
As you shaped the hills and moun - tains,
You are food for all your crea - tures,
You, O Spir - it of sal - va - tion,

You who light the stars a - bove,
Formed the land and filled the deep,
You are hun - ger in the soul,
You a - lone, be - neath, a - bove,

All the heav - ens tell the sto - ry of your love. *(To verse 2)*
Let your hand re - new and wak - en all who sleep. *(To refrain)*
In your hands the bro - ken - heart - ed are made whole. *(To verse 4)*
Come, re - new your whole cre - a - tion in your love. *(To refrain)*

Refrain

Spir-it re-new-ing the earth, re-new-ing the hearts of all

peo-ple; Burn in the wea-ry souls,

blow through the si-lent lips, come now a - wake us,

Spir-it of God.

Text: Marty Haugen, b.1950
Tune: Marty Haugen, b.1950
© 1987, GIA Publications, Inc.

## Come Down, O Love Divine 556

1. Come down, O Love di - vine, Seek now this soul of
2. O let it free - ly burn, Till earth - ly pas - sions
3. And so the yearn-ing strong, With which the soul will

mine, And vis - it it with your own ar - dor glow-ing;
turn To dust and ash - es in its heat con - sum - ing;
long, Shall far out-pass the pow'r of hu - man tell - ing;

O Com-fort - er, draw near, With - in my heart ap -
And let your glo - rious light Shine ev - er on my
No soul can guess Love's grace Till it be - come the

pear, And kin - dle it, your ho - ly flame be - stow-ing.
sight, And clothe me round, the while my path il - lum-ing.
place Where - in the Ho - ly Spir - it makes a dwell-ing.

Text: *Discendi, Amor Santo*; Bianco da Siena, d.1434; tr. by Richard F. Littledale, 1833–1890
Tune: DOWN AMPNEY, 66 11 D; Ralph Vaughan Williams, 1872–1958

# 557  Send Down the Fire

Text: Marty Haugen, b.1950
Tune: Marty Haugen, b.1950
© 1989, GIA Publications, Inc.

# Veni Creátor Spíritus 558

1. Ve - ni Cre - á - tor Spí - ri - tus,
2. Qui dí - ce - ris Pa - rá - cli - tus,
3. Tu se - pti - fór - mis mú - ne - re,
4. Ac - cén - de lu - men sén - si - bus,
5. Ho - stem re - pél - las lón - gi - us,
6. Per te sci - á - mus da Pa - trem,
7. De - o Pa - tri sit gló - ri - a,

Men - tes tu - ó - rum ví - si - ta:
Al - tís - si - mi do - num De - i,
Dí - gi - tus pa - tér - nae déx - te - rae,
In - fún - de a - mó - rem cór - di - bus,
Pa - cém - que do - nes pró - ti - nus:
No - scá - mus at - que Fí - li - um
Et Fí - li - o, qui a mór - tu - is

Im - ple su - pér - na grá - ti - a
Fons vi - vus, i - gnis, cá - ri - tas,
Tu ri - te pro - mís - sum Pa - tris,
In - fír - ma no - stri cór - po - ris
Du - ctó - re sic te práe - vi - o,
Te - que u - tri - ús - que Spí - ri - tum
Sur - ré - xit, ac Pa - rá - cli - to,

Quae tu cre - á - sti pé - cto - ra.
Et spi - ri - tá - lis ún - cti - o.
Ser - mó - ne di - tans gút - tu - ra.
Vir - tú - te fir - mans pér - pe - ti.
Vi - té - mus o - mne nó - xi - um.
Cre - dá - mus o - mni tém - po - re.
In sae - cu - ló - rum saé - cu - la. A - men.

Text: *Veni Creator Spiritus*, attr. to Rabanus Maurus, 776–856
Tune: VENI CREATOR SPIRITUS, LM; Mode VIII; acc. by Richard Proulx, 1937–2010, © 1975, GIA Publications, Inc.

# 559 Come, Holy Ghost

1. Come, Ho - ly Ghost, Cre - a - tor blest, And in our
2. O Com - fort - er, to thee we cry, Thou heav'n - ly
3. O Ho - ly Ghost, through thee a - lone Know we the
4. Praise we the Lord, Fa - ther and Son, And Ho - ly

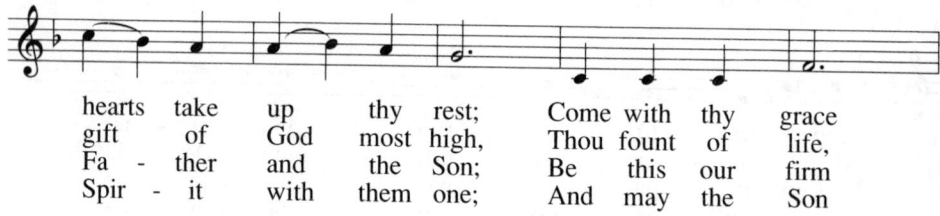

hearts take up thy rest; Come with thy grace
gift of God most high, Thou fount of life,
Fa - ther and the Son; Be this our firm
Spir - it with them one; And may the Son

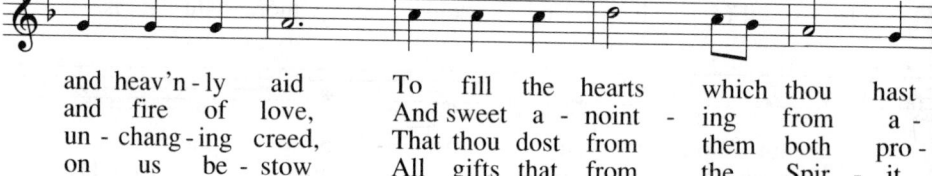

and heav'n - ly aid To fill the hearts which thou hast
and fire of love, And sweet a - noint - ing from a -
un - chang - ing creed, That thou dost from them both pro -
on us be - stow All gifts that from the Spir - it

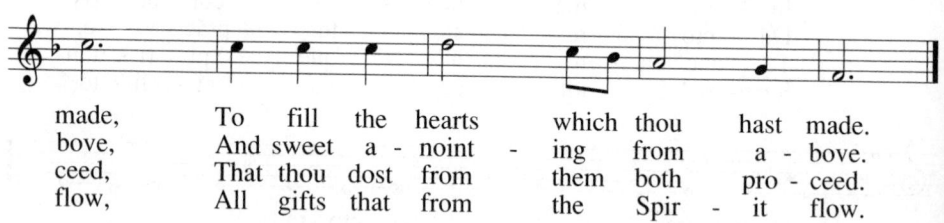

made, To fill the hearts which thou hast made.
bove, And sweet a - noint - ing from a - bove.
ceed, That thou dost from them both pro - ceed.
flow, All gifts that from the Spir - it flow.

Text: *Veni, Creator Spiritus;* attr. to Rabanus Maurus, 776–856; tr. by Edward Caswall, 1814–1878, alt.
Tune: LAMBILLOTTE, LM with repeat; Louis Lambillotte, SJ, 1796–1855; harm. by Richard Proulx, 1937–2010, © 1986, GIA Publications, Inc.

# Spirit Wind 560

**Refrain**

Spir-it Wind, Breath of God, breathe new life in - to the world.

Spir-it Wind, Breath of God, breathe new life in - to the world.

**Verses**

1. My soul cries out, "O bless the Lord!" O God, you
2. If you should take a - way our breath, what could we
3. All praise and thanks are yours, O God; may you re -

are the Ho - ly One; so man - y works your hands have
do but fall to dust? When you send forth the breath of
joice in all your works. May you find joy in us as

**D.C.**

made through - out the earth.
life we rise a - gain!
we re - joice in you!

Text: Psalm 104; Scott Soper, b.1961
Tune: Scott Soper, b.1961

# 561  Let There Be Light

Refrain

Ho - ly and bless - ed Three, glo - ri - ous Trin - i - ty:

Wis - dom, Love, and Might! Let there be light! Let there be light!

Verses 1, 2

1. You, whose al - might - y word cha - os and dark - ness heard.
2. Hope for all you bring, on your re - deem - ing wing.

Let there be light! Vic - tor of sin and death,
Let there be light! Dawn out of sin - ful night,

**D.C.**

giv - er of ho - ly breath. Let there be light!
mak - ing the dark - ness bright. Let there be light!

Verse 3

3. Spir - it of truth and love, life - giv - ing Ho - ly Dove.

Let there be light! Bring - er of ho - ly fire,

aim of our heart's de - sire. Let there be light!

Final Refrain

Ho - ly and bless - ed Three, glo - ri - ous Trin - i -

ty: Wis - dom, Love, and Might! Let there be light! Let there be

light! Oh, let there be light!

Text: John Marriott, 1780–1825; adapt. by Paul Melley, b.1973
Tune: Paul Melley, b.1973
© 2008, GIA Publications, Inc.

## Come Now, Almighty King  562

1. Come now, al - might - y King,  Help us your
2. Come now, in - car - nate Word,  Mer - ci - ful,
3. Come, ho - ly Com - fort - er,  Your sa - cred
4. To the great One in Three,  E - ter - nal

name to sing,  Help us to praise.
might - y Lord,  Our prayer at - tend.
wit - ness bear  In this glad hour.
prais - es be  For - ev - er - more!

Fa - ther all glo - ri - ous,  Ev - er vic - to - ri - ous,
Come and your peo - ple bless,  And give your word suc - cess,
Your grace to us im - part,  Now rule in ev - 'ry heart,
Your sov - 'reign maj - es - ty  May we in glo - ry see

Come and reign o - ver us,  An - cient of Days.
Grant us your ho - li - ness,  Sav - ior and Friend.
Nev - er from us de - part,  Spir - it of pow'r.
And, to e - ter - ni - ty,  Love and a - dore.

Text: Anon.; *Collection of Hymns for Social Worship*, 1757, alt.
Tune: ITALIAN HYMN, 66 4 666 4; Felice de Giardini, 1716–1796

# 563  How Wonderful the Three-in-One

1. How won - der - ful the Three - in - One, Whose
2. Be - fore the flow of dawn and dark, Cre -
3. The Lov - er's own Be - lov'd, in time, Be -
4. Their E - qual Friend all life sus - tains With
5. How won - der - ful the Liv - ing God: Di -

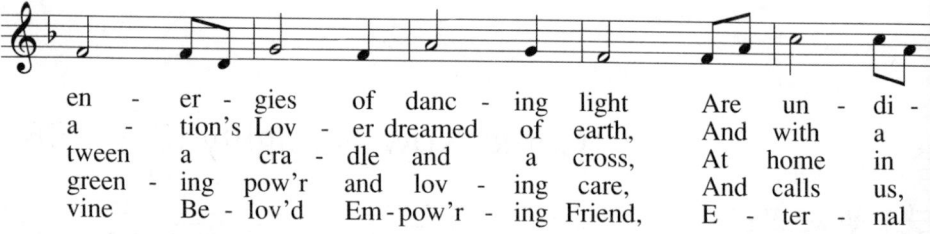

en - er - gies of danc - ing light Are un - di -
a - tion's Lov - er dreamed of earth, And with a
tween a cra - dle and a cross, At home in
green - ing pow'r and lov - ing care, And calls us,
vine Be - lov'd Em - pow'r - ing Friend, E - ter - nal

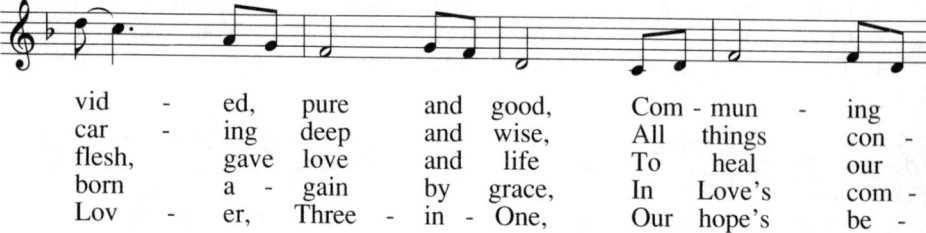

vid - ed, pure and good, Com - mun - ing
car - ing deep and wise, All things con -
flesh, gave love and life To heal our
born a - gain by grace, In Love's com -
Lov - er, Three - in - One, Our hope's be -

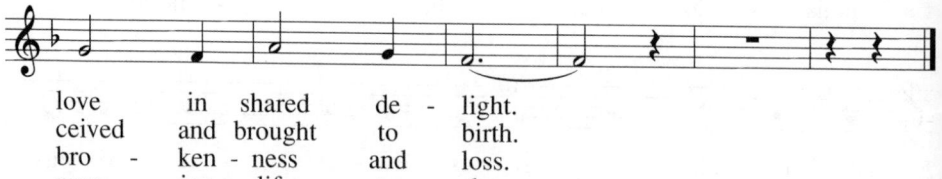

love in shared de - light.
ceived and brought to birth.
bro - ken - ness and loss.
mun - ing life to share.
gin - ning, way and end.

Text: Brian Wren, b.1936, © 1989, Hope Publishing Company
Tune: PROSPECT, LM; *Southern Harmony*; arr. by Marty Haugen, b.1950, © 1991, GIA Publications, Inc.

# The Play of the Godhead  564

1. The play of the God-head, the Trin - i - ty's dance,
2. The warm mists of sum-mer, cool wa - ters that flow,
3. In God's gra-cious im - age of co - e - qual parts,

Em - brac - es the earth in a sa - cred ro - mance,
Turn crys - tal as ice when the win - try winds blow.
We gath - er as danc - ers, u - nit - ing our hearts.

With God the Cre - a - tor, and Christ the true Son,
The tap - root that nur - tures, the shoot grow - ing free,
Men, wom - en, and chil - dren, and all liv - ing things,

En - twined with the Spir - it, a web dai - ly spun
The life - giv - ing fruit, full and ripe on the tree:
We join in the round of bright na - ture that rings

In span - gles of mys - t'ry, the great Three-in - One.
More mys - tic and won-drous, the great One - in - Three.
With rap - ture and rhy - thm: Cre - a - tion now sings!

Text: Mary Louise Bringle, b.1953
Tune: BEDFORD PARK, 11 11 11 11 11; Robert J. Batastini, b.1942
© 2002, 2003, GIA Publications, Inc.

# 565 Stand Up, Friends!

Verses

1. Praise the God who chang - es plac - es, Leaves the loft - y seat,
2. Praise the Rab - bi, speak - ing, do - ing All that God in - tends,
3. Praise the Breath of Love, whose free-dom Spreads our wak-ing wings,
4. Praise, un - til we join the sing-ing Far be-yond our sight,

Wel-comes us with warm em-brac - es, Stoops to wash our feet.
Dy - ing, ris - ing, faith re - new-ing, Call - ing us his friends.
Lift - ing ev - 'ry blight and bur-den Till our spir - it sings;
With the End - ing and Be - gin-ning Danc - ing in the light.

Refrain

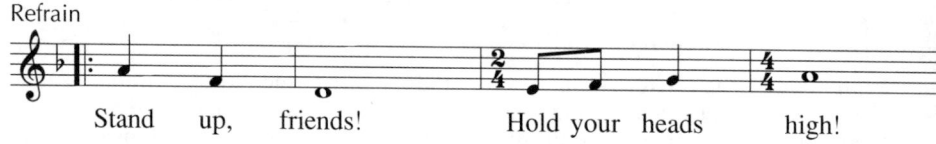

Stand up, friends! Hold your heads high!

Free-dom is our song! Al - le - lu - ia! Free-dom is our song!

Al - le - lu - ia! ia!

1. 2. 3

Text: Brian Wren, b.1936, © 1986, Hope Publishing Co.
Tune: David Haas, b.1957, © 1993, GIA Publications, Inc.

# 566 O God, Almighty Father

1. O God, al - might - y Fa - ther, Cre - a - tor of all things, The
2. O Je - sus, Word in - car - nate, Re - deem - er most a - dored, All
3. O God, the Ho - ly Spir - it, Who lives with - in our soul, Send

heav - ens stand in won - der, While earth your glo - ry sings.
glo - ry, praise, and hon - or Be yours, O sov - 'reign Lord.
forth your light and lead us To our e - ter - nal goal.

O most ho - ly Trin - i - ty, Un - di - vid - ed u - ni - ty,

Ho - ly God, might - y God, God im - mor - tal be a - dored!

Text: *Gott Vater sei gepriesen*; anon; tr. by Irvin Udulutsch, OFM Cap., 1920–2010, alt. © 1959, 1977, Order of Saint Benedict, admin. Liturgical Press
Tune: GOTT VATER SEI GEPRIESEN, 7 6 7 6 with refrain; *Limburg Gesangbuch*, 1838; harm. by Healey Willan, 1880–1968, © 1958,
Ralph Jusko Publications, Inc.

## Holy, Holy, Holy! Lord God Almighty! 567

1. Ho - ly, Ho - ly, Ho - ly! Lord God Al - might - y!
2. Ho - ly, Ho - ly, Ho - ly! All the saints a - dore thee,
3. Ho - ly, Ho - ly, Ho - ly! Though the dark - ness hide thee,
4. Ho - ly, Ho - ly, Ho - ly! Lord God Al - might - y!

Ear - ly in the morn - ing our song shall rise to thee.
Cast - ing down their gold - en crowns a - round the glass - y sea;
Though the eye made blind by sin thy glo - ry may not see,
All thy works shall praise thy Name in earth and sky and sea.

Ho - ly, Ho - ly, Ho - ly, mer - ci - ful and might - y!
Cher - u - bim and ser - a - phim fall - ing down be - fore thee,
On - ly thou art ho - ly; there is none be - side thee,
Ho - ly, Ho - ly, Ho - ly, mer - ci - ful and might - y!

God in three Per - sons, bless - ed Trin - i - ty.
God ev - er - last - ing through e - ter - ni - ty.
Per - fect in pow'r, in love, and pu - ri - ty.
God in three Per - sons, bless - ed Trin - i - ty.

Text: Reginald Heber, 1783–1826, alt.
Tune: NICAEA, 11 12 12 10; John Bacchus Dykes, 1823–1876

# 568 Rejoice, the Lord Is King!

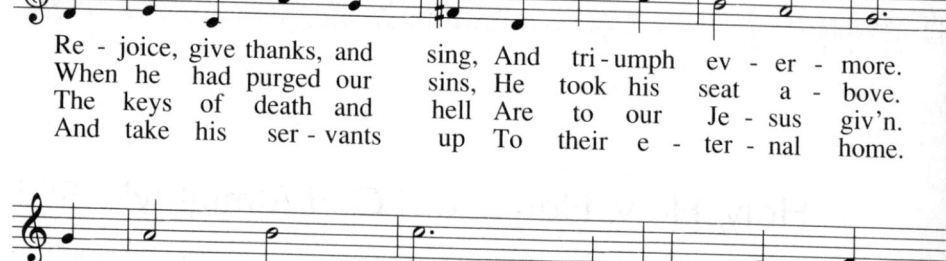

1. Re - joice, the Lord is King! Your Lord and King a - dore!
2. The Lord, our Sav - ior, reigns, The God of truth and love.
3. His king-dom can - not fail, He rules o'er earth and heav'n.
4. Re - joice in glo - rious hope! For Christ the Judge shall come

Re - joice, give thanks, and sing, And tri - umph ev - er - more.
When he had purged our sins, He took his seat a - bove.
The keys of death and hell Are to our Je - sus giv'n.
And take his ser - vants up To their e - ter - nal home.

Lift up your heart, lift up your voice!

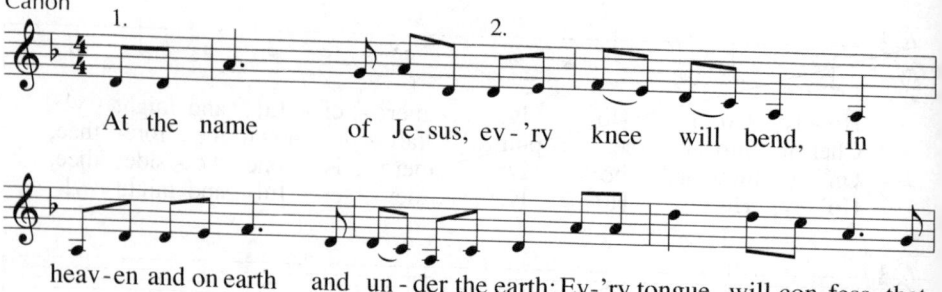

Re - joice, a - gain I say, re - joice!

Text: Charles Wesley, 1707–1788, alt.
Tune: DARWALL'S 148TH, 6 6 6 6 88; John Darwall, 1731–1789; harm. from *The Hymnal 1940*

# 569 At the Name of Jesus

Canon

At the name of Je-sus, ev-'ry knee will bend, In

heav-en and on earth and un - der the earth; Ev-'ry tongue will con-fess that

Je-sus Christ is Lord, To the glo - ry of God the Fa - ther.

Text: Philippians 2:10–11
Tune: IN THE NAME, 11 11 12 9; James E. Clemens, © 2008, James E. Clemens

# All Hail the Power of Jesus' Name! 570

1. All hail the pow'r of Je - sus' name! Let
2. Crown him, you mar - tyrs of our God Who
3. O seed of Is - rael's cho - sen race Now
4. Oh, that with yon - der sa - cred throng We

an - gels pros - trate fall. Bring forth the roy - al
from his al - tar call: Ex - tol the stem of
ran - somed from the fall, Hail him who saves you
at his feet may fall! We'll join the ev - er -

di - a - dem, And crown him Lord of
Jes - se's rod, And crown him Lord of
by his grace, And crown him Lord of
last - ing song And crown him Lord of

all, And crown him Lord of all, And
all, And crown him Lord of all, And
all, And crown him Lord of all, And
all, And crown him Lord of all, And

crown him Lord of all. Bring forth the roy - al
crown him Lord of all. Ex - tol the stem of
crown him Lord of all. Hail him who saves you
crown him Lord of all. We'll join the ev - er -

di - a - dem, And crown him Lord of all!
Jes - se's rod, And crown him Lord of all!
by his grace, And crown him Lord of all!
last - ing song And crown him Lord of all!

Text: Edward Perronet, 1726–1792; alt. by John Rippon, 1751–1836, alt.
Tune: DIADEM, CM with repeats; from the *Primitive Baptist Hymn and Tune Book*, 1902; harm. by Richard Proulx, 1937–2010, © 1975,
GIA Publications, Inc.

## 571 Christ Is the King!

1. Christ is the King! O friends, re - joice;
2. O mag - ni - fy the Lord, and raise
3. They with a faith for ev - er new
4. O Chris - tian wom - en, Chris - tian men,
5. Christ through all a - ges is the same;

Broth - ers and sis - ters, with one voice
An - thems of joy and ho - ly praise
Fol - lowed the King, and round him drew
All the world o - ver, seek a - gain
Place the same hope in his great name;

Let the world know he is your choice.
For Christ's brave saints of an - cient days.
Thou - sands of men and wom - en true.
The Way dis - ci - ples fol - lowed then.
With the same faith his word pro - claim.

Al - le - lu - ia, al - le - lu - ia, al - le - lu - ia.

6. Let Love's all reconciling might
Your scattered companies unite
In service to the Lord of light.
Alleluia, alleluia, alleluia.

7. So shall the Church at last be one;
So shall God's will on earth be done,
New lamps be lit, new tasks begun.
Alleluia, alleluia, alleluia.

Text: George K. A. Bell, 1883–1958, alt., © Oxford University Press
Tune: GELOBT SEI GOTT, 888 with alleluias; Melchior Vulpius, c.1560–1616

## 572 The King of Glory

Refrain

The King of glo - ry comes, the na - tion re - joic - es.

*Last time*

O - pen the gates be - fore him, lift up your voic - es.

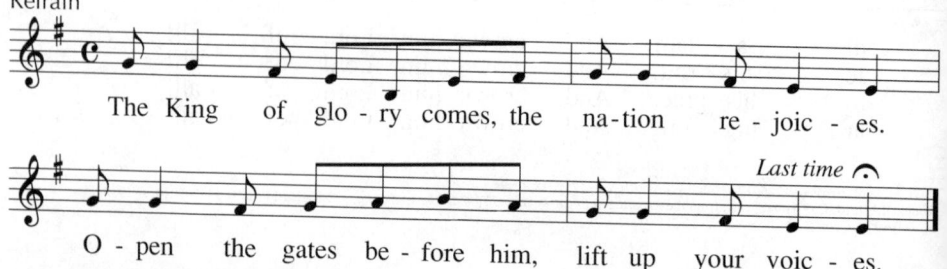

Verses

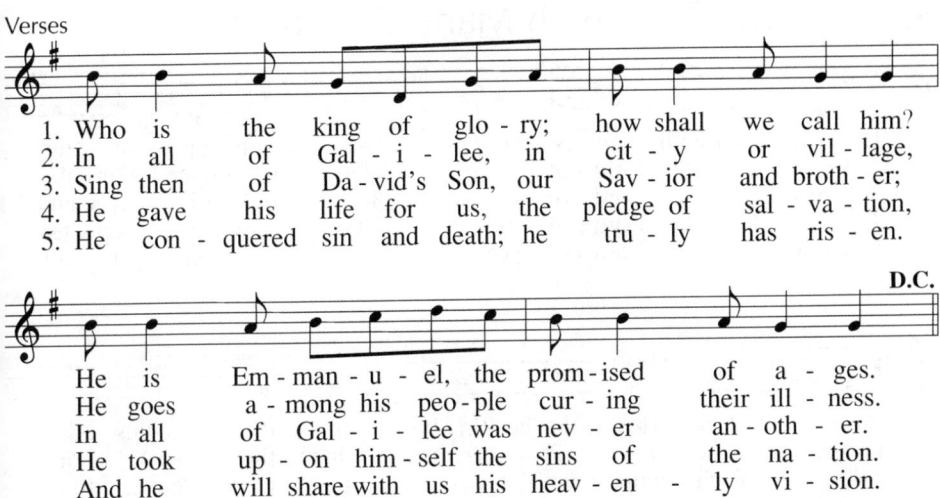

1. Who is the king of glo - ry; how shall we call him?
2. In all of Gal - i - lee, in cit - y or vil - lage,
3. Sing then of Da - vid's Son, our Sav - ior and broth - er;
4. He gave his life for us, the pledge of sal - va - tion,
5. He con - quered sin and death; he tru - ly has ris - en.

D.C.

He is Em - man - u - el, the prom - ised of a - ges.
He goes a - mong his peo - ple cur - ing their ill - ness.
In all of Gal - i - lee was nev - er an - oth - er.
He took up - on him - self the sins of the na - tion.
And he will share with us his heav - en - ly vi - sion.

Text: Willard F. Jabusch, b.1930, © 1966, 1982, Willard F. Jabusch. Administered by OCP.
Tune: KING OF GLORY, 12 12 with refrain; Israeli; harm. by Richard Proulx, 1937–2010, © 1986, GIA Publications, Inc.

# To Jesus Christ, Our Sovereign King   573

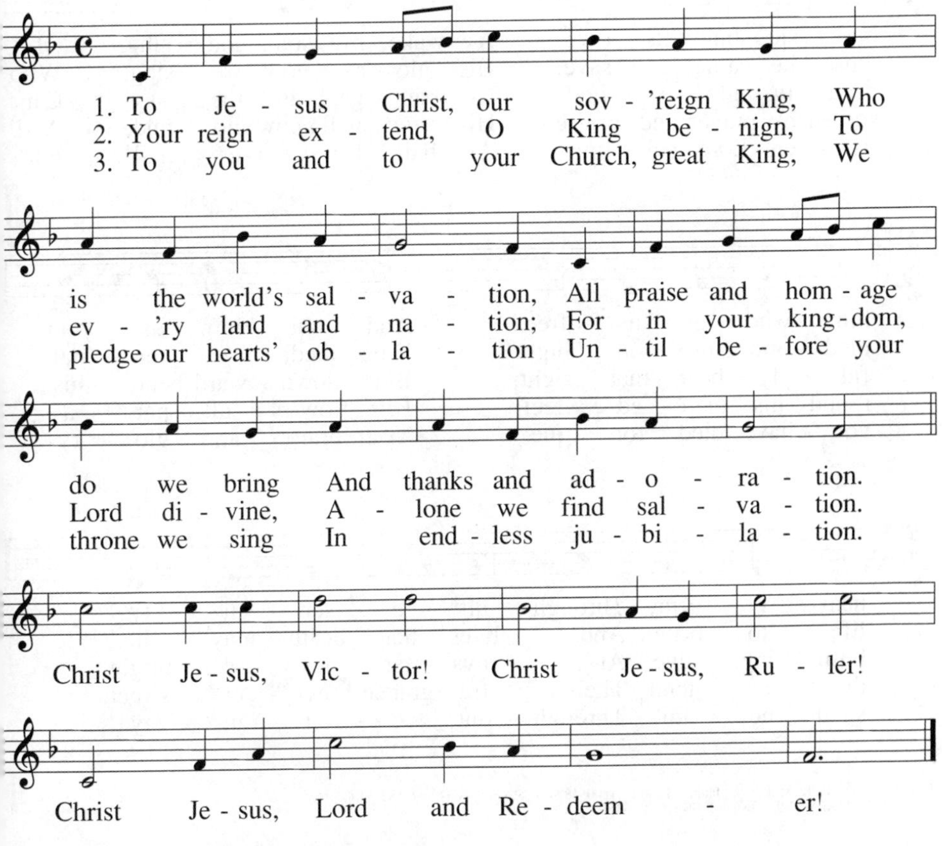

1. To Je - sus Christ, our sov - 'reign King, Who
2. Your reign ex - tend, O King be - nign, To
3. To you and to your Church, great King, We

is the world's sal - va - tion, All praise and hom - age
ev - 'ry land and na - tion; For in your king - dom,
pledge our hearts' ob - la - tion Un - til be - fore your

do we bring And thanks and ad - o - ra - tion.
Lord di - vine, A - lone we find sal - va - tion.
throne we sing In end - less ju - bi - la - tion.

Christ Je - sus, Vic - tor! Christ Je - sus, Ru - ler!

Christ Je - sus, Lord and Re - deem - er!

Text: Martin B. Hellriegel, 1890–1981, alt., © 1941, Irene C. Mueller
Tune: ICH GLAUB AN GOTT, 8 7 8 7 with refrain; *Mainz Gesangbuch*, 1870; harm. by Richard Proulx, 1937–2010, © 1986, GIA Publications, Inc.

# 574 Crown Him with Many Crowns

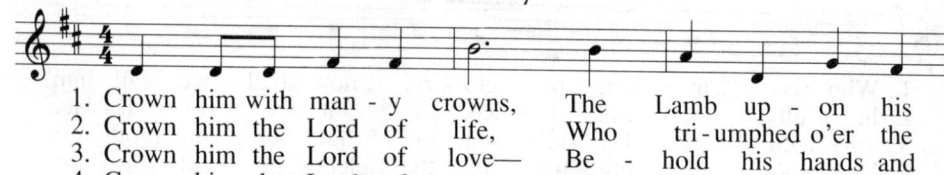

1. Crown him with man - y crowns, The Lamb up - on his
2. Crown him the Lord of life, Who tri - umphed o'er the
3. Crown him the Lord of love— Be - hold his hands and
4. Crown him the Lord of peace, Whose power a scep - ter
5. Crown him the Lord of years, The mas - ter of all

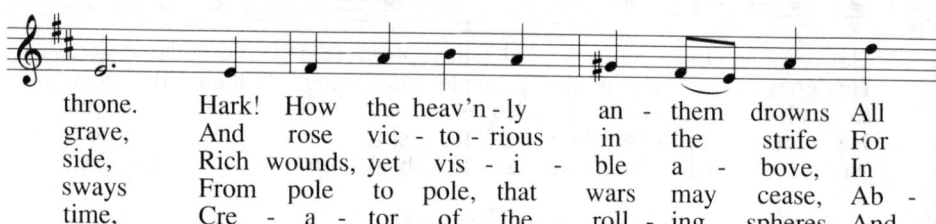

throne. Hark! How the heav'n - ly an - them drowns All
grave, And rose vic - to - rious in the strife For
side, Rich wounds, yet vis - i - ble a - bove, In
sways From pole to pole, that wars may cease, Ab -
time, Cre - a - tor of the roll - ing spheres, And

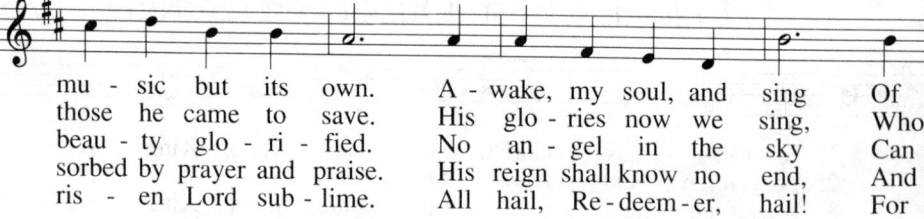

mu - sic but its own. A - wake, my soul, and sing Of
those he came to save. His glo - ries now we sing, Who
beau - ty glo - ri - fied. No an - gel in the sky Can
sorbed by prayer and praise. His reign shall know no end, And
ris - en Lord sub - lime. All hail, Re - deem - er, hail! For

him who set us free, And hail him as your
died and rose on high, Who died, e - ter - nal
ful - ly bear that sight, But down - ward bends his
round his pierc - ed feet Fair flow'rs of par - a -
you have died for me; Your praise and glo - ry

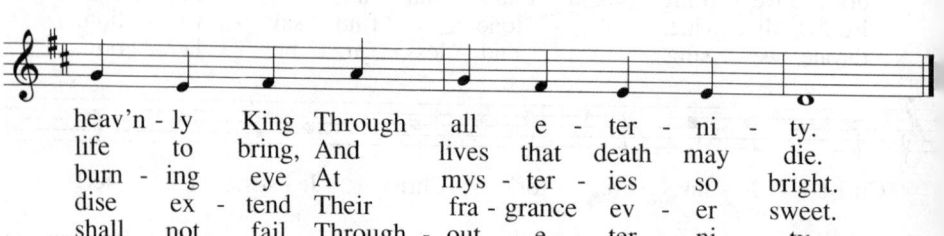

heav'n - ly King Through all e - ter - ni - ty.
life to bring, And lives that death may die.
burn - ing eye At mys - ter - ies so bright.
dise ex - tend Their fra - grance ev - er sweet.
shall not fail Through - out e - ter - ni - ty.

Text: Revelation 19:12; st. 1, 3–5, Matthew Bridges, 1800–1894; st. 2, Godfrey Thring, 1823–1903
Tune: DIADEMATA, SMD; George J. Elvey, 1816–1893

# All You Works of God   575

Refrain

All you works of God, ev-'ry moun-tain, star and tree, bless the One who shapes your beau - ty, who has caused you all to be one great song of love and grace, ev - er an - cient, ev - er new. Raise your voic - es, all you works of God!

Verses

*Solo:*    *All:*    *Solo:*

1. Sun    and  moon:                           Stars  of   heav - en:
2. Winds  of   God:                            Cold   and  win - ter:
3. Night  and  day:                            Light  and  dark - ness:
4. All     the  earth:   Bless your Mak - er!   Hills  and  moun - tains:
5. Wells  and springs:                         Seas   and  riv - ers:
6. Fly - ing  birds:                           Beasts and  cat - tle:
7. All    who  live:                           Men    and  wom - en:

*All:*    *Solo:*

                     Show  -  ers     and   dew:
                     Snow  -  storms   and   ice:
                     Light  -  nings   and   clouds:
Chant your praise!  Green     things    that   grow:
                     Whales    in       the    deep:
                     Chil - dren    at     play:
                     Ser - vants   of     God:

*All:*                                   **D.C.**

Raise    up    your    joy - ful    song.

Text: Based on Daniel 3:57–85; Marty Haugen, b.1950
Tune: Marty Haugen, b.1950
© 1989, GIA Publications, Inc.

# 576 Canticle of the Sun

**Refrain**

The heav-ens are tell-ing the glo-ry of God,

and all cre-a-tion is shout-ing for joy. Come,

dance in the for-est, come, play in the field, and

sing, sing to the glo-ry of the Lord.

**Verses**

1. Praise for the sun, the bring-er of day, He car-ries the
2. Praise for the wind that blows through the trees, The seas' might-y
3. Praise for the rain that wa-ters our fields, And bless-es our
4. Praise for the fire who gives us his light, The warmth of the
5. Praise for the earth who makes life to grow, The crea-tures you
6. Praise for our death that makes our life real, The knowl-edge of

light of the Lord in his rays; The moon and the stars who
storms, ⁊ the gen-tl-est breeze; They blow where they will, they
crops ⁊ so all the earth yields; From death un-to life her
sun ⁊ to bright-en our night; He danc-es with joy, his
made ⁊ to let your life show; The flow-ers and trees that
loss ⁊ that helps us to feel; The gift of your-self, your

**D.C.**

light up the way Un-to your throne.
blow where they please To please the Lord.
mys-t'ry re-vealed Springs forth in joy.
spir-it so bright, He sings of you.
help us to know The heart of love.
pres-ence re-vealed To lead us home.

Text: *Altissimu, onnipotente bon Signore*; St. Francis of Assisi, 1181–1226; adapt. by Marty Haugen, b.1950
Tune: Marty Haugen, b.1950
© 1980, GIA Publications, Inc.

# Sing Out, Earth and Skies! 577

**Verses**

*Cantor:* / *All:*

1. Come, O God of all the earth: Come to us, O
2. Come, O God of wind and flame: Fill the earth with
3. Come, O God of flash-ing light: Twin-kling star and
4. Come, O God of snow and rain: Show-er down up -
5. Come, O Jus-tice, Come, O Peace: Come and shape our

*Cantor:*

Right-eous One; Come, and bring our love to birth:
right-eous-ness; Teach us all to sing your name:
burn-ing sun; God of day and God of night:
on the earth; Come, O God of joy and pain:
hearts a-new; Come and make op - pres-sion cease:

*All:*

In the glo - ry of your Son.
May our lives your love con - fess.
In your light we all are one.
God of sor - row, God of mirth.
Bring us all to life in you.

**Refrain**

Sing out, earth and skies! Sing of the God who

loves you! Raise your joy - ful cries!

Dance to the life a - round you!

Text: Marty Haugen, b.1950
Tune: SING OUT, 7 7 7 7 with refrain; Marty Haugen, b.1950
© 1985, GIA Publications, Inc.

# 578 How Great Thou Art

1. O Lord my God, when I in awe-some
2. When through the woods and for - est glades I
3. And when I think that God, his Son not
4. When Christ shall come with shout of ac - cla -

won - der Con - sid - er all the works thy hands have
wan - der And hear the birds sing sweet - ly in the
spar - ing, Sent him to die, I scarce can take it
ma - tion And take me home, what joy shall fill my

made, I see the stars, I hear the roll - ing
trees, When I look down from loft - y moun-tain
in That on the cross, my bur - den glad - ly
heart! Then I shall bow in hum - ble ad - o -

thun - der, Thy pow'r through-out the un - i - verse dis - played!
gran - deur And hear the brook and feel the gen - tle breeze,
bear - ing, He bled and died to take a - way my sin!
ra - tion And there pro - claim, "My God, how great thou art!"

Then sings my soul, my Sav-ior God, to thee: How great thou

art, how great thou art! Then sings my soul, my Sav-ior God, to

thee: How great thou art, how great thou art!

Text: Stuart K. Hine, 1899–1989
Tune: HOW GREAT THOU ART, 11 10 11 10 with refrain; Stuart K. Hine, 1899–1989
© 1949, 1953, Stuart K. Hine Trust. Print rights administered by Hope Publishing Company in the USA.

# Over My Head 579

**Refrain**

O - ver my head, I hear mu - sic in the air; o - ver my head,

I hear mu - sic in the air; o - ver my head, I hear

mu - sic in the air; there must be a God some - where.

**Verses**

*Solo:*     *Assembly:*     *Solo:*

1. Oh when the world is si - lent,    oh
2. And when I'm feel-ing lone-ly, I hear mu-sic in the air;    and
3. Now when I think on Je - sus,    now

*Assembly:*     *Solo:*

when the world is si - lent,    oh
when I'm feel - ing lone - ly, I hear mu - sic in the air;    and
when I think on Je - sus,    now

*Assembly:*

when the world is si - lent,
when I'm feel - ing lone - ly, I hear mu - sic in the air;
when I think on Je - sus,

*All:*     **D.C.**

there must be a God some - where.

Text: African American spiritual
Tune: African American spiritual; arr. by John L. Bell, b.1949, © 1997, Iona Community, GIA Publications, Inc., agent

# 580   For God So Loved the World

Refrain

For God so loved the world, God gave the on - ly Son,

so that ev-'ry-one who be-lieves in him may not die, but have life.

*Last time to Coda ⊕*

So much God loved the world, so much God loves the world.

Verses 1, 2

1. The Word be - came flesh and dwelt a - mong us; full of
2. As Mo - ses lift - ed up the ser - pent so that

grace, full of truth he made his home. He came to his own who would
all who looked to it might live, the Son of Man must be

know him not, though all who be - hold him,
lift - ed up so that all who be - lieve,

**D.C.**

all who re-ceive him are called the chil - dren of God.
all who look to him may have e - ter - nal life.

Verse 3

3. God's Son came not to con - demn the world, but that the

world may be saved through him, and all who be-lieve in the

PROVIDENCE

Son     of     God     shall     come     to  the  light,         and

D.C.

live     in  the  light,     and     dwell     in  the  heart     of     God.

Coda

much     God     loves     the     world,             so     much  God

loves     the     world.

Text: John 1:11–12, 14, 3:14–17, 21; Marty Haugen, b.1950, and Susan Briehl, b.1952
Tune: Marty Haugen, b.1950
© 2005, GIA Publications, Inc.

# 581   O God, You Search Me

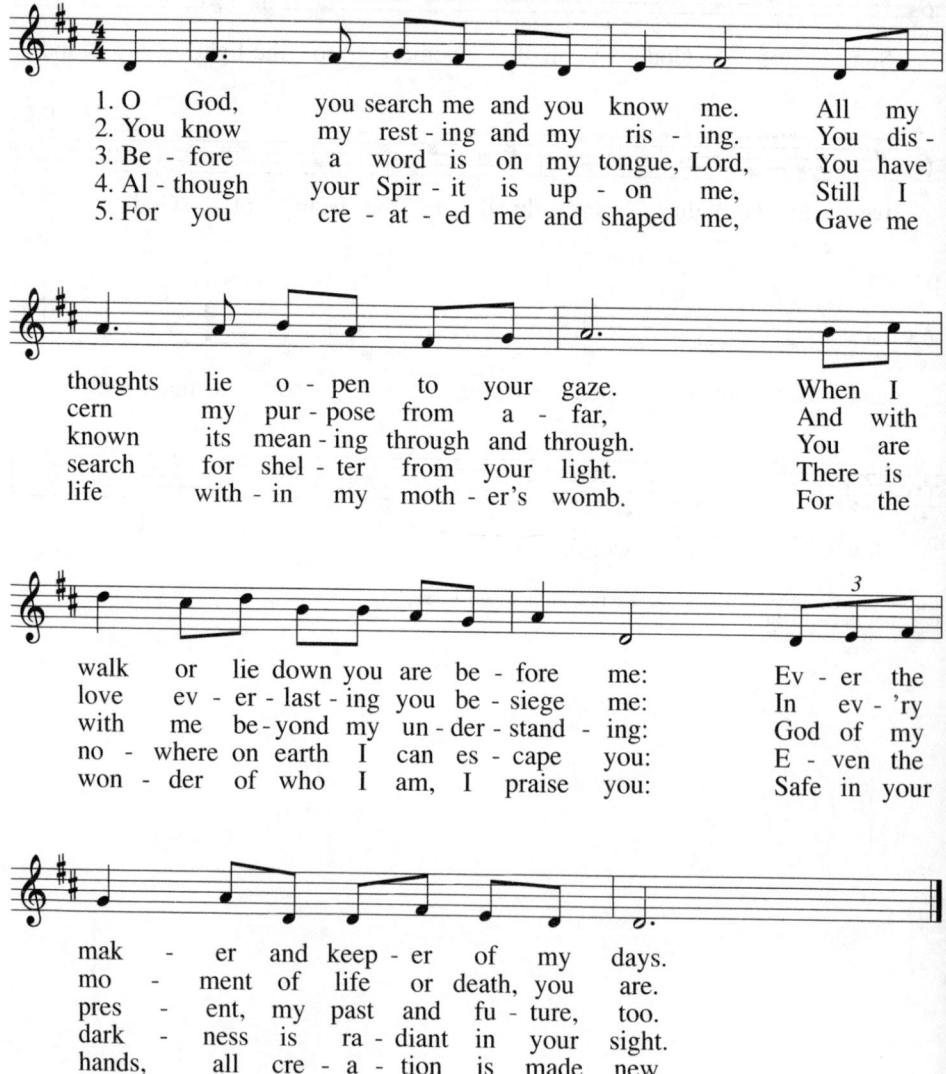

1. O God,     you search me and you know me.   All my
2. You know    my rest - ing and my ris - ing.   You dis -
3. Be - fore    a word is on my tongue, Lord,   You have
4. Al - though   your Spir - it is up - on me,   Still I
5. For you     cre - at - ed me and shaped me,   Gave me

thoughts   lie o - pen to your gaze.   When I
cern     my pur - pose from a - far,   And with
known    its mean - ing through and through.   You are
search    for shel - ter from your light.   There is
life     with - in my moth - er's womb.   For the

walk   or lie down you are be - fore   me:   Ev - er the
love   ev - er - last - ing you be - siege   me:   In ev - 'ry
with   me be - yond my un - der - stand - ing:   God of my
no - where on earth I can es - cape   you:   E - ven the
won - der of who I am, I praise   you:   Safe in your

mak - er and keep - er of my days.
mo - ment of life or death, you are.
pres - ent, my past and fu - ture, too.
dark - ness is ra - diant in your sight.
hands, all cre - a - tion is made new.

Text: Based on Psalm 139; Bernadette Farrell, b.1957
Tune: Bernadette Farrell, b.1957
© 1992, Bernadette Farrell. Published by OCP.

# Rain Down   582

**Refrain**

Rain     down,     rain     down,     rain down your

love on your peo - ple.     Rain     down,     rain

down,     rain down your     love, God   of     life.

**Verses**

1. Faith - ful    and     true     is     the     word   of    our     God.
2. We     who    re - vere    and    find     hope    in    our     God
3. God     of     cre - a - tion,    we     long    for    your     truth;

All    of    God's   works   are    so     wor - thy    of     trust.
live    in     the    kind - ness   and    joy    of   God's   wing.
you    are     the    wa - ter    of     life    that    we    thirst.

God's   mer - cy     falls    on     the    just   and    the    right;
God    will    pro - tect    us    from   dark - ness   and   death;
Grant   that   your    love    and   your   peace touch   our    hearts,

**D.C.**

full    of    God's   love    is     the    earth.
God    will    not    leave   us    to     starve.
all    of    our    hope   lies    in     you.

Text: Based on Psalm 33; Jaime Cortez, b.1963
Tune: Jaime Cortez, b.1963; acc. by Craig S. Kingsbury, b.1952
© 1991, 1992, Jaime Cortez. Published by OCP.

# 583 Wisdom, My Road

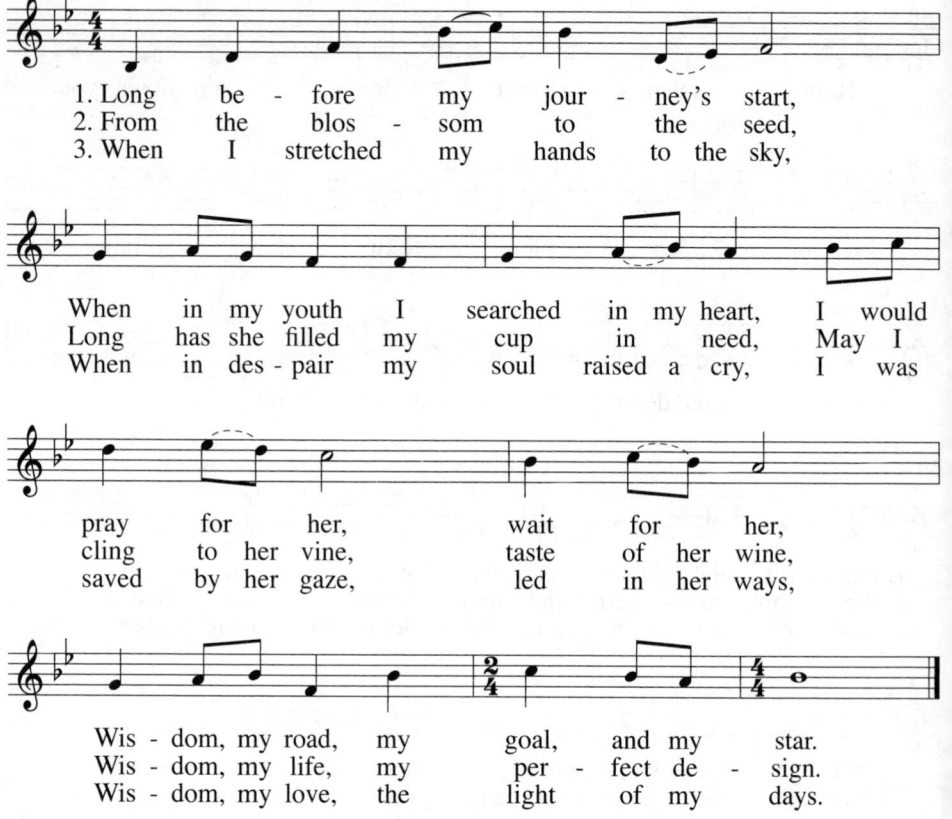

1. Long be - fore my jour - ney's start,
2. From the blos - som to the seed,
3. When I stretched my hands to the sky,

When in my youth I searched in my heart, I would
Long has she filled my cup in need, May I
When in des - pair my soul raised a cry, I was

pray for her, wait for her,
cling to her vine, taste of her wine,
saved by her gaze, led in her ways,

Wis - dom, my road, my goal, and my star.
Wis - dom, my life, my per - fect de - sign.
Wis - dom, my love, the light of my days.

Text: Based on Ecclesiasticus 51:13–22; Steven C. Warner, b.1954
Tune: Leslie Palmer Barnhart
© 1993, World Library Publications

# Come to the Water  584

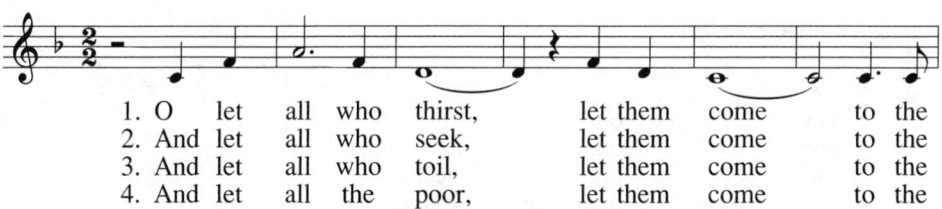

1. O   let   all   who   thirst,      let them   come      to   the
2. And let   all   who   seek,       let them   come      to   the
3. And let   all   who   toil,        let them   come      to   the
4. And let   all   the   poor,       let them   come      to   the

wa - ter.                    And   let   all   who have   noth - ing,
wa - ter.                    And   let   all   who have   noth - ing,
wa - ter.                    And   let   all   who are    wea - ry,
wa - ter.                    Bring  the   ones  who are    lad - en,

let    them come    to   the Lord:   With - out   mon - ey,
let    them come    to   the Lord:   With - out   mon - ey,
let    them come    to   the Lord:   All  who    la - bor,
bring them    all    to   the Lord:   Bring the    chil - dren

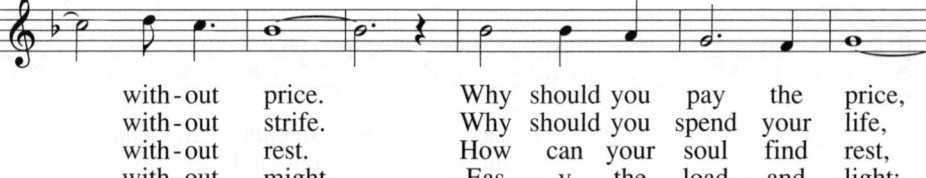

with - out   price.      Why should you   pay   the   price,
with - out   strife.      Why should you   spend your   life,
with - out   rest.       How  can  your   soul  find   rest,
with - out   might.      Eas - y   the   load  and   light:

ex - cept for the   Lord?
ex - cept for the   Lord?
ex - cept for the   Lord?
𝄪 come to the   Lord.

Text: Isaiah 55:1, 2, Matthew 11:28–30; John Foley, SJ, b.1939
Tune: John Foley, SJ, b.1939
© 1978, John B. Foley, SJ, and OCP

# 585 Come to the Feast

*Solo or S, A:*                                                                 *All:*

1. Oh,      ev - 'ry - one  who    thirsts:
   and      ev - 'ry - one  who    la - bors:
2. Oh,      ev - 'ry - one  who    seeks:
   and      ev - 'ry - one  who    mourns:
3. Let      all   who  seek their  God:            Come  to  the  wa-ters!
   the      ev - er - last - ing   stream:
4. And      you   who  are  en - slaved:
   To       all   who  live in     fear:
5. And      all   who  are  op - pressed:
   and      you,  the  lost and    bro - ken:

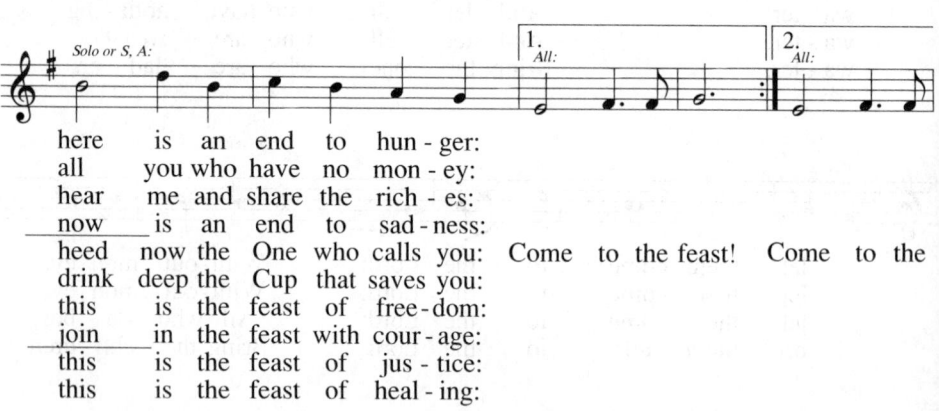

*Solo or S, A:*                              1. *All:*          2. *All:*

here     is   an   end   to   hun - ger:
all      you who have  no   mon - ey:
hear     me and share the  rich - es:
now      is   an   end   to   sad - ness:
heed     now the One  who calls you:   Come  to the feast!  Come  to the
drink    deep the Cup  that saves you:
this     is   the feast of   free - dom:
join     in   the feast with cour - age:
this     is   the feast of   jus - tice:
this     is   the feast of   heal - ing:

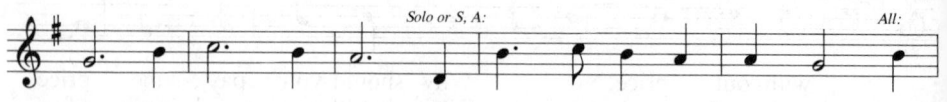

*Solo or S, A:*                                          *All:*

                              1. the  wa - ters of the   Jor - dan:
                              2. the streams of joy and  glad - ness:
feast! For this    is  life: 3. the floods that o - ver-whelm you:    For
                              4. the  wa - ters that have freed you:
                              5. to   die  and rise in   Je - sus:

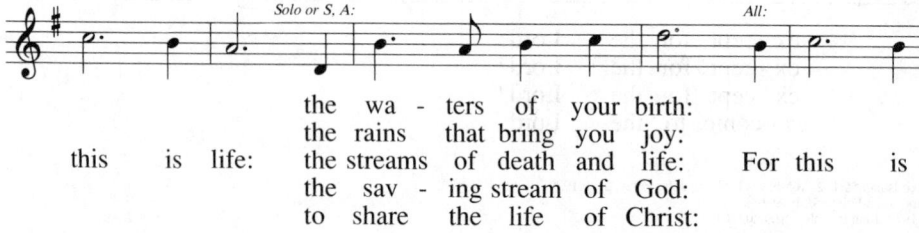

*Solo or S, A:*                              *All:*

                 the  wa - ters of   your birth:
                 the  rains    that bring you  joy:
this  is  life:  the streams  of   death and  life:   For this  is
                 the  sav - ing stream of   God:
                 to   share   the  life  of   Christ:

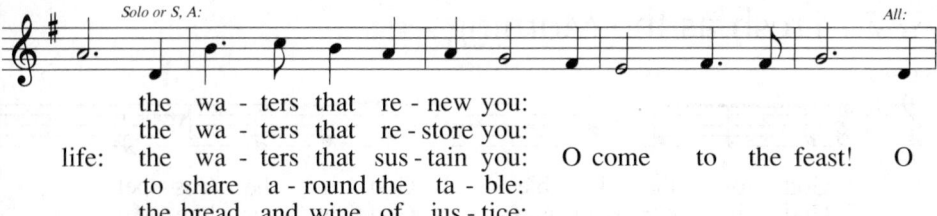

Solo or S, A:                                                                                    All:

life:  the  wa - ters  that  re - new  you:
       the  wa - ters  that  re - store  you:
       the  wa - ters  that  sus - tain  you:   O come   to   the feast!   O
       to  share  a - round  the  ta - ble:
       the  bread  and  wine  of  jus - tice:

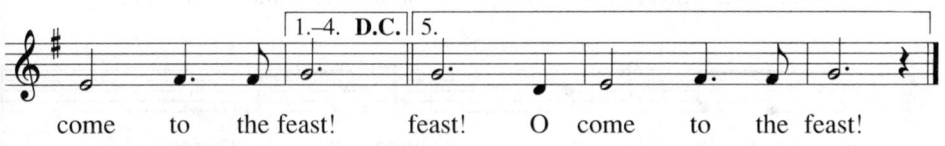

1.–4.  D.C.  5.

come    to    the feast!    feast!    O    come    to    the feast!

Text: Isaiah 55; Marty Haugen, b.1950
Tune: Marty Haugen, b.1950
© 1991, GIA Publications, Inc.

## You Are All We Have    586

Refrain

You   are all  we   have.   You give  us what we   need.   Our

lives  are in  your hands,  O Lord,  our lives  are in  your hands.

Verses

1. Protect me, Lord; I come to you for safety.
   I say, "You are my God."
   All good things, Lord, all good things
   that I have come from you,
   the God of my salvation.

2. How wonderful are your gifts to me,
   how good they are!
   I praise the Lord who guides me
   and teaches me the way of truth and life.

3. You are near, the God I seek.
   Nothing can take me from your side.
   All my days I rest secure;
   you will show me the path that leads to life.

Text: Francis Patrick O'Brien, b.1958
Tune: Francis Patrick O'Brien, b.1958
© 1992, GIA Publications, Inc.

## 587 Fresh as the Morning

Verses

1. God of the Bi - ble, God in the Gos - pel,
2. God in our strug-gles, God in our hun - ger,
3. Those with - out sta - tus, those who are noth - ing,
4. Not by your fin - ger, not by your an - ger
5. Hope we must car - ry, shin - ing and cer - tain

hope seen in Je - sus, hope yet to come,
suf - fer - ing with us, tak - ing our part,
you have made roy - al, gift - ed with rights,
will our world or - der change in a day,
through all our tur - moil, ter - ror and loss,

you are our cen - ter, day - light or dark - ness,
still you em - pow'r us, moth - er - ing Spir - it,
cho - sen as part - ners, mid - wives of jus - tice,
but by your peo - ple, fear - less and faith - ful,
bond - ing us glad - ly one to the oth - er,

free - dom or pris - on, you are our home.
feed - ing, sus - tain - ing, from your own heart.
birth - ing new sys - tems, light - ing new lights.
small pa - per lan - terns, light - ing the way.
till our world chang - es fac - ing the Cross.

Refrain

Fresh as the morn - ing, sure as the sun - rise,

God al - ways faith - ful, you do not change.

PROVIDENCE

Fresh as the morn - ing, sure as the sun - rise,

God al - ways faith - ful, you do not change.

Text: Shirley Erena Murray, b.1931, © 1996, Hope Publishing Co.
Tune: Tony E. Alonso, b.1980, © 2001, GIA Publications, Inc.

## I Have Loved You 588

Refrain

I have loved you with an ev - er - last - ing love, I have

called you and you are mine; I have loved you with an

ev - er - last - ing love, I have called you and you are mine.

Verses

1. Seek the face of the Lord and long for
2. Seek the face of the Lord and long for
3. Seek the face of the Lord and long for

D.C.

him: He will bring you his light and his peace.
him: He will bring you his joy and his hope.
him: He will bring you his care and his love.

Text: Jeremiah 31:3, Psalm 24:3; Michael Joncas, b.1951
Tune: Michael Joncas, b.1951
© 1979, OCP

# 589 Lord Jesus Christ / Jésus le Christ

Ostinato Refrain

Lord Je - sus Christ, your light shines with - in us.
*French: Jé - sus le Christ, lu - mière in - té - rieu - re,*
*Spanish: Cris - to Je - sús, oh fue - go que a-bra - sa,*
*Polish: Je - zu, Tyś jest świat - łoś - cią mej du - szy.*

Let not my doubts nor my dark - ness speak to me.
*ne lais - se pas mes té - nè - bres me par - ler.*
*que las ti - nie - blas en mí no ten - gan voz.*
*Niech ciem-ność ma nie prze - ma - wia do mnie już.*

Lord Je - sus Christ, your light shines with - in us.
*Jé - sus le Christ, lu - mière in - té - rieu - re,*
*Cris - to Je - sús, di - si - pa mis som - bras.*
*Je - zu, Tyś jest świat - łoś - cią mej du - szy.*

Let my heart al - ways wel - come your love.
*don - ne - moi d'ac-cueil - lir ton a - mour.*
*Y que en mí só - lo ha - ble tu A - mor.*
*Daj mi moc przy - jąć dziś mi - łość Twą.*

Text: Psalm 139
Tune: Jacques Berthier, 1923–1994
© 1998, Les Presses de Taizé, GIA Publications, Inc., agent

# Christ, Be Our Light! 590

**Verses**

1. Long - ing for light, we wait in dark - ness.
2. Long - ing for peace, our world is trou - bled.
3. Long - ing for food, man - y are hun - gry.
4. Long - ing for shel - ter, man - y are home - less.
5. Man - y the gifts, man - y the peo - ple,

Long - ing for truth, we turn to you.
Long - ing for hope, man - y de - spair.
Long - ing for wa - ter, man - y still thirst.
Long - ing for warmth, man - y are cold.
man - y the hearts that yearn to be - long.

Make us your own, your ho - ly peo - ple,
Your word a - lone has pow'r to save us.
Make us your bread, bro - ken for oth - ers,
Make us your build - ing, shel - ter - ing oth - ers,
Let us be ser - vants to one an - oth - er,

light for the world to see.
Make us your liv - ing voice.
shared un - til all are fed.
walls made of liv - ing stone.
mak - ing your king - dom come.

**Refrain**

Christ, be our light! Shine in our hearts.

Shine through the dark - ness. Christ, be our light!

Shine in your Church gath-ered to - day.

Text: Bernadette Farrell, b.1957
Tune: Bernadette Farrell, b.1957
© 1993, 2000, Bernadette Farrell. Published by OCP.

# 591 This Little Light of Mine

1. This lit - tle light of mine    I'm gon-na let it    shine,
2. Ev - 'ry - where I    go,    I'm gon-na let it    shine,
3. Je - sus    gave it to me,    I'm gon-na let it    shine,

This lit - tle light of mine    I'm gon-na let it    shine;
Ev - 'ry - where I    go,    I'm gon-na let it    shine;
Je - sus    gave it to me,    I'm gon-na let it    shine;

This lit - tle light of mine    I'm gon - na let it    shine,
Ev - 'ry - where I    go,    I'm gon - na let it    shine,
Je - sus    gave it to me,    I'm gon - na let it    shine,

Let it    shine,    let it    shine,    let it    shine.
Let it    shine,    let it    shine,    let it    shine.
Let it    shine,    let it    shine,    let it    shine.

Text: Harry Dixon Loes, 1895–1965
Tune: Harry Dixon Loes, 1895–1965; harm by Horace Clarence Boyer, 1935–2009, © 1992

# We Are the Light of the World 592

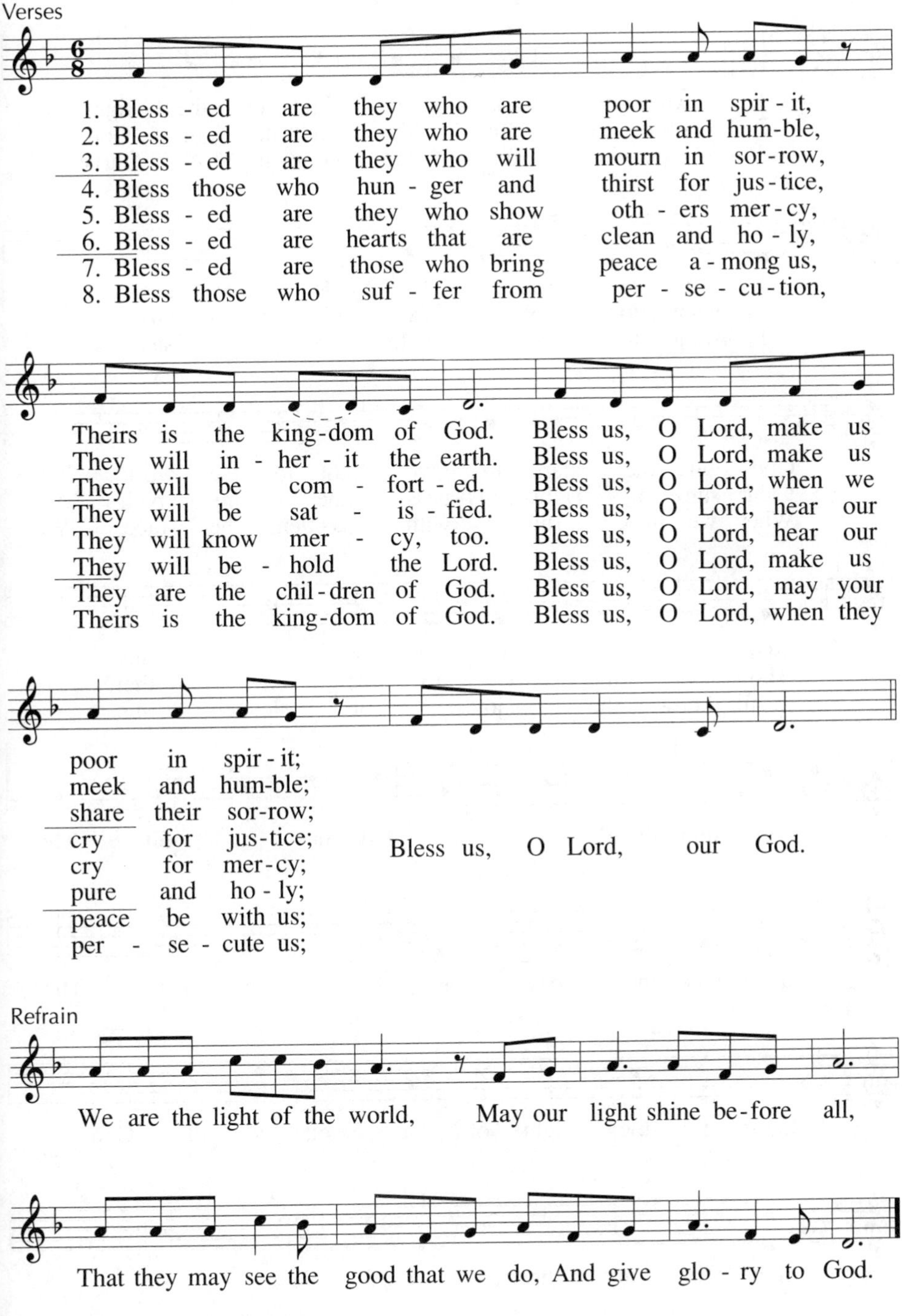

**Verses**

1. Bless - ed are they who are poor in spir - it,
2. Bless - ed are they who are meek and hum-ble,
3. Bless - ed are they who will mourn in sor-row,
4. Bless those who hun - ger and thirst for jus-tice,
5. Bless - ed are they who show oth - ers mer-cy,
6. Bless - ed are hearts that are clean and ho - ly,
7. Bless - ed are those who bring peace a - mong us,
8. Bless those who suf - fer from per - se - cu-tion,

Theirs is the king-dom of God. Bless us, O Lord, make us
They will in - her - it the earth. Bless us, O Lord, make us
They will be com - fort - ed. Bless us, O Lord, when we
They will be sat - is - fied. Bless us, O Lord, hear our
They will know mer - cy, too. Bless us, O Lord, hear our
They will be - hold the Lord. Bless us, O Lord, make us
They are the chil - dren of God. Bless us, O Lord, may your
Theirs is the king-dom of God. Bless us, O Lord, when they

poor in spir - it;
meek and hum-ble;
share their sor-row;
cry for jus-tice;
cry for mer-cy;
pure and ho - ly;
peace be with us;
per - se - cute us;

Bless us, O Lord, our God.

**Refrain**

We are the light of the world, May our light shine be-fore all,

That they may see the good that we do, And give glo - ry to God.

Text: Matthew 5:3–11, 14–16; Jean A. Greif, 1898–1981
Tune: Jean A. Greif, 1898–1981
© 1966, Vernacular Hymns Publishing Co.

# 593   I Want to Walk as a Child of the Light

1. I want to walk as a child of the light.
2. I want to see the bright-ness of God.
3. I'm look - ing for the com - ing of Christ.

I want to fol - low Je - sus.
I want to look at Je - sus.
I want to be with Je - sus.

God set the stars to give light to the world. The
Clear sun of right - eous - ness shine on my path And
When we have run with pa - tience the race, We

star of my life is Je - sus.
show me the way to the Fa - ther.
shall know the joy of Je - sus.

In him there is no dark - ness at all. The

night and the day are both a - like. The

Lamb is the light of the cit - y of God. The

Shine in my heart, Lord Je - sus.

Text: Ephesians 5:8–10, Revelation 21:23, John 12:46, 1 John 1:5, Hebrews 12:1; Kathleen Thomerson, b.1934, © 1970, 1975, Celebration
Tune: HOUSTON, 10 7 10 8 9 9 10 7; Kathleen Thomerson, b.1934, © 1970, 1975, Celebration; acc. by Robert J. Batastini, b.1942, © 1987, GIA
Publications, Inc.

# We Are Marching / Siyahamba 594

*Alternate text: dancing, singing, praying*

Text: South African
Tune: South African
© 1984, Utryck, Walton Music Corporation, agent

# 595 God Is Still Speaking

**Refrain**

God is still speak-ing: bless-ed in-vi-ta-tion. God is still speak-ing: lis-ten and draw near. God is still speak-ing: see a new cre-a-tion. God is still speak-ing: stand and do not fear.

**Verses**

*Cantor:*      *All:*

1. O - pen up your ears to hear:
2. In the bleak and mid-night hour:
3. Though the na - tions rage and fight:   God is still speak - ing.
4. All cre-a - tion groans and yearns:
5. Hear the sound of jus - tice ring:

*Cantor:*      *All:*

Liv - ing Good News, strong and clear:
Sing the word of truth to pow'r:
Hear God's voice of grace and light:   lis-ten and draw near.
"Seek the way that life re-turns":
Hear the song of mer - cy sing:

*Cantor:*      *All:*

Through the strug - gle, grief and pain:
To our frag - ile, wound-ed earth:
Choose the way that leads to peace:   God is still speak - ing.
Through our bro - ken, wound-ed earth:
To the ones in deep de - spair:

*Cantor:*      *All:*      **D.C.**

God can raise us up a - gain:
God can bring new hope to birth:
True com-pas - sion, sweet re - lease:   stand and do not fear.
God can bring new seeds to birth:
Be the sign of hope and care:

Text: Marty Haugen, b.1950
Tune: Marty Haugen, b.1950
© 2009, GIA Publications, Inc.

# Praise to You, O Christ, Our Savior 596

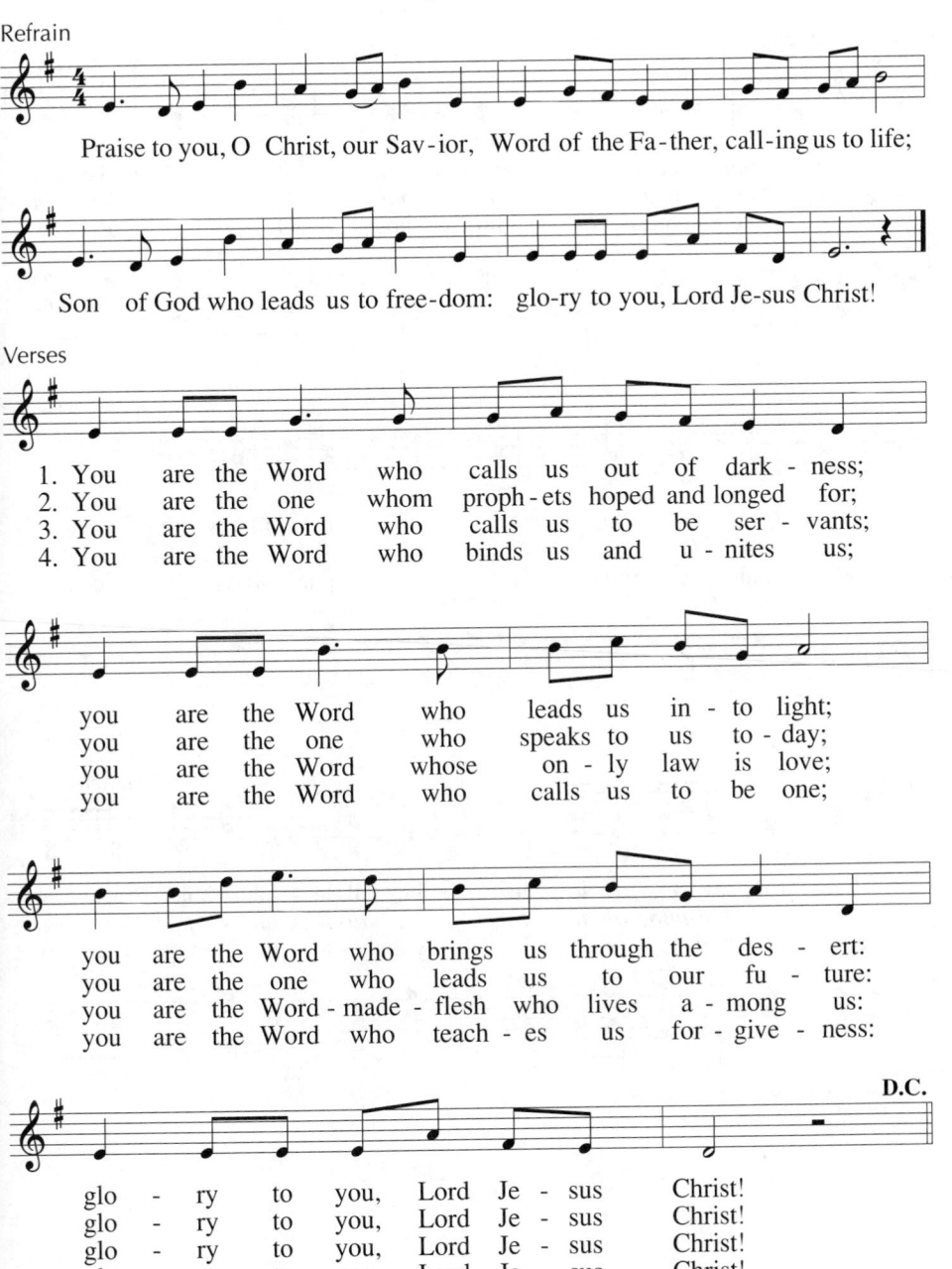

**Refrain**

Praise to you, O Christ, our Sav-ior, Word of the Fa-ther, call-ing us to life;

Son of God who leads us to free-dom: glo-ry to you, Lord Je-sus Christ!

**Verses**

1. You are the Word who calls us out of dark - ness;
2. You are the one whom proph - ets hoped and longed for;
3. You are the Word who calls us to be ser - vants;
4. You are the Word who binds us and u - nites us;

you are the Word who leads us in - to light;
you are the one who speaks to us to - day;
you are the Word whose on - ly law is love;
you are the Word who calls us to be one;

you are the Word who brings us through the des - ert:
you are the one who leads us to our fu - ture:
you are the Word - made - flesh who lives a - mong us:
you are the Word who teach - es us for - give - ness:

**D.C.**

glo - ry to you, Lord Je - sus Christ!
glo - ry to you, Lord Je - sus Christ!
glo - ry to you, Lord Je - sus Christ!
glo - ry to you, Lord Je - sus Christ!

Text: Bernadette Farrell, b.1957
Tune: Bernadette Farrell, b.1957
© 1986, Bernadette Farrell. Published by OCP.

# 597 Praise Our God and Savior

Ostinato Refrain

Praise our God and Sav - ior, O praise our
*Polish:* Wy - sła - wiaj - cie Pa - na, O Wy - sła -
*Spanish:* En - to - ne - mos him - nos, O al Se -

God and Sav - ior, O for God's love en -
wiaj - cie Pa - na, O Śpie - waj Pa - nu
ñor can - te - mos, O pue - blos to - dos,

*Last time*

dures for - ev - er, al - le - lu - ia, al - le - lu - ia! Praise our
ca - ła zie-mio, al - le - lu - ja, al - le - lu - ja! Wy - sła -
a - la - bad-le, ¡a - le - lu - ya, a - le - lu - ya! En - to -

*Last time*

Text: Psalm 136, Luke, 1:68–79; Taizé Community
Tune: Taizé Community
© 2007, 2011, Les Presses de Taizé, GIA Publications, Inc., agent

# O God beyond All Praising 598

1. O God be-yond all prais-ing, we wor-ship you to - day
*2. The flow'r of earth - ly splen-dor in time must sure - ly die,
3. Then hear, O gra-cious Sav - ior, ac - cept the love we bring,

And sing the love a - maz-ing that songs can - not re - pay;
Its frag - ile bloom sur - ren - der to you, the Lord most high;
That we who know your fa - vor may serve you as our King;

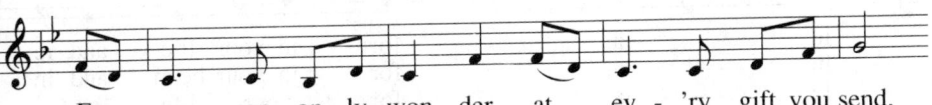

For we can on - ly won - der at ev - 'ry gift you send,
But hid - den from all na - ture the e - ter - nal seed is sown,
And wheth - er our to - mor-rows be filled with good or ill,

At bless-ings with - out num-ber and mer - cies with-out end.
Though small in mor - tal stat - ure to heav-en's gar - den grown.
We'll tri-umph through our sor-rows and rise to bless you still,

We lift our hearts be - fore you and wait up - on your word;
For Christ, the man from heav-en, from death has set us free,
To mar - vel at your beau - ty and glo - ry in your ways,

We hon - or and a - dore you, our great and might-y Lord.
And we through him are giv - en the fin - al vic - to - ry!
And make a joy-ful du - ty our sac - ri - fice of praise.

*May be omitted.

Text: Michael Perry, 1942–1996, © 1982, The Jubilate Group (admin. by Hope Publishing Company)
Tune: THAXTED, 13 13 13 13 13 13; Gustav Holst, 1874–1934

## 599 Heaven Is Singing for Joy / El Cielo Canta Alegría

Verses

1. Heav - en is sing - ing for joy, al - le - lu - ia, for in your life and in mine is shin - ing the glo - ry of God.
2. Heav - en is sing - ing for joy, al - le - lu - ia, for in your heart and in mine a - bides the one love of our God.
3. Heav - en is sing - ing for joy, al - le - lu - ia, for your life and mine u - nite in the love of our God.

1. El cie - lo can - ta_a - le - grí - a, ¡a - le - lu - ya! por - que_en tu vi - da_y la mí - a bri - lla la glo - ria de Dios.
2. El cie - lo can - ta_a - le - grí - a, ¡a - le - lu - ya! por - que_a tu vi - da_y la mí - a las u-ne_el a - mor de Dios.
3. El cie - lo can - ta_a - le - grí - a, ¡a - le - lu - ya! por - que tu vi - da_y la mí - a pro - cla-ma - rán al Se - ñor.

Refrain

Al - le - lu - ia, al - le - lu - ia! Al - le - lu - ia, al - le - lu - ia!
¡A - le - lu - ya, a - le - lu - ya! ¡A - le - lu - ya, a - le - lu - ya!

Text: Pablo Sosa, b.1933
Tune: Pablo Sosa, b.1933
© 1958, GIA Publications, Inc.

# Sing Praise to God   600

1. Sing praise to God, look not to earth - ly rul - ers. Sing praise to God, not in hu - man might. Sing praise to God, our help and our sal - va - tion. Sing praise to God, our hope and our de - light.
2. Sing praise to God, who shaped the earth and heav - ens. Sing praise to God, who formed the bound - less sea. Sing praise to God, whose prom - is - es are faith - ful. Sing praise to God, who sets the pris - 'ner free.
3. Sing praise to God, when those op - pressed find jus - tice. Sing praise to God, who gives the hun - gry food. Sing praise to God, who heals all your af - flic - tions. Sing praise to God, who grants us ev - 'ry good.
4. Sing praise to God, who watch - es o - ver stran - gers. Sing praise to God, who rais - es those bowed low. Sing praise to God, who holds the wid - ow, or - phan. Sing praise to God, as long as you shall live.
5. Sing praise to God, who brings the wick - ed ru - in. Sing praise to God, who loves the right - eous one. Sing praise to God, in ev - 'ry gen - er - a - tion. Sing praise to God, O praise the Ho - ly One.

Text: Based on Psalm 146; Marty Haugen, b.1950
Tune: Marty Haugen, b.1950
© 2009, GIA Publications, Inc.

## 601 Laudáte, Laudáte Dóminum

**Refrain**

Lau - dá - te, lau - dá - te Dó - mi - num, o - mnes
*We praise you, we praise your ho - ly name, God of*

gen - tes, lau - dá - te Dó - mi - num. Ex - sul - tá - te, ju - bi -
*jus - tice, e - ter-nal - ly the same. May our liv - ing be thanks-*

lá - te per an - nos Dó - mi - ni, om - nes gen - tes. Lau -
*giv - ing, re - joic-ing in your name now and al-ways. We*

dá - te, lau - dá - te Dó-mi-num, o - mnes gen - tes, lau -
*praise you, we praise your ho - ly name, God of jus - tice, e -*

dá - te Dó - mi - num. Ex - sul - tá - te, ju - bi -
*ter - nal-ly the same. May our liv - ing be thanks-*

*Last time*

lá - te per an - nos Dó - mi - ni, om - nes gen - tes.
*giv - ing, re - joic-ing in your name now and al - ways.*

**Verses 1–3**

1. In the faith of Christ we walk hand in hand,
2. In the name of Christ we will spread the seed;
3. In the pow'r of Christ we pro - claim one Lord.

1. *Ca - mi - na - mos jun - tos en la fe de Cris - to.*
2. *Con los po - bres com - par - ti - mos luz de Cris - to,*
3. *Los bau - ti - za - dos en un so - lo Se - ñor,*

| light | be - fore | our | path | as | the | Lord | has | planned; |
|---|---|---|---|---|---|---|---|---|
| share | the Word | of | God | with | all | those | in | need, |
| All | who put | on | Christ | are | by | faith | re - stored; |
| Luz | en nues - tra | sen - da | es | el | don | de Dios, | an - |
| y | sem - bra - mos | la | pa - la - bra | del | Se - ñor, |
| res - tau - ra - dos | to - dos | por | la | fe | en Cris - to, |

| shin - ing | the | torch | of | faith in | our | land: |
| faith - ful | in | thought | and | word | and | deed: |
| shar - ing new | life, | sal - va - tion's re - ward: |
| tor - cha de | fe | que i - lu - mi - na al | mun - do, |
| fie - les en | o - bra | y | nues - tro pen - sar, |
| al - can - za - mos | la | nue - va | vi - da, |

D.C.

| in | the | name | of | Christ | Je - sus. |
| en | el | nom - bre | de | Cris - to. |

Verses 4–6

4. In the life of Christ, through the blood he shed,
we are justified, and by him are fed,
nourished by word and living bread:
in the name of Christ Jesus.

5. In the Church of God we are unified,
by the Spirit's pow'r we are sanctified,
temples of grace, where God may abide:
by the pow'r of the Spirit.

6. Praise to God the Father while ages run.
Praise to Christ the Savior, God's only Son,
praise to the Holy Spirit be sung:
omnes gentes, laudáte.

4. Oigan al Señor y síganle,
vengan a alabar y comer de Él,
alimentados con pan de vida,
en el nombre de Cristo.

5. En la Iglesia estamos unidos,
santificados por el Espíritu,
morada de la gracia de Dios,
por el poder del Espíritu.

6. Siempre bendito sea el Padre,
siempre bendito sea el Hijo de Dios,
siempre bendito el Espíritu Santo,
omnes gentes, laudáte.

*Ordination Verses*
1. In the Church we answer the Savior's call,
serving, as he showed us, both great and small,
sharing the Lord's compassion for all:
in the name of Christ Jesus.

2. In the name of Christ we baptize and teach,
truth upon our lips in the way we preach,
raising the cup of blessing for each:
in the name of Christ Jesus.

Text: Christopher Walker, b.1947
Tune: Christopher Walker, b.1947
© 1997, Christopher Walker. Published by OCP.

# 602   Lord, I Lift Your Name on High

Lord, I lift your name on high.        Lord, I love to sing your

prais - es.        I'm so glad you're in        my        life.

I'm so glad you came to        save us.        save us.

You came from heav - en to earth        to show        the way.        From the earth

to the cross, my debt        to pay.        From the cross        to the grave,

from the grave        to the sky;  Lord, I lift your name on high.

high.        Lord, I        lift your name on        high.

Lord, I lift your name on  high.        Lord, I lift your name on high.

Text: Rick Founds, b.1954
Tune: Rick Founds, b.1954; arr. by Ed Bolduc, b.1969
© 1989, Universal Music—Brentwood Benson Publishing

# I Will Sing a Song of Love    603

**Refrain**

I will sing a song of love to the one who first loved me,

and I'll sing it as a child of God who is

named and known and free. For the love of God is good,

it is broad and deep and long, and a-bove all else that

mat - ters God is wor - thy of my song.

**Verses**

1. And      I      will      not      sing      a  -  lone      But  with
2. And      I'll     sing    with     ev - 'ry     soul,       Ev - 'ry
3. And      I'll     sing    for      what    is       right       And  a -
4. As        I       bring    to       God     my      joy,        So   I'll
5. While  my      life      on      earth   still    runs,       May  my

earth       and      sky      and      sea,        For     cre  -  a  -  tion
lan - guage,        ev - 'ry      race,       Which pro - claims  this
gainst      all       that     is        wrong,     Be - cause  God     is
bring       to        God     my      pain,       For      there     is       no
song        to        God     be       giv'n,      Till     through grace    I

**D.C.**

raised     its      voice well     in      ad - vance    of      me.
world     is       good   for      God    has      blessed  this     place.
nev - er          neu - tral  who     in - spires  my      song.
hurt       which   God    re - quires  me      to       re - tain.
join       the      har - mo - ny    of      all      in      heav'n.

Text: John L. Bell, b.1949
Tune: NAMED AND KNOWN, 7 7 13 with refrain; John L. Bell, b.1949
© 2005, Iona Community, GIA Publications, Inc., agent

# 604 All the Ends of the Earth

Refrain

All the ends of the earth, all you crea-tures of the sea, lift up your eyes to the won - ders of the Lord. For the Lord of the earth, the Mas - ter of the sea, has come with jus - tice for the world.

Verse 1

1. Break in - to song at the deeds of the Lord, the won - ders he has done in ev - 'ry age. *D.C.*

Verse 2

2. Heav - en and earth shall re - joice in his might; ev - 'ry heart, ev - 'ry na - tion call him Lord. *D.C.*

Verse 3

3. The Lord has made sal - va - tion known, faith-ful to the prom- is - es of old. Let the ends of the earth, let the sea and all it holds make mu - sic be - fore our King! *D.C.*

Text: Psalm 98; Bob Dufford, SJ, b.1943
Tune: Bob Dufford, SJ, b.1943; acc. by Bob Dufford and Chris Morash, alt.
© 1981, Robert J. Dufford, SJ, and OCP

# All Glory Is Yours 605

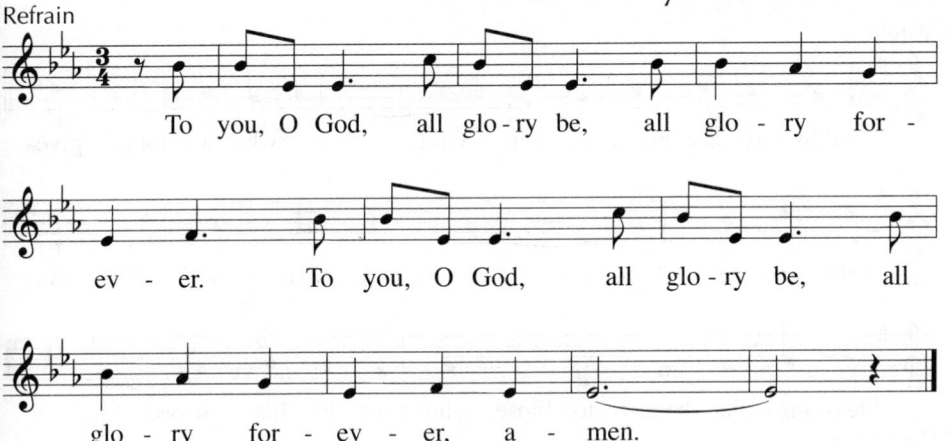

Refrain

To you, O God, all glo - ry be, all glo - ry for -
ev - er. To you, O God, all glo - ry be, all
glo - ry for - ev - er, a - men.

Verses

1. How deep are your riches, your wisdom profound.
   Your knowledge surpasses all we dare imagine.
   You are God: all glory is yours!

2. God, how can we know you? Who knows your mind?
   What more can we do but serve you and love you?
   You are God: all glory is yours!

3. God, all things are from you, conceived and brought forth.
   Through you all things move, move and have being.
   Creation exults: all glory is yours!

Text: Romans 11:33–36; Bob Moore, b.1962
Tune: Bob Moore, b.1962
© 1999, GIA Publications, Inc.

# 606 Glory and Praise to Our God

Refrain

Glo - ry and praise to our God, who a - lone gives light to our days. Man - y are the bless-ings he bears to those who trust in his ways.

Verses 1–3

1. We, the daugh - ters and sons of him who built the
2. In his wis - dom he strength - ens us, like gold that's
3. Ev - 'ry mo - ment of ev - 'ry day our God is

val - leys and plains, Praise the won - ders our God has
test - ed in fire. Though the pow - er of sin pre -
wait-ing to save, Al - ways read - y to seek the

D.C.

done in ev - 'ry heart that sings.
vails, our God is there to save.
lost, to an - swer those who pray.

Verse 4

4. God has wa - tered our bar - ren land and spent his
mer - ci - ful rain. Now the riv - ers of life run

D.C.

full for an - y - one to drink.

Text: Psalm 65, 66; Dan Schutte, b.1947
Tune: Dan Schutte, b.1947; acc. by Sr. Theophane Hytrek, OSF, 1915–1992, alt.
© 1976, Daniel L. Schutte and OCP

# Sing a New Song   607

Refrain

Sing a new song un - to the Lord; let your song be

sung from moun - tains high. Sing a new song

un - to the Lord, sing-ing al - le - lu - ia.

Verses

1. Shout with glad - ness! Dance for joy! O come be -
2. Rise, O chil - dren, from your sleep; your Sav - ior
3. Glad my soul for I have seen the glo - ry

fore the Lord. And play for God on
now has come. He has turned your
of the Lord. The trum - pet sounds; the

D.C.

glad tam - bou - rines, and let your trum - pet sound.
sor - row to joy, and filled your soul with song.
dead shall be raised. I know my Sav - ior lives.

Text: Psalm 98; Dan Schutte, b.1947
Tune: Dan Schutte, b.1947
© 1972, OCP

# 608　We Praise You

**Verses**

*Cantor:* ... *All:* We praise you,

1. For your sun that bright-ens the day:
2. For the glo - ry of all cre - a - tion:
3. For your love that greets the morn-ing: praise you,
4. For the treas - ure of joy and laugh-ter:
5. For your Word, your Ho - ly Wis - dom:

Lord!　*Cantor:* ... *All:* We

Lord!

For your moon that guides the night:
For all crea - tures great and small:
For your faith - ful - ness through night: We
For the mys - t'ry of sor - row and tears:
For the bread, the work of our hands:

praise you, Lord!　*Cantor:*

praise you, Lord!

For your source of light
For the seas, the hills
For your voice that sings
For the gift of love
For the wine, the cup

*All:* We praise you, Lord!

and breath:
and val - leys:
in all of us: praise you, Lord!
and heal - ing:
of bless - ing,

*Cantor:* ... *All:* We praise you,

For your song of death to life:
For the moun - tains strong and tall:
For your call to love and serve: We praise you,
For the awe - some pow'r of prayer:
For us all, your sa - cred pres - ence,

Lord!

Lord! We praise you, Lord! You

hear our cry! We praise you, Lord!

You are the an - swer! We praise you, Lord!

You are al - ways near! With

all our be-ing we praise you, Lord!

Text: David Haas, b.1957
Tune: David Haas, b.1957
© 2002, GIA Publications, Inc.

# 609 You Are the Voice

Refrain

You are the voice of the liv - ing God,

call - ing us now to live in your love, to be

chil - dren of God once a - gain!

Verses

*Cantor:*

1. Praise for the light that shines through the night, from
2. Praise for the wa - ter that springs from the sea, the
3. Praise for the sing - ing and praise for the dance, with

dark - ness to light, from death to new life, and
seed that gives life to all who be - lieve, God's
new heart and voice, all raise the song of

praise to the morn - ing that brings forth the sun, to
love o - ver - flow - ing, our hearts know the joy to be
praise to cre - a - tion; all heav - en and earth, come

*All:*

o - pen our eyes to the Lord! To
daugh - ters and sons of the Lord! To be
sing of the glo - ry of God! Come

**D.C.**

o - pen our eyes to the Lord! For
daugh - ters and sons of the Lord! For
sing of the glo - ry of God! For

Text: David Haas, b.1957
Tune: David Haas, b.1957; acc. by Jeanne Cotter, b.1964
© 1983, 1987, GIA Publications, Inc.

# Sing of the Lord's Goodness 610

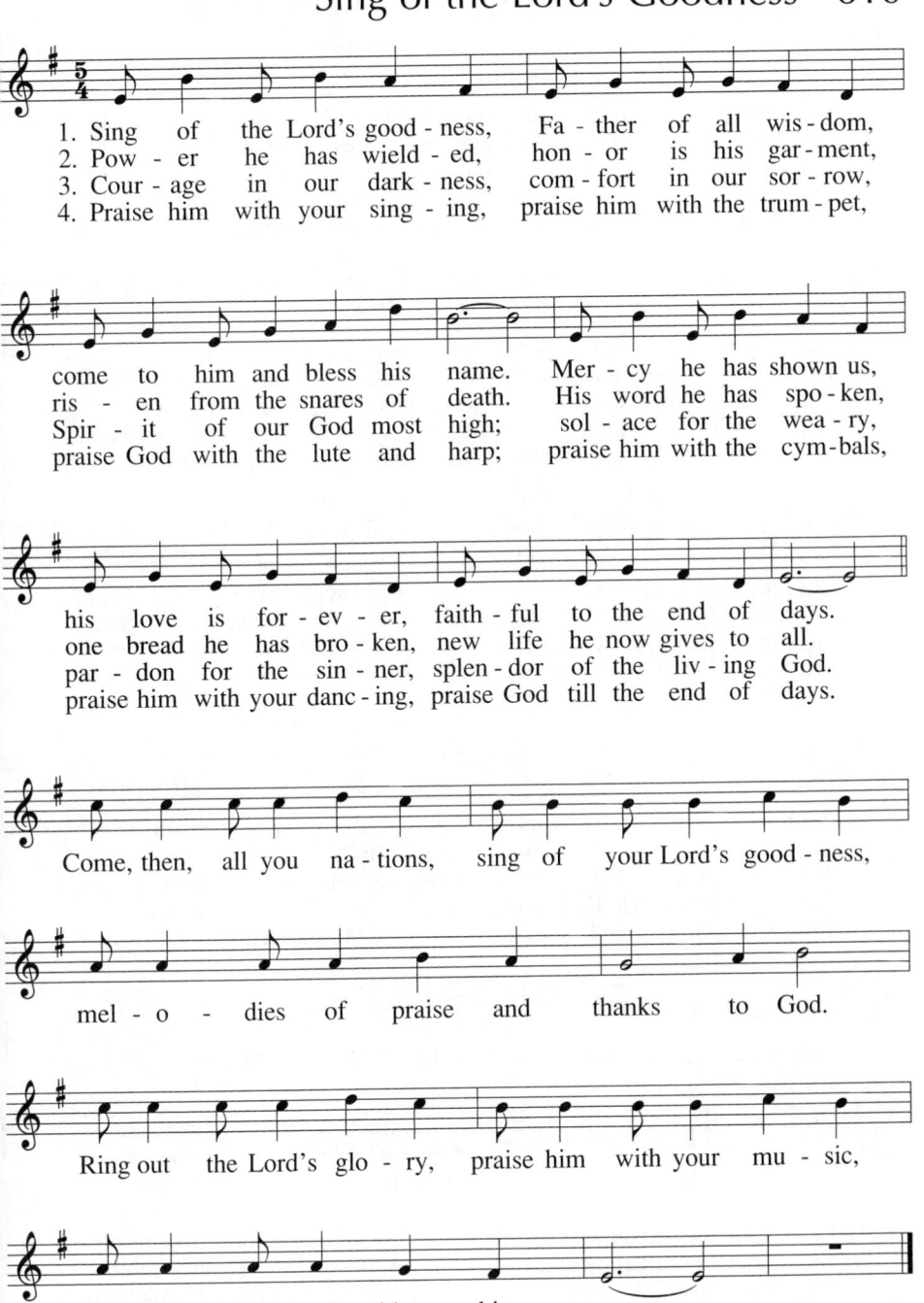

1. Sing of the Lord's good - ness, Fa - ther of all wis - dom,
2. Pow - er he has wield - ed, hon - or is his gar - ment,
3. Cour - age in our dark - ness, com - fort in our sor - row,
4. Praise him with your sing - ing, praise him with the trum - pet,

come to him and bless his name. Mer - cy he has shown us,
ris - en from the snares of death. His word he has spo - ken,
Spir - it of our God most high; sol - ace for the wea - ry,
praise God with the lute and harp; praise him with the cym - bals,

his love is for - ev - er, faith - ful to the end of days.
one bread he has bro - ken, new life he now gives to all.
par - don for the sin - ner, splen - dor of the liv - ing God.
praise him with your danc - ing, praise God till the end of days.

Come, then, all you na - tions, sing of your Lord's good - ness,

mel - o - dies of praise and thanks to God.

Ring out the Lord's glo - ry, praise him with your mu - sic,

wor - ship him and bless his name.

Text: Ernest Sands, b.1949, © 1981, Ernest Sands
Tune: Ernest Sands, b.1949, © 1981, Ernest Sands; acc. by Paul Inwood, b.1947, © 1986, Paul Inwood
Published by OCP.

# 611 All Creatures of Our God and King

1. All crea-tures of our God and King, Lift
2. O rush-ing wind and breez-es soft, O
3. O flow-ing wa-ter, pure and clear, Make
4. Dear moth-er earth, who day by day Un -
5. And ev-'ry one of ten - der heart, For -

up your voice and with us sing: Al - le - lu - ia!
clouds that ride the winds a - loft, Sing your prais-es!
mu - sic for your Lord to hear. Sing your prais-es!
fold rich bless-ings on our way, Sing your prais-es!
giv - ing oth - ers, take your part, Sing your prais-es!

Al - le - lu - ia! O burn - ing sun with gold - en beam
Al - le - lu - ia! O ris - ing morn, in praise re - joice,
Al - le - lu - ia! O fire so mas - ter - ful and bright,
Al - le - lu - ia! The flow'rs and fruits that in you grow,
Al - le - lu - ia! All you who pain and sor - row bear,

And sil - ver moon with soft - er gleam,
O lights of eve - ning, find a voice.
Pro - vid - ing us with warmth and light,
Let them God's glo - ry al - so show.
Praise God and cast on him your care.

Sing your prais - es! Al - le - lu - ia! Al - le - lu - ia,

al - le - lu - ia, al - le - lu - ia!

6. And you, most kind and gentle death,
   Waiting to hush our final breath,
   Sing your praises! Alleluia!
   You lead to heav'n the child of God,
   Where Christ our Lord the way has trod.
   Sing your praises! Alleluia!
   Alleluia, alleluia, alleluia!

7. Let all things their Creator bless,
   And worship God in humbleness,
   Sing your praises! Alleluia!
   Praise God the Father, God the Son,
   And God the Spirit, Three in One!
   Sing your praises! Alleluia!
   Alleluia, alleluia, alleluia!

Text: *Altissimu, onnipotente bon Signore*; Francis of Assisi, 1182–1226; tr. by William H. Draper, 1855–1933, alt.
Tune: LASST UNS ERFREUEN, LM with alleluias; *Geistliche Kirchengesänge*, 1623; harm. by Ralph Vaughan Williams, 1872–1958

# When in Our Music God Is Glorified   612

1. When in our mu - sic God is glo - ri - fied,
2. How of - ten, mak - ing mu - sic, we have found
3. So has the Church, in lit - ur - gy and song,
4. And did not Je - sus sing a psalm that night
5. Let ev - 'ry in - stru-ment be tuned for praise!

And ad - o - ra - tion leaves no room for pride,
A new di - men - sion in the world of sound,
In faith and love, through cen - tu - ries of wrong,
When ut - most e - vil strove a - gainst the light?
Let all re - joice who have a voice to raise!

It is as though the whole cre - a - tion cried:
As wor - ship moved us to a more pro - found
Borne wit - ness to the truth in ev - 'ry tongue:
Then let us sing, for whom he won the fight:
And may God give us faith to sing al - ways:

Al - le - lu - ia!

Text: Mark 14:26; Fred Pratt Green, 1903–2000, © 1972, Hope Publishing Company
Tune: ENGELBERG, 10 10 10 with alleluia; Charles V. Stanford, 1852–1924

# 613 Praise, My Soul, the King of Heaven

1. Praise, my soul, the King of heav - en; To his
2. Praise him for his grace and fa - vor To his
3. Fa - ther - like he tends and spares us; Well our
4. Frail as sum-mer's flow'r we flour - ish, Blows the
5. An - gels, help us to a - dore him; You be -

feet your trib - ute bring. Ran - somed, healed, re - stored, for -
peo - ple in dis - tress. Praise him, still the same as
fee - ble frame he knows. In his hands he gent - ly
wind and it is gone. But while mor - tals rise and
hold him face to face. Sun and moon, bow down be -

giv - en, Ev - er - more his prais - es sing. Al - le - lu - ia!
ev - er, Slow to chide and swift to bless. Al - le - lu - ia!
bears us, Res - cues us from all our foes. Al - le - lu - ia!
per - ish, God en - dures un - chang - ing on. Al - le - lu - ia!
fore him, Dwell-ers all in time and space. Al - le - lu - ia!

Al - le - lu - ia! Praise the ev - er - last - ing King.
Al - le - lu - ia! Glo - rious in his faith - ful - ness.
Al - le - lu - ia! Wide - ly yet his mer - cy flows.
Al - le - lu - ia! Praise the high e - ter - nal one.
Al - le - lu - ia! Praise with us the God of grace.

Text: Psalm 103; Henry F. Lyte, 1793–1847, alt.
Tune: LAUDA ANIMA, 8 7 8 7 8 7; John Goss, 1800–1880

# Joyful, Joyful, We Adore You    614

1. Joy - ful, joy - ful, we a - dore you, God of glo - ry,
2. All your works with joy sur - round you, Earth and heav'n re -
3. You are giv - ing and for - giv - ing, Ev - er bless - ing,
4. Mor - tals, join the might - y cho - rus, Which the morn - ing

Lord of love; Hearts un - fold like flow'rs be - fore you,
flect your rays, Stars and an - gels sing a - round you,
ev - er blest, Well - spring of the joy of liv - ing,
stars be - gan; God's own love is reign - ing o'er us,

O - p'ning to the sun a - bove. Melt the clouds of
Cen - ter of un - bro - ken praise. Field and for - est,
O - cean - depth of hap - py rest! God our Fa - ther,
Join - ing peo - ple hand in hand. Ev - er sing - ing,

sin and sad - ness; Drive the dark of doubt a - way;
vale and moun - tain, Flow - 'ry mead - ow, flash - ing sea,
Christ our broth - er, Let your light up - on us shine;
march we on - ward, Vic - tors in the midst of strife;

Giv - er of im - mor - tal glad - ness, Fill us with the light of day!
Chant - ing bird, and flow - ing foun - tain, Sound their praise e - ter - nal - ly!
Teach us how to love each oth - er, Lift us to the joy di - vine.
Joy - ful mu - sic leads us sun - ward In the tri - umph - song of life.

Text: Henry van Dyke, 1852–1933, alt.
Tune: HYMN TO JOY, 8 7 8 7 D; arr. from Ludwig van Beethoven, 1770–1827, by Edward Hodges, 1796–1867

# 615 Holy God, We Praise Thy Name

1. Ho - ly God, we praise thy name;
2. Hark! the loud ce - les - tial hymn
3. Lo, the ap - os - tol - ic train
4. Ho - ly Fa - ther, Ho - ly Son,

Lord of all, we bow be - fore thee!
An - gel choirs a - bove are rais - ing;
Joins, the sa - cred name to hal - low;
Ho - ly Spir - it, Three we name thee;

All on earth thy scep - ter claim,
Cher - u - bim and Ser - a - phim,
Proph - ets swell the loud re - frain,
While in es - sence on - ly One,

All in heav'n a - bove a - dore thee;
In un - ceas - ing cho - rus prais - ing,
And the white - robed mar - tyrs fol - low;
Un - di - vid - ed God we claim thee;

*Repeat ad lib.*

In - fi - nite thy vast do - main,
Fill the heav'ns with sweet ac - cord:
And from morn to set - ting sun,
And a - dor - ing bend the knee,

Ev - er - last - ing is thy reign.
"Ho - ly, ho - ly, ho - ly Lord!"
Through the Church the song goes on.
While we own the mys - ter - y.

Text: *Grosser Gott, wir loben dich;* ascr. to Ignaz Franz, 1719–1790; tr. by Clarence Walworth, 1820–1900
Tune: GROSSER GOTT, 7 8 7 8 77; *Katholisches Gesangbuch*, Vienna, c.1774

# Praise to the Lord, the Almighty   616

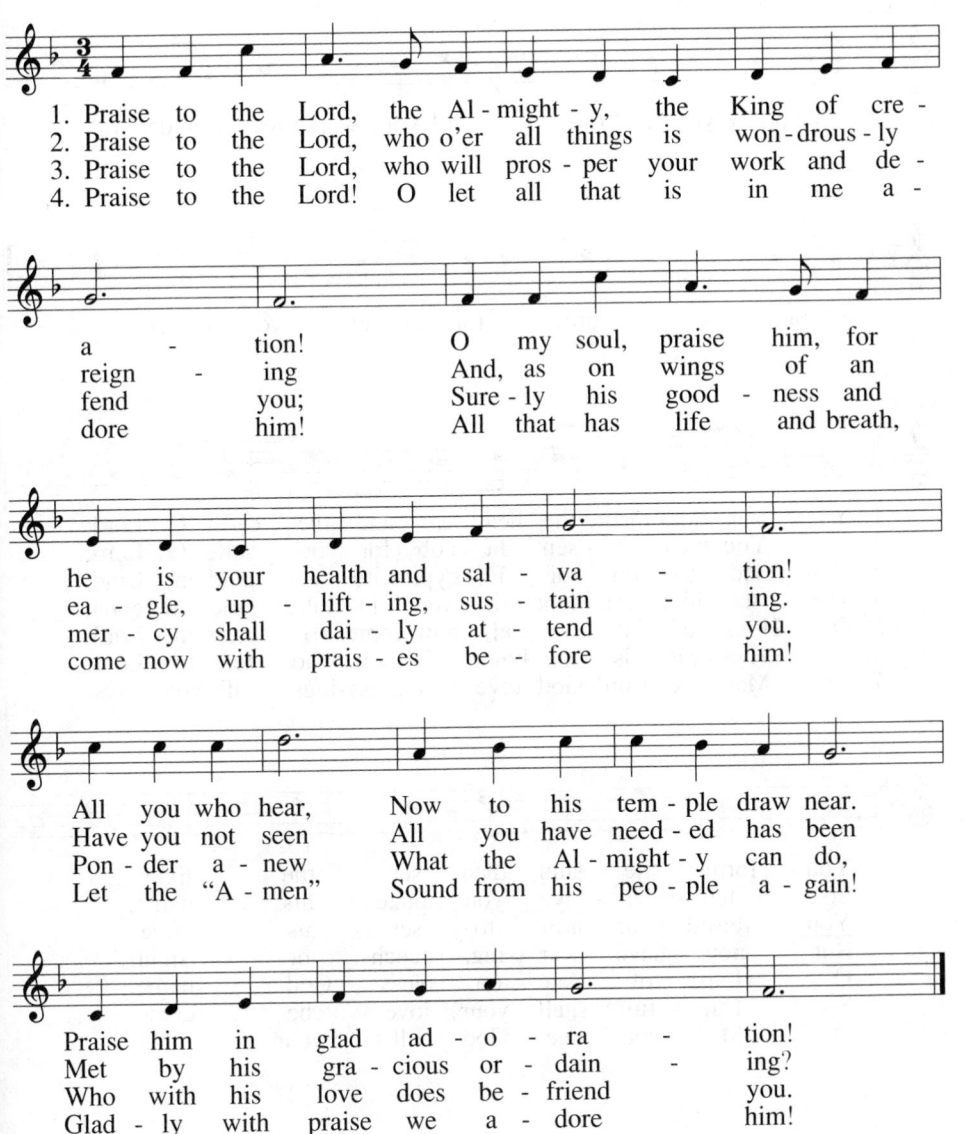

1. Praise to the Lord, the Al-might-y, the King of cre-a - tion! O my soul, praise him, for he is your health and sal - va - tion! All you who hear, Now to his tem-ple draw near. Praise him in glad ad - o - ra - tion!

2. Praise to the Lord, who o'er all things is won-drous-ly reign - ing And, as on wings of an ea - gle, up - lift - ing, sus - tain - ing. Have you not seen All you have need-ed has been Met by his gra - cious or - dain - ing?

3. Praise to the Lord, who will pros - per your work and de-fend you; Sure - ly his good - ness and mer - cy shall dai - ly at - tend you. Pon - der a - new What the Al - might - y can do, Who with his love does be - friend you.

4. Praise to the Lord! O let all that is in me a-dore him! All that has life and breath, come now with prais - es be - fore him! Let the "A - men" Sound from his peo - ple a - gain! Glad - ly with praise we a - dore him!

Text: *Lobe den Herren, den mächtigen König*; Joachim Neander, 1650–1680; tr. by Catherine Winkworth, 1827–1878, alt.
Tune: LOBE DEN HERREN, 14 14 47 8; *Stralsund Gesangbuch*, 1665; descant by C. S. Lang, 1891–1971, © 1953, Novello & Company Limited

# 617 We Praise You

**Refrain**

We praise you, O Lord, for all your works are won-der-ful.

We praise you, O Lord, for ev - er is your love.

**Verses**

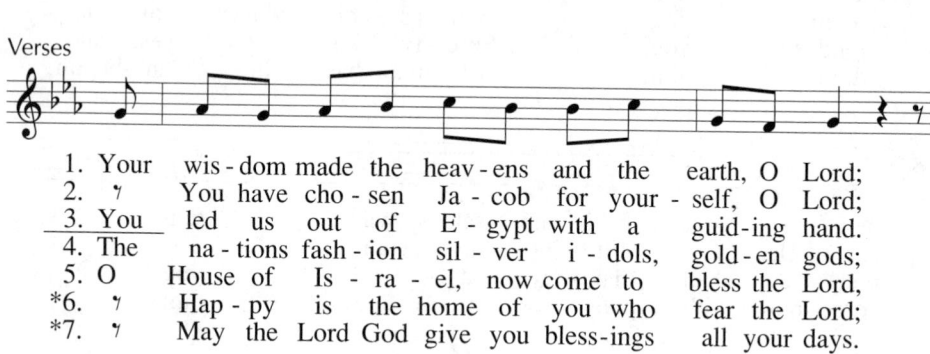

1. Your wis - dom made the heav - ens and the earth, O Lord;
2. ⅞ You have cho - sen Ja - cob for your - self, O Lord;
3. You led us out of E - gypt with a guid-ing hand.
4. The na - tions fash - ion sil - ver i - dols, gold-en gods;
5. O House of Is - ra - el, now come to bless the Lord,
*6. ⅞ Hap - py is the home of you who fear the Lord;
*7. ⅞ May the Lord God give you bless-ings all your days.

You formed the land then set the lights;
So ten - der - ly you spoke his name;
You raised your arm to set us free.
But none have hear - ing, speech or sight.
O House of Aar - on, bless God's name.
So fruit - ful shall your love be - come.
⅞ May you see God fill your land

And like your love the sun will rule the day,
Then called a ho - ly na - tion, Is - ra - el,
And like a ten - der vine you plant - ed us
Their mak - ers shall be like their emp - ty gods,
O bless the Lord, all you who hon - or God,
Your chil - dren flour - ish like the ol - ive plants,
Un - til your chil - dren bring their chil - dren home

*wedding verses

D.C.

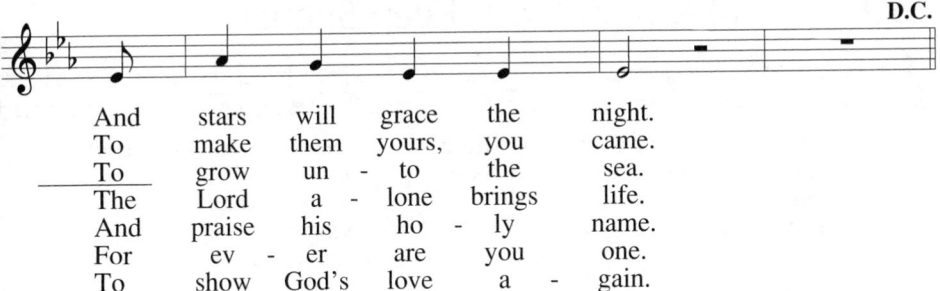

| And | stars | will | grace | the | night. |
| To | make | them | yours, | you | came. |
| To | grow | un - | to | the | sea. |
| The | Lord | a - | lone | brings | life. |
| And | praise | his | ho - ly | | name. |
| For | ev - | er | are | you | one. |
| To | show | God's | love | a - | gain. |

Text: Mike Balhoff, b.1946
Tune: Darryl Ducote, b.1945, Gary Daigle, b.1957
© 1978, Damean Music. Distributed by GIA Publications, Inc.

## Jubiláte, Sérvite   618

Canon

1.   2.

Ju - bi - lá - te   De - o   o - mnis ter - ra.
*Raise a song of glad-ness,   peo - ples of the earth.*
*Al Se - ñor a - cla - ma,   tie - rra en - te - ra.*

Sér - vi - te   Dó - mi - no   in lae - tí - ti - a.
*Christ has come,   bring-ing peace,   joy to ev - 'ry heart.*
*Sír - ve - lo,   dán - do - le   gra - cias por su a - mor.*

Al - le - lú - ia,   al - le - lú - ia,   in lae - tí - ti - a!
*Al - le - lu - ia,   al - le - lu - ia,   joy to ev - 'ry heart!*
*¡A - le - lu - ya,   a - le - lu - ya,   gra - cias por su a - mor!*

Al - le - lú - ia,   al - le - lú - ia,   in lae - tí - ti - a!
*Al - le - lu - ia,   al - le - lu - ia,   joy to ev - 'ry heart!*
*¡A - le - lu - ya,   a - le - lu - ya,   gra - cias por su a - mor!*

Text: Psalm 100, *Rejoice in God, all the earth, Serve the Lord with gladness*; Taizé Community, 1978
Tune: Jacques Berthier, 1923–1994
© 1979, 2011, Les Presses de Taizé, GIA Publications, Inc., agent

# 619 Let All Mortal Flesh Keep Silence

1. Let all mor - tal flesh keep si - lence,
2. King of kings, yet born of Mar - y,
3. Rank on rank the host of heav - en
4. At his feet the six - winged ser - aph;

And with fear and trem - bling stand;
As of old on earth he stood,
Spreads its van - guard on the way;
Cher - u - bim with sleep - less eye

Pon - der noth - ing earth - ly - mind - ed,
Lord of lords in hu - man ves - ture,
As the Light of Light, de - scend - ing
Veil their fac - es to the Pres - ence,

For with bless - ing in his hand
In the Bod - y and the Blood
From the realms of end - less day,
As with cease - less voice they cry:

Christ our God, to earth de - scend -
He will give to all the faith -
Comes, the pow'rs of hell to van -
"Al - le - lu - ia, al - le - lu -

ing, Comes, our hom - age to de - mand.
ful His own self for heav'n - ly food.
quish, As the dark - ness clears a - way.
ia! Al - le - lu - ia, Lord Most High!"

Text: Liturgy of St. James 5th C.; para. by Gerard Moultrie, 1829–1885, alt.
Tune: PICARDY, 8 7 8 7 8 7; French carol; harm. by Richard Proulx, 1937–2010, © 1986, GIA Publications, Inc.

# Bless the Lord 620

Ostinato Refrain

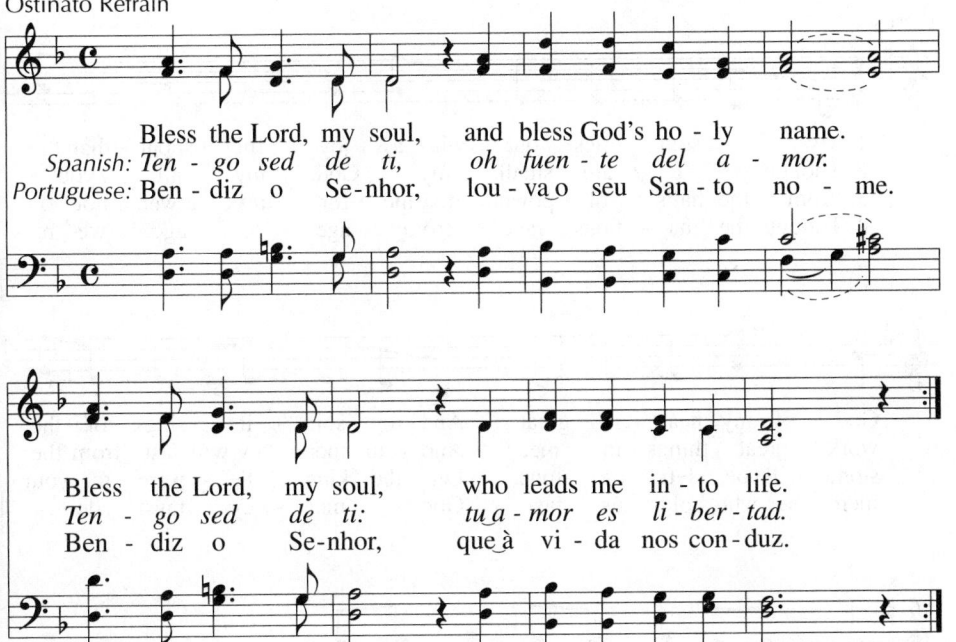

Bless the Lord, my soul, and bless God's ho - ly name.
*Spanish:* Ten - go sed de ti, oh fuen - te del a - mor.
*Portuguese:* Ben - diz o Se-nhor, lou - va_o seu San - to no - me.

Bless the Lord, my soul, who leads me in - to life.
Ten - go sed de ti: tu_a - mor es li - ber - tad.
Ben - diz o Se-nhor, que_à vi - da nos con - duz.

Text: Psalm 103
Tune: Jacques Berthier, 1923–1994
© 1998, Les Presses de Taizé, GIA Publications, Inc., agent

# Ad Te Jesu Christe 621

Canon*

Ad te Je - su Chri - ste le - vá - vi á - ni-mam
*I lift up my soul to you, Christ Je - sus, my re -*
Le - van - to mi al - ma, te_in - vo - co_a ti, oh

me - am. Sal - vá - tor mun - di, in te spe - rá - vi. Ad
*deem - er. All earth's sal - va - tion, my hope is in you. I*
Cris - to. Tú e - res Sal - va - ción; en ti es - pe - ro. Le -

*May be sung as a 2- or 4-part Canon.

Text: Psalm 25:1, 5; Taizé Community
Tune: Taizé Community
© 2007, 2011, Les Presses de Taizé, GIA Publications, Inc., agent

# 622 Canticle of the Turning

Verses

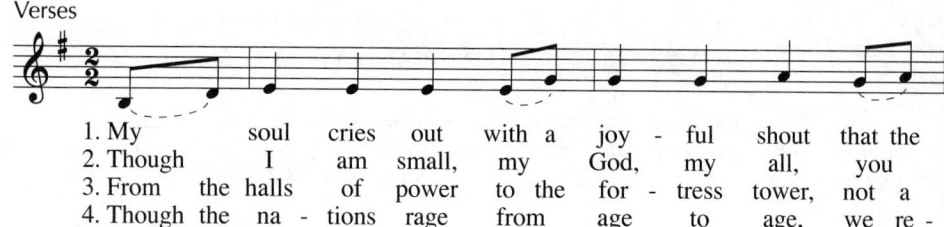

1. My soul cries out with a joy - ful shout that the
2. Though I am small, my God, my all, you
3. From the halls of power to the for - tress tower, not a
4. Though the na - tions rage from age to age, we re -

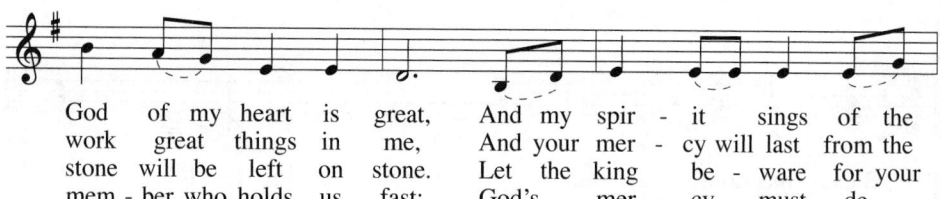

God of my heart is great, And my spir - it sings of the
work great things in me, And your mer - cy will last from the
stone will be left on stone. Let the king be - ware for your
mem - ber who holds us fast: God's mer - cy must de -

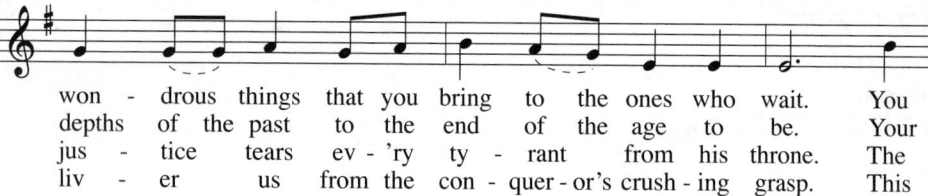

won - drous things that you bring to the ones who wait. You
depths of the past to the end of the age to be. Your
jus - tice tears ev - 'ry ty - rant from his throne. The
liv - er us from the con - quer - or's crush - ing grasp. This

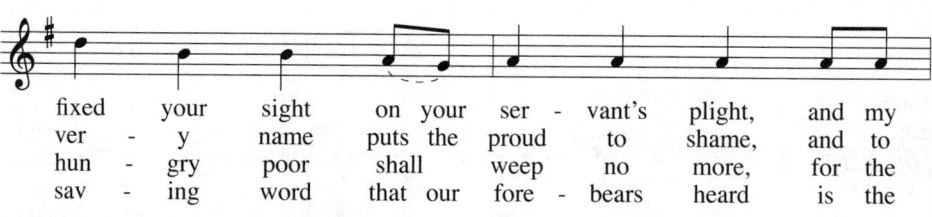

fixed your sight on your ser - vant's plight, and my
ver - y name puts the proud to shame, and to
hun - gry poor shall weep no more, for the
sav - ing word that our fore - bears heard is the

weak - ness you did not spurn, So from east to west shall my
those who would for you yearn, You will show your might, put the
food they can nev - er earn; There are ta - bles spread, ev - 'ry
prom - ise which holds us bound, 'Til the spear and rod can be

name      be      blest.   Could the   world   be   a - bout   to   turn?
strong    to      flight,  for the     world   is   a - bout   to   turn.
mouth     be      fed,     for the     world   is   a - bout   to   turn.
crushed   by      God,     who is      turn - ing the world   a -  round.

Refrain

My   heart   shall   sing   of the   day   you   bring.   Let   the

fires   of your   jus - tice   burn.   Wipe a - way   all   tears,   for the

dawn   draws   near,   and the   world   is   a - bout   to   turn!

Text: Luke 1:46–58; Rory Cooney, b.1952
Tune: STAR OF THE COUNTY DOWN; Irish traditional; arr. by Rory Cooney, b.1952
© 1990, GIA Publications, Inc.

## Laudáte Dóminum    623

Ostinato Refrain

Lau - dá - te   Dó - mi - num,   lau - dá - te   Dó - mi - num   o - mnes

1.
gen - tes,   al - le - lú - ia.

2.
al - le - lú - ia.

Text: Psalm 117, *Praise the Lord, all you peoples;* Taizé Community, 1980
Tune: Jacques Berthier, 1923–1994
© 1980, Les Presses de Taizé, GIA Publications, Inc., agent

# 624  Lift Up Your Hearts

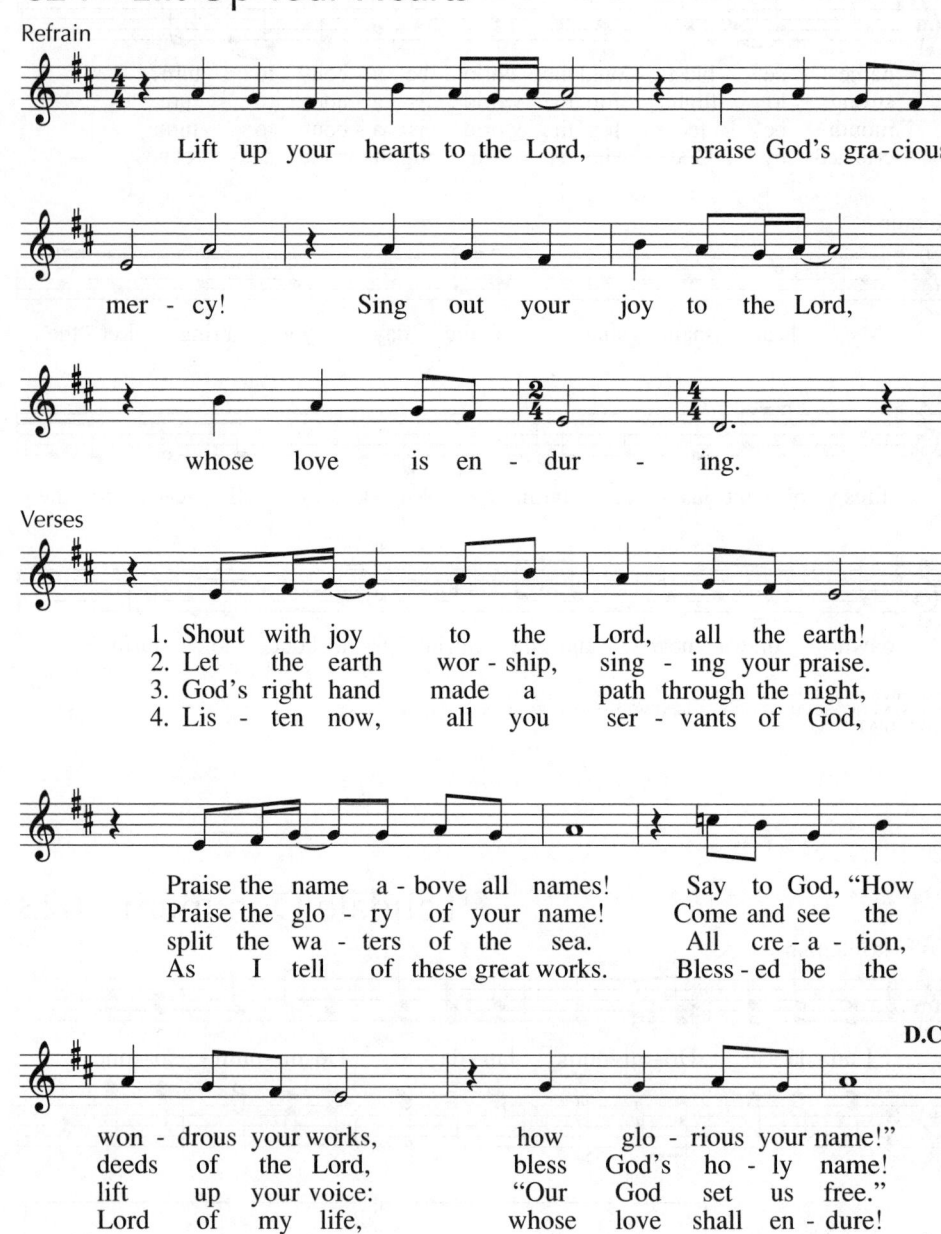

**Refrain**

Lift up your hearts to the Lord, praise God's gra-cious mer - cy! Sing out your joy to the Lord, whose love is en - dur - ing.

**Verses**

1. Shout with joy to the Lord, all the earth!
2. Let the earth wor - ship, sing - ing your praise.
3. God's right hand made a path through the night,
4. Lis - ten now, all you ser - vants of God,

Praise the name a - bove all names! Say to God, "How
Praise the glo - ry of your name! Come and see the
split the wa - ters of the sea. All cre - a - tion,
As I tell of these great works. Bless - ed be the

**D.C.**

won - drous your works, how glo - rious your name!"
deeds of the Lord, bless God's ho - ly name!
lift up your voice: "Our God set us free."
Lord of my life, whose love shall en - dure!

Text: Psalm 66; Roc O'Connor, SJ, b.1949
Tune: Roc O'Connor, SJ, b.1949; acc. by Robert J. Batastini, b.1942
© 1981, 1993, Robert F. O'Connor, SJ, and OCP

# Praise the One Who Breaks the Darkness 625

1. Praise the One who breaks the dark - ness With a
2. Praise the One who blessed the chil - dren With a
3. Praise the one true love in - car - nate: Christ, who

lib - er - at - ing light. Praise the One who frees the
strong yet gen - tle word. Praise the One who drove out
suf - fered in our place. Je - sus died and rose for

pris - 'ners, Turn - ing blind - ness in - to sight.
de - mons With a pierc - ing, two - edged sword.
man - y That we may know God by grace.

Praise the One who preached the gos - pel, Heal - ing
Praise the One who brings cool wa - ter To the
Let us sing for joy and glad - ness, See - ing

ev - 'ry dread dis - ease, Calm - ing storms and feed - ing
des - ert's burn - ing sand. From this well comes liv - ing
what our God has done. Praise the one re - deem - ing

thou - sands With the ver - y bread of peace.
wa - ter Quench-ing thirst in ev - 'ry land.
glo - ry; Praise the One who makes us one.

Text: Rusty Edwards, b.1955, © 1987, Hope Publishing Company
Tune: NETTLETON, 8 7 8 7 D, from Wyeth's *Repository of Sacred Music, Pt. II,* 1813

# 626 Halleluya! We Sing Your Praises

**Refrain**

Hal - le - lu - ya! We sing your prais-es, all our hearts are filled with glad - ness. Hal - le - lu - ya! We sing your prais-es, all our hearts are filled with glad - ness.

**Verses**

1. Christ the Lord to us said: I am wine, I am bread, I am wine, I am
2. Now he sends us all out, strong in faith, free of doubt, strong in faith, free of

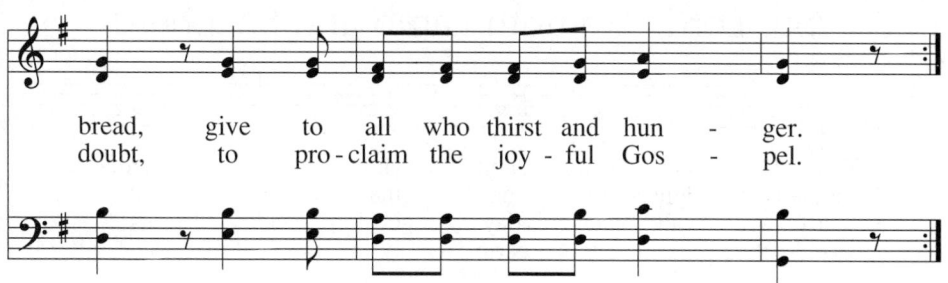

bread,   give   to   all  who thirst and hun - ger.
doubt,       to   pro - claim the  joy - ful  Gos - pel.

Text: South African
Tune: South African
© 1984, Utryck, Walton Music Corporation, agent

## Sing a New Song to the Lord 627

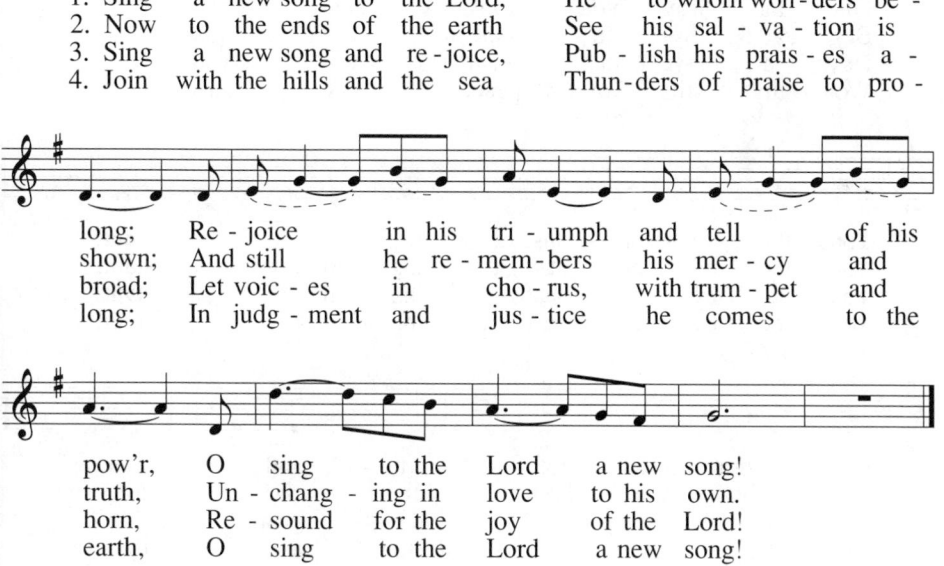

1. Sing   a  new song to  the Lord,     He    to whom won - ders be -
2. Now  to  the ends of  the earth     See   his sal - va - tion is
3. Sing   a  new song and re - joice,    Pub - lish his prais - es  a -
4. Join  with the hills and the sea   Thun - ders of praise to  pro -

long;  Re - joice    in his  tri - umph  and  tell     of his
shown;  And still    he  re - mem - bers his mer - cy    and
broad;  Let voic - es    in   cho - rus,  with trum - pet  and
long;  In judg - ment and   jus - tice  he  comes    to the

pow'r,  O   sing   to the  Lord  a  new  song!
truth,   Un - chang - ing in  love  to his  own.
horn,   Re - sound for the  joy  of the  Lord!
earth,  O   sing   to the  Lord  a new  song!

Text: Psalm 98; Timothy Dudley-Smith, b.1926, © 1973, Hope Publishing Company
Tune: CANTATE DOMINO (ONSLOW SQUARE), Irregular; David G. Wilson, b.1940, © 1973, The Jubilate Group (admin. Hope Publishing Company)

# 628 You, Lord, Are Both Lamb and Shepherd

1. You, Lord, are both Lamb and Shep - herd.
2. Clothed in light up - on the moun - tain,
3. You, who walk each day be - side us,
4. Wor - thy is our earth - ly Je - sus!

You, Lord, are both prince and slave.
Stripped of might up - on the cross,
Sit in pow - er at God's side.
Wor - thy is our cos - mic Christ!

You, peace - mak - er and sword - bring - er
Shin - ing in e - ter - nal glo - ry,
You, who preach a way that's nar - row,
Wor - thy your de - feat and vic - t'ry.

Of the way you took and gave.
Beg - gar'd by a sol - dier's toss.
Have a love that reach - es wide.
Wor - thy still your peace and strife.

You, the ev - er - last - ing in - stant;
You, the ev - er - last - ing in - stant;
You, the ev - er - last - ing in - stant;
You, the ev - er - last - ing in - stant;

You, whom we both scorn and crave.
You, who are both gift and cost.
You, who are our pil - grim guide.
You, who are our death and life.

Text: *Christus Paradox*, Sylvia Dunstan, 1955–1993, © 1991, GIA Publications, Inc.
Tune: PICARDY, 8 7 8 7 8 7; French Carol; harm. by Richard Proulx, 1937–2010, © 1986, GIA Publications, Inc.

# Holy God 629

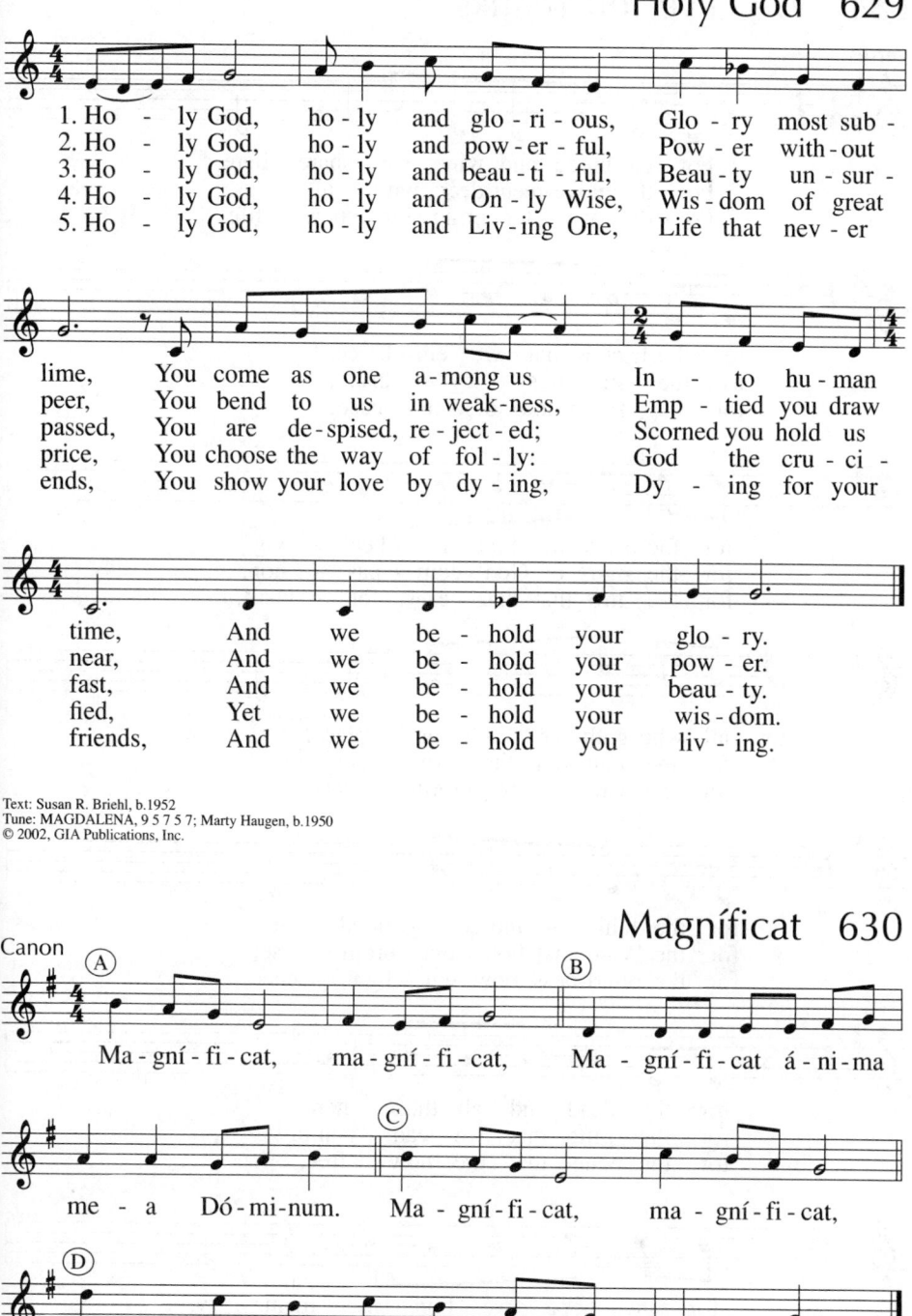

1. Ho - ly God, ho - ly and glo - ri - ous, Glo - ry most sub -
2. Ho - ly God, ho - ly and pow - er - ful, Pow - er with - out
3. Ho - ly God, ho - ly and beau - ti - ful, Beau - ty un - sur -
4. Ho - ly God, ho - ly and On - ly Wise, Wis - dom of great
5. Ho - ly God, ho - ly and Liv - ing One, Life that nev - er

lime, You come as one a - mong us In - to hu - man
peer, You bend to us in weak - ness, Emp - tied you draw
passed, You are de - spised, re - ject - ed; Scorned you hold us
price, You choose the way of fol - ly: God the cru - ci -
ends, You show your love by dy - ing, Dy - ing for your

time, And we be - hold your glo - ry.
near, And we be - hold your pow - er.
fast, And we be - hold your beau - ty.
fied, Yet we be - hold your wis - dom.
friends, And we be - hold you liv - ing.

Text: Susan R. Briehl, b.1952
Tune: MAGDALENA, 9 5 7 5 7; Marty Haugen, b.1950
© 2002, GIA Publications, Inc.

# Magníficat 630

Canon

Ma - gní - fi - cat, ma - gní - fi - cat, Ma - gní - fi - cat á - ni - ma

me - a Dó - mi - num. Ma - gní - fi - cat, ma - gní - fi - cat,

Ma - gní - fi - cat á - ni - ma me - a!

Text: Luke 1:46, *My soul magnifies the Lord;* Taizé Community, 1978
Tune: Jacques Berthier, 1923–1994
© 1979, Les Presses de Taizé, GIA Publications, Inc., agent

# 631 We Give You Thanks

Verses

1. For the bread and wine we share here,
2. For the move-ment deep with - in us,
3. For the wa - ter bring - ing new life,

for the friends that we em - brace,
for the sto - ries that we bring,
for the fra - grance of re - lease,

for the peace we find in heal - ing,
for the signs of God's com - pas - sion,
for the fire that blaz - es for - ward,

for all who gath - er in this place,
for the jour - ney that we sing,
for the call to bring forth peace,

for the faith of those a - round us,
for the Word that holds our prom - ise,
for the blind-ness now en - light - ened,

for the dead and all those here,
for the gifts that we can claim,
for the bound that are now free,

for the hope we find in mem - 'ry,
for the won - ders that sur - round us,
for the bright - ness of your new day,

for the love that draws us near:
for the song that sings our name:
for the king - dom we will be:

Refrain

We give you thanks, we give you thanks

for the grace to re - ceive, in you we be - lieve. We

give you thanks, we give you thanks. With

faith and hope and love, we give you thanks.

Text: David Haas, b.1957
Tune: WE GIVE YOU THANKS, 8 7 8 7 D with Refrain; David Haas, b.1957
© 1998, GIA Publications, Inc.

# 632 Father, We Thank You, Who Have Planted

1. Fa - ther, we thank you, who have plant - ed
2. Watch o'er your Church, O Lord, in mer - cy,

Your ho - ly name with - in our hearts.
Save it from e - vil, guard it still;

Knowl - edge and faith and life im - mor - tal
Per - fect it in your love, u - nite it,

Je - sus your Son to us im - parts.
Cleansed and con - formed un - to your will.

Lord, you have made all for your pleas - ure,
As grain, once scat - tered on the hill - sides,

And giv'n us food for all our days,
Was in this bro - ken bread made one,

Giv - ing in Christ the bread e - ter - nal;
So from all lands your Church be gath - ered

Yours is the pow'r, yours be the praise.
In - to your king - dom by your Son.

Text: From the *Didache*, c.110; tr. by F. Bland Tucker, 1895–1984, alt., © 1940, The Church Pension Fund
Tune: RENDEZ À DIEU, 9 8 9 8 D; *Genevan Psalter*, 1551; attr. to Louis Bourgeois, c.1510–1561

# For the Beauty of the Earth 633

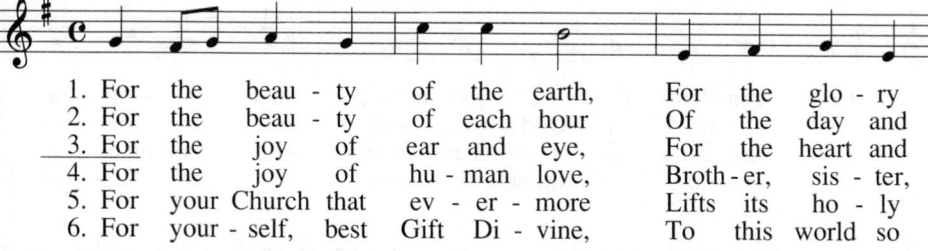

1. For the beau - ty of the earth, For the glo - ry
2. For the beau - ty of each hour Of the day and
3. For the joy of ear and eye, For the heart and
4. For the joy of hu - man love, Broth - er, sis - ter,
5. For your Church that ev - er - more Lifts its ho - ly
6. For your - self, best Gift Di - vine, To this world so

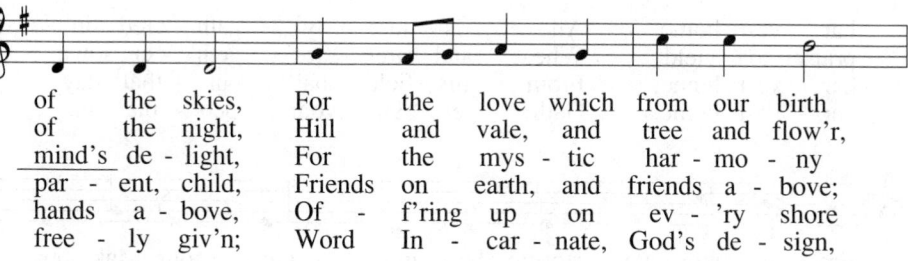

of the skies, For the love which from our birth
of the night, Hill and vale, and tree and flow'r,
mind's de - light, For the mys - tic har - mo - ny
par - ent, child, Friends on earth, and friends a - bove;
hands a - bove, Of - f'ring up on ev - 'ry shore
free - ly giv'n; Word In - car - nate, God's de - sign,

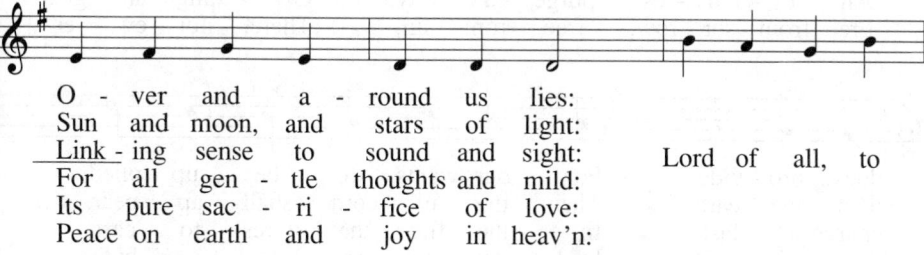

O - ver and a - round us lies:
Sun and moon, and stars of light:
Link - ing sense to sound and sight:        Lord of all, to
For all gen - tle thoughts and mild:
Its pure sac - ri - fice of love:
Peace on earth and joy in heav'n:

you we raise This our hymn of grate - ful praise.

Text: Folliot S. Pierpont, 1835–1917, alt.
Tune: DIX, 7 7 7 7 77; arr. from Conrad Kocher, 1786–1872, by William H. Monk, 1823–1889

# 634 Come, You Thankful People, Come

1. Come, you thank - ful peo - ple, come; Raise the song of
2. All the world is God's own field, Fruit un - to his
3. For the Lord our God shall come And shall take his
4. E - ven so, Lord, quick - ly come To your fi - nal

har - vest home. All is safe - ly gath - ered in
praise to yield; Wheat and tares to - geth - er sown,
har - vest home; From his field shall in that day
har - vest home. Gath - er all your peo - ple in,

Ere the win - ter storms be - gin. God, our Mak - er,
Un - to joy or sor - row grown. First the blade, and
All of - fens - es purge a - way, Giv - ing an - gels
Free from sor - row, free from sin, There, for ev - er

does pro - vide For our wants to be sup - plied.
then the ear, Then the full corn shall ap - pear.
charge at last In the fire the tares to cast,
pu - ri - fied, In your pres - ence to a - bide.

Come to God's own tem - ple, come.
Lord of har - vest, grant that we
But the fruit - ful ears to store
Come with all your an - gels, come!

Raise the song of har - vest home.
Whole - some grain and pure may be.
In God's gar - ner ev - er - more.
Raise the glo - rious har - vest home.

Text: Henry Alford, 1810–1871, alt.
Tune: ST. GEORGE'S WINDSOR, 77 77 D; George J. Elvey, 1816–1893; harm. by Richard Proulx, 1937–2010, © 1986, GIA Publications, Inc.

# Let All Things Now Living 635

1. Let all things now liv-ing A song of thanks-giv-ing
2. God rules all the forc-es: The stars in their cours-es

To God the Cre - a - tor tri - um - phant - ly raise,
And sun in its or - bit o - be - dient - ly shine;

Who fash-ioned and made us, Pro - tect - ed and stayed us,
The hills and the moun-tains, The riv - ers and foun-tains,

And guides us with care to the end of our days.
The deeps of the o - cean pro - claim God di - vine.

God's ban - ners are o'er us, God's light goes be - fore us,
We too should be voic-ing Our love and re - joic-ing;

A pil - lar of fire shin - ing forth in the night,
With glad ad - o - ra - tion a song let us raise

Till shad - ows have van-ished And dark - ness is ban-ished,
Till all things now liv - ing U - nite in thanks-giv - ing:

As for - ward we trav - el from light in - to light.
"To God in the high - est, ho - san - na and praise!"

Text: Katherine K. Davis, 1892–1980, alt., © 1939, 1966, E. C. Schirmer Music Co.
Tune: ASH GROVE, 66 11 66 11 D; Welsh; harm. by Gerald H. Knight, 1908–1979, © The Royal School of Church Music

## 636 Now Thank We All Our God

1. Now thank we all our God With hearts and hands and
2. O may this boun-teous God Through all our life be
3. All praise and thanks to God The Fa - ther now be

voic - es, Who won - drous things has done, In
near us, With ev - er joy - ful hearts And
giv - en, The Son, and him who reigns With

whom his world re - joic - es; Who from our moth-ers'
bless - ed peace to cheer us; Pre - serve us in his
them in high - est heav - en— The one e - ter - nal

arms Has blessed us on our way With
grace, And guide us in dis - tress, And
God, Whom earth and heav'n a - dore— For

count-less gifts of love, And still is ours to - day.
free us from all harm Till heav - en we pos - sess.
thus it was, is now, And shall be ev - er - more.

Text: *Nun danket alle Gott;* Martin Rinkart, 1586–1649; tr. by Catherine Winkworth, 1827–1878, alt.
Tune: NUN DANKET, 6 7 6 7 6 6 6 6; Johann Crüger, 1598–1662; harm. by A. Gregory Murray, OSB, 1905–1992

## 637 Confitémini Dómino / Come and Fill Our Hearts

Ostinato Refrain

Con - fi - té - mi - ni Dó - mi - no quó - ni - am
*Come and fill our hearts with your peace. You a -lone, O Lord, are*
Spanish: Llé - na-nos, Se - ñor, de tu paz. Por-que só - lo e - res
*Lithuanian: Aš pa - si - ti - kiu Vieš-pa - čiu, nes Jis mums*

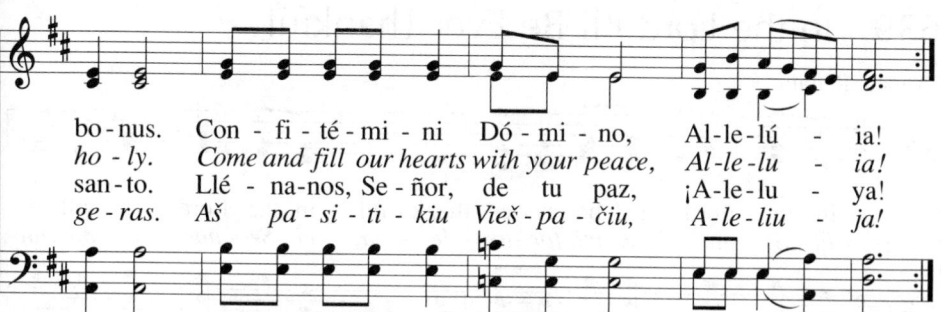

| bo - nus. | Con - fi - té - mi - ni | Dó - mi - no, | Al-le-lú - ia! |
| ho - ly. | *Come and fill our hearts with your peace,* | *Al-le-lu - ia!* |
| san - to. | Llé - na-nos, Se - ñor, de tu paz, | ¡A-le-lu - ya! |
| ge - ras. | *Aš pa - si - ti - kiu Vieš-pa - čiu,* | *A-le-liu - ja!* |

Text: Psalm 136, *Give thanks to the Lord for he is good;* Taizé Community, 1982
Tune: Jacques Berthier, 1923–1994
© 1982, 1991, 2011, Les Presses de Taizé, GIA Publications, Inc., agent

## We Gather Together    638

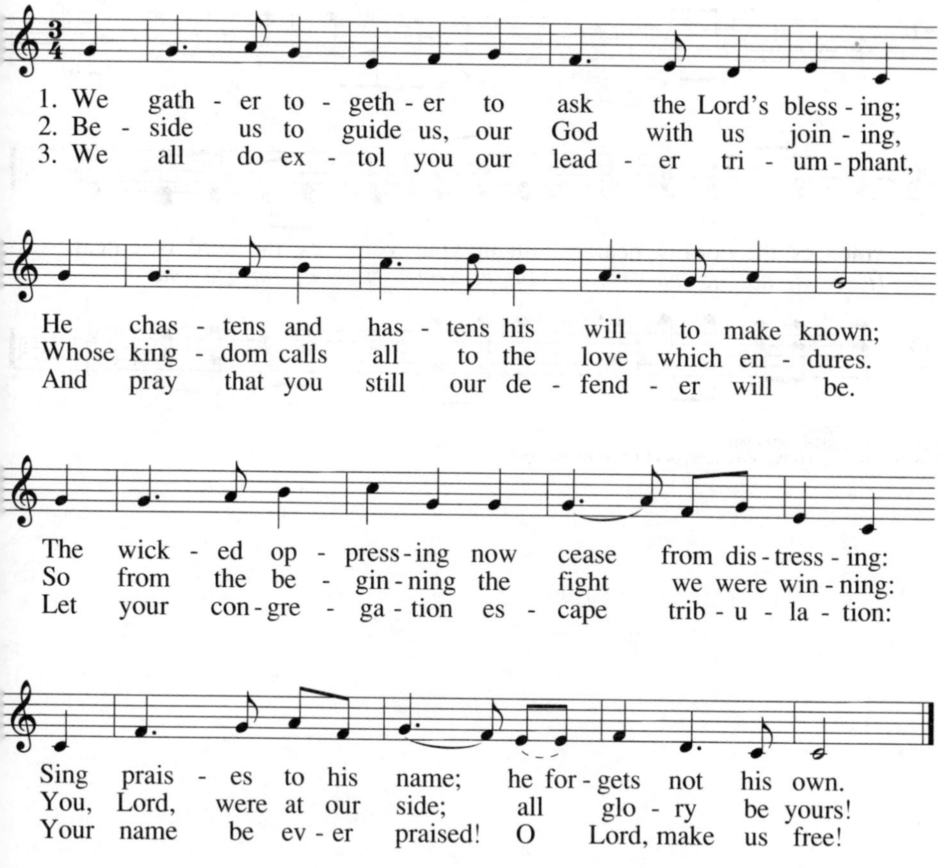

1. We   gath - er   to - geth - er   to   ask   the Lord's bless - ing;
2. Be - side   us to   guide us,   our   God   with us   join - ing,
3. We   all   do ex - tol you our   lead - er   tri - um-phant,

He   chas - tens and   has - tens his   will   to make known;
Whose king - dom calls   all   to the   love   which en - dures.
And   pray   that you   still   our de - fend - er   will   be.

The   wick - ed op - press-ing now   cease   from dis - tress - ing:
So   from   the be - gin-ning the   fight   we were win - ning:
Let   your   con - gre - ga - tion es - cape   trib - u - la - tion:

Sing   prais - es   to his   name;   he for - gets   not   his own.
You,   Lord,   were at   our   side;   all   glo - ry   be yours!
Your   name   be ev - er   praised!   O   Lord, make   us   free!

Text: *Wilt heden nu treden,* Netherlands folk hymn; tr. by Theodore Baker, 1851–1934, alt.
Tune: KREMSER, 12 11 12 11; *Nederlandtsch Gedenck-clanck,* 1626; harm. by Edward Kremser, 1838–1914

# 639 In the Lord I'll Be Ever Thankful

Ostinato Refrain

In the Lord I'll be ev - er thank - ful, in the Lord I will re -
*El Se - ñor es mi for -ta - le - za, el Se -ñor es mi can-*

joice! Look to God, do not be a - fraid. Lift up your
*ción. Él nos da la sal - va - ción. En él con -*

voic - es, the Lord is near; lift up your voic - es, the Lord is near.
*fí - o, no te -me - ré. En él con - fí - o, no te -me - ré.*

Text: Taizé Community
Tune: Jacques Berthier, 1923–1994
© 1986, 1991, 2011, Les Presses de Taizé, GIA Publications, Inc., agent

# There Is a Balm in Gilead 640

Refrain

There is a balm in Gil - e - ad To

make the wound - ed whole; There is a

balm in Gil - e - ad To heal the sin - sick soul.

Verses

1. Some - times I feel dis - cour - aged And
2. Don't ev - er be dis - cour - aged, For
3. If you can - not preach like Pe - ter, If you

think my work's in vain, But then the Ho - ly
Je - sus is your friend; And if you lack for
can - not pray like Paul, You can tell the love of

D.C.

Spir - it Re - vives my soul a - gain.
knowl - edge, He'll ne'er re - fuse to lend.
Je - sus And say, "He died for all."

Text: Jeremiah 8:22, African American spiritual
Tune: BALM IN GILEAD, Irregular with refrain; African American spiritual; acc. by Robert J. Batastini, b.1942, © 1987, GIA Publications, Inc.

# 641 Love Divine, All Loves Excelling

1. Love di - vine, all loves ex - cel - ling,
2. Come, Al - might - y, to de - liv - er,
3. Fin - ish then your new cre - a - tion,

Joy of heav'n, to earth come down!
Let us all your life re - ceive;
Pure and spot - less, gra - cious Lord.

Fix in us your hum - ble dwell - ing,
Sud - den - ly re - turn and nev - er,
Let us see your great sal - va - tion

All your faith - ful mer - cies crown.
Nev - er - more your tem - ples leave.
Per - fect - ly in you re - stored.

Je - sus, source of all com - pas - sion,
You we would be al - ways bless - ing,
Changed from glo - ry in - to glo - ry,

Love un - bound - ed, love all pure;
Serve you as your hosts a - bove,
Till in heav'n we take our place,

Vis - it us with your sal - va - tion,
Pray, and praise you with - out ceas - ing,
Till we sing be - fore the Al - might - y,

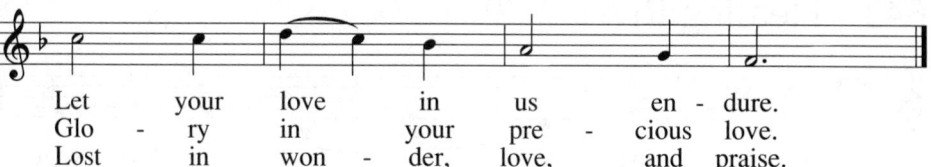

Let      your     love     in     us     en - dure.
Glo - ry     in     your     pre - cious     love.
Lost     in     won - der,     love,     and     praise.

Text: Charles Wesley, 1707–1788, alt.
Tune: HYFRYDOL, 8 7 8 7 D; Rowland H. Prichard, 1811–1887

## What Wondrous Love Is This 642

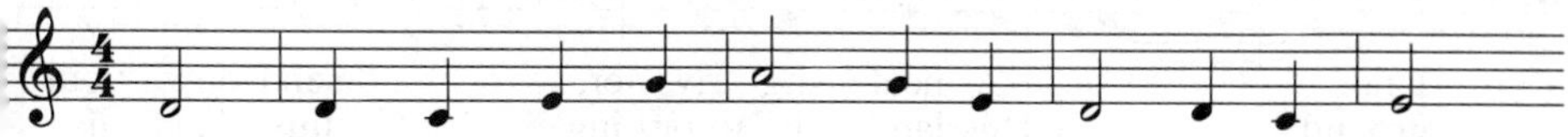

1. What     won - drous     love     is     this,     O     my     soul,     O     my     soul!
2. To     God     and     to     the     Lamb     I     will     sing,     I     will     sing;
3. And     when from death I'm     free,     I'll sing     on,     I'll sing     on;

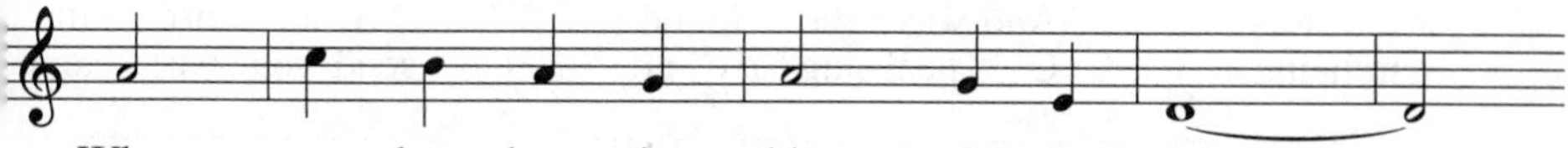

What     won - drous     love     is     this,     O     my     soul!
To     God     and     to     the     Lamb     I     will     sing.
And     when from death I'm     free,     I'll sing     on.

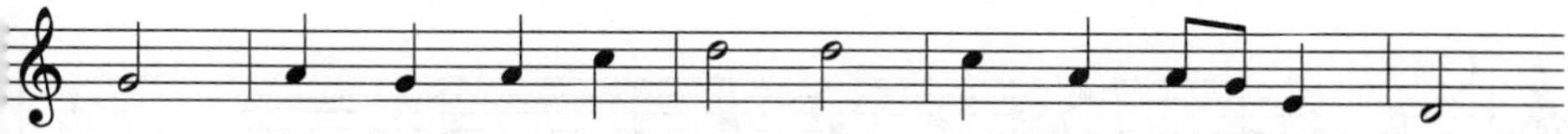

What     won - drous     love     is     this     that     caused the     Lord of     bliss
To     God     and     to     the     Lamb, who     is     the     great I     AM,
And     when from death I'm     free,     I'll     sing and     joy - ful     be,

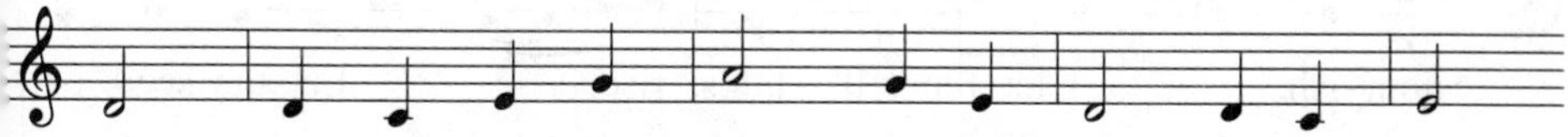

To     bear     the     dread - ful     curse     for     my     soul,     for     my     soul;
While     mil - lions join     the     theme,     I     will     sing,     I     will     sing;
And     through e - ter - ni - ty     I'll sing     on,     I'll sing     on;

To     bear     the     dread - ful     curse     for     my     soul!
While     mil - lions join     the     theme,     I     will     sing.
And     through e - ter - ni - ty     I'll sing     on.

Text: Alexander Means, 1801–1883
Tune: WONDROUS LOVE, 12 9 12 12 9; *Southern Harmony*, 1835; harm. from *Cantate Domino*, 1980, © 1980, World Council of Churches

## 643 Healing River

Cantor:*

1., 4. O heal - ing riv - er, send down your this land is
2. This land is thirst - ing,

wa - ters, Send down your wa - ters up - on this
parch - ing, No seed is grow-ing in the bar - ren

land. O heal - ing riv - er, send down your
ground. This land is thirst-ing, this land is

wa - ters, And wash the blood from off the
parch-ing, O heal-ing riv - er, send your wa - ters

1., 3. | Last time | 2.
sand. down. 3. Let the seed of

free - dom, a-wake and flour - ish, Let the deep roots

nour-ish, let the tall stalks rise. Let the seed of

free - dom, a-wake and flour-ish, Proud leaves un-

D.C.

curl - ing a - gainst the skies.

*The assembly echoes each phrase of the cantor at the interval of one half measure.*

Text: Fran Minkoff
Tune: Fred Hellerman, b.1927; arr. by Michael Joncas, b.1951
© 1964 (renewed), Appleseed Music, Inc.

# There's a Wideness in God's Mercy 644

1. There's a wide-ness in God's mer-cy Like the wide-ness
2. For the love of God is broad-er Than the meas-ures
3. Trou-bled souls, why will you scat-ter Like a crowd of

of the sea; There's a kind-ness in God's jus-tice
of the mind; And the heart of the E - ter - nal
fright-ened sheep? Fool - ish hearts, why will you wan-der

Which is more than lib - er - ty. There is plen - ti -
Is most won - der - ful - ly kind. If our love were
From a love so true and deep? There is wel-come

ful re-demp-tion In the blood that has been shed;
but more faith-ful, We should rest up - on God's word;
for the sin-ner, And more grac-es for the good;

There is joy for all the mem - bers
And our lives would be thanks-giv - ing
There is mer - cy with the Sav - ior,

In the sor - rows of the Head.
For the good - ness of our Lord.
There is heal - ing in his blood.

Text: Frederick W. Faber, 1814–1863, alt.
Tune: IN BABILONE, 8 7 8 7 D; *Oude en Nieuwe Hollantse Boerenlieties*, c.1710

# 645 Amazing Grace

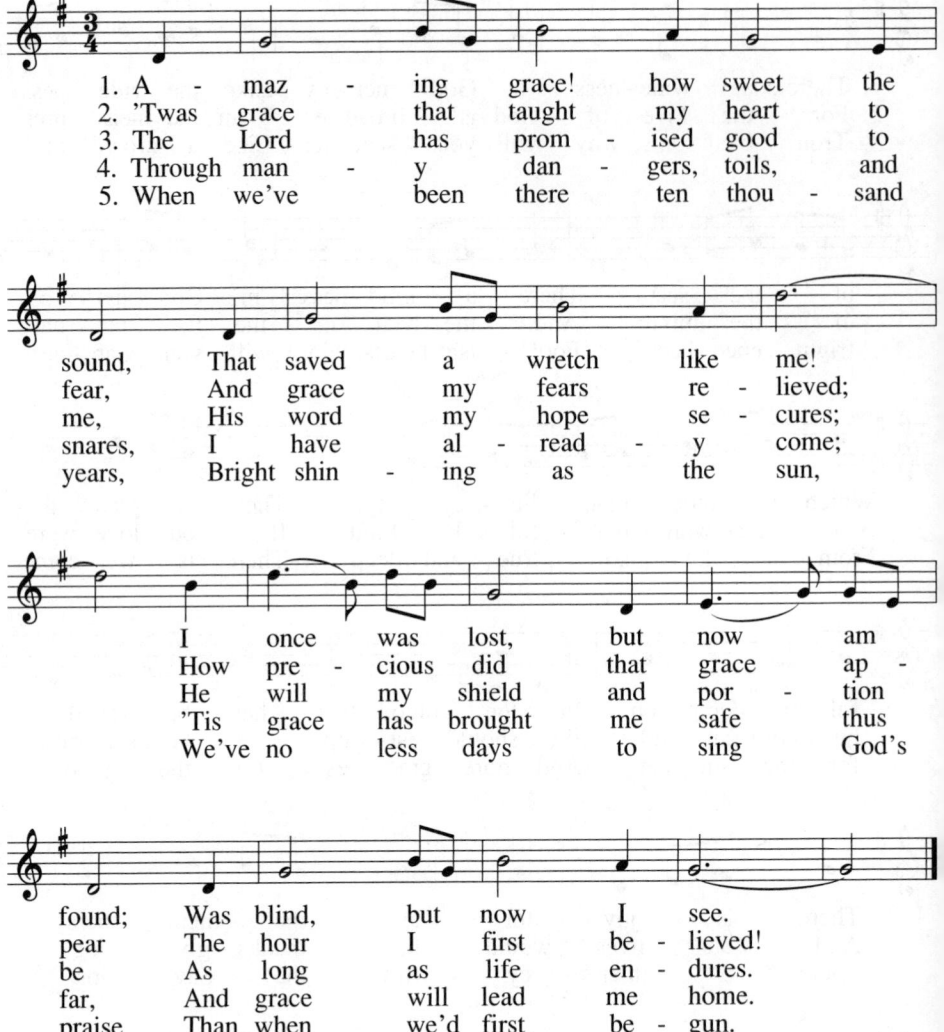

1. A - maz - ing grace! how sweet the
2. 'Twas grace that taught my heart to
3. The Lord has prom - ised good to
4. Through man - y dan - gers, toils, and
5. When we've been there ten thou - sand

sound, That saved a wretch like me!
fear, And grace my fears re - lieved;
me, His word my hope se - cures;
snares, I have al - read - y come;
years, Bright shin - ing as the sun,

I once was lost, but now am
How pre - cious did that grace ap -
He will my shield and por - tion
'Tis grace has brought me safe thus
We've no less days to sing God's

found; Was blind, but now I see.
pear The hour I first be - lieved!
be As long as life en - dures.
far, And grace will lead me home.
praise Than when we'd first be - gun.

Text: St. 1–4, John Newton, 1725–1807; st. 5, attr. to John Rees, fl.1859
Tune: NEW BRITAIN, CM; *Virginia Harmony*, 1831; harm. by Edwin O. Excell, 1851–1921

# Keep in Mind 646

**Refrain**

Keep in mind that Je - sus Christ has died for
us and is ris - en from the dead. He is our sav-ing
Lord, he is joy for all a - ges.

**Verse 1**    D.C.

1. If we die with the Lord, we shall live with the Lord.
   If we en - dure with the Lord, we shall reign with the Lord.

**Verses 2, 3**    D.C.

2. In Christ all our sor - row, in Christ all our joy.
   In him hope of glo - ry, in him all our love.
3. In Christ our re - demp - tion, in Christ all our grace.
   In him our sal - va - tion, in him all our peace.

Text: 2 Timothy 2:8–12, Lucien Deiss, CSSp, 1921–2007
Tune: Lucien Deiss, CSSp, 1921–2007
© 1965, World Library Publications

# 647 Neither Death nor Life

Refrain

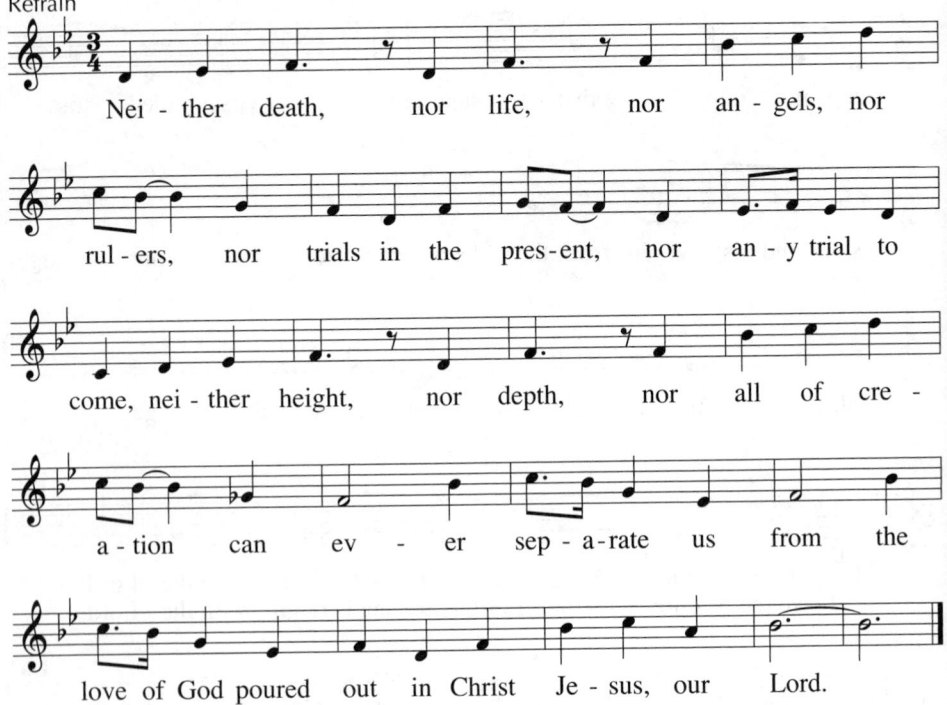

Nei - ther death, nor life, nor an - gels, nor
rul - ers, nor trials in the pres-ent, nor an - y trial to
come, nei - ther height, nor depth, nor all of cre -
a - tion can ev - er sep - a-rate us from the
love of God poured out in Christ Je - sus, our Lord.

Verses

1. Dwell in the One who raised Christ from the dead;
   Though your body shall die, in Christ you shall rise
   through the Spirit who brings you to life.

2. All who are led by the Spirit shall live as children of God,
   and heirs with Christ Jesus,
   God's adopted and chosen and loved.

3. All of the suffering we now must endure
   is nothing to the glory so soon to be revealed
   when creation itself is set free.

4. All of creation awaits the new birth,
   the fullness of redemption, through labor pains of love,
   and so we wait in patience and hope.

5. All things work for good for the ones who love God,
   and if God is for us, then who can be against us?
   God's justified cannot be condemned.

6. Who can separate us from the love of Christ?
   Will hardship or distress, persecution or famine,
   or nakedness or peril or sword?

Text: Romans 8:11–19, 22–25, 28–35, 38; Marty Haugen, b.1950
Tune: Marty Haugen, b.1950
© 2001, GIA Publications, Inc.

# O God of Exodus 648

1. O God of Ex - o - dus, of mer - cy sweet and
2. You call your ser - vant band to trust in you a -
3. Each morn - ing man - na fair, a feast of fin - est
4. Then when our jour-ney's done, our pil - grim - age com -

strong, On free - dom's shore we dance and sing you
lone, And guide us by your hand on paths as
grace, Re - shapes our hearts to share your gifts in
plete, A song will still be sung of mer - cy

Mir - yam's song. A - cross the dead - ly
yet un - known. Through doubt - filled nights and
ev - 'ry place. Till with all pil - grims
strong and sweet; And sto - ries we from

wa - ters chill, You bring your sons and daugh - ters still, With
tear - ful days, Be - yond our stub - born, fear - ful ways, Your
free - ly fed By com - mon cup and bro - ken bread, We
el - ders heard, Of won - drous deeds and sav - ing Word, Our

Christ, in whom we now be - long.
faith - ful prom - ise is our home.
taste your peace, be - hold your face.
chil - dren's chil - dren will re - peat.

Text: Susan Briehl, b.1952
Tune: MIRYAM'S SONG, 12 12 88 8; Marty Haugen, b.1950
© 2009, GIA Publications, Inc.

# 649 Shall Tribulation or Distress

1. Shall trib - u - la - tion or dis - tress, Shall per - se -
2. Shall ill - ness, hun - ger, or de - spair, Shall lone - ly
3. No, nei - ther an - gel hosts nor thrones, Nor height nor

cu - tion, fire, or sword, Or an - y per - il of this
grief or anx - ious fears, Or deeds of ha - tred and dis -
depth of e - vil's reach, Nor pres - ent things, nor things to

world— Or e - ven death, Or e - ven death— Shall an - y
dain— Or e - ven death, Or e - ven death— Shall an - y
come— Not e - ven death, Not e - ven death— Not an - y

pow'r of earth or heav'n Di - vide us from your love, O Christ?
pow'r of earth or heav'n Di - vide us from your love, O Christ?
pow'r of earth or heav'n Can part us from your love, O Christ.

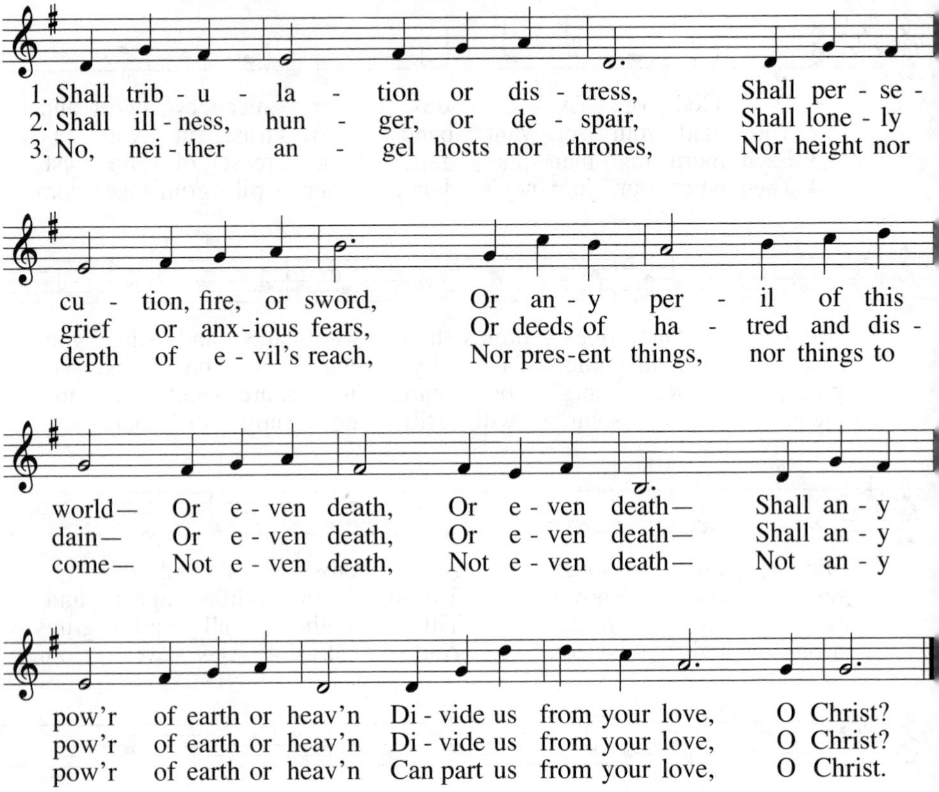

Text: Romans 8:35, 38; Mary Louise Bringle, b.1953
Tune: ROMANS 8, 8 8 8 4 4 8 8; Sally Ann Morris, b.1952
© 2006, GIA Publications, Inc.

# 650 These Alone Are Enough

1. Take my heart, O Lord, take my hopes and dreams.
2. Take my thoughts, O Lord, and my mem - o - ry.
3. I sur - ren - der, Lord, all I have and hold.
4. When the dark - ness falls on my fi - nal days,

Take my mind with all its plans and schemes.
Take my tears, my joys, my lib - er - ty.
I re - turn to you your gifts un - told.
take the ver - y breath that sang your praise.

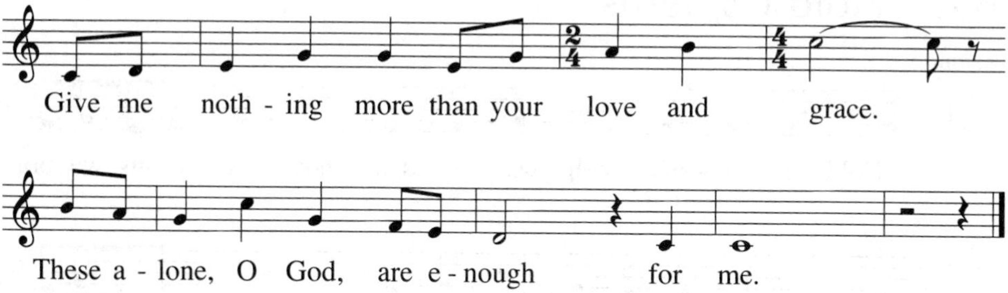

Give me noth - ing more than your love and grace.

These a - lone, O God, are e - nough for me.

Text: Based on *"Suscipe"* Prayer of Ignatius of Loyola; Dan Schutte, b.1947
Tune: Dan Schutte, b.1947
© 2004, Dan Schutte. Published by OCP.

## Open My Eyes 651

Verses

1. O - pen my eyes, Lord. Help me to see your face.
2. O - pen my ears, Lord. Help me to hear your voice.
3. O - pen my heart, Lord. Help me to love like you.
4. I live with - in you. Deep in your heart, O Love.

O - pen my eyes, Lord. Help me to see. *(To verse 2)*
O - pen my ears, Lord. Help me to hear. *(To verse 3)*
O - pen my heart, Lord. Help me to love. *(To bridge)*
I live with - in you. Rest now in me.

Bridge

And the first shall be last, and our eyes are o - pened,

and we'll hear like nev-er be - fore. And we'll speak in new ways,

D.C.

and we'll see God's face in plac-es we've nev-er known.

Text: Based on Mark 8:22–25; Jesse Manibusan, b.1958
Tune: Jesse Manibusan, b.1958; acc. by Ed Bolduc, b.1969, choral arr. by Ken Canedo, b.1953
© 1988, 1998, 1999, Jesse Manibusan. Published by OCP.

# 652  Hold Us, Jesus

Refrain

Hold us, Je - sus, help us, Je - sus, heal us, Je-sus, we pray.

Hold us, Je - sus, help us, Je - sus, heal us, Je-sus, we pray.

Ky-ri-e e-le - i - son, Chri-ste e-le - i - son.

Verses

*Cantor:*

*Cantor:*  *All:*  In the

1. In the des-ert of de-spair,
2. In the des-ert of pain,  be with us, Lord, quench our thirst.
3. In the des-ert of sin,

*All:*

dark-ness of doubt,
dark-ness of a-buse,  walk with us, Lord, light our path.
dark-ness of hate,

D.C.

Give us hope, give us peace, give us strength.

Text: Chris de Silva, b.1967
Tune: Chris de Silva, b.1967
© 2007, GIA Publications, Inc.

# There Is a Longing  653

**Refrain**

There is a long-ing in our hearts, O Lord, for
you to re - veal your - self to us.
There is a long-ing in our hearts for love we
on - ly find in you, our God.

**Verses**

1. For jus - tice, for free - dom, for mer - cy:
2. For wis - dom, for cour - age, for com - fort:
3. For heal - ing, for whole-ness, for new life:
4. Lord save us, take pit - y, light in our

hear our prayer. In sor - row, in grief:
hear our prayer. In weak-ness, in fear:
hear our prayer. In sick - ness, in death:
dark - ness. We call you, we wait:

**D.C.**

be near, hear our prayer, O God.

Text: Anne Quigley
Tune: Anne Quigley
© 1992, 1994, Anne Quigley. Published by OCP.

# 654 O Lord, the Guardian of My Heart

**Refrain**

O Lord, the guard-ian of my heart, who rules the day and night, you guide me through my dark-est hours and lead me in-to light.

**Verses**

1. Teach me the way of your truth,
2. Take my weak-ness, O God.
3. Wipe a-way my fear,

help me to know your wis-dom. Keep me in your
Build my strength in faith. Save me in your
lift me from my sor-row. Wash a-way my

**D.C.**

pres-ence, Lord, show me how to love.
mer-cy, Lord, clothe me with your grace.
bro-ken-ness, heal my wound-ed soul.

Text: Carol E. Browning, b.1956
Tune: Carol E. Browning, b.1956
© 2000, GIA Publications, Inc.

# Increase Our Faith 655

**Refrain**

Lord, in-crease our faith. With all our heart, may we al-ways fol-low you. Teach us to pray al - ways.

**Verses 1, 3**

1. So I say to you: "ask, you will re-ceive;
3. If you, with all your sins, know how to give,

seek and you will find. Knock, it shall be
how much more will God give to all those who

**D.C.**

o - pened to you."
cry from their hearts!

**Verse 2**

2. Who-ev-er asks, they shall re-ceive; who-ev-er seeks shall

**D.C.**

find. Who-ev-er knocks, the door will be o - pened.

Text: Based on Luke 11:1–13, 17:5; David Haas, b.1957
Tune: David Haas, b.1957
© 1997, GIA Publications, Inc.

# 656   Lead Me, Guide Me

**Refrain**

Lead me, guide me, a - long the way, For if you
lead me, I can - not stray. Lord, let me walk each
day with thee. Lead me, O Lord, lead me.

**Verses**

1. I am weak and I need thy strength and pow'r to
2. Help me tread in the paths of right - eous-ness, Be my
3. I am lost if you take your hand from me, I am

help me o - ver my weak - est hour. Help me through the
aid when Sa - tan and sin op - press. I am put - ting
blind with - out thy Light to see. Lord, just al - ways

dark-ness thy face to see. Lead me, O Lord, lead me.
all my trust in thee. Lead me, O Lord, lead me.
let me thy ser - vant be. Lead me, O Lord, lead me.

# We Cannot Measure How You Heal   657

1. We can - not meas - ure how you heal
2. The pain that will not go a - way,
3. So some have come who need your help,

an - swer ev - 'ry suf - f'rer's prayer, Yet
guilt that clings from things long past, The
some have come to make a - mends, As

we be - lieve your grace re - sponds Where faith and
fear of what the fu - ture holds, Are pres - ent
hands which shaped and saved the world Are pres - ent

doubt u - nite to care. Your hands, though blood - ied
as if meant to last. But pres - ent too is
in the touch of friends. Lord, let your Spir - it

on the cross, Sur - vive to hold and heal and
love which tends The hurt we nev - er hoped to
meet us here To mend the bod - y, mind, and

warn, To car - ry all through death to
find, The pri - vate ag - o - nies in -
soul, To dis - en - tan - gle peace from

life And cra - dle chil - dren yet un - born.
side, The mem - o - ries that haunt the mind.
pain, And make your bro - ken peo - ple whole.

Text: John L. Bell, b.1949
Tune: YE BANKS AND BRAES, 8 8 8 8 D; Scottish traditional; arr. by John L. Bell, b.1949
© 1989, Iona Community, GIA Publications, Inc., agent

# 658  Seek Ye First

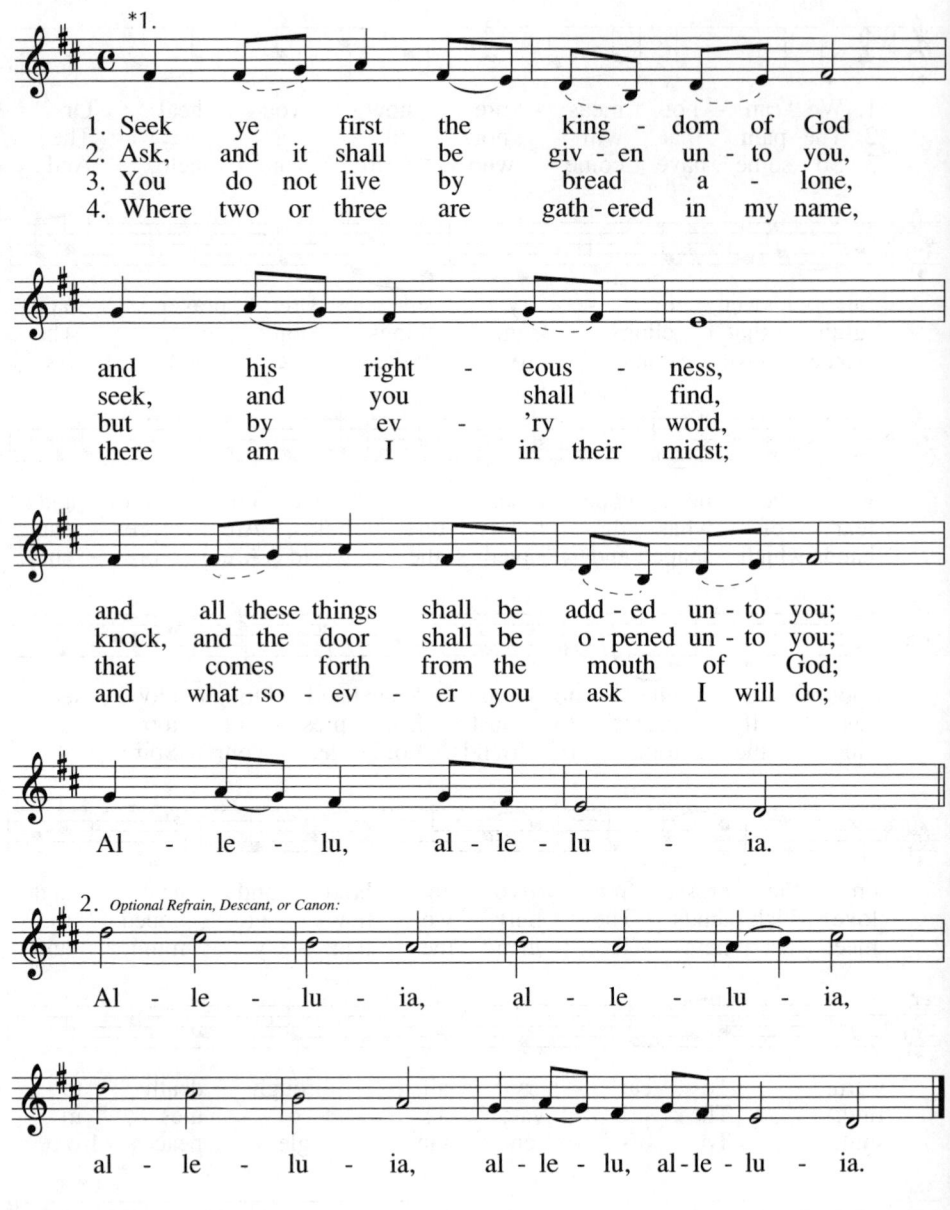

1. Seek ye first the king - dom of God
2. Ask, and it shall be giv - en un - to you,
3. You do not live by bread a - lone,
4. Where two or three are gath - ered in my name,

and his right - eous - ness,
seek, and you shall find,
but by ev - 'ry word,
there am I in their midst;

and all these things shall be add - ed un - to you;
knock, and the door shall be o - pened un - to you;
that comes forth from the mouth of God;
and what - so - ev - er you ask I will do;

Al - le - lu, al - le - lu - ia.

2. *Optional Refrain, Descant, or Canon:*

Al - le - lu - ia, al - le - lu - ia,

al - le - lu - ia, al - le - lu, al - le - lu - ia.

*May be sung as a two-voice canon.*

Text: Matthew 6:33, 7:7; adapt. by Karen Lafferty, b.1948
Tune: SEEK YE FIRST, Irregular; Karen Lafferty, b.1948
© 1972, Universal Music - Brentwood Benson Publishing / CCCM Music

# I Lift My Soul to You 659

**Refrain**

I lift my soul to you, O Lord. To you I lift my hands, I lift my heart, my soul. I lift my soul to you, O Lord. To you I lift my hands, I lift my heart, my soul.

**Verses 1, 2**

1. Lord, make me know your ways, keep me on your path. Walk with me in your truth and teach me. You save my life, you are my song.

2. Your ways are good and just. You find the lost, you lead the hum-ble to right - eous - ness. You help the poor to find the way.

**D.C.**

**Verse 3**

3. You hold true to your prom-ise, your friend-ship is with those who keep your cov-e - nant. Let us hum - bly walk in your name. For - give the past and wash a-way our guilt.

**D.C.**

Text: Psalm 25:1, 4–5, 8–11; Lori True, b.1961
Tune: Lori True, b.1961; acc. by Paul A. Tate, b.1968

# 660 Turn My Heart, O God

**Refrain**

Turn my heart, O God. Turn my heart, O God. Take my pain and bro - ken - ness; shape my life for you. Come and turn my heart, O God.

*To verses* | *To repeat refrain and last time*

**Verses**

turn my heart, O God.

*Cantor:*

1. From all that leads to death, to
2. From bit - ter - ness and hate, to
3. O let your Spir - it come and
4. O bring me home to you, Most

*All:*

Come and turn my heart, O

seek the way of life: From
ten - der-ness and care: From
cleanse my in - most heart: Give
Ho - ly, Bless-ed One: And

God.                                                    Come and

all   that leads to   sin,       to   ho - li - ness and grace:
self - ish - ness and greed,    to   gen- 'rous car - ing  love:
back to   me the   joy          of  walk - ing   in   your way:
let   my  spir - it   rest       with - in   your lov - ing  heart:

turn      my    heart,   O      God.

From   all    de - spair  and  grief,            to
From   all    de - ceit   and  lies,             to
O       fill   me  with your grace             that
For    you    a - lone  can  raise             my

D.C.

Come and turn  my  heart,  O    God.

hope  of    life  re - newed:
faith - ful - ness and   truth:
I     might sing your praise:
wea - ry   soul  to    life:

Text: Marty Haugen, b.1950
Tune: Marty Haugen, b.1950
© 2002, GIA Publications, Inc.

# 661 Song over the Waters

Refrain

God, you have moved up-on the wa-ters, you have sung in the rush of wind and flame; and in your love, you have called us sons and daugh-ters, make us peo-ple of the wa-ter and your name.

Verses

1. Come fill our wait-ing hearts with the
2. Give us a thirst for love, give us a
3. You are the breath of life, you are the
4. Come, o-pen ev-'ry heart, come now and

spir - it of Je - sus, let us shine with your
hun - ger for jus - tice, make us one with the
hope of the hope - less, come and fill us with
wake us to won - der, make us ves - sels of

D.C.

light and peace.
mind of Christ.
light and peace.
light and peace.

Sprinkling Rite

Cantor:  All:

(Invocation) Re - new us!

Cantor:  All:  D.C.

(Invocation) Re - new us!

Text: Marty Haugen, b.1950
Tune: Marty Haugen, b.1950
© 1987, GIA Publications, Inc.

# Make Us Worthy  662

Refrain

Lord, make us wor-thy. Make us wor-thy to see your face.

Fill us with your word, O Lord, and heal us with your grace.

Verses

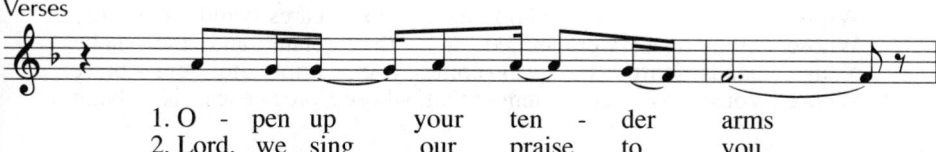

1. O - pen up your ten - der arms
2. Lord, we sing our praise to you,
3. You are strength when we are weak.
4. Fash - ion plough - shares from our swords.
5. Lord, you sent your heal - ing word

for your lost ones have come home.
who have blessed us with great love.
You are warmth when we are cold.
Rip the ha - tred from our minds.
to re - deem us from our sins.

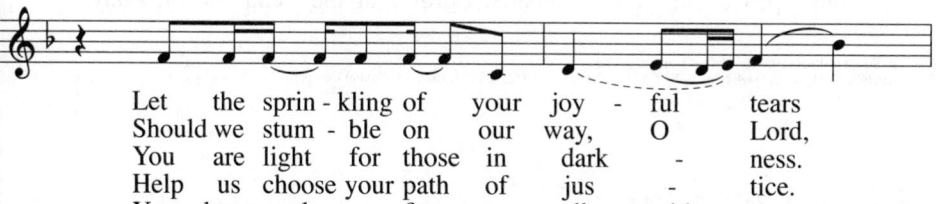

Let the sprin - kling of your joy - ful tears
Should we stum - ble on our way, O Lord,
You are light for those in dark - ness.
Help us choose your path of jus - tice.
You have made us fit to walk with you

D.C.

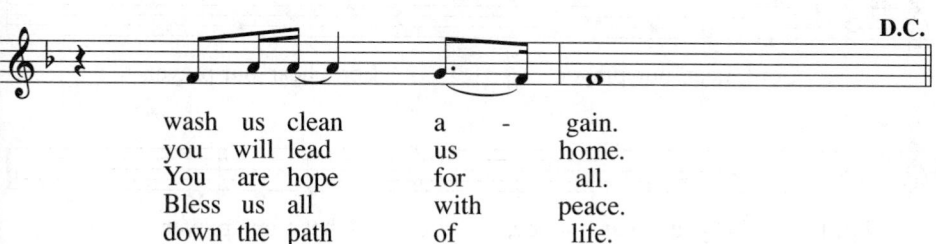

wash us clean a - gain.
you will lead us home.
You are hope for all.
Bless us all with peace.
down the path of life.

Text: Michael Mahler, b.1981
Tune: Michael Mahler, b.1981
© 2003, GIA Publications, Inc.

# 663　Lord of All Hopefulness

1. Lord of all hope - ful - ness, Lord of all joy,
2. Lord of all ea - ger - ness, Lord of all faith,
3. Lord of all kind - li - ness, Lord of all grace,
4. Lord of all gen - tle - ness, Lord of all calm,

Whose trust, ev - er child - like, no cares could de - stroy,
Whose strong hands were skilled at the plane and the lathe,
Your hands swift to wel - come, your arms to em - brace,
Whose voice is con - tent - ment, whose pres - ence is balm,

Be there at our wak - ing, and give us, we pray,
Be there at our la - bors, and give us, we pray,
Be there at our hom - ing, and give us, we pray,
Be there at our sleep - ing, and give us, we pray,

Your bliss in our hearts, Lord, at the break of the day.
Your strength in our hearts, Lord, at the noon of the day.
Your love in our hearts, Lord, at the eve of the day.
Your peace in our hearts, Lord, at the end of the day.

Text: Jan Struther, 1901–1953, © Oxford University Press
Tune: SLANE, 10 11 11 12; Gaelic; harm. by Erik Routley, 1917–1982, © 1975, Hope Publishing Company

# 664　A Celtic Rune

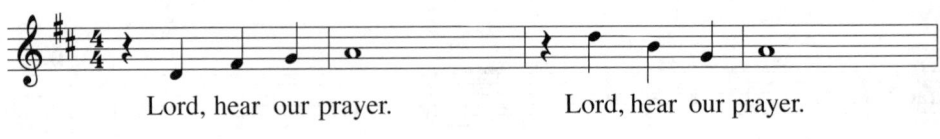

Lord, hear our prayer.　　　Lord, hear our prayer.

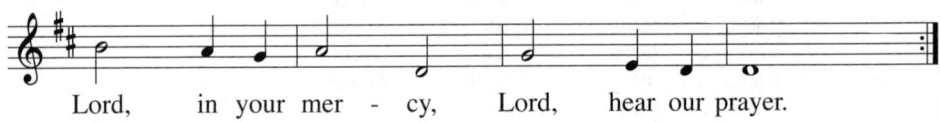

Lord, in your mer - cy, Lord, hear our prayer.

Text: Liam Lawton, b.1959
Tune: Liam Lawton, b.1959; arr. by Ian Callanan, b.1971
© 1995, Veritas Publications/Liam Lawton, GIA Publications, Inc., agent

# Healing River of the Spirit   665

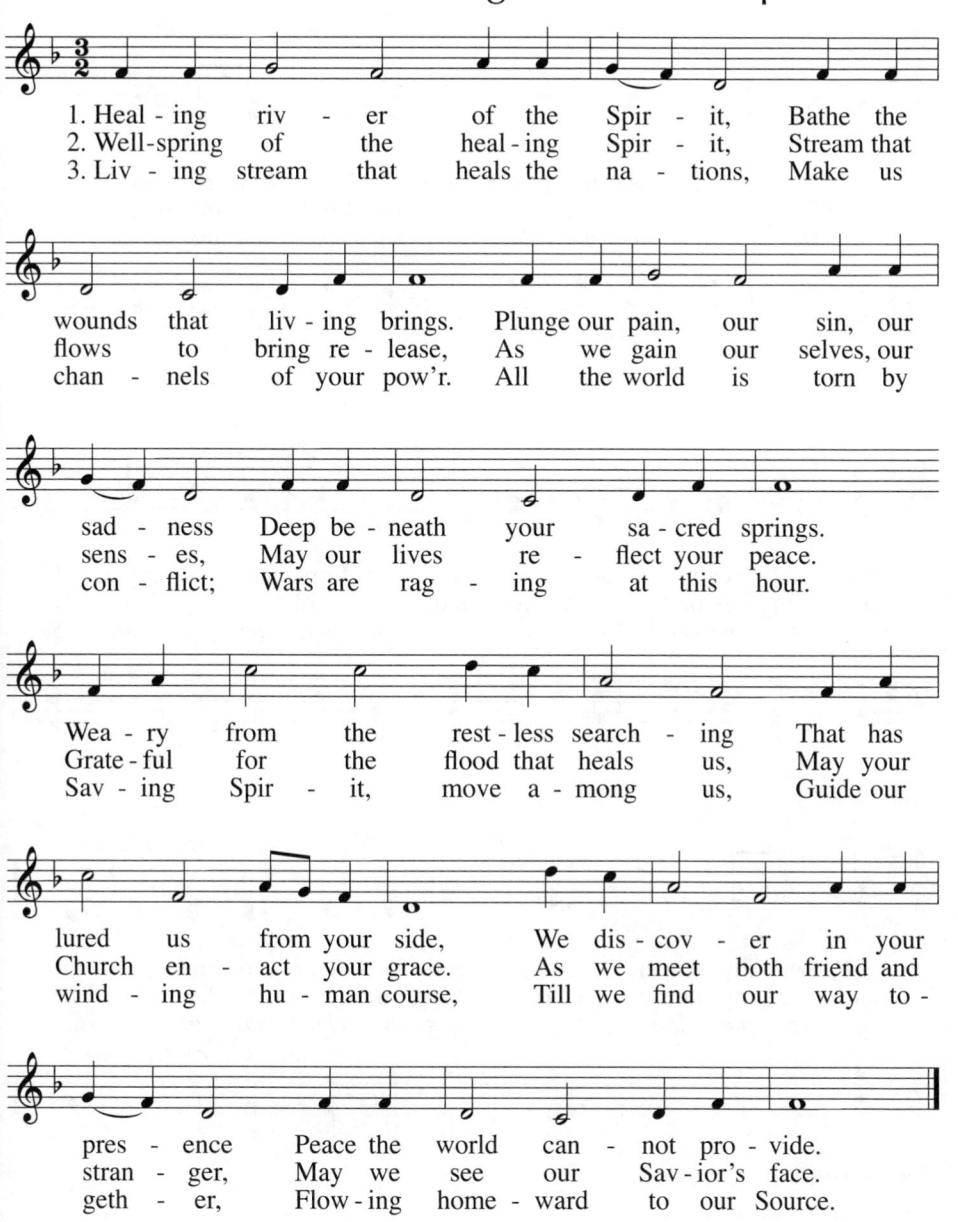

1. Heal - ing   riv - er   of   the   Spir - it,   Bathe the
2. Well-spring   of   the   heal - ing   Spir - it,   Stream that
3. Liv - ing   stream   that   heals the   na - tions,   Make us

wounds   that   liv - ing   brings.   Plunge our pain,   our   sin, our
flows   to   bring re - lease,   As   we gain   our   selves, our
chan - nels   of   your pow'r.   All   the world   is   torn by

sad - ness   Deep be - neath   your   sa - cred springs.
sens - es,   May our   lives   re - flect your peace.
con - flict;   Wars are   rag - ing   at this   hour.

Wea - ry   from   the   rest - less search - ing   That has
Grate - ful   for   the   flood that heals   us,   May your
Sav - ing   Spir - it,   move a - mong   us,   Guide our

lured   us   from your side,   We dis - cov - er   in your
Church   en - act   your grace.   As we meet   both friend and
wind - ing   hu - man course,   Till we find   our   way to -

pres - ence   Peace the   world   can - not pro - vide.
stran - ger,   May we   see   our   Sav - ior's face.
geth - er,   Flow - ing   home - ward   to   our Source.

Text: Ruth Duck, b.1947, © 1996, The Pilgrim Press
Tune: BEACH SPRING, 8 7 8 7 D; *The Sacred Harp*, 1844; harm. by Ronald A. Nelson, b.1927, © 1978, *Lutheran Book of Worship*

# 666 O Lord, Hear My Prayer

Ostinato Chorale

O        Lord,    hear my prayer,    O   Lord,   hear my prayer:
*The     Lord     is  my  song,      the Lord    is  my  praise:
*Se  -  ñor,    ten pie - dad,     Se - ñor,   ten pie - dad:*

when     I     call     an - swer me.    O  Lord, hear my prayer,   O
all      my    hope     comes  from God.  The Lord  is  my  song,    the
*si      te_in - vo - co,   ó  -  ye - me.   Se - ñor,   ten pie - dad,   Se -*

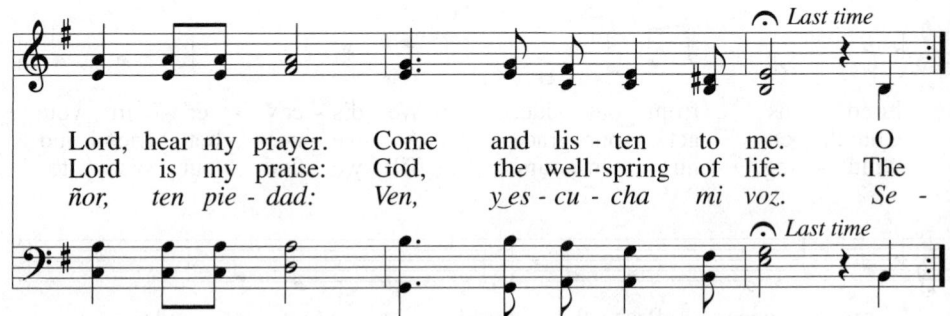

*Last time*

Lord,  hear my prayer.    Come    and lis - ten   to me.    O
Lord   is  my  praise:    God,    the well-spring  of life.  The
*ñor,   ten pie - dad:     Ven,    y_es - cu - cha   mi voz.   Se -*

*Last time*

*Alternate text

Text: Psalm 102; Taizé Community, 1982
Tune: Jacques Berthier, 1923–1994
© 1982, 2011, Les Presses de Taizé, GIA Publications, Inc., agent

# How Shall We Name God? 667

Verses

1. Source and Sov - 'reign, Rock and Cloud, For - tress, Foun - tain,
2. Word and Wis - dom, Root and Vine, Shep - herd, Sav - ior,
3. Storm and Still - ness, Breath and Dove, Thun - der, Tem - pest,

Shel - ter, Light, Judge, De - fend - er, Mer - cy, Might,
Ser - vant, Lamb, Well and Wa - ter, Bread and Wine,
Whirl - wind, Fire, Com - fort, Coun - sel - or, Pres - ence,

**1., 2.** *To refrain* **3.** *To refrain*

Life whose life all life en - dowed:
Way who leads us to I AM:
En - er - gies that nev - er tire:

Refrain

May the church at prayer re - call That no sin - gle ho - ly

name But the truth be - hind them all Is the

*To verses* **D.C.** *Last time*

God whom we pro - claim. claim.

Text: Thomas H. Troeger, b.1945, © 1986, Oxford University Press
Tune: BIRINUS, 7 7 7 7 D; Paul Inwood, b.1947, © 2003, GIA Publications, Inc.

# 668 O God, Why Are You Silent?

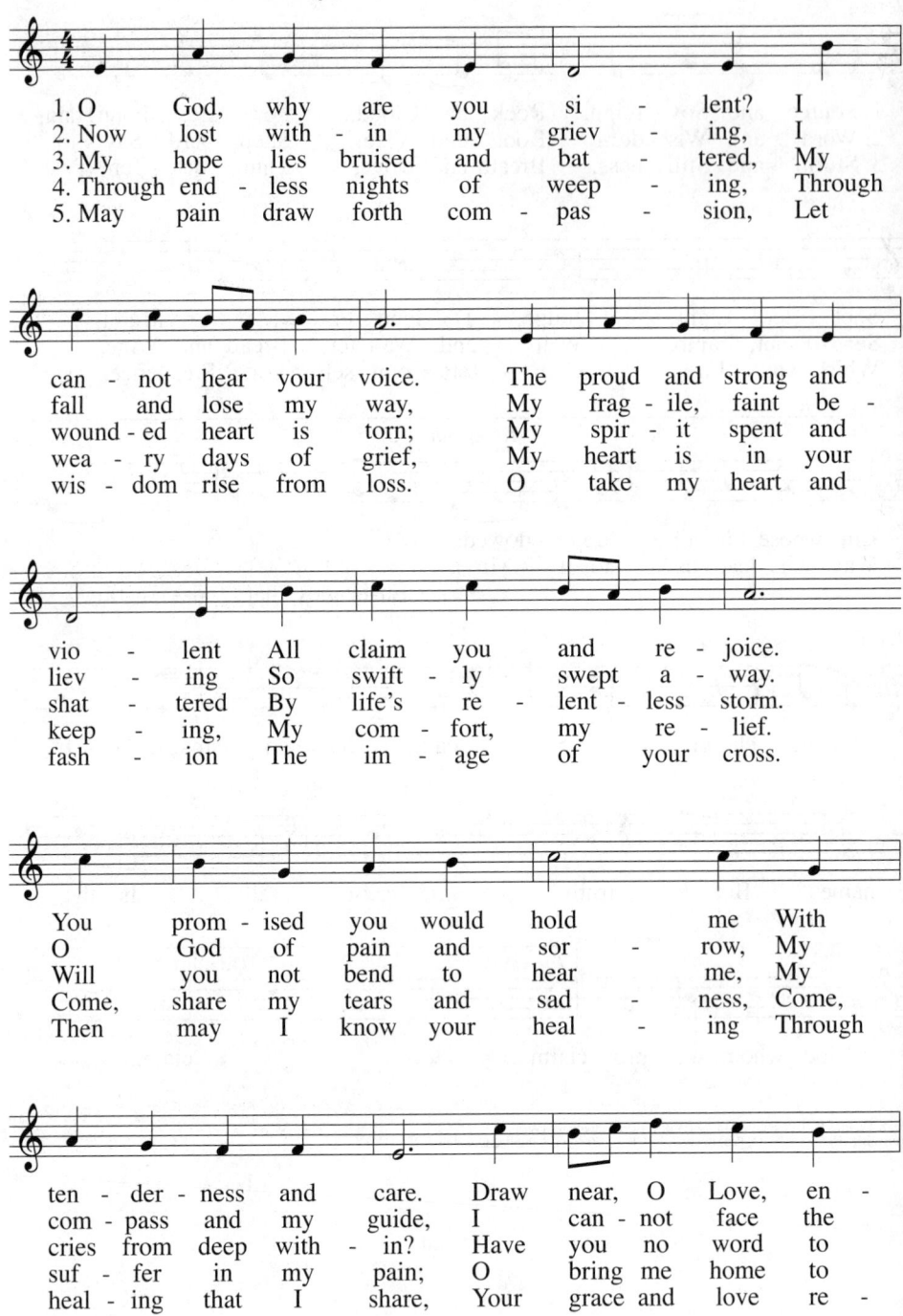

1. O God, why are you si - lent? I
2. Now lost with - in my griev - ing, I
3. My hope lies bruised and bat - tered, My
4. Through end - less nights of weep - ing, Through
5. May pain draw forth com - pas - sion, Let

can - not hear your voice. The proud and strong and
fall and lose my way, My frag - ile, faint be -
wound - ed heart is torn; My spir - it spent and
wea - ry days of grief, My heart is in your
wis - dom rise from loss. O take my heart and

vio - lent All claim you and re - joice.
liev - ing So swift - ly swept a - way.
shat - tered By life's re - lent - less storm.
keep - ing, My com - fort, my re - lief.
fash - ion The im - age of your cross.

You prom - ised you would hold me With
O God of pain and sor - row, My
Will you not bend to hear me, My
Come, share my tears and sad - ness, Come,
Then may I know your heal - ing Through

ten - der - ness and care. Draw near, O Love, en -
com - pass and my guide, I can - not face the
cries from deep with - in? Have you no word to
suf - fer in my pain; O bring me home to
heal - ing that I share, Your grace and love re -

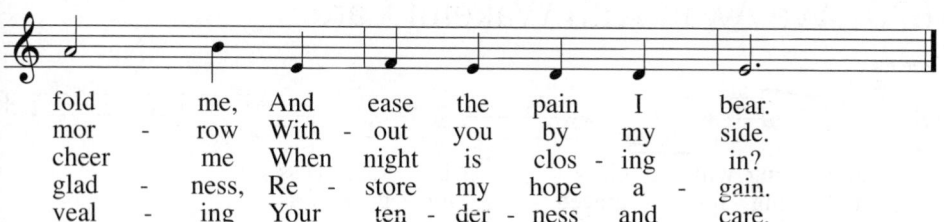

| fold | me, | And | ease | the | pain | I | bear. |
|------|-----|-----|------|-----|------|---|-------|
| mor - | row | With - | out | you | by | my | side. |
| cheer | me | When | night | is | clos - | ing | in? |
| glad - | ness, | Re - | store | my | hope | a - | gain. |
| veal - | ing | Your | ten - | der - | ness | and | care. |

Text: Marty Haugen, b.1950, © 2003, GIA Publications, Inc.
Tune: PASSION CHORALE, 7 6 7 6 D; Hans Leo Hassler, 1564–1612; harm. by Marty Haugen, b.1950, © 2003, GIA Publications, Inc.

## God Remembers 669

1. God re-mem-bers pain:    Nail by nail,    thorn by thorn,
2. God re-mem-bers joy:    Touch of love,    taste of food,
3. God re-mem-bers us:    All we were,    all we are,

Hun - ger, thirst, and mus - cles torn.    Time may dull our griefs    And
All our sens - es know is good.    Love and life flow by    And
Lives with - in our Lov - er's care.    Time may dull our minds    And

heal our less - er wounds,    But in e-ter-nal Love    Yes-ter-day is
pre - cious days are gone,    But in e-ter-nal Love    Ev - 'ry day is
death will take us all,    But in e-ter-nal Love    Ev - 'ry life is

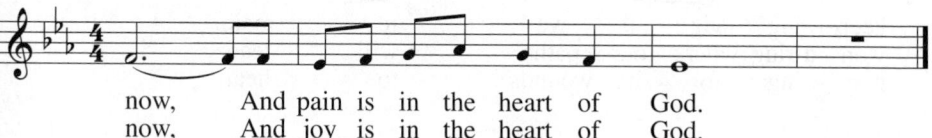

now,    And pain is in the heart of    God.
now,    And joy is in the heart of    God.
now:    Our life is hid with Christ in    God.

Text: Colossians 3:3–4; Brian Wren, b.1936, © 1993, Hope Publishing Company
Tune: GOD REMEMBERS, 5 6 7 5 6 6 5 8; Marty Haugen, b.1950, © 2003, GIA Publications, Inc.

# 670  We Await with Wakeful Care

Verses

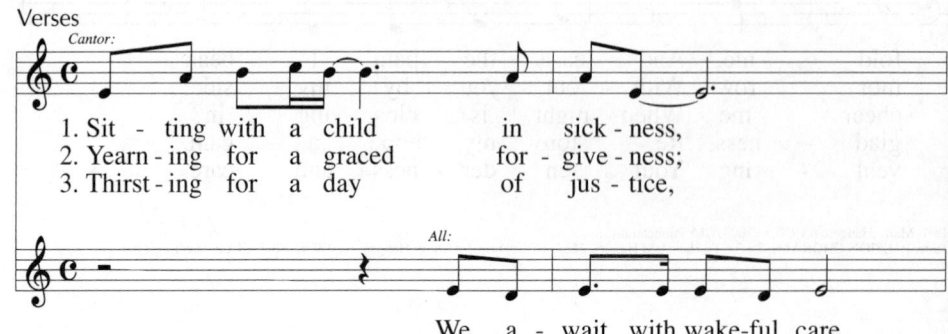

Cantor:

1. Sit - ting with a child in sick - ness,
2. Yearn - ing for a graced for - give - ness;
3. Thirst - ing for a day of jus - tice,

All:

We a - wait with wake-ful care.

list - 'ning for a cry of pain,
sore, re - pent - ing; deep in need;
hun - g'ring, plead - ing, now we kneel;

We a - wait with wake - ful care.

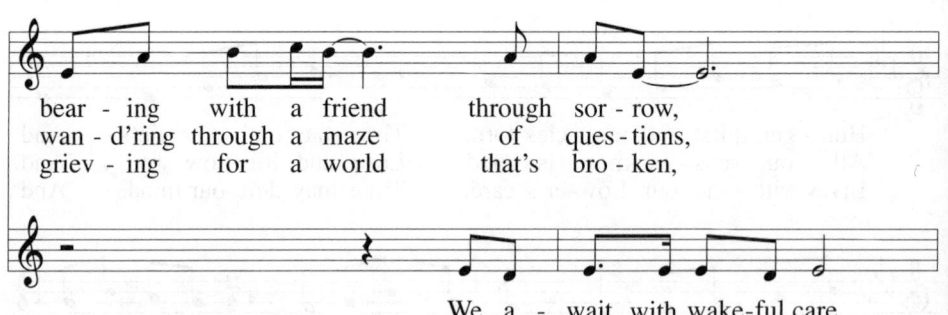

bear - ing with a friend through sor - row,
wan - d'ring through a maze of ques - tions,
griev - ing for a world that's bro - ken,

We a - wait with wake-ful care.

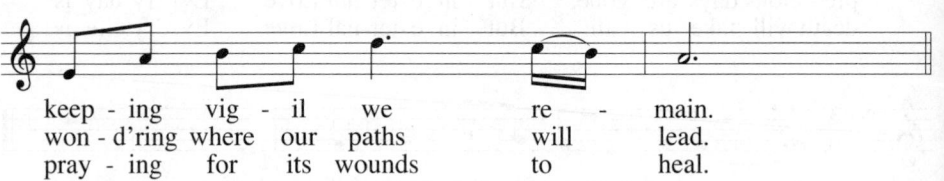

keep - ing vig - il we re - main.
won - d'ring where our paths will lead.
pray - ing for its wounds to heal.

Refrain

More than watch - ers for the morn - ing, we a -

wait with wake - ful care, hop - ing through the night of weep - ing our

God will lift us from de - spair.

Text: Mary Louise Bringle, b.1953, © 2002, GIA Publications, Inc.
Tune: Lori True, b.1961, © 2003, GIA Publications, Inc.

## Why Stand So Far Away 671

1. Why stand so far a - way, my God? Why
2. Why do you hide when, full of lies, they
3. The weak are crushed and fall to earth; the
4. In a - ges past you heard the voice of
5. A - rise, O God, and lift your hand; bring

hide in times of need? The proud, un - bri - dled,
mur - der and be - tray? They wait to pounce up -
wick - ed strut and preen. Why in these cruel, cha -
those the proud op - press. Re - mem - ber those who
jus - tice to the poor. Come, help us stop the

chase the poor, and curse you in their greed.
on the weak as li - ons stalk their prey.
ot - ic times can - not your face be seen?
suf - fer now, who cry in deep dis - tress.
flow of blood! Let ter - ror reign no more!

Text: Based on Psalm 10, Ruth Duck, b.1947, © 1992, GIA Publications, Inc.
Tune: Michael Mahler, b.1981, © 2003, GIA Publications, Inc.

# 672 By the Waters of Babylon

**Refrain**

By the wa-ters of Bab-y-lon, we shall cry,

we shall rest, and re-mem-ber Zi-on.

**Verses**

1. We long to play our harps
2. ⁷ May we not for - get
3. ⁷ Lord, we need your strength!

and raise a song to you.
be-lov-ed Je-ru - sa - lem!
⁷ Fill us with your spir - it!

But how can we sing our song in a
Lord, help us to sing our song in this
In - spire us to bring your song to this

**D.C.**

for-eign land?
for-eign land!
for-eign land!

Text: Psalm 137; Paul A. Tate, b.1968
Tune: Paul A. Tate, b.1968
© 1996, World Library Publications

# God Weeps with Us Who Weep and Mourn  673

1. God weeps with us who weep and mourn, God's
2. Through tears and sor - row, God, we share A
3. And yet, be - cause, like us, you weep, We

tears flow down with ours, And God's own heart is
sense of your vast grief; The weight of bear - ing
trust you will re - ceive And in your ten - der

bruised and worn From all the heav - y hours Of
ev - 'ry prayer For heal - ing and re - lief, The
heart will keep The ones for whom we grieve, While

watch - ing while the soul's bright fire Burned
bur - den of our ques - tions why, The
with your tears our hearts will taste The

low - er day by day, And pulse and breath and
doubts that they en - gage, And as our friends and
deep, dear core of things From which both life and

love's de - sire Dimmed down to ash and clay.
loved ones die, Our hope - less - ness and rage.
death are graced By love's re - new - ing springs.

Text: Thomas H. Troeger, b.1945, © 2002, Oxford University Press
Tune: MOSHIER, CMD; Sally Ann Morris, b.1952, © 1998, GIA Publications, Inc.

## 674  May the Peace of Christ / Ki Ri Su To No

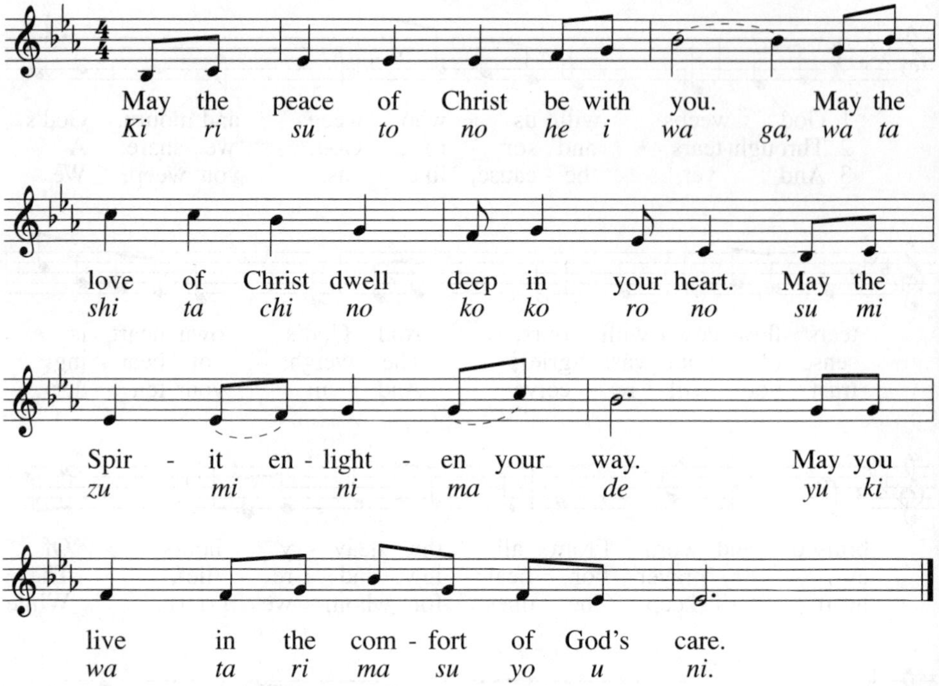

May    the    peace    of    Christ    be with    you.         May the
*Ki     ri      su      to     no     he  i     wa          ga,   wa  ta*

love    of    Christ  dwell    deep    in    your heart.    May    the
*shi     ta    chi     no      ko    ko    ro    no      su    mi*

Spir  -  it   en - light  -  en   your    way.            May  you
*zu      mi         ni      ma      de            yu   ki*

live    in    the    com - fort    of    God's    care.
*wa      ta    ri     ma    su      yo    u       ni.*

Text: Japanese blessing; additional text by Lori True, b.1961, © 2008, GIA Publications, Inc.
Tune: Japanese folk melody

## 675  May God Bless and Keep You

*Priest:* May God bless and    keep  you,    may God smile on    you.
*All:* May God bless and    keep  us,    may God smile on    us.

May God show  you    kind - ness,    fill    you with  peace.
May God show  us     kind - ness,    fill    us with  peace.

And may  God    bless you,    Fa - ther, Son, and    Spir - it;
And may  God    bless us,     Fa - ther, Son, and    Spir - it;

may we al-ways love and serve, filled with God's peace.
may we al-ways love and serve, filled with God's peace.

Text: Numbers 6:24–26; David Haas, b.1957, © 1997, GIA Publications, Inc.
Tune: ADORO TE DEVOTE, Mode V; adapt. by David Haas, b.1957, © 1997, GIA Publications, Inc.

## I Say "Yes," Lord / Digo "Sí," Señor 676

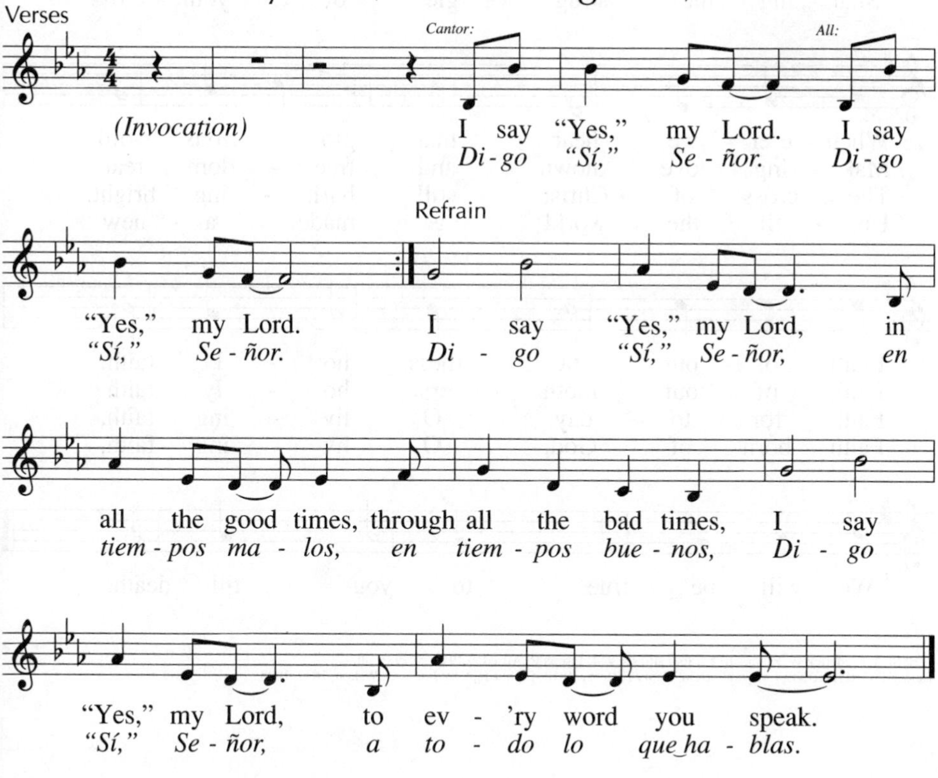

Verses

*(Invocation)*

Cantor:

All:

I say "Yes," my Lord. I say
*Di - go* *"Sí,"* *Se - ñor.* *Di - go*

Refrain

"Yes," my Lord. I say "Yes," my Lord, in
*"Sí,"* *Se - ñor.* *Di - go* *"Sí,"* *Se - ñor,* *en*

all the good times, through all the bad times, I say
*tiem - pos ma - los,* *en* *tiem - pos bue - nos,* *Di - go*

"Yes," my Lord, to ev - 'ry word you speak.
*"Sí,"* *Se - ñor,* *a* *to - do lo que_ha - blas.*

Text: Donna Peña, b.1955
Tune: Donna Peña, b.1955; arr. by Marty Haugen, b.1950
© 1989, GIA Publications, Inc.

# 677 A Living Faith

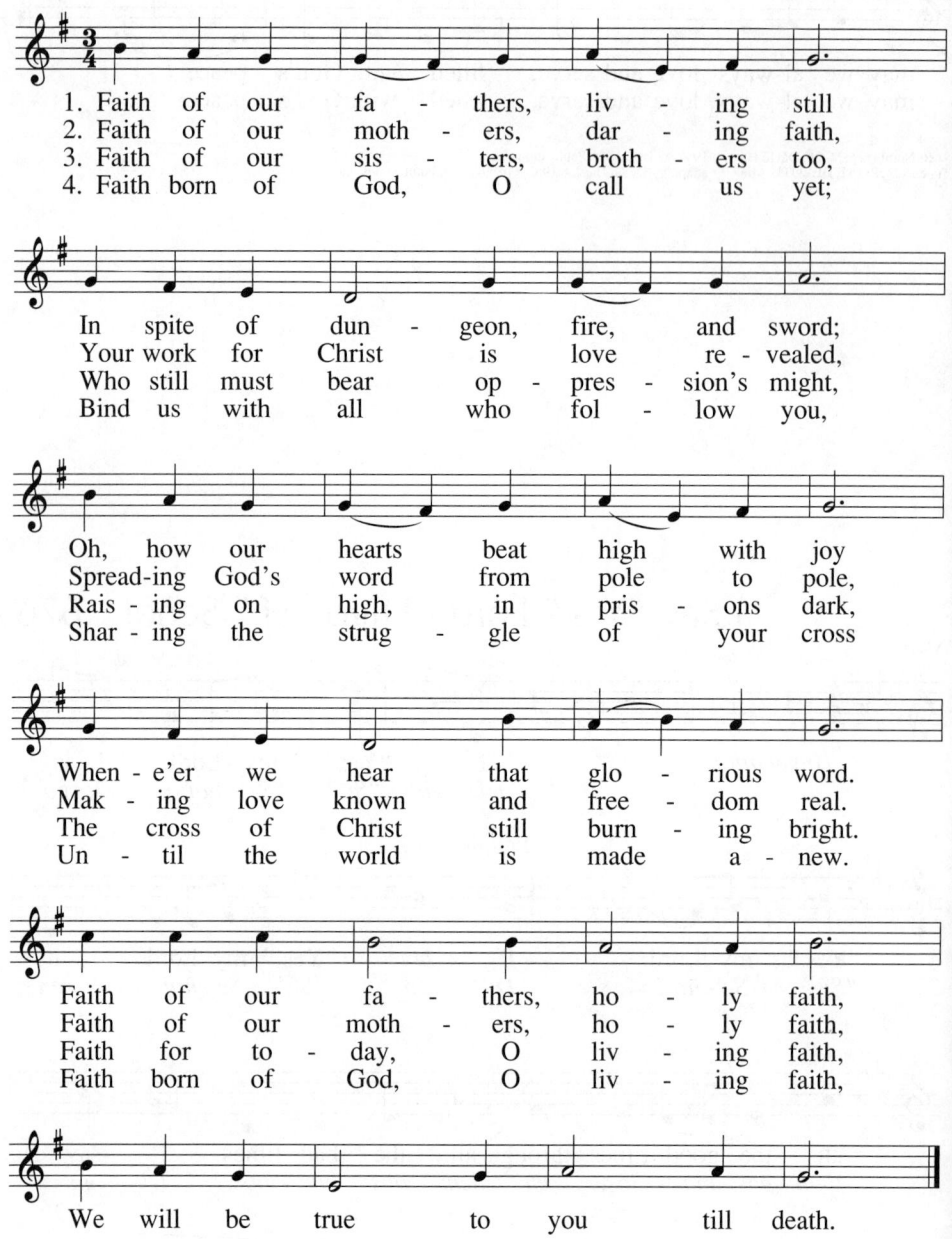

1. Faith of our fa - thers, liv - ing still
2. Faith of our moth - ers, dar - ing faith,
3. Faith of our sis - ters, broth - ers too,
4. Faith born of God, O call us yet;

In spite of dun - geon, fire, and sword;
Your work for Christ is love re - vealed,
Who still must bear op - pres - sion's might,
Bind us with all who fol - low you,

Oh, how our hearts beat high with joy
Spread-ing God's word from pole to pole,
Rais - ing on high, in pris - ons dark,
Shar - ing the strug - gle of your cross

When - e'er we hear that glo - rious word.
Mak - ing love known and free - dom real.
The cross of Christ still burn - ing bright.
Un - til the world is made a - new.

Faith of our fa - thers, ho - ly faith,
Faith of our moth - ers, ho - ly faith,
Faith for to - day, O liv - ing faith,
Faith born of God, O liv - ing faith,

We will be true to you till death.

Text: St. 1, Frederick W. Faber, 1814–1863, alt.; sts. 2–4, Joseph R. Alfred, b.1947, © 1981, alt.
Tune: ST. CATHERINE, LM with refrain; Henry F. Hemy, 1818–1888; adapt. by James G. Walton, 1821–1905

# Dwelling Place 678

**Verses 1, 2, 4**

1., 4. I fall on my knees to the Fa - ther of Je-sus, the
2. May Christ in his love give us strength for our liv-ing, the

Lord who has shown us the glo - ry of God. *(To verse 2)*
strength of the Spir - it the glo - ry of God.

**𝄋 Refrain**

May Christ find a dwell - ing place of faith in our hearts.

May our lives be root - ed in love,

root - ed in love.

**Verse 3**

3. May grace and peace be yours in God our

**D.S.**

Fa - ther, and in the Son.

Text: Ephesians 3:14–17; 1:2; John Foley, SJ, b.1939
Tune: John Foley, SJ, b.1939
© 1976, John B. Foley, SJ, and OCP

# 679 Center of My Life

**Refrain**

O Lord, you are the cen-ter of my life:

I will al-ways praise you, I will al-ways serve you,

I will al-ways keep you in my sight.

**Verses 1–3**

1. Keep me safe, O God, I take ref-uge in you. I
2. I will bless the Lord who gives me coun - sel, who
3. And so my heart re - joic - es, my soul is glad;

say to the Lord, "You are my God. My
e - ven at night di - rects my heart. I
e - ven in safe - ty shall my bod-y rest. For

hap - pi - ness lies in you a - lone; my
keep the Lord ev - er in my sight: since
you will not leave my soul a-mong the dead, nor

**D.C.**

hap - pi - ness lies in you a - lone."
he is at my right hand, I shall stand firm.
let your be - lov - ed know de - cay.

Verse 4

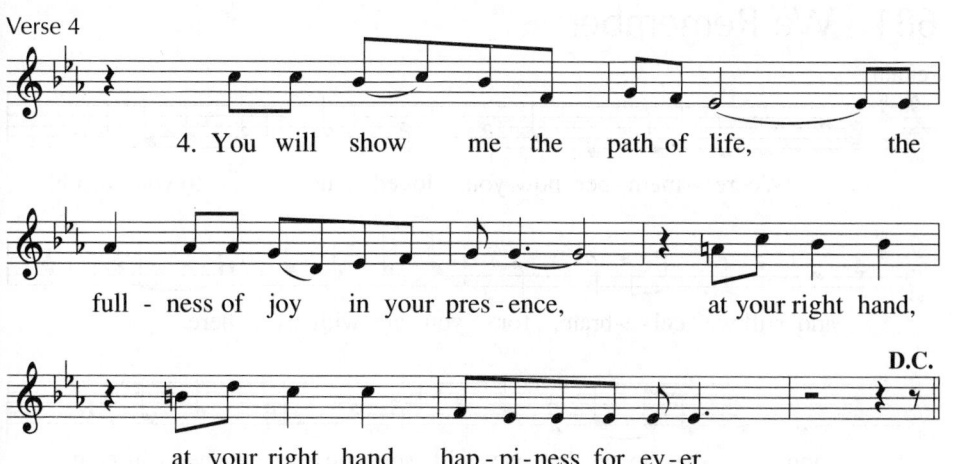

4. You will show me the path of life, the

full - ness of joy in your pres - ence, at your right hand,

**D.C.**

at your right hand hap - pi - ness for ev - er.

Text: Psalm 16; verses trans. © 1963, The Grail, GIA Publications, Inc., agent; refrain, Paul Inwood, b.1947, © 1985, Paul Inwood
Tune: Paul Inwood, b.1947, © 1985, Paul Inwood
Published by OCP.

## We Walk by Faith  680

1., 5. We walk by faith, and not by sight; No
2. We may not touch his hands and side, Nor
3. Help then, O Lord, our un - be - lief; And
4. That, when our life of faith is done, In

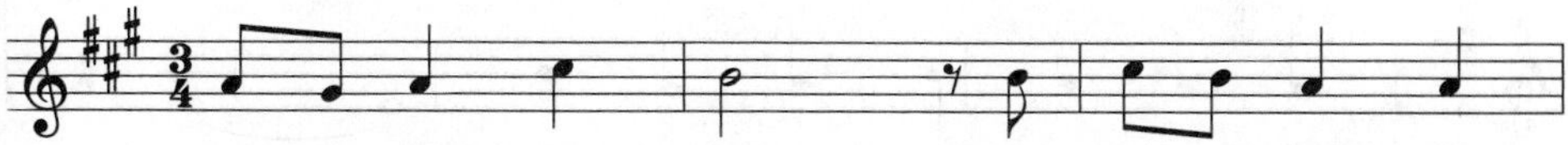

gra - cious words we hear From him who spoke as
fol - low where he trod; But in his prom - ise
may our faith a - bound To call on you when
realms of clear - er light We may be - hold you

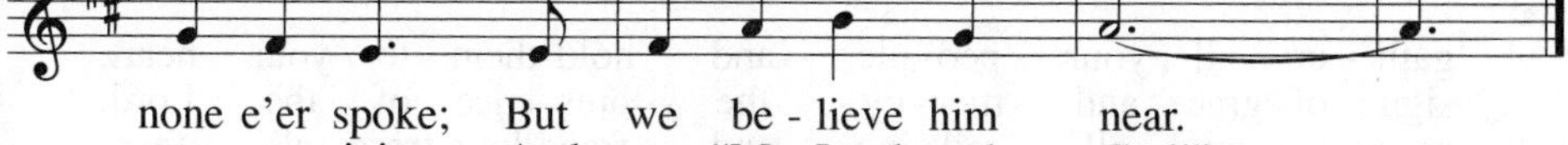

none e'er spoke; But we be - lieve him near.
we re - joice, And cry, "My Lord and God!"
you are near, And seek where you are found:
as you are, With full and end - less sight.

Text: Henry Alford, 1810–1871, alt.
Tune: SHANTI, CM; Marty Haugen, b.1950, © 1984, GIA Publications, Inc.

# 681 We Remember

Refrain

We re-mem-ber how you loved us to your death,

and still we cel-e-brate, for you are with us here;

and we be-lieve that we will see you when you come

in your glo-ry, Lord. We re-mem-ber, we

cel-e-brate, we be-lieve.

Verses

1. Here, a mil - lion wound - ed souls are
2. Now we re - cre - ate your love, we
3. Christ, the Fa - ther's great "A - men" to
4. See the face of Christ re - vealed in

1. yearn-ing just to touch you and be healed;
2. bring the bread and wine to share a meal:
3. all the hopes and dreams of ev - 'ry heart,
4. ev - 'ry per - son stand - ing by your side:

**D.C.**

1. gath - er all your peo-ple, and hold them to your heart.
2. sign of grace and mer-cy, the pres-ence of the Lord.
3. peace be-yond all tell-ing, and free-dom from all fear.
4. gifts to one an - oth-er, and tem-ples of your love.

Text: Marty Haugen, b.1950
Tune: Marty Haugen, b.1950
© 1980, GIA Publications, Inc.

# I Am Sure I Shall See    682

Ostinato Refrain

I am sure I shall see the good-ness of the Lord in the
*Ten - go fe que ve - ré la di - cha del Se - ñor por sen -*

land of the liv - ing. Yes, I shall see the
*de - ros de vi - da. Si, voy a ver la*

good-ness of our God. Hold firm, trust in the Lord.
*di - cha del Se - ñor. Ten fir - me_el co - ra - zón.*

*Last time*

Text: Psalm 27:13–14; Taizé Community
Tune: Taizé Community
© 2007, 2011, Les Presses de Taizé, GIA Publications, Inc., agent

# 683  Be Not Afraid

pow'r of hell and death is at your side,

know that I am with you through it all.

Verse 3

3. Bless - ed are your poor, for the king - dom shall be

theirs. Blest are you that weep and mourn, for

one day you shall laugh. And if wick-ed tongues in -

sult and hate you all be-cause of me,

bless-ed, bless-ed are you!

Text: Isaiah 43:2–3, Luke 6:20ff; Bob Dufford, SJ, b.1943
Tune: Bob Dufford, SJ, b.1943; acc. by Sr. Theophane Hytrek, OSF, 1915–1992
© 1975, 1978, Robert J. Dufford, SJ, and OCP

# 684  Psalm of Hope

Refrain

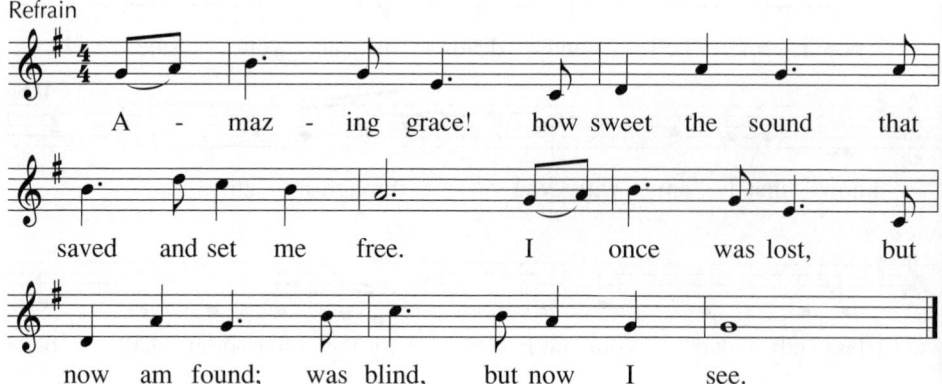

A - maz - ing grace! how sweet the sound that

saved and set me free. I once was lost, but

now am found; was blind, but now I see.

Verses

1. My God, my God, why have you abandoned me?
   Far from my prayers, far from my cries, all day and night I call.
   Yet, our ancestors put their trust in you.
   You rescued them, you saved them from all foes.

2. But here am I, the scorn of all my people.
   They say, "if God is now your friend, let God rescue you."
   From my mother's womb you are my God.
   You held me up, you placed me in your arms.

3. The evildoers circle in around me.
   I am enslaved in chains of death, I can count all my bones.
   O my strength, hasten to my aid.
   Come save my life, come quickly to my help.

4. I shall proclaim your name to the full assembly.
   Those who fear God, exult and praise;
   Glorify the Lord. All generations, all children of the earth:
   Proclaim for ever the wondrous deeds of God.

*1. You did not turn your face from all your people.
   You rescued them from chains of death, you raised them from despair.
   Ev'ry nation on earth from end to end
   Shall turn to you and bow before your throne.

*2. And so my soul shall live for you, O Lord of hope.
   My children shall bring forth your deeds and magnify your name.
   All my descendants shall know your ways, O Lord.
   May they proclaim the justice you have shown.

*Alternate Easter verses used with vs. 4 above.

Text: Refrain, John Newton, 1725–1807; verses, Psalm 22, adapt. by Felix Goebel-Komala, b.1961
Tune: PSALM OF HOPE; Irregular with refrain; Felix Goebel-Komala, b.1961
© 1994, GIA Publications, Inc.

# How Can I Keep from Singing? 685

1. My life flows on in end-less song. A -
2. Through all the tu - mult and the strife I
3. What though my joys and com-fort die? The
4. The peace of Christ makes fresh my heart, A

bove earth's lam - en - ta - tion I hear the clear though
hear that mu - sic ring - ing. It finds an ech - o
Lord my sav - ior liv - eth. What though the dark - ness
foun - tain ev - er spring-ing! All things are mine since

far - off hymn That hails a new cre - a - tion.
in my soul. How can I keep from sing-ing?
gath - er round? Songs in the night he giv - eth.
I am his! How can I keep from sing-ing?

No storm can shake my in-most calm While to that Rock I'm

cling-ing. Since Christ is Lord of heav-en and earth,

How can I keep from sing-ing?

Text: Robert Lowry, 1826–1899, alt.
Tune: HOW CAN I KEEP FROM SINGING, 8 7 8 7 with refrain; Robert Lowry, 1826–1899; harm. by Robert J. Batastini, b.1942, © 1988, GIA
    Publications, Inc.

# 686  Blest Be the Lord

**Refrain**

Blest be the Lord; blest be the Lord, the God of mer-cy, the God who saves. I shall not fear the dark of night, nor the ar-row that flies by day.

**Verse 1**

1. He will re-lease me from the nets of all my foes. He will pro-tect me from their wick-ed hands. Be-neath the shad-ow of his wings I will re-joice to find a dwell-ing place se-cure.

**D.C.**

**Verse 2**

2. I need not shrink be-fore the ter-rors of the night nor stand a-lone be-fore the light of day.

No harm shall come to me, no ar-row strike me down, no e-vil set-tle in my soul.

**D.C.**

Verse 3

3. Al-though a thou-sand strong have fall-en at my side, I'll not be shak-en with the Lord at hand.

His faith-ful love is all the ar-mor that I need to wage my bat-tle with the foe.

**D.C.**

Text: Psalm 91; Dan Schutte, b.1947
Tune: Dan Schutte, b.1947; arr. by Sr. Theophane Hytrek, OSF, 1915–1992
© 1976, 1979, Daniel L. Schutte and OCP

# 687 A Mighty Fortress Is Our God

1. A might-y for-tress is our God,
2. No strength of ours can match his might!
3. Though hordes of dev-ils fill the land
4. God's Word for-ev-er shall a-bide,

A sword and shield vic-to-rious, Who breaks the
We would be lost, re-ject-ed. But now a
All threat-'ning to de-vour us, We trem-ble
No thanks to foes, who fear it; For God, our

cruel op-pres-sor's rod And wins sal-va-tion
cham-pion comes to fight, Whom God a-lone e-
not, un-moved we stand; They can-not o-ver-
Lord, fights by our side With weap-ons of the

glo-rious. The old sa-tan-ic foe
lect-ed. You ask who this may be?
pow'r us. Let this world's ty-rant rage;
Spir-it. Were they to take our house,

Has sworn to work us woe! With craft and
The Lord of hosts is he! Christ Je-sus,
In bat-tle we'll en-gage! His might is
Goods, hon-or, child, or spouse, Though life be

dread-ful might He arms him-self to fight.
might-y Lord, God's on-ly Son, a-dored.
doomed to fail; God's judge-ment must pre-vail!
wrenched a-way, They can-not win the day.

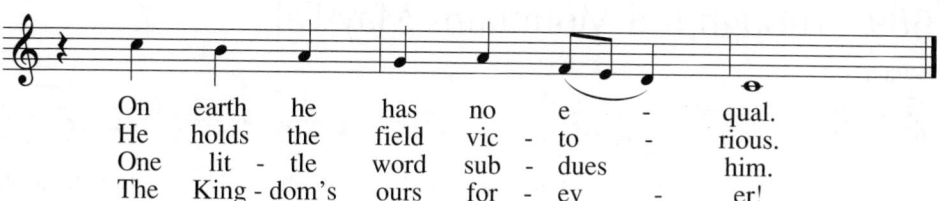

On    earth   he      has    no     e    -   qual.
He    holds   the     field  vic  - to    -   rious.
One   lit  -  tle      word   sub  - dues       him.
The   King - dom's   ours   for  - ev    -   er!

Text: Psalm 46; *Ein' feste Burg ins unser Gott*; Martin Luther, 1483–1546; tr. © 1978, *Lutheran Book of Worship*, alt.
Tune: EIN' FESTE BURG, 8 7 8 7 66 66 7; Martin Luther, 1483–1546; harm by J. S. Bach, 1685–1750

# O God, Our Help in Ages Past    688

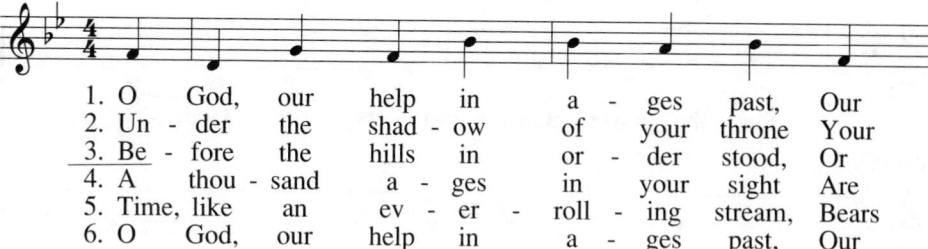

1. O     God,    our      help   in      a   -  ges     past,    Our
2. Un -  der     the      shad - ow      of      your   throne   Your
3. Be -  fore    the      hills  in      or  -  der     stood,   Or
4. A     thou -  sand     a   -  ges     in      your   sight    Are
5. Time, like    an       ev  -  er   -  roll - ing     stream,  Bears
6. O     God,    our      help   in      a   -  ges     past,    Our

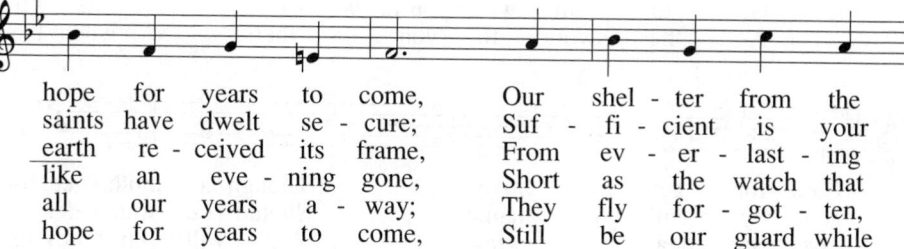

hope    for    years    to     come,    Our    shel - ter   from    the
saints  have   dwelt    se  -  cure;    Suf  - fi  - cient  is      your
earth   re  -  ceived   its    frame,   From   ev  - er  - last - ing
like    an     eve  -   ning   gone,    Short  as     the   watch   that
all     our    years    a   -  way;     They   fly    for - got  -  ten,
hope    for    years    to     come,    Still  be     our   guard  while

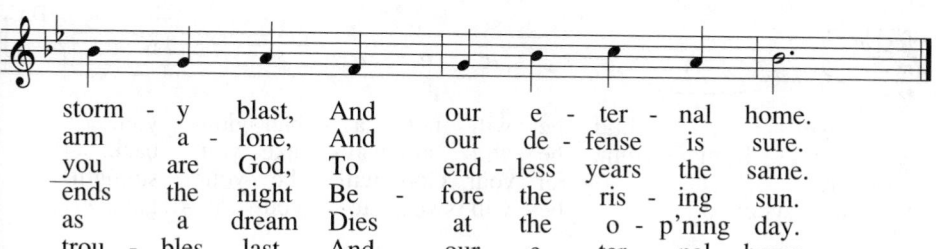

storm - y      blast,   And      our    e  -  ter - nal   home.
arm     a  -   lone,    And      our    de - fense   is    sure.
you     are    God,     To       end - less  years   the   same.
ends    the    night    Be   -   fore   the    ris - ing   sun.
as      a      dream    Dies     at     the    o  - p'ning day.
trou -  bles   last,    And      our    e  -  ter - nal   home.

Text: Psalm 90; Isaac Watts, 1674–1748, alt.
Tune: ST. ANNE, CM; attr. to William Croft, 1678–1727; harm. composite from 18th C. versions

# 689 Though the Mountains May Fall

Text: Isaiah 54:6–10, 49:15, 40:31–32; Dan Schutte, b.1947
Tune: Dan Schutte, b.1947; acc. by Michael Pope, SJ
© 1975, Daniel L. Schutte and OCP

# The Lord Is My Light   690

Verses 1, 3

1. The Lord is my light and my sal - va - tion, the Lord is my
3. Wait on the Lord and be of good cour - age, O wait on the

light and my sal - va - tion, the Lord is my light and
Lord and be of good cour - age, wait on the Lord and

my sal - va - tion; whom shall I fear?
be of good cour - age. He shall strength-en thine heart.

Refrain

Whom shall I fear, whom shall I fear? The Lord is the

strength of my life; whom shall I fear?

Verse 2

2. In the time of trou-ble he shall hide me, O in the time of

trou-ble, he shall hide me, in the time of trou-ble,

D.S.

he shall hide me; whom shall I fear?

Text: Lillian Bouknight
Tune: Lillian Bouknight; arr. by Paul Gainer
© 1981, arr. © 2011, Peermusic III, Ltd. and Savgos Music, Inc.

# 691 On Eagle's Wings

Verse 1

1. You who dwell in the shel-ter of the Lord, who a-
bide in his shad-ow for life, say to the Lord: "My
ref - uge, my rock in whom I trust!"

Refrain

And he will raise you up on ea - gle's wings, bear you on the
breath of dawn, make you to shine like the sun, and

*Last time to Coda* 𝄐   *To verses*

hold you in the palm of his hand.   2. The

Verse 2

snare of the fowl - er will nev - er cap-ture you, and
fam-ine will bring you no fear:   un - der his wings your

**D.S.**

ref - uge, his faith-ful-ness your shield.

Verse 3

3. You need not fear the ter - ror of the night, nor the ar - row that flies by day; though thou - sands fall a - bout you, near you it shall not come.

**D.S.**

Verse 4

4. For to his an - gels he's giv - en a com - mand to guard you in all of your ways; up - on their hands they will bear you up, lest you dash your foot a - gainst a stone.

**D.S.**

Coda

And hold you, hold you in the palm of his hand.

Text: Psalm 91; Michael Joncas, b.1951
Tune: Michael Joncas, b.1951

# 692  The Lord Is Near

Refrain*

O the Lord is near to all who call on him; he is
**May the an - gels lead you in - to par - a - dise; may the

close to all who seek his face, slow to an - ger and full of com-
mar - tyrs come to wel - come you, and take you to the ho - ly

pas - sion and a - bound - ing in mer - ci - ful love.
cit - y, the new and e - ter - nal Je - ru - sa - lem.

Verse 1

1. The Lord is my light and my sal - va - tion, there is

noth - ing at all I fear; the Lord is the

D.C.

ref - uge of my life; of whom should I be a - fraid?

Verse 2

2. One thing I ask of the Lord; there is

on - ly one thing I seek: to dwell in the

D.C.

house of the Lord all the days of my life.

Verse 3

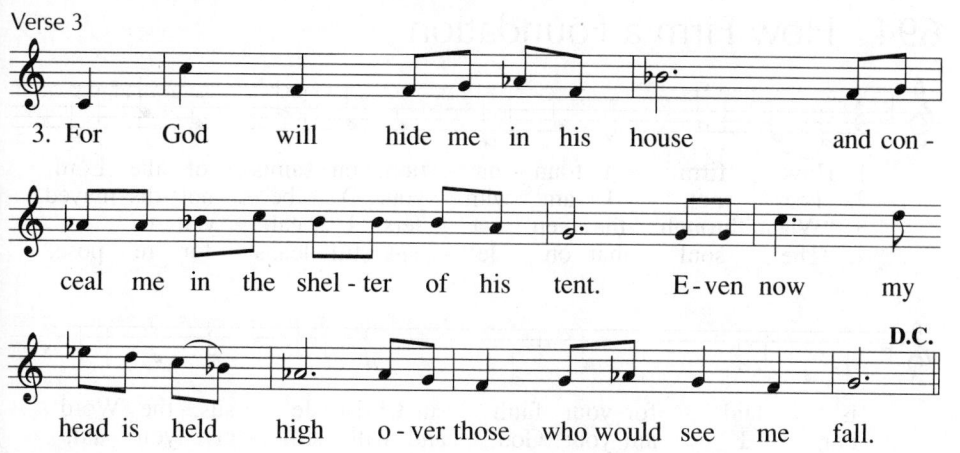

3. For God will hide me in his house and con-

ceal me in the shel-ter of his tent. E-ven now my

**D.C.**

head is held high o-ver those who would see me fall.

*The refrain may be sung in a two-voice canon at a distance of one measure, or a three-voice canon at a distance of one-half measure.*

**Alternate refrain for funerals*

Text: Psalm 27; Michael Joncas, b.1951
Tune: Michael Joncas, b.1951
© 1979, OCP

# All Will Be Well  693

Ostinato Refrain

All will be well, and all will be well, all

*To repeat*

man - ner of things will be well.

*Last time*

well, will be well, will be well.

Text: *The Revelations of Divine Love,* Julian of Norwich; adapt. by Steven C. Warner, b.1954
Tune: Steven C. Warner, b.1954
© 1993, World Library Publications

## 694 How Firm a Foundation

1. How    firm    a   foun - da - tion, you  saints    of   the   Lord,
2. "Fear   not,    I   am    with   you,  O    be    not  dis-mayed,
3. "When  through  the deep  wa - ters  I     call    you   to   go,
4. "The    soul   that on   Je - sus still leans   for   re - pose,

Is     laid    for your  faith   in Christ  Je -  sus,  the Word!
For    I      am your  God,   and will  still   give you  aid;
The    riv -   ers  of   woe   shall not  you    o - ver - flow;
I      will   not, I    will   not de - sert   to   its  foes;

What   more   can  God  say   than to   you    has been  said,
I'll   strength - en  you,  help  you, and cause   you  to  stand,
For    I      will  be   with  you, your trou - bles  to  bless,
That   soul,  though all  hell  should en - deav - or   to  shake,

To     you    who for  ref - uge  to    Je -  sus have fled?
Up -   held   by  my   right - eous, om - nip - o - tent hand.
And    sanc - ti - fy   to    you your deep - est dis - tress.
I'll   nev - er,  no   nev - er,  no   nev - er  for - sake!"

Text: 2 Peter 1:4; "K" in John Rippon's *A Selection of Hymns,* 1787, alt.
Tune: FOUNDATION, 11 11 11 11; Funk's *Compilation of Genuine Church Music,* 1832; harm. by Richard Proulx, 1937–2010, © 1975,
GIA Publications, Inc.

# You Are Near  695

**Refrain**

O Lord, I know you are near, stand-ing al - ways

at my side. You guard me from the foe, and you

lead me in ways ev - er - last-ing.

**Verses**

1. Lord, you have searched my heart, and you
2. Where can I run from your love? If I
3. You know my heart and its ways, you who
4. Mar - vel - ous to me are your works; how pro -

know when I sit and when I stand. Your
climb to the heav - ens you are there; if I
formed me be - fore I was born, in the
found are your thoughts, my Lord. E - ven

hand is up - on me, pro - tect - ing me from death,
fly to the sun - rise or sail be - yond the sea,
se - cret of dark - ness be - fore I saw the sun,
if I could count them, they num - ber as the stars,

*D.C.*

keep - ing me from harm.
still I'd find you there.
in my moth - er's womb.
you would still be there.

Text: Psalm 139; Dan Schutte, b.1947
Tune: Dan Schutte, b.1947; acc. by Sr. Theophane Hytrek, OSF, 1915–1992
© 1971, Daniel L. Schutte. Administered by OCP.

# 696 Ubi Cáritas

Refrain

*U - bi cá - ri - tas   est ve - ra,   est ve - ra:

De - us i - bi est,   De - us i - bi est.

Verses

1. The love of Christ joins us to - geth - er. Let
2. In true com - mu - nion let us gath - er. May
3. May we who gath - er at this ta - ble to
4. For those in need make us your mer - cy, for
5. May we one day be - hold your glo - ry and

1. U - ni - dos co - mo_un so - lo cuer - po, 
2. Reu - ni - dos y a - li - men - ta - dos, ya
3. Que_el pan de vi - da que nos u - ne nos
4. Y pa - ra los ne - ce - si - ta - dos de_a -
5. Con - cé - de - nos ya ver tu glor - ia y_en

us re - joice in him,   and in our love and
all di - vi - sions cease   and in their place be
share the bread of life   be - come a sac - ra -
those op - pressed, your might.   Make us, your Church, a
see you face to face,   re - joic - ing with the

en la co - mu - nión   de - mos - tre - mos
li - bres del ren - cor,   vi - va - mos nues - tra
cam - bie_el co - ra - zón   pa - ra dar al
mor y de bon - dad   se - a - mos la_es - pe -
tu pre - sen - cia_es - tar;   y_u - ni - dos a los

*Where there is true charity, God is present.

D.C.

care    for    all         now    love God    in    re - turn.
Christ the Lord,            our    ris - en Prince of Peace.
ment   of    love,          your   heal - ing touch, O    Christ.
ho  -  ly    sign           of     jus - tice and new    life.
saints of    God            to     sing   e - ter - nal praise.

*nues - tro_a - mor*        *a*      *quien pri - me - ro_a - mó.*
*co  -  mu - nión*          *en*     *Cris - to,    Sal - va - dor.*
*pró - ji - mo*             *a  -  mor   y    sa - na - ción.*
*ran    -    za,*           *jus   -  ti  -  cia   y   paz.*
*san    -    tos,*          *can   -  tar - te   sin   ce - sar.*

Text: Refrain and vss. 1, 2 and 5 based on *Ubi Cáritas*, 9th c.; vss. 3, 4, Bob Hurd, b.1950; Spanish by Pedro Rubalcava, b.1958
Tune: Bob Hurd b.1950; acc. by Craig K. Kingsbury, b.1952
© 1996, 2004, Bob Hurd. Published by OCP.

# Nothing Can Ever    697

Refrain  A

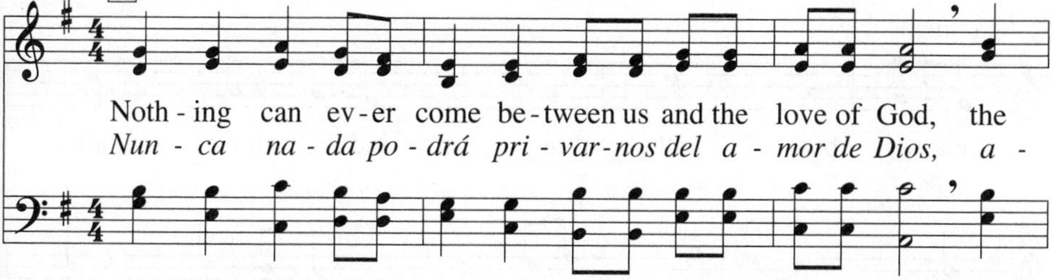

Noth - ing    can    ev - er   come be - tween us and the   love of God,   the
*Nun - ca    na - da po - drá   pri - var - nos del   a - mor de Dios,   a -*

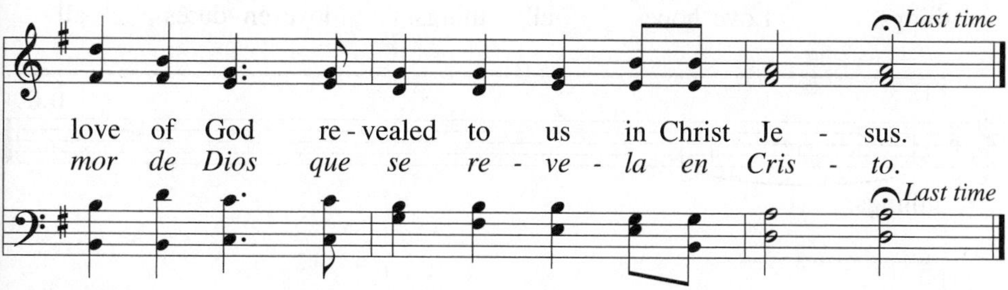

*Last time*

love    of    God    re - vealed   to    us    in Christ  Je  -  sus.
*mor   de   Dios    que   se    re - ve - la   en   Cris  -  to.*

*Last time*

Verses  B

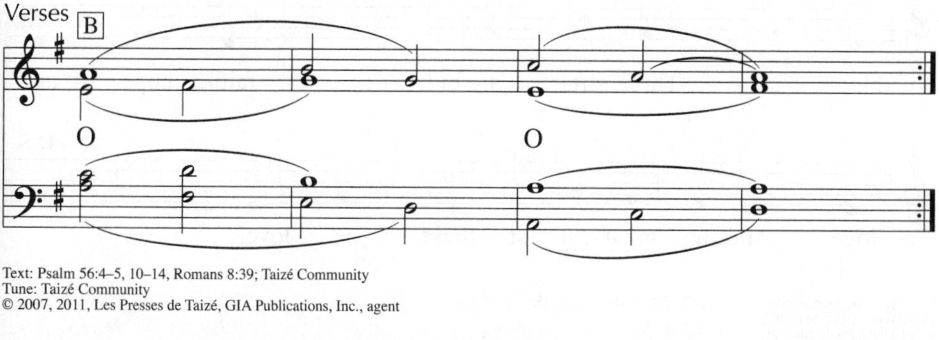

O

O

Text: Psalm 56:4–5, 10–14, Romans 8:39; Taizé Community
Tune: Taizé Community
© 2007, 2011, Les Presses de Taizé, GIA Publications, Inc., agent

# 698 Love Endures All Things

Verses

1. Seek the high-est gift of all, seek the gift be-yond all
2. Love is pa-tient, love is kind, nev-er jeal-ous, nev-er
3. Love does not re-joice in wrong, love re-joic-es in the

meas - ure: Love, the sign of God's de - light;
boast - ful, nev - er seek - ing its own way,
true word; love is God's own self - less song,

love, the heart's most sa - cred treas - ure. *(To verse 2 or refrain)*
nev - er an - gry or re - sent - ful. *(To refrain)*
here re - flect - ed in these vows heard. *(To refrain)*

𝄋 Refrain

Love will bear all things and be - lieve all

things. Love hopes all things, love en-dures all

1., 3.                        **D.C.**

things.

2.

things. Three gifts a - bide: faith, hope and

**D.S.**

love. And the great-est of these is love.

Text: Based on 1 Corinthians 13:1–3; adapt. Marty Haugen, b.1950
Tune: Marty Haugen, b.1950
© 2010, GIA Publications, Inc.

# God Is Love 699

Refrain

God is love, and all who live in love, live in God.

Verse 1

1. God is light, in God there is no dark - ness. Come

D.C.

live in the love of the Lord.

Verse 2

2. Come to the Lord, re - ceive the light, and

D.C.

live in the love of the Lord.

Verse 3

3. We are called to be God's own chil - dren, to

D.C.

live in the love of the Lord.

Verse 4

4. All of you are one, u - nit - ed in Je - sus, to

D.C.

live in the love of the Lord.

Text: 1 John 1:5, 3:2, 4:15, Psalm 33:6, Galatians 3:28; David Haas, b.1957
Tune: David Haas, b.1957
© 1987, GIA Publications, Inc.

# 700  Boundless Love / Tình Chúa Cao Vòi

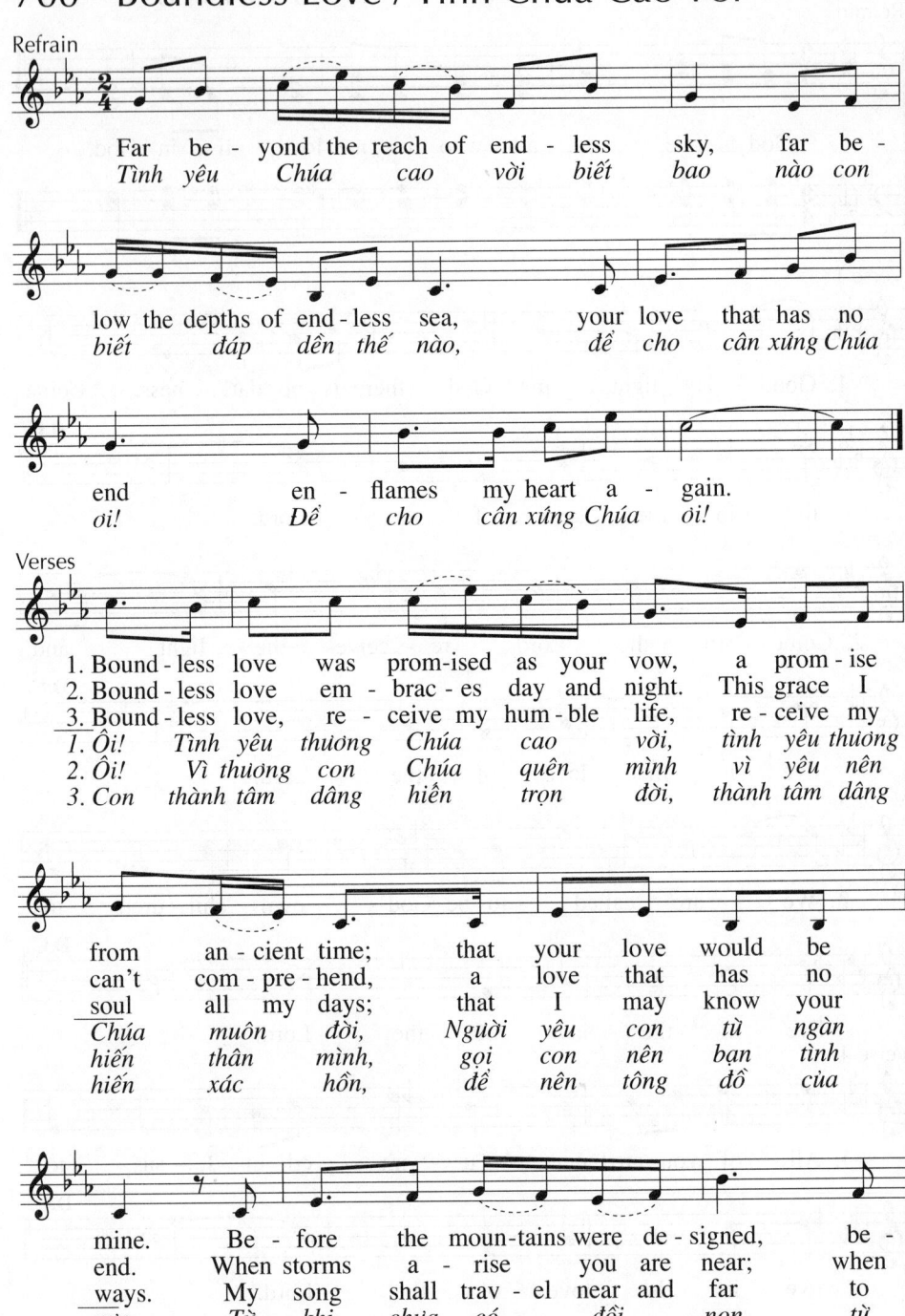

**Refrain**

Far be - yond the reach of end - less sky, far be -
*Tình yêu Chúa cao vòi biết bao nào con*

low the depths of end - less sea, your love that has no
*biết đáp dền thế nào, dể cho cân xứng Chúa*

end en - flames my heart a - gain.
*ơi! Dể cho cân xứng Chúa ơi!*

**Verses**

1. Bound - less love was prom-ised as your vow, a prom - ise
2. Bound - less love em - brac - es day and night. This grace I
3. Bound - less love, re - ceive my hum - ble life, re - ceive my
1. *Ôi! Tình yêu thương Chúa cao vòi, tình yêu thương*
2. *Ôi! Vì thương con Chúa quên mình vì yêu nên*
3. *Con thành tâm dâng hiến trọn dời, thành tâm dâng*

from an - cient time; that your love would be
can't com - pre - hend, a love that has no
soul all my days; that I may know your
*Chúa muôn dời, Người yêu con từ ngàn*
*hiến thân mình, gọi con nên bạn tình*
*hiến xác hồn, dể nên tông dồ của*

mine. Be - fore the moun-tains were de - signed, be -
end. When storms a - rise you are near; when
ways. My song shall trav - el near and far to
*xưa. Từ khi chúa có dồi non, từ*
*Cha. Dù bao sóng gió hiểm nguy, dìu*
*Cha, và nên nhân chứng của Cha. Truyền*

LOVE

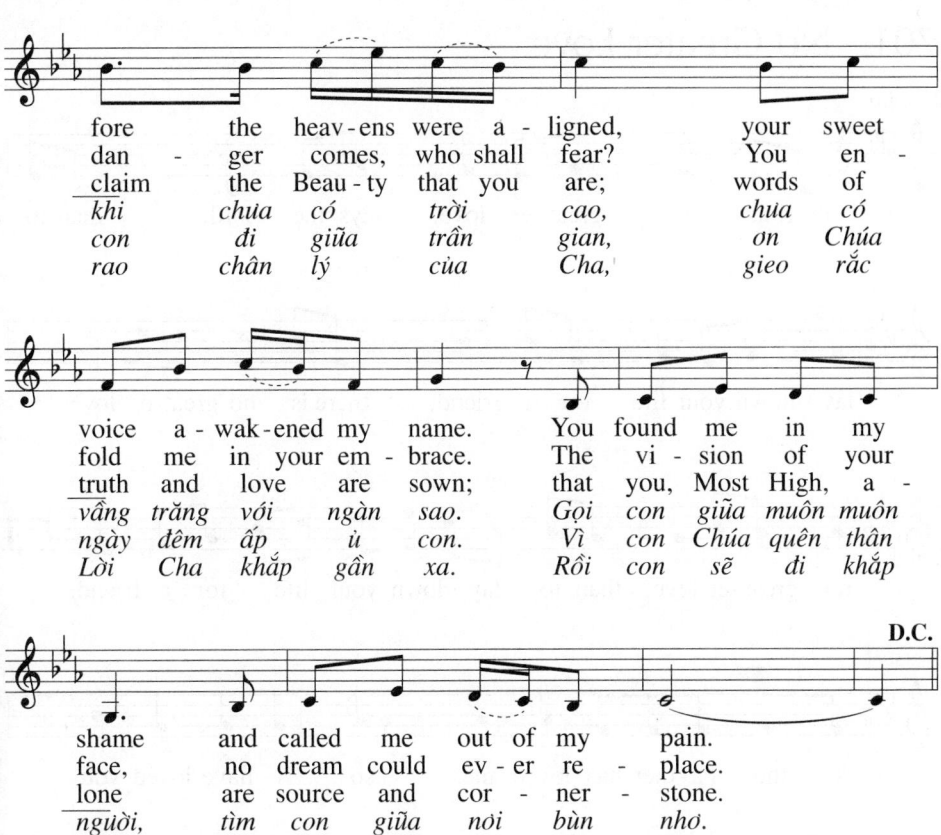

fore    the  heav-ens  were  a - ligned,       your  sweet
dan  -  ger  comes,  who shall  fear?      You  en -
claim   the  Beau-ty  that you  are;     words  of
*khi    chúa  có    trời   cao,     chúa  có*
*con    đi   giữa  trần   gian,    ơn  Chúa*
*rao   chân  lý   của   Cha,     gieo  rắc*

voice  a - wak-ened my  name.   You found me  in  my
fold  me  in your em - brace.   The  vi - sion of  your
truth  and  love  are  sown;   that  you, Most High, a -
*vẵng  trăng với  ngàn  sao.   Gọi  con giữa muôn muôn*
*ngày  đêm  ấp  ủ  con.   Vì  con Chúa quên thân*
*Lời  Cha  khắp  gần  xa.   Rồi  con sẽ  đi  khắp*

**D.C.**

shame   and  called  me  out of my   pain.
face,    no  dream  could  ev - er re - place.
lone    are  source  and  cor - ner - stone.
*người,  tìm  con  giữa  nơi  bùn  nhơ.*
*mình,  đời  con  dám  mơ  gì  hơn.*
*miền  làm  nhân  chứng  cho  tình  yêu.*

Text: Duy Thiên; tr. by Rufino Zaragoza, OFM
Tune: Duy Thiên; keyboard acc. by Kelly Dobbs Mickus, b.1966
© 1987, 2000, Duy Thiên. Published by OCP.

# 701 No Greater Love

Refrain

There is no great-er love, says the Lord, than to

lay down your life for a friend; there is no great-er love,

no great-er love, than to lay down your life for a friend.

Verse 1

1. As the Fa-ther has loved me, so I have loved you.

Live on in my love. You will live in my love if you

keep my com-mands, ev-en as I have kept my Fa-ther's. D.C.

Verse 2

2. All this I tell you that my joy may be yours and

your joy may be com-plete. Love one an-oth-er as

LOVE

I have loved you: This is my com - mand.

Verse 3

3. You are my friends if you keep my com - mands; no long-er slaves but friends to me. All I heard from my Fa - ther, I have made known to you: Now I call you friends.

Verse 4

4. It was not you who chose me, it was I who chose you, chose you to go forth and bear fruit. Your fruit must en - dure, so you will re - ceive all you ask the Fa - ther in my name.

Text: John 15:9–17; Michael Joncas, b.1951
Tune: Michael Joncas, b.1951
© 1988, GIA Publications, Inc.

# 702 Faith, Hope and Love

Refrain

Faith, hope and love, let these en-dure a-mong you; and the great-est of these is love, the great-est of these is love.

Verses

1. If I speak with the voice of angels but do not love,
   I am like a noisy gong, a clanging cymbal.
   I am nothing, I am nothing without love.

2. If I see all that's held in mystery, feed and clothe the poor,
   if my faith should call me on to move a mountain,
   still I'm nothing, I am nothing without love.

3. In the end, when the earth is silent, when all things pass away,
   we shall see the face of God in shining splendor;
   there are three things that will lead us to that day.

Text: 1 Corinthians 13:1–2, 8, 13; Francis Patrick O'Brien, b.1958
Tune: Francis Patrick O'Brien, b.1958
© 2001, GIA Publications, Inc.

# 703 Lord of All Nations, Grant Me Grace

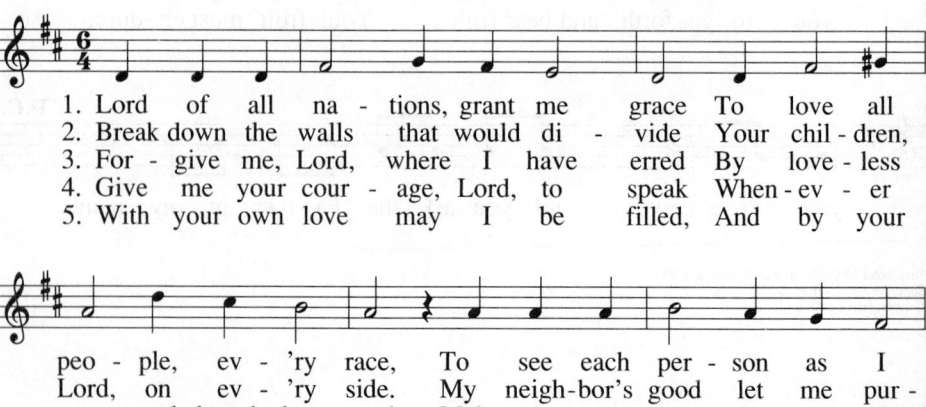

1. Lord of all na - tions, grant me grace To love all peo - ple, ev - 'ry race, To see each per - son as I
2. Break down the walls that would di - vide Your chil - dren, Lord, on ev - 'ry side. My neigh-bor's good let me pur -
3. For - give me, Lord, where I have erred By love - less act and thought-less word. Make me to see the wrong I
4. Give me your cour - age, Lord, to speak When-ev - er strong op - press the weak. Should I my - self as vic - tim
5. With your own love may I be filled, And by your Ho - ly Spir - it willed, That all whose lives are touched by

ought,   My   kin - dred,  whom   your  love  has     bought.
sue;    Let  Chris - tian   love    bind  warm and      true.
do     Will  cru - ci - fy    my  Lord  a   -  new.
live,   Re - mem - b'ring you,    may   I  for   -  give.
mine   May know   your heal - ing  touch di  -  vine.

Text: Philippians 2:1–18; Olive W. Spannaus, b.1916, © 1969, Concordia Publishing House
Tune: BEATUS VIR, LM; Slovak; harm. by Richard Hillert, 1923–2010, © 1969, Concordia Publishing House

## My Song Will Be for You Forever   704

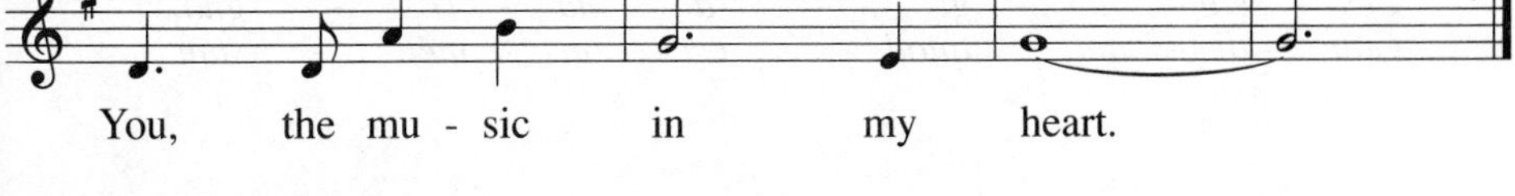

1. My   song   will   be   for   you   for - ev - er,
2.   You   have clothed me   in   your  prom - ise,
3.   I   am  here   to   be   your  ser - vant,
4.   With  your voice, you  sing   with - in   me,
5.   I   will  pledge my  love   for - ev - er,

you,   the  mu - sic   in   my  heart.   For   your  love   is
you,   my  love,  my   light,  my  friend.  You,   the  way   and
you   a - noint me   with  your  love.   You   will  hold   me
you,   the  one  who  knows me   well.   You,   my  joy,   my
I   will  call  your  name  out   loud.   I   will  reach   my

all   a - round me,   and   your good - ness   al - ways   here.
path  be - fore me,   you   will  lead  and   guide  me   home.
in   my  long - ing,   all   my  hope   in   your  em - brace.
life  and bless - ing,  when  you  call,  you   know  my   name.
hand  out  to  you,   and   I  know you'll  reach  for   me.

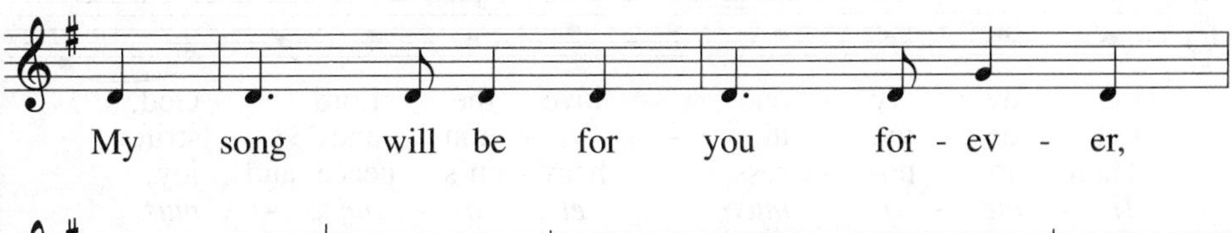

My   song   will   be   for   you   for - ev - er,

You,   the  mu - sic   in   my  heart.

Text: David Haas, b.1957
Tune: David Haas, b.1957
© 1995, GIA Publications, Inc.

## 705 Where True Love and Charity Are Found / Ubi Cáritas

Where true love and char-i-ty are found, God is al-ways there.
*U - bi cá - ri - tas et a - mor De-us i - bi est.*

1. Since the love of Christ has brought us
2. There-fore when we gath - er as one
3. Bring us with your saints to be - hold
*1. Con - gre - gá - vit nos in u - num*
*2. Si - mul er - go cum in u - num*
*3. Si - mul quo - que cum be - á - tis*

all to - geth - er, Let us all re -
in Christ Je - sus, Let our love en -
your great beau - ty, There to see you,
*Chri - sti a - mor. Ex - sul - té - mus*
*con - gre - gá - mur: Ne nos men - te*
*vi - de - á - mus. Glo - ri - án - ter*

joice and be glad, now and al - ways.
fold each race, creed, ev - 'ry per - son.
Christ our God, throned in great glo - ry;
*et in i - pso iu - cun - dé - mur.*
*di - vi - dá - mur, ca - ve - á - mus.*
*vul - tum tu - um, Chri - ste De - us:*

Let ev - 'ry - one love the Lord God,
Let en - vy, di - vi - sion and strife
There to pos - sess heav - en's peace and joy,
*Ti - me - á - mus et a - mé - mus*
*Ces - sent iúr - gi - a ma - lí - gna,*
*Gáu - di - um, quod est im - mén - sum*

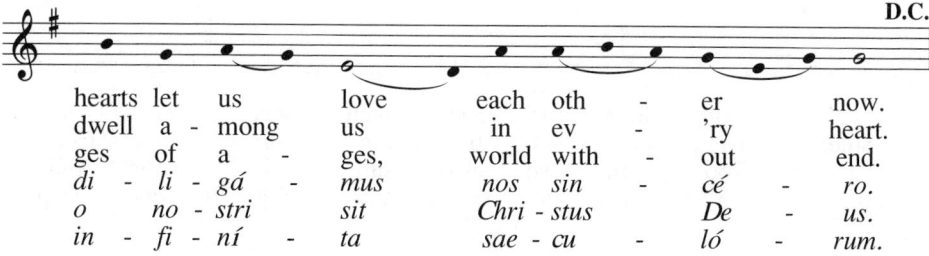

Text: Latin, 9th C.; tr. by Richard Proulx, 1937–2010, © 1975, 1986, GIA Publications, Inc.
Tune: UBI CÁRITAS, 12 12 12 12 with refrain; Mode VI; acc. by Richard Proulx, 1937–2010, © 1986, GIA Publications, Inc.

## Where Charity and Love Prevail 706

Text: *Ubi cáritas;* tr. by Omer Westendorf, 1916–1998
Tune: CHRISTIAN LOVE, CM; Paul Benoit, OSB, 1893–1979
© 1960, World Library Publications

## 707 The Call Is Clear and Simple

1. The call is clear and sim - ple: "Love God and hu - man -
2. God, help us sort our mo - tives, That lov - ing may be
3. God, teach us strength and wis - dom When false love takes the
4. O wise and ho - ly Lov - er, Teach us as sea - sons

kind," But love de - mands much wis - dom And
whole. High aims or base am - bi - tion? Com -
lead. Too well we learn sub - mis - sion And
turn To know our - selves and oth - ers— Deep,

clar - i - ty of mind. "Be wi - ly as a
pas - sion or con - trol? Then help us clear our
si - lence our own need. When oth - ers would mis -
hon - est love to learn. So may we nur - ture

ser - pent, Though gen - tle as a dove," For
sched - ules Of ev - 'ry fran - tic task That
use us Or lure us t'ward the wrong, God,
liv - ing In all we say and do, In

man - y are the dan - gers Up - on the path of love.
leads a - way from do - ing The one thing that you ask.
tem - per love with cour - age To keep our bound - 'ries strong.
strong and gen - tle giv - ing To hu - man - kind and you.

Text: Ruth Duck, b.1947, © 1992, GIA Publications, Inc.
Tune: PASSION CHORALE, 7 6 7 6 D; Hans Leo Hassler, 1564–1612; harm. by J. S. Bach, 1685–1750

*Alternate tune:* AURELIA

# Set Your Heart on the Higher Gifts   708

Refrain

Set your heart on the high-er gifts, on the things that come from your Mak - er in heav - en. These three gifts are all that re-main: faith, hope and love, and the great - est is love.

Verses

1. If I speak with the tongues of the liv - ing,
2. And if I un - der - stand ev - 'ry mys - t'ry,
3. And if I should re - nounce all my rich - es,

and of an - gels, but speak with-out love, I am
hav - ing wis - dom, but think with-out love, had I
feed the hun - gry, give o - ver my life; with - out

D.C.

on - ly brass with-out song, an emp - ty noise on the wind.
faith to scat - ter the hills, I am noth - ing at all.
love my prof - it is loss, my car - ing finds no re - ward.

Text: 1 Corinthians 12:31–13:13; Steven C. Warner, b.1954
Tune: Steven C. Warner, b.1954
© 1992, 1994, World Library Publications

## 709 Not for Tongues of Heaven's Angels

1. Not for tongues of heav - en's an - gels,
2. Love is hum - ble, love is gen - tle,
3. Nev - er jeal - ous, nev - er self - ish,
4. In the day this world is fad - ing

Not for wis - dom to dis - cern,
Love is ten - der, true, and kind;
Love will not re - joice in wrong;
Faith and hope will play their part;

Not for faith that mas - ters moun - tains,
Love is gra - cious, ev - er pa - tient,
Nev - er boast - ful nor re - sent - ful,
But when Christ is seen in glo - ry

For this bet - ter gift we yearn:
Gen - er - ous of heart and mind:
Love be - lieves and suf - fers long:
Love shall reign in ev - 'ry heart:

May love be ours, Lord; may love be ours.

May love be ours, O Lord.

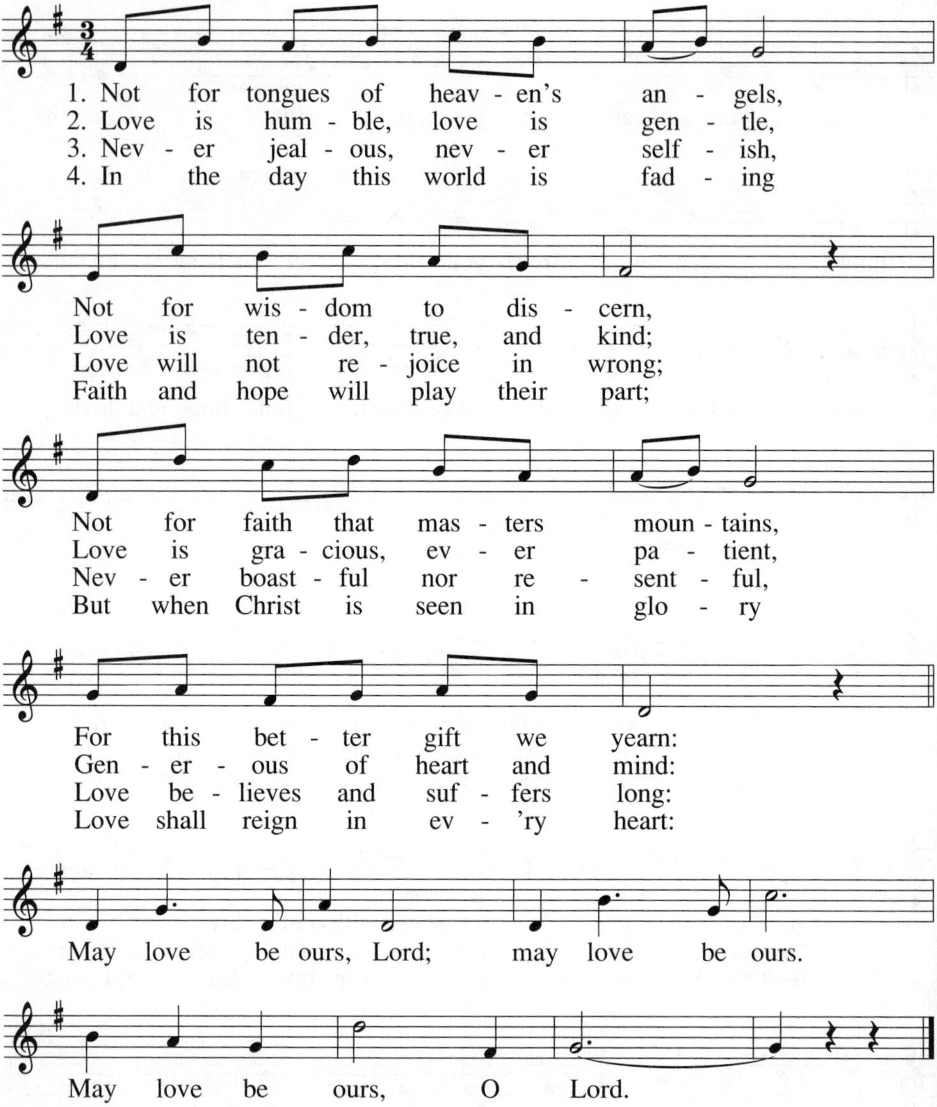

Text: 1 Corinthians 13:1–13; Timothy Dudley-Smith, b.1926, © 1985, Hope Publishing Company
Tune: COMFORT, 8 7 8 7 with refrain; Michael Joncas, b.1951, © 1988, GIA Publications, Inc.

## 710 The Clouds' Veil

Refrain

E - ven though the rain hides the stars, e - ven though the

mist swirls the hills, e - ven when the dark clouds

veil the sky, God is by my side. E-ven when the

sun shall fall in sleep, e - ven when at dawn the sky shall

weep, e-ven in the night when storms shall rise,

God is by my side. God is by my side.

Verses

1. Bright the stars at night that
2. Deep the feast of life where
3. Blest are they who sing the

mir - ror heav-en's way to you. Bright the stars in
saints shall gath - er in deep peace. Deep in heav - en's
fel - low-ship of saints in light. Blest is heav - en's

D.C.

light where dwell the saints in love and truth.
light where sor - rows pass be - yond death's sleep.
King. All saints a - dore the Lord, Most High.

Text: Liam Lawton, b.1959
Tune: Liam Lawton, b.1959; arr. by John McCann, b.1961
© 1997, GIA Publications, Inc.

# 711 Rest Now in Me

**Verses**

*Cantor or choir:*

1. Don't be a - fraid,    for I am with you:
2. You are my sheep,    the flock that I love:
3. Peace is my gift,    of - fered to you:
4. I am your God,    the Lamb who was slain:

*All:*

rest now in me,    rest now in me.

*Cantor or choir:*

All that you need,    I will pro - vide:
Trust and be - lieve,    I call you by name:
I bring you peace    the world can - not give:
I am the Way,    the Truth, and the Life:

*All:*

rest now in me,    rest now in me.

*Cantor or choir:*

Oh, let all who have ears hear now the mys-ter-ies of the king - dom!

**Refrain**

Come to me, all you who la - bor and I will give you rest! Take my yoke up - on you and learn from me for I am meek and hum - ble of

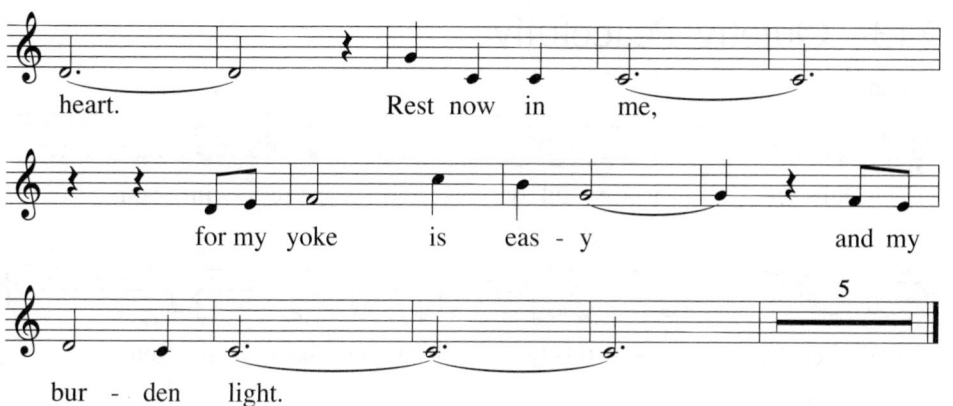

heart.　　　　　　Rest now in　me,

for my yoke　is　eas - y　　　　and my

bur - den　light.

Text: Based on Matthew 11:25–30; Paul A. Tate, b.1968
Tune: Paul A. Tate, b.1968
© 2005, GIA Publications, Inc.

## The King of Love My Shepherd Is　712

1. The　King　of　love　my　shep - herd　is,　Whose　good-ness
2. Where　streams　of　liv - ing　wa - ter　flow,　My　ran-somed
3. Con - fused　and　fool - ish　oft　I strayed,　But　yet　in
4. In　death's　dark　vale　I　fear　no　ill　With　you, dear
5. You　spread　a　ta - ble　in　my sight,　Your　sav - ing
6. And　so,　through all　the length　of　days　Your　good-ness

fails　me　nev　-　er;　I　noth - ing　lack　if
soul　he's　lead　-　ing,　And, where　the　ver - dant
love　he　sought　me,　And　on　his　shoul - der
Lord,　be - side　me,　Your　rod　and　staff　my
grace　be - stow　-　ing;　And,　oh,　what trans - port
fails　me　nev　-　er;　Good　Shep - herd, may　I

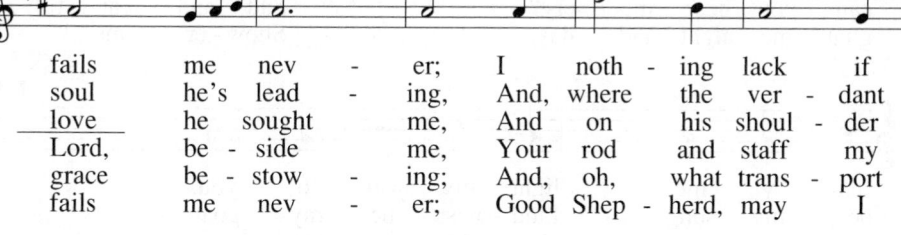

I　am　his　And　he　is　mine　for - ev - er.
pas - tures grow,　With　food　ce - les - tial　feed - ing.
gent - ly　laid,　And　home,　re - joic - ing, brought　me.
com - fort　still,　Your　cross　be - fore　to　guide　me.
of　de - light　From　your　pure chal - ice　flow - ing!
sing　your praise　With - in　your house　for - ev - er.

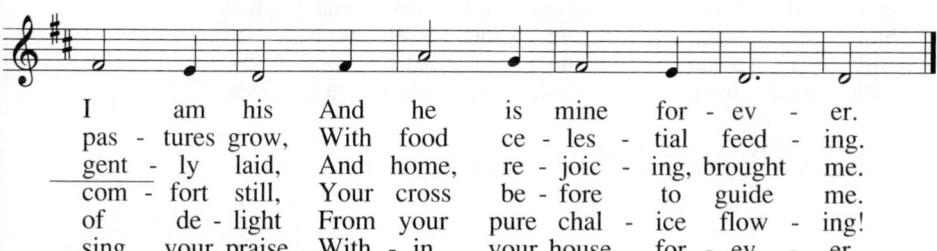

Text: Psalm 23; Henry W. Baker, 1821–1877, alt.
Tune: ST. COLUMBA, 8 7 8 7; Gaelic; harm. by A. Gregory Murray, OSB, 1905–1992, © Downside Abbey

# 713 Quietly, Peacefully

**Refrain**

Qui - et-ly, peace - ful-ly let me rest in you.

Qui - et-ly, peace - ful-ly lead me back to you.

**Verses**

1. In my weak - ness I have strayed,
2. Breathe your law deep in me,
3. Save me from my self - ish ways,
4. Lov - ing wis - dom, you a - lone
5. Hap - py is the heart that's free,
6. In the night I call to you;
7. Heal - ing grace, take my pain,

drift - ing far from you. In your good - ness
plant it in my soul. Let your jus - tice
keep me from my pride. By your grace,
know all I can be. You, the hope my
choos - ing life with you. Break the chains that
can you hear me cry? Sad and fear - ful,
guard me night and day. Show - er me

**D.C.**

stead - y me, light my path to you.
be my song, kind - ness be my goal.
bring me home, safe - ly by your side.
spir - it seeks, come and set me free.
bind my soul, let me walk with you.
still I plead: do not pass me by.
with your love, wash my tears a - way.

Text: Lori True, b.1961, © 2007, GIA Publications, Inc.
Tune: Antonin Dvořák, 1841–1904; adapt. by Lori True, b.1961, © 2007, GIA Publications, Inc.

# In the Arms of God  714

**Refrain**

Come and rest in the arms of God, leave your wor-ry and fear; make your home in the heart of God, God will dry ev-'ry tear. For the bur-den you car-ry will fade with-in God's care, come and rest in the arms of God.

**Verses**

1. Gen - tle is God's way and hum - ble is God's heart. God's
2. Do not be a - fraid; God heals the bro - ken heart. Through
3. You are not a - lone, for God is al - ways near. Come,

1. love will light the way that leads to peace.
2. grief and dis - be - lief God still re - mains.
3. place your doubt and fear with - in God's care.

1. Sure - ly you shall see God's good - ness and God's grace:
2. God and God a - lone will be your soul's true rest:
3. God will give you rest and soothe your wea - ry soul:

**D.C.**

1. Rest now in God's em - brace.
2. Fall in the arms of God.
3. Dwell in the heart of God.

Text: Tony E. Alonso, b.1980
Tune: Tony E. Alonso, b.1980
© 2009, GIA Publications, Inc.

# 715 God Will Wipe the Tears

Refrain

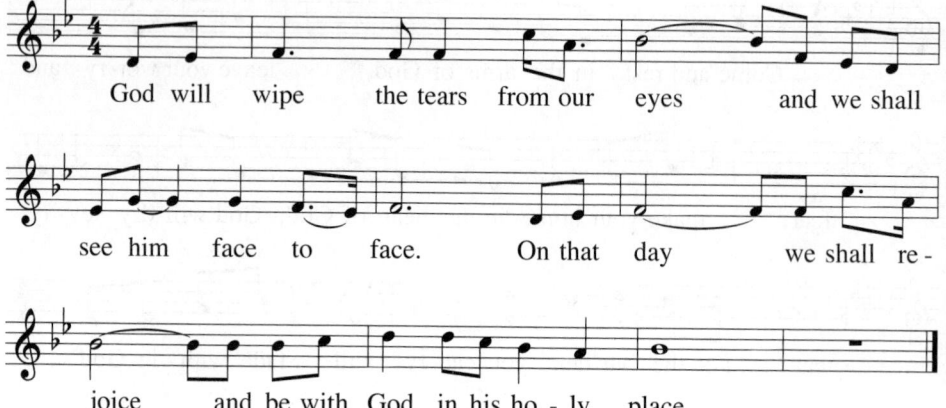

God will wipe the tears from our eyes and we shall

see him face to face. On that day we shall re-

joice and be with God in his ho - ly place.

Verses

1. God will turn our mourning to dancing. God will turn our sorrow to joy.
   God brings light into the darkness. Let us sing praise forevermore.

2. God has not abandoned us. God knows us each by name.
   Our loving shepherd will lead us home for we are God's own.

3. No hurricane or storm, no earthquake or flood can keep us from the love of God!
   No powers that be and not even death can keep us from the love of God!

Text: Stephen Pishner
Tune: Stephen Pishner
© 2006, GIA Publications, Inc.

# 716 In Every Age

Verse 1

1. Long before the mountains came to be and the land and sea and stars of the night,
   through the endless seasons of all time, you have always been, you will always be.

Refrain

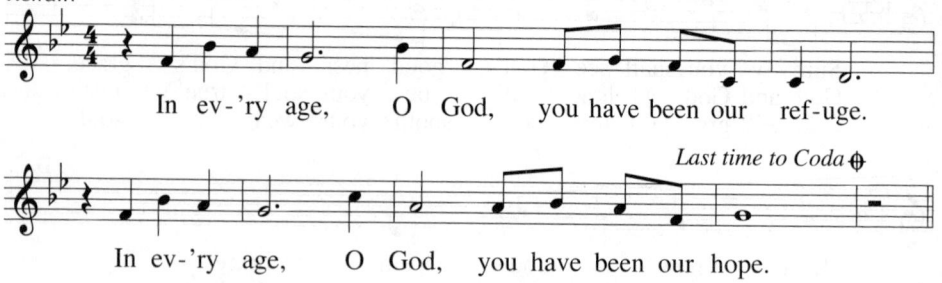

In ev-'ry age, O God, you have been our ref-uge.

*Last time to Coda* ⊕

In ev-'ry age, O God, you have been our hope.

Verses 2, 3

2. Destiny is cast, and at your silent word we return to dust and scatter to the wind.
   A thousand years are like a single moment gone,
   as the light that fades at the end of day.

3. Teach us to make use of the time we have. Teach us to be patient even as we wait.
   Teach us to embrace our ev'ry joy and pain,
   to sleep peacefully, and to rise up strong.

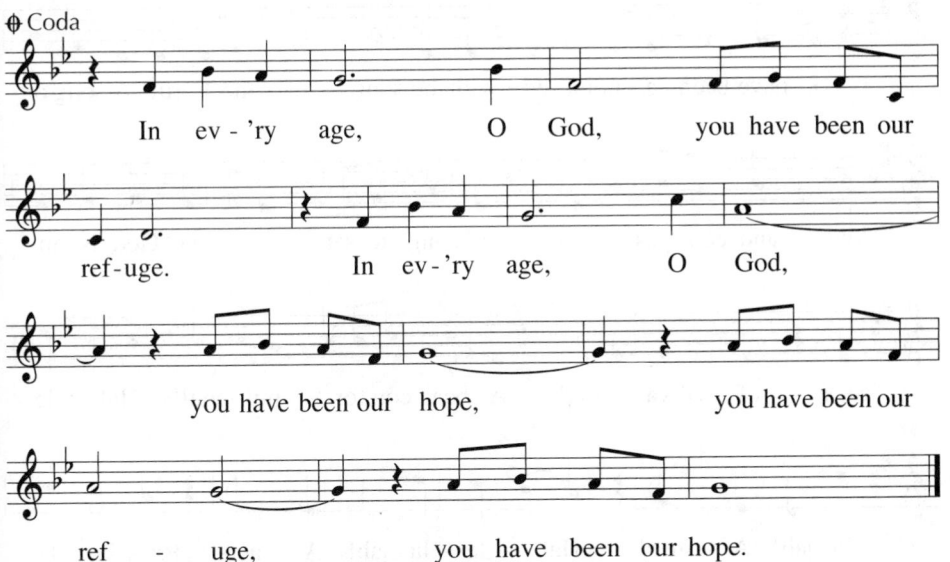

Coda

In ev - 'ry age, O God, you have been our

ref - uge. In ev - 'ry age, O God,

you have been our hope, you have been our

ref - uge, you have been our hope.

Text: Based on Psalm 90:1–4, 12, Janèt Sullivan Whitaker, b.1958
Tune: Janèt Sullivan Whitaker, b.1958
© 1998, 2000, Janèt Sullivan Whitaker. Published by OCP.

## Shelter Me, O God    717

Refrain

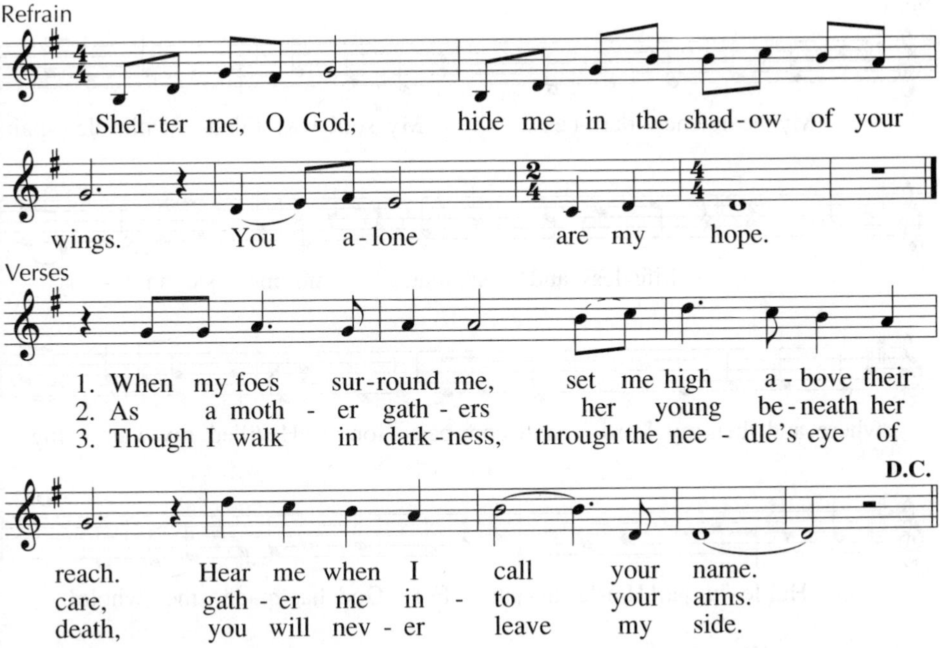

Shel - ter me, O God; hide me in the shad - ow of your

wings. You a - lone are my hope.

Verses

1. When my foes      sur-round me,      set me high      a - bove their
2. As      a moth - er gath - ers      her young      be - neath her
3. Though I walk      in dark - ness,      through the nee - dle's eye of

D.C.

reach.      Hear me when I      call      your name.
care,      gath - er me in - to      your arms.
death,      you will nev - er      leave      my side.

Text: Psalm 16:1, 61:5, Luke 13:34; Bob Hurd, b.1950, © 1984, Bob Hurd
Tune: Bob Hurd, b.1950, © 1984, Bob Hurd; harm. by Craig S. Kingsbury, b.1952, © 1984, OCP
Published by OCP.

# 718  I Have Been Anointed

Refrain

I have been a-noint-ed with the song of the Lord! A song of

love and com-pas-sion, a song to set me free! God is my

rock of sal-va-tion! A bea-con for my soul! Hal-le-

lu-jah! A-men! Hal-le-lu-jah! A-men! Praise to the

1. *Last time*  |  2. *To verse*

rock and the well-spring, cre-a-tor of my soul! Oh, soul!

Verse

My heart knew dark-ness, My soul was filled with de-spair,

Life-less and si-lent, no mu-sic an-y-

where, and then my Lord and com-pan-ion, He filled my wait-ing

D.C.

soul: Hal-le-lu-jah! Hal-le-lu-jah! For God has made me whole!

Text: Steven C. Warner, b.1954
Tune: Steven C. Warner, b.1954; arr. by Peter M. Kolar, b.1973
© 1996, 1999, World Library Publications

# Don't Be Afraid 719

**Ostinato Refrain**

Don't be a - fraid. My love is strong - er,

my love is strong - er than your fear.

Don't be a - fraid. My love is strong - er and

I have prom-ised, prom-ised to be al - ways near.

Text: John L. Bell, b.1949
Tune: John L. Bell, b.1949

# 720 Come to Me

Ostinato Refrain

Come to me, come to me, weak and heav-y lad-en; lad-en;

To repeat | Last time

trust in me, lean on me. I will give you rest. give you rest.

Text: Matthew 11:28; John L. Bell, b.1949
Tune: John L. Bell, b.1949
© 2008, Iona Community, GIA Publications, Inc., agent

# 721 You Are Mine / Contigo Estoy

Verses

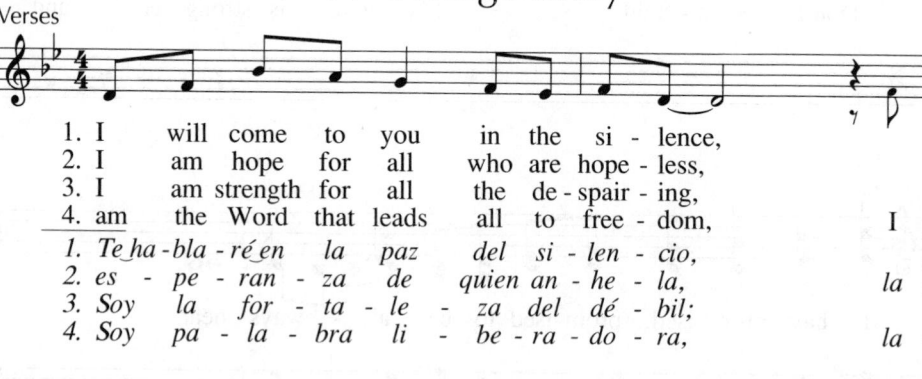

1. I     will come    to    you    in the si - lence,
2. I     am hope     for    all    who are hope - less,
3. I     am strength for    all    the de - spair - ing,
4. am    the Word that leads all    to free - dom,        I

1. Te_ha -bla - ré_en  la   paz   del si - len - cio,
2. es - pe - ran - za  de   quien an - he - la,         la
3. Soy  la  for - ta - le - za  del dé - bil;            
4. Soy  pa - la - bra  li - be - ra - do - ra,          la

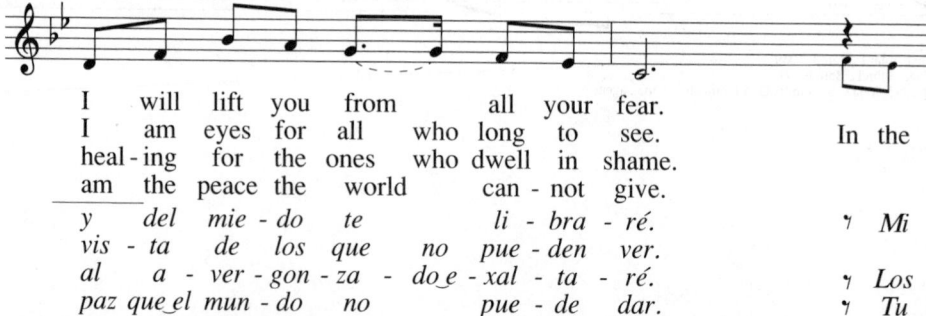

I    will lift  you   from    all  your  fear.
I    am  eyes for   all  who long  to   see.          In the
heal - ing for   the  ones who dwell in  shame.
am   the peace the  world      can - not give.

y    del mie - do   te       li - bra - ré.          Mi
vis - ta  de  los  que   no  pue - den ver.          Los
al   a - ver - gon - za - do_e - xal - ta - ré.
paz que_el mun - do   no       pue - de dar.          Tu

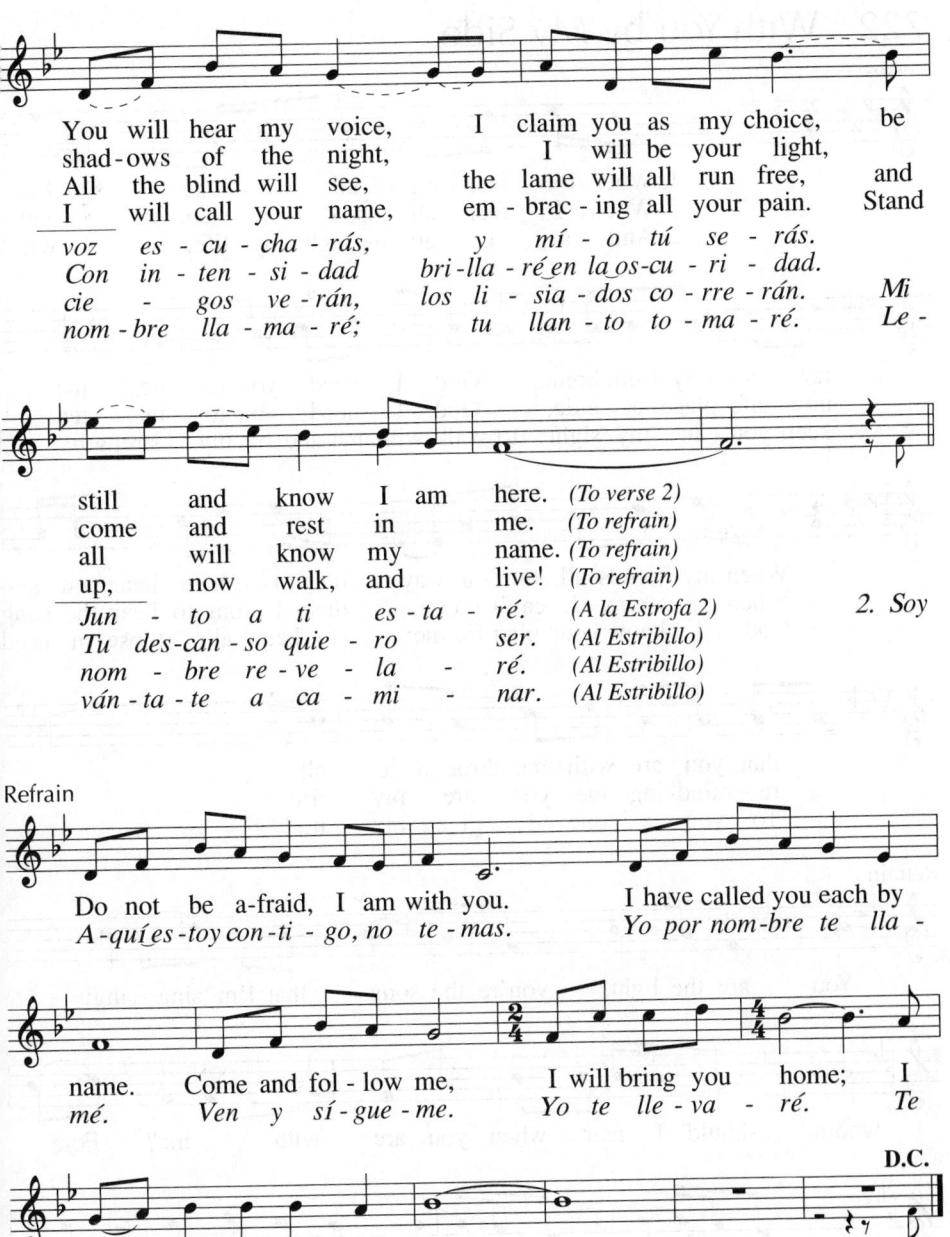

You will hear my voice, I claim you as my choice, be
shad-ows of the night, I will be your light,
All the blind will see, the lame will all run free, and
I will call your name, em - brac-ing all your pain. Stand

*voz es - cu - cha - rás, y mí - o tú se - rás.*
*Con in - ten - si - dad bri -lla - ré_en la_os-cu - ri - dad.*
*cie - gos ve - rán, los li - sia - dos co - rre - rán.* Mi
*nom - bre lla - ma - ré; tu llan - to to - ma - ré.* Le -

still and know I am here. *(To verse 2)*
come and rest in me. *(To refrain)*
all will know my name. *(To refrain)*
up, now walk, and live! *(To refrain)*

*Jun - to a ti es - ta - ré. (A la Estrofa 2)* 2. Soy
*Tu des-can - so quie - ro ser. (Al Estribillo)*
*nom - bre re - ve - la - ré. (Al Estribillo)*
*ván - ta - te a ca - mi - nar. (Al Estribillo)*

**Refrain**

Do not be a-fraid, I am with you. I have called you each by
*A -quí_es -toy con -ti - go, no te -mas. Yo por nom-bre te lla -*

name. Come and fol - low me, I will bring you home; I
*mé. Ven y sí - gue - me. Yo te lle - va - ré. Te*

**D.C.**

love you and you are mine.
*a - mo_y con - ti - go_es - toy.* 4. I

Text: David Haas, b.1957; tr. by Santiago Fernández, b.1971
Tune: David Haas, b.1957

## 722 With You by My Side

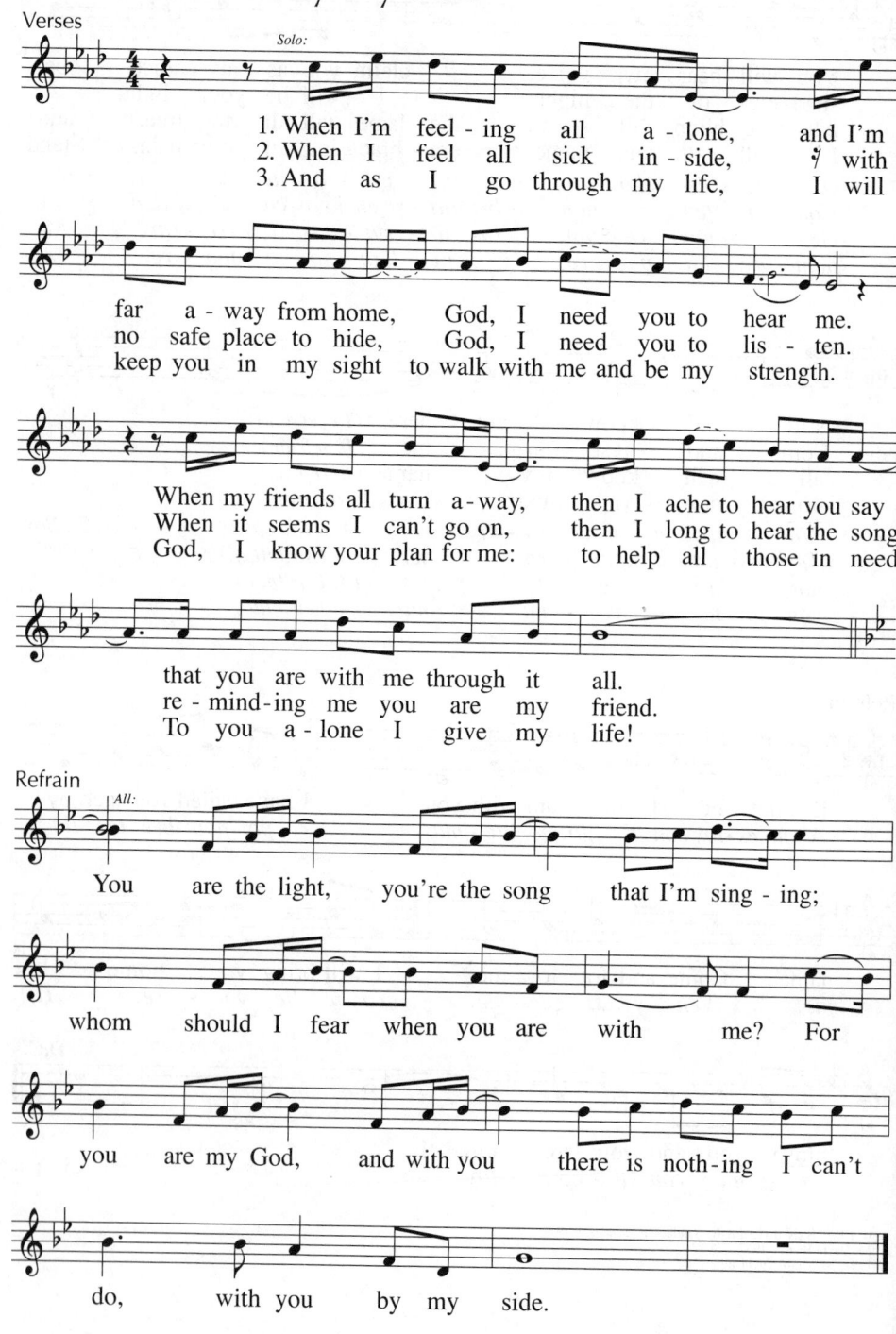

Verses

1. When I'm feel-ing all a-lone, and I'm
2. When I feel all sick in-side, ⁊ with
3. And as I go through my life, I will

far a-way from home, God, I need you to hear me.
no safe place to hide, God, I need you to lis-ten.
keep you in my sight to walk with me and be my strength.

When my friends all turn a-way, then I ache to hear you say
When it seems I can't go on, then I long to hear the song
God, I know your plan for me: to help all those in need

that you are with me through it all.
re-mind-ing me you are my friend.
To you a-lone I give my life!

Refrain

All:

You are the light, you're the song that I'm sing-ing;

whom should I fear when you are with me? For

you are my God, and with you there is noth-ing I can't

do, with you by my side.

Text: David Haas, b.1957
Tune: David Haas, b.1957; choral arr. by David Haas and Kate Cuddy, b.1953
© 1998, GIA Publications, Inc.

# Shepherd of My Heart 723

Verses

1. My shep-herd is the Lord, for noth-ing shall I want;
2. If I should walk one day in - to the vale of dark-ness,
3. You a-noint my head with oil; my cup is o - ver-flow-ing;

green are the pas - tures where I'm led to re - pose.
no e - vil shall I fear with God at my side.
good - ness and kind-ness crown the days of my life.

Near wa - ters still and deep God will re - fresh my soul.
There with your crook and staff you give me strength and com-fort;
With - in the Lord's own house I dwell in peace for ev - er;

I am led on - ward in ways true to the Name.
you spread a ban-quet in the sight of my foes.
with - in the house of God my soul is at rest.

Refrain

Guide me, O shep-herd of my heart; lead me home-ward through the

dark, in - to ev-er-last-ing day. Show me the way of truth and

light; keep me al - ways in your sight. May my life nev - er

part from the shep-herd of my heart.

Text: Psalm 23; Francis Patrick O'Brien, b.1958
Tune: Francis Patrick O'Brien, b.1958
© 1992, GIA Publications, Inc.

## 724 I Heard the Voice of Jesus Say

1. I heard the voice of Je - sus say, "Come
2. I heard the voice of Je - sus say, "Be -
3. I heard the voice of Je - sus say, "I

un - to me and rest; Lay down, O wea - ry
hold, I free - ly give The liv - ing wa - ter;
am this dark world's light; Look un - to me, your

one, lay down Your head up - on my breast." I
thirst - y one, Stoop down and drink and live." I
morn shall rise, And all your day be bright." I

came to Je - sus as I was, So
came to Je - sus, and I drank Of
looked to Je - sus, and I found In

wea - ry, worn, and sad; I found in him a
that life - giv - ing stream; My thirst was quenched, my
him my star, my sun; And in that light of

rest - ing place, And he has made me glad.
soul re - vived, And now I live in him.
life I'll walk Till trav - 'ling days are done.

Text: Horatius Bonar, 1808–1889
Tune: KINGSFOLD, CMD; English; harm. by Ralph Vaughan Williams, 1872–1958

# With a Shepherd's Care 725

**Refrain**

With a shep-herd's care  God  leads us.  With  a  fa-ther's

strength  God  guides us.  With a moth-er's love  God

nur-tures  us  and  cra-dles us  in gen - tle  arms.

**Verses**

1. When  we  are  lost  and  can - not find  the  way,  God
2. When  we  are  weak,  and  cares press all  a - round,  God
3. When  we  are  scared  and  feel  so  all  a - lone,  God

cares  for  us  and  keeps  us  safe.  For
strength - ens  us  to  face  each  day.  For
loves  us  and  is  by  our  side.  For

God  is  our light  and  our  faith - ful  guide,  who
God  is  our rock  and  our  sav - ing  help,  who
God  is  our hope  and  our  con - stant friend,  who

**D.C.**

leads  us  with  a  shep - herd's  care.
guides  us  with  a  fa - ther's  strength.
nur - tures  with  a  moth - er's  love.

Text: James J. Chepponis, b.1956
Tune: James J. Chepponis, b.1956
© 1992, GIA Publications, Inc.

# 726 You Are All I Want

**Refrain**

You are all I want, you are all I need, you a - lone are my de - light. You shep - herd me with love, you lead me through the dark - ness of night. In you my heart shall rest.

**Verse 1**

1. O Lord, you are my God, my shep - herd and my life. There's noth - ing I shall want. As I lie in fields of green, near cool and gen - tle streams, my heart is calm, my spir - it re - freshed.

*D.C.*

**Verses 2, 3**

2. With your staff, strong and true, you guide my life for you.
3. You have spread a lav - ish feast, for all my foes to see. You

Faith - ful is your name.   You are al - ways near, you
give me all I need.   You a - noint my head with oil, you

com - fort all my fears. In the face of death, I shall not hide.
soothe and heal my soul. My heart is full. I sing for joy.

*D.C.*

Verse 4

4. Your good - ness shall pur - sue me, your

kind - ness o - ver - whelms me. You shel - ter all my days.

In your house I will dwell, and live with you for -

**D.C.**

ev - er. In your arms of love, I am home.

Text: Psalm 23; Lori True, b.1961
Tune: Lori True, b.1961; acc. by David Haas, b.1957
© 2003, GIA Publications, Inc.

## Come to Me, O Weary Traveler  727

1. Come to me, O wea - ry trav - 'ler; Come to me with
2. Do not fear, my yoke is eas - y; Do not fear, my
3. Take my yoke and leave your trou - bles; Take my yoke and
4. Rest in me, O wea - ry trav - 'ler; Rest in me and

your dis - tress; Come to me, you heav - y bur-dened;
bur - den's light; Do not fear the path be - fore you;
come with me. Take my yoke, I am be - side you;
do not fear. Rest in me, my heart is gen - tle;

Come to me and find your rest.
Do not run from me in fright.
Take and learn hu - mil - i - ty.
Rest and cast a - way your care.

Text: Matthew 11:28–30; Sylvia G. Dunstan, 1955–1993, © 1991, GIA Publications, Inc.
Tune: DUNSTAN, 8 7 8 7; Bob Moore, b.1962, © 1993, GIA Publications, Inc.

# 728 Eye Has Not Seen

Refrain

Eye has not seen, ear has not heard what God has read-y for
those who love him; Spir-it of love, come, give us the mind of
Je - sus, teach us the wis-dom of God.

Verses 1-3

1. When pain and sor - row weigh us down, be near to us, O
2. Our lives are but a sin - gle breath, we flow-er and we
3. To those who see with eyes of faith, the Lord is ev - er

Lord; for - give the weak - ness of our faith, and
fade, yet all our days are in your hands, so
near, re - flect - ed in the fac - es of

D.C.

bear us up with - in your peace-ful word.
we re - turn in love what love has made.
all the poor and low - ly of the world.

Verse 4

4. We sing a mys-t'ry from the past in halls where saints have

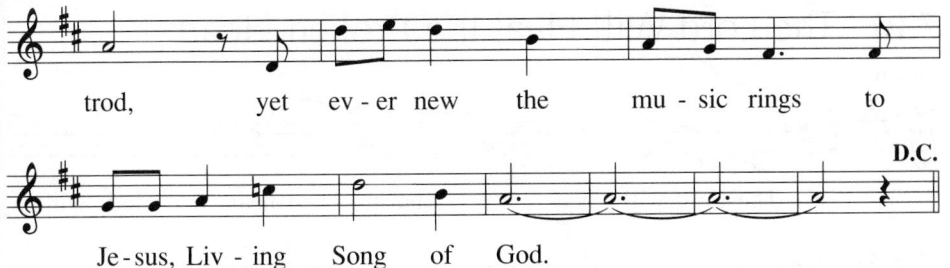

trod, yet ev - er new the mu - sic rings to

**D.C.**

Je-sus, Liv - ing Song of God.

Text: 1 Corinthians 2:9–10; Marty Haugen, b.1950
Tune: Marty Haugen, b.1950
© 1982, GIA Publications, Inc.

## Only You, O God  729

Refrain

On - ly you, O God, and you a-lone, the

bro - ken heart con - sole, On - ly you, O God, and

you a-lone, the wound - ed world make whole.

Verses

1. O God, our rock and ha - ven, Our
2. You guard us, faith - ful fa - ther, With -
3. We pray do not a - ban - don The

strong - hold, safe and sure, Though earth be torn and
in your shel - t'ring palm; You nurse us, lov - ing
ones you call your own; Our com - fort and com -

**D.C.**

shak - en, In you we stand se - cure.
moth - er, With milk and heal - ing balm.
pan - ion, We trust in you a - lone.

Text: Susan R. Briehl, b.1952, © 2003, GIA Publications, Inc.
Tune: BALM IN GILEAD, 7 6 7 6 with refrain; African American spiritual; acc. by Marty Haugen, b.1950, © 2003, GIA Publications, Inc.

# 730 The Lord Will Heal the Broken Heart

Refrain

The Lord will heal the bro - ken heart. God will

seek the lost and find them.

Verses

1. I     will bless the Lord     all  of  my days,     I     will
2. When the poor shall cry,     they shall be saved.     God will
3. You  who live  in  love     shall nev - er  die.     You who

bless the Lord     and give God praise,     For the     hum - ble
hear your cry,     live not in  shame.     God will     guard your
keep your word     need nev - er  hide.'     For the     Lord  will

heart     the  Lord  will  guard.     In     the
life     from sin's  dis - tress.     Let  us
seek     the  right - eous  soul.     May the

D.C.

Fa - ther's care     may  you     rest     from     harm.
fear  the  Lord,     may God's     name     be     blessed.
peace of  God     be  your     life     and     hope.

Text: Psalm 34; Liam Lawton, b.1959
Tune: Liam Lawton, b.1959; arr. John McCann, b.1961
© 2000, GIA Publications, Inc.

# Come to Me 731

**Refrain**

Come to me, come to me, come when you are wea - ry;

come to me, come to me, and I will give you rest.

**Verses 1, 2**

1. All who la - bor and are bur - dened,
2. Take my yoke up - on your shoul - ders,

all who la - bor and are bur - dened, let them come to me,
take my yoke up - on your shoul - ders, come and learn from me,

**D.C.**

come to me, and I will give them rest.
learn from me, for I am gen - tle of heart.

**Verse 3**

3. For the heart I hold is hum - ble, yes, the

heart I hold is hum - ble, and my yoke is eas - y, my

**D.C.**

bur - den light, and you will find rest for your souls.

Text: Matthew 11:28–30; Michael Joncas, b.1951
Tune: Michael Joncas, b.1951
© 1989, GIA Publications, Inc.

## 732 Jesus, Lead the Way

1. Je - sus, lead the way Through our life's long day. When at
2. Je - sus, be our light In the midst of night. Let not
3. When we seek re - lief From a long - felt grief; When temp -
4. Je - sus, still lead on Till our rest be won. If you

times the way is cheer - less, Help us fol - low, calm and
faith - less fears o'er - take us; Let not faith and hope for -
ta - tions come al - lur - ing, Make us pa - tient and en -
lead us through rough plac - es, Grant us your re - deem-ing

fear - less. Guide us by your hand To the prom - ised land.
sake us. May we feel you near As we wor - ship here.
dur - ing. Lord, we seek your grace In this ho - ly place.
grac - es. When our course is o'er, O - pen heav - en's door.

Text: *Jesu, geh voran;* Nicholas L. von Zinzendorf, 1700–1760; tr. by Jane Borthwick, 1813–1897, alt.
Tune: ROCHELLE, 55 88 55; Adam Drese, 1620–1701; harm. alt.

## 733 Nada Te Turbe / Nothing Can Trouble

Ostinato Refrain

Na - da te tur - be, na - da te es-pan - te. Quien a Dios tie - ne
*Noth-ing can trou-ble, noth-ing can fright-en. Those who seek God shall*

na - da le fal - ta. So - lo Dios bas - ta.
*nev-er go want - ing. God a - lone fills us.*

Text: St. Teresa of Jesus; Taizé Community, 1986, 1991
Tune: Jacques Berthier, 1923–1994
© 1986, 1991, Les Presses de Taizé, GIA Publications, Inc., agent

# Bring Forth the Kingdom 734

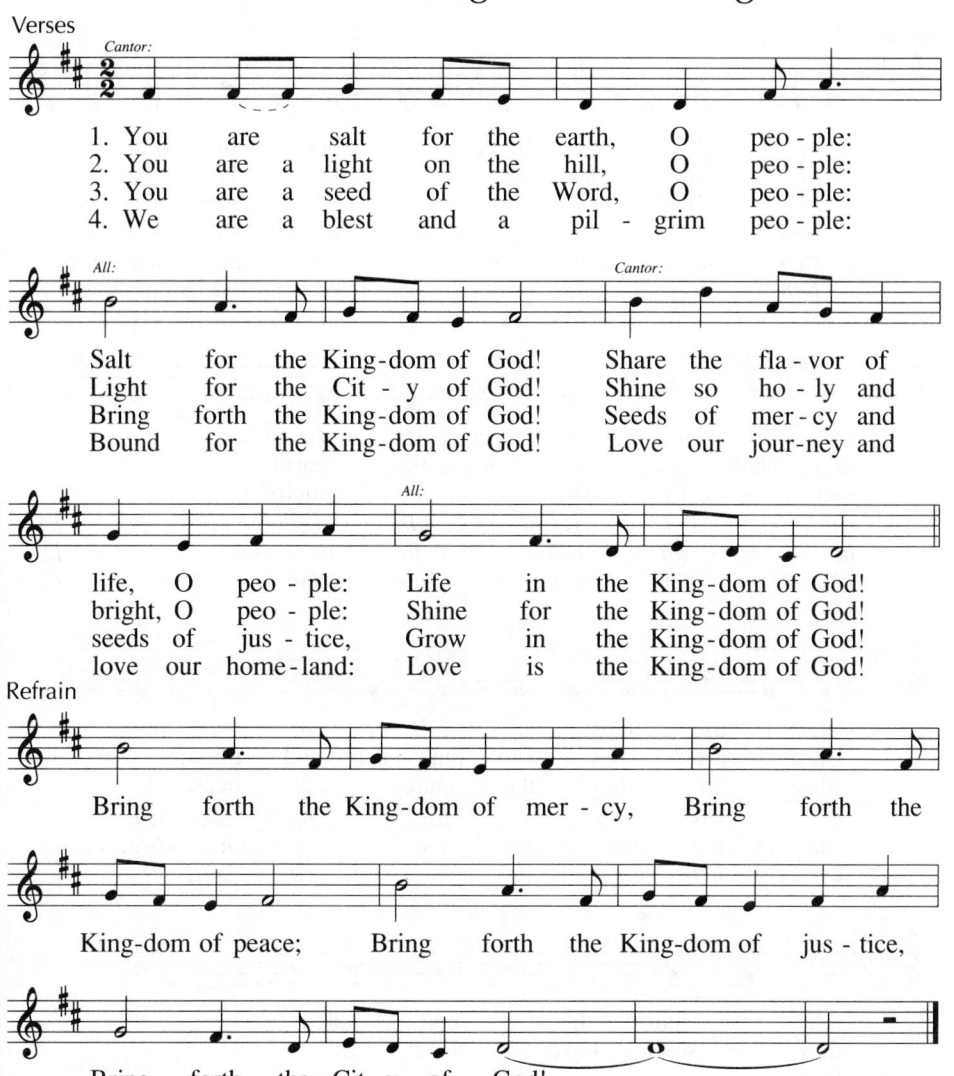

Verses

*Cantor:*

1. You are salt for the earth, O peo-ple:
2. You are a light on the hill, O peo-ple:
3. You are a seed of the Word, O peo-ple:
4. We are a blest and a pil-grim peo-ple:

*All:* ... *Cantor:*

Salt for the King-dom of God! Share the fla-vor of
Light for the Cit-y of God! Shine so ho-ly and
Bring forth the King-dom of God! Seeds of mer-cy and
Bound for the King-dom of God! Love our jour-ney and

*All:*

life, O peo-ple: Life in the King-dom of God!
bright, O peo-ple: Shine for the King-dom of God!
seeds of jus-tice, Grow in the King-dom of God!
love our home-land: Love is the King-dom of God!

Refrain

Bring forth the King-dom of mer-cy, Bring forth the

King-dom of peace; Bring forth the King-dom of jus-tice,

Bring forth the Cit-y of God!

Text: Marty Haugen, b.1950
Tune: Marty Haugen, b.1950
© 1986, GIA Publications, Inc.

# 735 Blest Are They / Benditos los Pobres

Verses 1–3

1. Blest are they, the poor in spir - it;
2. Blest are they, the low - ly ones;
3. Blest are they who show mer - cy;

1. Ben - di - tos los po - bres en el es - pí - ri - tu,
2. Ben - di - tos son los pa - cien - tes,
3. Ben - di - tos son los com - pa - si - vos,

theirs is the king - dom of God.
they shall in - her - it the earth.
mer - cy shall be theirs.

su - yo_es el rei - no de Dios. Di -
he - re - da - rán la tie - rra. Di -
ob - ten - drán pie - dad. Di -

Blest are they, full of sor - row;
Blest are they who hun - ger and thirst;
Blest are they, the pure of heart;

cho - sos son los que llo - ran,
cho - sos los que tie - nen sed y ham - bre,
cho - sos los lim - pios de co - ra - zón,

they shall be con - soled.
they shall have their fill.
they shall see God.

re - ci - bi - rán con - sue - lo.
por - que se - rán sa - cia - dos.
e - llos ve - rán a Dios.

Refrain

Re - joice and be glad! Bless-ed are
¡A - lé - gren - se y con - tén - ten - se! ¡Son los ben -

Verses 4, 5

you, ho - ly are you! Re - joice and be glad!
*di - tos de nues-tro Dios! ¡A - lé-gren-se y con - tén-ten -se!*

Yours is the king-dom of God!
*¡Su - yo_es el rei - no de Dios!*

4. Blest are they who seek peace;
5. Blest are you who suf - fer hate,
*4. Ben - di - tos los que por la paz tra - ba-jan,*
*5. Ben - di - tos son los per - se - gui-dos,*

they are the chil - dren of God. Re -
all be - cause of me.
*e - llos son hi - jos de Dios. Di -*
*to - do por cau - sa mí - a. ¡A -*

Blest are they who suf - fer in faith; the
joice and be glad, yours is the king - dom;
*cho - sos los que por la fe su - fren,*
*lé - gren - se! Su re - com - pen - sa*

To refrain

glo - ry of God is theirs.
shine for all to see.
*su - ya_es la glo - ria de Dios.*
*gran -de_en el cie - lo se - rá.*

Text: Matthew 5:3–12; David Haas, b.1957, tr. by Ronald F. Krisman, b.1946
Tune: David Haas, b.1957; vocal arr. by David Haas and Michael Joncas, b.1951
© 1985, 2005, GIA Publications, Inc.

## 736 The Kingdom of God

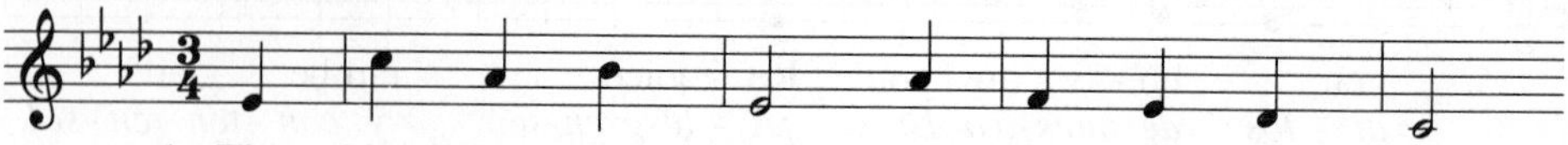

1. The king-dom of God is jus-tice and joy;
2. The king-dom of God is mer-cy and grace;
3. The king-dom of God is chal-lenge and choice:
4. God's king-dom is come, the gift and the goal;

For Je-sus re-stores what sin would de-stroy.
The cap-tives are freed, the sin-ners find place,
Be-lieve the good news, re-pent and re-joice!
In Je-sus be-gun, in heav-en made whole.

God's pow-er and glo-ry in Je-sus we know;
The out-cast are wel-comed God's ban-quet to share;
God's love for us sin-ners brought Christ to his cross:
The heirs of the king-dom shall an-swer his call;

And here and here-af-ter the king-dom shall grow.
And hope is a-wak-ened in place of de-spair.
Our cri-sis of judge-ment for gain or for loss.
And all things cry "Glo-ry!" to God all in all.

Text: Bryn A. Rees, 1911–1983, © 1973, Alexander Scott
Tune: LAUDATE DOMINUM, 10 10 11 11; Charles H. H. Parry, 1848–1918

## 737 We Will Walk with God

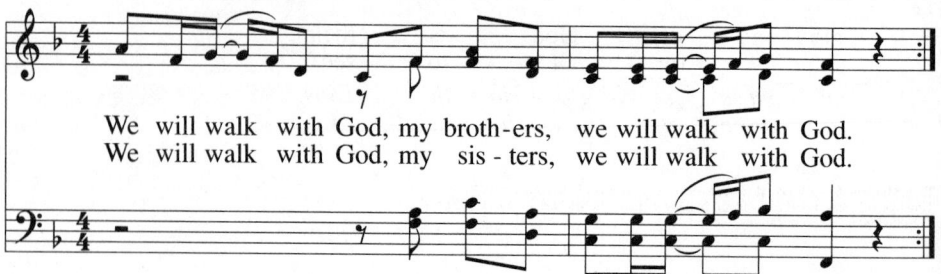

We will walk with God, my broth-ers, we will walk with God.
We will walk with God, my sis-ters, we will walk with God.

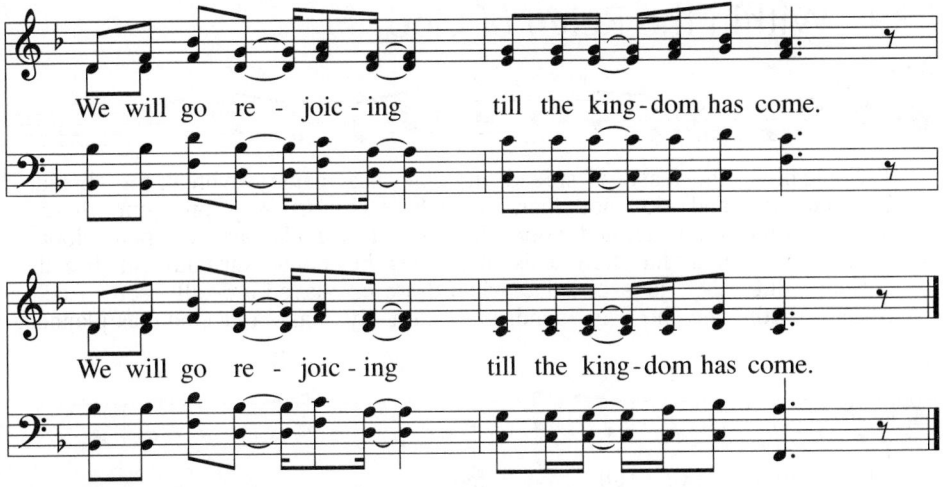

We will go re - joic - ing till the king - dom has come.

We will go re - joic - ing till the king - dom has come.

Text: Swaziland traditional; transcribed by Swedish Youth Exchange Project, ©; tr. by John L. Bell, b.1949, © 2002, Iona Community,
    GIA Publications, Inc., agent
Tune: Swaziland traditional; transcribed by Swedish Youth Exchange Project, ©

## The Reign of God   738

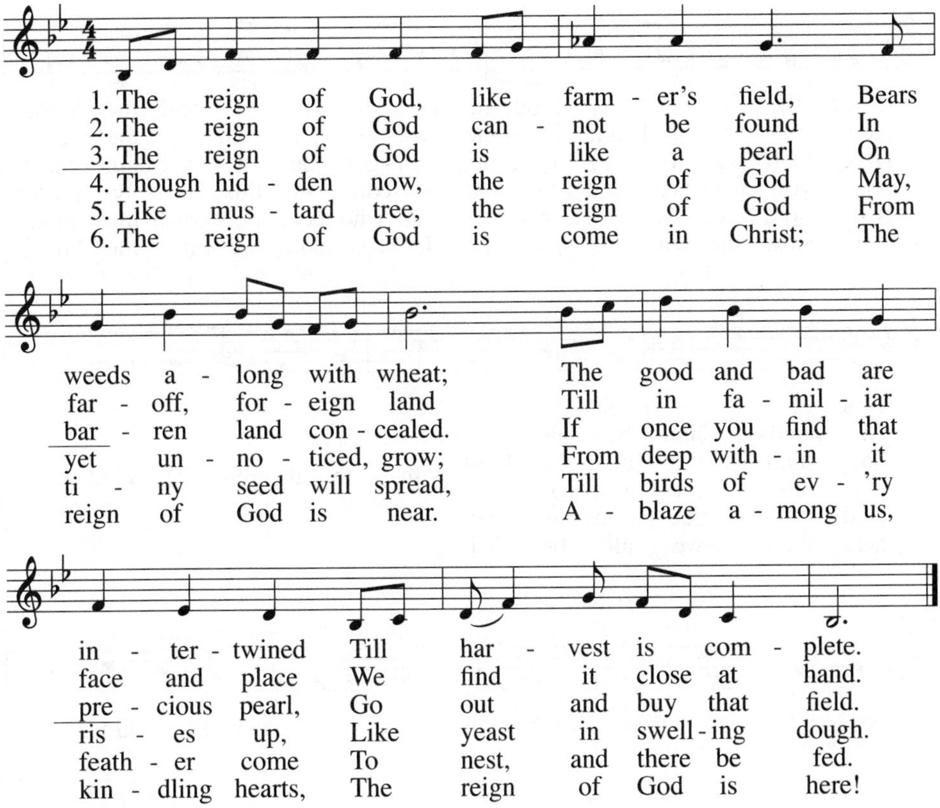

| | | | | | | | | |
|---|---|---|---|---|---|---|---|---|
| 1. The | reign | of | God, | like | farm - | er's | field, | Bears |
| 2. The | reign | of | God | can - | not | be | found | In |
| 3. The | reign | of | God | is | like | a | pearl | On |
| 4. Though hid - | den | now, | the | reign | of | God | May, |
| 5. Like | mus - tard | tree, | the | reign | of | God | From |
| 6. The | reign | of | God | is | come | in | Christ; | The |

| | | | |
|---|---|---|---|
| weeds | a - long with wheat; | The | good and bad are |
| far - off, | for - eign land | Till | in fa - mil - iar |
| bar - ren | land con - cealed. | If | once you find that |
| yet | un - no - ticed, grow; | From | deep with - in it |
| ti - ny | seed will spread, | Till | birds of ev - 'ry |
| reign of | God is near. | A - | blaze a - mong us, |

| | | | |
|---|---|---|---|
| in - ter - twined | Till | har - vest is com - plete. |
| face and place | We | find it close at hand. |
| pre - cious pearl, | Go | out and buy that field. |
| ris - es up, | Like | yeast in swell - ing dough. |
| feath - er come | To | nest, and there be fed. |
| kin - dling hearts, | The | reign of God is here! |

Text: Matthew 13:24–33, 44–49, Mark 4:26–34; Delores Dufner, OSB, b.1939, © 1995, 2003, GIA Publications, Inc.
Tune: McKEE, CM; African American; adapt. by Harry T. Burleigh, 1866–1949

# 739 Within the Reign of God

**Verses**

*Cantor:*

1. Come now, the feast is spread; in Je-sus' name we break the bread.
2. Stand up and do not fear, for Christ is tru - ly pres-ent here.
3. Wel-come the weak and poor, the sin-ner finds an o - pen door,
4. All fear and ha-tred ends and foes be-come our faith-ful friends,
5. Sing out the ju - bi - lee when those en-slaved are all set free,
6. One earth, one ho - ly band, one fam-'ly as our God has planned,

*All:*

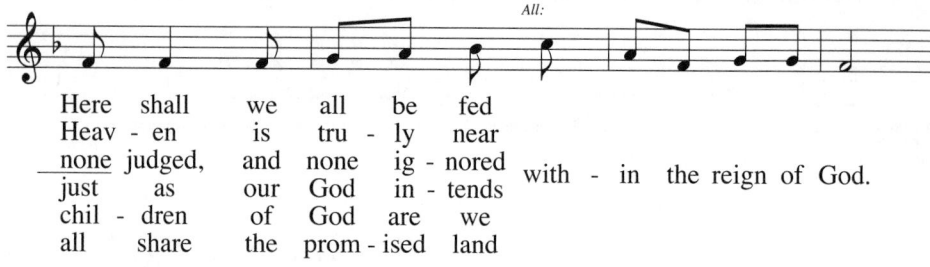

Here shall we all be fed
Heav - en is tru - ly near
none judged, and none ig - nored    with - in the reign of God.
just as our God in - tends
chil - dren of God are we
all share the prom - ised land

*Cantor:*

Come take this ho - ly food; re - ceive the bod - y and the blood.
Now at the wed-ding feast, the great-est here shall be the least.
Here shall the wea - ry rest, the stran-ger be a wel-come guest.
All you who seek God's face are wel-come in this ho - ly place;
No more can we for - get the ones who bear life's crush-ing debt;
Come now, the feast is spread, in Je - sus' name we break the bread;

*All:*

Grace is a might - y flood
All bonds shall be re - leased
So shall we all be blest    with - in the reign of God.
join in the feast of grace
God's jus - tice guides us yet
here shall we all be fed

**Refrain**

Bless-ed are they who will feast in the reign of God.

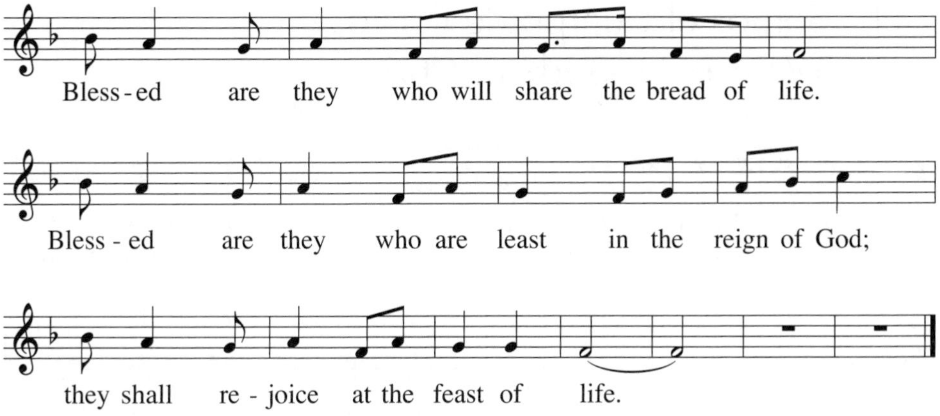

Bless-ed are they who will share the bread of life.

Bless - ed are they who are least in the reign of God;

they shall re - joice at the feast of life.

Text Marty Haugen, b.1950
Tune: Marty Haugen, b.1950
© 1999, GIA Publications, Inc.

## The Kingdom of God  740

Ostinato Refrain

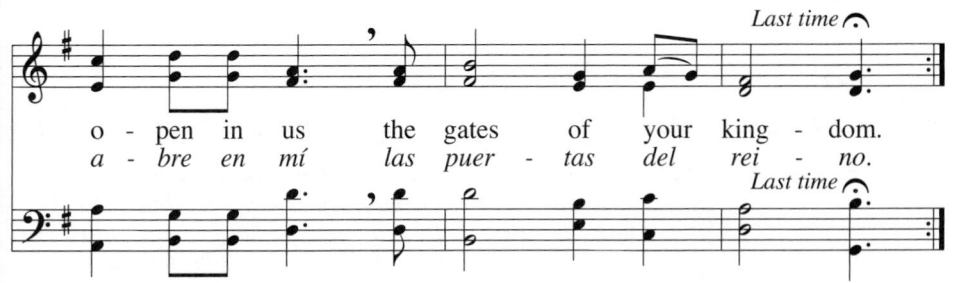

The king - dom of God is jus - tice and peace and
*El rei - no de Dios es rei - no de paz, jus -*

joy in the Ho - ly Spir - it. Come, Lord, and
*ti - cia y a - le - grí - a. Ven, Dios, y*

Last time

o - pen in us the gates of your king - dom.
*a - bre en mí las puer - tas del rei - no.*

Last time

Text: Taizé Community
Tune: Taizé Community
© 2001, 2011, Les Presses de Taizé, GIA Publications, Inc., agent

# 741 Somos el Cuerpo de Cristo / We Are the Body of Christ

**Refrain**

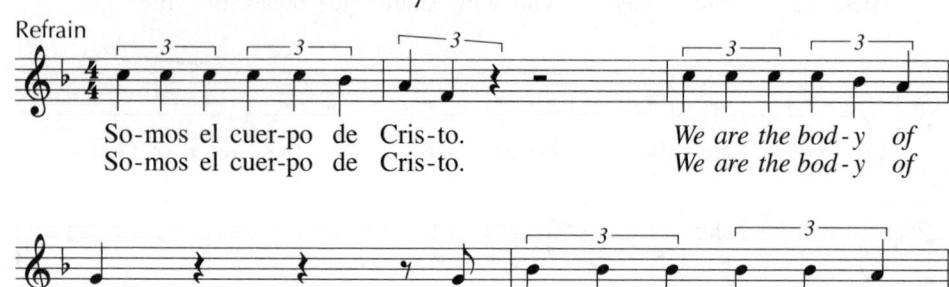

So-mos el cuer-po de Cris-to. We are the bod-y of
So-mos el cuer-po de Cris-to. We are the bod-y of

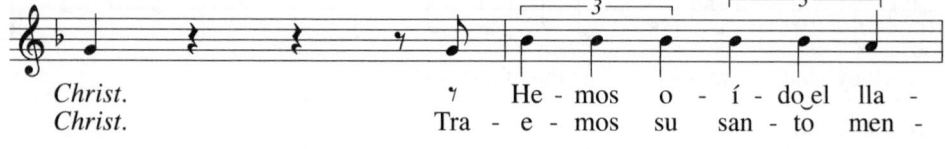

Christ. He - mos o - í - do el lla -
Christ. Tra - e - mos su san - to men -

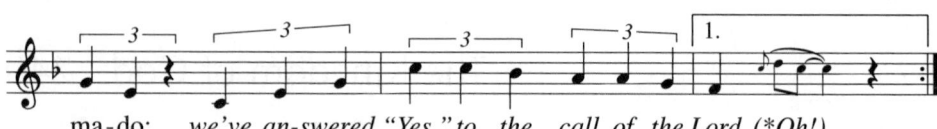

ma-do; we've an-swered "Yes," to the call of the Lord. (*Oh!)
sa - je. We come to bring the good news to the

world.
world. (*Oh!)
3. Que

**Verses** *Cantor:*

1. Dios vie-ne al mun-do a tra - vés de no - so-tros.
   mun-do a cum-plir la mi - sión de la I-gle-sia,
2. Ca - da per - so - na es par-te del rei-no;
   To - das las ra - zas que ha-bi-tan la tie-rra,
3. nues-tras ac - cio - nes re - fle-jen jus - ti - cia;
   Va - mos al mun-do a cui - dar su re - ba-ño.

So-mos el cuer-po de

*Cantor:*

Cris-to.

God is re-vealed when we love one an-oth - er.
Bring-ing the light of God's mer - cy to oth - ers,
Put - ting a stop to all dis-crim - i - na - tion,
All are in - vit - ed to feast in the ban-quet.
Stop - ping a - buse and re - liev-ing the hun - gry,
Serv - ing each oth - er we build up the king-dom;

*Sing after Verse 2 (optional)

CHURCH

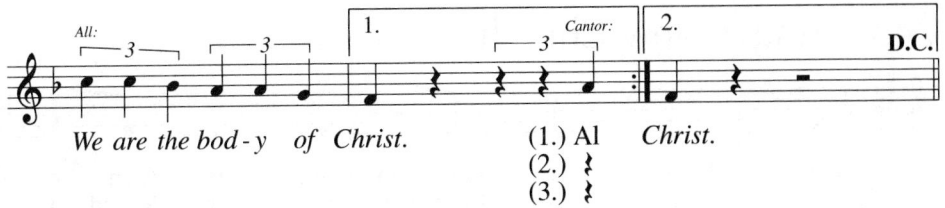

We are the bod-y of Christ.     (1.) Al     Christ.
                                (2.) 
                                (3.) 

Text: Jaime Cortez, b.1963, and Bob Hurd, b.1950
Tune: Jaime Cortez, b.1963, acc. by Jeffrey Honoré, b.1956
© 1994, Jaime Cortez. Published by OCP.

## The Church's One Foundation  742

1. The Chur-ch's one foun - da - tion Is Je - sus Christ, her
2. E - lect from ev - 'ry na - tion, Yet one o'er all the
3. Through toil and trib - u - la - tion And tu - mult of her
4. Yet she on earth has u - nion With God, the Three in

Lord; She is his new cre - a - tion By wa - ter
earth; Her char - ter of sal - va - tion: One Lord, one
war She waits the con - sum - ma - tion Of peace for -
One, And mys - tic sweet com - mun - ion With those whose

and the Word. From heav'n he came and sought her To
faith, one birth. One ho - ly name she bless - es, Par -
ev - er - more Till with the vi - sion glo - rious Her
rest is won. O bless - ed heav'n - ly cho - rus! Lord,

be his ho - ly bride; With his own blood he
takes one ho - ly food, And to one hope she
long - ing eyes are blessed, And the great Church vic -
save us by your grace That we, like saints be -

bought her, And for her life he died.
press - es With ev - 'ry grace en - dued.
to - rious Shall be the Church at rest.
fore us, May see you face to face.

Text: Samuel J. Stone, 1839–1900, alt.
Tune: AURELIA, 7 6 7 6 D; Samuel S. Wesley, 1810–1876

# 743 Sing a New Church

1. Sum-moned by the God who made us Rich in
2. Ra - diant ris - en from the wa - ter, Robed in
3. Trust the good - ness of cre - a - tion; Trust the
4. Bring the hopes of ev - 'ry na - tion; Bring the
5. Draw to - geth - er at one ta - ble All the

our di - ver - si - ty, Gath-ered in the name of
ho - li - ness and light, Male and fe - male in God's
Spir - it strong with - in. Dare to dream the vi - sion
art of ev - 'ry race. Weave a song of peace and
hu - man fam - i - ly; Shape a cir - cle ev - er

Je - sus, Rich - er still in u - ni - ty:
im - age, Male and fe - male, God's de - light:
prom - ised, Sprung from seed of what has been.
jus - tice; Let it sound through time and space.
wid - er And a peo - ple ev - er free.

Let us bring the gifts that dif - fer And, in

splen - did, var - ied ways, Sing a new Church in - to

be - ing, One in faith and love and praise.

Text: Delores Dufner, OSB, b.1939, © 1991, Sisters of St. Benedict. Published by OCP.
Tune: NETTLETON, 8 7 8 7 D, from *Wyeth's Repository of Sacred Music, Pt. II*, 1813

# As a Fire Is Meant for Burning 744

1. As a fire is meant for burning
With a bright and warm-ing flame,
So the Church is meant for mis - sion,
Giv - ing glo - ry to God's name.
As we wit - ness to the gos - pel,
We would build a bridge of care,
Join-ing hands a - cross the na - tions,
Find-ing neigh - bors ev - 'ry - where.

2. We are learn - ers; we are teach - ers;
We are pil - grims on the way.
We are seek - ers; we are giv - ers;
We are ves - sels made of clay.
By our gen - tle, lov - ing ac - tions,
We would show that Christ is light.
In a hum - ble, lis - t'ning Spir - it,
We would live to God's de - light.

3. As a green bud in the spring - time
Is a sign of life re - newed,
So may we be signs of one - ness
Mid earth's peo - ples, man - y hued.
As a rain - bow lights the heav - ens
When a storm is past and gone,
May our lives re - flect the ra - diance
Of God's new and glor - ious dawn.

Text: Ruth Duck, b.1947, © 1992, GIA Publications, Inc.
Tune: BEACH SPRING, 8 7 8 7 D; *The Sacred Harp*, 1844; harm. by Marty Haugen, b.1950, © 1985, GIA Publications, Inc.

# 745 Christ Is Made the Sure Foundation

1. Christ is made the sure foun - da - tion, Christ, our Head and
2. To this tem - ple, where we call you, Come, O Lord of
3. Here be - stow on all your ser - vants What they ask of
4. Praise and hon - or to the Fa - ther, Praise and hon - or

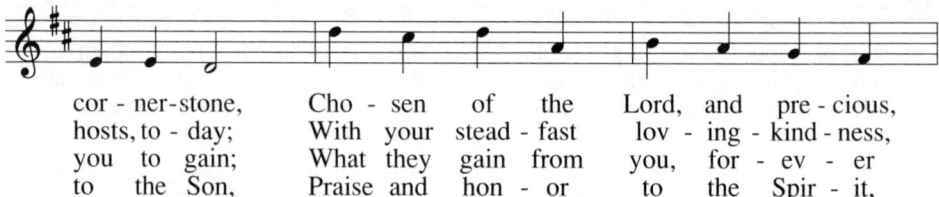

cor - ner-stone, Cho - sen of the Lord, and pre - cious,
hosts, to - day; With your stead - fast lov - ing - kind - ness,
you to gain; What they gain from you, for - ev - er
to the Son, Praise and hon - or to the Spir - it,

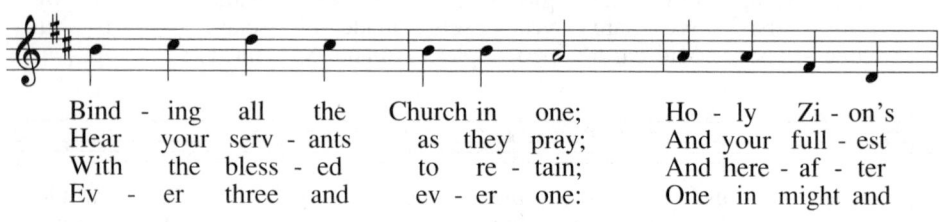

Bind - ing all the Church in one; Ho - ly Zi - on's
Hear your serv - ants as they pray; And your full - est
With the bless - ed to re - tain; And here - af - ter
Ev - er three and ev - er one: One in might and

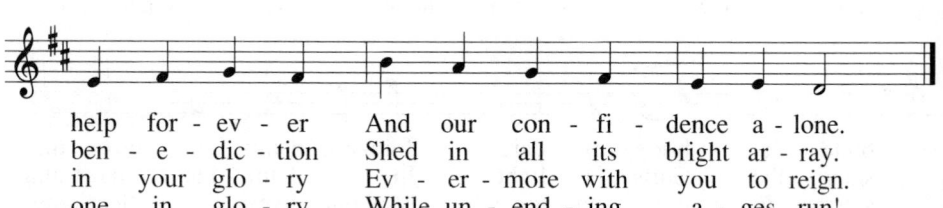

help for - ev - er And our con - fi - dence a - lone.
ben - e - dic - tion Shed in all its bright ar - ray.
in your glo - ry Ev - er - more with you to reign.
one in glo - ry While un - end - ing a - ges run!

Text: *Angularis fundamentum*; 11th C.; tr. by John M. Neale, 1818–1866, alt.
Tune: ST. THOMAS, 8 7 8 7 8 7; John Wade, 1711–1786

# 746 All That Is Hidden

1. If you would fol - low me, fol - low where life will lead:
2. If you would hon - or me, hon - or the least of these:
3. If you would speak of me, live all your life in me:
4. If you would rise with me, rise through your des - ti - ny:

do not look for me      a - mong the  dead,      for      I      am
you will not find me dressed in      fin - er - y.      My  Word  cries
my ways are not the  ways    that   you would choose; my thoughts are
do   not re-fuse the  death which brings you  life,      for     as      the

hid - den   in    pain,                  ris  -  en    in    love;
out     to    be   heard;               breaks through the   world:
far   be - yond  yours,         as   heav  -  en   from  earth:
grain  in    the    earth        must   die     for   re - birth,

there   is    no    har - vest with - out   sow - ing   of   grain.
my   Word   is     on  your  lips  and   lives   in   your  heart.
if      you  be - lieve   in    me    my   voice  will   be   heard.
so      I    have plant - ed  your  life  deep  with - in   mine.

All that is hid-den      will be made clear.          All that is

dark now will  be   re - vealed.          What you have heard in the dark

pro-claim in the light;      what  you    hear     in  whis-pers

pro-claim from the house - tops.

Text: Refrain based on Luke 12:2–3, Bernadette Farrell, b.1957
Tune: Bernadette Farrell, b.1957; choral arr. by Paul Inwood, b.1947
© 1986, 1988, Bernadette Farrell. Published by OCP.

# 747 Whatever Be the Love

1. What-ev-er be the love, it is en-fold-ed, O God of
2. What-ev-er be our small-est acts of cour-age, O God of
3. What-ev-er be the ques-tion or the chal-lenge, O God of
4. What-ev-er be our faith, it is up-lift-ed, O God of
5. What-ev-er be the song, it is your mu-sic, O God of

Love, with-in your arms' em-brace— Our
Strength, they wit-ness to your pow'r That
Wis - dom, Source of ho-ly speech, It
Mys - t'ry far be-yond our sight. Through
Hope, sus-tain-ing ev-'ry breath, With

hu - man pas-sions, part-ner-ships, and yearn-ings Re -
reach-es through our anx-ious fear and trem-bling And
is your call that sum-mons us to jus-tice And
shad-owed lands, our wan-d'ing, up-ward path-ways Con -
morn-ing stars and moun-tain peaks u-nit-ed In

fined with-in the ra-diance of your grace.
nur-tures us to grow to full-est flow'r.
o - pens hearts to live the truth you teach.
verge with-in your fi-nal realm of light.
sym-pho-nies of joy, out-liv-ing death!

Text: Mary Louise Bringle, b.1953, © 2006, GIA Publications, Inc.
Tune: Lori True, b.1961, © 2010, GIA Publications, Inc.

# 'Tis the Gift to Be Simple 748

'Tis the gift to be sim-ple, 'tis the gift to be free, 'Tis the

gift to come down where we ought to be; And

when we find our-selves in the place just right, 'Twill

be in the val - ley of love and de - light.

When true sim - plic - i - ty is gained, To bow and to bend we

shan't be a-shamed; to turn, turn, will be our de-light, Till by

turn - ing, turn - ing we come round right.

Text: Joseph Brackett, Jr., 1797–1882
Tune: SIMPLE GIFTS, Joseph Brackett, Jr., 1797–1882; acc. Margaret W. Mealy, b.1922, © 1984

# 749 Where Your Treasure Is

**Refrain**

Where your treas-ure is, there your heart shall be. All that
you pos-sess will nev - er set you free. Seek the
things that last; come and learn from me. Where your

*Fourth time to Vs. 4* | *To verses 1–3* | *Last time*

treas-ure is, your heart shall be. be.

**Verses 1–3**

1. What do you gain from all your wor - ry,
2. Look at the ra - vens high a - bove you.
3. Be - hold the lil - ies in their splen - dor.

What you should eat or what to wear?
They do not work their whole life through,
In grace and beau - ty are they dressed,

There is no peace in stress or hur - ry. Do you not
And yet God feeds them and pro - tects them. So how much
And yet so soon their bloom is fad - ed. So how much

**D.C.**

know that you are held with - in God's care?
more will God pro - tect and care for you?
more will those who look to God be blessed?

Verse 4

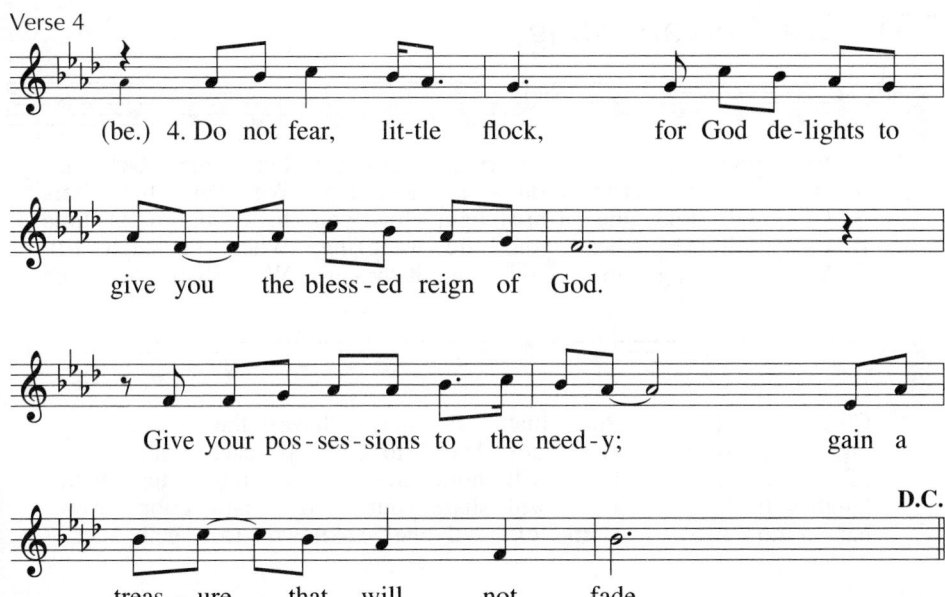

(be.) 4. Do not fear, lit-tle flock, for God de-lights to

give you the bless-ed reign of God.

Give your pos-ses-sions to the need-y; gain a

**D.C.**

treas - ure that will not fade.

Text: Luke 12:22–34; Marty Haugen, b.1950
Tune: Marty Haugen, b.1950
© 2000, GIA Publications, Inc.

## Deliver Us, O Lord of Truth  750

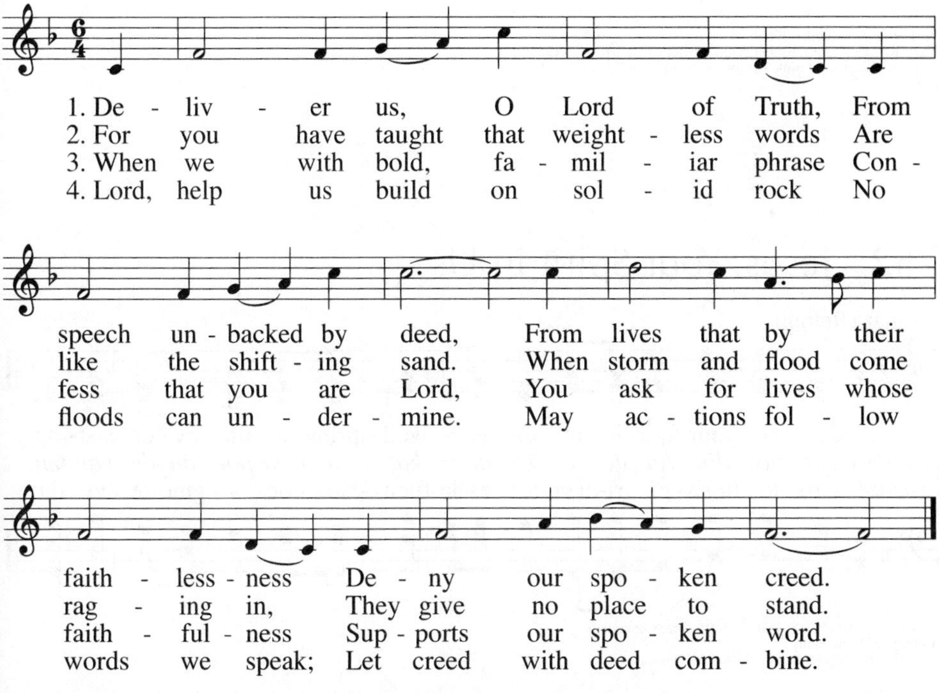

1. De - liv - er us, O Lord of Truth, From
2. For you have taught that weight - less words Are
3. When we with bold, fa - mil - iar phrase Con -
4. Lord, help us build on sol - id rock No

speech un - backed by deed, From lives that by their
like the shift - ing sand. When storm and flood come
fess that you are Lord, You ask for lives whose
floods can un - der - mine. May ac - tions fol - low

faith - less - ness De - ny our spo - ken creed.
rag - ing in, They give no place to stand.
faith - ful - ness Sup - ports our spo - ken word.
words we speak; Let creed with deed com - bine.

Text: Herman G. Stuempfle, Jr., 1923–2007, © 1997, GIA Publications, Inc.
Tune: LAND OF REST, CM; American; adapt. by Annabel M. Buchanan, 1888–1983, © 1938 (renewed), this arr. © 2011, The H.W. Gray Company

# 751 The Servant Song

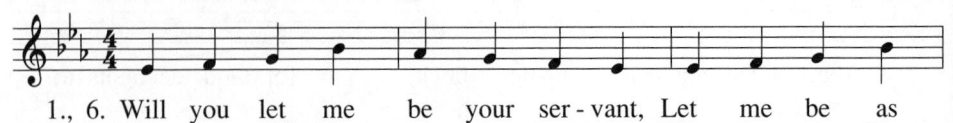

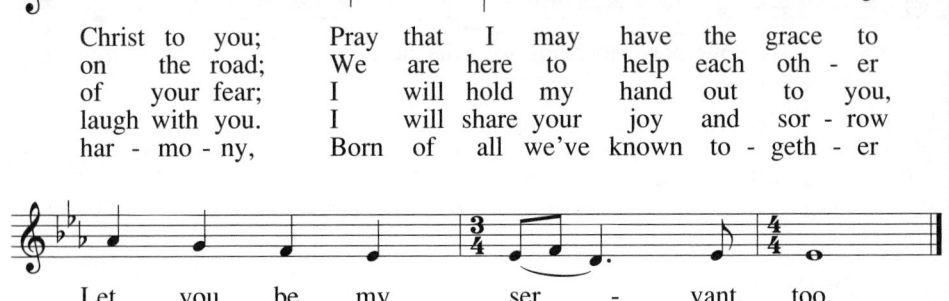

```
1., 6. Will  you   let   me    be    your   ser - vant,  Let   me    be    as
2.  We  are  pil - grims  on   a     jour - ney,  We   are   trav - 'lers
3.  I    will hold  the   Christ-light for  you   In    the   night - time
4.  I    will weep when  you   are   weep-ing;  When you  laugh I'll
5.  When we  sing   to    God   in    heav - en   We   shall find  such
```

```
Christ  to    you;    Pray  that   I     may   have  the   grace  to
on      the   road;   We    are    here  to    help  each  oth - er
of      your  fear;   I     will   hold  my    hand  out   to    you,
laugh   with  you.    I     will   share your  joy   and   sor - row
har - mo - ny,        Born  of     all   we've known to - geth - er
```

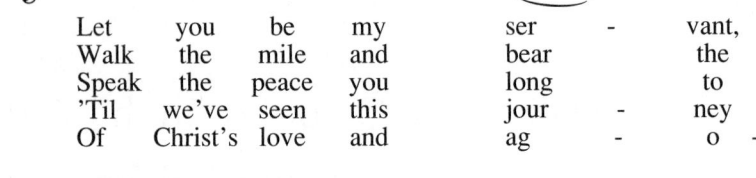

```
Let    you     be      my      ser  -    vant,  too.
Walk   the     mile    and     bear      the    load.
Speak  the     peace   you     long      to     hear.
'Til   we've   seen    this    jour  -   ney    through.
Of     Christ's love    and     ag   -    o   -  ny.
```

Text: Richard Gillard, b.1953
Tune: Richard Gillard, b.1953; harm. by Betty Pulkingham, b.1929
© 1977, Universal Music — Brentwood Benson Publishing

# 752 Jesus, Your Spirit in Us

Ostinato Refrain

```
              Je - sus, your Spir-it  in   us   is  a  well-spring of  life  ev - er - last-ing.
Swedish: Kris-tus, din  An - de   i   oss  är en käl - la  med por-lan-de vat-ten.
Spanish: Cris-to, tu Es-pí - ri-tu en mí  es la fuen - te  con a - gua de  vi - da.
```

Text: Psalm 63:1–4, 7–8, John 7:37–39; Taizé Community
Tune: Taizé Community
© 2003, 2011, Les Presses de Taizé, GIA Publications, Inc., agent

# We Will Serve the Lord 753

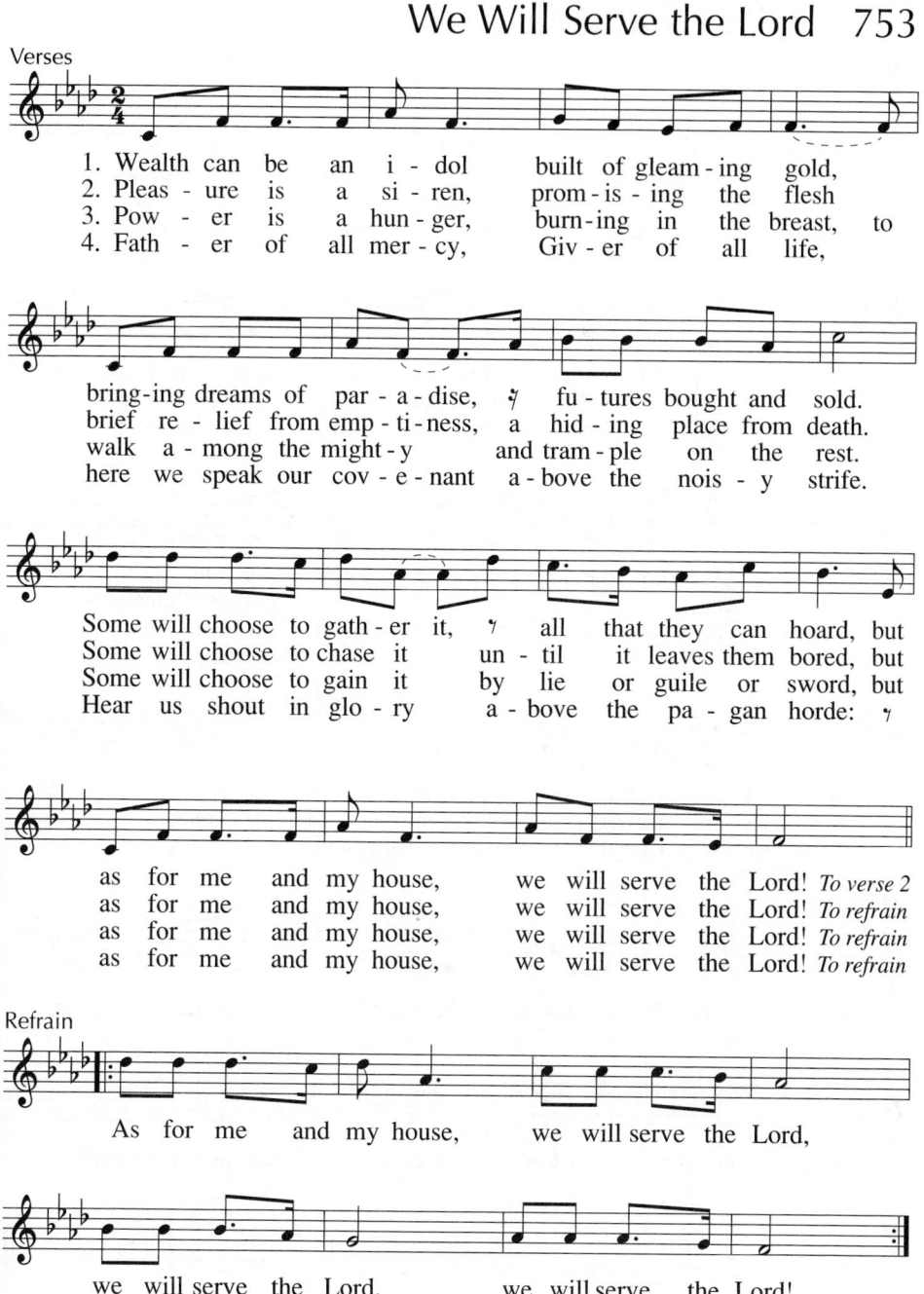

**Verses**

1. Wealth can be an i - dol built of gleam - ing gold,
2. Pleas - ure is a si - ren, prom - is - ing the flesh
3. Pow - er is a hun - ger, burn - ing in the breast, to
4. Fath - er of all mer - cy, Giv - er of all life,

bring-ing dreams of par - a - dise, fu - tures bought and sold.
brief re - lief from emp - ti - ness, a hid - ing place from death.
walk a - mong the might - y and tram - ple on the rest.
here we speak our cov - e - nant a - bove the nois - y strife.

Some will choose to gath - er it, all that they can hoard, but
Some will choose to chase it un - til it leaves them bored, but
Some will choose to gain it by lie or guile or sword, but
Hear us shout in glo - ry a - bove the pa - gan horde:

as for me and my house, we will serve the Lord! *To verse 2*
as for me and my house, we will serve the Lord! *To refrain*
as for me and my house, we will serve the Lord! *To refrain*
as for me and my house, we will serve the Lord! *To refrain*

**Refrain**

As for me and my house, we will serve the Lord,

we will serve the Lord, we will serve the Lord!

Text: Rory Cooney, b.1952
Tune: Rory Cooney, b.1952
© 1986, North American Liturgy Resources. Published by OCP.

# 754  Build Us a Table

Verses

1. Walls mark our bound-'ries and keep us a - part;
2. Walls make us sure who is in and who's out;
3. Once we were stran-gers, di - vid - ed, a - lone.

Walls keep the world from our eyes and our heart.
Walls keep us safe from all ques - tion and doubt,
Hate and dis - trust built a wall stone by stone.

Ta - bles are round, mak - ing room for one more,
But at a ta - ble in o - pen ex - change
Now at a ta - ble the bread that we share

Wel - com-ing friends we had not known be - fore. So
New ties are formed as our lives re - ar - range. So
Joins us to Christ in a cir - cle of care. So

Refrain

build us a ta-ble and tear down the wall! Christ is our host. There is

room for us all! Build us a ta-ble and tear down the wall!

Christ is our host. There is room for us all!

Text: Ruth Duck, b.1947, alt., © 1996, The Pilgrim Press
Tune: Lori True, b.1961; acc. by Paul A. Tate, b.1968, © 2007, GIA Publications, Inc.

# Bambelela / Never Give Up    755

Text: Traditional South African
Tune: Traditional South African; tr. by Mairi Munro and Martine Stemerick; adapt. by Mairi Munro and Philip Jakob
© 2002, JL Zwane Memorial Congregation

# 756 When We Are Living / Pues Si Vivimos

1. When we are liv - ing, we are in Christ
2. While we are liv - ing, we have fruit to
3. When sad or hurt - ing, when we feel a -
4. Through-out this wide world man - y peo - ple

1. *Pues si vi - vi - mos, pa - ra él vi -*
2. *En es - ta vi - da fru - tos hay que*
3. *En la tris - te - za y en el do -*
4. *En es - te mun - do por do - quier ha -*

Je - sus, And when we die,
bear. Good works of serv - ice:
lone, When glimps - ing beau - ty,
mourn, Seek-ing con - so - la - tion

*vi - mos; Y si mo - ri - mos,*
*dar, Y bue - nas o - bras*
*lor, En la be - lle - za*
*brá Gen - te que llo - ra*

we re - main in him. Both in our
these are ours to share. If we are
and when love is known: Both in our
for their sor - rows borne; And when we

*pa - ra él mo - ri - mos. Se - a que vi -*
*he - mos de_o - fren - dar. Se - a ya que*
*y en el a - mor, Se - a que su -*
*y sin con - so - lar. Se - a que_a - yu -*

liv - ing, and in our dy - ing,
giv - ing or are re - ceiv - ing,
suf - f'ring and our re - joic - ing,
help them or when we feed them,

*va - mos o que mu - ra - mos,*
*de - mos o que re - ci - ba - mos,*
*fra - mos o que go - ce - mos,*
*de - mos o que_a - li - men - te - mos,*

we are the Lord's, we be-long to him.
*so-mos del Se - ñor,* *so-mos del Se - ñor.*

Text: Verse 1, Romans 14:8; traditional Spanish; vss. 2–4, Roberto Escamilla, b.1931, © 1983, Abingdon Press; tr. by Ronald F. Krisman, b.1946,
   © 2004, Abingdon Press
Tune: SOMOS DEL SEÑOR, Irregular; arr. by Ronald F. Krisman, b.1946, © 2004, GIA Publications, Inc.

## Jesus in the Morning 757

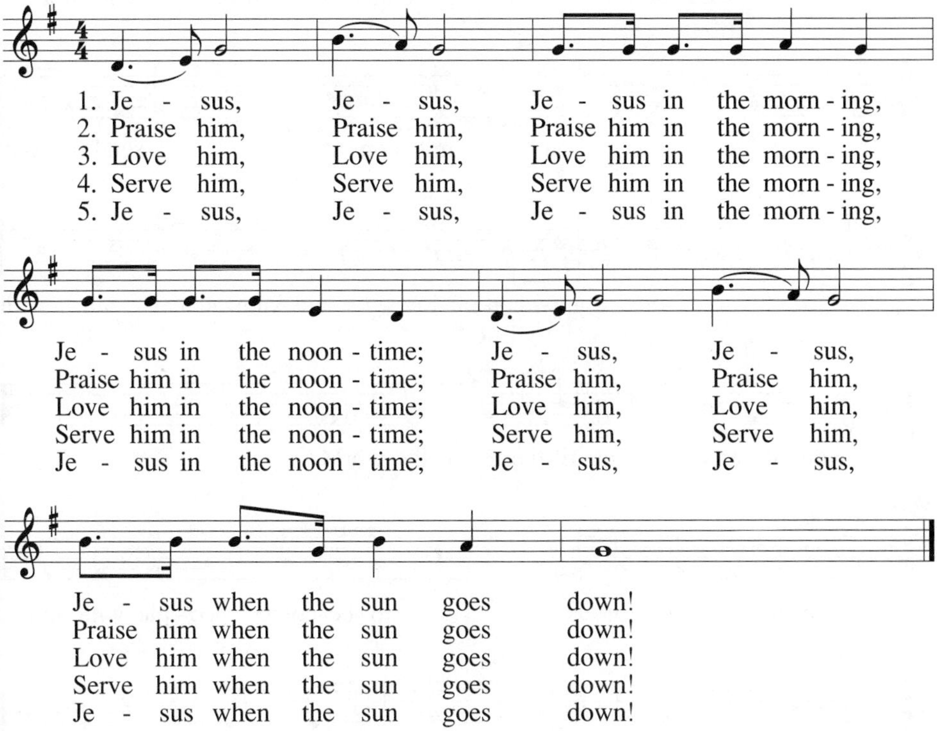

1. Je - sus, Je - sus, Je - sus in the morn - ing,
2. Praise him, Praise him, Praise him in the morn - ing,
3. Love him, Love him, Love him in the morn - ing,
4. Serve him, Serve him, Serve him in the morn - ing,
5. Je - sus, Je - sus, Je - sus in the morn - ing,

Je - sus in the noon - time; Je - sus, Je - sus,
Praise him in the noon - time; Praise him, Praise him,
Love him in the noon - time; Love him, Love him,
Serve him in the noon - time; Serve him, Serve him,
Je - sus in the noon - time; Je - sus, Je - sus,

Je - sus when the sun goes down!
Praise him when the sun goes down!
Love him when the sun goes down!
Serve him when the sun goes down!
Je - sus when the sun goes down!

Text: African American folk song
Tune: African American folk song

# 758 I Send You Out

**Verse 1**

*Cantor:*

1. I bap-tize you in the name of the Fa-ther. I bap-tize you in the name of the Son. I bap-tize you with the Ho-ly Spir-it. Go out and spread Good News!

*All:*

**Refrain**

I send you out on a mis-sion of love. I send you out on a mis-sion of love. I send you out on a mis-sion of love, and know that I am with you al-ways un-til the end of the world.

**Verse 2**

*Cantor:*

2. Well, it's time for us to be-come peo-ple with spir-it. It's time for us to be-come peo-ple of love. It's time for

us to know that Je - sus Christ is ris - en, for -

*All:* **D.S.**

gives our sins, and brings us new life! I send you out

Text: John Angotti, b.1963
Tune: John Angotti, b.1963; arr. by Paul A. Tate, b.1968
© 2000, World Library Publications

## God Sends Us Forth  759

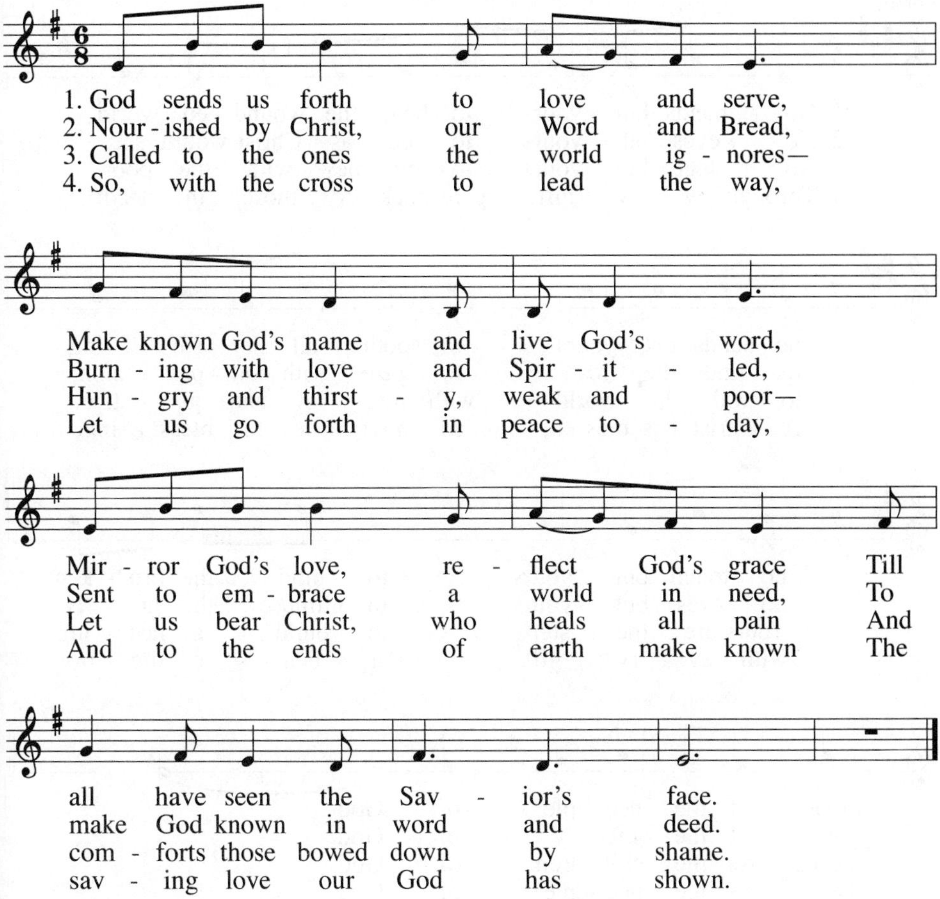

1. God sends us forth to love and serve,
2. Nour - ished by Christ, our Word and Bread,
3. Called to the ones the world ig - nores—
4. So, with the cross to lead the way,

Make known God's name and live God's word,
Burn - ing with love and Spir - it - led,
Hun - gry and thirst - y, weak and poor—
Let us go forth in peace to - day,

Mir - ror God's love, re - flect God's grace Till
Sent to em - brace a world in need, To
Let us bear Christ, who heals all pain And
And to the ends of earth make known The

all have seen the Sav - ior's face.
make God known in word and deed.
com - forts those bowed down by shame.
sav - ing love our God has shown.

Text: Tony E. Alonso, b.1980
Tune: Tony E. Alonso, b.1980
© 2009, GIA Publications, Inc.

# 760 Christ Has No Body Now But Yours

**Refrain**

Christ has no bod-y now but yours, no hands but yours. Here on this earth yours is the work, to serve with the joy of com-pas-sion.

**Verses**

1. No hands but yours to heal the wound-ed world,
2. No eyes but yours to see as Christ would see,
3. No feet but yours to jour-ney with the poor,
4. Through ev-'ry gift, give back to those in need:

1. no hands but yours to soothe all its suf-f'ring,
2. to find the lost, to gaze with com-pas-sion;
3. to walk this world with mer-cy and jus-tice.
4. As Christ has blessed, so now be his bless-ing,

1. no touch but yours to bind the bro-ken
2. no eyes but yours to glimpse the ho-ly
3. Yours are the steps to build a last-ing
4. with ev-'ry gift a ben-e-dic-tion

**D.C.**

1. hope of the peo-ple of God.
2. joy of the cit-y of God.
3. peace for the chil-dren of God.
4. be to the peo-ple of God.

Text: St. Teresa of Ávila, 1515–1582, adapt. by Steven C. Warner, b.1954
Tune: Steven C. Warner, b.1954
© 2003, World Library Publications

# God Has Chosen Me 761

Verses

1. God has cho - sen me, God has cho - sen me to
2. God has cho - sen me, God has cho - sen me to
3. God is call - ing me, God is call - ing me in

bring good news to the poor. God has cho - sen me,
set a - light a new fire. God has cho - sen me,
all whose cry is un - heard. God is call - ing me,

God has cho - sen me to bring new sight to those
God has cho - sen me to bring to birth a new
God is call - ing me to raise up the voice with no

search - ing for light: God has cho - sen me, cho - sen me:
king - dom on earth: God has cho - sen me, cho - sen me:
pow - er or choice: God is call - ing me, call - ing me:

Refrain

And to tell the world that God's king - dom is near, to re -

move op - pres - sion and break down fear, yes, God's time is near,

God's time is near, God's time is near, God's time is near.

Text: Bernadette Farrell, b.1957
Tune: Bernadette Farrell, b.1957

# 762 Go Out to the World

Verses

1. With hands of jus - tice and faith, we go to
(2. With lives of ) cour - age and strength, we spread the
(3. With gen - tle) spir - its, we go to share the

serve the world, to bring good news to the poor and op - pressed.
mes-sage of love to all the weak, the lone - ly, the hurt.
mes-sage of peace with all the trou - bled, lost, and dis - tressed.

With hearts of love and of hope, we go to
With lives that an - swer the call, we spread the
With hum - ble spir - its, we go to share the

live the word that em - pow-ers us to new life.
word of God that em - pow-ers us to new life.
love of God that em - pow-ers us to new life.

𝄉 Refrain

Go out to the world and tell all the good news,

tell all the good news of God's end - less love.

Go out to the world and tell all the good news,

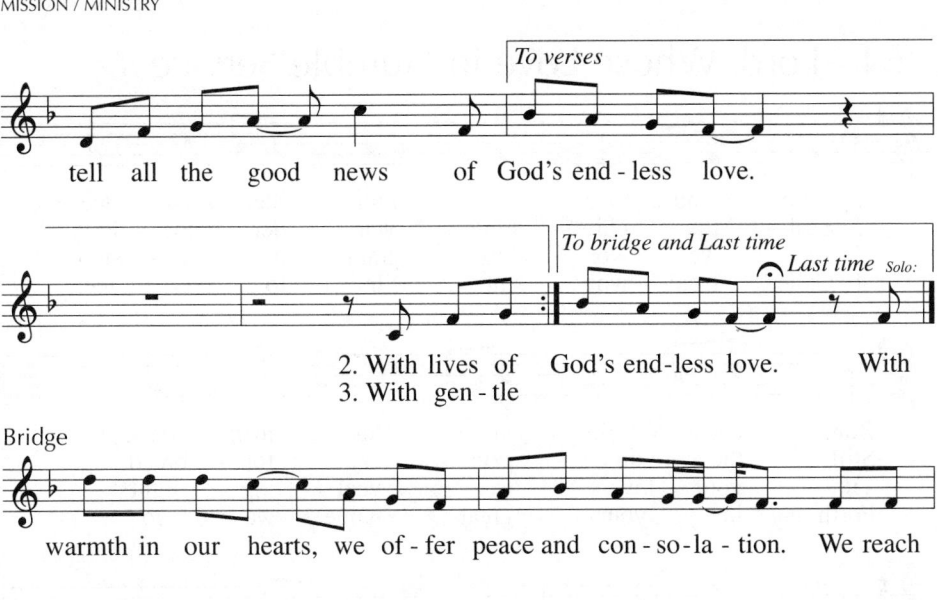

tell all the good news of God's end - less love.

*To bridge and Last time*

*Last time* Solo:

2. With lives of God's end-less love. With
3. With gen - tle

Bridge

warmth in our hearts, we of - fer peace and con - so-la - tion. We reach

D.S.

out to the world, reach out to the world!

Text: Chris de Silva, b.1967
Tune: Chris de Silva, b.1967
© 2007, GIA Publications, Inc.

## Stand Firm 763

Stand, O stand firm; stand, O stand firm;

stand, O stand firm and see what the Lord can do.

Text: Cameroon traditional
Tune: Cameroon traditional; arr. by John L. Bell, b.1949, © 1998, The Iona Community, GIA Publications, Inc., agent

# 764 Lord, Whose Love in Humble Service

1. Lord, whose love in hum - ble serv - ice
2. Still the chil - dren wan - der home - less,
3. As we wor - ship, grant us vi - sion,
4. Called from wor - ship in - to serv - ice,

Bore the weight of hu - man need,
Still the hun - gry cry for bread.
Till your love's re - veal - ing light
Forth in your great name we go

Who up - on the cross, for - sak - en,
Still the cap - tives long for free - dom,
In its height and depth and great - ness
To the child, the youth, the a - ged,

Of - fered mer - cy's per - fect deed:
Still in grief we mourn our dead.
Dawns up - on our hu - man sight,
Love in liv - ing deeds to show.

We, your ser - vants, bring the wor - ship
As you, Lord, in deep com - pas - sion,
Mak - ing known the needs and bur - dens
Hope and health, good - will and com - fort,

Not of voice a - lone, but heart,
Healed the sick and freed the soul,
Your com - pas - sion bids us bear,
Coun - sel, aid, and peace we give

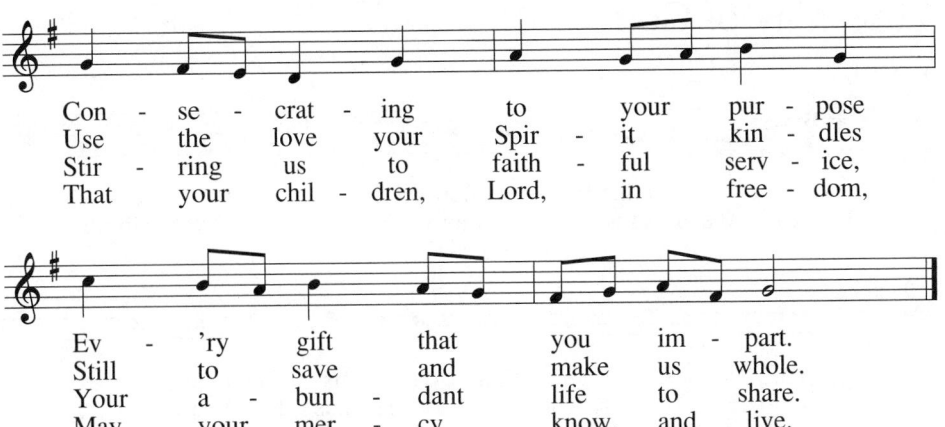

Con - se - crat - ing    to    your    pur - pose
Use    the    love    your    Spir - it    kin - dles
Stir - ring    us    to    faith - ful    serv - ice,
That    your    chil - dren,    Lord,    in    free - dom,

Ev - 'ry    gift    that    you    im - part.
Still    to    save    and    make    us    whole.
Your    a - bun - dant    life    to    share.
May    your    mer - cy    know,    and    live.

Text: Albert F. Bayly, 1901–1984, alt., © 1988, Oxford University Press
Tune: IN BABILONE, 8 7 8 7 D; *Oude en Nieuwe Hollantse Boerenlieties en Contredansen*, c.1710

## The Church of Christ    765

1. The Church    of    Christ,    in    ev - 'ry    age    Be - set    by
2. A - cross    the    world,    a - cross    the    street,    The    vic - tims
3. Then    let    the    ser - vant    Church    a - rise,    A    car - ing
4. For    he    a - lone,    whose    blood    was    shed,    Can    cure    the
5. We    have    no    mis - sion    but    to    serve    In    full    o -

change,    but    Spir - it - led,    Must    claim    and    test    its    her - it -
of    in - jus - tice    cry    For    shel - ter    and    for    bread    to
Church    that    longs    to    be    A    part - ner    in    Christ's    sac - ri -
fe - ver    in    our    blood,    And    teach    us    how    to    share    our
be - dience    to    our    Lord:    To    care    for    all,    with - out    re -

age    And    keep    on    ris - ing    from    the    dead.
eat,    And    nev - er    live    un - til    they    die.
fice,    And    clothed    in    Christ's    hu - man - i - ty.
bread    And    feed    the    starv - ing    mul - ti - tude.
serve,    And    spread    his    lib - er - at - ing    Word.

Text: Fred Pratt Green, 1903–2000, © 1972, Hope Publishing Company
Tune: O WALY WALY, LM; English; harm. by Martin West, b.1929, © 1983, Hope Publishing Company

# 766  City of God

Verses 1, 2

1.  A-wake from your slum-ber!     A - rise from your
2. We are sons  of  the morn-ing;     we are daugh-ters of

sleep!     A  new  day  is  dawn-ing
day.     The  One  who has  loved us

for  all  those who weep.     The  peo - ple  in
has bright-ened  our  way.     The  Lord  of all

dark - ness  have seen  a great light.     The Lord  of our
kind - ness  has called us  to  be  a  light  for his

long-ing  has con-quered the  night.     
peo - ple  to  set  their hearts  free.

Refrain

Let us  build the  cit-y  of  God.     May our  tears  be

turned in - to danc - ing!     For the Lord,  our light and our

love,  has  turned  the night in - to  day!

Verse 3

3. God is light; in him there is no dark-ness. Let us walk in his light, his chil - dren, one and all.

O com-fort my peo-ple; make gen-tle your words. Pro - claim to my cit-y

**D.S.**

the day of her birth.

Verse 4

4. O cit-y of glad-ness, now lift up your voice. Pro - claim the good tid - ings

**D.S.**

that all may re - joice!

Text: Dan Schutte, b.1947
Tune: Dan Schutte, b.1947; acc. by Robert J. Batastini, b.1942
© 1981, Daniel L. Schutte and OCP

# 767 Called by Christ

Verses

1. Called by Christ, you built on the bed - rock,
2. Called by Christ, you of - fer God's chil - dren
3. Called by Christ, you thirst af - ter good - ness.

God who was faith - ful through each pass - ing year.
Food for their hun - ger and songs for the soul.
Seek - ing God's pres - ence you sure - ly will find.

Spir - it - led, you wel - come the stran - ger,
Spir - it - led, you look to the fu - ture,
Spir - it - led, you plant for the har - vest,

Prom - ise of new life a - wak-en-ing here.
hand to your la - bor and eye on the goal.
Peace, love, and jus - tice for all hu - man - kind.

Refrain

Sing, sing, sing of God's good-ness. Cel - e - brate love a -

live here to - day. Share, share life in the Spir - it.

Look for God's reign and seek Je - sus' way.

Text: Ruth Duck, b.1947, © 2005, GIA Publications, Inc.
Tune: Kate Cuddy, b.1953, © 2007, GIA Publications, Inc.

# Good News 768

Verses

1. When Je - sus worked here on earth he
2. The eld - ers of the syn - a - gogue were
3. The way he lived was proof of it: he
4. So pass it on to - day, good friend: the

preached in his home - town, I - sa - iah's hopes
shocked by Mar - y's son, That he was des -
qui - et - ed our strife. The cross it - self he
mes - sage is the same. De - liv - 'rance Christ a -

now ful - filled, those claims of great re - nown.
tined to be the Christ for ev - 'ry - one.
would not flee e'en though it cost his life.
lone can give, for this to earth he came.

Refrain

To bring good news to the need - y, to make the

blind to see, the bro - ken hearts healed a - gain, to

1.

set the cap - tive free.

2.

cap - tive free.

Text: Howard S. Olson, 1922–2010
Tune: Almaz Belihu; Yemissrach Dimts Literature Program, Ethiopia
© 1993, Estate of Howard S. Olson

# 769 Go Make of All Disciples

1. "Go make of all dis - ci - ples." We hear the call, O
2. "Go make of all dis - ci - ples," Bap - tiz - ing in the
3. "Go make of all dis - ci - ples." We at your feet would
4. "Go make of all dis - ci - ples." We wel - come your com -

Lord, That comes from you, our Fa - ther, In
name Of Fa - ther, Son, and Spir - it— From
stay Un - til each life's vo - ca - tion Shows
mand. "Lo, I am with you al - ways." We

your e - ter - nal Word. In - spire our ways of
age to age the same. We call each new dis -
forth your ho - ly way. We cul - ti - vate the
take your guid - ing hand. The task looms large be -

learn - ing Through earn - est, fer - vent prayer, And
ci - ple To fol - low you, O Lord, Re -
na - ture God plants in ev - 'ry heart, Re -
fore us— We fol - low with - out fear. In

let our dai - ly liv - ing Re - veal you ev - 'ry - where.
deem - ing soul and bod - y By wa - ter and the Word.
veal - ing in our wit - ness The Mas - ter Teach-er's art.
heav'n and earth your pow - er Shall bring God's king - dom here.

Text: Matthew 28:19–20; Leon M. Adkins, 1896–1986, alt. © 1964, Abingdon Press
Tune: ELLACOMBE, 7 6 7 6 D; *Gesangbuch der Herzogl*, Wirtemberg, 1784

# One Lord 770

**Refrain**

One Lord, one faith, one call to serve

each oth - er. One heart, one mind,

*To verses* | **Final ending**

one com - mon ground; we stand all as one.

**Verses** *Solo:*

1. Give us new hands, o - pen and free,
2. Give us new eyes, lov - ing and wise,
3. Give us new hearts, hum - ble yet strong,
4. Breathe out your Spir - it up - on the land.

to serve with grace and dig - ni - ty. May we be wor-
to seek the good we all have in - side. May we be wor-
to love like you our whole life long. May we be wor-
In hope and peace we'll firm - ly stand, to live lives wor-

**D.C.**

thy of our call.
thy of our call.
thy of our call. We have but
thy of our call.

Text: Ephesians 4:1–24; Lori True, b.1961
Tune: Lori True, b.1961
© 2003, GIA Publications, Inc.

## 771 Go in Peace, Go in Love

Go in peace. Go in love.

Go to seek. Go to serve.

Go in hope to work and pray. And

1.
God goes with you all the way.

2.
And God goes with you all the way.

Text: Mary Louise Bringle, b.1953
Tune: GIPGIL; Sally Ann Morris, b.1952
© 2011, GIA Publications, Inc.

# How Can We Be Silent   772

**Verses**

1. How can we be si-lent when we know our God is near, bring-ing
2. How can we be si-lent when our God has con-quered death, stretch-ing
3. How can we be si-lent as we turn our eyes a - way and ig -
4. How can we be si-lent, not give praise with all our hearts, for Christ
5. How can we be si-lent when our souls are filled with awe at the

light   to those in dark-ness, to the worth-less, end-less worth?
out   his arms to suf - fer so that we might have new life?
nore   the poor and bro-ken who lie bleed-ing in the street?
Je - sus is our Sav-ior and com-pas-sion is our king?
beau-ty of cre - a - tion and the mer - cy of our Lord?

How can we be si-lent when we are the voice of Christ, speak-ing
How can we be si-lent when we know that Je - sus rose, and will
How can we be si-lent when we're called to heal and serve in the
How can we be si-lent when God gave us life to be vi-brant
How can we be si-lent when we yearn to sing new songs? In our

jus - tice to the na-tions, breath-ing love to all the earth?
come a - gain in glo - ry, end - ing suf - fer - ing and strife?
im - age of Lord Je - sus, who has stooped to wash our feet?
in - stru-ments of wor-ship, made to laugh and dance and sing?
hearts a fire is burn-ing and it will not be ig - nored!

**Refrain***   1.   2.

None can stop the Spir - it   burn-ing now in-side us.

3.   4.

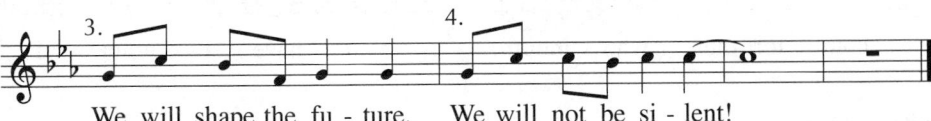

We will shape the fu - ture.   We will not be si - lent!

*May be sung as a canon.*

Text: Michael Mahler, b.1981
Tune: Michael Mahler, b.1981
© 2003, GIA Publications, Inc.

# 773 You Have Anointed Me

**Verse 1**

1. To bring glad tid - ings to the low - ly, to heal the bro-ken heart, You have a - noint - ed me. To pro - claim lib-er-ty to cap - tives, re - lease to pris - on - ers, You have a - noint - ed me.

**Refrain**

Your Spir - it, O God, is up - on me, You have a - noint - ed me.

**Verse 2**

2. To an-nounce a year of fa - vor, to com - fort those who mourn, You have a - noint - ed me. To give to them the oil of glad - ness, and

D.S.

share   a man-tle of   joy,   You   have   a - noint - ed   me.

## You Are Called to Tell the Story   774

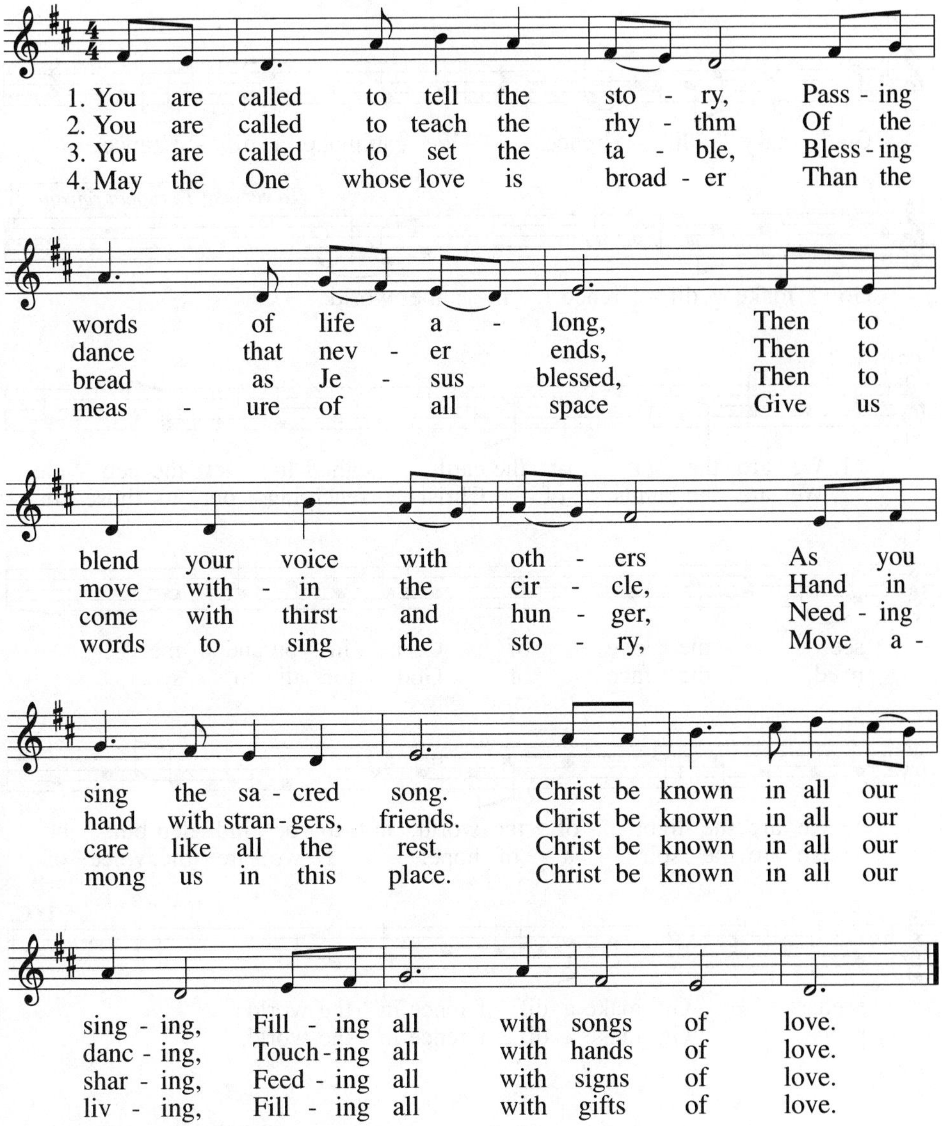

1. You   are   called   to   tell   the   sto - ry,   Pass - ing
2. You   are   called   to   teach   the   rhy - thm   Of   the
3. You   are   called   to   set   the   ta - ble,   Bless - ing
4. May   the   One   whose love   is   broad - er   Than   the

words   of   life   a -   long,   Then   to
dance   that   nev - er   ends,   Then   to
bread   as   Je - sus   blessed,   Then   to
meas - ure   of   all   space   Give   us

blend   your   voice   with   oth - ers   As   you
move   with - in   the   cir - cle,   Hand   in
come   with   thirst   and   hun - ger,   Need - ing
words   to   sing   the   sto - ry,   Move   a -

sing   the   sa - cred   song.   Christ be   known   in all   our
hand   with stran - gers,   friends.   Christ be   known   in all   our
care   like   all   the   rest.   Christ be   known   in all   our
mong   us   in   this   place.   Christ be   known   in all   our

sing - ing,   Fill - ing   all   with   songs   of   love.
danc - ing,   Touch - ing   all   with   hands   of   love.
shar - ing,   Feed - ing   all   with   signs   of   love.
liv - ing,   Fill - ing   all   with   gifts   of   love.

# 775  Go Make a Difference

Refrain

Go make a dif - f'rence. We can make a dif - f'rence.

Go make a dif - f'rence in the world.

Go make a dif - f'rence. We can make a dif - f'rence.

*To verses* | *To repeat refrain*

Go make a dif - f'rence in the world.

Verses 1, 2

1. We are the salt of the earth, called to let the peo - ple
2. We are the hands of Christ reach-ing out to those in

see the love of God in you and me.
need, the face of God for all to see.

We are the light of the world, not to be hid - den but be
We are the spir - it of hope; we are the voice of

**D.C.**

seen. Go make a dif - f'rence in the world.
peace. Go make a dif - f'rence in the world.

Verse 3

3. So let your love shine on, let it shine for all to see.

Go make a dif - f'rence in the world. And the

spir - it of Christ will be with us as we go.

D.C.

Go make a dif -f'rence in the world.

Text: Matthew 5:13–16; Steve Angrisano, b.1965, and Tom Tomaszek, b.1950
Tune: Steve Angrisano, b.1965, and Tom Tomaszek, b.1950; acc. by Rick Modlin, b.1966
© 1997, 1998, Steve Agrisano and Thomas N. Tomaszek. Published by OCP.

## Thuma Mina / Send Me, Jesus    776

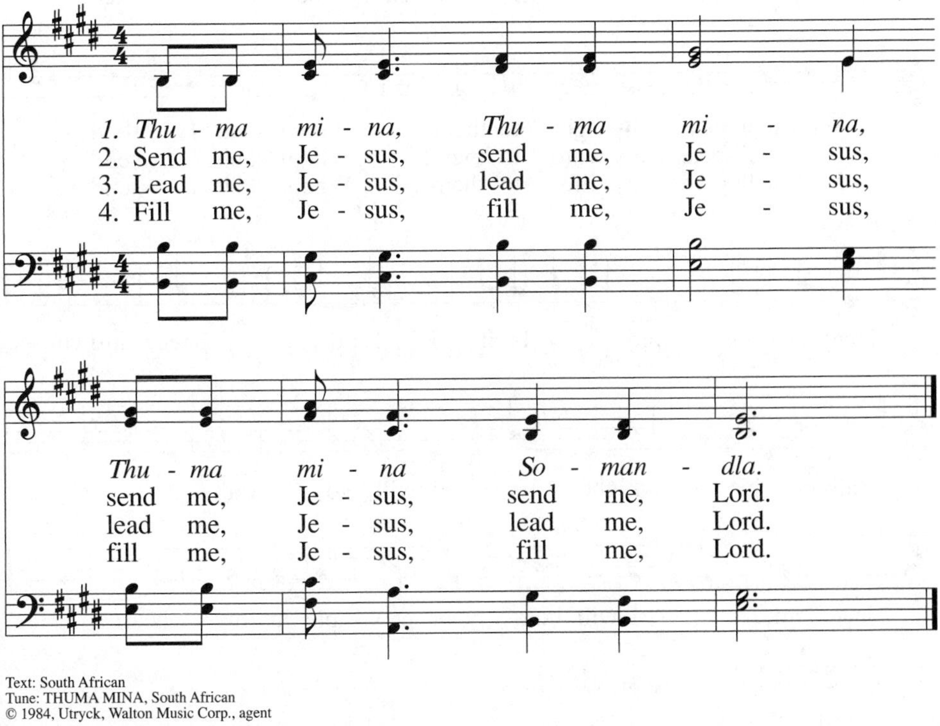

1. *Thu - ma   mi - na,*   *Thu - ma   mi - na,*
2. Send me,   Je - sus,   send   me,   Je - sus,
3. Lead me,   Je - sus,   lead   me,   Je - sus,
4. Fill me,   Je - sus,   fill   me,   Je - sus,

*Thu - ma   mi - na*   *So - man - dla.*
send me,   Je - sus,   send   me,   Lord.
lead me,   Je - sus,   lead   me,   Lord.
fill me,   Je - sus,   fill   me,   Lord.

Text: South African
Tune: THUMA MINA, South African
© 1984, Utryck, Walton Music Corp., agent

# 777 Here I Am, Lord

Verses

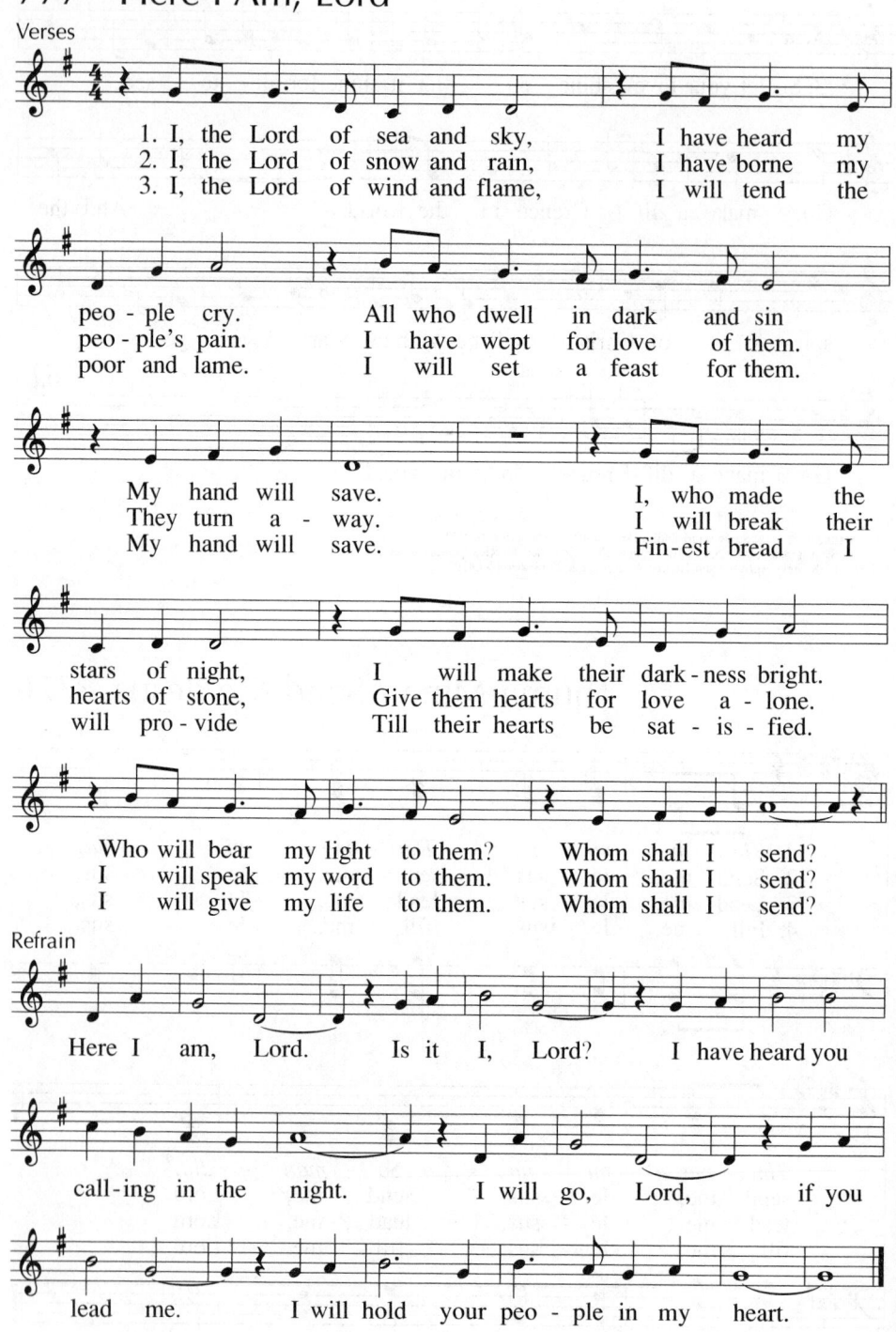

1. I, the Lord of sea and sky, I have heard my
2. I, the Lord of snow and rain, I have borne my
3. I, the Lord of wind and flame, I will tend the

peo - ple cry. All who dwell in dark and sin
peo - ple's pain. I have wept for love of them.
poor and lame. I will set a feast for them.

My hand will save. I, who made the
They turn a - way. I will break their
My hand will save. Fin - est bread I

stars of night, I will make their dark - ness bright.
hearts of stone, Give them hearts for love a - lone.
will pro - vide Till their hearts be sat - is - fied.

Who will bear my light to them? Whom shall I send?
I will speak my word to them. Whom shall I send?
I will give my life to them. Whom shall I send?

Refrain

Here I am, Lord. Is it I, Lord? I have heard you

call - ing in the night. I will go, Lord, if you

lead me. I will hold your peo - ple in my heart.

Text: Isaiah 6; Dan Schutte, b.1947
Tune: Dan Schutte, b.1947; arr. by Michael Pope, SJ, and John Weissrock

# Anthem 778

**Refrain**

We are called, we are cho-sen. We are Christ for one an-oth-er. We are

prom-ised to to-mor-row, while we are for him to-day. We are

sign, we are won-der. We are sow-er, we are seed. We are

har-vest, we are hun-ger. We are ques-tion, we are creed.

**Verses**

1. Then where can we stand jus-ti-fied? In what can we be-
2. Then how are we to stand at all, this world of bend-ed
3. Then shall we not stand emp-ty at the al-tar of our

lieve? In no one else but Christ who suf-fered, noth-ing
knee? In noth-ing more than bar-ren shad-ows. No one
dreams: When Christ prom-ised us our-selves. Who mark

more than Christ who rose. Who was jus-tice for the poor.
else but Christ could save us. Who was jus-tice for the poor.
time a-gainst to-mor-row. Who are jus-tice for the poor.

Who was rage a-gainst the night. Who was
Who was rage a-gainst the night. Who was
Who are rage a-gainst the night. Who are

**D.C.**

hope for peace-ful peo-ple. Who was light.
hope for peace-ful peo-ple. Who was light.
hope for peace-ful peo-ple. Who are light.

Text: Tom Conry, b.1951
Tune: Tom Conry, b.1951; acc. by Robert J. Batastini, b.1942
© 1978, OCP

# 779 Look to Christ

Refrain

Look to Christ to be your light; fol - low,

Leave be-hind your for - mer self and live.

Don't look back, don't be a-fraid; fol - low,

1.–4.    To verses    5.

Come to Christ, walk with Christ, and live.    live.

Verses

1. Who is the one who calls us to live our life to the full?
2. Who is the one who sees ev-'ry-thing we say and do?
3. Who is the one who gives new sight to those who are blind?
4. Who is the one who weeps for us? Who can this be?

Who is the one who calls us to bear the
Who is the one who knows us and still for -
Who is the one who wash-es and makes us
Who is the one who rolls the stone a -

cross? Who is the one who calls us all to
gives? Who is the source and foun-tain of grace that
new? Who is the one who o - pens our eyes that
way? Who is the one who cries to us all to

sell   what  we  have?               Je - sus,  the  Christ:     the
quench-es  our  thirst?           Je - sus,  the  Christ:     the
we   may  be - lieve?           Je - sus,  the  Christ:     the
come  out  and  live?            Je - sus,  the  Christ:  Res-ur -

**D.C.**

Son  of  the  Liv  -  ing     God!
Wa - ter  of  Life     and     Love!
Liv  -  ing  Light  of     God!
rec-tion  and  Life   for     all!

Text: David Haas, b.1957
Tune: David Haas, b.1957
© 2007, GIA Publications, Inc.

## Guide My Feet   780

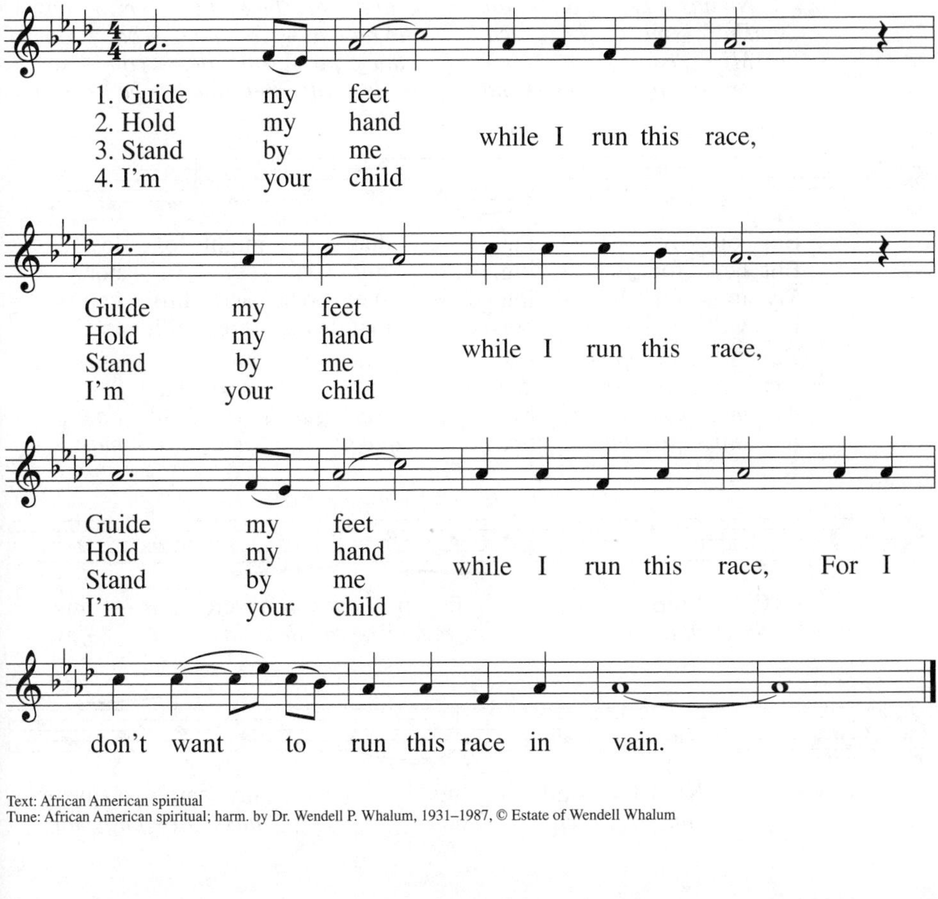

1. Guide     my     feet
2. Hold     my     hand
3. Stand    by     me          while  I   run this  race,
4. I'm     your   child

Guide     my     feet
Hold     my     hand
Stand    by     me          while  I   run this  race,
I'm     your   child

Guide     my     feet
Hold     my     hand
Stand    by     me          while  I   run this  race,    For  I
I'm     your   child

don't  want    to   run this race in    vain.

Text: African American spiritual
Tune: African American spiritual; harm. by Dr. Wendell P. Whalum, 1931–1987, © Estate of Wendell Whalum

# 781 Lord, When You Came / Pescador de Hombres

**Verses**

1. Lord, when you came to the sea - shore
2. Lord, you knew what my boat car - ried:
3. Lord, have you need of my la - bor,
4. Lord, send me where you would have me,

*1. Tú has ve - ni - do a la o - ri - lla,*
*2. Tú sa - bes bien lo que ten - go;*
*3. Tú ne - ce - si - tas mis ma - nos,*
*4. Tú, pes - ca - dor de o - tros la - gos,*

You weren't seek - ing the wise or the wealth - y,
Nei - ther mon - ey nor weap - ons for fight - ing,
Hands for serv - ice, a heart made for lov - ing,
To a vil - lage, or heart of the cit - y;

*No has bus - ca - do ni a sa - bios, ni a ri - cos;*
*En mi bar - ca no hay o - ro ni es - pa - das,*
*Mi can - san - cio que a o - tros des - can - se,*
*an - sia e - ter - na de al - mas que es - pe - ran,*

But on - ly ask - ing that I might fol - low.
But nets for fish - ing, my dai - ly la - bor.
My arms for lift - ing the poor and bro - ken?
I will re - mem - ber that you are with me.

*Tan só - lo quie - res que yo te si - ga.*
*Tan só - lo re - des y mi tra - ba - jo.*
*A - mor que quie - ra se - guir a - man - do.*
*A - mi - go bue - no, que a - sí me lla - mas.*

**Refrain**

O Lord, in my eyes you were gaz - ing,
*Se - ñor, me has mi - ra - do a los o - jos,*

Kind - ly smil - ing, my name you were
*son - ri - en - do has di - cho mi*

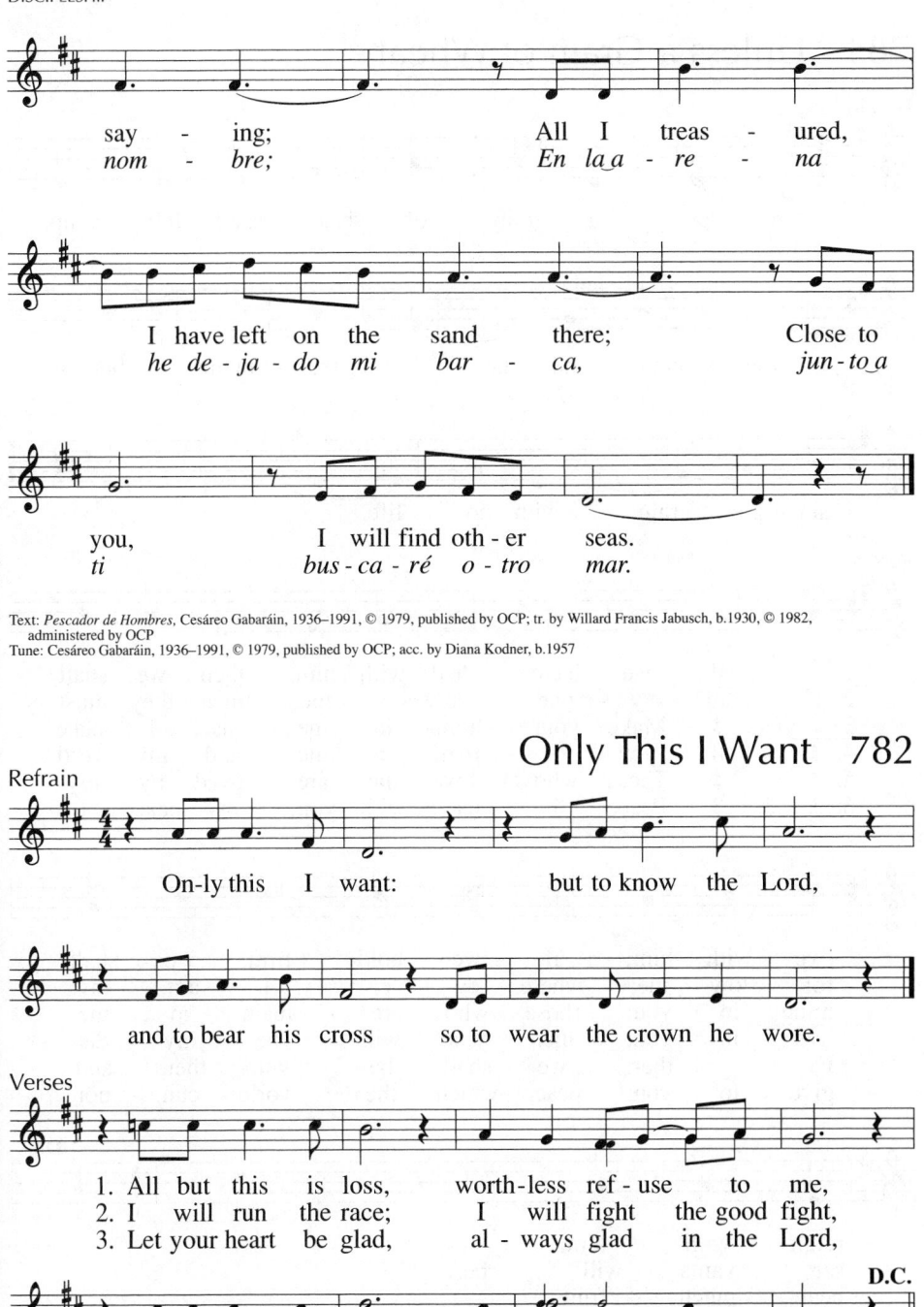

say - ing;
*nom - bre;*

All I treas - ured,
*En la_a - re - na*

I have left on the sand there;
*he de - ja - do mi bar - ca,*

Close to
*jun - to_a*

you,
*ti*

I will find oth - er seas.
*bus - ca - ré o - tro mar.*

Text: *Pescador de Hombres*, Cesáreo Gabaráin, 1936–1991, © 1979, published by OCP; tr. by Willard Francis Jabusch, b.1930, © 1982, administered by OCP
Tune: Cesáreo Gabaráin, 1936–1991, © 1979, published by OCP; acc. by Diana Kodner, b.1957

## Only This I Want    782

Refrain

On - ly this I want: but to know the Lord,

and to bear his cross so to wear the crown he wore.

Verses

1. All but this is loss, worth - less ref - use to me,
2. I will run the race; I will fight the good fight,
3. Let your heart be glad, al - ways glad in the Lord,

D.C.

for to gain the Lord is to gain all I need.
so to win the prize of the King - dom of my Lord.
so to shine like stars in the dark - ness of the night.

Text: Philippians 3:7–16; 2:15, 18; Dan Schutte, b.1947
Tune: Dan Schutte, b.1947; arr. by Michael Pope, SJ
© 1981, Daniel L. Schutte and OCP

# 783 Unless a Grain of Wheat

Refrain

Un - less a grain of wheat shall fall up -
on the ground and die, it re - mains but a
sin - gle grain with no life.

Verses

1. If we have died with him, then we shall
2. If an - y - one serves me, then they must
3. Make your home in me as I make
4. If you re - main in me and my word
5. Those who love me are loved by my
6. Peace I leave with you, my peace I

live with him; if we hold firm, we shall
fol - low me; where - ev - er I am, my
mine in you; those who re - main in me
lives in you, then you will be my dis -
Fa - ther; we shall be with them and
give to you; peace which the world can - not

D.C.

reign with him.
ser - vants will be.
bear much fruit.
ci - ples.
dwell in them.
give is my gift.

Text: John 12:24; Bernadette Farrell, b.1957
Tune: Bernadette Farrell, b.1957
© 1983, Bernadette Farrell. Published by OCP.

# We Have Been Told  784

**Refrain**

We have been told, we've seen his face and

heard his voice a-live in our hearts:

"Live in my love with all your heart;

as the Fa-ther has loved me, so I have loved

you."

**Verse 1**

1. "I am the vine, you are the branch-es, and

D.C.

all who live in me will bear great fruit."

**Verses 2, 3**

2. "You are my friends, if you keep my com-mands;
3. "No great-er love is there than this: to

D.C.

no long-er slaves, I call you friends."
lay down one's life for a friend."

Text: David Haas, b.1957
Tune: David Haas, b.1957; vocal arr. by David Haas and Marty Haugen, b.1950
© 1983, GIA Publications, Inc.

# 785 Now We Remain

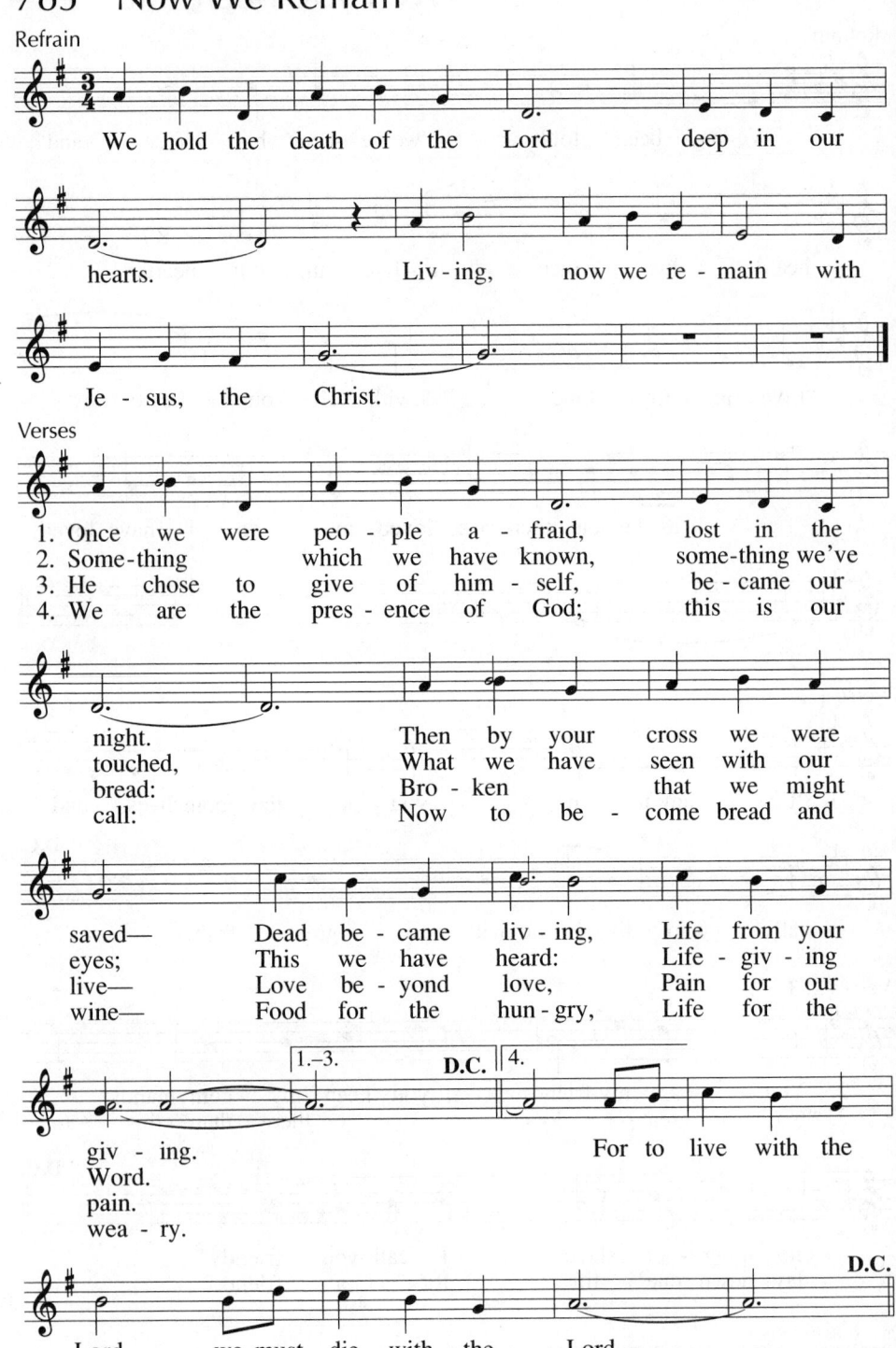

Refrain

We hold the death of the Lord deep in our hearts. Liv-ing, now we re-main with Je-sus, the Christ.

Verses

1. Once we were peo - ple a - fraid, lost in the
2. Some-thing which we have known, some-thing we've
3. He chose to give of him - self, be - came our
4. We are the pres - ence of God; this is our

night. Then by your cross we were
touched, What we have seen with our
bread: Bro - ken that we might
call: Now to be - come bread and

saved— Dead be - came liv - ing, Life from your
eyes; This we have heard: Life - giv - ing
live— Love be - yond love, Pain for our
wine— Food for the hun - gry, Life for the

1.–3. | D.C. | 4.

giv - ing.
Word.
pain.
wea - ry.

For to live with the

D.C.

Lord, we must die with the Lord.

Text: Corinthians, 1 John, 2 Timothy; David Haas, b.1957
Tune: David Haas, b.1957
© 1983, GIA Publications, Inc.

# Heart of a Shepherd / 786
# El Corazón de un Buen Pastor

**Refrain**

If you love me, feed my lambs; Be my heart, my voice, my
*Si me a - mas con fer - vor, sé mis ma - nos, voz, y_a -*

hands. If you love me, feed my sheep. And for my part, I give
*mor. Mis o - ve - jas cui - da - rás. El co - ra - zón de un*

you the heart of a shep - herd.
*buen pas - tor yo te_en - tre - go.*

**Verses**

1. Lord, you are my shepherd;
   there is nothing I shall want.
   Fresh and green are the pastures
   where you give me repose.
   Near restful waters you lead me,
   to revive my drooping spirit.

2. You guide me along the right path;
   you are true to your name.
   If I should walk in the valley of darkness
   no evil would I fear.
   You are there with your crook your staff;
   with these you give me comfort.

3. You have prepared a banquet for me
   in the sight of my foes.
   My head you have anointed with oil;
   my cup is overflowing.

4. Surely goodness and kindness shall
   follow me
   all the days of my life.
   In the Lord's own house shall I dwell
   for ever and ever.

5. To the Father and Son give glory,
   give glory to the Spirit,
   to God who is, who was, and who will be
   for ever and ever.

1. *Tú_eres, Señor, mi pastor;*
   *nada me falta.*
   *En praderas de hierba tierna*
   *tú me haces reposar.*
   *A las aguas de descanso me guías,*
   *y mi alma reconfortas.*

2. *Tú me guías por veredas de justicia,*
   *por amor de tu nombre.*
   *Aunque camine por cañadas oscuras,*
   *ningún mal temeré.*
   *Junto_a mí tu vara_y tu cayado:*
   *ellos me confortan.*

3. *Tú preparas ante mí una mesa,*
   *frente_a aquellos que me odian.*
   *Tú perfumas con óleo mi cabeza,*
   *desbordando_está mi copa.*

4. *Tu gracia_y tu favor me seguirán*
   *por los días de mi vida.*
   *Habitaré en la casa del Señor*
   *a lo largo de los días.*

5. *Gloria_a Dios Padre_omnipotente,*
   *y_a su Hijo, Jesucristo,*
   *y_al Espíritu que_habita_en nuestras*
   *almas,*
   *por los siglos de los siglos.*

Text: Refrain, Rory Cooney, b.1952, © 2005, GIA Publications, Inc.; verses, Psalm 23, The Grail, © 1963, 1993, The Grail, GIA Publications, Inc., agent;
tr. by Ronald F. Krisman, b.1946, © 2010, GIA Publications, Inc.
Tune: Refrain and verses arr., Rory Cooney, b.1952, © 2005, GIA Publications, Inc.; verses melody, Joseph Gelineau, SJ, 1920–2008, © 1963, 1993,
The Grail, GIA Publications, Inc., agent

# 787 Take Up Your Cross

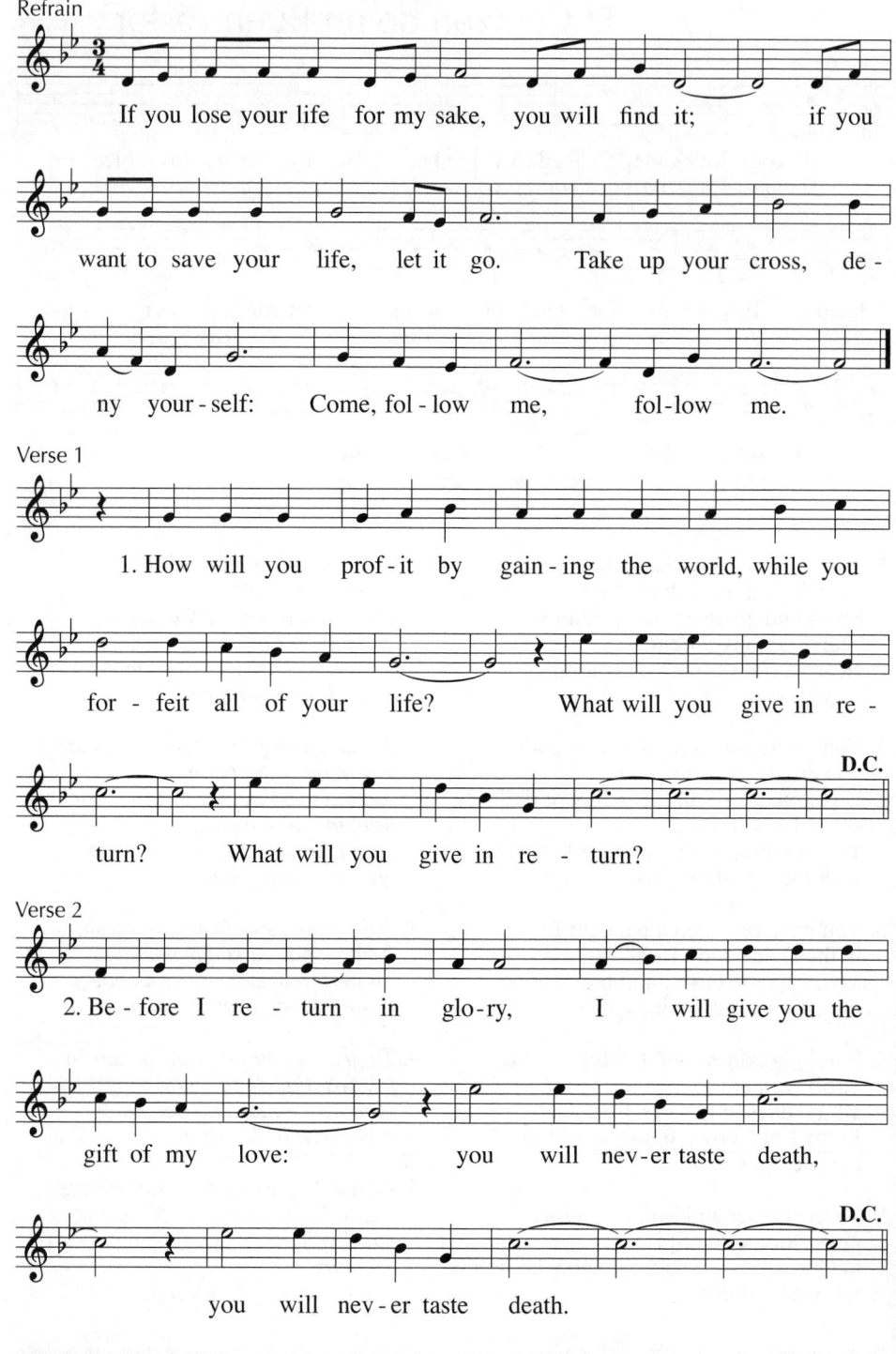

Refrain

If you lose your life for my sake, you will find it; if you want to save your life, let it go. Take up your cross, de-ny your-self: Come, fol-low me, fol-low me.

Verse 1

1. How will you prof-it by gain-ing the world, while you for-feit all of your life? What will you give in re-turn? What will you give in re-turn?

Verse 2

2. Be-fore I re-turn in glo-ry, I will give you the gift of my love: you will nev-er taste death, you will nev-er taste death.

Text: Matthew 16:24–28; David Haas, b.1957
Tune: David Haas, b.1957
© 2001, GIA Publications, Inc.

# Come and Journey with a Savior  788

1. Come and jour - ney with a Sav - ior Who has
2. Come and jour - ney, jour-ney in - ward, Come and
3. Come and jour - ney, jour-ney out - ward, Tell - ing
4. Come and jour - ney, jour-ney out - ward, Where that
5. Come and jour - ney, jour-ney up - ward, Sing his
6. Come and jour - ney, jour-ney on - ward, All our

called us from our birth, Who has washed us in the
seek him deep with - in, Where he meets us in our
oth - ers of his name, Tell - ing oth - ers of his
cross calls us to care, Where in - jus - tice and where
prais - es, of - fer prayer. In the storm and in the
gifts we now shall bring, To the build - ing of a

wa - ters, And who loved us on the earth.
liv - ing, In our striv - ing and our sin.
glo - ry, Of his cross and of the shame.
hun - ger And the poor call us to share.
still - ness, Find his pres - ence ev - 'ry - where.
cit - y That is ho - ly, Christ its king.

Come and jour - ney, come and jour - ney With a Sav-ior who has

come. We are all God's sons and daugh - ters. In the

Spir-it we are one. In the Spir-it we are one.

Text: Herbert O'Driscoll, b.1928, ©
Tune: COME AND JOURNEY, 8 7 8 7 with refrain; Marty Haugen, b.1950, © 1998, GIA Publications, Inc.

# 789 Blest Are We / Bendecidos, Somos Santos

**Refrain**

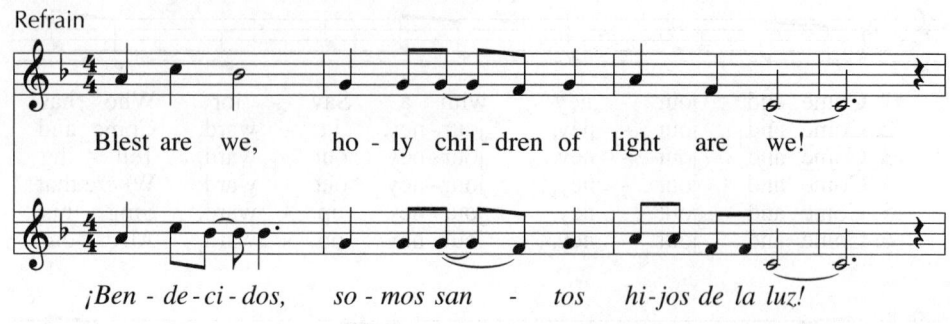

Blest are we, ho-ly chil-dren of light are we!

¡Ben - de-ci-dos, so - mos san - tos hi-jos de la luz!

Blest are we, cho - sen peo - ple of God.

Ben - de - ci - dos, y e - le - gi - dos por Dios.

Blest are we, God has plans for you and me.

Ben - de - ci - dos, Dios nos quie - re ha-cer cual Je - sús.

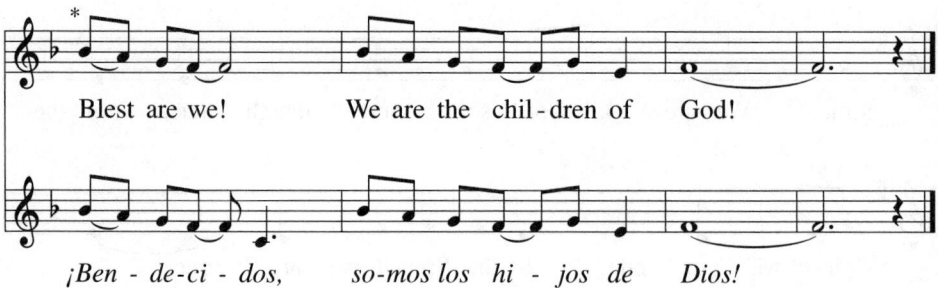

Blest are we! We are the chil-dren of God!

¡Ben - de-ci - dos, so-mos los hi - jos de Dios!

*Last time, repeat final 4 bars.

Verses

1. For our world, each sis - ter and broth - er: We are called,
2. For the poor, the meek and the low - ly: We are called,
3. For all those who yearn for free - dom: We are called,

1. Por el mun-do, por to - dos sus pue-blos: ¡So-mos lla-ma - dos
2. Por los po-bres, los man - sos y hu-mil - des: ¡So-mos lla-ma - dos
3. Por los que su-fren y quie-ren ser li - bra-dos: ¡So-mos lla-ma - dos

called to serve! We are here to love one an-oth - er:
called to serve! For the weak, the sick and the hun - gry:
called to serve! For the world, to be God's king - dom:

pa-ra ser-vir! Que nos a-me-mos los u - nos a los o - tros;
pa-ra ser-vir! Por los en-fer-mos, ham-brien - tos, y dé-bi-les:
pa-ra ser-vir! Ven-ga a no-so-tros el Rei-no de los Cie-los:

We are called, called to serve!
We are called, called to serve!
We are called, called to serve!

D.C.

¡So-mos lla - ma - dos pa-ra ser-vir!
¡So-mos lla - ma - dos pa-ra ser-vir!
¡So-mos lla - ma - dos pa-ra ser-vir!

D.C.

Text: David Haas, b.1957, Spanish tr. by Ronald F. Krisman, b.1946
Tune: David Haas, b.1957
© 2003, GIA Publications, Inc.

# 790 The Summons

Text: John L. Bell, b.1949, © 1987, Iona Community, GIA Publications, Inc., agent
Tune: KELVINGROVE, 7 6 7 6 777 6; Scottish traditional; arr. by John L. Bell, b.1949, © 1987, Iona Community, GIA Publications, Inc., agent

# Were I the Perfect Child of God 791

1. Were I the per-fect child of God Whose faith was deep and love was broad, Not doubt-ful, guilt-y, worn or flawed, I'd glad-ly fol-low Je-sus. But I'm the child of what I've been, Es-tranged by much I've done and seen, A-fraid to show the love I mean, Un-fit to fol-low Je-sus.

2. Yet God, who knows me first and last, Who's seen my best, my worst, my past, Has shown his love in-tense and vast By meet-ing me in Je-sus. For Christ, though killed at Cal-va-ry By sins like mine and folk like me, Has ris'n, for-giv'n and set me free, Fit to fol-low Je-sus.

3. Then sprin-kle wa-ter on my brow As, in this place, I make my vow To own and love my Sav-ior now And give my-self to Je-sus. God grant me what I still re-quire That I, in oth-ers, might in-spire The hid-den hope, the deep de-sire To love and fol-low Je-sus.

Text: John L. Bell, b.1949, © 2004, Iona Community, GIA Publications, Inc., agent
Tune: Scottish traditional; arr. by Tony E. Alonso, b.1980, and Michael Mahler, b.1981, © 2007, GIA Publications, Inc.

# 792   The Love of the Lord

1. All that I count - ed as gain
2. Rich - es and hon - ors will fade,
3. Sil - ver and gold have I none,
4. Faith is the wealth I pos - sess

now I con - sid - er as loss,
earth - ly de - light dis - ap - pear,
no land to count as my home, yet
Find - ing its source in my God:

emp - ty and worth - less to me in the
fade like the grass of the field in the
wealth be - yond meas - ure I own in the
faith in the prom - ise of Christ is my

1., 3.          2., 4.

light of the love of the Lord.
light of the love of the Lord.
light of the love of the Lord.
life and my love of the Lord.

What more could bring us hope than to know the pow'r of his

life? What more could bring us peace than to

share in his suf-f'ring and death? What more could be our

fi - nal wish than to live in the love of the Lord?

Text: Philippians 3:8–14; Michael Joncas, b.1951
Tune: Michael Joncas, b.1951
© 1988, GIA Publications, Inc.

# Song of St. Patrick 793

**Refrain**

May the Spir - it of Christ be our hope through the day, be our guard through the night, our com - pan - ion on the way.

**Verse 1**

1. Christ be ev-er be - fore us, Christ be ev-er be - hind us, Christ be ev-er with - in.

D.C.

**Verses 2–5**

2. Christ up - on our left hand watch - ing, At our right hand guid - ing, Christ a - bove, be - neath us guard - ing, Near to us a - bid - ing.
3. Christ be in each ho - ly si - lence, Christ be in our speak - ing, Christ in ev - 'ry work we of - fer, Ev - er in our seek - ing.
4. Let us be God's light in the dark - ness, Let us be God's kind - ness; Let us be God's jus - tice and mer - cy, Hands and feet of Christ.
5. God Cre - a - tor, bless and keep us, Christ, be ev - er near us; Spir - it be the light be - fore us, Gen - tle be our path - way.

D.C.

Text: Based on *St. Patrick's Breastplate*; Marty Haugen, b.1950
Tune: Marty Haugen, b.1950
© 1986, GIA Publications, Inc.

# 794   I Am for You

1. There is a moun-tain,       there is a sea.
2. There was a wom-an         small as a star,
3. There was a man        who walked in the storm,
4. We are a - noint - ed,       ser - vants of God;
5. There is a world        that waits in the womb;

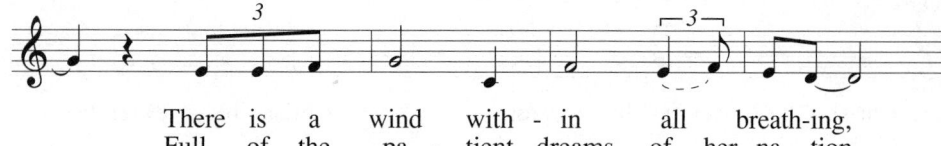

There is a wind with - in all breath-ing,
Full of the pa - tient dreams of her na - tion,
Caught in be - tween the waves and the light-ning,
We have been born a - gain of Spir - it.
There is a hope un - born God is bear-ing,

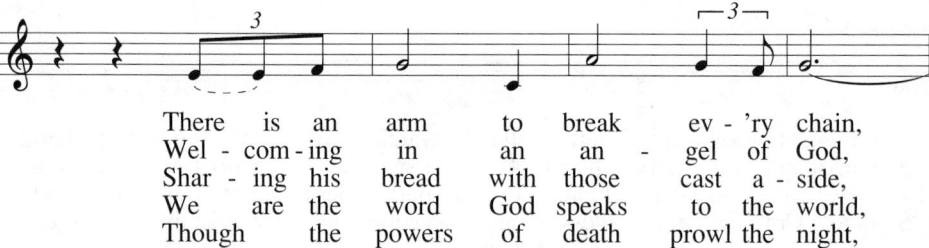

There is an arm to break ev - 'ry chain,
Wel - com - ing in an an - gel of God,
Shar - ing his bread with those cast a - side,
We are the word God speaks to the world,
Though the powers of death prowl the night,

There is a fire in all things
Wel - com - ing in God's bold in - vi -
Heal - ing by touch the lost and the
Free - dom and light to all who will
There is a day our God is pre -

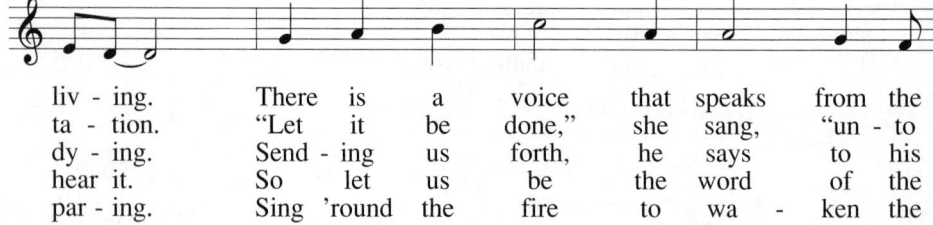

liv - ing.    There is a voice that speaks from the
ta - tion.    "Let it be done," she sang, "un - to
dy - ing.    Send - ing us forth, he says to his
hear it.    So let us be the word of the
par - ing.    Sing 'round the fire to wa - ken the

| flame: | "I | am | for | you, | I | am | for |
| me. | I | am | for | you, | I | am | for |
| friends: | "I | am | for | you, | I | am | for |
| Lord: | I | am | for | you, | I | am | for |
| dawn: | I | am | for | you, | I | am | for |

| you, | I | am | for | you | is | my name." |
| you, | I | am | for | you: | let | it be." |
| you, | I | am | for | you | to | the end." |
| you, | I | am | for | you | ev - | er - more. |
| you, | I | am | for | you: | We | are one. |

Text: Rory Cooney, b.1952
Tune: Rory Cooney, b.1952
© 1993, GIA Publications, Inc.

## Take, O Take Me As I Am    795

Ostinato Refrain

Take, O take me as I am; sum - mon out what I shall

be; set your seal up-on my heart and live in me.

Text: John L. Bell, b.1949
Tune: John L. Bell, b.1949
© 1995, Iona Community, GIA Publications, Inc., agent

# 796 I Danced in the Morning

1. I danced in the morn-ing when the world was be-gun, And I
2. I danced for the scribe and the phar - i - see, But
3. I danced on the Sab-bath and I cured the lame: The
4. I danced on a Fri - day when the sky turned black; It's
5. They cut me down and I leapt up high;

danced in the moon and the stars and the sun, And I
they would not dance, and they would-n't fol-low me; I
ho - ly peo - ple said it was a shame. They
hard to dance with the dev - il on your back. They
I am the life that - 'll nev - er, nev - er die; I'll

came down from heav - en and I danced on the earth; At
danced for the fish - er - men, for James and John; They
whipped and they stripped and they hung me high, And
bur - ied my bod - y and they thought I'd gone; But
live in you if you'll live in me:

Beth - le - hem I had my birth.
came with me and the dance went on.
left me there on a Cross to die.
I am the dance and I still go on.
I am the Lord of the Dance, said he.

Dance, then, wher - ev - er you may be; I am the

Lord of the Dance, said he, And I'll lead you all, wher -

ev - er you may be, And I'll lead you all in the Dance, said he.

Text: Sydney Carter, 1915–2004, © 1963, Stainer & Bell, Ltd., London, England. (Admin. by Hope Publishing Company)
Tune: LORD OF THE DANCE, Irregular with refrain; adapted from a traditional Shaker melody by Sydney Carter, 1915–2004, © 1963,
Stainer & Bell, Ltd., London, England. (Admin. by Hope Publishing Company)

## You Walk along Our Shoreline 797

1. You walk a - long our shore-line, Where land meets un - known sea.
2. You call us, Christ, to gath - er The peo - ple of the earth.
3. We cast our net, O Je - sus; We cry the king-dom's name;

We hear your voice of pow - er, "Now come and fol - low me.
We can - not fish for on - ly Those lives we think have worth.
We work for love and jus - tice; We learn to hope through pain.

And if you still will fol - low Through storm and wave and shoal,
We spread your net of gos - pel A - cross the wa - ter's face,
You call us, Lord, to gath - er God's daugh-ters and God's sons,

Then I will make you fish - ers, But of the hu - man soul."
Our boat a com - mon shel - ter For all found by your grace.
To let your judg-ment heal us So that all may be one.

Text: Sylvia G. Dunstan, 1955–1993, © 1991, GIA Publications, Inc.
Tune: AURELIA, 7 6 7 6 D; Samuel S. Wesley, 1810–1876

# 798 Two Fishermen

1. Two fish - er - men, who lived a - long The Sea of Gal - i -
2. And as he walked a - long the shore, 'Twas James and John he'd
3. O Si - mon Pe - ter, An - drew, James, And John, be - lov - ed
4. And you, good Chris - tians, one and all, Who'd fol - low Je - sus'

lee, Stood by the shore to cast their nets In -
find; And these two sons of Zeb - e - dee Would
one, You heard Christ's call to speak good news Re -
way, Come, leave be - hind what keeps you bound To

to an age - less sea. Now, Je - sus watched them
leave their boats be - hind. Their work and all they
vealed to God's own Son. Su - san - na, Mar - y,
trap - pings of our day. And lis - ten as he

from a - far, Then called them each by name. It
held so dear They left be - side their nets. Their
Mag - da - lene, Who trav - eled with your Lord, You
calls your name To come and fol - low near, For

changed their lives, these sim - ple men; They'd nev - er be the same.
names they'd heard as Je - sus called; They came with - out re - gret.
min - is - tered to him with joy For he is God a - dored.
still he speaks in var - ied ways To those his call will hear.

Leave all things you have And come and fol - low

me, And come and fol - low me.

Text: Suzanne Toolan, SM, b.1927, © 1986, GIA Publications, Inc.
Tune: LEAVE ALL THINGS, CMD with refrain; Suzanne Toolan, SM, b.1927, © 1970, GIA Publications, Inc.

# You Are Strong, You Are Holy   799

**Verses**

1. Lord, you lead through sea and des - ert, You
2. Lord, you lead to cool - ing wa - ters, You
3. So we fol - low where you lead us, Where you

lead to prom - ised lands. We are your own ho - ly
lead to green - ing fields. Lord, you lead to deep - 'ning
walk a - long the shore, Where you suf - fer in the

peo - ple, In your cov - e - nant we stand!
val - leys Where your com - fort is re - vealed!
gar - den, When you rise to die no more!

**Refrain**

You are strong, you are ho - ly, you are mer - cy and

peace. You are love, you are jus - tice. Your

grace and fa - vor nev - er cease!

Text: Sylvia Dunstan, 1955–1993, © 1991, GIA Publications, Inc.
Tune: JUSTICE, 8 6 8 7 with refrain; Paul A. Tate, b.1968, © 2003, GIA Publications, Inc.

# 800 Come and Follow Me

Verses

1. Come, be my light, be my voice to the na -
2. Go, take your gift to the poor and the lone -

tions. Be my hands, be my heart for the world.
ly. As you love, so will I live in you.

Would you go where I go? Where I lead,
Will you feed, feed my lambs? Share your hope

will you fol - low? Would you leave ev-'ry - thing
with the hope - less? Bring new sight to the blind

for my sake? By the pow - er of the Spir-
in my name? With a tow - el and a ba -

it, ev - 'ry - one with ears to hear it will em-
sin, t'ward the king - dom we will has - ten, through the

brace the call to love with - in their heart.
nar - row gate that leads to Cal - va - ry.

𝄋 Refrain

If an - y-one would come and fol-low me, my dis-

ci - ple you would be. Leave the past be-hind, seek and you will

find all you're called to be. If an - y - one would

come and fol-low me, know the truth will make you free.

Give and you re - ceive. Trust me and be -

lieve. Come and fol - low me.

With a tow - el and a ba -

sin, t'ward the king-dom we will has - ten, through the

nar - row gate that leads to Cal - va - ry.

Text: Tom Franzak, b.1954
Tune: Tom Franzak, b.1954; acc. by Gerard Chiusano, b.1953
© 1997, GIA Publications, Inc.

## 801 Take Up Your Cross

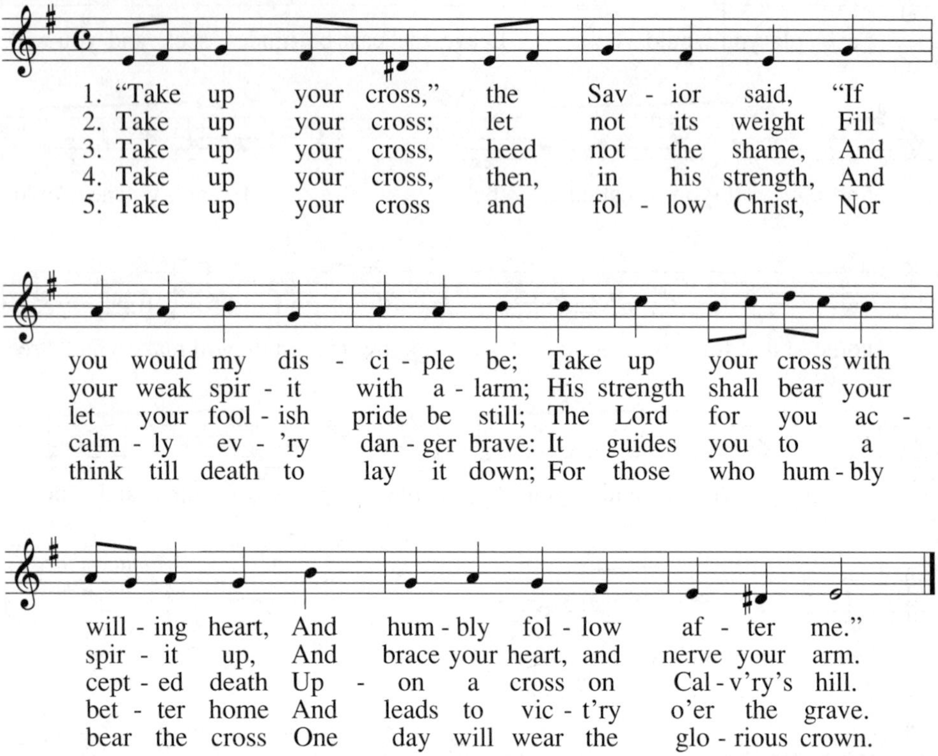

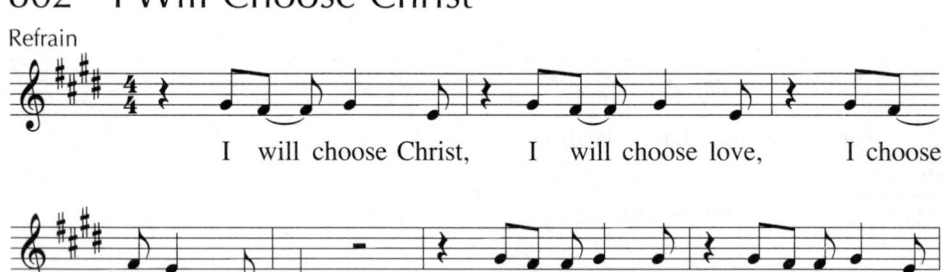

1. "Take up your cross," the Sav - ior said, "If
2. Take up your cross; let not its weight Fill
3. Take up your cross, heed not the shame, And
4. Take up your cross, then, in his strength, And
5. Take up your cross and fol - low Christ, Nor

you would my dis - ci - ple be; Take up your cross with
your weak spir - it with a - larm; His strength shall bear your
let your fool - ish pride be still; The Lord for you ac -
calm - ly ev - 'ry dan - ger brave: It guides you to a
think till death to lay it down; For those who hum - bly

will - ing heart, And hum - bly fol - low af - ter me."
spir - it up, And brace your heart, and nerve your arm.
cept - ed death Up - on a cross on Cal - v'ry's hill.
bet - ter home And leads to vic - t'ry o'er the grave.
bear the cross One day will wear the glo - rious crown.

Text: Charles W. Everest, 1814–1877, alt.
Tune: ERHALT UNS HERR, LM; Klug's *Geistliche Lieder*, 1543; harm. by J. S. Bach, 1685–1750

*Alternate tune:* O WALY WALY

## 802 I Will Choose Christ

Refrain

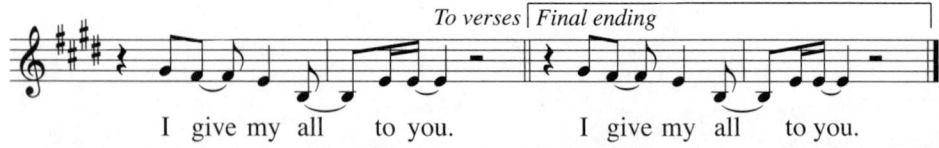

I will choose Christ, I will choose love, I choose

to serve. I give my heart, I give my life,

*To verses* | *Final ending*

I give my all to you. I give my all to you.

Verse 1

1. How man-y times must he call my name and show to me that he is God? And as a ser-vant he calls to me, "You must serve too."

Verse 2

2. Christ, my teach - er and heal - er, teach my heart and heal my soul. And as I walk this road with you, teach me to love.

Verse 3

3. As I look up - on your cross, so too must I die with you. And with the death of my own de - sires, I'll rise with you.

Text: Tom Booth, b.1961
Tune: Tom Booth, b.1961; acc. by Ed Bolduc, b.1969
© 1997, Tom Booth. Published by OCP.

## 803   For the Healing of the Nations

1. For the heal-ing of the na-tions, Lord, we pray with
2. Lead your peo-ple in-to free-dom, From de-spair your
3. All that kills a-bun-dant liv-ing, Let it from the
4. You, cre-a-tor God, have writ-ten Your great name on

one ac-cord; For a just and e-qual shar-ing
world re-lease That, re-deemed from war and ha-tred,
earth be banned: Pride of sta-tus, race, or school-ing,
hu-man-kind; For our grow-ing in your like-ness

Of the things that earth af-fords. To a life of
All may come and go in peace. Show us how, through
Dog-mas that ob-scure your plan. In our com-mon
Bring the life of Christ to mind, That by our re-

love in ac-tion Help us rise and pledge our word.
care and good-ness, Fear will die and hope in-crease.
quest for jus-tice May we hal-low life's brief span.
sponse and serv-ice Earth its des-ti-ny may find.

Text: Fred Kaan, 1929–2009, alt., © 1968, Hope Publishing Company
Tune: ST. THOMAS, 8 7 8 7 8 7; John Wade, 1711–1786

## 804   Here Am I

1. Here am I, Where un-der-neath the bridg - es
2. Here am I, With peo-ple in the line - up,
3. Here am I, Where two or three are gath - ered,

Of our win-ter cit - ies Home-less peo-ple sleep.
Anx-ious for a hand - out, Ach-ing for a job.
Read-y to be al - tered, Shar-ing wine and bread.

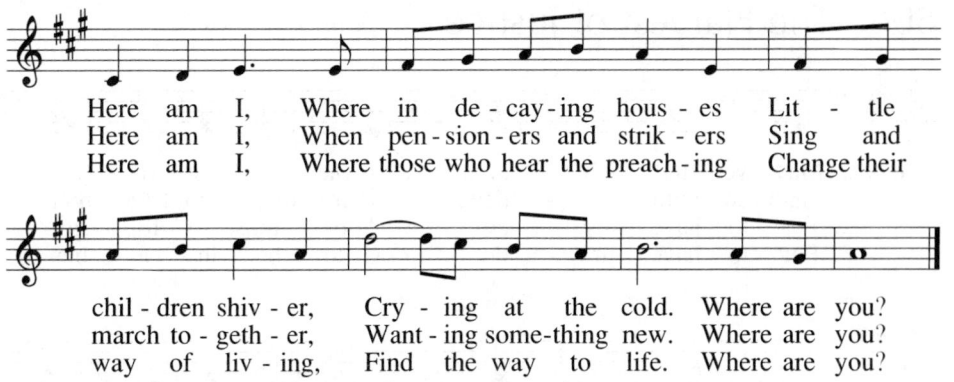

Here am  I,    Where  in   de - cay-ing  hous - es   Lit - tle
Here am  I,    When  pen - sion - ers and  strik - ers  Sing  and
Here am  I,    Where those who hear the preach-ing   Change their

chil - dren shiv - er,   Cry - ing  at  the  cold.  Where are you?
march to - geth - er,   Want - ing some-thing new.  Where are you?
way  of  liv - ing,   Find  the  way  to  life.  Where are you?

Text: Brian Wren, b.1936
Tune: STANISLAUS, 3 7 6 5 D 3; Daniel Charles Damon, b.1955
© Words 1983, music 1995, Hope Publishing Co.

## Touch the Earth Lightly    805

1. Touch    the earth   light - ly,    Use    the earth   gen - tly,
2. We       who en - dan - ger,    Who    cre - ate   hun - ger,
3. Let      there be   green - ing,    Birth  from the   burn - ing,
4. God      of all   liv - ing,    God    of all   lov - ing,

Nour - ish   the   life  of   the   world  in   our   care:
A - gents   of   death for  all   crea - tures that  live,
Wa - ter   that   bless - es,  and   air   that  is   sweet,
God  of   the   seed - ling, the   snow,  and  the   sun,

Gift    of great   won - der,   Ours   to   sur - ren - der,
We      who would  fos - ter   Clouds  of   dis - as - ter—
Health  in God's   gar - den,   Hope   in God's  chil - dren,
Teach   us, de - flect us,   Christ  re - con - nect us,

Trust   for  the   chil - dren  to - mor - row  will   bear.
God     of  our   plan - et,   fore - stall  and  for - give!
Re - gen - er - a - tion  that  peace  will  com - plete.
Us - ing  us   gen - tly,  and  mak - ing  us   one.

Text: Shirley Erena Murray, b.1931, © 1992, Hope Publishing Company
Tune: Tony E. Alonso, b.1980, © 2007, GIA Publications, Inc.

# 806  The Harvest of Justice

*Refrain:* May we find rich - ness in the har - vest of jus -
1. Gath - er with pa - tience   for those who have noth -
2. For to have mer - cy   on those for - got -
3. For to have lit - tle is to be in a - bun -

tice which Christ Je - sus has rip-ened for
ing. Leave them your rich - es, and you will re -
ten, this is my true law, this is my com -
dance. To give what re - mains, to give all we

us. Bread for the jour - ney,
ceive.   Make room for the poor ones,
mand: Clothe the na - ked,
have, is to walk with the poor ones,

bread for the hun - gry, all for the
make way for the stran - ger; for I am the
be home for the or - phan, be hope for the
and be - come the stran - ger, one with the

glo - ry and praise of God.
Lord, the Lord your God.
wid - ow, and wel - come the lost.
Lord, the Lord our God.

Text: Philippians 1:11, Leviticus 19:9, 23:22, Deuteronomy 24:19; David Haas, b.1957
Tune: David Haas, b.1957
© 1985, GIA Publications, Inc.

# We Are Called 807

1. Come! Live in the light! Shine with the
2. Come! O - pen your heart! Show your
3. Sing! Sing a new song! Sing of that

joy and the love of the Lord! We are called
mer - cy to all those in fear! We are called
great day when all will be one! God will reign,

to be light for the king - dom, to
to be hope for the hope - less so all
and we'll walk with each oth - er as

live in the free - dom of the cit - y of God!
ha - tred and blind-ness will be no more!
sis - ters and broth-ers u - nit - ed in love!

We are called to act with jus-tice, we are called to

love ten - der - ly, we are called to serve one an - oth-er,

to walk hum - bly with God!

Text: Micah 6:8; David Haas, b.1957
Tune: David Haas, b.1957
© 1988, GIA Publications, Inc.

# 808 We Come with Joy

1. We come with joy in Je - sus Christ, Who
2. A lit - tle bread is all we have, So
3. Like rip - ples in a pool, our gifts, How -

knows our hu - man need, Who, moved with pit - y
mea - ger our sup - ply; A lit - tle time, a
ev - er small they are, Will reach and heal a

for the poor, Would ev - 'ry hun - ger feed.
lit - tle love Can hard - ly sat - is - fy.
need - y world, Will com - fort near and far.

He blessed the fish and bar - ley loaves Till
But let us bring the best we have, De -
For Christ will bless our bit of bread, The

food was mul - ti - plied. His boun - ty o - ver -
spite our pov - er - ty, And of - fer all our
loaves our hands pro - vide, Till emp - ty bas - kets

flowed their want And all were sat - is - fied.
gifts to Christ, Im - per - fect though they be.
o - ver - flow And all are sat - is - fied.

Text: Delores Dufner, OSB, b.1939, © 1994, GIA Publications, Inc., alt.
Tune: FOREST GREEN, CMD; English; harm. by Ralph Vaughan Williams, 1872–1958, alt.

# On Holy Ground 809

**Verses**

1. The heav - ens em - brace the earth, as they
2. *Á - bran - se los cie - los, en el*
3. Let heav - en and earth sing praise to the
4. Bless earth, wa - ter, fire, and wind. Bless your
5. *La his - to - ria de los pue - blos se - rá*
6. U - nit - ed we join the light. We are

sing of the new birth. The earth ech - oes and re -
*nom - bre de Cris - to Dios. Trans - for - men la tie - rra cau -*
one who from death was raised. Let hearts ut - ter words pro -
peo - ple with - out, with - in. Let beau - ty and birth sur -
*li - bre por la ver - dad. La cau - sa_es jus - ti - fi -*
born of the same right. We've come to re - lease what's

sounds that we are on ho - ly ground.
*ti - va en u - na tie - rra con li - ber - tad.*
found in pro - claim - ing this ho - ly ground.
round in re - claim - ing this ho - ly ground.
*ca - da. San - ta tie - rra nues - tra se - rá.*
bound, for we are on ho - ly ground.

**Refrain**

*Assembly:* Do you be - lieve in free - dom? Yes, we do Lord! *Assembly:* Do you be - lieve in jus - tice? Jus - tice for all!

*Assembly:* ¿Y en la nue - va vi - da? ¡En su es - pí - ri - tu! *Assembly:* ¿Quién es su li - be - ra - ción? ¡Tú, Se - ñor!

¡A - rri - ba! ¡Pro - cla - men! ¡San - ta Tie - rra!

We are on ho - ly ground!

Text: Donna Peña, b.1955
Tune: Donna Peña, b.1955; acc. by Diana Kodner, b.1957
© 1992, 1994, GIA Publications, Inc.

# 810 Let Justice Roll Like a River

**Refrain**

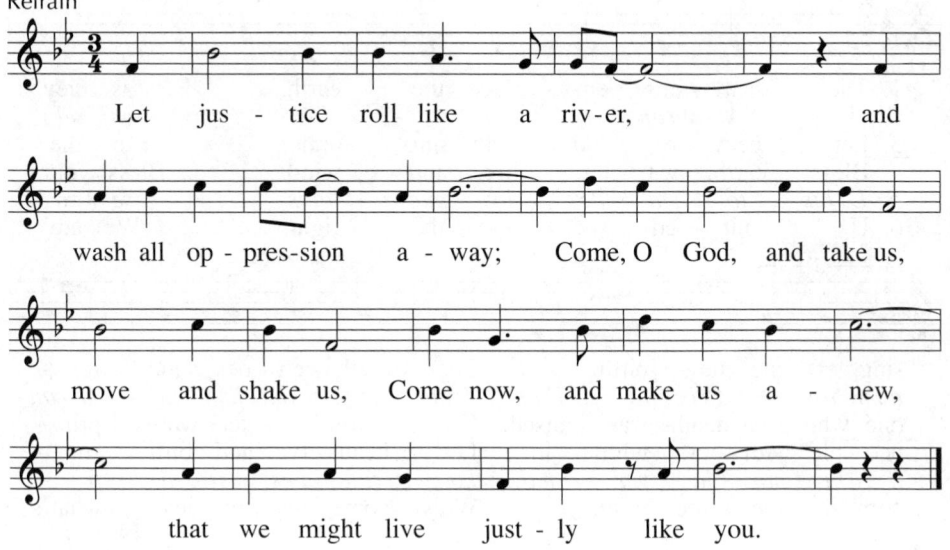

Let jus - tice roll like a riv-er, and wash all op - pres-sion a - way; Come, O God, and take us, move and shake us, Come now, and make us a - new, that we might live just - ly like you.

Verses

1. Take from me your holy feasts, all your off'rings and your music;
   Let justice flow like waters, and integrity like an ever-flowing stream.

2. How long shall we wait, O God, for the day of your mercy to dawn,
   the day we beat our swords into ploughs, when your peace reigns over the earth?

3. Hear this, all of you who use the poor in your thirst of power and riches:
   the Lord will turn your laughter to tears, on the wondrous Day of our God.

4. Even now return to me, let your hearts be broken and humble,
   for I am gracious, gen'rous and kind; come and seek the mercies of God.

5. You have been told the way of life, the way of justice and peace;
   to act justly, to love gently, and walk humbly with God.

Text: Amos 5:21–24, 8:4, Micah 4:3–4, 6:8, Joel 2:12–14; Marty Haugen, b.1950
Tune: Marty Haugen, b.1950
© 1991, GIA Publications, Inc.

# Abundant Life 811

1. We can-not own the sun-lit sky, The
2. When bod-ies shiv-er in the night And,
3. God calls hu-man-i-ty to join As

moon, the wild-flow'rs grow-ing, For we are
wea - ry, wait for morn-ing, When chil-dren
part - ners in cre - at-ing A fu-ture

part of all that is With - in life's
have no bread but tears, And war - horns
free from want or fear, Life's good - ness

riv - er flow-ing. With o - pen
sound their warn-ing, God calls hu -
cel - e - brat-ing. That new world

hands re-ceive and share The gifts of God's cre -
man-i-ty to wake, To join in com-mon
beck-ons from a - far, In - vites our shared en -

a - tion, That all may have a - bun - dant
la - bor, That all may have a - bun - dant
deav-or, That all may have a - bun - dant

life In ev - 'ry earth - ly na - tion.
life In one - ness with their neigh-bor.
life And peace en - dure for - ev - er.

Text: Ruth Duck, b.1947, © 1992, GIA Publications, Inc.
Tune: LA GRANGE, 8 7 8 7 D; Marty Haugen, b.1950, © 1994, GIA Publications, Inc.

# 812  A Place at the Table

Verses

1. For ev - 'ry - one born, a place at the ta - ble, for
2. For wom - an and man, a place at the ta - ble, re -
3. For young and for old, a place at the ta - ble, a
4. For just and un - just, a place at the ta - ble, a -
5. For ev - 'ry - one born, a place at the ta - ble, to

ev - 'ry - one born, clean wa - ter and bread, a
vis - ing the roles, de - cid - ing the share, with
voice to be heard, a part in the song, the
bus - er, a - bused, with need to for - give, in
live with - out fear, and sim - ply to be, to

shel - ter, a space, a safe place for grow - ing, for
wis - dom and grace, di - vid - ing the pow - er, for
hands of a child in hands that are wrin - kled, for
an - ger, in hurt, a mind - set of mer - cy, for
work, to speak out, to wit - ness and wor - ship, for

ev - 'ry - one born, a star o - ver - head.
wom - an and man, a sys - tem that's fair.
young and for old, the right to be - long. And
just and un - just, a new way to live.
ev - 'ry - one born, the right to be free.

Refrain

God will de - light when we are cre - a - tors of

jus - tice and joy, yes, God will de - light

when we are cre - a - tors of jus - tice,

jus - tice and joy!

Text: Shirley Erena Murray, b.1931, © 1998, Hope Publishing Co.
Tune: Lori True, b.1961, © 2001, GIA Publications, Inc.

## God, Whose Purpose Is to Kindle   813

1. God, whose pur-pose is to kin - dle, Now ig - nite us
2. God, who still a sword de - liv - ers Rath - er than a
3. God, who in your ho - ly gos-pel Wills that all should

with your fire. While the earth a - waits your burn-ing,
plac - id peace, With your sharp-ened Word dis - turb us,
tru - ly live, Make us sense our share of fail - ure,

With your pas - sion us in-spire. O - ver-come our
From com - pla - cen - cy re-lease! Save us now from
Our tran - quil - i - ty for-give. Teach us cour - age

sin - ful calm-ness, Stir us with your sav - ing name.
sat - is - fac - tion, When we pri - vate - ly are free,
as we strug - gle In all lib - er - at - ing strife.

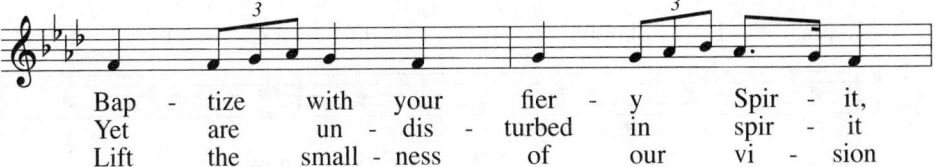

Bap - tize with your fier - y Spir - it,
Yet are un - dis - turbed in spir - it
Lift the small - ness of our vi - sion

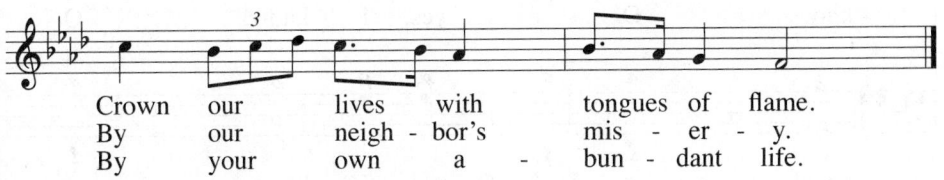

Crown our lives with tongues of flame.
By our neigh - bor's mis - er - y.
By your own a - bun - dant life.

Text: Luke 12:49; David E. Trueblood, 1900–1994, alt., © 1967, David Elton Trueblood
Tune: EBENEZER, 8 7 8 7 D; Thomas J. Williams, 1869–1944

*Alternate tune:* HOLY MANNA

# 814 Freedom Is Coming

O  yes,  I  know.

O  yes,  I  know.

yes,  I  know.  O  yes,  I

O  yes,  I

O  yes,  I  know.  O  yes,  I

1.  O  2.

know.  O  yes.  I  yes,  I  know.

Text: South African
Tune: South African
© 1984, Utryck, Walton Music Corp., agent

## The Thirsty Cry for Water, Lord   815

1. The thirst - y cry for wa - ter, Lord; The
2. The cup of wa - ter poured in love The
3. But help us al - so hear the cry Of
4. And come to us, O ris - en Christ, Our

hun - gry plead for bread. And man - y long to
pangs of thirst will still. The bread of earth you
hun - g'ring, thirst - ing hearts For liv - ing wa - ter,
rest - less souls re - lieve; And sat - is - fy our

rise a - gain Where hope, cast down, lies dead.
bid us share, The fam - ished child can fill.
bread of life Your grace a - lone im - parts.
starv - ing hearts That we may rise and live.

Text: Herman G. Stuempfle, Jr., 1923–2007, © 1997, GIA Publications, Inc.
Tune: SHANTI, CM; Marty Haugen, b.1950, © 1984, GIA Publications, Inc.

# 816 What You Have Done for Me

her - it    the    king - dom    pre - pared    for    you.    For

you    are    my    chil-dren,    called    to    serve    as    keep-ers    of    the

**D.S.**

vi - sion    and    speak-ers    of    the    word.

Verse 3

3. I    will    look to you    when    life    on    earth    has    end - ed.

Those    who    give    will    re-ceive,    those    who    seek    will    find;    so

**D.S.**

seek    my face    in    ev-'ry    face    and    see    the eyes    of    God!

Text: Based on Matthew 25:24–41; Tony E. Alonso, b.1980
Tune: Tony E. Alonso, b.1980
© 2001, GIA Publications, Inc.

# 817  We Shall Overcome

1. We shall o - ver - come, we shall o - ver - come,
2. We'll walk hand in hand, we'll walk hand in hand,
3. We shall live in peace, we shall live in peace,
4. We are not a - fraid, we are not a - fraid,

we shall o - ver - come some - day. Oh,
we'll walk hand in hand some - day. Oh,
we shall live in peace some - day. Oh,
we are not a - fraid to - day. Oh,

deep in my heart I do be - lieve
deep in my heart I do be - lieve
deep in my heart I do be - lieve
deep in my heart I do be - lieve

we shall o - ver - come some - day.
we'll walk hand in hand some - day.
we shall live in peace some - day.
we are not a - fraid to - day.

5. We shall stand together...
6. The truth will make us free...
7. The Lord will see us through...
8. We shall be like him...
9. The whole wide world around...

Text: Spiritual
Tune: Spiritual; harm. by J. Jefferson Cleveland, 1937–1986, © 1981, Abingdon Press

# 818  If You Believe and I Believe

If you be - lieve and I be-lieve And we to-geth - er

pray, The Ho - ly Spir - it must come down And

set God's peo - ple free, And set God's peo - ple

free, And set God's peo - ple free; The

Ho - ly Spir - it must come down And set God's peo - ple free.

Text: Zimbabwean traditional
Tune: Zimbabwean traditional; adapt. of English traditional; as taught by Tarasai; arr. by John L. Bell, b.1949, © 1991, Iona Community, GIA Publications, Inc., agent

## Peace Is Flowing Like a River  819

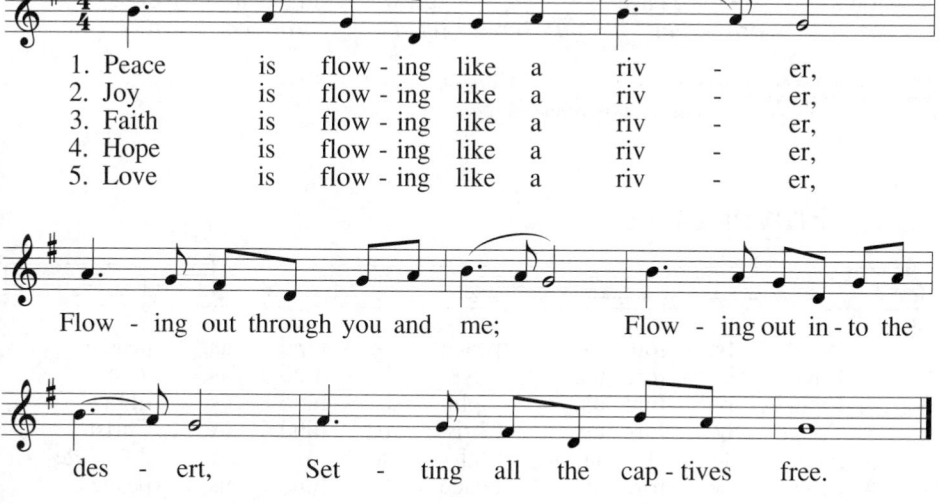

1. Peace is flow - ing like a riv - er,
2. Joy is flow - ing like a riv - er,
3. Faith is flow - ing like a riv - er,
4. Hope is flow - ing like a riv - er,
5. Love is flow - ing like a riv - er,

Flow - ing out through you and me; Flow - ing out in - to the

des - ert, Set - ting all the cap - tives free.

Text: Anonymous
Tune: Anonymous; acc. by Diana Kodner, b.1957, © 1993, GIA Publications, Inc.

## 820 The Peace of the Earth / La Paz de la Tierra

The peace of the earth be with you, the
*La paz de la tie-rra es - té con ti - go, la*

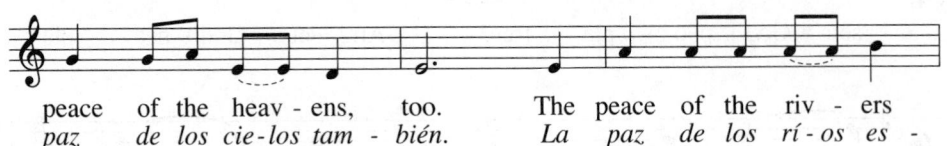

peace of the heav - ens, too. The peace of the riv - ers
*paz de los cie-los tam - bién. La paz de los rí-os es -*

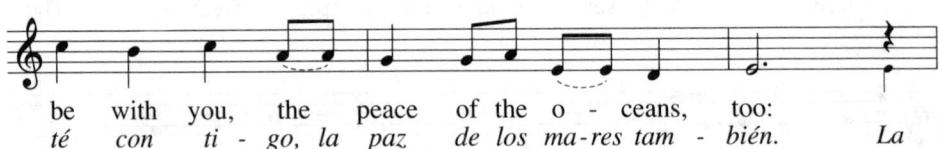

be with you, the peace of the o - ceans, too:
*té con ti - go, la paz de los ma-res tam - bién. La*

deep peace fall - ing o - ver you,
*paz pro - fun - da ca - yen - do so - bre ti. La*

God's peace grow - ing in you.
*paz pro - fun - da cre - cien - do en ti.*

Text: Traditional Guatemalan; trans. by Christine Carson
Tune: Traditional Guatemalan; arr. by John L. Bell, b.1949
© 1998, Christine Carson and Iona Community, GIA Publications, Inc., agent

## 821 Prayer of Peace

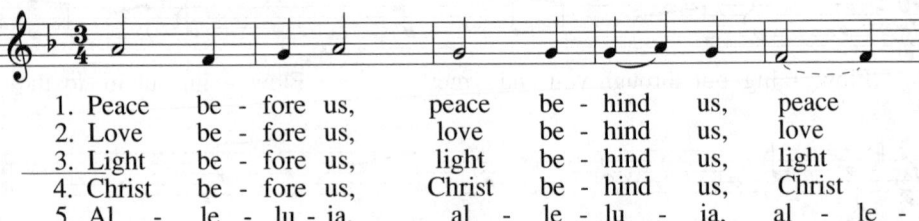

1. Peace be - fore us, peace be - hind us, peace
2. Love be - fore us, love be - hind us, love
3. Light be - fore us, light be - hind us, light
4. Christ be - fore us, Christ be - hind us, Christ
5. Al - le - lu - ia, al - le - lu - ia, al - le -
6. Peace be - fore us, peace be - hind us, peace

un - der our feet.    Peace with - in us,    peace
un - der our feet.    Love with - in us,    love
un - der our feet.    Light with - in us,    light
un - der our feet.    Christ with - in us,    Christ
lu - ia,    Al - le - lu - ia,    al - le -
un - der our feet.    Peace with - in us,    peace

o - ver us, let all a - round us be peace.
o - ver us, let all a - round us be love.
o - ver us, let all a - round us be light.
o - ver us, let all a - round us be Christ.
lu - ia, al - le - lu - ia.
o - ver us, let all a - round us be peace.

Text: Based on a Navajo prayer; David Haas, b.1957
Tune: David Haas, b.1957
© 1987, GIA Publications, Inc.

## Dona Nobis Pacem    822

Canon

1.
Do - na no - bis pa - cem, pa - cem.

Do - na no - bis pa - cem.

2.
Do - na no - bis pa - cem.

Do - na no - bis pa - cem.

3.
Do - na no - bis pa - cem.

Do - na no - bis pa - cem.

Text: *Grant us peace*
Tune: Traditional; acc. by Diana Kodner, b.1957, © 1994, GIA Publications, Inc.

# 823 The Peace of God

Refrain

Let your gen-tle-ness be known, so all may know the Lord is near. Do not wor-ry, do not wor-ry; reach out to God in prayer. Stay with all that you have learned, and all that you have heard and seen, and the peace of God, the peace of God will be with you.

Verse 1

1. What-ev-er is true, what-ev-er is just, all that is pure and pleas-ing and all that is wor-thy of praise: think on these things.

D.C.

Verse 2

2. And the peace of God, the peace of God be-

yond all un-der-stand-ing will guard your hearts, and

**D.C.**

guide your minds in Christ Je - sus.

Text: Based on Philippians 4:5–9, David Haas, b.1957
Tune: David Haas, b.1957
© 2002, GIA Publications, Inc.

## Put Peace into Each Other's Hands  824

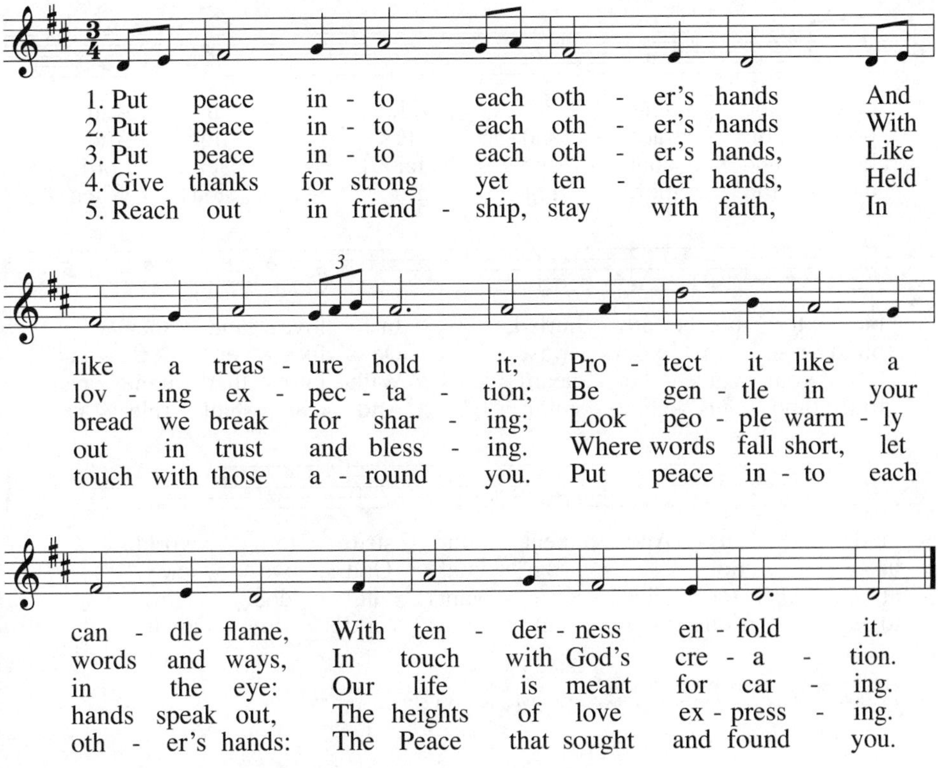

| 1. Put | peace | in - to | each | oth | - | er's | hands | And |
| 2. Put | peace | in - to | each | oth | - | er's | hands | With |
| 3. Put | peace | in - to | each | oth | - | er's | hands, | Like |
| 4. Give | thanks | for strong | yet | ten | - | der | hands, | Held |
| 5. Reach | out | in friend - | ship, | stay | | with | faith, | In |

| like | a | treas - ure | hold | it; | Pro - tect | it | like | a |
| lov - ing | ex - | pec - ta | - tion; | Be | gen - tle | in | your |
| bread | we | break | for shar | - ing; | Look | peo - ple warm | - ly |
| out | in | trust | and bless | - ing. | Where words | fall short, | let |
| touch | with | those | a - round | you. | Put | peace in - to | each |

| can | - dle | flame, | With ten | - der - ness | en - fold | it. |
| words | and | ways, | In touch | with God's | cre - a | - tion. |
| in | the | eye: | Our life | is meant | for car | - ing. |
| hands | speak | out, | The heights | of love | ex - press | - ing. |
| oth | - er's | hands: | The Peace | that sought | and found | you. |

Text: Fred Kaan, 1929–2009, © 1989, Hope Publishing Company
Tune: ST. COLUMBA, 8 7 8 7; Gaelic; harm. by A. Gregory Murray, OSB, 1905–1992, © Downside Abbey

# 825 O God of Every Nation

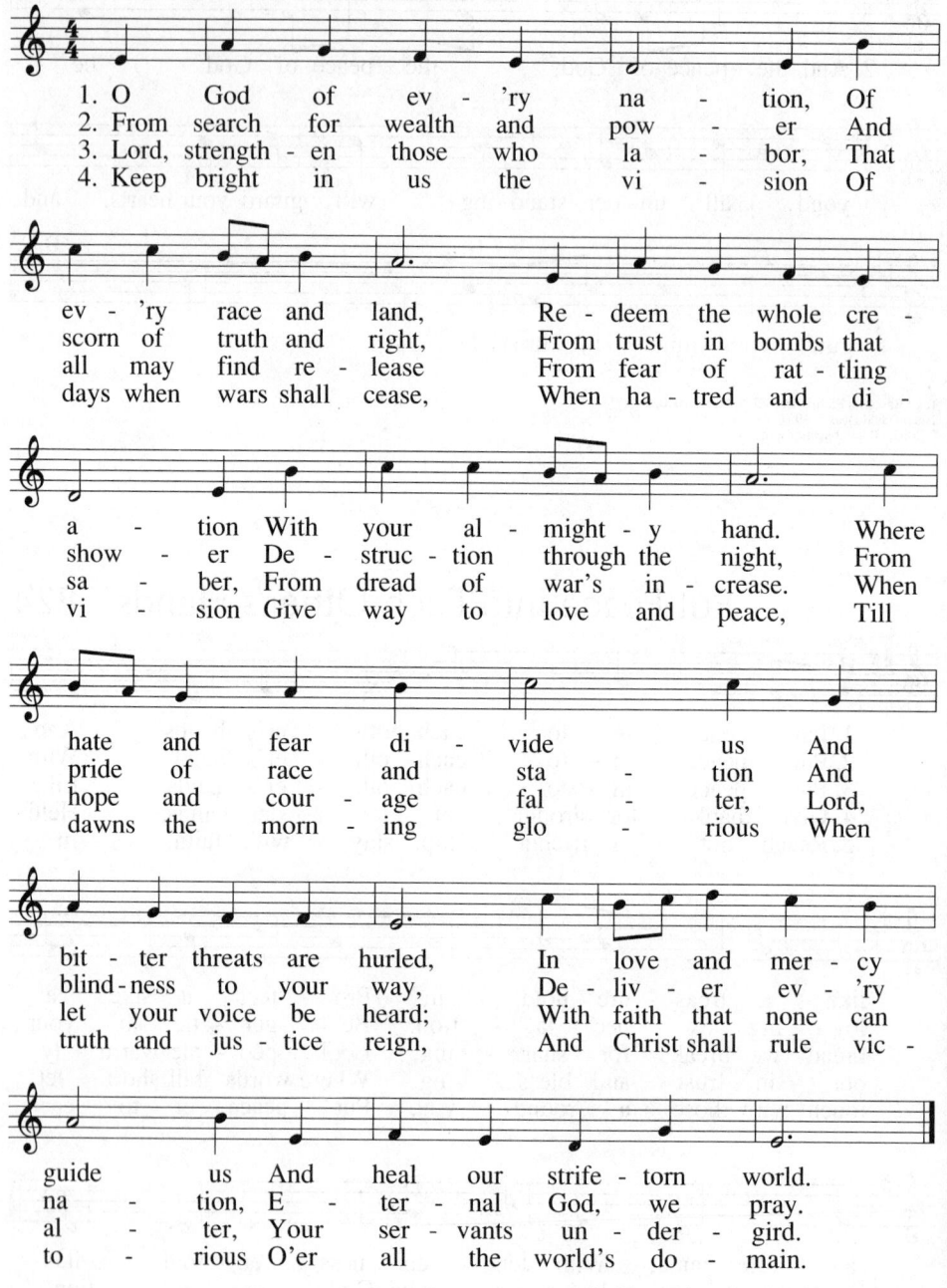

1. O God of ev - 'ry na - tion, Of
2. From search for wealth and pow - er And
3. Lord, strength - en those who la - bor, That
4. Keep bright in us the vi - sion Of

ev - 'ry race and land, Re - deem the whole cre -
scorn of truth and right, From trust in bombs that
all may find re - lease From fear of rat - tling
days when wars shall cease, When ha - tred and di -

a - tion With your al - might - y hand. Where
show - er De - struc - tion through the night, From
sa - ber, From dread of war's in - crease. When
vi - sion Give way to love and peace, Till

hate and fear di - vide us And
pride of race and sta - tion And
hope and cour - age fal - ter, Lord,
dawns the morn - ing glo - rious When

bit - ter threats are hurled, In love and mer - cy
blind - ness to your way, De - liv - er ev - 'ry
let your voice be heard; With faith that none can
truth and jus - tice reign, And Christ shall rule vic -

guide us And heal our strife - torn world.
na - tion, E - ter - nal God, we pray.
al - ter, Your ser - vants un - der - gird.
to - rious O'er all the world's do - main.

Text: William W. Reid, b.1923, alt., © 1958, 1986, The Hymn Society (admin. by Hope Publishing Company)
Tune: PASSION CHORALE, 7 6 7 6 D; Hans Leo Hassler, 1564–1612; harm. by J. S. Bach, 1685–1750

# Give Us Your Peace  826

%  Refrain

Je - sus, give us your peace. Bring us to - geth-
er. Let all the fight - ing cease.
Shat - ter all our hearts of stone. Give us a heart
for love a - lone. Oh woh

*Repeat each time*
*To verses*
*Last time*

Verses

1. Some days the road I walk is lone - ly,
2. Some days the walk - ing makes me wea - ry,
3. Some days the strength I need is fail - ing,

and it's so hard to find a friend.
and my soul yearns to be re - lieved.
and then, O Lord, I turn to you.

E - ven then I know, some-where in my soul,
You, my Lord, are strong. You pull me a - long.
I need nev - er fear, you are al - ways near.

D.S.

your love is far too great to com-pre-hend. Oh woh
Your love is far too great to be be - lieved. Oh woh
What-ev - er hap-pens, you will pull me through. Oh woh

Text: Michael Mahler, b.1981
Tune: Michael Mahler, b.1981
© 2001, GIA Publications, Inc.

# 827 World Peace Prayer

Text: Refrain, Upanishads, Satish Kumar, ©; verses, Marty Haugen, b.1950, © 1985, GIA Publications, Inc.
Tune: Marty Haugen, b.1950, © 1985, GIA Publications, Inc.

# Make Me a Channel of Your Peace  828

Verses 1, 2, 4

1. Make me a chan - nel of your peace. Where
2. Make me a chan - nel of your peace. Where
4. Make me a chan - nel of your peace. It

there is ha - tred, let me bring your love. Where
there's de - spair in life, let me bring hope. Where
is in par - don - ing that we are par - doned, in

there is in - ju - ry, your par - don, Lord, And
there is dark - ness, on - ly light, And
giv - ing of our - selves that we re - ceive, and in

1.
where there's doubt, true faith in you.
2., 4.
where there's sad - ness, ev - er joy.
dy - ing that we're born to e - ter - nal life.

Verse 3

3. Oh, Mas-ter, grant that I may nev-er seek So much to be con -

soled as to con - sole. To be un-der-stood as to un-der-

D.C.

stand. To be loved as to love with all my soul.

Text: Prayer of St. Francis; adapt. by Sebastian Temple, 1928–1997
Tune: Sebastian Temple, 1928–1997; acc. by Robert J. Batastini, b.1942
© 1967, OCP
Dedicated to Mrs. Frances Tracy

# 829 Let There Be Peace on Earth

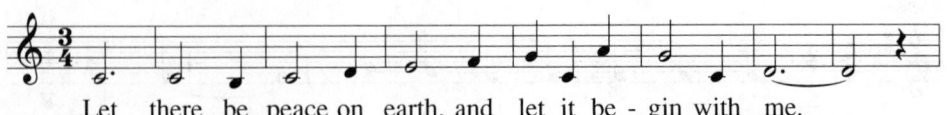

Let there be peace on earth, and let it be - gin with me.

Let there be peace on earth, the peace that was meant to be. With

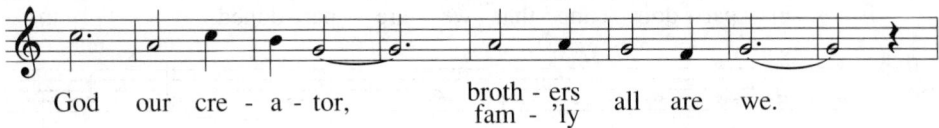

God our cre - a - tor, broth - ers / fam - 'ly all are we.

Let me / us walk with my broth-er / each oth - er in per-fect har-mo - ny.

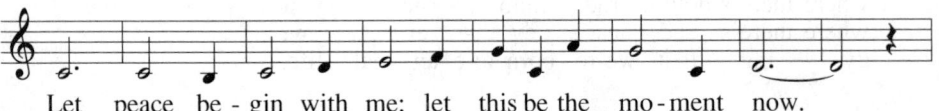

Let peace be - gin with me; let this be the mo - ment now.

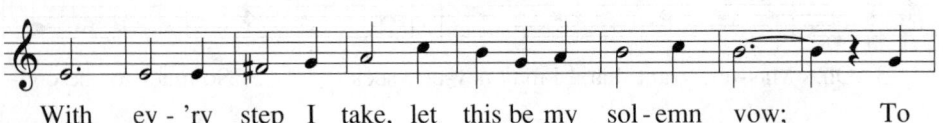

With ev - 'ry step I take, let this be my sol - emn vow; To

take each mo-ment, and live each mo-ment in peace e - ter-nal - ly!

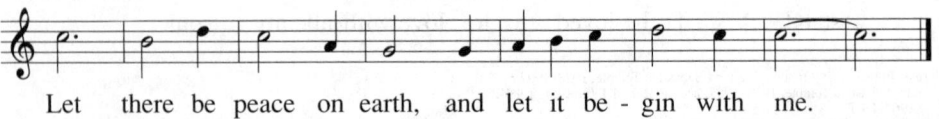

Let there be peace on earth, and let it be - gin with me.

Text: Jill Jackson, 1913–1995, © 1955, 1983, Jan-Lee Music
Tune: Sy Miller, 1908-1941, © 1955, 1983, Jan-Lee Music; acc. by Diana Kodner, b.1957, © 1993, GIA Publications, Inc.

# Peace, Be Not Anxious 830

Refrain

Peace now I give to you. My peace I pour through you.

Not as the world gives, but ev - er more sure.

Past all un - der - stand-ing, this gra - cious com - mand - ing:

peace, be not anx - ious, God holds you se - cure.

Verses

1. Peace, be not anxious. Our Maker is gracious.
   Think now of the lilies: they toil not, nor spin.
   Fields lush with adornment, all Solomon's raiment,
   still never could rival the splendor therein.

2. Fret not for tomorrow. In joy or in sorrow,
   each tiniest sparrow God will not forget.
   Bright Spirit descending, warm comfort unending—
   peace, be not anxious: God cares for you yet.

3. In mansions of heaven, blest life will be given.
   There, one with our Maker, I'll welcome you home.
   Lo, I go before you. So, now I implore you:
   peace, be not anxious, for you are my own.

## 831  Oh, Look and Wonder / Miren Qué Bueno

**Refrain**

Oh, look and won - der how good it is!
¡Mir - en qué bue - no, qué bue - no es!

**Verses**

1. How good it is when broth - ers dwell in
2. How good it is when sis - ters dwell in
3. How good it is when all earth's peo - ple

1. ¡Mi - ren qué bue - no_es cuan - do los her -
2. ¡Mi - ren qué bue - no_es cuan - do las her -
3. ¡Mi - ren qué bue - no_es cuan - do nos reu -

peace with one an - oth - er: it is like pre - cious
peace with one an - oth - er: fresh like the morn - ing
dwell in peace to - geth - er: there is where God will

ma - nos es - tán jun - tos! Es co - mo_a - cei - te
ma - nas es - tán jun - tas! Se pa - re - ce_al ro -
ni - mos to - dos jun - tos! Por - que_el Se - ñor ahí

**D.C.**

oil when run - ning fresh on Aa - ron's beard.
dew that falls on Zi - on's ho - ly hill.
pour the bless - ing, life for - ev - er - more.

bue - no de - rra - ma - do so - bre_Aa - rón.
cí - o so - bre los mon - tes de Sión.
man - da vi - da_e - ter - na_y ben - di - ción.

Text: Psalm 133; Pablo D. Sosa, b.1933
Tune: Pablo D. Sosa, b.1933
© 1972, GIA Publications, Inc.

## 832  In Christ There Is No East or West

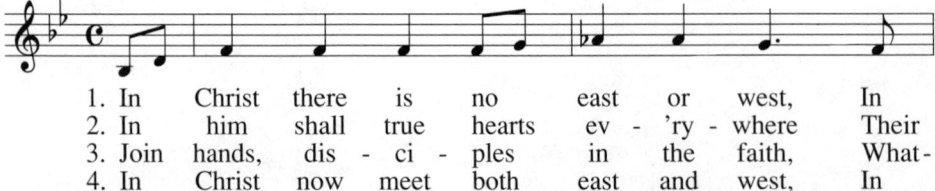

1. In Christ there is no east or west, In
2. In him shall true hearts ev - 'ry - where Their
3. Join hands, dis - ci - ples in the faith, What -
4. In Christ now meet both east and west, In

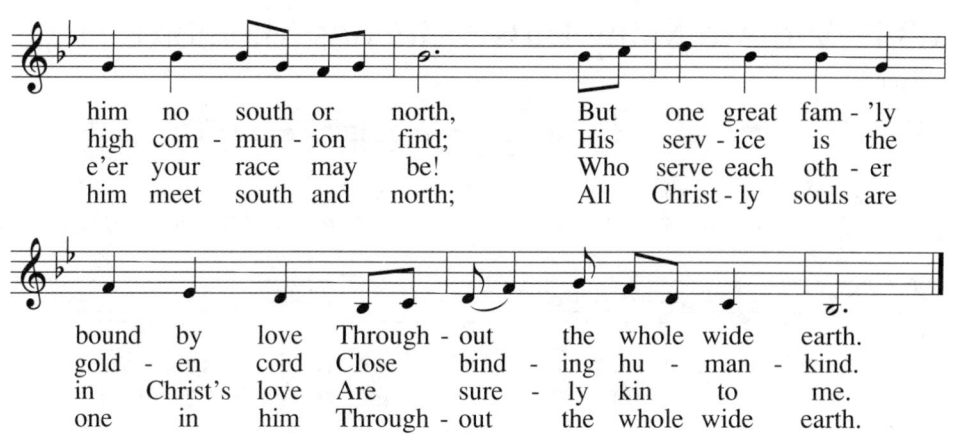

| | | | | | | | | |
|---|---|---|---|---|---|---|---|---|
| him | no | south or | north, | But | one great | fam - 'ly |
| high com | - mun - ion | find; | His | serv - ice | is | the |
| e'er | your | race may | be! | Who | serve each | oth - er |
| him | meet | south and | north; | All | Christ - ly | souls are |

| | | | | | | | |
|---|---|---|---|---|---|---|---|
| bound | by | love | Through - out | the whole wide | earth. |
| gold | - en | cord | Close | bind - ing | hu - man - kind. |
| in | Christ's | love | Are | sure - ly | kin | to | me. |
| one | in | him | Through - out | the whole wide | earth. |

Text: Galatians 3:23; William A. Dunkerley, 1852–1941, alt.
Tune: McKEE, CM; African American; adapt. by Harry T. Burleigh, 1866–1949

## Diverse in Culture, Nation, Race     833

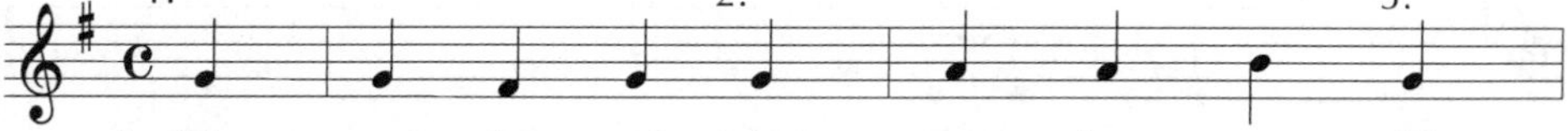

| | | | | | | | | |
|---|---|---|---|---|---|---|---|---|
| 1. Di | - verse | in | cul - ture, | na - tion, | race, | We |
| 2. God, | let | us | be | a | bridge | of | care | Con - |
| 3. When | cha - sms | wid - en, | storms | a - rise, | O |
| 4. God, | let | us | be | a | ta - ble | spread | With |

| | | | | | | | |
|---|---|---|---|---|---|---|---|
| come to - geth - er | by | your grace. | God, | let | us | be | a |
| nect - ing peo - ple | ev - 'ry - where. | Help | us | con - front | all |
| Ho - ly Spir - it, | make | us | wise. | Let | our | re - solve, like |
| gifts | of | love and | bro - ken bread, | Where | all | find wel - come, |

| | | | | | | | |
|---|---|---|---|---|---|---|---|
| meet - ing ground | Where | hope | and heal - ing | love | are | found. |
| fear | and | hate | And | lust | for pow'r that | sep - a - rate. |
| steel, | be | strong | To | stand | with those who | suf - fer wrong. |
| grace | at - tends, | And | en - e - mies | a - rise | as | friends. |

*May be sung as a two- or four-voice canon.*

Text: Ruth Duck, b.1947, © 1992, GIA Publications, Inc.
Tune: TALLIS' CANON, LM; Thomas Tallis, c.1510–1583

## 834 We Are Many Parts / Muchos Miembros Hay

Refrain

We are man-y parts, we are all one bod-y,
*Mu-chos miem-bros hay, en un so-lo cuer-po;*

and the gifts we have we are giv-en to share.
*nues-tros do-nes son pa-ra dar y ser-vir.*

May the Spir-it of love make us one in-deed;
*Que_el Es-pí-ri-tu de Dios nos u-na en su_a-mor;*

one, the love that we share, one, our hope in de-
*com-par-tien-do_el do-lor, com-ba-tien-do_el te-*

Last time

spair, one, the cross that we bear.
*mor, com-pla-cien-do_al Se-ñor.*

Verses

1. God of all, we look to you, We would be your
2. So my pain is pain for you, In your joy is
3. All you seek-ers, great and small, Seek the great-est

1. *Oh Se-ñor, que-re-mos ser Ser-vi-do-res*
2. *Mi do-lor te due-le_a ti; Si te go-zas,*
3. *Quie-nes bus-can de ver-dad Su ma-yor fe-*

D.C.

ser-vants true, Let us be your love to all the world.
my joy, too; All is brought to-geth-er in the Lord.
gift of all; If you love, then you will know the Lord.

*por do-quier; Y_a la_hu-ma-ni-dad lle-var tu_a-mor.*
*soy fe-liz; To-do se_u-ne_en tor-no al Se-ñor.*
*li-ci-dad: A-men y co-no-ce-rán a Dios.*

Text: 1 Corinthians 12, 13; Marty Haugen, b.1950; tr. by Santiago Fernández, b.1971
Tune: Marty Haugen, b.1950
© 1980, 1986, 2005, GIA Publications, Inc.

# They'll Know We Are Christians 835

1. We are one in the Spir - it, we are
   one in the Lord, We are one in the
   Spir - it, we are one in the Lord, And we
   pray that all u - ni - ty may one day be restored:

2. We will walk with each oth - er, we will
   walk hand in hand, We will walk with each
   oth - er, we will walk hand in hand, And to-
   geth - er we'll spread the news that God is in our
   land:

3. We will work with each oth - er, we will
   work side by side, We will work with each
   oth - er, we will work side by side, And we'll
   guard hu - man's dig - ni - ty and save hu - man's
   pride:

4. All praise to the Fa - ther, from
   whom all things come, And all praise to Christ
   Je - sus, his on - ly Son, And all
   praise to the Spir - it, who makes us
   one:

And they'll know we are Chris - tians by our
love, by our love, Yes, they'll know we are
Chris - tians by our love.

Text: Peter Scholtes, b.1938
Tune: ST. BRENDAN'S, 7 6 7 6 8 6 with refrain; Peter Scholtes, b.1938
© 1966, F.E.L. Publications, assigned to The Lorenz Corp., 1991

# 836 Coming Together for Wine and for Bread

Verses 1–3

1. Com - ing to - geth - er for Wine and for Bread,
2. Who will be hun - gry if, hear - ing the call,
3. Here at this ta - ble, we're wel - comed by name;

Tast - ing the sto - ry and hear - ing it read,
We of - fer seats at our ban - quet to all?
All are in - vit - ed, each seat is the same.

Know - ing our hun - ger and shar - ing the meal
Who is for - got - ten? Whom will we ig - nore?
Serv - ing, re - ceiv - ing, and eat - ing the feast

1., 2.

O - pens our eyes to see Je - sus is real.
Who is the out - cast that knocks at our door?
Hum - bles the haugh - ty and hon - ors the least.

Verse 4

3.

4. Bless - ing this ta - ble the Spir - it is here

Grant - ing us vi - sion, so sud - den - ly clear:

Shar - ing and serv - ing, the bod - y is fed,

Nour - ished by Je - sus, the Wine and the Bread,

Nour - ished by Je - sus, the Wine and the Bread.

Text: Adam M. L. Tice, b.1979, © 2009, GIA Publications, Inc.
Tune: BLACKHAWK LANE, 10 10 10 10; David Haas, b.1957, © 2010, GIA Publications, Inc.

# Gather Your People  837

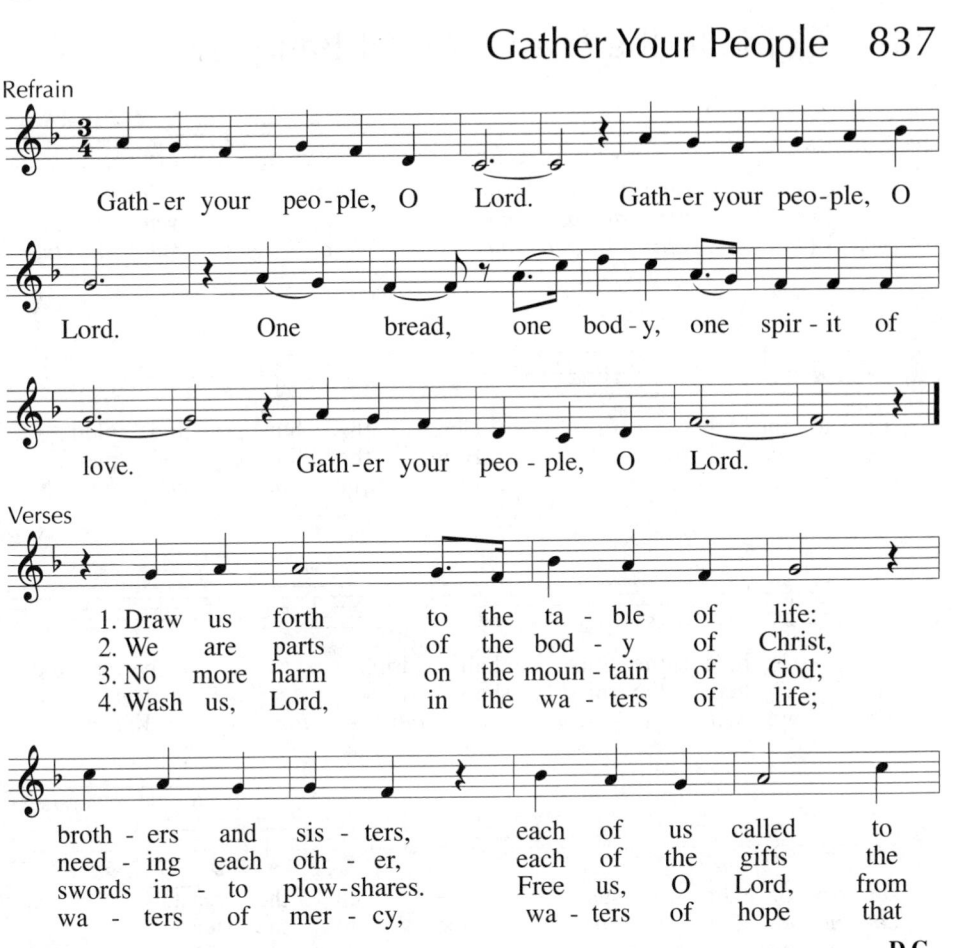

**Refrain**

Gath-er your peo-ple, O Lord. Gath-er your peo-ple, O

Lord. One bread, one bod-y, one spir-it of

love. Gath-er your peo - ple, O Lord.

**Verses**

1. Draw us forth to the ta - ble of life:
2. We are parts of the bod - y of Christ,
3. No more harm on the moun - tain of God;
4. Wash us, Lord, in the wa - ters of life;

broth - ers and sis - ters, each of us called to
need - ing each oth - er, each of the gifts the
swords in - to plow-shares. Free us, O Lord, from
wa - ters of mer - cy, wa - ters of hope that

**D.C.**

walk in your light.
Spir - it pro - vides.
hard - ness of heart.
flow from your side.

Text: 1 Corinthians 12, Isaiah 2:3–4, 11:9; Bob Hurd, b.1950
Tune: Bob Hurd. b.1950; choral arr. by Craig S. Kingsbury, b.1952; acc. by Dominic MacAller, b.1959
© 1991, Bob Hurd. Published by OCP.

# 838 Come to the Feast / Ven al Banquete

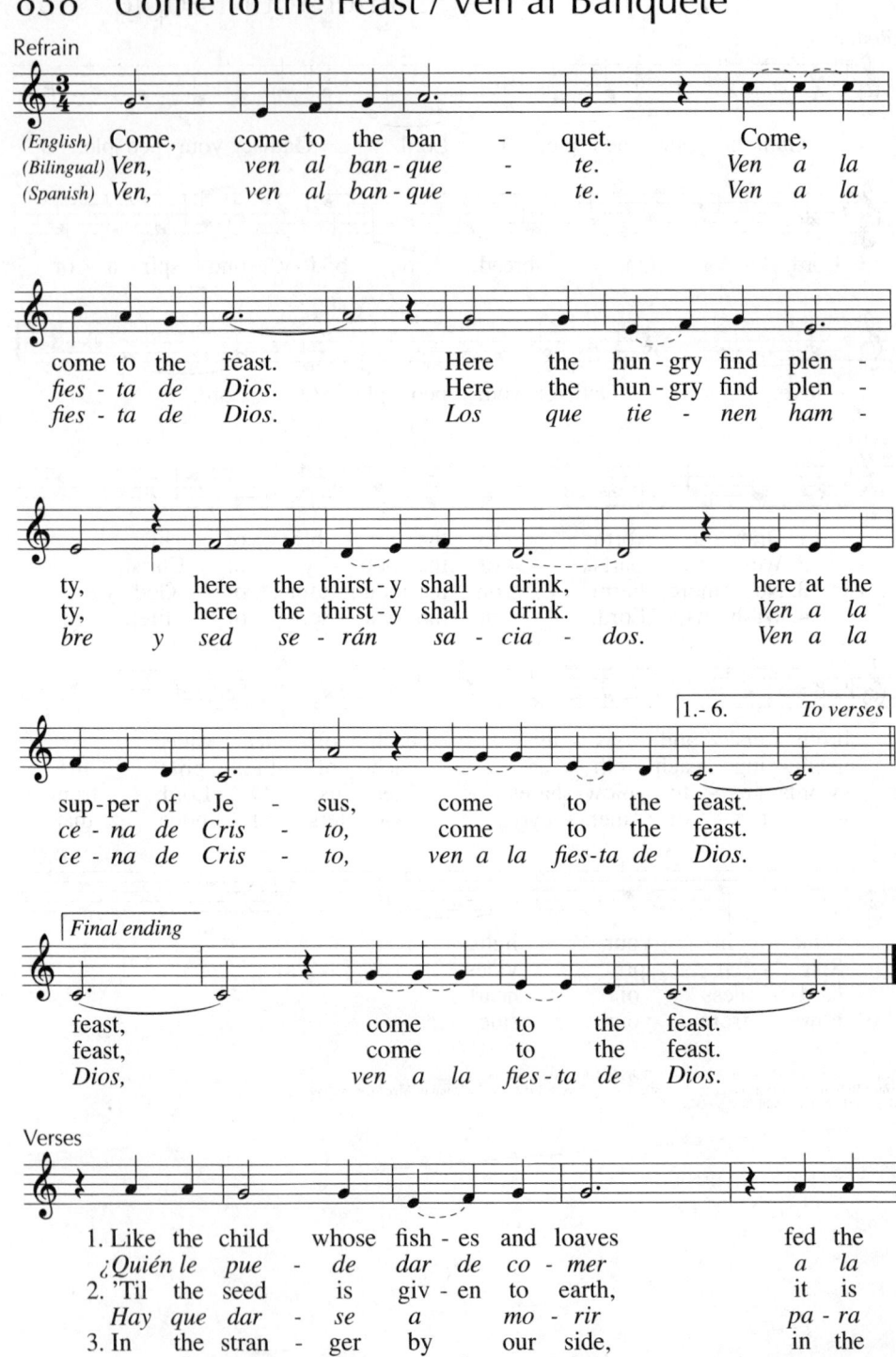

Refrain

(English) Come, come to the ban - quet. Come,
(Bilingual) *Ven, ven al ban - que - te. Ven a la*
(Spanish) *Ven, ven al ban - que - te. Ven a la*

come to the feast. Here the hun - gry find plen -
*fies - ta de Dios. Here the hun - gry find plen -*
*fies - ta de Dios. Los que tie - nen ham -*

ty, here the thirst - y shall drink, here at the
ty, *here the thirst - y shall drink. Ven a la*
*bre y sed se - rán sa - cia - dos. Ven a la*

1.- 6.  To verses

sup - per of Je - sus, come to the feast.
*ce - na de Cris - to, come to the feast.*
*ce - na de Cris - to, ven a la fies - ta de Dios.*

Final ending

feast, come to the feast.
feast, come to the feast.
*Dios, ven a la fies - ta de Dios.*

Verses

1. Like the child whose fish - es and loaves fed the
   *¿Quién le pue - de dar de co - mer a la*
2. 'Til the seed is giv - en to earth, it is
   *Hay que dar - se a mo - rir pa - ra*
3. In the stran - ger by our side, in the
   *Los de - sam - pa - ra - dos ven - drán a par -*

| mul - ti - tude, | in the Lord the |
| *mul - ti - tud?* | *Con Je - sús, al* |
| just one grain; | but once sown its |
| *co - se - char,* | *las se - mi - llas* |
| least and last, | in the thirst for |
| *tir el pan* | *y ve - rán su* |

| lit - tle we have, | bro - ken and shared, be - |
| *com - par - tir lo* | *po - co que hay, re - ci -* |
| death brings new birth, the | har - vest is rich; what's |
| *de li - ber - tad y* | *re - su - rrec - ción, la pro -* |
| jus - tice we share, | Christ is here in the |
| *dig - ni - dad de* | *nue - vo en Je - sús, Sal - va -* |

**D.C.**

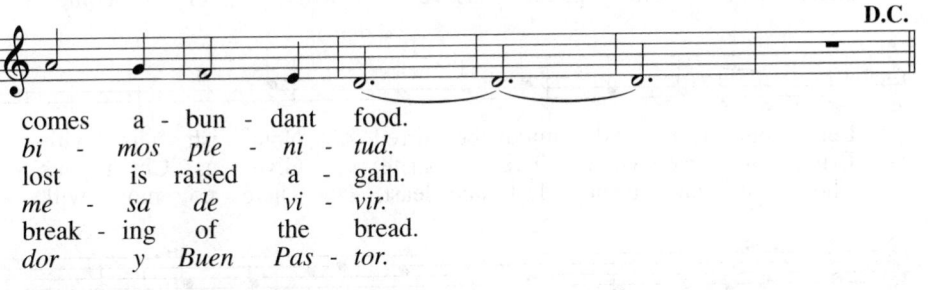

| comes a - bun - dant food. |
| *bi - mos ple - ni - tud.* |
| lost is raised a - gain. |
| *me - sa de vi - vir.* |
| break - ing of the bread. |
| *dor y Buen Pas - tor.* |

Text: Bob Hurd, b.1950, Pia Moriarty, b.1948, Jaime Cortez, b.1963
Tune: Bob Hurd, b.1950; acc. by Dominic MacAller, b.1959, alt.
© 1994, 1995, Bob Hurd and Pia Moriarty. Published by OCP.

# 839 As We Gather at Your Table

1. As we gath - er at your ta - ble,
2. Turn our wor - ship in - to wit - ness
3. Gra - cious Spir - it, help us sum - mon

As we lis - ten to your word,
In the sac - ra - ment of life;
Oth - er guests to share that feast

Help us know, O God, your pres - ence;
Send us forth to love and serve you,
Where tri - um - phant Love will wel - come

Let our hearts and minds be stirred. Nour - ish us with
Bring - ing peace where there is strife. Give us, Christ, your
Those who had been last and least. There no more will

sa - cred sto - ry Till we claim it as our own;
great com - pas - sion To for - give as you for - gave;
en - vy blind us, Nor will pride our peace de - stroy,

Teach us through this ho - ly ban - quet
May we still be - hold your im - age
As we join with saints and an - gels

How to make Love's vic - t'ry known.
In the world you died to save.
To re - peat the sound - ing joy.

Text: Carl P. Daw, Jr., b.1944, © 1989, Hope Publishing Company
Tune: HOLY MANNA, 8 7 8 7 D; William Moore, fl.1830; acc. by Kelly Dobbs Mickus, b.1966, © 2003, GIA Publications, Inc.

# Jesus Is the Resurrection    840

**Refrain**

Je-sus is the res-ur - rec-tion and the life.

*To repeat and last time* | *To verses*

All who be - lieve will live.

**Verse 1**

1. We come to this house, we gath - er in his name. We

| 1. | 2. | D.C. |

know that our Sav - ior lives.

**Verse 2**

2. Just as Laz - a - rus rose and Mar - tha be - lieved, the

| 1. | 2. | D.C. |

glo - ry of the Lord shall be re - vealed.

Text: Derek W. Campbell, 1963–2004
Tune: Derek W. Campbell, 1963–2004
© 2002, GIA Publications, Inc.

# 841 Gathered as One

Verses

*Cantor:*

1. Man - y fac - es, the young and the old,
2. Man - y pil - grims, ⁊ shar - ing at feast,
3. Man - y voic - es, ⁊ raised up in song,

*All:*

gath-ered as one in our God!

*Cantor:*

Through-out his-t'ry the
All are wel-come the
In one fam-'ly where

sto - ry's re - told,
great-est and least,
all can be - long,

*All:*

gath-ered as one in our God!

*Cantor:*

Like those come be-fore us, we lis - ten and learn. We re -

mem - ber the prom-ise and a - wait your re - turn. So with-

out hes - i - ta - tion a new gen - er - a - tion pro-

**Refrain**

*All:*

claims the sal-va - tion of God! Gath-ered as one in

Je - sus your Son, lift-ing our voic-es in praise, we

know and be - lieve and long to re - ceive the

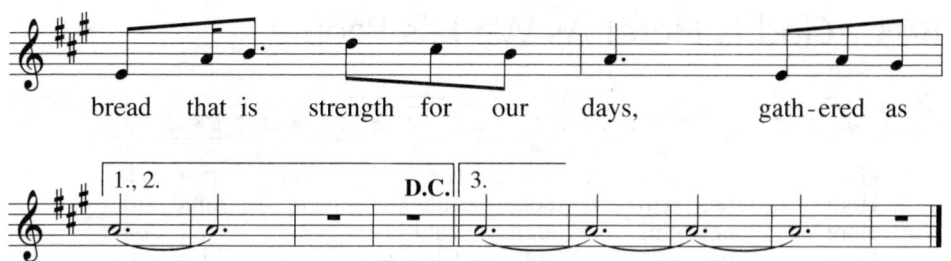

bread that is strength for our days, gath-ered as

**1., 2.** **D.C.** **3.**

one! one!

Text: Deanna Light, b.1967, and Paul A. Tate, b.1968
Tune: Deanna Light, b.1967, and Paul A. Tate, b.1968
© 1997, World Library Publications

## Come to Us 842

1. Come to me, come to us, you who are bur-dened.
2. Come to me, come to us, pil - grim or stran - ger,
3. Come to me, come to us, bro - ken or build - ing,

Come to the word, and come to the meal.
look - ing for change, or chal - lenge, or light.
Come with your chil - dren, your choic - es, your chains.

Come with-out ques - tion or pres - sure or price:
We are the peo - ple whose call - ing is care,
All are in - vit - ed to friend-ship or rest, to

Come, be em - braced by the bod - y of Christ.
bear - ers of mer - cy, nour - ished in prayer.
share in our strug - gle, our call and our quest.

Text: Rory Cooney, b.1952
Tune: Rory Cooney, b.1952
© 1986, North American Liturgy Resources. Published by OCP.

# 843  God Is Here! As We His People

1. God is here! As we his peo - ple
2. Here are sym - bols to re - mind us
3. Here our chil - dren find a wel - come
4. Lord of all, of Church and king - dom,

Meet to of - fer praise and prayer,
Of our life - long need of grace;
In the Shep - herd's flock and fold;
In an age of change and doubt,

May we find in ful - ler meas - ure
Here are ta - ble, font, and pul - pit;
Here, as bread and wine are tak - en,
Keep us faith - ful to the Gos - pel;

What it is in Christ we share.
Here the cross has cen - tral place.
Christ sus - tains us as of old.
Help us work your pur - pose out.

Here, as in the world a - round us,
Here in hon - es - ty of preach - ing,
Here the ser - vants of the Ser - vant
Here, in this day's ded - i - ca - tion,

All our var - ied skills and arts
Here in si - lence, as in speech,
Seek in wor - ship to ex - plore
All we have to give, re - ceive;

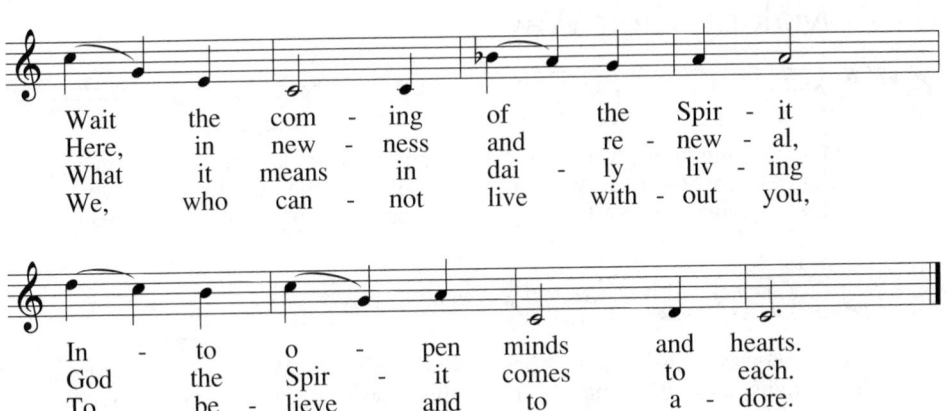

Wait | the | com - ing | of | the | Spir - it
Here, | in | new - ness | and | re - new - al,
What | it | means | in | dai - ly | liv - ing
We, | who | can - not | live | with - out | you,

In - to | o - pen | minds | and | hearts.
God | the | Spir - it | comes | to | each.
To | be - lieve | and | to | a - dore.
We | a - dore | you! | We | be - lieve!

Text: Fred Pratt Green, 1903–2000, © 1979, Hope Publishing Company
Tune: ABBOT'S LEIGH, 8 7 8 7 D; Cyril V. Taylor, 1907–1991, © 1942, 1970, Hope Publishing Company

## Alleluia! Give the Glory 844

Refrain

Al - le - lu - ia! Al - le - lu - ia! Al - le -

1.
lu - ia! Give the glo - ry and the

hon - or to the Lord!

2.
glo - ry and the hon - or to the Lord!

Text: Matthew 18:20, John 15:5; adapt. by Ken Canedo, b.1953, and Bob Hurd, b.1950
Tune: Ken Canedo, b.1953; choral arr. by Craig S. Kingsbury, b.1952; acc. by Dominic MacAller, b.1959
© 1991, Ken Canedo and Bob Hurd. Published by OCP.

## 845 Making Their Way

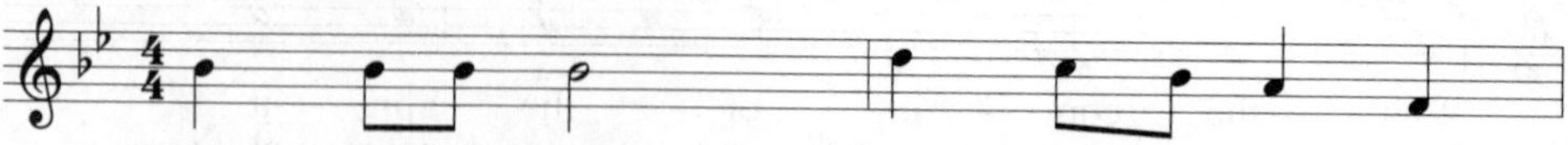

1. Mak - ing their way down through the a - ges,
2. Mak - ing their way all the world o - ver,
3. Mak - ing our way sea - son by sea - son,

Sin - ners and saints have heard God's call: Wealth-y and poor,
Chris - tians as - sem - ble on this day, Hear - ing the Word,
Pil - grims, we jour - ney till life's end, Trav - el-ing light,

pow - er-ful, low - ly, Je - sus' dis - ci - ples, one and all.
shar - ing the Ban-quet, Learn-ing to walk in Je - sus' way.
shar - ing the rich - es, Car - ing for stran - ger as for friend,

Gath - ered for wor - ship, of - fer-ing thanks, The great - est
Mem - bers of Christ, u - nit - ed in love, They seek our
Till in the joy of long - ing ful-filled, To - geth - er

with the least Have come to share this feast.
God to know, And so to - geth - er grow.
we will come To our e - ter - nal home.

Text: Delores Dufner, OSB, b.1939, © 2010, GIA Publications, Inc.
Tune: KOMT NU MET ZANG, 9 8 9 8 9 66; Valerius' *Neder-landtsche gedenck-klanck;* acc. by Robert J. Batastini, b.1942, © 1987,
GIA Publications, Inc.

## 846 Come, Host of Heaven's High Dwelling Place

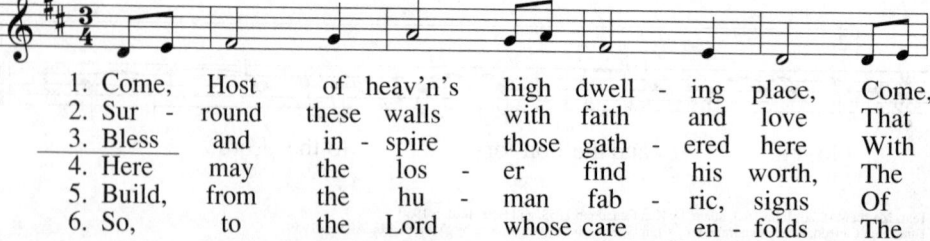

1. Come, Host of heav'n's high dwell - ing place, Come,
2. Sur - round these walls with faith and love That
3. Bless and in - spire those gath - ered here With
4. Here may the los - er find his worth, The
5. Build, from the hu - man fab - ric, signs Of
6. So, to the Lord whose care en - folds The

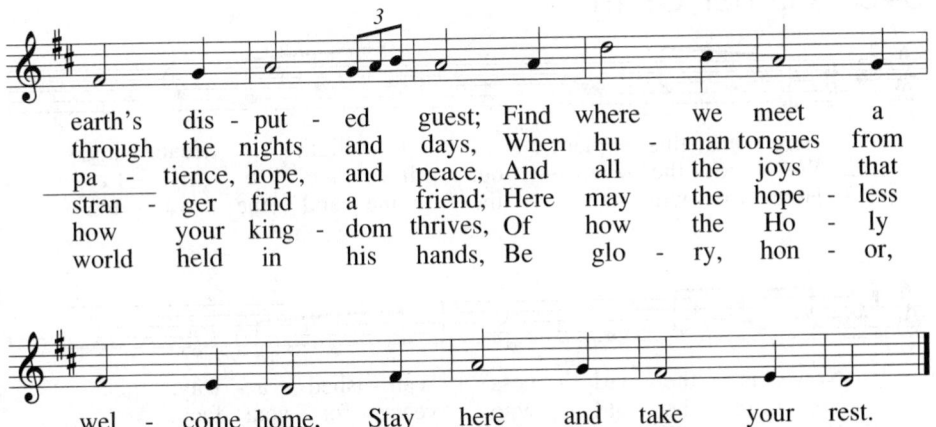

earth's · dis - put - ed guest; Find where we meet a
through the nights and days, When hu - man tongues from
pa - tience, hope, and peace, And all the joys that
stran - ger find a friend; Here may the hope - less
how your king - dom thrives, Of how the Ho - ly
world held in his hands, Be glo - ry, hon - or,

wel - come home, Stay here and take your rest.
speak - ing cease, These stones may ech - o praise.
know the depth In which all sor - rows cease.
find their faith And aim - less find an end.
Spir - it chang - es life By chang - ing lives.
pow'r and praise For which this com - p'ny stands.

Text: John L. Bell, b.1949, © 1989, Iona Community, GIA Publications, Inc., agent
Tune: ST. COLUMBA, 8 6 8 6; Irish traditional; arr. by John L. Bell, b.1949, © 1989, Iona Community, GIA Publications, Inc., agent

# Jesus Christ, Yesterday, Today, and for Ever / 847
## Jesucristo Ayer
Ostinato Refrain

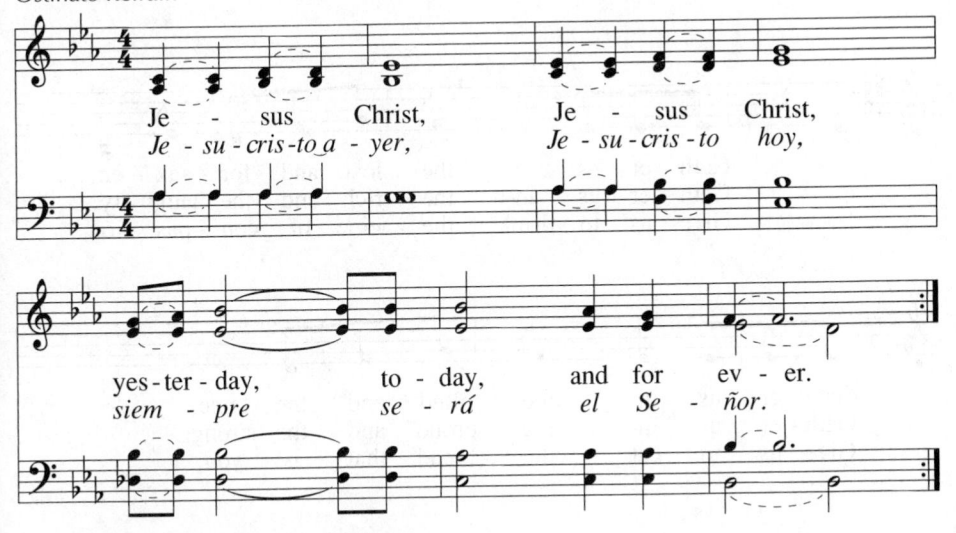

Je - sus Christ, Je - sus Christ,
Je - su - cris - to_a - yer, Je - su - cris - to hoy,

yes - ter - day, to - day, and for ev - er.
siem - pre se - rá el Se - ñor.

Text: Suzanne Toolan, SM, b.1927; Spanish tr. by Ronald F. Krisman, b.1946
Tune: Suzanne Toolan, SM, b.1927
© 1988, 2004, GIA Publications, Inc.

# 848 Gather Us In

1. Here in this place new light is stream - ing,
2. We are the young— our lives are a mys - t'ry,
3. Here we will take the wine and the wa - ter,

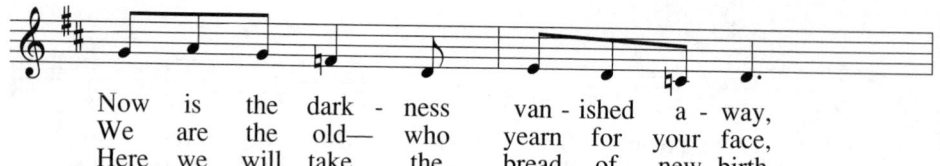

Now is the dark - ness van - ished a - way,
We are the old— who yearn for your face,
Here we will take the bread of new birth,

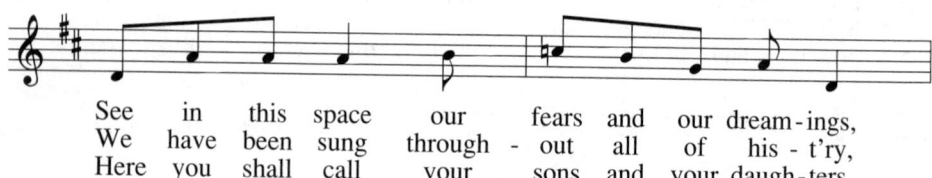

See in this space our fears and our dream-ings,
We have been sung through - out all of his - t'ry,
Here you shall call your sons and your daugh-ters,

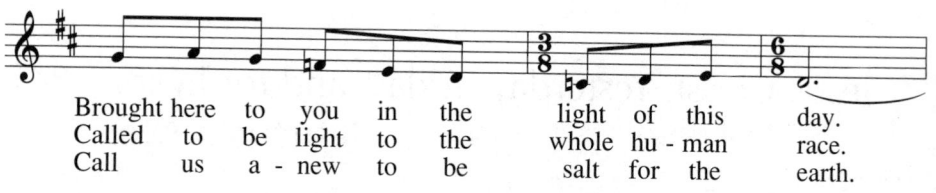

Brought here to you in the light of this day.
Called to be light to the whole hu - man race.
Call us a - new to be salt for the earth.

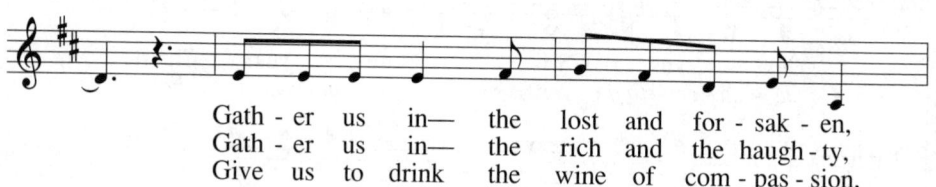

Gath - er us in— the lost and for - sak - en,
Gath - er us in— the rich and the haugh - ty,
Give us to drink the wine of com - pas - sion,

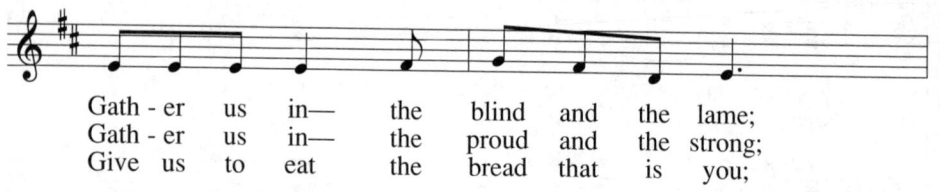

Gath - er us in— the blind and the lame;
Gath - er us in— the proud and the strong;
Give us to eat the bread that is you;

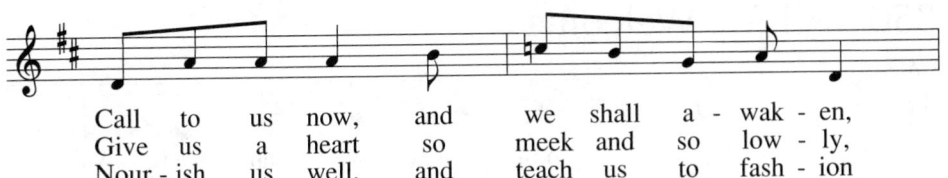

Call to us now, and we shall a - wak - en,
Give us a heart so meek and so low - ly,
Nour - ish us well, and teach us to fash - ion

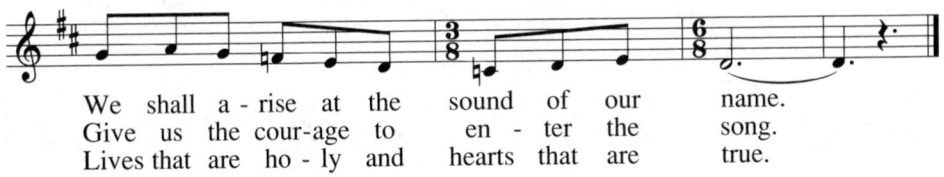

We shall a - rise at the sound of our name.
Give us the cour - age to en - ter the song.
Lives that are ho - ly and hearts that are true.

Text: Marty Haugen, b.1950
Tune: GATHER US IN, Irregular; Marty Haugen, b.1950
© 1982, GIA Publications, Inc.

## Uyai Mose / Come All You People   849

Ostinato Refrain

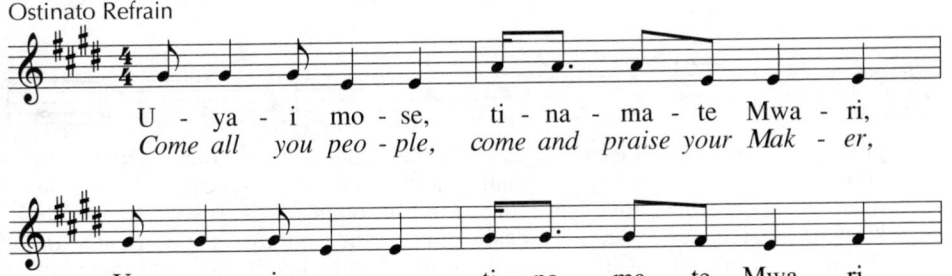

U - ya - i mo - se, ti - na - ma - te Mwa - ri,
*Come all you peo - ple, come and praise your Mak - er,*

U - ya - i mo - se, ti - na - ma - te Mwa - ri,
*Come all you peo - ple, come and praise your Mak - er,*

U - ya - i mo - se, ti - na - ma - te Mwa - ri,
*Come all you peo - ple, come and praise your Mak - er,*

3

U - ya - i mo - se zvi - no.
*Come now and wor - ship the Lord.*

Text: Alexander Gondo, b.1936
Tune: Alexander Gondo, b.1936; arr. by John L. Bell, b.1949, © 1994, Iona Community, GIA Publications, Inc., agent

# 850  All Are Welcome

1. Let us build a house where love can dwell And
2. Let us build a house where proph - ets speak, And
3. Let us build a house where love is found In
4. Let us build a house where hands will reach Be -
5. Let us build a house where all are named, Their

all can safe - ly live, A place where saints and
words are strong and true, Where all God's chil - dren
wa - ter, wine and wheat: A ban - quet hall on
yond the wood and stone To heal and strength - en,
songs and vi - sions heard And loved and treas - ured,

chil - dren tell How hearts learn to for -
dare to seek To dream God's reign a -
ho - ly ground, Where peace and jus - tice
serve and teach, And live the Word they've
taught and claimed As words with - in the

give. Built of hopes and dreams and vi - sions, Rock of
new. Here the cross shall stand as wit - ness And as
meet. Here the love of God, through Je - sus, Is re -
known. Here the out - cast and the stran - ger Bear the
Word. Built of tears and cries and laugh - ter, Prayers of

faith and vault of grace; Here the
sym - bol of God's grace; Here as
vealed in time and space; As we
im - age of God's face; Let us
faith and songs of grace, Let this

love    of  Christ  shall  end  di - vi - sions:
one    we  claim  the  faith  of  Je - sus:
share   in  Christ  the  feast  that  frees  us:
bring   an  end  to  fear  and  dan - ger:
house  pro - claim  from  floor  to  raft - er:

All   are wel-come,  all   are wel-come,  all   are wel-come

in   this   place.

Text: Marty Haugen, b.1950
Tune: TWO OAKS, 9 6 8 6 8 7 10 with refrain; Marty Haugen, b.1950
© 1994, GIA Publications, Inc.

## Christ Has Promised to Be Present   851

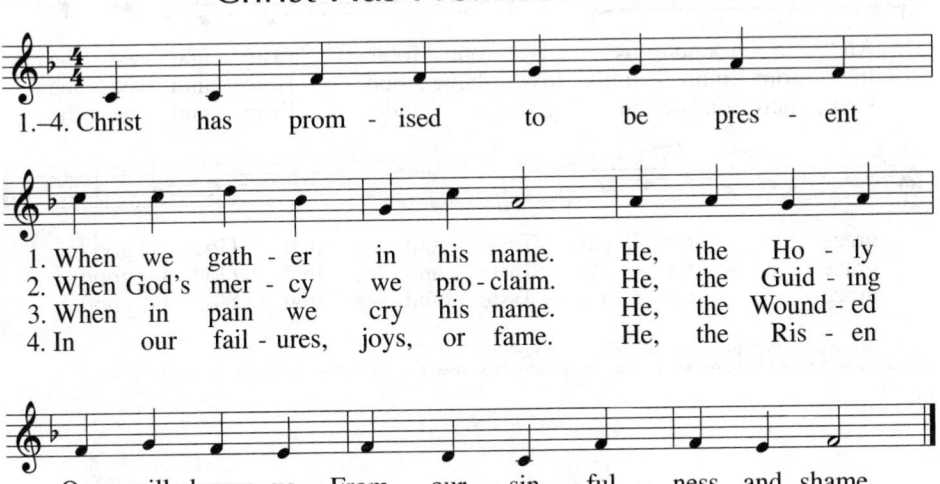

1.–4. Christ  has  prom - ised  to  be  pres - ent

1. When  we  gath - er  in  his  name.  He,  the  Ho - ly
2. When God's mer - cy  we  pro - claim.  He,  the  Guid - ing
3. When  in  pain  we  cry  his  name.  He,  the  Wound - ed
4. In   our  fail - ures,  joys,  or  fame.  He,  the  Ris - en

One, will cleanse us  From  our  sin - ful - ness and shame.
One, will teach us  Words  of  wis - dom  in  his name.
One, will touch us  With  his  Spir - it's  heal - ing flame.
One, will save us  Through his  pow'r - ful,  glo - rious name.

Text: Rae E. Whitney, b.1927, © 1994, Selah Publishing Co., Inc.
Tune: STUTTGART, 8 7 8 7; *Psalmodia Sacra*, 1715; adapt. and harm. by William Henry Havergal, 1793–1870, alt.

# 852 All Who Hunger, Gather Gladly

1. All who hun - ger, gath - er glad - ly;
2. All who hun - ger, nev - er stran - gers,
3. All who hun - ger, sing to - geth - er;

Ho - ly man - na is our bread. Come from wil - der -
Seek - er, be a wel - come guest. Come from rest - less -
Je - sus Christ is liv - ing bread. Come from lone - li -

ness and wan - d'ring. Here, in truth, we will be fed.
ness and roam - ing. Here, in joy, we keep the feast.
ness and long - ing. Here, in peace, we have been led.

You that yearn for days of full - ness,
We that once were lost and scat - tered
Blest are those who from this ta - ble

All a - round us is our food. Taste and see the
In com - mun - ion's love have stood. Taste and see the
Live their days in grat - i - tude. Taste and see the

grace e - ter - nal. Taste and see that God is good.
grace e - ter - nal. Taste and see that God is good.
grace e - ter - nal. Taste and see that God is good.

Text: Sylvia G. Dunstan, 1955–1993, © 1991, GIA Publications, Inc.
Tune: HOLY MANNA, 8 7 8 7 D; William Moore, fl.1830; harm. by Charles Anders, b.1929, © 1969, *Contemporary Worship I: Hymns*

# All People That on Earth Do Dwell 853

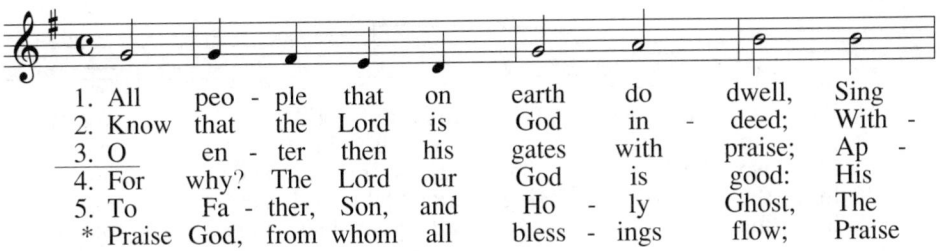

1. All peo - ple that on earth do dwell, Sing
2. Know that the Lord is God in - deed; With -
3. O en - ter then his gates with praise; Ap -
4. For why? The Lord our God is good: His
5. To Fa - ther, Son, and Ho - ly Ghost, The
\* Praise God, from whom all bless - ings flow; Praise

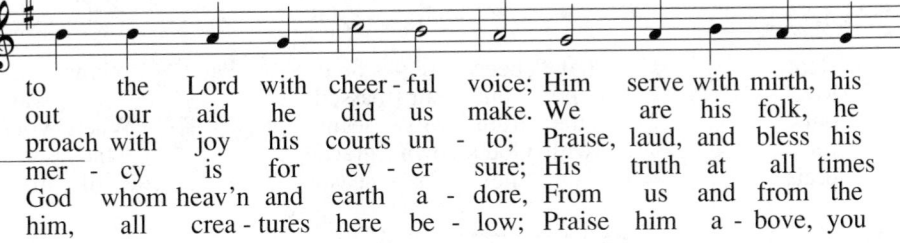

to the Lord with cheer - ful voice; Him serve with mirth, his
out our aid he did us make. We are his folk, he
proach with joy his courts un - to; Praise, laud, and bless his
mer - cy is for ev - er sure; His truth at all times
God whom heav'n and earth a - dore, From us and from the
him, all crea - tures here be - low; Praise him a - bove, you

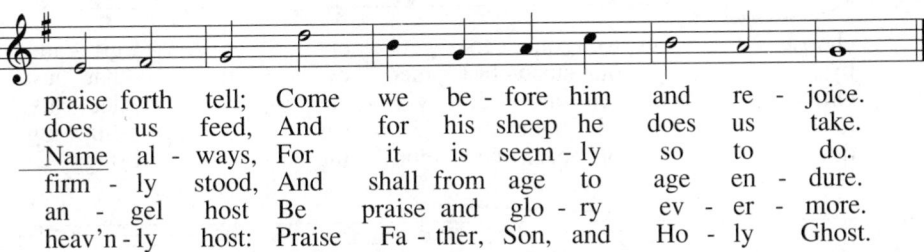

praise forth tell; Come we be - fore him and re - joice.
does us feed, And for his sheep he does us take.
Name al - ways, For it is seem - ly so to do.
firm - ly stood, And shall from age to age en - dure.
an - gel host Be praise and glo - ry ev - er - more.
heav'n - ly host: Praise Fa - ther, Son, and Ho - ly Ghost.

*May be sung alone or as an alternate to stanza 5.*

Text: Psalm 100; William Kethe, d. c.1593; Doxology, Thomas Ken, 1637–1711
Tune: OLD HUNDREDTH, LM; Louis Bourgeois, c.1510–1561

# 854 We Arise

Verses

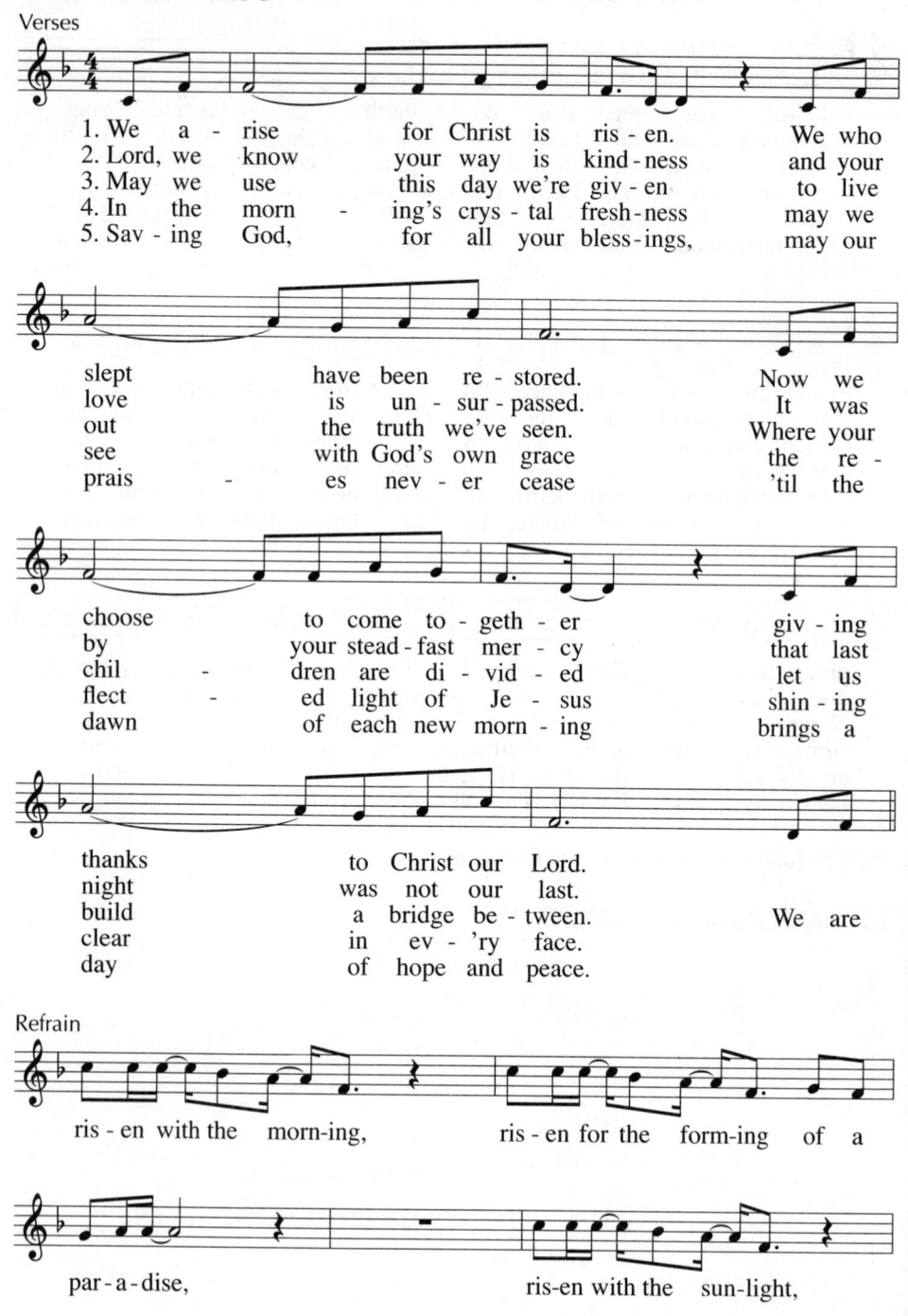

1. We a - rise for Christ is ris - en. We who
2. Lord, we know your way is kind - ness and your
3. May we use this day we're giv - en to live
4. In the morn - ing's crys - tal fresh - ness may we
5. Sav - ing God, for all your bless - ings, may our

slept have been re - stored. Now we
love is un - sur - passed. It was
out the truth we've seen. Where your
see with God's own grace the re -
prais - es nev - er cease 'til the

choose to come to - geth - er giv - ing
by your stead - fast mer - cy that last
chil - dren are di - vid - ed let us
flect - ed light of Je - sus shin - ing
dawn of each new morn - ing brings a

thanks to Christ our Lord.
night was not our last.
build a bridge be - tween. We are
clear in ev - 'ry face.
day of hope and peace.

Refrain

ris - en with the morn-ing, ris - en for the form-ing of a

par - a - dise, ris - en with the sun-light,

ris - en with the    one light    in our    o - pen eyes.

We    a - rise!

1.–4.    **D.C.**  5.                                    *Repeat as desired*

We    a - rise!

Text: Michael Mahler, b.1981
Tune: Michael Mahler, b.1981
© 2004, GIA Publications, Inc.

## Morning Has Broken    855

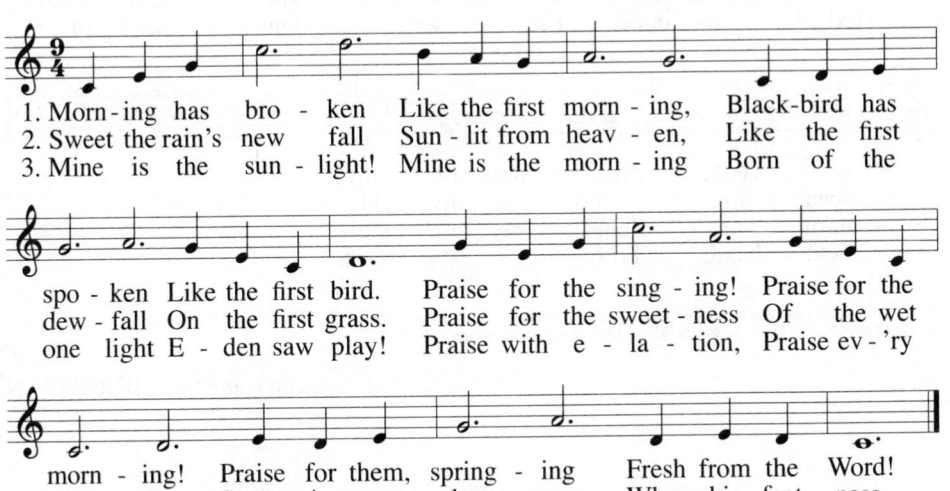

1. Morn - ing has    bro - ken  Like the first   morn - ing,    Black-bird has
2. Sweet the rain's   new    fall  Sun - lit from heav - en,    Like   the   first
3. Mine  is  the    sun - light!  Mine is  the   morn - ing   Born  of   the

spo - ken  Like the first bird.    Praise  for   the   sing - ing!  Praise for the
dew - fall  On   the first grass.  Praise  for   the   sweet - ness  Of    the wet
one  light E - den saw  play!    Praise with  e - la - tion,  Praise ev - 'ry

morn - ing!  Praise for them, spring - ing    Fresh from the    Word!
gar - den,  Sprung in  com - plete - ness   Where his feet    pass.
morn - ing,  God's  re - cre - a - tion    Of    the new    day!

Text: Eleanor Farjeon, 1881–1965, *The Children's Bells,* © David Higham Assoc. Ltd.
Tune: BUNESSAN, 5 5 5 4 D; Gaelic; acc. by Robert J. Batastini, b.1942, © 1999, GIA Publications, Inc.

# 856 This Day God Gives Me

1. This day God gives me Strength of high
2. This day God sends me Strength as my
3. God's way is my way, God's shield is
4. Ris - ing I thank you, Might - y and

heav - en, Sun and moon shin - ing,
guar - dian, Might to up - hold me,
'round me, God's host de - fends me,
strong One, King of cre - a - tion,

Flame in my hearth, Flash - ing of light - ning,
Wis - dom as guide. Your eyes are watch - ful,
Sav - ing from ill. An - gels of heav - en,
Giv - er of rest, Firm - ly con - fess - ing

Wind in its swift - ness, Depths of the
Your ears are lis - t'ning, Your lips are
Drive from me al - ways All that would
God in three Per - sons, One - ness of

o - cean, Firm - ness of earth.
speak - ing, Friend at my side.
harm me, Stand by me still.
God - head, Trin - i - ty blest.

Text: Ascribed to St. Patrick; James Quinn, SJ, 1919–2010, © 1969. Used by permission of Selah Publishing Co., Inc.
Tune: ANDREA, 5 5 5 4 D; David Haas, b.1957, © 1993, GIA Publications, Inc.

*Alternate tune:* BUNESSAN

# At Evening 857

1. Now it is eve - ning: Lights of the cit - y
2. Now it is eve - ning: Lit - tle ones sleep - ing
3. Now it is eve - ning: Food on the ta - ble
4. Now it is eve - ning: Here in our meet - ing

Bid us re - mem - ber Christ is our Light.
Bid us re - mem - ber Christ is our Peace.
Bids us re - mem - ber Christ is our Life.
May we re - mem - ber Christ is our Friend.

Man - y are lone - ly, Who will be neigh - bor?
Some are ne - glect - ed, Who will be neigh - bor?
Man - y are hun - gry, Who will be neigh - bor?
Some may be stran - gers, Who will be neigh - bor?

Where there is car - ing Christ is our Light.
Where there is car - ing Christ is our Peace.
Where there is shar - ing Christ is our Life.
Where there's a wel - come Christ is our Friend.

Text: Fred Pratt Green, 1903–2000, © 1974, Hope Publishing Company
Tune: EVENING HYMN, 5 5 5 4 D; David Haas, b.1957, © 1985, GIA Publications, Inc.

# 858 Day Is Done

1. Day is done, but Love un - fail - ing Dwells ev - er
2. Dark de - scends, but Light un - end - ing Shines through our
3. Eyes will close, but you un - sleep - ing Watch by our

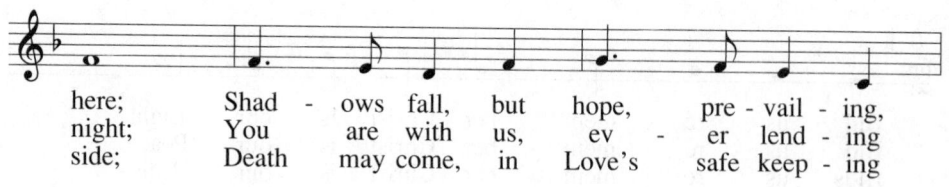

here; Shad - ows fall, but hope, pre - vail - ing,
night; You are with us, ev - er lend - ing
side; Death may come, in Love's safe keep - ing

Calms ev - 'ry fear. God, our Mak - er, none for - sak - ing,
New strength to sight. One in love, your truth con - fess - ing,
Still we a - bide. God of love, all e - vil quell-ing,

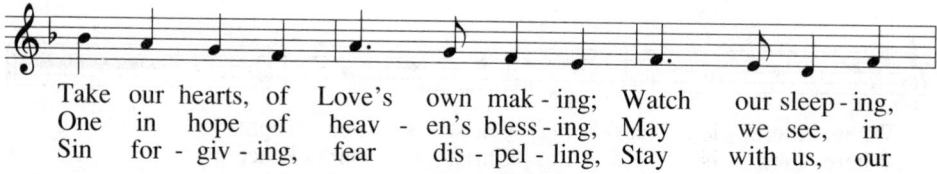

Take our hearts, of Love's own mak - ing; Watch our sleep - ing,
One in hope of heav - en's bless - ing, May we see, in
Sin for - giv - ing, fear dis - pel - ling, Stay with us, our

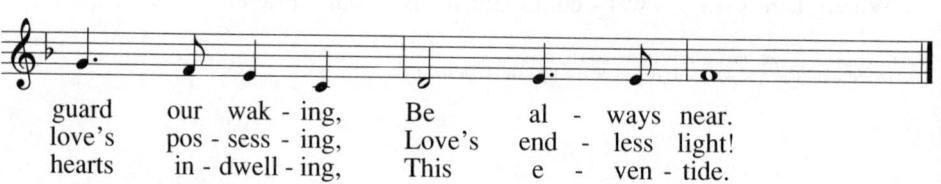

guard our wak - ing, Be al - ways near.
love's pos - sess - ing, Love's end - less light!
hearts in - dwell - ing, This e - ven - tide.

Text: James Quinn, SJ, 1919–2010, © 1969, Used by permission of Selah Publishing Co., Inc.
Tune: AR HYD Y NOS, 8 4 8 4 888 4; Welsh

# God of Day and God of Darkness 859

1. God of day and God of darkness, Now we stand be-fore the night; As the shad-ows stretch and deep-en, Come and make our dark-ness bright. All cre-a-tion still is groan-ing For the dawn-ing of your might, When the Sun of peace and jus-tice Fills the earth with ra-diant light.

2. Still the na-tions curse the darkness, Still the rich op-press the poor; Still the earth is bruised and bro-ken By the ones who still want more. Come and wake us from our sleep-ing, So our hearts can-not ig-nore All your peo-ple lost and bro-ken, All your chil-dren at our door.

3. You shall be the path that guides us, You the light that in us burns; Shin-ing deep with-in all peo-ple, Yours the love that we must learn. For our hearts shall wan-der rest-less 'Til they safe to you re-turn; Find-ing you in one an-oth-er, We shall all your face dis-cern.

4. Praise to you in day and darkness, You our source and you our end; Praise to you who love and nur-ture As a fa-ther, moth-er, friend. Grant us all a peace-ful rest-ing, Let each mind and bod-y mend, So we rise re-freshed to-mor-row, Hearts re-newed to King-dom tend.

Text: Marty Haugen, b.1950, © 1985, 1994, GIA Publications, Inc.
Tune: BEACH SPRING, 8 7 8 7 D; *The Sacred Harp*, 1844; harm. by Marty Haugen, b.1950, © 1985, GIA Publications, Inc.

# 860 Watch, O Lord

Refrain

Watch, O Lord, with all those a - wake this night,

Watch, O Lord, with all those who weep; Give your

an-gels and saints charge o - ver all who sleep.

Verses

*Cantor:*            *All:*            *Cantor:*

1. Tend your ail - ing ones:
2. Soothe your suf-f'ring ones:
3. Hold your griev-ing ones:
4. Guard your lit - tle ones:

in your love, Lord;

Rest your
Heal af -
Raise your
Guide your

*All:*            *Cantor:*

wea - ry ones:
flict - ed ones:
fal - len ones:
search - ing ones:

in your love, Lord;

Bless your
Shield your
Mend your
Grant us

*All:*            D.C.

dy - ing ones:
joy-ous ones:
bro-ken ones:
all your peace:

in your love, O Lord of all.

Text: St. Augustine; adapt. by Marty Haugen, b.1950
Tune: Marty Haugen, b.1950
© 2003, GIA Publications, Inc.

# Praise and Thanksgiving   861

1. Praise and thanks - giv - ing,   Fa - ther, we   of - fer,
2. Lord, bless the la - bor   We bring to serve you,
3. Fa - ther, pro - vid - ing   Food for your chil - dren,
4. Then will your bless - ing   Reach ev - 'ry peo - ple,

For all things liv - ing   You have made good:
That with our neigh - bor   We may be fed.
By your wise guid - ing   Teach us to share
Free - ly con - fess - ing   Your gra - cious hand.

Har - vest of sown fields,   Fruits of the or - chard,
Sow - ing or till - ing,   We would work with you,
One with an - oth - er,   So that, re - joic - ing
Where you are reign - ing   No one will hun - ger,

Hay from the mown fields,   Blos - som and wood.
Har - vest - ing, mill - ing,   For dai - ly bread.
With us, all oth - ers   May know your care.
Your love sus - tain - ing,   Fruit - ful the land.

Text: Albert F. Bayly, 1901–1984, © 1988, Oxford University Press
Tune: BUNESSAN, 5 5 5 4 D; Gaelic; harm. by Robert J. Batastini, b.1942, © 1999, GIA Publications, Inc.

# 862 On That Day

**Refrain**

On that day, on that hal - le - lu - jah day, on that

day, on that hal - le - lu - jah day there'll be

sing - in', there'll be shout - in', and joy flows like a foun-

*Last time to Coda*

tain on that day.

**Verses**

1. We'll see the ho - ly cit - y there; the
2. Twelve gates to the king-dom we shall see; all
3. No need of the sun or moon to shine; the

new Je - ru - sa - lem. No more
na - tions will walk as one. Lift - ing our
glo - ry of God is there. Dark - ness to

sor - row, no more cry - in'.
voic - es, claim - ing our choic - es.
light, God's face in our sight.

**D.C.**

No more death, no more pain.
Glo - ry and hon - or shall be:
Joy from God's love we will share:

✟ Coda

day,                    on that    day.

Text: Kate Cuddy, b.1953
Tune: Kate Cuddy, b.1953
© 1997, GIA Publications, Inc.

# O Holy City, Seen of John   863

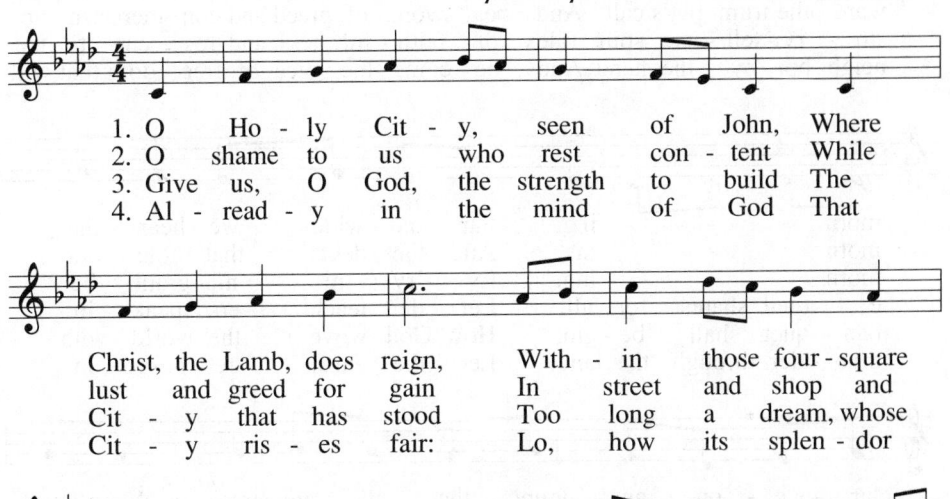

1. O       Ho - ly    Cit - y,    seen    of    John,    Where
2. O    shame   to     us    who    rest    con - tent   While
3. Give   us,    O    God,    the  strength   to    build    The
4. Al - read - y    in    the    mind    of    God    That

Christ, the Lamb, does  reign,    With - in    those four - square
lust    and greed   for    gain     In    street    and   shop   and
Cit - y    that   has   stood    Too    long    a   dream, whose
Cit - y    ris - es    fair:    Lo,    how    its    splen - dor

walls    shall come No    night,    nor    need, nor    pain,    And
ten - e - ment Wring   gold   from    hu - man    pain,    And
laws    are   love, Whose  ways,   the   com - mon   good,    And
chal - leng - es The    souls   that   great - ly   dare:    Yea,

where the tears are wiped from eyes That   shall   not   weep a - gain.
bit - ter  lips  in  blind de - spair Cry, "Christ has  died  in  vain."
where the shin-ing sun  be - comes God's grace  for  hu - man good.
bids    us seize the whole of    life And   build   its  glo - ry  there.

Text: Revelation 21; W. Russell Bowie, 1882–1969
Tune: MORNING SONG, 8 6 8 6 8 6; *Kentucky Harmony*, 1816; harm. by C. Winfred Douglas, 1867–1944, © 1940, The Church Pension Fund

# 864   The Trumpet in the Morning

Verses

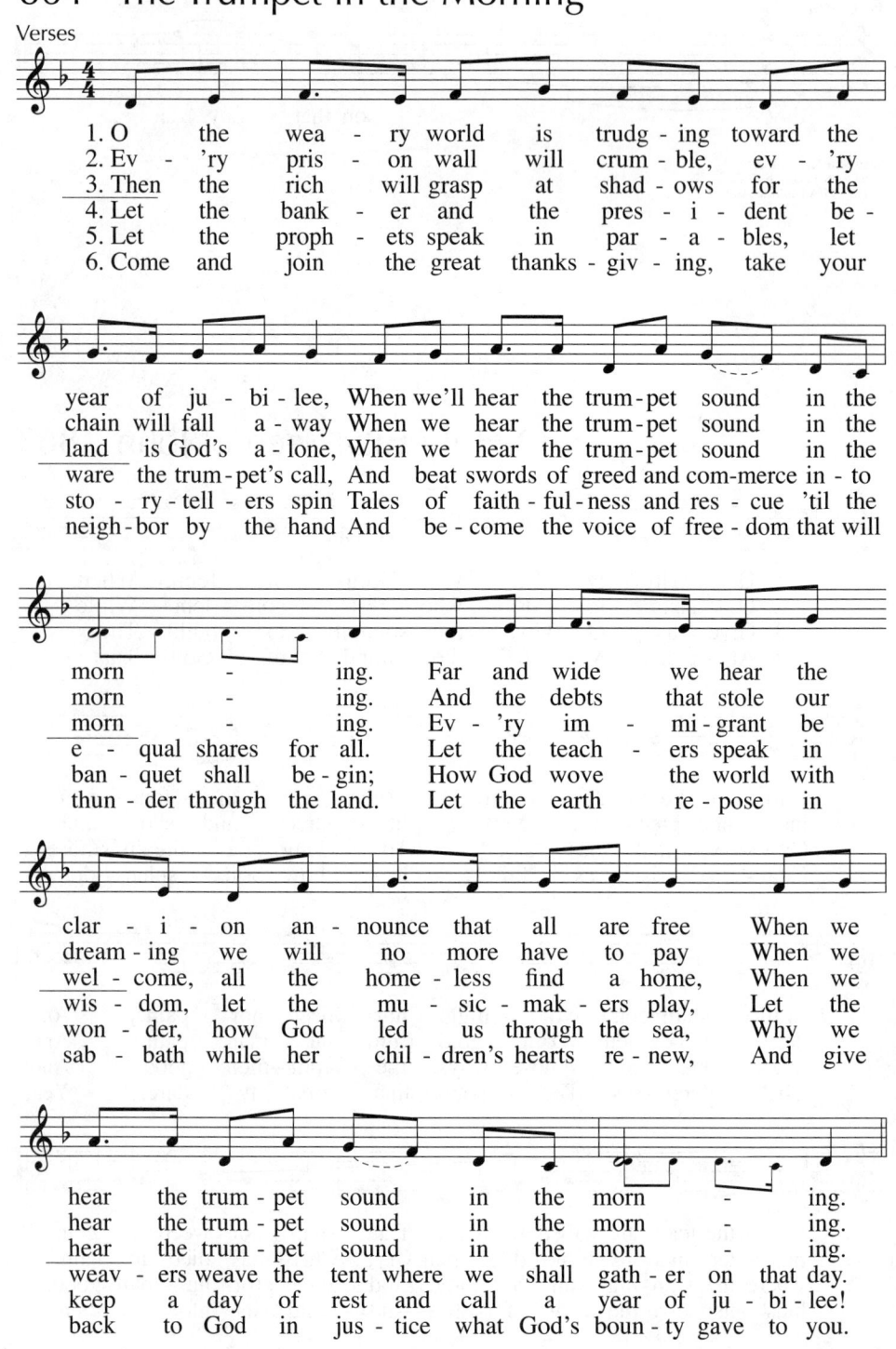

1. O the wea - ry world is trudg - ing toward the
2. Ev - 'ry pris - on wall will crum - ble, ev - 'ry
3. Then the rich will grasp at shad - ows for the
4. Let the bank - er and the pres - i - dent be -
5. Let the proph - ets speak in par - a - bles, let
6. Come and join the great thanks - giv - ing, take your

year of ju - bi - lee, When we'll hear the trum-pet sound in the
chain will fall a - way When we hear the trum-pet sound in the
land is God's a - lone, When we hear the trum-pet sound in the
ware the trum-pet's call, And beat swords of greed and com-merce in - to
sto - ry - tell - ers spin Tales of faith - ful-ness and res - cue 'til the
neigh-bor by the hand And be - come the voice of free - dom that will

morn - ing. Far and wide we hear the
morn - ing. And the debts that stole our
morn - ing. Ev - 'ry im - mi - grant be
e - qual shares for all. Let the teach - ers speak in
ban - quet shall be - gin; How God wove the world with
thun - der through the land. Let the earth re - pose in

clar - i - on an - nounce that all are free When we
dream - ing we will no more have to pay When we
wel - come, all the home - less find a home, When we
wis - dom, let the mu - sic - mak - ers play, Let the
won - der, how God led us through the sea, Why we
sab - bath while her chil - dren's hearts re - new, And give

hear the trum - pet sound in the morn - ing.
hear the trum - pet sound in the morn - ing.
hear the trum - pet sound in the morn - ing.
weav - ers weave the tent where we shall gath - er on that day.
keep a day of rest and call a year of ju - bi - lee!
back to God in jus - tice what God's boun - ty gave to you.

Refrain

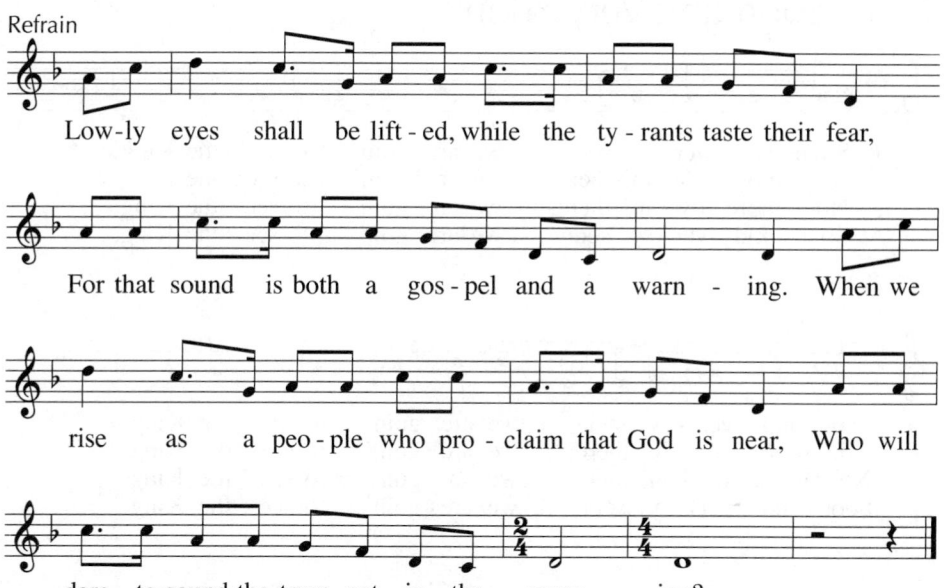

Low-ly eyes shall be lift-ed, while the ty-rants taste their fear,

For that sound is both a gos-pel and a warn - ing. When we

rise as a peo-ple who pro - claim that God is near, Who will

dare to sound the trum-pet in the morn - ing?

Text: Leviticus 25, Deuteronomy 15, Joel 2; Rory Cooney, b.1952, © 1998, GIA Publications, Inc.
Tune: MORNING TRUMPET, 15 11 15 11 with refrain; B. F. White, 1800–1879, from *Southern Harmony*; arr. by Rory Cooney, b.1952,
    © 1998, GIA Publications, Inc.

# 865 Soon and Very Soon

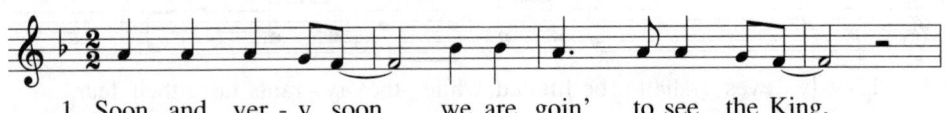

1. Soon and ver - y soon     we are goin'   to see   the King,
2. No more cry - in' there,    we are goin'   to see   the King,
3. No more dy - in' there,    we are goin'   to see   the King,
4. Soon and ver - y soon     we are goin'   to see   the King,

Soon and ver - y soon     we are goin'   to see   the King,
No more cry - in' there,    we are goin'   to see   the King,
No more dy - in' there,    we are goin'   to see   the King,
Soon and ver - y soon     we are goin'   to see   the King,

Soon and ver - y soon     we are goin'   to see   the King.
No more cry - in' there,    we are goin'   to see   the King.
No more dy - in' there,    we are goin'   to see   the King.    Hal-le-
Soon and ver - y soon     we are goin'   to see   the King.

1., 2.

lu - jah,   hal-le-lu - jah,   we're goin'   to see   the King!

3., 4.

Hal - le - lu - jah, hal - le - lu -

jah, hal - le - lu - jah, hal - le - lu - jah.

Text: Andraé Crouch, b.1942
Tune: SOON AND VERY SOON, 12 12 12 14; Andraé Crouch, b.1942
© 1976, Crouch Music/Bud John Songs, admin. at EMICMGPublishing.com

# Take Me Home 866

**Refrain**

Take me home, to your dwell-ing place, in your sweet em-

brace, read-y to hold me in your arms. Take me

home, to your lov-ing eyes, with you a-lone I'll

rise, sing-ing for-ev-er, in your arms, take me home.

**Verses**

1. O my God, you've led me through it all,
2. With you all pain is left be-hind, no
3. O my God, the road is long and hard,

through all the hurt and my shame.
sor - row or death, on that day.
o - pen your heart, come to me.

O my God, I have trav-eled far to meet you, to
O my God, how I've longed to know your love, come
God, with you, my sor - row turns to danc - ing, reach

**D.C.**

see your face and call up - on your name!
wipe my tears, and take my fear a - way!
out your hand and set my spir - it free!

Text: David Haas, b.1957
Tune: David Haas, b.1957
© 2001, GIA Publications, Inc.

# 867 There Are Many Rooms

Refrain

There are man-y rooms in my Fa - ther's house.

Do not be a-fraid, and have no doubt;

I am go-ing there to pre - pare a place.

Come and fol-low me, come and you will see,

come and take your rest in God's safe em - brace.

Verses 1, 2

1. I am the Way, the Truth, the Life;
2. I will not leave you or - phans;

those who be-lieve in me will nev - er die, will
I will re-turn to you and you will live, and

D.C.

nev - er die, but live a - gain!
you will live for - ev - er!

**Verse 3**

3. Peace I leave; my peace I give. Do not be trou-bled;

do not be a-fraid, I calm your fear.

I am near!

Text: Based on John 14; adapt. Liam Lawton, b.1959
Tune: Liam Lawton; arr. Paul A. Tate, b.1968
© 2009, GIA Publications, Inc.

## Steal Away to Jesus 868

**Refrain**

Steal a-way, steal a-way, steal a-way to Je-sus!

Steal a-way, steal a-way home, I ain't got long to stay here.

**Verses**

1. My Lord, he calls me, He calls me by the thun-der; The
2. Green trees are bend-ing, Poor sin-ners stand a trem-bling; The
3. My Lord, he calls me, He calls me by the light-ning; The

trum-pet sounds with-in my soul; I ain't got long to stay here.

Text: African American spiritual
Tune: African American spiritual

# 869  Do Not Let Your Hearts Be Troubled

Refrain

Do not let your hearts be trou - bled, have

faith in God and faith in me. I will go forth to pre -

pare a place for you, then I'll come back to take you

with me, that where I am, you may al - so be.

Verse 1

1. In God's house there are man - y plac - es for you a -

lone to dwell in safe - ty. You know the way to

D.C.

where I'll lead you, if you are lost, I will show the way.

Verses 2, 3

2. I am the way, the truth and the life,
3. The words I speak are not on - ly of my-self,

on - ly through me can you know what I know. If you knew
it is your God who lives with - in me. If you be -

me,       you would see the vi - sion,       if you see
lieve     that your God and I are   one,      I will pro -

D.C.

me,       you      see   your   God.
vide      when     you   call   my     name.

Text: John 14:1–3, 6–7, 10–14; David Haas, b.1957
Tune: David Haas, b.1957
© 1995, GIA Publications, Inc.

## Jerusalem, My Happy Home   870

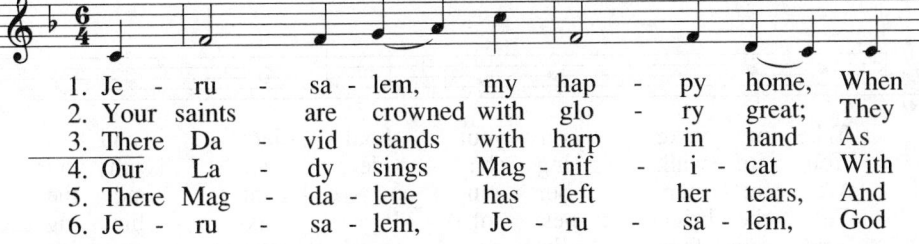

1. Je - ru - sa - lem,     my   hap - py   home,   When
2. Your saints    are   crowned with glo - ry   great;   They
3. There Da - vid   stands with harp   in   hand   As
4. Our La - dy   sings Mag - nif - i - cat   With
5. There Mag - da - lene   has left   her   tears,   And
6. Je - ru - sa - lem,   Je - ru - sa - lem,   God

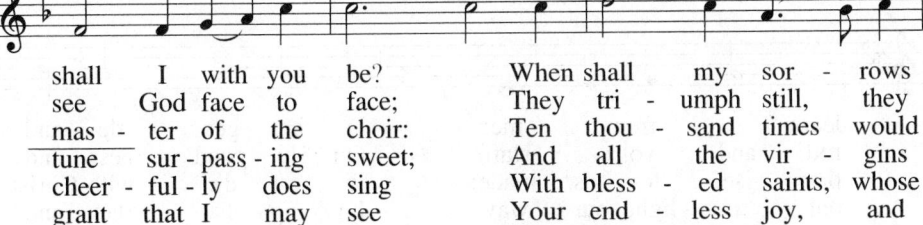

shall    I   with you   be?   When shall   my   sor - rows
see      God face  to   face;   They tri - umph still,   they
mas - ter of   the   choir:   Ten thou - sand times   would
tune     sur - pass - ing  sweet;   And all   the   vir - gins
cheer - ful - ly   does   sing   With bless - ed saints, whose
grant    that I   may   see   Your end - less joy,   and

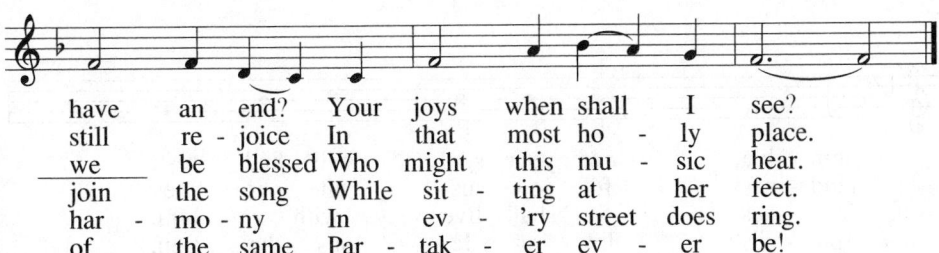

have     an   end?   Your   joys   when shall   I   see?
still     re - joice   In   that   most ho - ly   place.
we       be   blessed Who might   this   mu - sic   hear.
join      the   song   While sit - ting at   her   feet.
har - mo - ny   In   ev - 'ry   street   does   ring.
of        the   same   Par - tak - er   ev - er   be!

Text: F.B.P., 16th C., alt.
Tune: LAND OF REST, CM; American; harm. by Richard Proulx, 1937–2010, © 1975, GIA Publications, Inc.

# 871   We Shall Rise Again

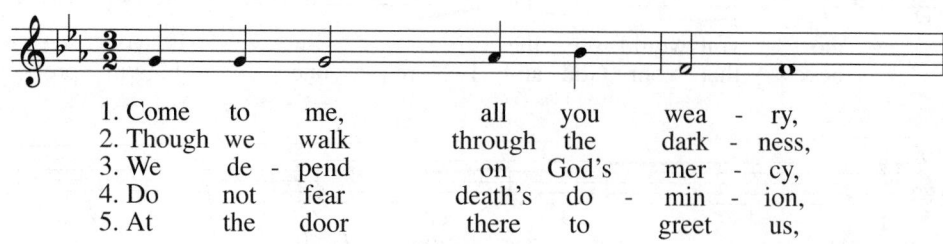

1. Come to me, all you wea - ry,
2. Though we walk through the dark - ness,
3. We de - pend on God's mer - cy,
4. Do not fear death's do - min - ion,
5. At the door there to greet us,

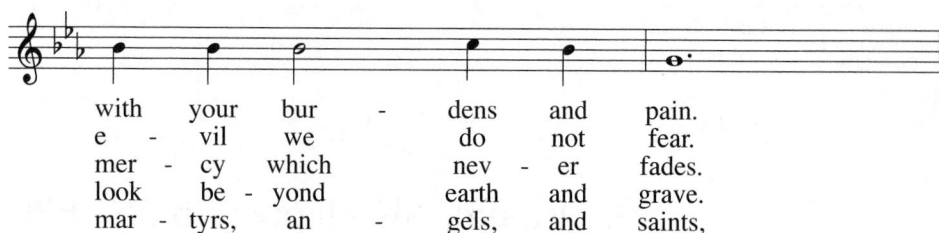

with your bur - dens and pain.
e - vil we do not fear.
mer - cy which nev - er fades.
look be - yond earth and grave.
mar - tyrs, an - gels, and saints,

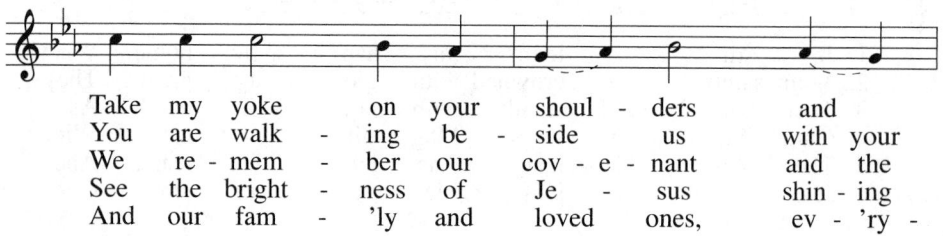

Take my yoke on your shoul - ders and
You are walk - ing be - side us with your
We re - mem - ber our cov - e - nant and the
See the bright - ness of Je - sus shin - ing
And our fam - 'ly and loved ones, ev - 'ry -

learn from me: I am gen - tle and
rod and your staff. On - ly good - ness and
prom - ise Je - sus made: If we die with Christ
out to light our way. Lov - ing Fa - ther and
one freed from their chains. We shall feel their ac -

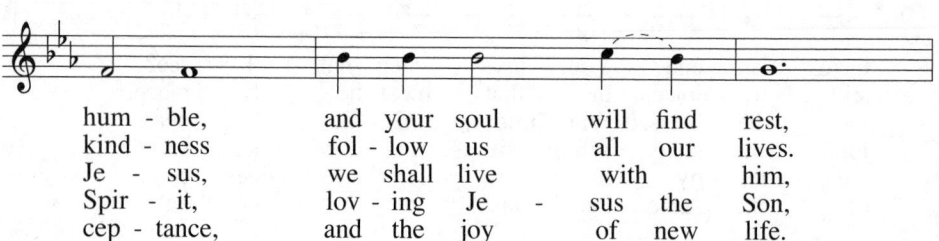

hum - ble, and your soul will find rest,
kind - ness fol - low us all our lives.
Je - sus, we shall live with him,
Spir - it, lov - ing Je - sus the Son,
cep - tance, and the joy of new life.

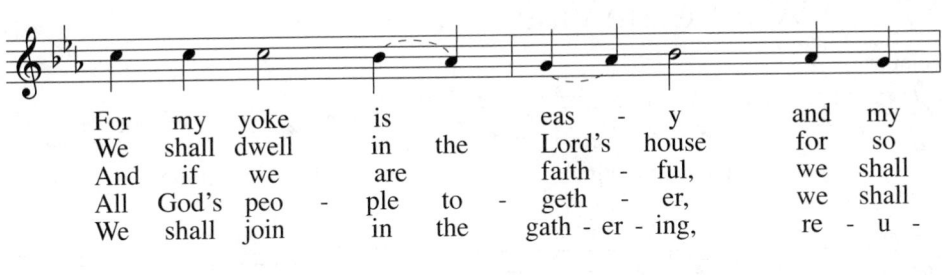

For my yoke is eas - y and my
We shall dwell in the Lord's house for so
And if we are faith - ful, we shall
All God's peo - ple to - geth - er, we shall
We shall join in the gath - er - ing, re - u -

bur - den is light.
man - y years to come!
reign with him!
live on as one!
nit - ed in God's love!

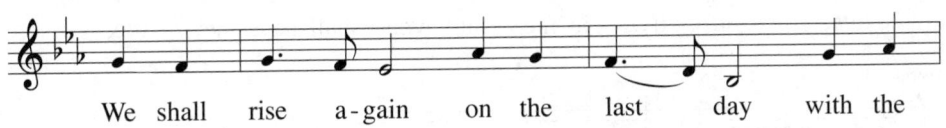

We shall rise a - gain on the last day with the

faith - ful, rich and poor. Com-ing to the house of Lord

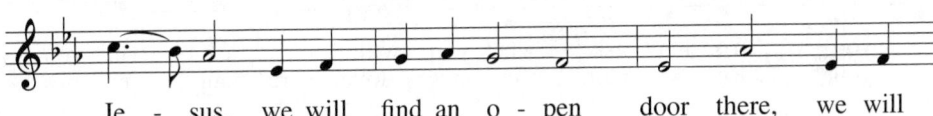

Je - sus, we will find an o - pen door there, we will

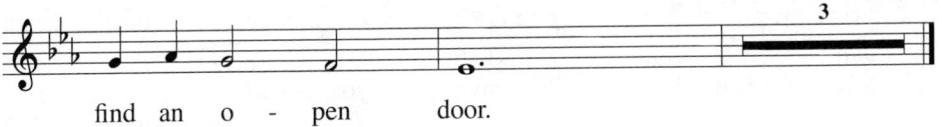

find an o - pen door.

Text: Matthew 11:29–30, Psalm 23, John 11, 2 Timothy 2; Jeremy Young, b.1948
Tune: RESURRECTION; Irregular with refrain; Jeremy Young, b.1948
© 1987, GIA Publications, Inc.

# 872   I Will Be the Vine

Refrain

I will be the vine    and    you will be the branch-es.    All

you    who    live    in    me    will    nev - er, nev - er    die.

I will be the sign,    I will of - fer man - y    chanc-es;    so

live,    oh    live    in me    and    you    shall have    new    life.

Verses 1, 2

1. Re - main    in    me,    as    I    re-main in
2. As the Fa - ther loved    me,    so have    I    loved

you.    You may    ask    what you    will,    ask    what you
you.    Re - main    in    my    love,    re - main    in    my

D.C.

will,    and    you    shall    re - ceive.
love,    and    I    will    give    you    life.

Verse 3

3. If    you    are my    friends,    you will    live    my com -

mands.    There is    no    great - er    love,    no    great - er

**D.C.**

love     than to     lay     down your     life         for your     friends.

Text: Based on John 15:5–14; Liam Lawton, b.1959
Tune: Liam Lawton, b.1959; arr. by John McCann, b.1961
© 1998, GIA Publications, Inc.

## Shall We Gather at the River     873

1. Shall   we   gath - er   at   the   riv - er,   Where bright
2. On   the   mar - gin of   the   riv - er,   Wash - ing
3. Ere   we   reach   the shin - ing riv - er,   Lay   we
4. Soon   we'll   reach   the shin - ing riv - er,   Soon   our

an - gel feet have trod,   With   its   crys - tal tide for
up its sil - ver spray,   We   will   walk and wor - ship
ev - 'ry bur - den down;   Grace   our   spir - its will de -
pil-grim-age will cease;   Soon   our   hap - py hearts will

ev - er   Flow - ing   by   the throne   of   God?
ev - er,   All   the   hap - py   gold - en   day.
liv - er,   And pro - vide   a   robe   and   crown.
quiv - er   With the   mel - o - dy   of   peace.

Yes,   we'll gath - er at   the riv - er,   The beau - ti - ful, the

beau - ti - ful   riv - er,   Gath - er with the saints   at   the

riv - er   That   flows   by   the throne   of   God.

Text: Robert Lowry, 1826–1899
Tune: HANSON PLACE, 8 7 8 7 with refrain; Robert Lowry, 1826–1899

# 874 Now Let Your Servant Go in Peace

1. Now let your ser - vant go in peace;
2. Be - fore the peo - ples you pre - pare
3. Child, you are cho - sen as a sign
4. Now let us sing our Sav - ior's praise,

Let praise and bless - ing here in - crease;
Your way of life which all may share.
To test the hu - man heart and mind;
And tell God's good - ness all our days.

For in our midst your word is done And
Your sav - ing pow'r is now made known; A -
For se - crets hid - den in the night Shall
While breath is ours, let praise be heard For

you have sent your Prom - ised One.
mong the na - tions love is shown.
be re - vealed in pierc - ing light.
God's own faith - ful, sav - ing word.

Text: *Nunc dimittis*, Luke 2:29–35, adapt. by Ruth Duck, b.1947, © 1992, GIA Publications, Inc.
Tune: DICKSON, LM; Norah Duncan IV, b.1952, © 2010, GIA Publications, Inc.

*Alternate tune:* CONDITOR ALME SIDERUM

# Praise We the Lord This Day 875

1. Praise we the Lord this day, This day so long fore - told, Whose prom - ise shone with cheer - ing ray On wait - ing saints of old.
2. The proph - et gave the sign For faith - ful folk to read: A vir - gin, born of Da - vid's line, Shall bear the prom - ised seed.
3. Ask not how this should be, But wor - ship and a - dore Like her whom God's own maj - es - ty Came down to shad - ow o'er.
4. She meek - ly bowed her head To hear the gra - cious word: Hail, Mar - y, pure and low - ly maid, Most fa - vored of the Lord.
5. How blest shall be her name In all the Church on earth! Through her that won - drous mys - t'ry came, The in - car - nate Sav - ior's birth.
6. Praise Christ, the Vir - gin's Son, Whom earth and heav'n a - dore, With Fa - ther, Spir - it, Three in One Both now and ev - er - more.

Text: Matthew 1:23; *Hymns for the Festivals and Saints' Days*, 1846, alt.
Tune: SWABIA, SM; Johann M. Speiss, 1715–1772; adapt. by William H. Havergal, 1793–1870

# 876 No Wind at the Window

1. No wind at the win - dow, No knock on the door; No light from the lamp - stand, No foot on the floor; No dream born of tired - ness, No ghost raised by fear: Just an an - gel and a wom - an And a voice in her ear.

2. "O Mar - y, O Mar - y, Don't hide from my face. Be glad that you're fa - vored And filled with God's grace. The time for re - deem - ing The world has be - gun; And you are re - quest - ed To moth - er God's son.

3. "This child must be born that The king - dom might come: Sal - va - tion for man - y, De - struc - tion for some; Both end and be - gin - ning, Both mes - sage and sign; Both vic - tor and vic - tim, Both yours and di - vine."

4. No pay - ment was prom - ised, No prom - is - es made; No wed - ding was dat - ed, No blue - print dis - played. Yet Mar - y, con - sent - ing To what none could guess, Re - plied with con - vic - tion, "Tell God I say yes."

Text: John L. Bell, b.1949
Tune: COLUMCILLE, Irregular; Gaelic, arr. by John L. Bell, b.1949
© 1992, Iona Community, GIA Publications, Inc., agent

# How Good, Lord, to Be Here!  877

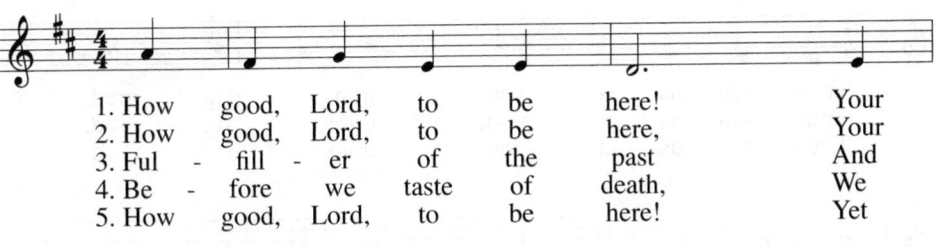

1. How good, Lord, to be here! Your
2. How good, Lord, to be here, Your
3. Ful - fill - er of the past And
4. Be - fore we taste of death, We
5. How good, Lord, to be here! Yet

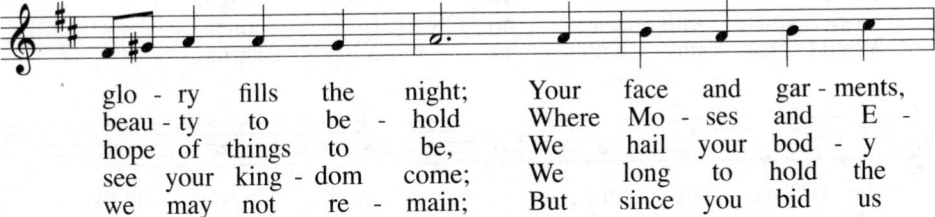

glo - ry fills the night; Your face and gar - ments,
beau - ty to be - hold Where Mo - ses and E -
hope of things to be, We hail your bod - y
see your king - dom come; We long to hold the
we may not re - main; But since you bid us

like the sun, Shine with un - bor - rowed light.
li - jah stand, Your mes - sen - gers of old.
glo - ri - fied And our re - demp - tion see.
vi - sion bright And make this hill our home.
leave the mount, Come with us to the plain.

Text: Luke 9:32–33; Joseph A. Robinson, 1858–1933, alt.
Tune: SWABIA, SM; Johann M. Speiss, 1715–1772; adapt. by William H. Havergal, 1793–1870

## 878 Transform Us

1. Trans - form us as you, trans - fig - ured,
2. Trans - form us as you, trans - fig - ured,
3. Trans - form us as you, trans - fig - ured,

Stood a - part on Ta - bor's height.
Once spoke with those ho - ly ones.
Would not stay with - in a shrine.

Lead us up our sa - cred moun - tains,
We, sur - round - ed by the wit - ness
Keep us from our great temp - ta - tion—

Search us with re - veal - ing light.
Of those saints whose work is done,
Time and truth we quick - ly bind.

Lift us from where we have fall - en,
Live in this world as your Bod - y,
Lead us down those dai - ly path - ways

Full of ques - tions, filled with fright.
Cho - sen daugh - ters, cho - sen sons.
Where our love is not con - fined.

Text: Sylvia Dunstan, 1955–1993, © 1993, GIA Publications, Inc.
Tune: PICARDY, 8 7 8 7 8 7; French Carol; harm. by Richard Proulx, 1937–2010, © 1986, GIA Publications, Inc.

# Hail, Holy Queen Enthroned Above  879

1. Hail, ho - ly Queen en - throned a - bove,    O  Ma - rí - a.  Hail,
2. The cause of  joy  to    all  be - low,    O  Ma - rí - a.  The
3. O    gen - tle,  lov - ing,  ho - ly one,    O  Ma - rí - a.  The

Queen  of    mer - cy  and   of love,    O  Ma - rí - a.
spring through which  all   grac - es  flow,    O  Ma - rí - a.
God   of   light  be - came your Son,    O  Ma - rí - a.

Tri - umph,  all   ye  Cher - u - bim;   Sing  with  us,   ye
An - gels,  all   your prais - es  bring;  Earth and  heav - en,
Tri - umph,  all   ye  Cher - u - bim;   Sing  with  us,   ye

Ser - a - phim.   Heav'n and  earth  re - sound the hymn:
with  us   sing;   All    cre - a - tion   ech - o - ing:
Ser - a - phim.   Heav'n and  earth  re - sound the hymn:

Sal - ve,   Sal - ve,   Sal - ve, Re - gí - na.

Text: *Salve, Regina, mater misericordia*; c.1080; tr. *Roman Hymnal*, 1884; st. 2–3, adapt. by M. Owen Lee, CSB, b.1930
Tune: SALVE REGINA COELITUM, 8 4 8 4 777 4 5; *Choralmelodien zum Heiligen Gesänge*, 1808; harm. by Healey Willan, 1880–1968,
© Willis Music Co.

# 880  Salve Regína / Hail, Queen of Heaven

Sal - ve Re - gí - na,  ma - ter mi - se - ri - cór - di - ae:
*Hail, Queen of Heav-en,  hail, our Moth-er com-pas-sion-ate,*

Vi - ta, dul - cé - do  et spes no - stra sal - ve.
*True life and com - fort  and our hope, we greet you!*

Ad te cla - má - mus,  éx - su - les fí - li - i He - vae.
*To you we ex - iles,  chil-dren of Eve, raise our voic - es.*

Ad te sus - pi - rá - mus,  ge - mén - tes et flen - tes
*We send up sighs to you,  as mourn-ing and weep-ing,*

in hac la - cri - má - rum val - le.  E - ia er - go,
*we pass through this vale of sor - row.  Then turn to us,*

ad - vo - cá - ta no - stra,  il - los tu - os
*O most gra - cious Wom - an,  those eyes of yours,*

mi - se - ri - cór - des ó - cu - los  ad nos con - vér - te.
*so full of love and ten - der-ness,  so full of pit - y.*

Et Je - sum, be - ne - dí - ctum fru - ctum ven - tris tu - i,
*And grant us af - ter these, our days of lone - ly ex - ile,*

no - bis  post  hoc  ex - sí - li - um  o - stén - de.
*the sight  of  your  blest  Son  and  Lord,  Christ  Je - sus.*

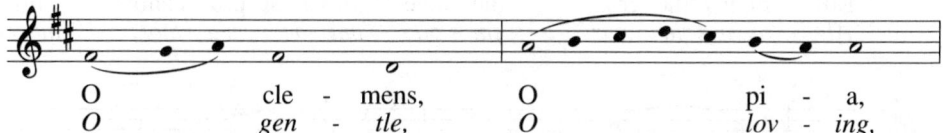

O  cle - mens,  O  pi - a,
*O  gen - tle,  O  lov - ing,*

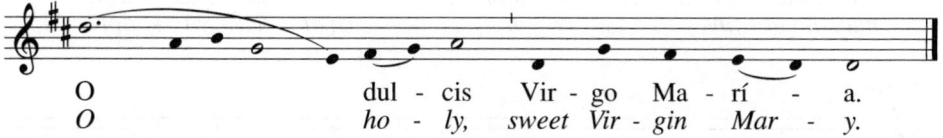

O  dul - cis  Vir - go  Ma - rí - a.
*O  ho - ly,  sweet  Vir - gin  Mar - y.*

Text: Latin, c.1080, tr. by John C. Selner, SS, 1904–1992, © 1954, GIA Publications, Inc.
Tune: SALVE REGINA, Irregular; Mode V; acc. by Gerard Farrell, OSB, 1919–2009, alt., © 1986, GIA Publications, Inc.

# 881  Lift High the Cross / Alcen la Cruz

**Refrain**

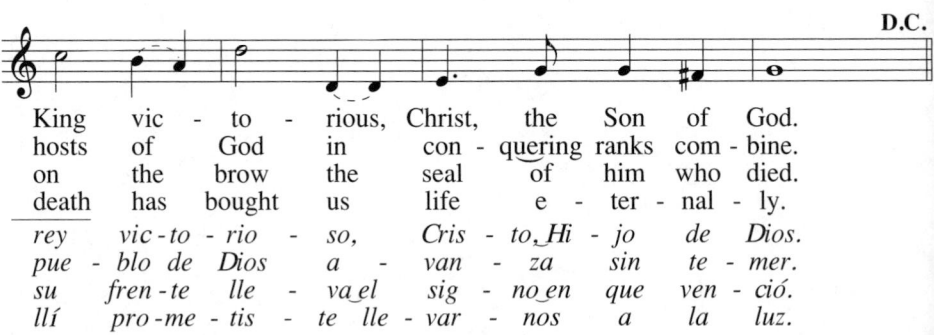

Lift    high    the    cross,    the    love    of Christ pro - claim    till
*Al - cen    la    cruz,    em - ble - ma de    su_a - mor;    que_el*

all    the    world    a - dore    his    sa - cred    name.
*mun - do_al    fin    co - noz    -    ca_al    Sal - va - dor.*

**Verses**

| | | | | | | | | |
|---|---|---|---|---|---|---|---|---|
| 1. Come, | Chris - tians, | fol - low | where | our | Sav - ior | trod, | Our |
| 2. Led | on | their | way | by | this | tri - um - phant | sign, | The |
| 3. Each | new - born | ser - vant | of | the | Cru - ci - fied | Bears |
| 4. O | Lord, | once | lift - ed | on | the | glo - rious | tree, | Your |

*1. Va - mos, cris - tia - nos, tras nues - tro Se - ñor;    El*
*2. Ba - jo_es - te sig - no de su gran po - der    El*
*3. Ca - da cre - yen - te del que_en cruz mu - rió    En*
*4. Cuan - do te_al - za - ron glo - rio - so_en la cruz,    A -*

**D.C.**

King    vic - to - rious,    Christ,    the    Son    of    God.
hosts    of    God    in    con - quering ranks    com - bine.
on    the    brow    the    seal    of    him    who    died.
death    has    bought    us    life    e - ter - nal - ly.

*rey    vic - to - rio - so,    Cris - to, Hi - jo    de    Dios.*
*pue - blo de    Dios    a - van - za    sin    te - mer.*
*su    fren - te    lle - va_el    sig - no_en que    ven - ció.*
*llí    pro - me - tis - te lle - var - nos    a    la    luz.*

5. So shall our song of triumph ever be:    *5. Himnos de gloria_alcemos sin cesar;*
Praise to the Crucified for victory!    *Al rey vencedor que en cruz supo triunfar.*

Text: 1 Corinthians 1:18; George W. Kitchin, 1827–1912, and Michael R. Newbolt, 1874–1956, alt.; tr. by Dimas Planas-Belfort, 1934–1992, and Ángel Mattos, alt.
Tune: CRUCIFER, 10 10 with refrain; Sydney H. Nicholson, 1875–1947
© 1974, 1997, Hope Publishing Company

# Ye Watchers and Ye Holy Ones  882

1. Ye watch - ers and ye ho - ly ones,
2. O high - er than the cher - u - bim,
3. Re - spond, ye souls in end - less rest,
4. O friends, in glad - ness let us sing,

Bright
More
Ye
Su -

ser - aphs, cher - u - bim, and thrones,
glo - rious than the ser - a - phim,
pa - tri - archs and proph - ets blest:
per - nal an - thems ech - o - ing:

Raise the
Lead their
"Al - le -
"Al - le -

[⌢]

glad strain: "Al - le - lu - ia!" Cry out, do - min - ions, prince-doms,
prais - es: "Al - le - lu - ia!" O bear - er of the_e - ter - nal
lu - ia, Al - le - lu - ia!" Ye ho - ly twelve, ye mar - tyrs
lu - ia, Al - le - lu - ia!" To God the Fa - ther, God the

pow'rs, Vir - tues, arch - an - gels, an - gels' choirs:
Word, Most gra-cious, mag - ni - fy the Lord:
strong, All saints tri - um-phant, raise the song:
Son, And God the Spir - it, Three in One:

"Al - le - lu - ia! Al - le - lu - ia!" Al - le - lu - ia,

al - le - lu - ia, al - le - lu - ia!

Text: John Athelstan Riley, 1858–1945
Tune: LASST UNS ERFREUEN, LM with alleluias; *Geistliche Kirchengasänge*, Cologne, 1623; harm. by Ralph Vaughan Williams, 1872–1958

# 883 For the Faithful Who Have Answered

1. For the faith - ful who have an - swered
2. Man - y eyes have glimpsed the prom - ise.
3. For this cloud of faith - ful wit - ness,

When they heard your call to serve, For the man - y
Man - y hearts have yearned to see. Man - y ears have
For the com - mon life we share, For the work of

ways you led them Test - ing will and stretch-ing nerve,
heard you call - ing Us to great - er lib - er - ty.
peace and jus - tice, For the gos - pel that we bear,

For their work and for their wit - ness As they strove a -
Some have fal - len in the strug - gle. Oth - ers still are
For the vi - sion that our home-land Is your love— deep,

gainst the odds, For their cour - age and o - be-dience
fight - ing on. You are not a - shamed to own us.
high, and broad— For the dif - f'rent roads we trav - el

We give thanks and praise, O God.
We give thanks and praise, O God.
We give thanks and praise, O God.

Text: Sylvia Dunstan, 1955–1993, © 1991, GIA Publications, Inc.
Tune: PLEADING SAVIOR, 8 7 8 7 D; *Christian Lyre*, 1830; harm. by Richard Proulx, 1937–2010, © 1986, GIA Publications, Inc.

*Alternate tune:* BEACH SPRING

# For All the Saints   884

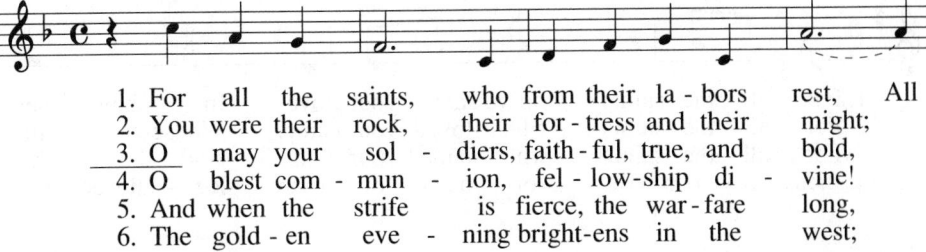

1. For all the saints, who from their la - bors rest, All
2. You were their rock, their for - tress and their might;
3. O may your sol - diers, faith - ful, true, and bold,
4. O blest com - mun - ion, fel - low-ship di - vine!
5. And when the strife is fierce, the war - fare long,
6. The gold - en eve - ning bright-ens in the west;

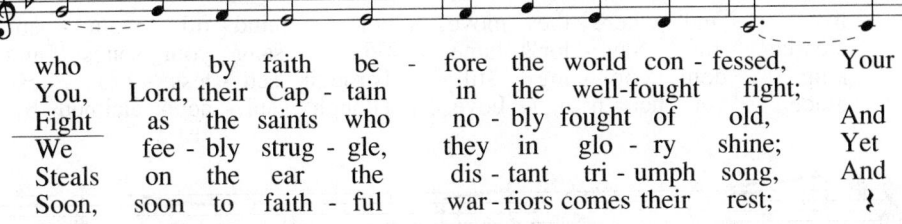

who by faith be - fore the world con - fessed, Your
You, Lord, their Cap - tain in the well-fought fight;
Fight as the saints who no - bly fought of old, And
We fee - bly strug - gle, they in glo - ry shine; Yet
Steals on the ear the dis - tant tri - umph song, And
Soon, soon to faith - ful war - riors comes their rest;

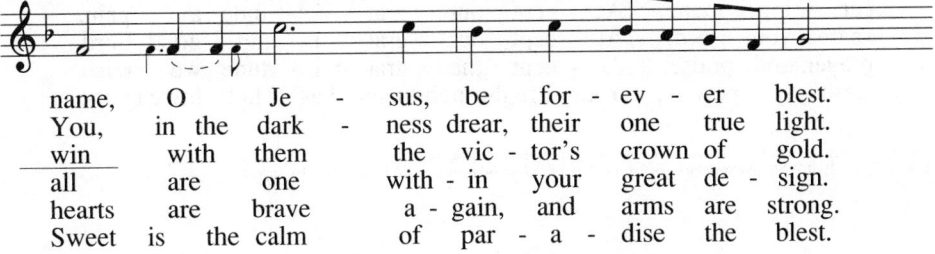

name, O Je - sus, be for - ev - er blest.
You, in the dark - ness drear, their one true light.
win with them the vic - tor's crown of gold.
all are one with - in your great de - sign.
hearts are brave a - gain, and arms are strong.
Sweet is the calm of par - a - dise the blest.

Al - le - lu - ia!   Al - le - lu - ia!

7. But then there breaks a yet more glorious day;
   The saints triumphant rise in bright array;
   The King of glory passes on his way.
   Alleluia! Alleluia!

8. From earth's wide bounds, from ocean's farthest coast,
   Through gates of pearl streams in the countless host,
   Singing to Father, Son, and Holy Ghost:
   Alleluia! Alleluia!

Text: William Walsham How, 1823–1897, alt.
Tune: SINE NOMINE, 10 10 10 with alleluias; Ralph Vaughan Williams, 1872–1958

## 885 For All the Saints Who've Shown Your Love

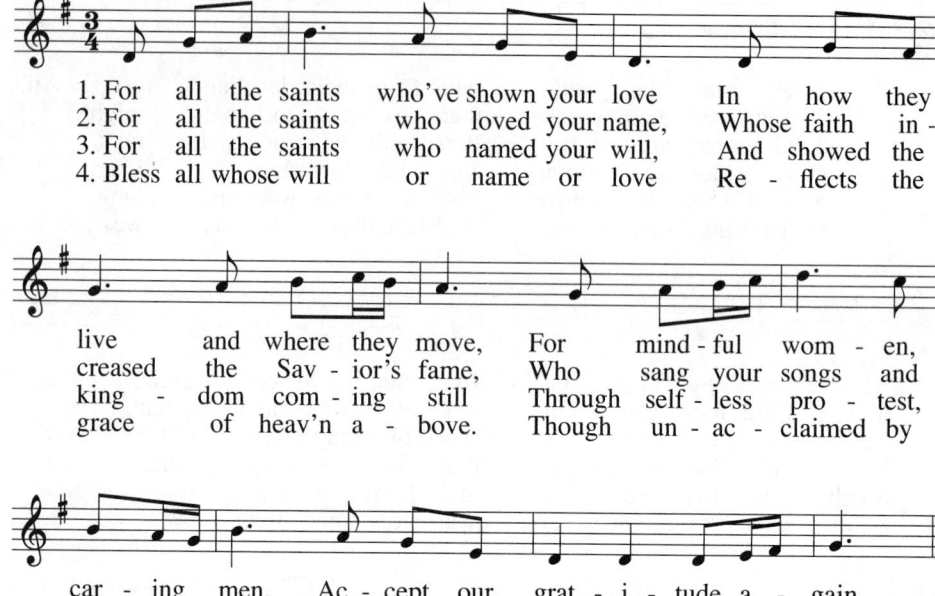

1. For all the saints who've shown your love In how they
2. For all the saints who loved your name, Whose faith in -
3. For all the saints who named your will, And showed the
4. Bless all whose will or name or love Re - flects the

live and where they move, For mind - ful wom - en,
creased the Sav - ior's fame, Who sang your songs and
king - dom com - ing still Through self - less pro - test,
grace of heav'n a - bove. Though un - ac - claimed by

car - ing men, Ac - cept our grat - i - tude a - gain.
shared your word, Ac - cept our grat - i - tude, good Lord.
prayer, and praise, Ac - cept the grat - i - tude we raise.
earth - ly pow'rs, Your life through theirs has hal - lowed ours.

Text: John L. Bell, b.1949, © 1996, Iona Community, GIA Publications, Inc., agent
Tune: O WALY WALY, LM; arr. by John L. Bell, b.1949, © 1989, Iona Community, GIA Publications, Inc., agent

## 886 Immaculate Mary

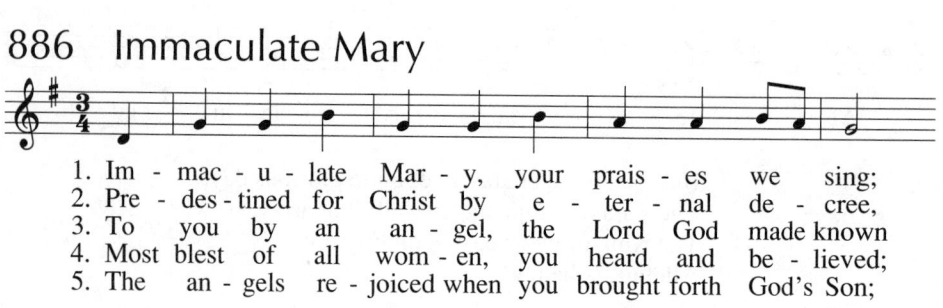

1. Im - mac - u - late Mar - y, your prais - es we sing;
2. Pre - des - tined for Christ by e - ter - nal de - cree,
3. To you by an an - gel, the Lord God made known
4. Most blest of all wom - en, you heard and be - lieved;
5. The an - gels re - joiced when you brought forth God's Son;

You reign now in splen - dor with Je - sus our King.
God willed you both vir - gin and moth - er to be.
The grace of the Spir - it, the gift of the Son.
Most blest is the fruit of your womb then con - ceived.
Your joy is the joy of all a - ges to come.

A - ve, A - ve, A - ve, Ma - rí - a.

A - ve, A - ve, Ma - rí - a.

6. Your child is the Savior, all hope lies in him:
   He gives us new life and redeems us from sin.

7. In glory for ever now close to your Son,
   All ages will praise you for all God has done.

Text: St. 1, Jeremiah Cummings, 1814–1866, alt.; sts. 2–7, Brian Foley, 1919–2000, © 1971, Faber Music Ltd.
Tune: LOURDES HYMN, 11 11 with refrain; *Grenoble*, 1882

# Ave María 887

A - ve Ma - rí - a, grá - ti - a ple - na,

Dó - mi - nus te - cum, be - ne - dí - cta tu in mu - li - é -

ri - bus, et be - ne - dí - ctus fru - ctus ven-tris tu - i, Je - sus.

San - cta Ma - rí - a, Ma-ter De - i, o - ra pro no - bis pec - ca -

tó - ri - bus, nunc et in ho - ra mor-tis no - strae. A - men.

Text: *Hail, Mary, full of grace*, Luke 1:29; Latin, 13th C.
Tune: AVE MARIA, Irregular; Mode I; acc. by Robert LeBlanc, b.1948, © 1986, GIA Publications, Inc.

# 888 Among All

**Refrain**

A-mong all, you are blessed, and full of grace and ho-li-ness. A-mong all, you said yes to do God's will with o - pen-ness. O La - dy, full of grace, Mar-y, Moth-er of God, be with us, pray for us.

*Last time to Coda* ⊕

*Solo or section:*

1. You
2. You
3. You

**Verses**

1. teach us to o - bey the liv - ing word of God. You show us
2. teach us how to serve God's king-dom here on earth. You bring to
3. teach us how to pray with hum - ble - ness of heart. You guide us

**D.C.**

1. how to lis - ten to his voice that calls us each by name.
2. birth a wil-ling - ness to share our lives with joy and love.
3. to be in - stru-ments of peace and hope for all the world.

⊕ **Coda**

*Solo:* **Litany of Petitions**

That we may love like Christ,
peace in ev - 'ry land,
we may spread God's word,

*All:*

us.* Mar-y,

*Sing on repeat.*

Text: Chris de Silva, b.1967
Tune: Chris de Silva, b.1967

## 889 Hail Mary: Gentle Woman

Hail Mar - y, full of grace, the
Lord is with you. Bless-ed are you a-mong
wom-en, and blest is the fruit of your womb, Je - sus.
Ho-ly Mar - y, Moth-er of God,
pray for us sin - ners now and at the hour of
death. A - men.

**Refrain**

Gen - tle wom - an, qui-et light, morn-ing
star, so strong and bright, gen - tle
Moth - er, peace-ful dove, teach us
wis - dom; teach us love.

Verse 1

1. You were cho - sen by the Fa - ther;

you were cho - sen for the Son.

You were cho - sen from all wom-en

**D.S.**

and for wom-an, shin-ing one.

Verse 2

2. Bless-ed are you a - mong wom-en,

blest in turn all wom-en, too.

Bless-ed they with peace - ful spir-its.

**D.S.**

Bless-ed they with gen - tle hearts.

Text: *Hail Mary*, alt.; Carey Landry, b.1944
Tune: Carey Landry, b.1944; arr. by Martha Lesinski, alt.
© 1975, 1978, Carey Landry and North American Liturgy Resources. Published by OCP.

# 890 Litany of Mary /
## Letanía de la Santísima Virgen María

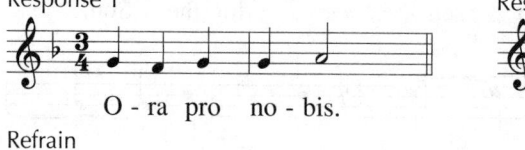

*Cantor:*
1. Holy Mary, *Response 1*
   Mother of God, *Response 1*
   Mother of the Church, *Response 2*

*Cantor:*
1. *Santa María,* Response 1
   *Madre de Dios,* Response 1
   *Madre de la Iglesia,* Response 2

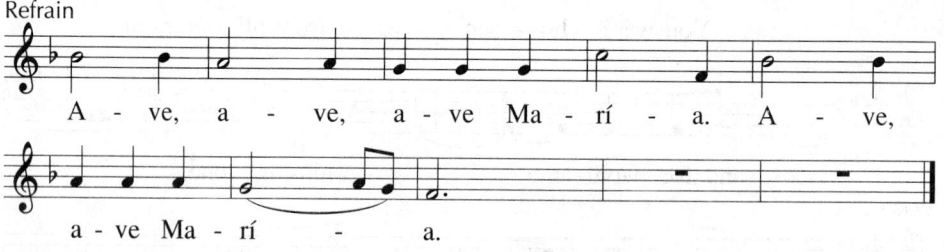

*Cantor:*
2. Mother of good counsel, *Response 1*
   Mother most pure, *Response 1*
   Mirror of justice, *Response 2*

3. Refuge of sinners, *Response 1*
   Morning star, *Response 1*
   Mary, Queen of peace, *Response 2*

4. Gate of heaven, *Response 1*
   Queen of angels, *Response 1*
   Health of the sick, *Response 2*

*Cantor:*
2. *Madre del buen consejo,* Response 1
   *Madre purísima,* Response 1
   *Espejo de justicia,* Response 2

3. *Refugio de los pecadores,* Response 1
   *Estrella de la mañana,* Response 1
   *Reina de la paz,* Response 2

4. *Puerta del cielo,* Response 1
   *Reina de los ángeles,* Response 1
   *Salud de los enfermos,* Response 2

Text: Based on the Litany of Loretto; Tony E. Alonso, b.1980
Tune: Refrain based on LOURDES HYMN; Tony E. Alonso, b.1980
© 2008, GIA Publications, Inc.

# Ave María 891

**Verses**

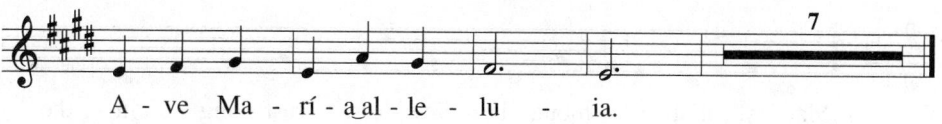

1. Hail Mar - y full of grace, the
2. Ho - ly Mar - y moth-er of God, the

Lord is with you.
Lord is with you.

Bless - ed are you a - mong all wom-en,
Pray for us sin - ners, pray for us sin - ners,

Blest is the fruit of your womb.
Now and at the hour of our death.

**Refrain**

Je - sus, formed in your faith, A - ve Ma - rí - a al - le -

lu - ia. Je - sus, born in your love,

A - ve Ma - rí - a al - le - lu - ia.

Text: Hail Mary; additional text by Dan Kantor, b.1960
Tune: Dan Kantor, b.1960; arr. by Rob Glover, b.1950
© 1993, GIA Publications, Inc.

## 892 Magníficat

Refrain

All that I am sings of the God who brings new life to birth in me. My spir-it soars on the wings of my Lord.

Verses

1. My soul gives glory to the Lord, rejoicing in my saving God,
Who looks upon me in my state, and all the world will call me blest;
For God works marvels in my sight, and holy, holy is God's name!

2. God's mercy is from age to age, on those who follow in fear;
Whose arm is power and strength, and scatters all the proud of heart;
Who casts the mighty from their thrones and raises up the lowly ones!

3. God fills the starving with good things, the rich are left with empty hands;
Protecting all the faithful ones, rememb'ring Israel with mercy,
The promise known to those before and to their children for ever!

Text: Luke 1:46–55; David Haas, b.1957
Tune: David Haas, b.1957
© 1990, GIA Publications, Inc.

## 893 Mary, First among Believers

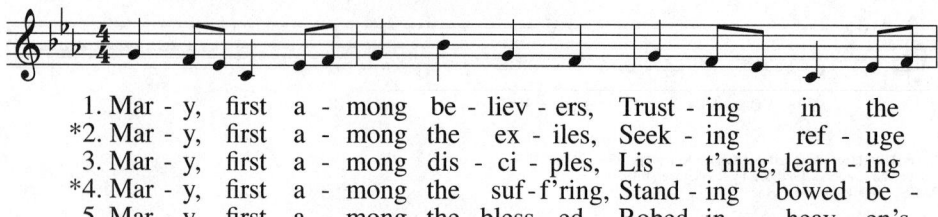

1. Mar - y, first a - mong be - liev - ers, Trust - ing in the
*2. Mar - y, first a - mong the ex - iles, Seek - ing ref - uge
3. Mar - y, first a - mong dis - ci - ples, Lis - t'ning, learn - ing
*4. Mar - y, first a - mong the suf-f'ring, Stand - ing bowed be -
5. Mar - y, first a - mong the bless - ed, Robed in heav - en's

*These stanzas may be omitted.

an - gel's word, You con - sent - ed and, con - ceiv - ing,
in the night, You left home with spouse and In - fant,
from your Son, You held dear his words and ac - tions,
neath the cross, You knew all the pain and an - guish
beau - ty bright, You re - joice with saints and an - gels

Brought to birth the Son of God. Moth - er now of
Flee - ing Her - od's sword in fright. Moth - er now of
Pon - d'ring each, for - get - ting none. Moth - er now of
Of op - pres - sion, grief, and loss. Moth - er now of
In your Son's re - splen - dent light. Moth - er now of

all be - liev - ers, Give our frag - ile faith in - crease;
all the ex - iles, Give them sleep with - out a - larm;
all dis - ci - ples, Help us lis - ten day by day;
all the suf - f'ring, May we show Com - pas - sion's face;
all the bless - ed, Make your pil - grim peo - ple strong;

May we, trust - ing in God's prom - ise,
Give them cloth - ing, food, and shel - ter;
O - pen to the Spir - it's prompt - ing,
May the vic - tims of in - jus - tice
Keep us faith - ful till we join you,

Doubts and use - less fears re - lease.
Keep them safe and free from harm.
Help us fol - low Je - sus' way.
Know, through us, God's love and grace.
Prais - ing God in end - less song.

Text: Delores Dufner, OSB, b.1939, © 2010, GIA Publications, Inc.
Tune: PLEADING SAVIOR, 8 7 8 7 D; *Christian Lyre*, 1830; harm. by Richard Proulx, 1937–2010, © 1986, GIA Publications, Inc.

# 894 My Soul Gives Glory

1. My soul gives glo - ry to my God, Who
2. God's mer - cy com - forts all who fear, Em -
3. God's jus - tice sends the rich a - way, But

reach - es down with lov - ing grace To lift me from
brac - ing with a stead-fast arm That casts the might-
feeds the poor with lav - ish things. Each hun - gry soul

my low es - tate And set me in the high - est
y from their thrones, But keeps the hum - ble safe from
now fills with joy And joins the song that Mar - y

place. Ma - gní - fi - cat, ma - gní - fi - cat! With
harm. Ma - gní - fi - cat, ma - gní - fi - cat! The
sings: Ma - gní - fi - cat, ma - gní - fi - cat! To

all my heart, I an - swer Yes When God an - nounc - es
weak find strengh; the wea - ry, rest. God's prom-ise sounds from
God, Cre - a - tor, Christ the Son; And Ho - ly Spir - it—

won - drous news. And ev - 'ry age shall call me blest.
age to age: The need - y of the world are blest.
tri - une God: All prais - es to the Three - in - One.

Text: Mary Louise Bringle, b.1953, © 2003, GIA Publications, Inc.
Tune: DUKTA, LMD; Norah Duncan IV, b.1952, © 2010, GIA Publications, Inc.

# O Sanctíssima / O Most Holy One   895

1. O san - ctís - si - ma, O pi - ís - si - ma,
2. Tu so - lá - ti - um Et re - fú - gi - um,
3. Ec - ce dé - bi - les, Per - quam flé - bi - les,
4. Vir - go ré - spi - ce, Ma - ter, á - spi - ce,

1. *O most ho - ly one, O most low - ly one,*
2. *Com - fort in our tears, Ref - uge in our fears,*
3. *See us pow - er - less. In our hope - less - ness*
4. *Maid - en, look on us, Moth - er, care for us.*

Dul - cis vir - go Ma - rí - a!
Vir - go ma - ter Ma - rí - a!
Sal - va nos, O Ma - rí - a!
Au - di nos, O Ma - rí - a!

*Praise to you, vir - gin Mar - y!*
*Vir - gin moth - er, sweet Mar - y!*
*Save us! Aid us, O Mar - y!*
*Hear our plead - ing, O Mar - y!*

Ma - ter a - má - ta, In - te - me - rá - ta,
Quid - quid o - ptá - mus, Per te spe - rá - mus,
Tol - le lan - guó - res, Sa - na do - ló - res,
Tu me - di - cí - nam, Por - tas di - ví - nam;

*Kind, lov - ing Moth - er, Graced like no oth - er,*
*What - e'er our souls need Grant us, as we plead:*
*Come, take our sad - ness; Fill us with glad - ness.*
*You bring us heal - ing, God's love re - veal - ing.*

O - ra, o - ra pro no - bis.
O - ra, o - ra pro no - bis.
O - ra, o - ra pro no - bis.
O - ra, o - ra pro no - bis.

*Pray, O pray for us, Mar - y!*
*Pray, O pray for us, Mar - y!*
*Pray, O pray for us, Mar - y!*
*Pray, O pray for us, Mar - y!*

Text: St. 1, *Stimmen der Völker in Liedern*, 1807; st. 2, *Arundel Hymnal*, 1902; tr. Neil Borgstrom, b.1953, © 1994, 2011, GIA Publications, Inc.
Tune: O DU FRÖLICHE, 55 7 55 7; Tattersall's *Improved Psalmody*, 1794

# 896 Christ Be in Your Senses

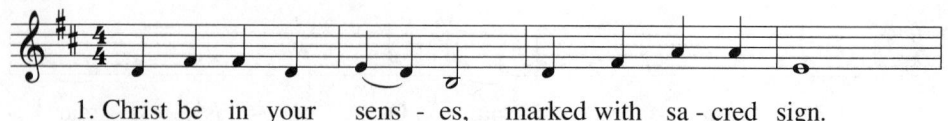

1. Christ be in your sens - es, marked with sa - cred sign.
2. Christ be in your vi - sion, guard you day and night;
3. Christ be in your breath-ing, con - stant - ly im - part

In the In - car - na - tion flesh be - came di - vine.
Keep your feet from stum - bling, shine God's ho - ly light.
Grace to ev - 'ry move - ment, peace with - in your heart.

Christ be in your hear - ing, tune you to re - joice;
Christ be in your speak - ing, train your ev - 'ry word.
Christ be in your sens - es, marked with sa - cred sign.

In each shout or whis - per, hear God's call - ing voice.
In your dai - ly wit - ness let God's truth be heard.
In the Spir - it's pres - ence, flesh be - comes di - vine.

Text: Mary Louise Bringle, b.1953
Tune: APPALACHIAN FALL, 11 11 11 11; William P. Rowan, b.1951
© 2002, GIA Publications, Inc.

# 897 You Have Been Enlightened

You have been en - light - ened by Christ. Walk al - ways as

chil - dren of the light and keep the flame of

To repeat    Last time

faith a - live in your hearts.    hearts;    and

keep the flame of faith a-live in your hearts.

Text: *Rite of Christian Initiation of Adults*, © 1985, ICEL
Tune: Kate Cuddy, b.1953, © 2007, GIA Publications, Inc.

## Wade in the Water 898

**Refrain**

Wade in the wa-ter, wade in the wa-ter, chil-dren,

wade in the wa-ter, God's a gon-na trou-ble the wa-ter.

**Verses**

*Cantor:*

1. See that host all dressed in white,
2. See that band all dressed in red,
3. Look o - ver yon - der, what do I see?
4. If you don't be - lieve I've been re - deemed,

*All:*

God's a gon - na trou - ble the wa - ter;

*Cantor:*

The lead - er looks like the Is - ra - el - ite,
Looks like the band that Mo - ses led,
The Ho - ly Ghost a com - in' on me,
Just fol - low me down to Jor - dan's stream,

*All:*                                                    **D.C.**

God's a gon - na trou - ble the wa - ter.

Text: African American spiritual
Tune: African American spiritual; harm. by Diana Kodner, b.1957, © 1994, GIA Publications, Inc.

# 899 Sweet Refreshment

Refrain

Cantor: Come to the wa-ter. All: Come to the wa-ter. Cantor: Drink of it free-ly.

All: Drink of it free-ly. Cantor: Taste God's own Spir-it. All: Taste God's own

Cantor: Spir-it. Sweet re-fresh-ment. All: Sweet re-fresh-ment.

Verses

Cantor:
1. At the dawn of cre - a - tion, your
2. When your peo - ple were cap - tive, you
3. In the wa - ters of Jor - dan, your
4. Liv - ing wa - ters, e - ter - nal,

Spir - it, O God, moved on the wa - ters. You
led them, O God, led them from bond - age. You
Son was bap - tized; with Spir - it a - noint - ed, that
quench ev - 'ry thirst, cleanse ev - 'ry soul.

D.C.

breathed and the wa - ters were life.
led them through wa - ters to life.
we might be raised to new life.
You are the foun - tain of life.

Text: Based on *Blessing of Water,* Easter Vigil; adapt. by Bob Moore, b.1962
Tune: Bob Moore, b.1962
© 1999, GIA Publications, Inc.

# Who Calls You by Name   900

Refrain

*Cantor:*
Bless-ed be God! O Bless-ed be God!

*All:*
Bless-ed be God! O Bless-ed be God! Who

*All:*
calls you by name! Who calls you by name!

*Cantor:*
Ho - ly and cho - sen one!

*All:*
Ho - ly and cho - sen one!

Verses

1. Come, and re - turn to the Lord!
2. Seek to be chil - dren of light!
3. Sing now with all your heart!

Live by the Word of God, who
Live in the love of God, who
Praise and glo - ry be to our God, who

D.C.

calls you by name! Who calls you by name!
calls you by name! Who calls you by name!
calls you by name! Who calls you by name!

# 901 For the Life of the World

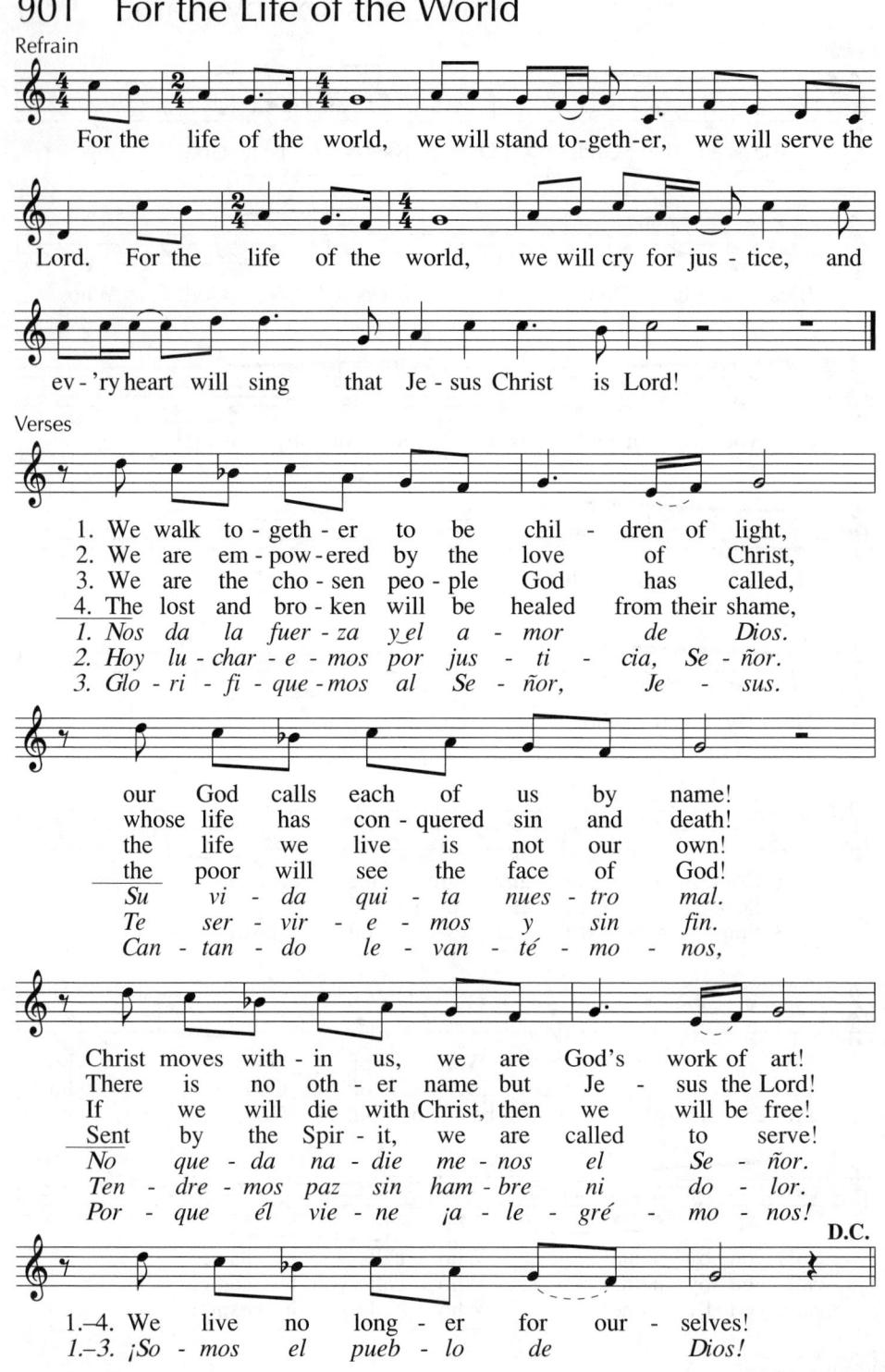

**Refrain**

For the life of the world, we will stand to-geth-er, we will serve the Lord. For the life of the world, we will cry for jus - tice, and ev - 'ry heart will sing that Je - sus Christ is Lord!

**Verses**

1. We walk to - geth - er to be chil - dren of light,
2. We are em - pow - ered by the love of Christ,
3. We are the cho - sen peo - ple God has called,
4. The lost and bro - ken will be healed from their shame,

1. Nos da la fuer - za y_el a - mor de Dios.
2. Hoy lu - char - e - mos por jus - ti - cia, Se - ñor.
3. Glo - ri - fi - que - mos al Se - ñor, Je - sus.

our God calls each of us by name!
whose life has con - quered sin and death!
the life we live is not our own!
the poor will see the face of God!

Su vi - da qui - ta nues - tro mal.
Te ser - vir - e - mos y sin fin.
Can - tan - do le - van - té - mo - nos,

Christ moves with - in us, we are God's work of art!
There is no oth - er name but Je - sus the Lord!
If we will die with Christ, then we will be free!
Sent by the Spir - it, we are called to serve!

No que - da na - die me - nos el Se - ñor.
Ten - dre - mos paz sin ham - bre ni do - lor.
Por - que él vie - ne ¡a - le - gré - mo - nos!

**D.C.**

1.–4. We live no long - er for our - selves!
1.–3. ¡So - mos el pueb - lo de Dios!

Text: David Haas, b.1957; Spanish verses by Jeffrey Judge
Tune: David Haas, b.1957; acc. by Jeanne Cotter, b.1964
© 1993, GIA Publications, Inc.

## O Breathe on Me, O Breath of God  902

1. O breathe on me, O Breath of God, Fill
2. O breathe on me, O Breath of God, Un -
3. O breathe on me, O Breath of God, My
4. O breathe on me, O Breath of God, So

me with life a - new, That I may love the
til my heart is pure; Un - til my will is
will to yours in - cline, Un - til this self - ish
shall I nev - er die, But live with you the

things you love And do what you would do.
one with yours, To do and to en - dure.
part of me Glows with your fire di - vine.
per - fect life Of your e - ter - ni - ty.

Text: Edwin Hatch, 1835–1889
Tune: ST. COLUMBA, CM; Gaelic; harm. by A. Gregory Murray, OSB, 1905–1992, © Downside Abbey

## Baptized in Water  903

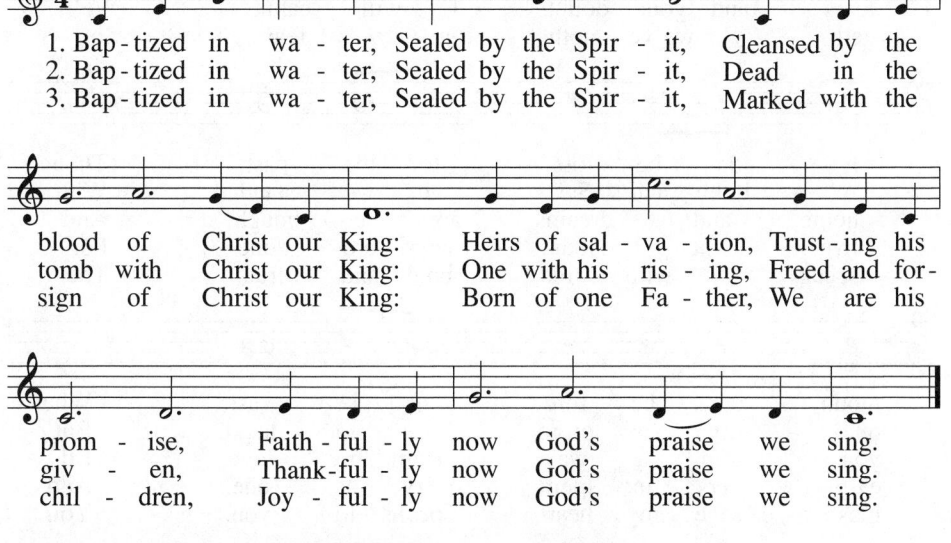

1. Bap - tized in wa - ter, Sealed by the Spir - it, Cleansed by the
2. Bap - tized in wa - ter, Sealed by the Spir - it, Dead in the
3. Bap - tized in wa - ter, Sealed by the Spir - it, Marked with the

blood of Christ our King: Heirs of sal - va - tion, Trust - ing his
tomb with Christ our King: One with his ris - ing, Freed and for-
sign of Christ our King: Born of one Fa - ther, We are his

prom - ise, Faith - ful - ly now God's praise we sing.
giv - en, Thank - ful - ly now God's praise we sing.
chil - dren, Joy - ful - ly now God's praise we sing.

Text: Michael Saward, b.1932, © 1982, The Jubilate Group (admin. by Hope Publishing Company)
Tune: BUNESSAN, 5 5 8 D; Gaelic melody; acc. by Marty Haugen, b.1950, © 1987, GIA Publications, Inc.

# 904 Covenant Hymn

1. Wher - ev - er you go, I will fol - low, Wher-
2. What - ev - er you dream, I am with you, When
3. And though you should fall, you will find me, When
4. Wher - ev - er you die, I will be there To
5. Wher - ev - er you go, I will fol - low, Be -

ev - er you live is my home. Though
stars call your name in the night. Though
no oth - er friend can you claim, When
sing you to sleep with a psalm, To
hold! The ho - ri - zon shines clear. The

days be of bless - ing or sor - row, Though
shad - ows and mist cloud the fu - ture, To -
foes beat you down or be - tray you And
soothe you with tales of our jour - ney, Your
pos - si - ble gleams like a cit - y: To -

house be of can - vas or stone, Though
geth - er we bear there a light. Like
oth - ers de - sert you in shame. When
fears and your doubts I will calm. We'll
geth - er we've noth - ing to fear. So

E - den be lost to the past, Though
A - bram and Sar - ah we stand, With
home and dreams aren't e - nough, And
live when jour - neys are done For -
speak with words bold and true The

moun - tains be - fore us be vast, Wher -
on - ly a prom - ise in hand. But
you run a - way from my love, I'll
ev - er in mem - 'ry as one. And
mes - sage my heart speaks to you. You

| | | | | | | | | |
|---|---|---|---|---|---|---|---|---|
| ev | - | er | you | go, | I | am | with you, | I |
| lead | | where | you | dream: | I | will | fol - low. | To |
| raise | | you | from | where | you | have | fall - en. | |
| we | | will | be | bur - | ied | to - | geth - er, | And |
| won't | | be | a - lone, | | I | have | prom - ised. | Wher - |

| | | | | | | | |
|---|---|---|---|---|---|---|---|
| nev | - | er | will | leave | you | a - | lone. |
| dream | | with | you | is | my | de - | light. |
| Faith | - | ful | to | you | is | my | name. |
| wak | - | en | to | greet | a | new | dawn. |
| ev | - | er | you | go, | I | am | here. |

Text: Ruth 1:16; Rory Cooney, b.1952
Tune: Gary Daigle, b.1957
© 1993, GIA Publications, Inc.

## There Is One Lord   905

Ostinato Refrain

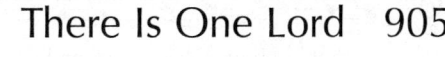

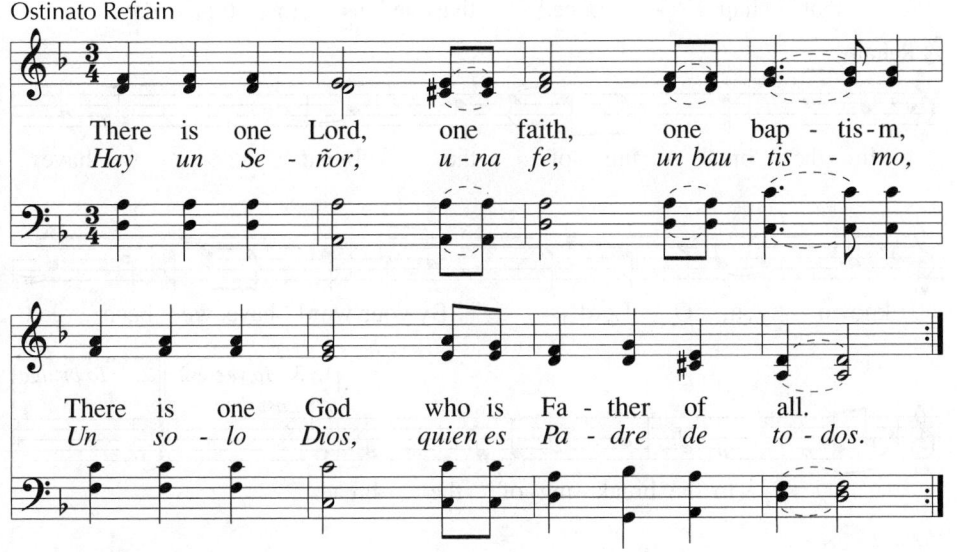

| | | | | | | | | | |
|---|---|---|---|---|---|---|---|---|---|
| There | is | one | Lord, | one | faith, | one | bap - tis - m, |
| *Hay* | *un* | *Se -* | *ñor,* | *u - na* | *fe,* | *un bau -* | *tis - mo,* |

| | | | | | | | |
|---|---|---|---|---|---|---|---|
| There | is | one | God | who is | Fa - ther | of | all. |
| *Un* | *so - lo* | *Dios,* | *quien es* | *Pa - dre* | *de* | *to - dos.* |

Text: Ephesians 4, Taizé Community, 1984
Tune: Jacques Berthier, 1923–1994
© 1984, 2007, Les Presses de Taizé, GIA Publications, Inc., agent

## 906 Emmaus

Verse 1

1. As we jour-neyed on our way and re-mem-bered Christ our friend, our eyes were slow to rec-og-nize, our hearts to com-pre-hend. Now a stran-ger at our side, we talked with him on the way of all the things that hap-pened that led us to this day.

℅ Refrain

In the break-ing of the bread we have known you, O Lord. By your word have we been led

1., 3. *To verse 2*    2. *To bridge*
*Last time*

to the break-ing of the bread.

Verse 2

2. Then he o-pened up the Word of the

proph-ets who had said, "Your Sav-ior first must suf - fer, then

rise from the dead." As our jour - ney found its end

and the dark of night drew near, we told the stran-

D.S.

ger, "Stay with us till morn-ing's light ap - pears."

Bridge

It was at ta - ble then we knew why our hearts were set a - blaze:

This stran-ger was our broth-er a - ris - en from the grave!

Interlude

4

D.S.

Text: Based on Luke 24:13–35; Tony E. Alonso, b.1980
Tune: Tony E. Alonso, b.1980
© 2007, GIA Publications, Inc.

# 907  Where Two or Three Are Gathered

**Refrain**

Here in the Bread that is bro-ken, here in the Cup that is poured, here in the Word that is spo-ken: Je-sus Christ is Lord! Here where the poor find their treas-ure, here where the great-est are least, come find a love be-yond meas-ure in this heav'n-ly feast.

**Verses**

1. Where two or three are gath-ered, gath-ered in my name, I come with words of com-fort
2. Where two or three are gath-ered, I am there as well, in-vit-ing my dis-ci-ples
3. Where two or three are gath-ered, I am there with you. I lead you in-to free-dom,
4. Where two or three are gath-ered, gath-ered in my name, I wash your feet in serv-ice.
5. Where two or three are gath-ered, I am there as well. The bless-ings of the king-dom
6. Where two or three are gath-ered, I am there with you. My gifts of peace and mer-cy

**D.C.**

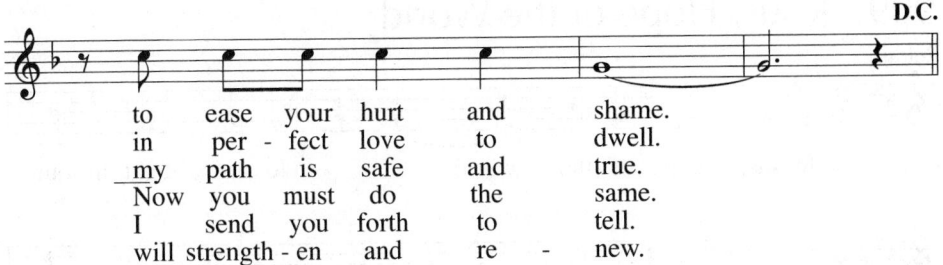

| to | ease | your | hurt | and | shame. |
|----|------|------|------|-----|--------|
| in | per - fect | love | to | | dwell. |
| my | path | is | safe | and | true. |
| Now | you | must | do | the | same. |
| I | send | you | forth | to | tell. |
| will | strength - en | and | re - | | new. |

Text: Liam Lawton, b.1959
Tune: Liam Lawton, b.1959; arr. by Paul A. Tate, b.1968
© 2009, Sumerset Recordings and GIA Publications, Inc.

## Take and Eat, This Is My Body   908

Refrain

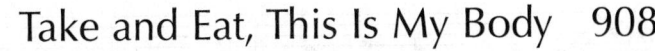

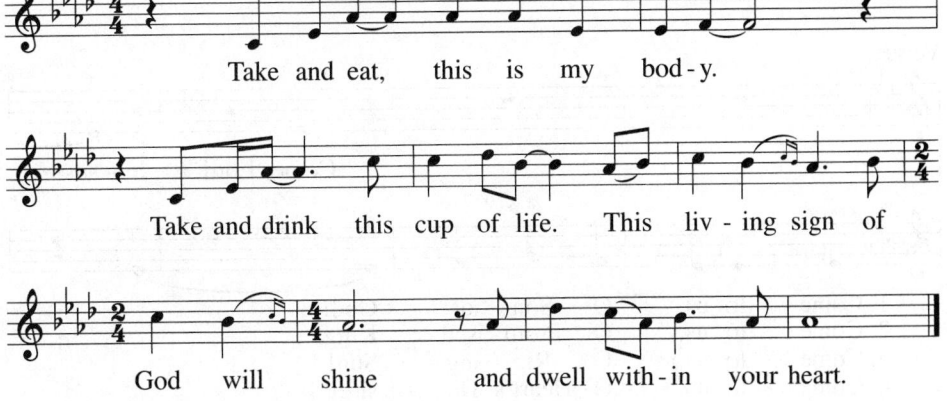

Take and eat, this is my bod-y.

Take and drink this cup of life. This liv-ing sign of

God will shine and dwell with-in your heart.

Verses

1. Come to me, all you who labor, and I will give you rest.
   Lay your burdens upon me; my yoke is light.
   I am strength for the weary, new sight for the blind.

2. Come to me, all you in darkness, Come, live in my light.
   Seek the justice which is hidden within your hearts.
   I have promised a new day. I have promised new life.

3. Is not the bread you break together a sharing in my life?
   Is not the wine poured out for you a sign
   for all the world of the life that I offer, of the life that I give?

Text: Ian Callanan, b.1971
Tune: Ian Callanan, b.1971
© 2006, GIA Publications, Inc.

# 909 Jesus, Hope of the World

Refrain

Je-sus, hope of the world, Je-sus, light in our dark-ness, here we a-wait you, O Mas-ter Di-vine. Here we re-ceive you in Bread and in Wine: Je-sus, hope of the world.

Verses

*All:*

Come, Lord Je-sus!

*Cantors:*

1. Come to us, O Son of God!
2. Come to us, O Prom-ised King!
3. Come to us, O Ris-ing Sun!
4. Come to us, O Heart's De - sire!

Come, Lord Je-sus!

Come to us, O Son of Man!
Come to us, O Prom-ised Peace!
Come to us, O End-less Light!
Come to us, O Sav-ing Love!

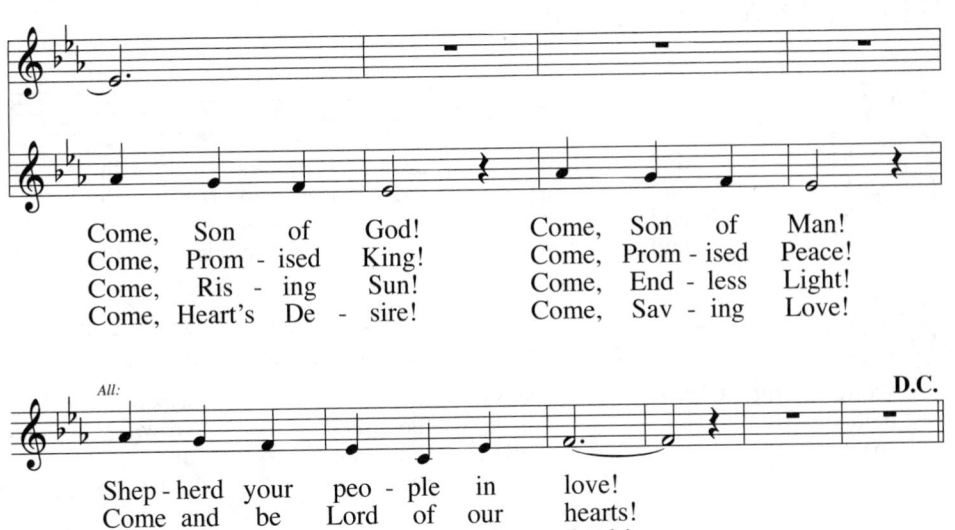

Come, Son of God!
Come, Prom - ised King!
Come, Ris - ing Sun!
Come, Heart's De - sire!

Come, Son of Man!
Come, Prom - ised Peace!
Come, End - less Light!
Come, Sav - ing Love!

*All:*

D.C.

Shep - herd your peo - ple in love!
Come and be Lord of our hearts!
Shat - ter the dark - ness of death!
Ban - ish our doubt and our fear!

Text: Deanna Light, b.1967, and Paul A. Tate, b.1968
Tune: Deanna Light, b.1967, and Paul A. Tate, b.1968
© 2001, World Library Publications

## Shepherd of Souls 910

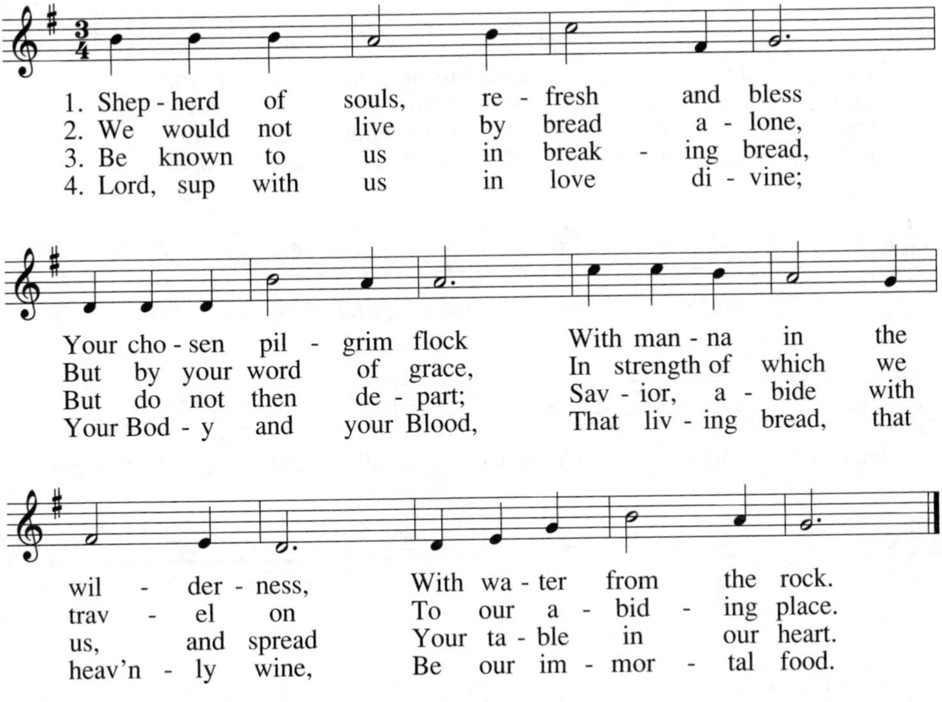

1. Shep - herd of souls, re - fresh and bless
2. We would not live by bread a - lone,
3. Be known to us in break - ing bread,
4. Lord, sup with us in love di - vine;

Your cho - sen pil - grim flock With man - na in the
But by your word of grace, In strength of which we
But do not then de - part; Sav - ior, a - bide with
Your Bod - y and your Blood, That liv - ing bread, that

wil - der - ness, With wa - ter from the rock.
trav - el on To our a - bid - ing place.
us, and spread Your ta - ble in our heart.
heav'n - ly wine, Be our im - mor - tal food.

Text: James Montgomery, 1771–1854, alt.
Tune: ST. AGNES, CM; John B. Dykes, 1823–1876; harm. by Richard Proulx, 1937–2010, © 1986, GIA Publications, Inc.

# 911 Many and Great

Verses

1. Man - y and great are bear - ers of the Word: the Christ speaks; the heart seeks.
2. Man - y and great are seeds up - on the field: the hand sows; the seeds grow.
3. Man - y and great are voic - es of de - spair: the rain falls; the voice calls.
4. Man - y and great are peb - bles in the sand: the sun glows; the wind blows.

Gath - ered as one, we lis - ten to the Word and share the meal of new birth.
Take now and eat the cov - e - nant ful - filled, the bread of prom - ise and life.
Take now and drink the wine of hope and care; our cup of bless - ing we share.
Take now and spread the Word to ev - 'ry land, the Word of good - ness and hope.

Refrain

The wheat grows from spring - time to fall; the wine flows; in Christ we re - call the shar - ing of our lives with one and all.

Text: Ricky Manalo, CSP, b.1965
Tune: Ricky Manalo, CSP, b.1965
© 1995, Ricky Manalo, CSP. Published by OCP.

# Amén. El Cuerpo de Cristo   912

**Refrain**

A - mén. El Cuer - po de Cris-to.   A - mén. La

San-gre del Se-ñor.   *Eat-ing your Bod-y,   drink-ing your Blood, we be-*

*come what we re-ceive.* A - mén.   A - mén.

**Verses**

| | | | | | | | |
|---|---|---|---|---|---|---|---|
| 1. A | - | mén. | *We re* | *- mem* | *- ber* | *your* | *dy - ing* |
| 2. A | - | mén. | *Now we* | *of* | *- fer* | *the* | *sac - ri -* |
| 3. A | - | mén. | *Lord, you* | *make* | *us* | *one* | *bod - y* |
| 4. A | - | mén. | *We find* | *you* | *when* | *we* | *serve the* |
| 5. A | - | mén. | *We look* | *for -* | *ward* | *to* | *your re -* |

| | | | | | | |
|---|---|---|---|---|---|---|
| *and* | *your* | *ris - ing.* | A - | mén. | Y con - ti - go, Se - |
| *fice* | *you* | *gave us.* | A - | mén. | Te o-fre - ce - mos, Se - |
| *and* | *one* | *spir - it.* | A - | mén. | En tu cuer - po, Se - |
| *poor* | *and* | *low - ly.* | A - | mén. | A ti mis - mo ser - |
| *turn* | *in* | *glo - ry.* | A - | mén. | Es - pe - ra - mos el |

**D.C.**

| | | | | | |
|---|---|---|---|---|---|
| ñor, | re - su - ci - | ta - mos. | A | - | mén. |
| ñor, | to - do lo que | so - mos. | A | - | mén. |
| ñor, | un pue - blo | san - to. | A | - | mén. |
| vi - mos en los | po - bres. | A | - | mén. | |
| día | de tu ve - | ni - da. | A | - | mén. |

Text: John Schiavone, b.1947
Tune: John Schiavone, b.1947
© 1995, John Schiavone. Published by OCP.

# 913 We Are One

**Refrain**

We are one, one in the bod - y, one in the Spir-it of the Lord. Here, we be - come food for the hun-gry, drink for the thirst - y. At this ta-ble of love, by faith, we are all made one.

**Verses**

1. Be - yond the bread we break, we live the prom-ise of new life. Be-yond the cup we take,
2. As we re - ceive your love, we look to give love in re - turn, and we be - lieve your love
3. Sum-moned as food for all, we take the gos - pel to the world. When we do good for all,

we share our lives with one an - oth - er:
will change our hearts to end di - vi - sion:
we hear the call to choose com - pas - sion:

Then we'll know the pres - ence of God.

**D.C.**

Text: Based on Ephesians 4:4–6; Chris de Silva, b.1967
Tune: Chris de Silva, b.1967
© 2007, GIA Publications, Inc.

# Lord, Who at Your First Eucharist 914

1. Lord, who at your first Eu - cha - rist did pray
2. For all your Church, O Lord, we in - ter - cede;
3. We pray for those who wan - der from your fold;
4. So, Lord, at length when sac - ra - ments shall cease,

That all your Church might be for - ev - er one,
O make our lack of char - i - ty to cease.
O bring them back, Good Shep - herd of the sheep,
May we be one with all your Church a - bove,

Help us at ev - 'ry Eu - cha - rist to say
Draw us the near - er each to each, we plead,
Back to the faith which saints be - lieved of old,
One with your saints in one un - bro - ken peace,

With long - ing heart and soul, "Your will be done."
By draw - ing all to you, O Prince of Peace.
Back to the Church which still that faith does keep.
One with your saints in one un - bound - ed love.

Thus may we all one Bread, one Bod - y be,
Thus may we all one Bread, one Bod - y be,
Thus may we all one Bread, one Bod - y be,
More bless - ed still, in peace and love to be

Through this blest Sac - ra - ment of U - ni - ty.
Through this blest Sac - ra - ment of U - ni - ty.
Through this blest Sac - ra - ment of U - ni - ty.
One with the Trin - i - ty in u - ni - ty.

Text: William H. Turton, 1859–1938, alt.
Tune: UNDE ET MEMORES, 10 10 10 10 with refrain; William H. Monk, 1823–1889, alt.

# 915  Gusten y Vean / Taste and See

**Refrain**

Gus-ten y ve-an, gus-ten y ve-an qué bue-no es el Se-ñor, qué bue-no es el Se-ñor. Taste and see, taste and see the good-ness of the Lord.

**Verses**

*Cantor:*

1. Ven - gan los ham-brien - tos:
2. Ven - gan los se - dien - tos:
3. Ven - gan los po - bres:
4. Ven - gan los do - lien - tos:
5. Ven - gan los que su - fren:
6. Ven - gan los can - sa - dos:
7. Ven - gan a la me - sa:

*All:*

4. ¡Gus-ten y ve - an!

*Cantor:*

Come all who hun - ger:
All you who thirst:
Come all you poor ones:
All who are griev - ing:
Come all who suf - fer:
All who are wea - ry:
Come to the ta - ble:

*All:*

Taste and see the good-ness of the Lord, the good-ness of the Lord.

D.C.

Psalm 34 Verses

1. I will bless the Lord at all times,
   God's praise always on my lips;
   in the Lord my soul shall make its boast.
   The humble shall hear and be glad.

2. Glorify the Lord with me.
   Together let us praise God's name.
   I sought the Lord and was heard;
   from all my terrors set free.

3. Look towards God and be radiant;
   let your faces not be abashed.
   When the poor cry out the Lord hears them
   and rescues them from all their distress.

4. The angel of the Lord is encamped
   around those who fear God, to rescue them.
   Taste and see that the Lord is good.
   They are happy who seek refuge in God.

1. *Bendigo al Señor en todo momento,*
   *su_alabanza está siempre en mi boca;*
   *mi alma se gloria_en el Señor:*
   *que los humildes lo escuchen y se_alegren.*

2. *Proclamen  conmigo la grandeza del Señor,*
   *ensalcemos juntos su nombre.*
   *Yo consulté al Señor y me respondió,*
   *me libró de todas mis ansias.*

3. *Contémplenlo, y quedarán radiantes,*
   *su rostro no se_avergonzará.*
   *Si_el afligido invoca al Señor,*
   *él lo escucha y lo salva de sus angustias.*

4. *El ángel del Señor acampa*
   *en torno a sus fieles, y los protege.*
   *Gusten y vean qué bueno_es el Señor,*
   *dichoso_el  que se_acoge a él.*

Text: Based on Psalm 34; Tony E. Alonso, b.1980, © 2008, GIA Publications, Inc.; verses, Psalm 34:2–9, © 1963, 2000, The Grail,
GIA Publications, Inc., agent; Spanish tr. from *Leccionario, Edición Hispanoamérica*, © 1970, 1972, Conferencia Episcopal Española
Tune: Tony E. Alonso, b.1980, © 2008, 2010, GIA Publications, Inc.

# 916　I Receive the Living God

Refrain

I re-ceive the liv-ing God, And my heart is full of joy. I re-ceive the liv-ing God, And my heart is full of joy.

Verses

1. Je - sus says: I am the Bread Sent to
2. Je - sus says: I am the Vine, Far from
3. Je - sus says: I am the Way, And my
4. Je - sus says: I am the Truth. If you
5. Je - sus says: I am the Life, Raised in
6. Je - sus says: I am the Day, Shin - ing

1. you from God Most High. Take and eat, and you will
2. whom no life can grow. If you join your-self to
3. path is straight and true. Fol - low me to where I
4. fol - low close to me, You will know me in your
5. tri - umph from the dead. As one Bod - y now re -
6. bright - ly through your night. Wel-come me, and you will

**D.C.**

1. live; You need nev - er fear to die.
2. me, A rich har - vest you will know.
3. lead; There my Fa - ther waits for you.
4. heart, And my word will make you free.
5. main, Mem - bers joined to me, the Head.
6. walk By the Spir - it's guid - ing light.

7. Jesus says: I am the Love
   Which can bind you close to me.
   Those who know this gift I bring
   Will find true community.

8. Jesus says: I am the Peace
   Which the world cannot bestow.
   Learn to love and live in me,
   And in you my Reign will grow.

9. Jesus says: I am the Lamb,
   And my death set sinners free.
   Those who drink the cup I drink
   Must take up this work with me.

Text: Vss. 1–3, 5–9, Bernard Geoffroy, b.1946; tr. by Ronald F. Krisman, b.1946, © 2011, GIA Publications, Inc.; vs. 4, anonymous
Tune: LIVING GOD, 7 7 7 7 with refrain; Dom Clément Jacob, OSB, 1906–1977, adapt.; harm. by Richard Proulx, 1937–2010, © 1986,
   GIA Publications, Inc.

## O Taste and See   917

Refrain

O taste, taste and see the
good - ness of God, the bless - ings of God.

Verses

1. I will sing God's praises all the days that I shall live.
   My soul will glory in my God, the lowly will hear and be glad.
   O glorify God's name with me, together let us rejoice.

2. For God has heard my anguished cries, and delivered me from all my foes.
   O look to God that you might shine, your faces be radiant with joy.

3. When the poor cry out, God hears and saves them,
   rescues them from their distress.
   God's angel watches near to those who look to their God to save them.

4. O taste and see that God is good, how happy the ones who find refuge.
   The mighty shall grow weak and hungry, those who seek God lack nothing.

5. Come, my children, hear me, I will teach you the fear of God.
   Come, all of you who thirst for life and seek joy in all of your days.

6. For God is close to the brokenhearted, near to those crushed in spirit.
   The hand of God redeems your life, a refuge for all those who seek.

Text: Psalm 34:2–4, 5–6, 7–8, 9, 11, 12–13, 19; Marty Haugen, b.1950
Tune: Marty Haugen, b.1950
© 1993, GIA Publications, Inc.

# 918 In the Breaking of the Bread / Cuando Partimos el Pan del Señor

**Refrain**

In the break - ing of the bread
*Cuan-do par - ti - mos el pan del Se - ñor,*

We have known him; we have been fed.
*lo co - no - ce - mos, nos da de co - mer.* Je -

Je - sus the stran - ger, Je - sus the Lord,
*sús des - co - no - ci - do, Je - sús Se - ñor,*

Be our com - pan - ion; be our hope.
*nues - tro com - pa - ñe - ro y fuen - te de fe.*

**Verses**

1. Bread for the jour - ney, strength for our years,
1. *Pan pa - ra el via - je, Pan de la vi - da,*
2. Bread of the prom - ise, peo - ple of hope,
2. *Pan de pro - me - sa, Pan de es - pe - ran - za,*

Man - na of a - ges, of strug - gle and tears.
*Pan de los si - glos de lu - cha y do - lor,*
Wine of com - pas - sion, life for the world.
*Vi - no de vi - da, de su com - pa - sión.*

Cup of sal - va - tion, fruit of the land,
*y es - te vi - no, fru - to de la tie - rra,* ben-
Gath - ered at ta - ble, joined as his bod - y,
*En es - ta me - sa, un so - lo cuer - po,*

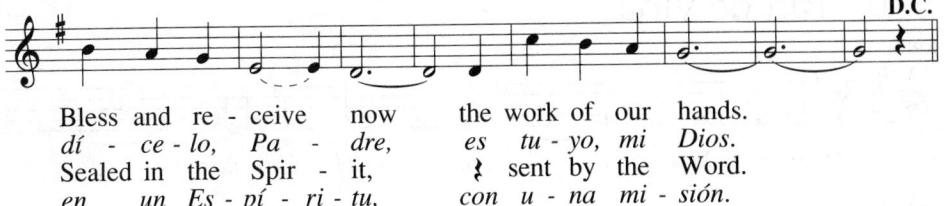

**D.C.**

Bless and re - ceive now the work of our hands.
*dí - ce - lo, Pa - dre, es tu - yo, mi Dios.*
Sealed in the Spir - it, ⟩ sent by the Word.
*en un Es - pí - ri - tu, con u - na mi - sión.*

*Original Verses:*

1. Once I was helpless, sad and confused; darkness surrounded me, courage removed.
And then I saw him by my side. Carry my burden, open my eyes.

2. There is no sorrow, pain or woe; there is no suffering he did not know.
He did not waver; he did not bend. He is the victor. He is my friend.

Text: Bob Hurd, b.1950, and Michael Downey, © 1984, 1987; Spanish text by Stephen Dean and Kathleen Orozco, © 1989, OCP
Tune: Bob Hurd, b.1950, © 1984; acc. by Dominic MacAller, b.1959, © 1984, OCP
Published by OCP.

## I Come with Joy  919

1. I come with joy, a child of God, For -
2. I come with Chris - tians far and near To
3. As Christ breaks bread, and bids us share, Each
4. The Spir - it of the ris - en Christ, Un -
5. To - geth - er met, to - geth - er bound By

giv - en, loved, and free, The life of Je - sus
find, as all are fed, The new com - mu - ni -
proud di - vi - sion ends. The love that made us,
seen, but ev - er near, Is in such friend - ship
all that God has done, We'll go with joy, to

to re - call, In love laid down for me.
ty of love In Christ's com - mu - nion bread.
makes us one, And strang - ers now are friends.
bet - ter known, A - live a - mong us here.
give the world The love that makes us one.

Text: Brian Wren, b.1936, © 1971, rev. 1995, Hope Publishing Company
Tune: LAND OF REST, CM; American; adapt. by Annabel M. Buchanan, 1888–1983, © 1938 (renewed), this arr. © 2011, The H.W. Gray Company

# 920 Pan de Vida

Refrain

*Pan de Vi - da, cuer-po del Se - ñor,

cup of bless - ing, blood of Christ the Lord.

At this ta - ble the last shall be first, **po-

der es ser - vir, por-que Dios es a - mor.

Verses

1. ⸲ We are the dwell-ing of God,
***2. Us - te - des me lla - man "Se - ñor," me in-
3. ⸲ There is no Jew or Greek,

fra - gile and wound-ed and weak. We are the
cli - no_a la - var - les los pies. Ha - gan lo
there is no slave or free; there is no

bod - y of Christ, called to be the com -
mis - mo, hu - mil - des, sir - vién - do - se
wom-an or man; on - ly heirs of the

D.C.

pas - sion of God.
u - nos a o - tros.
prom - ise of God.

*Bread of Life, body of the Lord,   **power is for service, because God is Love.
***You call me "Lord," and I bow to wash your feet:
you must do the same, humbly serving each other.

Text: John 13:1–15, Galatians 3:28–29; Bob Hurd, b.1950, and Pia Moriarty, b.1948
Tune: Bob Hurd, b.1950; acc. by Craig Kingsbury, b.1952
© 1988, Bob Hurd and Pia Moriarty. Published by OCP.

# The Living Bread of God   921

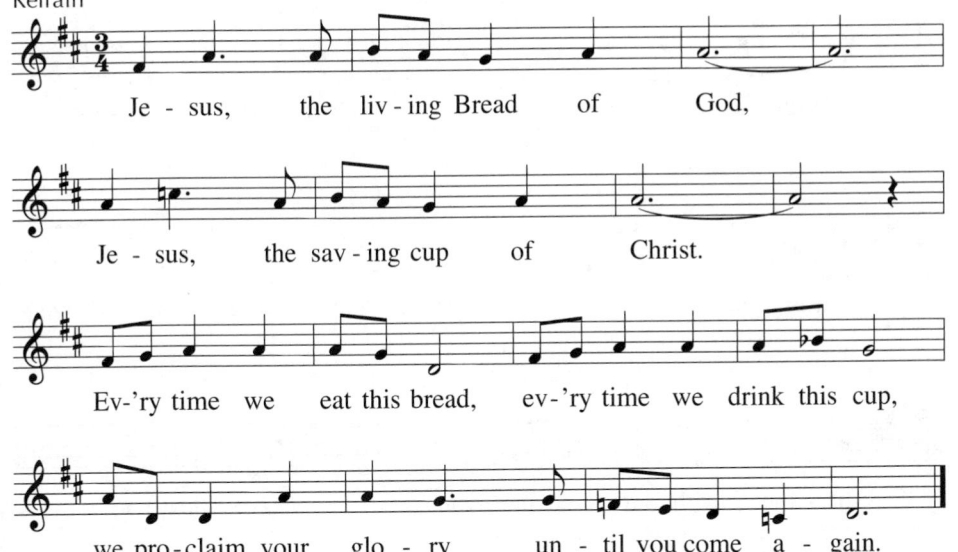

Refrain

Je - sus, the liv - ing Bread of God,

Je - sus, the sav - ing cup of Christ.

Ev-'ry time we eat this bread, ev-'ry time we drink this cup,

we pro-claim your glo - ry un - til you come a - gain.

Verses

1. You are the bread of life.
   If we come to you, we will never be in need.
   If we believe in you, we will never thirst, and we will live for ever.

2. You are the life of the world.
   If we come to you, we will never know death.
   If we eat of this bread, we will be renewed, and we will live for ever.

3. You are the living bread,
   our bread from heaven, our food from above.
   If we eat and drink, we will be like you, and we will live for ever.

4. You are the living Christ.
   If we follow you, we will see the face of God.
   If we die with you, we will rise again, and we will live for ever.

Text: 1 Corinthians 11:26; David Haas, b.1957
Tune: Kate Cuddy, b.1953
© 1992, GIA Publications, Inc.

# 922 Without Seeing You

**Refrain**

With-out see-ing you, we love you; with-out

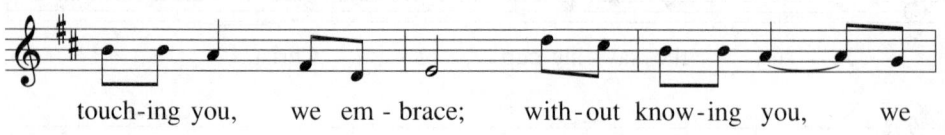

touch-ing you, we em-brace; with-out know-ing you, we

fol-low; with-out see-ing you, we be-lieve.

**Verses**

1. We re - turn to you deep with - in, leave the
2. The spar - row will find a home, near to
3. For ev - er we sing to you of your
4. For you are our shep - herd, there is

past to the dust; turn to you with tears and
you, O God; how hap - py, we who
good - ness, O God; pro - claim - ing to
noth - ing that we need; in green pas - tures we will

**D.C.**

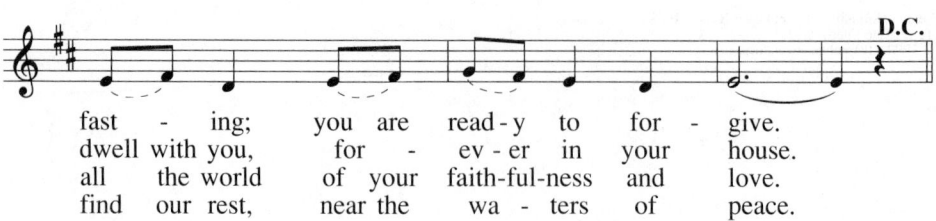

fast - ing; you are read - y to for - give.
dwell with you, for - ev - er in your house.
all the world of your faith-ful-ness and love.
find our rest, near the wa - ters of peace.

Text: Inspired by 1 Peter 1:8; David Haas, b.1957
Tune: David Haas, b.1957
© 1993, GIA Publications, Inc.

# Table Song 923

**Refrain**

We are the bod-y of Christ, Bro-ken and
poured out, prom-ise of life from death,
we are the bod-y of Christ.

**Verses**

1. Is not the bread of life we break a
2. How shall we make a re - turn to God, for
3. Un - less a grain of wheat shall fall up -
4. Come taste and see the good - ness, the

shar - ing in the life of God? Is not the cup of
good-ness un - sur - pass - ing? This sav - ing cup we
on the earth, it shall re - main a sin - gle grain; but
won - ders of the ris - en one! Come bless our God, in

**D.C.**

peace out-poured the blood of Christ?
shall hold high, and call out God's name!
if it dies, it will come to life!
all things, let praise be our song!

Text: David Haas, b. 1957
Tune: David Haas, b. 1957
© 1991, GIA Publications, Inc.

# 924 Song of the Body of Christ / Cancíon del Cuerpo de Cristo

Refrain

We come to share our sto - ry, we
*Hoy ve - ni - mos a con - tar nues-tra his - to - ria, com - par-*

come to break the bread, We come to
*tien - do el pan ce - les - tial. Hoy ve - ni - mos jun - tos*

know our ris - ing from the dead.
*a ce - le - brar tu mis - te - rio pas - cual.*

Verses

1. We come as your peo - ple, we
2. We are called to heal the bro - ken, to be
3. Bread of life and cup of prom - ise, in this
4. You will lead and we shall fol - low, you will
5. We will live and sing: "A - lo - ha," "Al - le -
   (live and sing your prais - es,)

come as your own, u - nit - ed with each
hope for the poor, we are called to feed the
meal we all are one. In our dy - ing and our
be the breath of life; liv - ing wa - ter, we are
lu - ia" is our song. May we live in love and

D.C.

oth - er, love finds a home.
hun - gry at our door.
ris - ing, may your king - dom come.
thirst - ing for your light.
peace our whole life long.

Estrofas

1. Hoy ve - ni - mos por - que so - mos tu pue - blo, re - na-
2. A sa - nar al en - fer - mo nos lla - mas, al an-
3. Pan de vi - da y san-gre de la_a - lian - za, haz - nos
4. Nos guia - rás y te se - gui - re - mos. Nues-tro_a-
5. Vi - vi - re - mos can - tan - do "A - lo - ja." "A - le-

ci - dos por tu per - dón, re - u - ni - dos
sio - so, tu_es - pe - ran - za tra - er, y_al ham - brien - to,
u - no_en es - ta co - mu - nión. Que tu rei - no
lien - to vi - tal tú se - rás. Nues - tra luz, en el
lu - ya" es nues - tra can - ción. Que vi - va - mos por

D.C.

en tu_a - mor, y de un co - ra - zón.
nues - tro_a - li - men - to o - fre - cer.
ven - ga en nues - tra trans - for-ma - ción.
dí - a y_en la no - che bri - lla - rás.
siem - pre en paz y fra - ter - na u - nión.

Text: David Haas, b.1957, Spanish translation by Donna Peña, b.1955, and Ronald F. Krisman, b.1946
Tune: NO KE ANO' AHI AHI, Irregular, Hawaiian traditional, arr. by David Haas, b.1957
© 1989, GIA Publications, Inc.

# 925 All Who Hunger

Verses

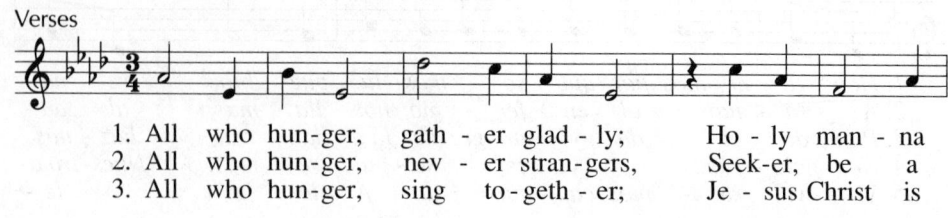

1. All who hun-ger, gath - er glad - ly; Ho - ly man - na
2. All who hun-ger, nev - er stran-gers, Seek-er, be a
3. All who hun-ger, sing to-geth - er; Je - sus Christ is

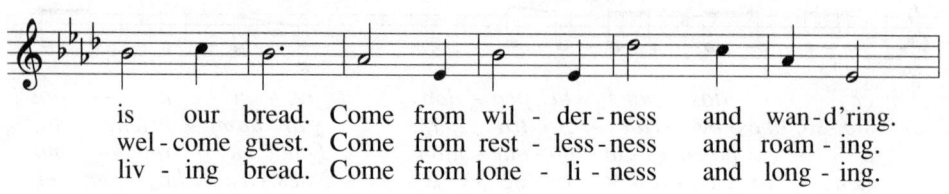

is our bread. Come from wil - der-ness and wan-d'ring.
wel-come guest. Come from rest - less-ness and roam - ing.
liv - ing bread. Come from lone - li - ness and long - ing.

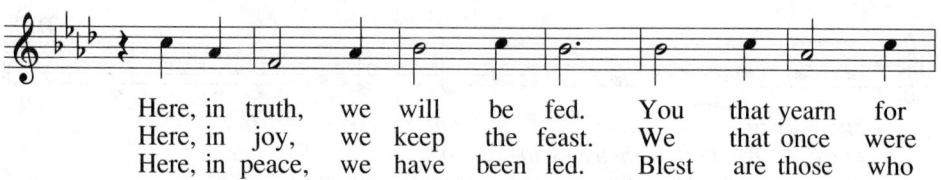

Here, in truth, we will be fed. You that yearn for
Here, in joy, we keep the feast. We that once were
Here, in peace, we have been led. Blest are those who

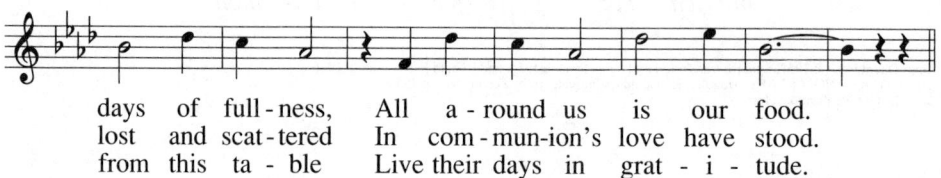

days of full - ness, All a - round us is our food.
lost and scat-tered In com - mun-ion's love have stood.
from this ta - ble Live their days in grat - i - tude.

Refrain

Taste and see the grace e - ter-nal. Taste and see that God is good.

Text: Sylvia G. Dunstan, 1955–1993, © 1991, GIA Publications, Inc.
Tune: Bob Moore, b.1962, © 1993, GIA Publications, Inc.

# Life-Giving Bread, Saving Cup  926

**Refrain**

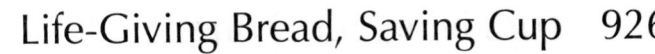

Life - giv-ing Bread,      sav - ing Cup,      we   of - fer in thanks-

giv-ing,      O  God.      Life  -  giv-ing Bread,

sav - ing  Cup,      we   of - fer  as    a   sign   of  our  love.

**Verses**

1. For  bread  that   is      bro - ken,   we  give  thanks;      for
2. We   thank  you,   O      Fa - ther,   for your  name,      which
3. Cre - a - tor  of     all,      we     of - fer  thanks;      you
4. Re - mem - ber  your Church, which  sings your  praise;      per-

wine      that   is  poured,      we  give  praise.      For
you      give   to  dwell      in   our  hearts.      You
give      us    a   share      in   your  life.      You
fect      it    in  truth      and  in   love.      And

life      and    for knowl-edge  of    the   king - dom:      all
bring      us    to - geth - er  as    one   fam - 'ly:      all
strength - en   our  bod - y   and   our   spir - it:      all
gath    -  er   your peo - ple  all   to - geth - er      to

**D.C.**

praise  to   you   un - til      the  end   of    time!
praise  to   you   un - til      the  end   of    time!
praise  to   you   un - til      the  end   of    time!
praise       you   un - til      the  end   of    time!

Text: Adapted from the *Didache*, 2nd C.; James J. Chepponis, b.1956
Tune: James J. Chepponis, b.1956
© 1987, GIA Publications, Inc.

# 927  For Living, for Dying

**Refrain**

Nour-ish us well. Teach us to be all that you long

for us to be. Al-ways to live, nev-er to thirst,

*To verses*

nev - er to hun - ger.

*Last time*

Al-ways to live, al-ways to live.

**Verses**

1. For living, for dying, Lord, for rising from the dead,
   we praise you with every breath we take.
   We come to you, remember you in the breaking of this bread,
   we drink the cup, the promise that you made.

2. Communion, community, is what we claim this day.
   Your body, your Spirit is our grace.
   With every heart, with every hand, with every word we say,
   of rich and poor, we welcome, we embrace.

3. For loving us, forgiving us, for sharing in our tears,
   for laughter, the tenderness you bring.
   You call to us, we follow. You guard us from our fears.
   Beside you our hearts will always sing.

4. So here we are, a part of you, a part of everyone;
   a river that flows into the sea.
   From east to west, from near and far, from every time and place,
   around the world we all join in your feast.

Text: Donna Peña, b.1955
Tune: Donna Peña, b.1955; arr. by Paul Gerike
© 1999, GIA Publications, Inc.

# Take and Eat This Bread  928

**Refrain**

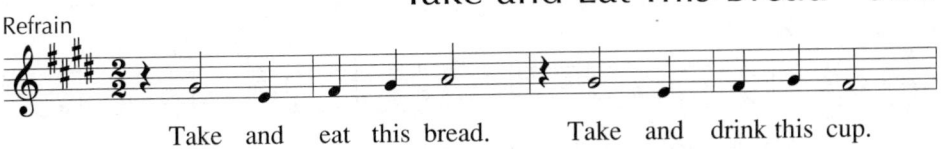

Take and eat this bread. Take and drink this cup.

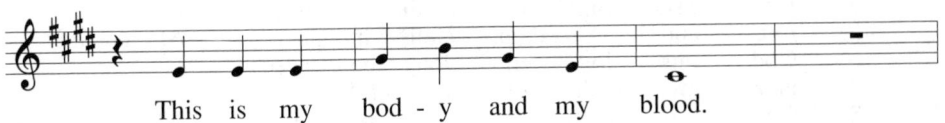

This is my bod-y and my blood.

When you eat this bread, when you drink this cup,

you live in me and I in you.

**Verses**

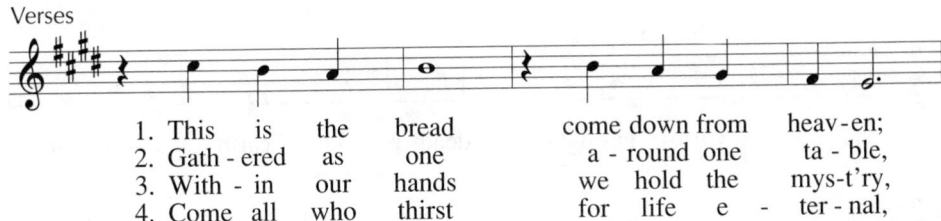

1. This is the bread    come down from    heav-en;
2. Gath-ered as one    a - round one    ta - ble,
3. With - in our hands    we hold the    mys-t'ry,
4. Come all who thirst    for life e - ter - nal,

D.C.

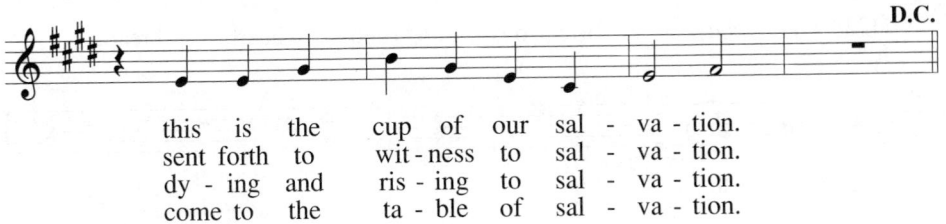

this is the cup of our sal - va - tion.
sent forth to wit - ness to sal - va - tion.
dy - ing and ris - ing to sal - va - tion.
come to the ta - ble of sal - va - tion.

Text: Francis Patrick O'Brien, b.1958
Tune: Francis Patrick O'Brien, b.1958
© 1992, GIA Publications, Inc.

# 929 Joyous Cup

**Verses**

*Cantor:*

1. Slaves and chil - dren, take a stand:
2. Sea, stand straight! And riv - ers, flee:
3. Trem - ble, earth, to see God's face:
4. Heav - ens, sing! O earth, in - tone:
5. Eve and A - dam, tell it plain:
6. God, our lov - er, long be - trayed
7. O hap - py fault, O need - ful sin:
8. Go pro - claim a ju - bi - lee:
9. Go pro - claim a ju - bi - lee:

*All:* Al - le - lu -

*Cantor:*

ia!

Come to milk and hon - ey land:
Moun-tains, skip like lambs to see:
Flint shall flow with wa - ter's grace:
Death and hell now wail and groan:
All was lost but more's the gain:
Pas - sion has our wed - ding made:
O Christ our sav - ior, Christ our kin:
Nei - ther rich nor poor shall be:
Now from ev - 'ry debt set free:

*All:* Al - le - lu -

**Refrain**

ia! Christ has died and death is dead: earth and heav - en

bold - ly wed. Joy - ous cup and heart - y bread.

Al - le - lu - ia.

Text: Based on Psalm 114 and the Exsultet; Gabe Huck, b.1941
Tune: Tony E. Alonso, b.1980
© 2004, GIA Publications, Inc.

# Taste and See  930

**Refrain**

Taste and see, taste and see the good - ness of the Lord. O taste and see, taste and see the good - ness of the Lord, of the Lord.

**Verses**

1. I will bless the Lord at all times.
2. Glo - ri - fy the Lord with me.
3. Wor - ship the Lord, all you peo - ple.

Praise shall al - ways be on my lips;
To - geth-er let us all praise God's name.
You'll want for noth-ing if you ask.

my soul shall glo - ry in the Lord
I called the Lord who an - swered me;
Taste and see that the Lord is good;

for God has been so good to me.
from all my trou-bles I was set free.
in God we need put all our trust.

Text: Psalm 34; James E. Moore, Jr., b.1951
Tune: James E. Moore, Jr., b.1951
© 1983, GIA Publications, Inc.

# 931 Come to the Banquet

Refrain

Come to the ban - quet, come to the feast. Eat the Bread of life! Share in the sing - ing, share in the joy. Drink the Cup of love!

*To verses*

*Last time* love! Share the joy!

Verses

1. Draw near and take the Bod - y of the Lord,
2. Our great Re - deem - er, God's e - ter - nal Son,
3. Let us ap - proach with faith - ful hearts sin - cere
4. With heav'n - ly bread Christ makes the hun - gry whole;

1. And drink with faith the Blood for you out - poured. Saved by his Bod - y, hal - lowed by his Blood, With souls re - freshed we give our thanks to God.
2. Has by his cross and blood the vic - t'ry won. He spent his life for great - est and for least. Praise Christ, the Pas - chal Vic - tim, Christ the Priest.
3. And claim the prom - ise of sal - va - tion here. Christ rules our hearts, and all his saints de - fends; He gives be - liev - ers life that nev - er ends.
4. His liv - ing wa - ter fills the thirst - ing soul. Be - fore your pres - ence, Lord, all peo - ple bow. In this your feast of love be with us now.

D.C.

Text: *Sancti, venite, corpus sumite*, 7th C., tr. John Mason Neale, 1818-1866, alt.; refrain, James J. Chepponis, b.1956, © 2000, GIA Publications, Inc.
Tune: James J. Chepponis, b.1956, © 2000, GIA Publications, Inc.

# One Bread, One Body  932

**Refrain**

One bread, one bod-y, one Lord of all,
one cup of bless - ing which we bless. And
we, though man - y, through-out the earth,
we are one bod - y in this one Lord.

**Verses**

1. Gen - tile or Jew, ser - vant or free,
2. Man - y the gifts, man - y the works,
3. Grain for the fields, scat-tered and grown,

D.C.

wom - an or man no more.
one in the Lord of all.
gath - ered to one for all.

Text: 1 Corinthians 10:16; 17, 12:4, Galatians 3:28; the *Didache* 9; John Foley, SJ, b.1939
Tune: John Foley, SJ, b.1939
© 1978, John B. Foley, SJ, and OCP

# 933 With This Bread

**Refrain**

With this bread we will walk with each oth - er,
with this cup we will fol-low the Lord. Com - pas - sion,
love o - ver - flow-ing, God's love ev - er know-ing, we
share it in our song.

**Verses 1, 2**

1. To of - fer as - sis - tance when oth - ers are blind to the need,
2. Wash-ing the wounds of di - vi - sion, we seek to ease pain.

to give lov - ing care to each oth -
Shar - ing the bur - den of oth -

er is plant - ing God's seed.
ers, like God's gen - tle rain.
Be -

Walk - ing the prom - ise and fall - ing on mer - cy, be -
friend-ing the one who is lone - ly and lost, be -

D.C.

liev - ing we'll walk with you.
liev - ing we'll walk with you.

Verse 3

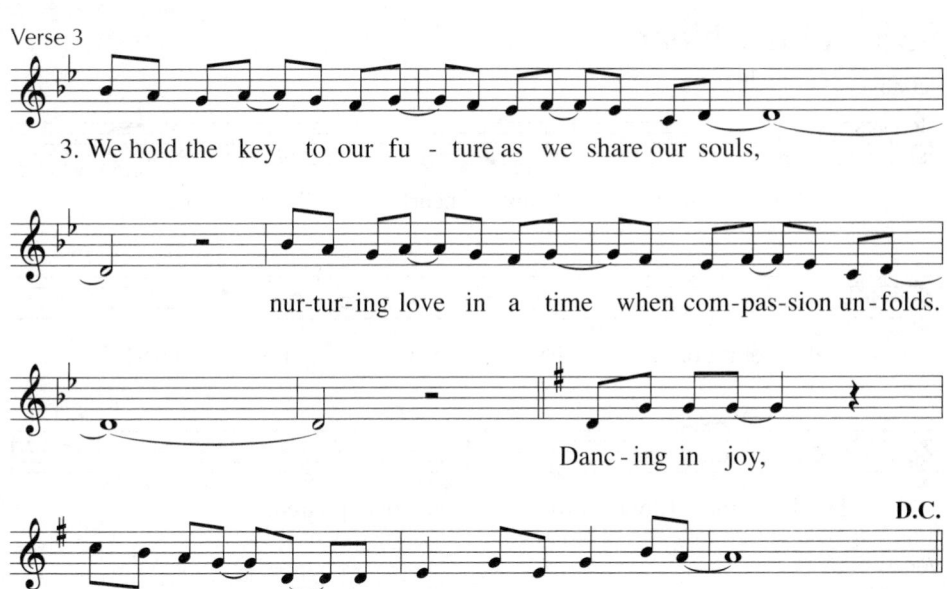

3. We hold the key to our fu - ture as we share our souls,

nur-tur-ing love in a time when com-pas-sion un-folds.

Danc-ing in joy,

D.C.

shar-ing in won - der the prayer that we sing to you.

Text: Kate Cuddy, b.1953
Tune: Kate Cuddy, b.1953
© 2001, GIA Publications, Inc.

## Jesus Is Here Right Now 934

Refrain

Je - sus is here right now. Je - sus is

here; With this bread and wine his peace you'll

find, Christ Je - sus is here right now.

Verses

1. Do not let your hearts be troubled.
   Have faith in God and have faith in me.
   In my Father's house there are many mansions;
   otherwise, why would I have told you so?

2. I am indeed going to prepare a place for you,
   and then I shall come back to take you with me;
   that where I am you also may be.
   For you know the way that leads to where I go.

Text: Leon C. Roberts, 1950–1999; verses, John 14:1–4
Tune: Leon C. Roberts, 1950–1999
© 1986, GIA Publications, Inc.

# 935  Draw Near

**Refrain**

Draw near, draw near! Take the Bod-y
of your Lord. Draw near, draw near!
Drink the Blood for you out-poured.

**Verses**

1. Draw near and take the Bod-y of the Lord,
2. Christ, our Re-deem - er, God's e-ter - nal Son,
3. Let us ap-proach with faith-ful hearts sin - cere
4. With heav'n-ly bread Christ makes the hun-gry whole;

 and drink with faith the Blood for you out-poured.
 has by his cross and blood the vic - t'ry won.
 and claim the prom-ise of sal - va - tion here.
 his liv-ing wa-ter fills the thirst - ing soul.

Saved by Christ's Bod - y and his ho - ly Blood, with
He spent his life for great-est and for least. Praise
Christ rules our hearts, and all his saints de-fends; he
Al - pha - O - me - ga, un - to whom shall bow all

**D.C.**

souls re-freshed we give our thanks to God.
Christ, the Pas - chal Vic - tim, Christ the Priest.
gives be-liev - ers life that nev - er ends.
na - tions of the earth, be with us now.

Text: *Sancti, venite, Christi corpus sumite*, 7th C.; tr. by John M. Neale, 1818–1866, alt.
Tune: Steven R. Janco, b.1961, © 1992, World Library Publications

# Gather in Your Name 936

Refrain

When two or more gath-er in your name, and see your
pres-ence in each face, we treas-ure the gift of this
sa-cred meal, blessed and poured out for all in this place.

Verses

Cantor:

1. Bread, the gift of your bod - y.
2. Bread, our light and our life.
3. Bread, your man - na from heav - en.
4. Bread, your mys - t'ry be - fore us.
5. Bread, the path for our jour - ney.
6. Bread, the food for our long - ing.
7. Bread for those who seek jus - tice.

Wine, your life blood out poured.
Wine, our truth and our way.
Wine, the fruit of your heart.
Wine, the hope of our dreams.
Wine, of wis - dom and grace.
Wine, the sweet taste of love.
Wine for the hum - ble of heart.

All:

Come, join the feast! Take and be - lieve! Be -

D.C.

come what you re - ceive!

Text: Lori True, b.1961
Tune: Lori True, b.1961
© 2003, GIA Publications, Inc.

# 937 Now in This Banquet

Refrain

Now in this ban-quet, Christ is our bread;
*Advent:* God of our jour-neys, day-break to night;
*Lent:* Lord, you can o-pen hearts that are stone;

Here shall all hun-gers be fed.
Lead us to jus-tice and light.
Live in our flesh and our bone;

Bread that is bro-ken, wine that is poured,
Grant us com-pas-sion, strength for the day,
Lead us to won-der, mys-t'ry and grace,

Love is the sign of our Lord.
Wis-dom to walk in your way.
One in your lov-ing em-brace.

Verses 1, 2

1. You who have touched us and graced us with love,
2. Let our hearts burn with the fire of your love;

D.C.

make us your peo-ple of good-ness and light.
o-pen our eyes to the glo-ry of God.

Verse 3

3. God who makes the blind to see, God who makes the

*May be sung in canon.*

**D.C.**

lame to walk, bring us danc - ing in - to day,

lead your peo - ple in your way.

Verse 4

4. Hope for the hope - less, light for the blind,

"Strong" is your name, Lord, "Gen - tle" and "Kind."

Verse 5

5. Call us to be your light, call us to be your love,

make us your peo - ple a - gain.

Verse 6

6. Come, O Spir - it! re - new our hearts!

We shall a - rise to be chil - dren of light.

Text: Marty Haugen, b.1950
Tune: Marty Haugen, b.1950
© 1986, GIA Publications, Inc.

# 938  We Come to Your Feast

**Verses**

*Cantor or choir:*

1. We place up-on your ta-ble    a gleam-ing cloth of
2. We place up-on your ta-ble    a hum-ble loaf of
3. We place up-on your ta-ble    a sim-ple cup of
4. We gath-er 'round your ta-ble,  we pause with-in our

white:    the weav-ing of our    sto - ries,
bread:    the gift of field and   hill - side,
wine:     the fruit of hu-man     la - bor,
quest,    we stand be-side our    neigh-bors,

the fab-ric of    our lives;    the dreams of those be-
the grain by which we're fed;    we come to taste the
the gift of sun   and vine;     we come to taste the
we name the stran-ger "guest."  The feast is spread be-

fore us,    the an-cient hope-ful    cries,
pres-ence  of him on whom we      feed,
pres-ence  of him we claim as     Lord,
fore us;   you bid us come and    dine:

the prom-ise of our   fu-ture:   our need-ing and our
to strength-en and con-nect us,  to chal-lenge and cor-
his dy-ing and his    liv-ing,   his lead-ing and his
in bless-ing we'll un-cov-er,    in shar-ing we'll dis-

nur-ture   lie here be-fore our    eyes.
rect us,   to love in word and     deed.
giv-ing,   his love in cup out-    poured.
cov-er     your sub-stance and your sign.

Refrain

We come to your feast, we come to your feast: the young and the old, the fright-ened, the bold, the great-est and the least. We come to your feast, we come to your feast with the fruit of our lands and the work of our hands, we come to your feast.

Text: Michael Joncas, b.1951
Tune: Michael Joncas, b.1951
© 1994, GIA Publications, Inc.

# 939 Behold the Lamb

Verses

1. Those who were in the dark are thank-ful for the
2. Peace-ful now, those whose hearts are blessed with un - der -
3. Gen - tle one, Child of God, join with us at this
4. Lord of all, give us light. De - liv - er us from

sun - light; We who live, we who die are
stand-ing Of the wheat, of the wine u -
ta - ble. Bless our lives; nour-ish all who
e - vil. Make us one; be our shield. Make

grate - ful for this gift, thank-ful for God's love.
nit - ed with God's word and the love we share.
hung - er for this feast; shel-ter them with peace.
still the winds that blow; cra - dle us with love.

Refrain

Be - hold, be - hold the Lamb of God. All who eat,

all who drink shall live; and all, all who dwell in

God, shall come to know God's glo-ry!

Text: Martin Willett, b.1960, alt.
Tune: Martin Willett, b.1960; acc. by Craig S. Kingsbury, b.1952
© 1984, OCP

# You Satisfy the Hungry Heart  940

**Refrain**

You sat - is - fy the hun - gry heart  With

gift  of fin - est wheat;  Come  give to us,  O

sav - ing Lord,  The bread  of life to  eat.

**Verses**

1. As when the shep - herd calls his sheep,  They
2. With joy - ful lips we sing to you  Our
3. Is not the cup we bless and share  The
4. The mys - t'ry of your pres - ence, Lord,  No
5. You give your - self to us, O Lord;  Then

know and heed his voice; So when you call your
praise and grat - i - tude, That you should count us
blood of Christ out - poured? Do not one cup, one
mor - tal tongue can tell: Whom all the world can -
self - less let us be, To serve each oth - er

**D.C.**

fam - 'ly, Lord, We fol - low and re - joice.
wor - thy, Lord, To share this heav'n - ly food.
loaf, de - clare Our one - ness in the Lord?
not con - tain Comes in our hearts to dwell.
in your name In truth and char - i - ty.

Text: Omer Westendorf, 1916–1998
Tune: BICENTENNIAL, CM with refrain; Robert E. Kreutz, 1922–1996
© 1977, Archdiocese of Philadelphia. Published by International Liturgy Publications

# 941 Eat This Bread

Refrain

Eat this bread, drink this cup,
*Co-man de_es-te pan, be-ban de_es-te cá-liz,*

come to him and nev-er be hun-gry.
*ven-gan, y no ten-drán ham-bre.*

Eat this bread, drink this cup,
*Co-man de_es-te pan, be-ban de_es-te cá-liz,*

trust in him and you will not thirst.
*cre-an, y no ten-drán sed.*

Text: John 6; adapt. by Robert J. Batastini, b.1942, and the Taizé Community
Tune: Jacques Berthier, 1923–1994
© 1984, 2005, Les Presses de Taizé, GIA Publications, Inc., agent

# Come and Eat This Living Bread   942

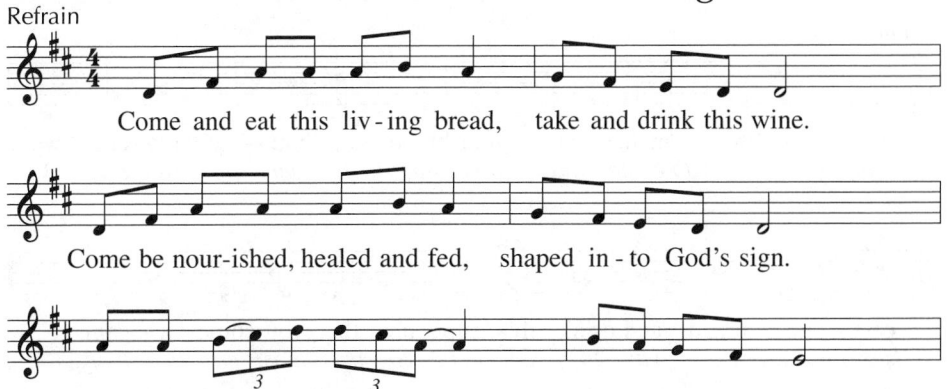

**Refrain**

Come and eat this liv-ing bread,   take and drink this wine.

Come be nour-ished, healed and fed,   shaped in-to God's sign.

Gath-ered 'round as fam-i-ly,   man-y are made one.

Form-ing love's com-mu-ni-ty,   one we now be-come.

**Verses**

1. Saint and sinner welcome in to this meal of harmony.
   Lonely people, next of kin journey toward the glory tree.
   Gathered strangers, scattered sheep, at this table all are fed.
   Blood and body bonds run deep as your kingdom feast is spread.

2. May we see the Christ revealed in the breaking of the bread.
   Living stories, holy meals, we become what we are fed.
   Broken shattered, fragile life, now received by you and me.
   Eating, drinking, joy and strife, Gospel living sets us free.

3. See the Christ in saddened sighs, blood poured out in every land.
   Wounded people, wailing cries lie upon our outstretched hands.
   Jesus is the way through death; truth beyond the present rage.
   Life unfolding, healing breath now enfleshed in youth and age.

4. Bless us, Lord, and these your gifts, fruit of vine and human hands.
   With our hearts and minds we lift all the goodness of these lands.
   Praise and thanks we shout and sing, from your bounty we are blessed.
   Joyfully all gifts we bring to receive our Lord and guest.

5. Death and life in water meet, drenching us in floods of light.
   Marking us with oil so sweet, clothing us in glorious white.
   Priest and prophet, spirit led, we are God's new living sign.
   Feeding on this holy bread, drinking of this holy wine.

6. Witnessing to love and peace, hands of blessing we remain.
   Helping fear and hate to cease, we bring forth God's wondrous reign.
   Strength and power here we find, given in this kingdom feast.
   We go forth to heal and sign everyone, both great and least.

Text: Rob Glover, b.1950
Tune: ADORO TE DEVOTE, 12 12 12 12; verses and arr. Rob Glover, b.1950
© 1997, GIA Publications, Inc.

# 943 Bread of Life from Heaven / Pan de Vida Eterna

**Refrain**

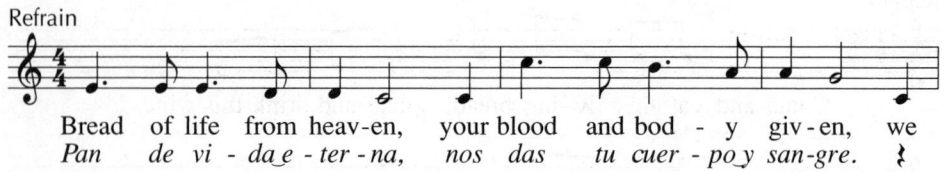

Bread of life from heav-en, your blood and bod - y giv-en, we
*Pan de vi - da_e - ter - na, nos das tu cuer - po_y san-gre.*

eat this bread and drink this cup un - til you come a - gain.
*Has - ta que vuel - vas tú, Se - ñor, co - me - mos en tu_a -mor.*

**Verses**

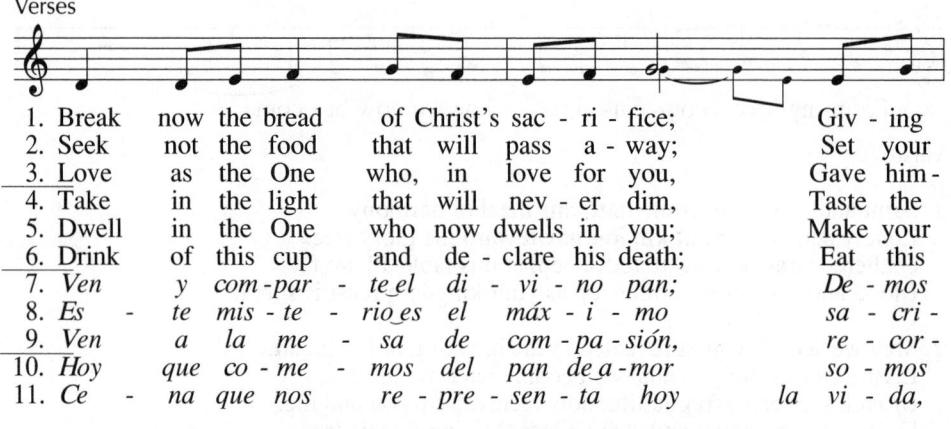

1. Break now the bread of Christ's sac - ri - fice; Giv - ing
2. Seek not the food that will pass a - way; Set your
3. Love as the One who, in love for you, Gave him -
4. Take in the light that will nev - er dim, Taste the
5. Dwell in the One who now dwells in you; Make your
6. Drink of this cup and de - clare his death; Eat this
7. *Ven y com -par - te_el di - vi - no pan; De - mos*
8. *Es - te mis - te - rio_es el máx - i - mo sa - cri -*
9. *Ven a la me - sa de com - pa - sión, re - cor -*
10. *Hoy que co - me - mos del pan de_a -mor so - mos*
11. *Ce - na que nos re - pre - sen - ta hoy la vi - da,*

thanks, hun - gry ones, gath - er round. Eat, all of you, and be
hearts on the food that en - dures. Come, learn the true and the
self for the life of the world. Come to the One who is
life that is strong - er than death. Live in the One who will
home in the life - giv - ing Word. Know on - ly Christ, Ho - ly
bread and be - lieve Eas - ter morn; Trust his re - turn and, with
*gra - cias con gran cor - a - zón. Cris - to_es sus - ten - to que*
*fi - cio de fe y de_a -mor. Pan que nos lla - ma_a con-*
*de - mos a Cris - to Je - sús. Él nos da vi - da con*
*u - no en Cris - to Je - sús. Ce - na que_es fuen - te de_in-*
*muer - te, y re - su -rrec - ción De Je - su - cris - to, que_es*

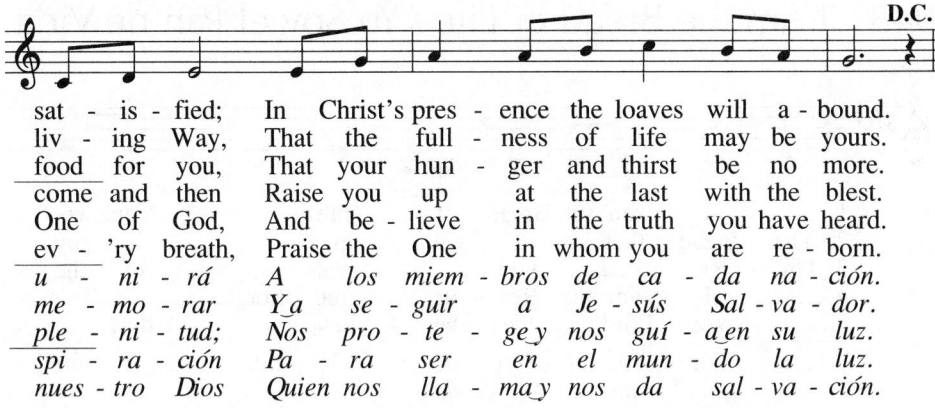

D.C.

| sat - is - fied; | In Christ's pres - ence the loaves will a - bound. |
| liv - ing Way, | That the full - ness of life may be yours. |
| food for you, | That your hun - ger and thirst be no more. |
| come and then | Raise you up at the last with the blest. |
| One of God, | And be - lieve in the truth you have heard. |
| ev - 'ry breath, | Praise the One in whom you are re - born. |
| u - ni - rá | A los miem - bros de ca - da na - ción. |
| me - mo - rar | Ya se - guir a Je - sús Sal - va - dor. |
| ple - ni - tud; | Nos pro - te - ge y nos guí - a en su luz. |
| spi - ra - ción | Pa - ra ser en el mun - do la luz. |
| nues - tro Dios | Quien nos lla - ma y nos da sal - va - ción. |

Text: Based on John 6; adapt. by Susan R. Briehl, b.1952; Spanish by Jaime Cortez, b.1963
Tune: ARGENTINE SANTO, 9 9 9 9 with refrain; Argentine melody; adapt. and verses by Marty Haugen, b.1950
© 2001, GIA Publications, Inc.

## In Remembrance of You 944

**Verses**

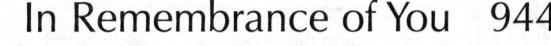

1. Je - sus, hope for all, teach us to be - lieve.
2. Je - sus, Son of God, you are liv - ing Word.
3. Je - sus, Lamb of God, bear - er of our sin,

Reach us, hope for all, in wa - ter, wine, and wheat.
Teach us, Son of God, to share what we have heard.
Free us, Lamb of God; come heal us from with - in.

**Refrain**

Gath - ered at ta - ble, gath - ered in love, food for the jour - ney

sent from a - bove. Strength - en and feed us in all that we do,

gath - ered at ta - ble in re - mem - brance of you.

Text: Paul A. Tate, b.1968
Tune: Paul A. Tate, b.1968
© 1997, World Library Publications

# 945 I Am the Bread of Life / Yo Soy el Pan de Vida

Verses

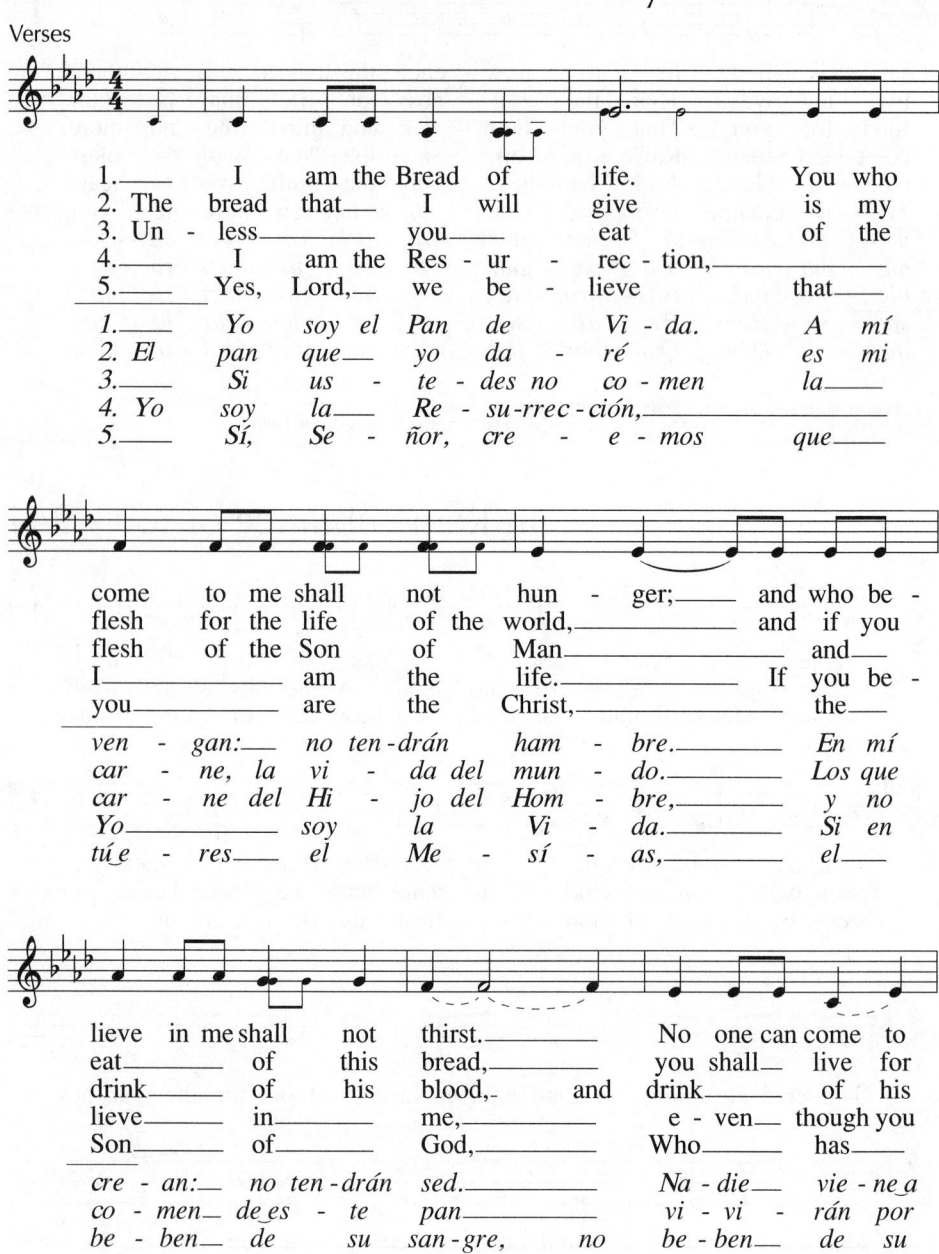

1.____ I am the Bread of life. You who
2. The bread that____ I will give is my
3. Un - less____ you____ eat of the
4.____ I am the Res - ur - rec - tion,____
5.____ Yes, Lord,— we be - lieve that____

1.____ Yo soy el Pan de Vi - da. A mí
2. El pan que____ yo da - ré es mi
3.____ Si us - te - des no co - men la____
4. Yo soy la____ Re - su-rrec - ción,
5.____ Sí, Se - ñor, cre - e - mos que____

come to me shall not hun - ger;____ and who be -
flesh for the life of the world,____ and if you
flesh of the Son of Man____ and____
I____ am the life.____ If you be -
you____ are the Christ,____ the____

ven - gan:__ no ten-drán ham - bre.____ En mí
car - ne, la vi - da del mun - do.____ Los que
car - ne del Hi - jo del Hom - bre,____ y no
Yo____ soy la Vi - da.____ Si en
tú_e - res____ el Me - sí - as,____ el____

lieve in me shall not thirst.____ No one can come to
eat____ of this bread,____ you shall__ live for
drink____ of his blood,- and drink____ of his
lieve____ in____ me,____ e - ven__ though you
Son____ of____ God,____ Who____ has__

cre - an:__ no ten-drán sed.____ Na - die__ vie - ne_a
co - men__ de_es - te pan____ vi - vi - rán por
be - ben__ de su san-gre, no be - ben__ de su
mí us - te - des cre - en,____ aun-que__ ha - yan
Hi - jo de Dios,— que has ve - ni - do_al

me un - less the Fa - ther beck - ons.
ev - er,_____ you shall live for ev - er.
blood, you shall not have life with - in you.
die,_____ you shall live for ev - er.
come in - to_____ the_____ world._____
*mí si mi Pa - dre no lo_a - tra - e.*
*siem - pre,_____ vi - vi - rán por siem - pre.*
*san - gre, no po -drán te - ner mi vi - da.*
*muer - to,_____ vi - vi - rán por siem - pre.*
*mun - do_____ pa - ra re - di - mir - nos.*

Refrain

And I will raise you up, and I will
*Yo los re - su - ci - ta - ré, Yo los re -*

raise you up, and I will raise you
*su - ci - ta - ré, Yo los re - su - ci - ta -*

up on the last day.
*ré en el dí - a fi - nal.*

Text: John 6 and 11; Suzanne Toolan, RSM, b.1927; tr. by anon., rev. by Ronald F. Krisman, b.1946
Tune: BREAD OF LIFE, Irregular with refrain; Suzanne Toolan, RSM, b.1927
© 1966, 1970, 1986, 1993, 2005, GIA Publications, Inc.

# 946 Let Us Be Bread

Refrain

Let us be bread, blessed by the Lord, bro-ken and shared, life for the world. Let us be wine, love free-ly poured. Let us be one in the Lord.

Verse 1

1. I am the bread of life, bro-ken for all. Eat now and hun-ger no more.

D.C.

Verse 2

2. You are my friends if you keep my com-mands, no long - er ser-vants but friends.

D.C.

Verse 3

3. See how my peo - ple have noth - ing to eat. Give them the bread that is you.

D.C.

Verse 4

4. As God has loved me so I have loved you.

**D.C.**

Go and live on in my love.

Text: Thomas J. Porter, b.1958
Tune: Thomas J. Porter, b.1958
© 1990, GIA Publications, Inc.

# Bread of Life, Cup of Blessing  947

Refrain

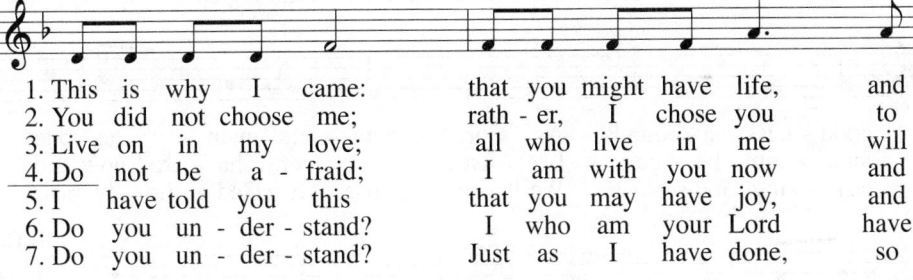

Bread of life, cup of bless-ing, gift of Christ the Lord!

Be the Bod - y you re - ceive now, bro - ken for the world.

Verses

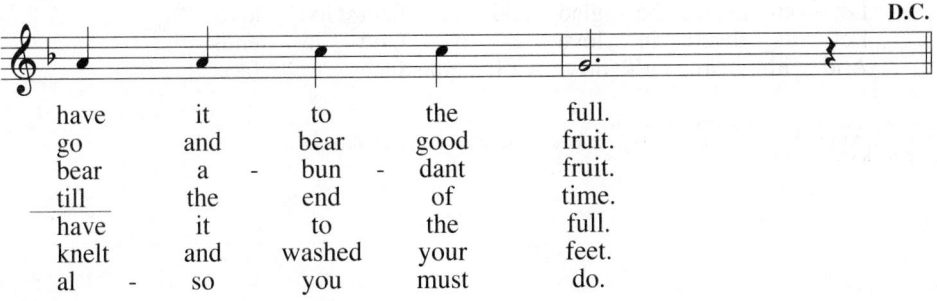

| 1. This | is | why | I | came: | that | you | might | have | life, | and |
| 2. You | did | not | choose | me; | rath - er, | | I | chose | you | to |
| 3. Live | on | in | my | love; | all | who | live | in | me | will |
| 4. Do | not | be | a - fraid; | | I | am | with | you | now | and |
| 5. I | have | told | you | this | that | you | may | have | joy, | and |
| 6. Do | you | un - der - stand? | | | I | who | am | your | Lord | have |
| 7. Do | you | un - der - stand? | | | Just | as | I | have | done, | so |

**D.C.**

| have | it | to | the | full. |
| go | and | bear | good | fruit. |
| bear | a - bun - dant | | | fruit. |
| till | the | end | of | time. |
| have | it | to | the | full. |
| knelt | and | washed | your | feet. |
| al - so | | you | must | do. |

Text: Delores Dufner, OSB, b.1939
Tune: Michel Guimont, b.1950
© 2008, GIA Publications, Inc.

# 948  At the Table of Jesus

**Refrain**

At the ta - ble of Je-sus we are nour - ished and fed  By the

bless - ing  cup  and  heav-en's liv - ing bread.  At the

ta - ble of Je - sus earth and heav - en are wed.  To a

hun - gry  world,  by our  God  we are led.

**Verses**

1. Where love and char - i - ty are found There God is  a - mong us; God's
2. Now,  as  we gath-er all as one, Di - vi - sion is end - ed, com-
3. Joined with the an - gels and the saints, Be - hold-ing God's glo - ry  and

good - ness  a - bounds.  As Christ  gath - ers man - y  as one,
mun - ion  be - gun.  Let  fear,  an - ger,  ha - tred now end.
tast - ing God's grace,  We'll sing  praise  in  God's ho - ly place,

**D.C.**

Let  our  hearts  be  glad  and  re - flect God's love.
Let  us  dwell  in  love  as  our  God  in - tends.
And with heav - en's hosts we'll come face  to  face.

Text: Based on *Ubi Caritas*; Tony E. Alonso, b.1980
Tune: SIMPLE GIFTS, Irregular with refrain; Joseph Brackett, Jr., 1797–1882; arr. by Marty Haugen, b.1950
© 2010, GIA Publications, Inc.

# Alleluia! Sing to Jesus! 949

1. Al - le - lu - ia! Sing to Je - sus! His the
2. Al - le - lu - ia! Not as or - phans Are we
3. Al - le - lu - ia! Bread of an - gels, Here on
4. Al - le - lu - ia! King e - ter - nal, You the

scep - ter, his the throne. Al - le - lu - ia! His the
left in sor - row now; Al - le - lu - ia! He is
earth our food, our stay! Al - le - lu - ia! Here the
Lord of lords we own; Al - le - lu - ia! Born of

tri - umph, His the vic - to - ry a - lone.
near us; Faith be - lieves, nor ques - tions how.
sin - ful Flee to you from day to day.
Mar - y, Earth your foot - stool, heav'n your throne.

Hark! The songs of peace - ful Zi - on Thun - der
Though the cloud from sight re - ceived him When the
In - ter - ces - sor, friend of sin - ners, Earth's re -
You with - in the veil have en - tered, Robed in

like a might - y flood: "Je - sus out of ev - 'ry
for - ty days were o'er, Shall our hearts for - get his
deem - er, plead for me, Where the songs of all the
flesh, our great high priest; Here on earth both priest and

na - tion Has re - deemed us by his blood."
prom - ise: "I am with you ev - er - more"?
sin - less Sweep a - cross the crys - tal sea.
vic - tim In the eu - cha - ris - tic feast.

Text: Revelation 5:9; William C. Dix, 1837–1898
Tune: HYFRYDOL, 8 7 8 7 D; Rowland H. Prichard, 1811–1887

# 950 Take and Eat

**Refrain**

Take and eat; take and eat: this is my bod - y giv-en up for you. Take and drink; take and drink: this is my blood giv - en up for you.

**Verses**

1. I am the Word that spoke and light was made;
2. I am the way that leads the ex - ile home;
3. I am the Lamb that takes a - way your sin;
4. I am the cor - ner - stone that God has laid;
5. I am the light that came in - to the world;
6. I am the first and last, the Liv - ing One;

I am the seed that died to be re - born;
I am the truth that sets the cap - tive free;
I am the gate that guards you night and day;
A cho - sen stone and pre - cious in his eyes;
I am the light that dark - ness can - not hide;
I am the Lord who died that you might live;

I am the bread that comes from heav'n a - bove;
I am the life that rais - es up the dead;
You are my flock: you know the shep-herd's voice;
You are God's dwell - ing place, on me you rest;
I am the morn - ing star that nev - er sets;
I am the bride-groom, this my wed - ding song;

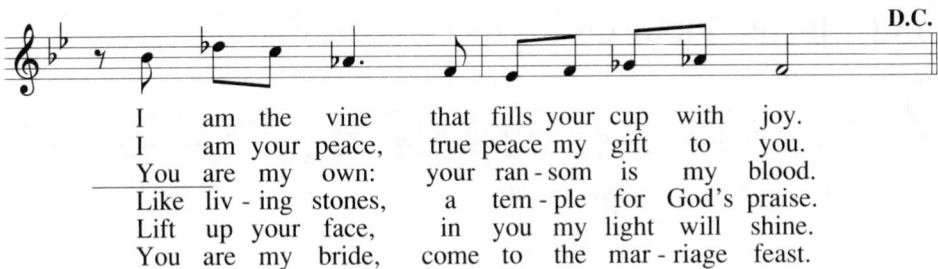

**D.C.**

I am the vine that fills your cup with joy.
I am your peace, true peace my gift to you.
You are my own: your ran-som is my blood.
Like liv-ing stones, a tem-ple for God's praise.
Lift up your face, in you my light will shine.
You are my bride, come to the mar-riage feast.

Text: Verse text, James Quinn, SJ, 1919–2010, © 1989. Used by permission of Selah Publishing Co., Inc.; refrain text, Michael Joncas, b.1951,
© 1989, GIA Publications, Inc.
Tune: Michael Joncas, b.1951, © 1989 GIA Publications, Inc.

## This Is the Body of Christ 951

This is the Bod-y of Christ, bro-ken that we may be

whole; this cup, as prom-ised by God, true to his word,

cra-dles our Lord: food for the good of the soul.

Text: John L. Bell, b.1949
Tune: John L. Bell, b.1949
© 1998, Iona Community, GIA Publications, Inc., agent

# 952  Jesus, Heal Us

Verse 4

4. All who trust the Lord: God will up - hold you. Let us cling to our God; let us fall in the arms of the Lord!

Text: David Haas, b.1957
Tune: David Haas, b.1957
© 1988, GIA Publications, Inc.

# He Healed the Darkness of My Mind 953

1. He healed the dark - ness of my mind The day he gave my sight to me. It was not sin that made me blind; It was no sin - ner made me see.
2. Let oth - ers call my faith a lie Or try to stir up doubt in me. Look at me now! None can de - ny I once was blind, and now I see!
3. Ask me not how! But I know who Has o - pened up new worlds to me. This Je - sus does what none can do; I once was blind, and now I see!

Text: John 9; Fred Pratt Green, 1903–2000, © 1982, Hope Publishing Company
Tune: ARLINGTON, LM; David Haas, b.1957, © 1988, GIA Publications, Inc.

*Alternate tune:* O WALY WALY

# 954 Hands of Healing

**Refrain***

1. Let our hands be hands of heal-ing, let our words be clear and true,
2.
3. In our work, God's love re-veal-ing, just and gen-tle in all we do.

**Verses**

*Cantor:*

1. Safe - ly lead the young ones:
2. Free the ones in bond - age:
3. Touch the ones who sor - row: hands of heal - ing,
4. Com - fort for the dy - ing:
5. May we al - ways be your

*Cantor:*

bring your joy and laugh - ter:
bring the reign of new hope:
hope be - yond all griev - ing: clear and true;
vi - sion of a new life:
make us in your im - age:

*Cantor:*

sing the God of chil - dren:
sing the God of free - dom:
sing the God of mer - cy: love re - veal - ing,
sing the res - ur - rec - tion:
give us voice to praise you:

**D.C.**

just and gen - tle in all we do.

*May be sung in canon.*

Text: Marty Haugen, b.1950
Tune: Marty Haugen, b.1950
© 1999, GIA Publications, Inc.

# Precious Lord, Take My Hand 955

1. Pre - cious Lord, take my hand, Lead me on, let me
2. When my way grows drear, Pre - cious Lord, lin - ger
3. When the dark - ness ap - pears And the night draws

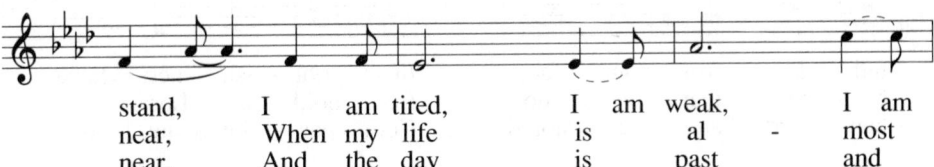

stand, I am tired, I am weak, I am
near, When my life is al - most
near, And the day is past and

worn. Through the storm, through the
gone, Hear my cry, hear my
gone, At the riv - er I

night, Lead me on to the light. Take my
call, Hold my hand lest I fall. Take my
stand, Guide my feet, hold my hand. Take my

hand, pre - cious Lord, lead me home.
hand, pre - cious Lord, lead me home.
hand, pre - cious Lord, lead me home.

Text: Thomas A. Dorsey, 1899–1993
Tune: PRECIOUS LORD, 66 9 D; George N. Allen, 1812–1877; adapt. by Thomas A. Dorsey, 1899–1993; arr. by Kelly Dobbs-Mickus, b.1966
© 1938, (renewed), arr. © 2011, Warner-Tamerlane Publishing Corp.

# 956 Our Father, We Have Wandered

1. Our Fa - ther, we have wan - dered And
2. And now at length dis - cern - ing The
3. O Lord of all the liv - ing, Both

hid - den from your face; In fool - ish - ness have
e - vil that we do, Be - hold us, Lord, re -
ban - ished and re - stored, Com - pas - sion - ate, for -

squan - dered Your leg - a - cy of grace. But
turn - ing With hope and trust to you. In
giv - ing, And ev - er - car - ing Lord, Grant

now, in ex - ile dwell - ing, We
haste you come to meet us And
now that our trans - gress - ing, Our

rise with fear and shame, As, dis - tant but com -
home re - joic - ing bring, In glad - ness there to
faith - less - ness may cease. Stretch out your hand in

pell - ing, We hear you call our name.
greet us With calf and robe and ring.
bless - ing, In par - don, and in peace.

Text: Kevin Nichols, 1929–2006, © 1980, ICEL
Tune: PASSION CHORALE, 7 6 7 6 D; Hans Leo Hassler, 1564–1612; harm. by J. S. Bach, 1685–1750

# If I Have Been the Source of Pain / 957
## Si Fui Motivo de Dolor

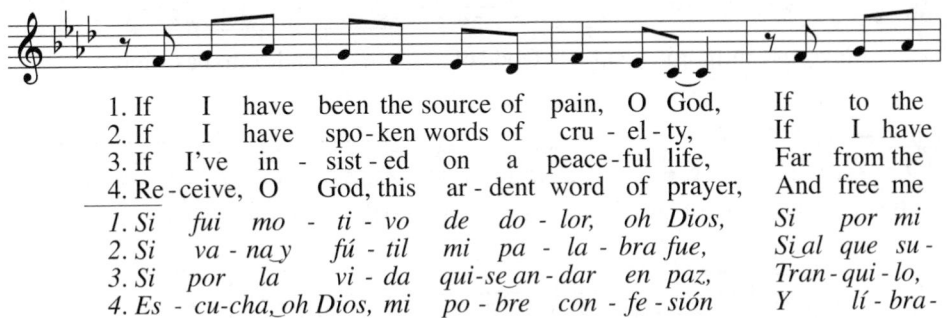

1. If I have been the source of pain, O God, If to the
2. If I have spo-ken words of cru - el - ty, If I have
3. If I've in - sist - ed on a peace-ful life, Far from the
4. Re-ceive, O God, this ar - dent word of prayer, And free me

1. Si fui mo - ti - vo de do - lor, oh Dios, Si por mi
2. Si va - na_y fú - til mi pa - la - bra fue, Si_al que su -
3. Si por la vi - da qui-se_an - dar en paz, Tran - qui - lo,
4. Es - cu-cha,_oh Dios, mi po - bre con - fe - sión Y lí - bra-

weak I have re - fused my strength, If, in re -
left some suf - f'ring un - re - lieved, Con - demn not
strug - gles that the gos - pel brings, When you pre -
from temp - ta - tion's sub - tle snare; With ten - der

cau - sa_el dé - bil tro - pe - zó, Si_en tus ca -
frí - a_en su do - lor de - jé, No me con -
li - bre_y sin lu - char por ti, Cuan - do_an - he -
me de ten - ta - ción su - til; Pre - ser - va

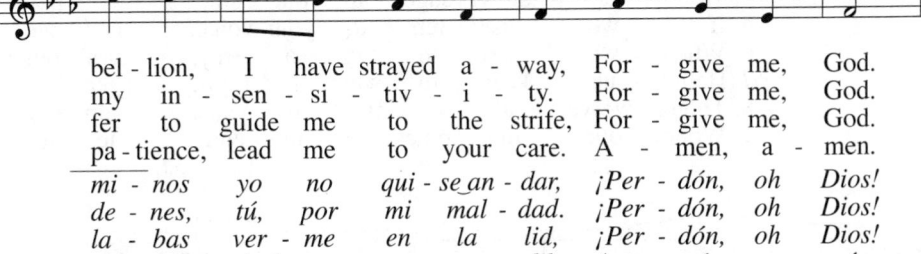

bel - lion, I have strayed a - way, For - give me, God.
my in - sen - si - tiv - i - ty. For - give me, God.
fer to guide me to the strife, For - give me, God.
pa - tience, lead me to your care. A - men, a - men.

mi - nos yo no qui - se_an - dar, ¡Per - dón, oh Dios!
de - nes, tú, por mi mal - dad. ¡Per - dón, oh Dios!
la - bas ver - me en la lid, ¡Per - dón, oh Dios!
siem-pre mi_al-ma_en tu re - dil. A - mén, a - mén.

Text: Sara Menéndez de Hall, alt., based on a text by C. Maude Battersby; tr. by Janet W. May, © 1992, The Pilgrim Press
Tune: CAMACUÁ, 10 10 10 4; Pablo D. Sosa, b.1933, © 1988, GIA Publications, Inc.

# 958 Make Us Turn to You

**Refrain**

Make us turn to you, God of love and com-pas-sion.

Bring us home to you to be with you for ev - er.

Make us turn to you, God of love and com-pas-sion.

Bring us home to you to be with you for ev - er.

**Verses**

1. We have turned a - way from you; we have
2. As we try to find the way, when we
3. In the things we've failed to do, and the
4. We ac - knowl-edge all our sin, a new
5. If we lis - ten to your voice, then we
6. When we start to go a - stray, turn our
7. Help us keep to what is right, keep us
8. Though we've al - ways tried in vain, help us
9. When our life comes to its end, Je - sus

failed in what we do; we are ask - ing for for -
have no words to say, as we seek the path of
wrongs that we've been through, our in - ad - e - qua - cies
life we must be - gin; now the time has come to
have no oth - er choice than to fol - low in your
dark - ness in - to day; shine a light-beam deep in -
walk - ing in your sight, give us sure and strong en -
try just once a - gain; with your strength and re - as -
Sav - ior, be our friend; take us gent - ly by the

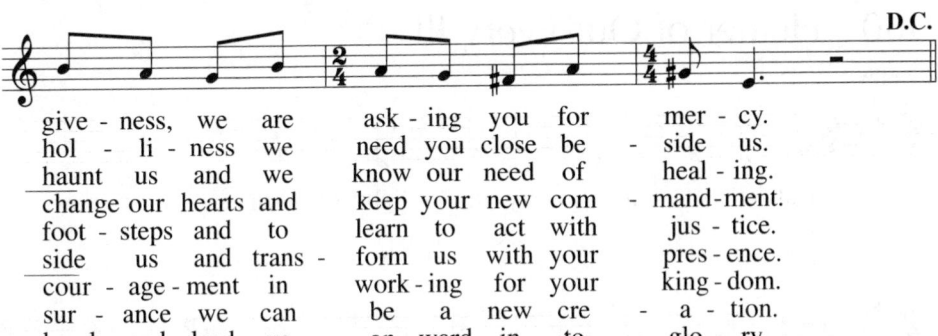

**D.C.**

| give - ness, | we | are | ask - ing | you | for | mer - cy. |
| hol - li - ness | we | | need you | close | be | - side us. |
| haunt | us | and | we | know our | need of | heal - ing. |
| change our | hearts | and | keep your | new | com | - mand-ment. |
| foot - steps | and | to | learn to | act | with | jus - tice. |
| side | us | and trans - | form us | with | your | pres - ence. |
| cour - age - ment | in | | work - ing | for | your | king - dom. |
| sur - ance | we | can | be | a | new cre | - a - tion. |
| hand | and | lead | us | on - ward | in - to | glo - ry. |

Text: Paul Inwood, b.1947
Tune: Paul Inwood, b.1947
© 2005, GIA Publications, Inc.

## God Is Forgiveness  959

**Ostinato Refrain**

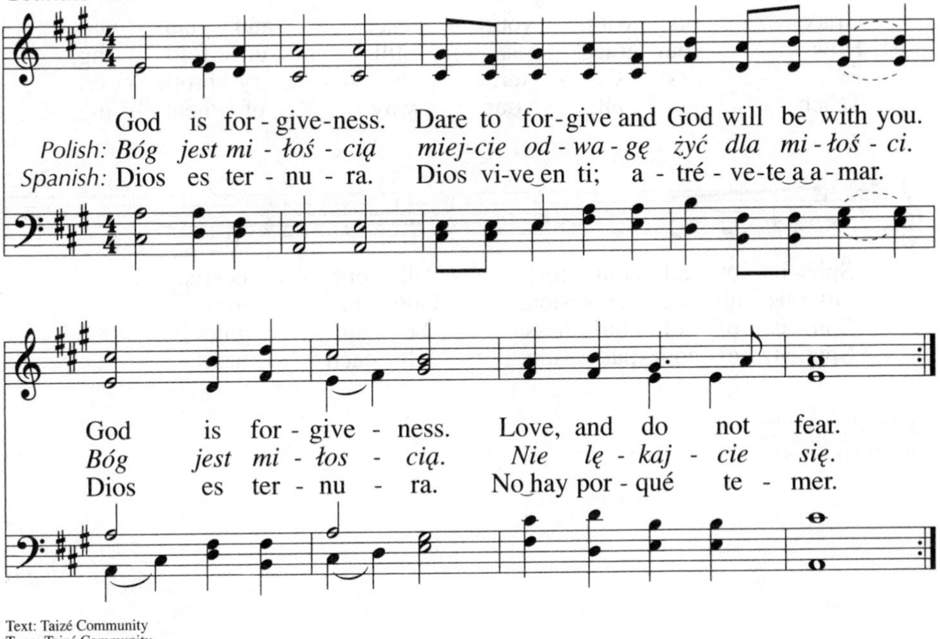

God     is for - give-ness.     Dare to  for-give and God will  be  with you.
*Polish:* Bóg  jest mi - łoś - cią     miej-cie od - wa - gę  żyć dla  mi - łoś - ci.
*Spanish:* Dios  es ter - nu - ra.     Dios vi - ve en ti;  a - tré - ve-te a a - mar.

God     is for - give - ness.     Love,  and  do    not   fear.
*Bóg     jest mi - łos - cią.     Nie  lę - kaj - cie   się.*
Dios     es ter - nu - ra.     No hay por - qué  te - mer.

Text: Taizé Community
Tune: Taizé Community
© 2007, 2011, Les Presses de Taizé, GIA Publications, Inc., agent

# 960　Healer of Our Every Ill

Refrain

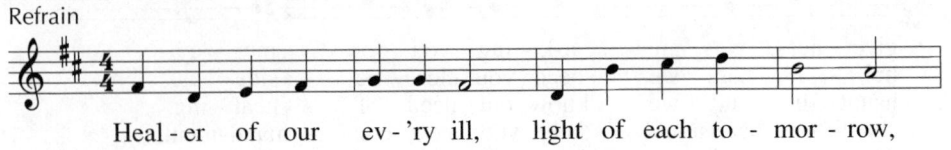

Heal-er of our ev-'ry ill, light of each to-mor-row,

give us peace be-yond our fear and hope be-yond our sor - row.

Verses

1. You who know our fears and sad - ness,
2. In the pain and joy, be - hold - ing
3. Give us strength to love each oth - er,
4. You who know each thought and feel - ing,

Grace us with your peace and glad - ness.
How your grace is still un - fold - ing,
Ev - 'ry sis - ter, ev - 'ry broth - er.
Teach us all your way of heal - ing.

D.C.

Spir - it of all com - fort, fill our hearts.
Give us all your vi - sion, God of love.
Spir - it of all kind - ness, be our guide.
Spir - it of com - pas - sion, fill each heart.

Text: Marty Haugen, b.1950
Tune: Marty Haugen, b.1950
© 1987, GIA Publications, Inc.

# Remember Your Love 961

**Refrain**

Re - mem - ber your love and your faith - ful - ness, O Lord. Re - mem - ber your peo - ple and have mer - cy on us, Lord.

**Verses**

1. The Lord is my light and my sal - va - tion,
2. If you dwelt, O Lord, up - on our sin - ful - ness,
3. O Lord, hear the sound of my call
4. As watch - man who waits up - on the day - light,
5. Be - fore all the moun - tains were be - got - ten

whom should I fear? The Lord is my
then who could stand? But with you there is
and an - swer me. My heart cries
wait for the Lord. I trust in your
and earth took shape, e - ven then, O

**D.C.**

life and my ref - uge, when I call God hears.
mer - cy and for - give - ness and a guid - ing hand.
out for your pres - ence; it is you I seek.
kind - ness and re - demp - tion; and your faith - ful word.
Lord, you were our ref - uge through - out ev - 'ry age.

Text: Psalm 27; Mike Balhoff, b.1946
Tune: Darryl Ducote, b.1945, and Gary Daigle, b.1957
© 1978, Damean Music. Distributed by GIA Publications, Inc.

## 962 Ashes

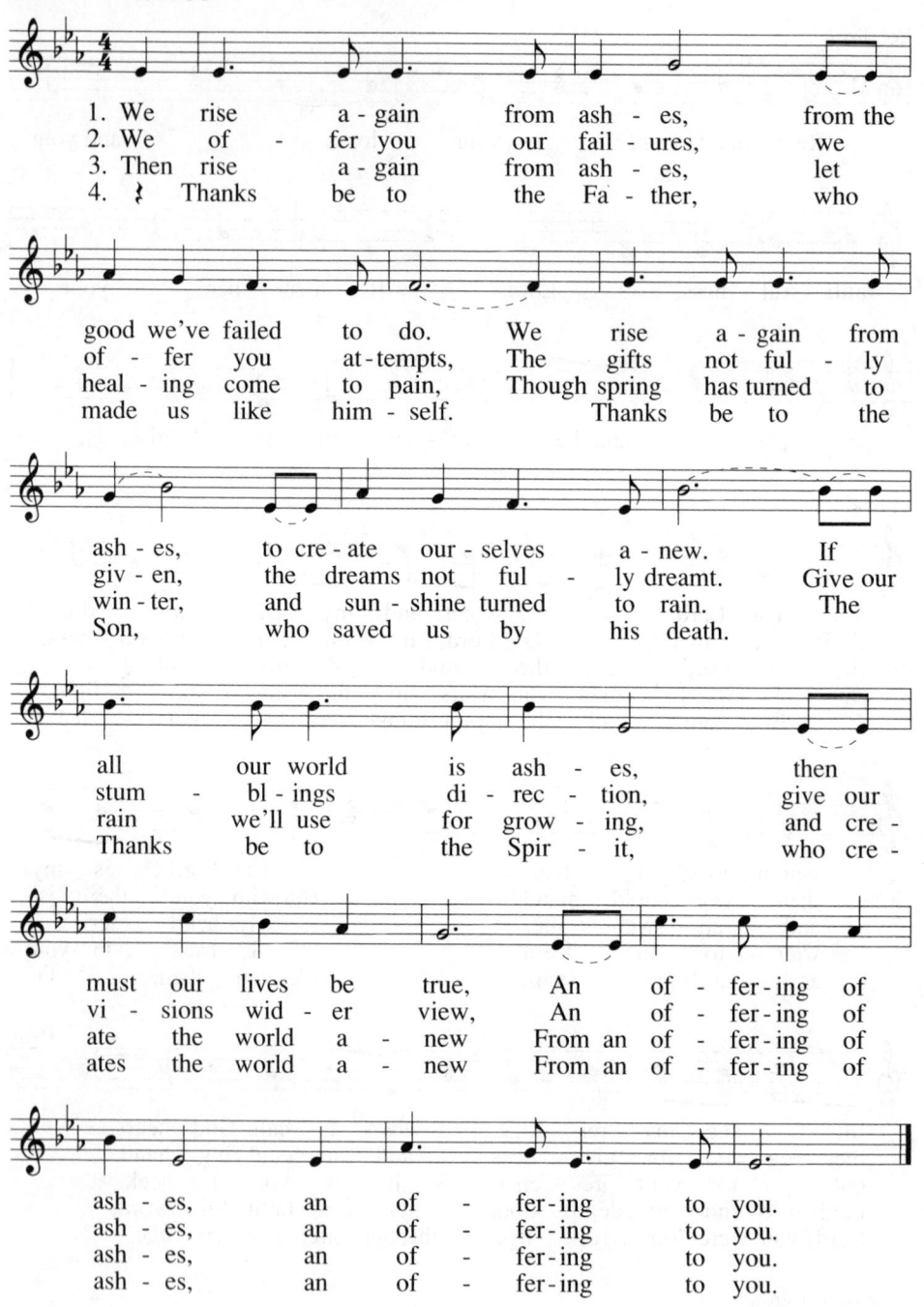

1. We rise a-gain from ash - es, from the
2. We of - fer you our fail - ures, we
3. Then rise a-gain from ash - es, let
4. ⁂ Thanks be to the Fa - ther, who

good we've failed to do. We rise a - gain from
of - fer you at-tempts, The gifts not ful - ly
heal - ing come to pain, Though spring has turned to
made us like him - self. Thanks be to the

ash - es, to cre-ate our-selves a - new. If
giv - en, the dreams not ful - ly dreamt. Give our
win - ter, and sun - shine turned to rain. The
Son, who saved us by his death.

all our world is ash - es, then
stum - bl - ings di - rec - tion, give our
rain we'll use for grow - ing, and cre -
Thanks be to the Spir - it, who cre -

must our lives be true, An of - fer-ing of
vi - sions wid - er view, An of - fer-ing of
ate the world a - new From an of - fer-ing of
ates the world a - new From an of - fer-ing of

ash - es, an of - fer-ing to you.
ash - es, an of - fer-ing to you.
ash - es, an of - fer-ing to you.
ash - es, an of - fer-ing to you.

Text: Tom Conry, b.1951
Tune: Tom Conry, b.1951; acc. by Michael Joncas, b.1951
© 1978, OCP

# Softly and Tenderly Jesus Is Calling   963

1. Soft - ly and ten - der - ly   Je - sus is call - ing,
2. Why should we tar - ry when   Je - sus is plead - ing,
3. Time is now fleet - ing, the   mo - ments are pass - ing,
4. O for the won - der - ful   love He has prom - ised,

Call - ing for you and for me;   See, on the
Plead - ing for you and for me?   Why should we
Pass - ing from you and from me;   Shad - ows are
Prom - ised for you and for me;   Though we have

por - tals He's wait - ing and watch - ing,
lin - ger and heed not His mer - cies,
gath - er - ing, death - beds are com - ing,
sinned He has mer - cy and par - don,

Watch - ing for you and for me.
Mer - cies for you and for me?
Com - ing for you and for me.
Par - don for you and for me.

Come home, come home, Ye who are wea - ry, come

home; Ear - nest-ly, ten - der - ly,

Je - sus is call - ing— Call-ing, "O sin-ner, come home!"

Text: Will L. Thompson, 1847-1909
Tune: Will L. Thompson, 1847-1909

## 964 The Master Came to Bring Good News

1. The Mas - ter came to bring good news, The
2. The Law's ful - filled through Je - sus Christ, The
3. To seek the sin - ners Je - sus came, To
4. For - give us, Lord, as we for - give And

news of love and free - dom, To heal the sick and
man who lived for oth - ers. The law of Christ is:
live a - mong the friend - less, To show them love that
seek to help each oth - er. For - give us, Lord, and

seek the poor, To build the peace - ful king - dom.
Serve in love Our sis - ters and our broth - ers.
they might share The king - dom that is end - less.
we shall live To pray and work to - geth - er.

Fa - ther, for - give us! Through Je - sus hear us!

As we for - give one an - oth - er!

Text: Ralph Finn, b.1941, © 1965, GIA Publications, Inc.
Tune: ICH GLAUB AN GOTT, 8 7 8 7 with refrain; *Mainz Gesangbuch*, 1870; harm. by Richard Proulx, 1937–2010, © 1986, GIA Publications, Inc.

## 965 Forgive Our Sins

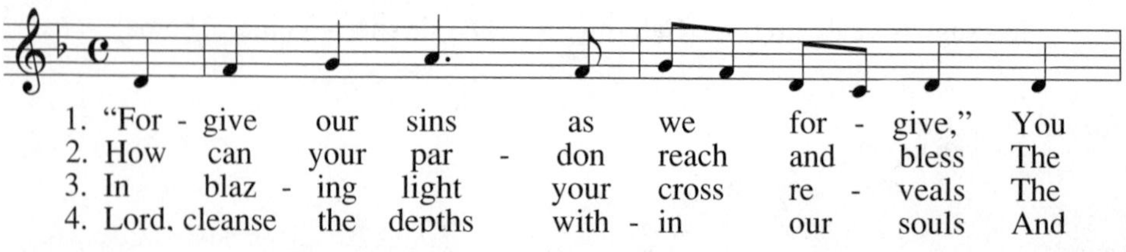

1. "For - give our sins as we for - give," You
2. How can your par - don reach and bless The
3. In blaz - ing light your cross re - veals The
4. Lord, cleanse the depths with - in our souls And

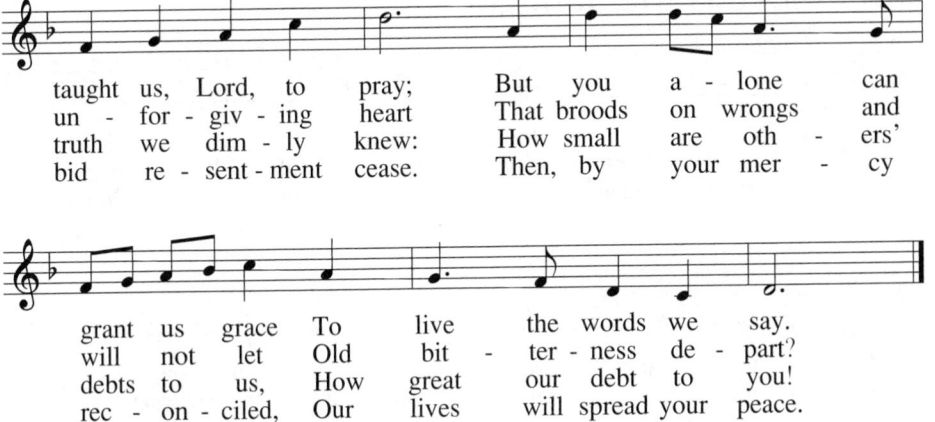

taught us, Lord, to pray; But you a - lone can
un - for - giv - ing heart That broods on wrongs and
truth we dim - ly knew: How small are oth - ers'
bid re - sent - ment cease. Then, by your mer - cy

grant us grace To live the words we say.
will not let Old bit - ter - ness de - part?
debts to us, How great our debt to you!
rec - on - ciled, Our lives will spread your peace.

Text: Rosamond E. Herklots, 1905–1987, alt., © Oxford University Press
Tune: DETROIT, CM; Supplement to *Kentucky Harmony*, 1820; harm. by Gerald H. Knight, 1908–1979, © The Royal School of Church Music

# When Love Is Found   966

1. When love is found and hope comes home, Sing and be
2. When love has flow'red in trust and care, Build both each
3. When love is tried as loved - ones change, Hold still to
4. When love is torn, and trust be - trayed, Pray strength to
5. Praise God for love, praise God for life, In age or

glad that two are one. When love ex - plodes and
day, that love may dare To reach be - yond home's
hope, though all seems strange, Till ease re - turns and
love till tor - ments fade, Till lov - ers keep no
youth, in calm or strife. Lift up your hearts! Let

fills the sky, Praise God, and share our Mak - er's joy.
warmth and light, To serve and strive for truth and right.
love grows wise Through lis - t'ning ears and o - pened eyes.
score of wrong But hear through pain love's Eas - ter song.
love be fed Through death and life in bro - ken bread.

Text: Brian Wren, b.1936, © 1983, Hope Publishing Co.
Tune: O WALY WALY, LM; English; harm. by Martin West, b.1929, © 1983, Hope Publishing Co.

# 967 Love Is the Sunlight

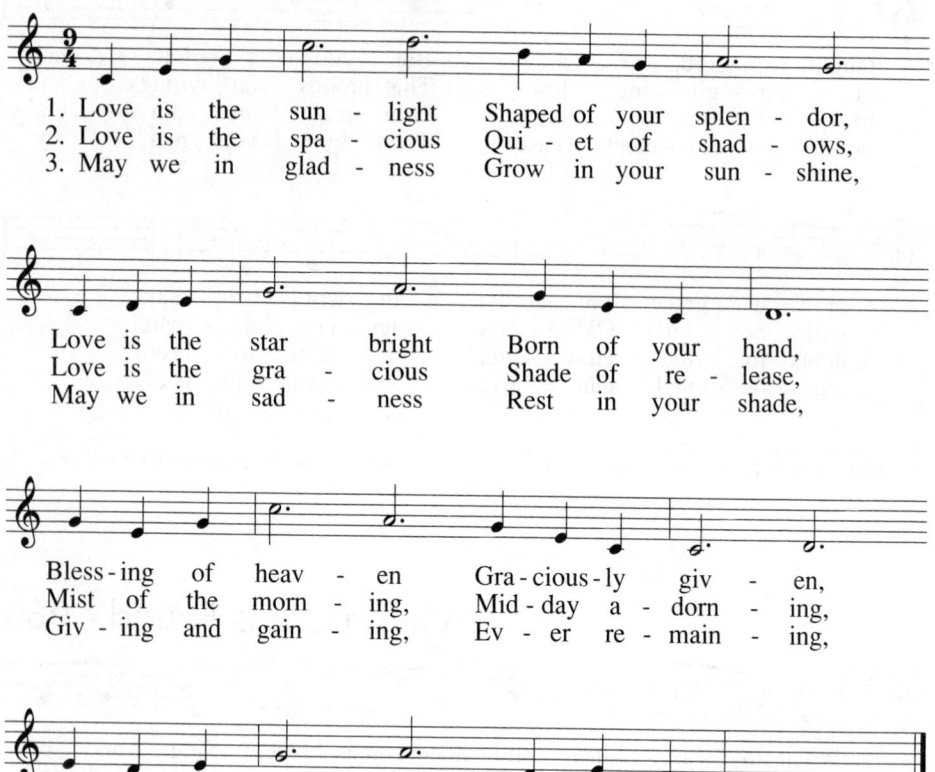

1. Love is the sun - light Shaped of your splen - dor,
2. Love is the spa - cious Qui - et of shad - ows,
3. May we in glad - ness Grow in your sun - shine,

Love is the star bright Born of your hand,
Love is the gra - cious Shade of re - lease,
May we in sad - ness Rest in your shade,

Bless - ing of heav - en Gra - cious - ly giv - en,
Mist of the morn - ing, Mid - day a - dorn - ing,
Giv - ing and gain - ing, Ev - er re - main - ing,

Ra - diant with glo - ry From your com - mand.
Cool with the twi - light Breath of your peace.
One in the mar - riage Your love has made.

Text: Borghild Jacobson, © 1981, Concordia Publishing House
Tune: BUNESSAN, 5 5 8 D; Gaelic melody; acc. by Marty Haugen, b.1950, © 1987, GIA Publications, Inc.

# Wherever You Go  968

Refrain

Wher - ev - er you go, I will go; wher - ev - er you

live, I'll be with you. Wher - ev - er you lie, I'll

be there be - side you. Wher - ev - er you go,

I'll be there.

Verses

1. Come, set me like a seal upon your heart; a seal protecting your arm.
   Deep waters cannot quench this love; the ocean will not sweep it away.

2. Arise my beloved, come to me; the rains are gone, the winter is past.
   The flowers appear, the vines are pruned, and the dove's song is heard in our land.

3. Wherever you stay, I will stay; your people will be my people.
   Wherever you die, so will I die with you in the arms of God!

Text: Ruth 1:16–17; Song of Songs 2:10–12, 7:6–7; David Haas, b.1957
Tune: David Haas, b.1957
© 1993, GIA Publications, Inc.

# 969 Love Has Brought Us Here Together

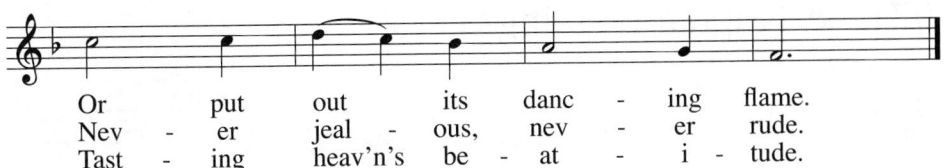

Or        put     out      its     danc  -  ing      flame.
Nev  -  er     jeal  -  ous,     nev  -  er      rude.
Tast  -  ing     heav'n's     be  -  at  -  i  -  tude.

Text: Mary Louise Bringle, b.1953, © 2010, GIA Publications, Inc.
Tune: HYFRYDOL, 8 7 8 7 D; Rowland H. Prichard, 1811–1887

## God, in the Planning   970

1. God,     in     the     plan - ning     and     pur - pose     of     life,
2. Je - sus     was     found,     at     a     sim - i - lar     feast,
3. There - fore     we     pray     that     his     spir - it     pre - side
4. Praise then     the     Mak - er,     the     Spir - it,     the     Son,

Hal - lowed     the     un - ion     of     hus - band     and     wife:
Tak - ing     the     roles     of     both     wait - er     and     priest,
O - ver     the     wed - ding     of     bride-groom and     bride,
Source of     the     love through which     two     are     made     one.

This     we     em - bod - y     where     love     is     dis - played,
Turn - ing     cre - at - ed     things     in - to     di - vine,
Help - ing     them share what     is     ten - der     and     true,
God's     is     the     glo - ry,     the     good - ness,     and     grace

Rings     are     pre - sent - ed     and     prom - is - es     made.
Tears     in - to     laugh - ter     and     wa - ter     to     wine.
Light - ing     with     love     all     they     dream of     and     do.
Seen     in     this     mar - riage     and     known in     this     place.

Text: John L. Bell, b.1949, © 1989, Iona Community, GIA Publications, Inc., agent
Tune: SLANE, 10 10 10 10; Irish traditional; harm. by Erik Routley, 1917–1982, © 1975, Hope Publishing Company

# 971 A Nuptial Blessing

Refrain

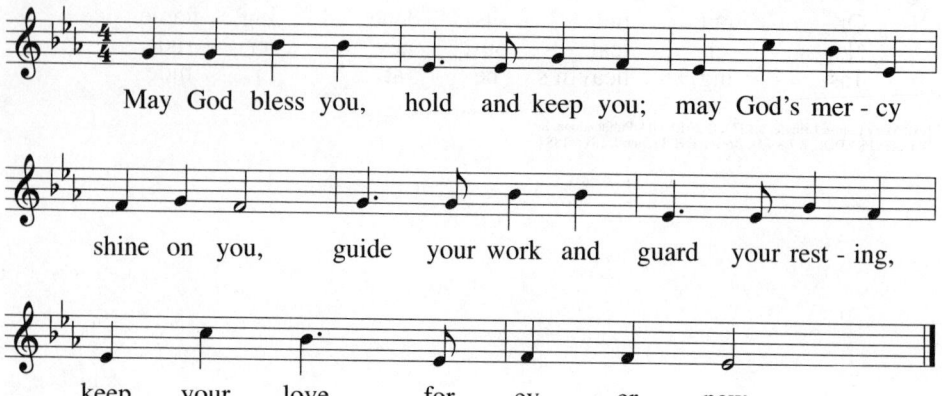

May God bless you, hold and keep you; may God's mer - cy

shine on you, guide your work and guard your rest - ing,

keep your love for ev - er new.

Verses

1. May God satisfy your longing, be refreshment at your table,
   and provide your daily bread,
   guard your going and your coming, be the solace in your silence:
   life within the lives you wed.

2. May God join your hopeful spirits, fill your hearts with truth and courage,
   trust to share both joy and tears,
   teach love to your children's children; may your household learn to witness
   living faith through all your years.

3. May God make your home a refuge where you warmly welcome strangers
   and the lowly find a place;
   make you caring, kind companions, help you meet the needs of neighbors,
   finding Christ in every face.

Text: Vicki Klima, b.1952; adapt. by Michael Joncas, b.1951, and George Szews, b.1951
Tune: Michael Joncas, b.1951
© 1989, GIA Publications, Inc.

# I Know That My Redeemer Lives    972

Refrain

I know that my re - deem - er lives: on the last day

I shall rise a - gain, and in my flesh I shall see

God. On the last day I shall rise a - gain!

Verses

*Cantor:*

1. I      shall   see    my   Sav - ior's face;   and my own
2. With - in my   heart  this  hope  I  hold;   that in my

*All:*

eyes    shall be - hold my  God.   On  the  last  day
flesh    I  shall see  my  God.   On  the  last  day

**D.C.**

I shall rise   a - gain!
I shall rise   a - gain!

Text: Job 19:25–27; David Haas, b.1957
Tune: David Haas, b.1957
© 1990, GIA Publications, Inc.

# 973   I Know That My Redeemer Lives

I know that my Re-deem-er lives, and on the

last day I shall rise a-gain; in my bod-y I shall

look on God, my Sav-ior, in my bod-y I shall look on God, my

Sav - ior. I my-self shall see him; my own eyes will

gaze on him, my own eyes will gaze on him; in my bod-y I shall

look on God, my Sav - ior, in my bod-y I shall look on God, my

Sav - ior. This is the hope I cher-ish, this is the hope I

cher - ish in my heart; in my bod - y I shall

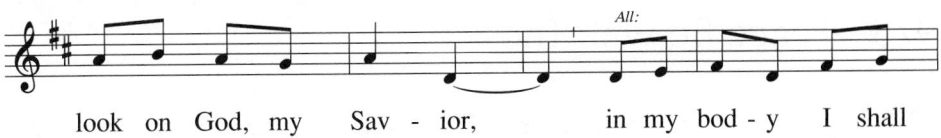

look on God, my Sav - ior, in my bod - y I shall

look on God, my Sav - ior.

Text: *Rite of Funerals*, © 1970, ICEL
Tune: *Music for Rite of Funerals and Rite of Baptism for Children*, Howard Hughes, SM, b.1930, © 1977, ICEL

## Song of Farewell 974

Refrain

Dy-ing you de-stroyed our death! Ris-ing you re - stored our life!

Lord Je - sus, Lord Je - sus, come in glo - ry!

Verses

1. May Christ who died for you lead you into his kingdom;
   may Christ who died for you lead you this day into paradise.

2. May Christ, the Good Shepherd, lead you home today
   and give you a place within his flock.

*Alternate children's verse:*
2. May Christ, the Good Shepherd, take you on his shoulders
   and bring you home, bring you home today.

3. May the angels lead you into paradise;
   may the martyrs come to welcome you
   and take you to the Holy City, the new and eternal Jerusalem.

4. May the choirs of angels come to meet you,
   may the choirs of angels come to meet you;
   where Lazarus is poor no longer, may you have eternal life in Christ.

*Alternate children's verse:*
4. May the choirs of angels come to meet you,
   may the choirs of angels come to meet you;
   and with all God's children may you have eternal life in Christ.

Text: Memorial Acclamation, © 1973, ICEL; *In paradisum;* Michael Marchal, b.1951, © 1988, GIA Publications, Inc.
Tune: Michael Joncas, b.1951, © 1988, GIA Publications, Inc.

# 975 Peace Be with Those

Refrain

Peace be with those who have gone to God. May they
be at peace, may they be with God. Peace be with
those who have gone to God. May they be at peace, may they

*To verses* | *Last time*

be with God. | Peace with God.

Verses

*Cantor or choir:*

1. May they be with the liv - ing God.
2. May they find their de - light in the Lord.
3. May they be where God's name is great.
4. May they find a for - giv - ing God.
5. May they dwell in the house of God.
6. May they know the peace of the Lord.

*All:*

Be at peace, be with God.

*Cantor or choir:*

May they see the im - mor - tal God.
May they rest se - cure in God.
May they live in e - ter - nal peace.
Now and on the judg - ment day.
May they live in e - ter - nal light.
May they rest for - ev - er in peace.

*All:*

D.C.

Be at peace, be with God.

Text: Based on text from the 1969 *Rite of Funerals*; Carol Browning, b.1956
Tune: Carol Browning, b.1956
© 2008, GIA Publications, Inc.

# Dwellers in the Holy City   976

1. Dwell - ers in the ho - ly cit - y,
2. Fam - 'ly born to God's own house - hold,
3. Sing - ers in the choir of heav - en,
4. Saints a - round the ban - quet gath - ered,

O - pen wide the gold - en door;
Bring our faith - ful friend with - in,
Let your prayer like in - cense rise;
Claim her/him now as next of kin;

May our friend from this world sum - moned
Free of suf - f'ring, pain and sor - row,
Let our friend, in song, now join you,
Lead her/him to the fam - 'ly ta - ble;

Know God's pres - ence ev - er - more.
Free of weak - ness, free of sin.
Prais - ing God in par - a - dise.
Let the feast of joy be - gin.

Saints and an - gels, make her/him wel - come,
May her/his pass - ing lead to glo - ry,
And may we, re - joic - ing, join you,
Friends at God's own ta - ble seat - ed,

Glad at home for ev - er - more.
Vic - t'ry o - ver death and sin.
Prais - ers all in par - a - dise.
Let the feast - ing now be - gin!

Text: Delores Dufner, OSB, b.1939, © 2010, GIA Publications, Inc.
Tune: ST. THOMAS, 8 7 8 7 8 7; John Wade, 1711–1786

*Alternate tune:* LAUDA ANIMA

# 977 In Paradísum / May Choirs of Angels

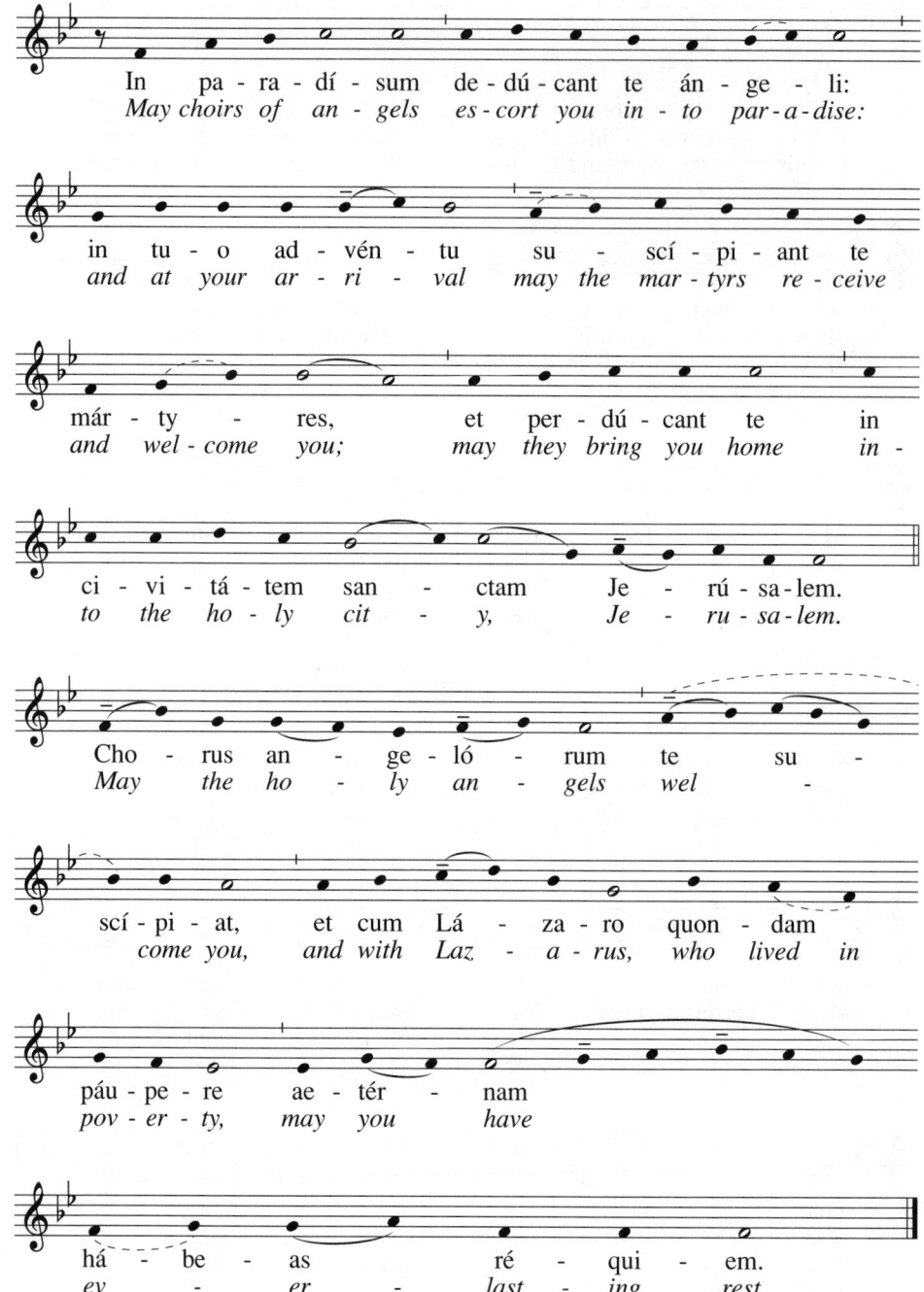

In pa - ra - dí - sum de - dú - cant te án - ge - li:
*May choirs of an - gels es - cort you in - to par - a - dise:*

in tu - o ad - vén - tu su - scí - pi - ant te
*and at your ar - ri - val may the mar - tyrs re - ceive*

már - ty - res, et per - dú - cant te in
*and wel - come you; may they bring you home in -*

ci - vi - tá - tem san - ctam Je - rú - sa - lem.
*to the ho - ly cit - y, Je - ru - sa - lem.*

Cho - rus an - ge - ló - rum te su -
*May the ho - ly an - gels wel -*

scí - pi - at, et cum Lá - za - ro quon - dam
*come you, and with Laz - a - rus, who lived in*

páu - pe - re ae - tér - nam
*pov - er - ty, may you have*

há - be - as ré - qui - em.
*ev - er - last - ing rest.*

Text: *In Paradísum* and *Chorus angelórum*, tr. © 1986, GIA Publications, Inc.
Tune: Mode VII; acc. by Richard Proulx, 1937–2010, © 1986, GIA Publications, Inc.

# May Holy Angels Lead You 978

May ho - ly an - gels lead you forth to par - a - dise,

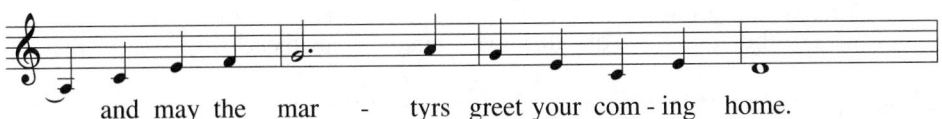

and may the mar - tyrs greet your com - ing home.

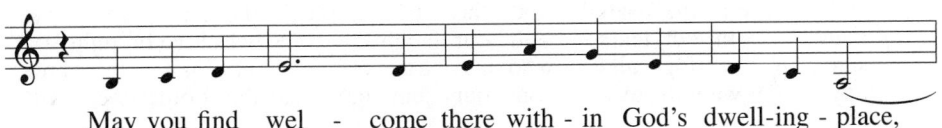

May you find wel - come there with - in God's dwell-ing - place,

the rad - iant cit - y, New Je - ru - sa - lem.

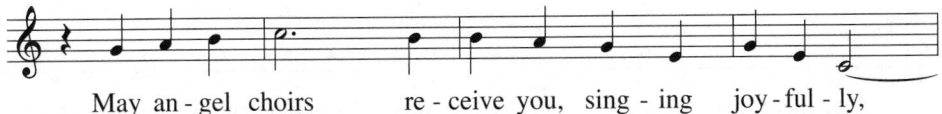

May an - gel choirs re - ceive you, sing - ing joy - ful - ly,

as you be - hold with La - za - rus, once poor,

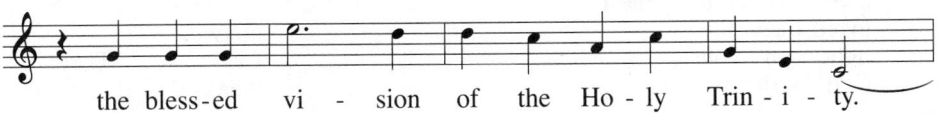

the bless-ed vi - sion of the Ho - ly Trin - i - ty.

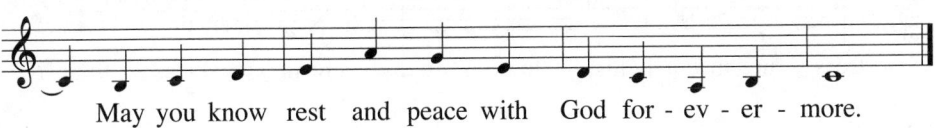

May you know rest and peace with God for - ev - er - more.

Text: *In Paradísum* and *Chorus angelórum*; Latin 11th C.; para. by Ronald F. Krisman, b.1946, © 2011, GIA Publications, Inc.
Tune: LONDONDERRY AIRE, 11 10 11 10 D; arr. by John L. Bell, b.1949, © 1996, Iona Community, GIA Publications, Inc., agent

# 979 There Is a Place

**Verses**

1. There's a time for re-mem-b'ring, a time to re-
2. There is gold that is gleam-ing, in a past we once
3. There's a prom-ise of God that is writ-ten in the
4. In the quiet of the eve-ning at the close of the

call, the trials and the tri-umphs, the fears and the
knew, in our tears and our laugh-ter 'twas love brought us
stars, for all who may trav-el, no mat-ter how
day, we will rest on our jour-ney to the Lord we will

falls. There's a time to be grate-ful for
through. There's a road we have trav-eled where
far. God will be your com-pan-ion each
pray. May we thank God for bless-ings, for the

mo-ments so blessed, the jewels of our mem-'ry where
sun-light has kissed, that car-ries us on-wards when
jour-ney you make, in the shad-ow of loved ones to
mo-ments we shared, as we seek for to-mor-row, our

**1.**

love is our guest.
loved ones are
light-en your
God will be

**2.-4.**

missed.
way. There is
there.

**Refrain**

treas-ure in our fields, there is treas-ure in our skies, there is

treas-ure in our dream-ing from the soul to the eye,

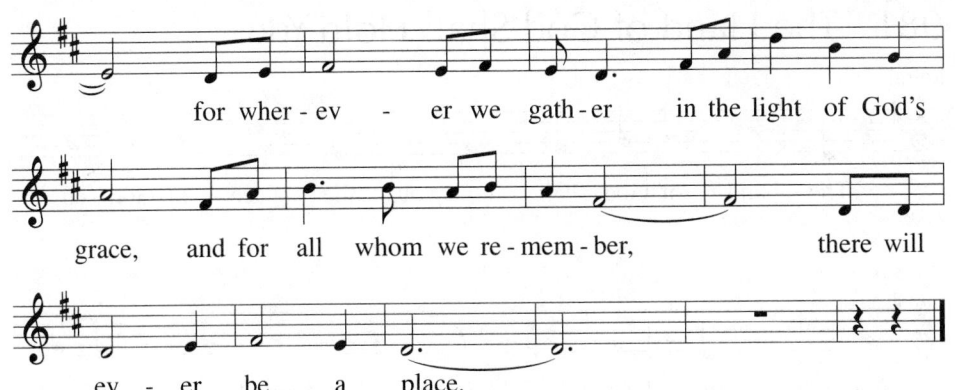

for wher - ev - er we gath - er in the light of God's

grace, and for all whom we re - mem - ber, there will

ev - er be a place.

Text: Liam Lawton, b.1959
Tune: Liam Lawton, b.1959; choral arr. by Gary Daigle, b.1957; acc. by Kelly Dobbs Mickus, b.1966
© 2002, GIA Publications, Inc.

## May the Angels Lead You into Paradise   980

*Cantor, then all:*

May the an - gels lead you in - to par - a - dise;

may the mar - tyrs come to wel - come you and

take you to the ho - ly cit - y, the

new and e - ter - nal Je - ru - sa - lem.

Text: *In paradísum; Rite of Funerals,* © 1970, ICEL
Tune: *Music for Rite of Funerals and Rite of Baptism for Children,* Howard Hughes, SM, b.1930, © 1977, ICEL

# 981 The Hand of God Shall Hold You

Refrain

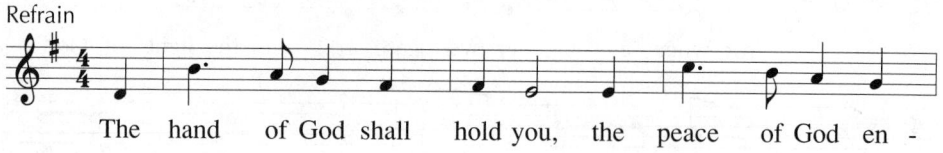

The hand of God shall hold you, the peace of God en -

fold you, the love that dreamed and formed you still sur -

rounds you here to-day; The light of God be - side you, a -

bove, be-neath, in - side you, the light that shines to

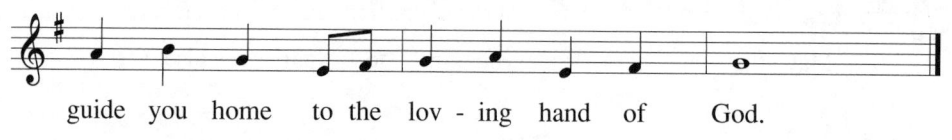

guide you home to the lov - ing hand of God.

Verses

1. May God's light shine ever upon you, may you rest in the arms of God;
   may you dwell for evermore in communion with all the blessed.

2. May the angels lead you into paradise; may the martyrs come to welcome you
   and take you to the holy city, the new and eternal Jerusalem.

Text: Marty Haugen, b.1950, © 1994, GIA Publications, Inc.; verse 2 from *In paradísum; Rite of Funerals,* © 1970, ICEL
Tune: Marty Haugen, b.1950, © 1994, GIA Publications, Inc.

# God of Adam, God of Joseph    982

Refrain

God of A - dam,    God of Jo - seph,

God of sow - ing,    soil and seed,    Thank you for    your

world of prom - ise:    Milk and hon - ey,    wine and bread.

Verses

1. God, you make    us    your    com - pan - ions,
2. May your pas - sion    for    cre - a - tion
3. Thank you for    all    men    en - trust - ed
4. Ab - ba (Fa - ther),    God    of    Jo - seph,

Shar - ers    of    your    lov - ing    cup;
Be    re - flect - ed    in    our    own;
With    the    charge    of    fa - ther - hood,
Hu - man    Christ    whose    name    we    bear,

Thank you for    the    gen - er - a - tions,
For    our role    in    birth    and    nur - ture
And    for those    who    have    no    chil - dren,
Spir - it, womb    of    life    and    wis - dom:

D.C.

Weave    of    names    and    threads    of    hope.
Make    through    us    your    pres - ence    known.
Yet    are    par - ents    un - der    God.
Thank    you,    God,    for    who    we    are!

# 983 God of Eve and God of Mary

**Refrain**

God of Eve and God of Mar - y,

God of love and moth - er earth, Thank you for the

ones who with us Shared their life and gave us birth.

**Verses**

1. As you came to earth in Je - sus,
2. Thank you, that the Church, our Moth - er,
3. Thank you for be - long - ing, shel - ter,
4. God of Eve and God of Mar - y,

So you come to us to - day;
Gives us bread and fills our cup,
Bonds of friend - ship, ties of blood,
Christ our broth - er, hu - man Son.

You are pres - ent in the car - ing
And the com - fort of the Spir - it
And for those who have no chil - dren,
Spir - it, car - ing like a moth - er,

**D.C.**

That pre - pares us for life's way.
Warms our hearts and lifts us up.
Yet are par - ents un - der God.
Take our love and make us one.

Text: Fred Kaan, 1929–2009, © 1989, Hope Publishing Company
Tune: FARRELL, 8 7 8 7 with refrain, Thomas J. Porter, b.1958, © 1994, GIA Publications, Inc.

# America the Beautiful  984

1. O beau - ti - ful for spa - cious skies, For
2. O beau - ti - ful for pil - grim feet, Whose
3. O beau - ti - ful for he - roes proved In
4. O beau - ti - ful for pa - triot dream That

am - ber waves of grain, For pur - ple moun - tain
stern, im - pas - sioned stress A thor - ough - fare for
lib - er - at - ing strife, Who more than self their
sees be - yond the years Thine al - a - bas - ter

maj - es - ties A - bove the fruit - ed plain! A -
free - dom beat A - cross the wil - der - ness! A -
coun - try loved, And mer - cy more than life! A -
cit - ies gleam, Un - dimmed by hu - man tears! A -

mer - i - ca! A - mer - i - ca! God
mer - i - ca! A - mer - i - ca! God
mer - i - ca! A - mer - i - ca! May
mer - i - ca! A - mer - i - ca! God

shed his grace on thee, And crown thy good with
mend thine ev - 'ry flaw, Con - firm thy soul in
God thy gold re - fine, Till all suc - cess be
shed his grace on thee, And crown thy good with

broth - er - hood From sea to shin - ing sea.
self - con - trol, Thy lib - er - ty in law.
no - ble - ness, And ev - 'ry gain di - vine.
broth - er - hood From sea to shin - ing sea.

Text: Katherine L. Bates, 1859–1929
Tune: MATERNA, CMD; Samuel A. Ward, 1848–1903

# 985  Mine Eyes Have Seen the Glory

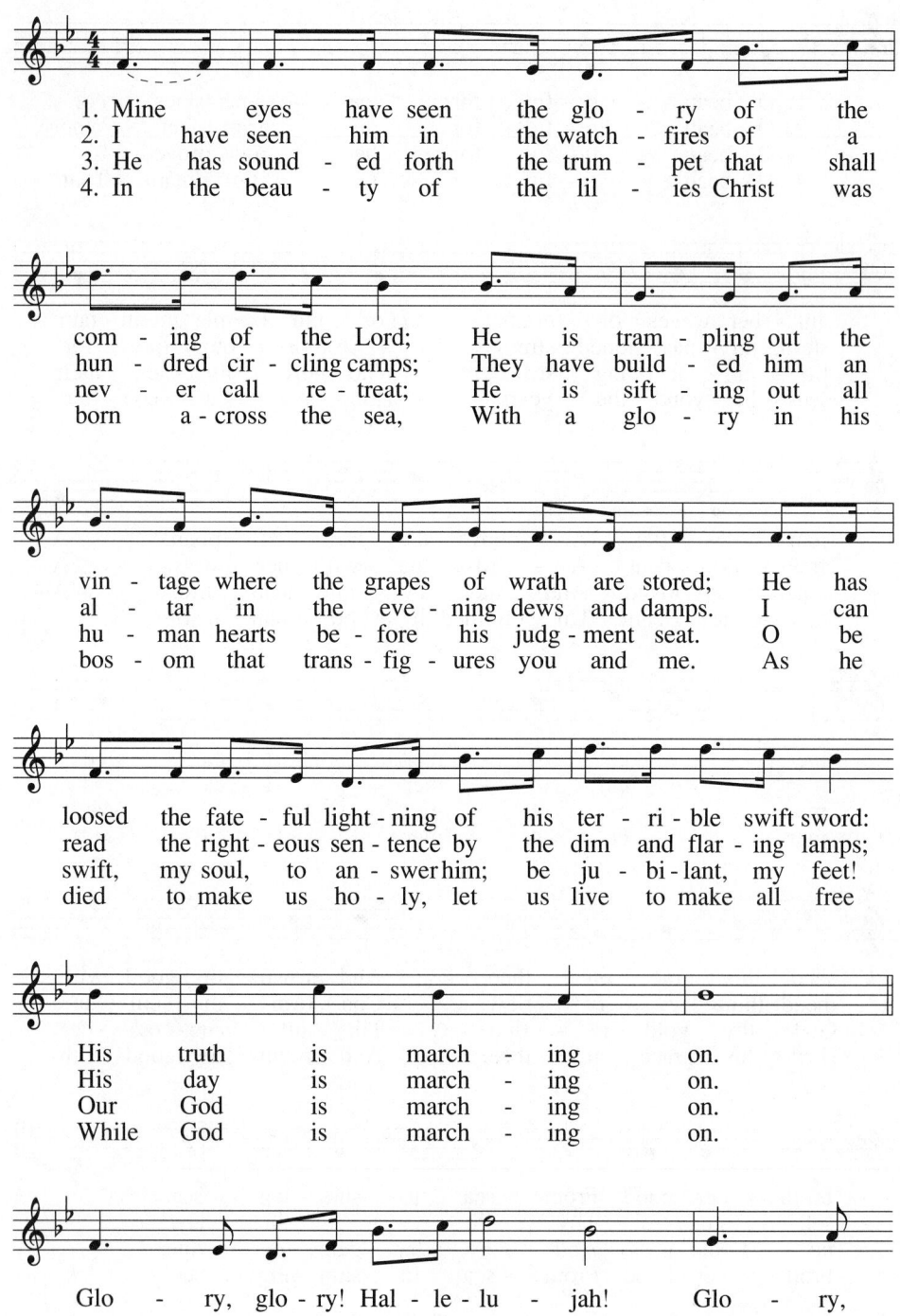

1. Mine eyes have seen the glo - ry of the
2. I have seen him in the watch - fires of a
3. He has sound - ed forth the trum - pet that shall
4. In the beau - ty of the lil - ies Christ was

com - ing of the Lord; He is tram - pling out the
hun - dred cir - cling camps; They have build - ed him an
nev - er call re - treat; He is sift - ing out all
born a - cross the sea, With a glo - ry in his

vin - tage where the grapes of wrath are stored; He has
al - tar in the eve - ning dews and damps. I can
hu - man hearts be - fore his judg - ment seat. O be
bos - om that trans - fig - ures you and me. As he

loosed the fate - ful light - ning of his ter - ri - ble swift sword:
read the right - eous sen - tence by the dim and flar - ing lamps;
swift, my soul, to an - swer him; be ju - bi - lant, my feet!
died to make us ho - ly, let us live to make all free

His truth is march - ing on.
His day is march - ing on.
Our God is march - ing on.
While God is march - ing on.

Glo - ry, glo - ry! Hal - le - lu - jah! Glo - ry,

glo - ry! Hal - le - lu - jah! Glo - ry, glo - ry! Hal - le -

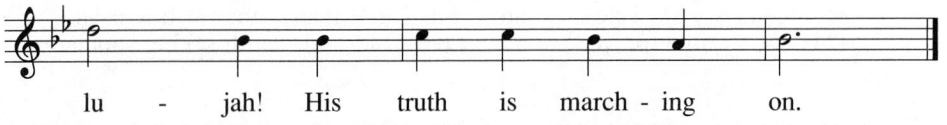

lu - jah! His truth is march - ing on.

Text: Julia W. Howe, 1819–1910, alt.
Tune: BATTLE HYMN OF THE REPUBLIC, 15 15 15 6 with refrain; attr. to William Steffe, d.1911

# 986   This Is My Song

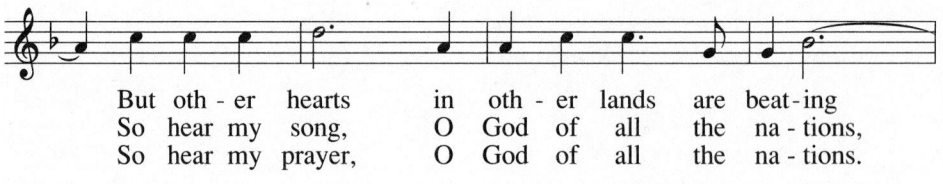

1. This is my song, O God of all the na - tions,
2. My coun - try's skies are blu - er than the o - cean,
3. This is my prayer, O Lord of all earth's king - doms:

A song of peace for lands a - far and mine.
And sun - light beams on clo - ver - leaf and pine.
Your king - dom come; on earth your will be done.

This is my home, the coun - try where my heart is;
But oth - er lands have sun - light too, and clo - ver,
Let Christ be lift - ed up till all shall serve him,

Here are my hopes, my dreams, my ho - ly shrine.
And skies are ev - 'ry - where as blue as mine.
And hearts u - nit - ed learn to live as one.

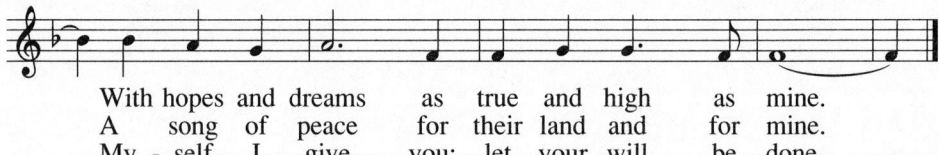

But oth - er hearts in oth - er lands are beat - ing
So hear my song, O God of all the na - tions,
So hear my prayer, O God of all the na - tions.

With hopes and dreams as true and high as mine.
A song of peace for their land and for mine.
My - self I give you; let your will be done.

Text: St. 1, 2, Lloyd Stone, 1912–1993; st. 3, Georgia Harkness, 1891–1974, © 1964, Lorenz Publishing Co.
Tune: FINLANDIA, 11 10 11 10 11 10; Jean Sibelius, 1865–1957

# We Have a Dream  987

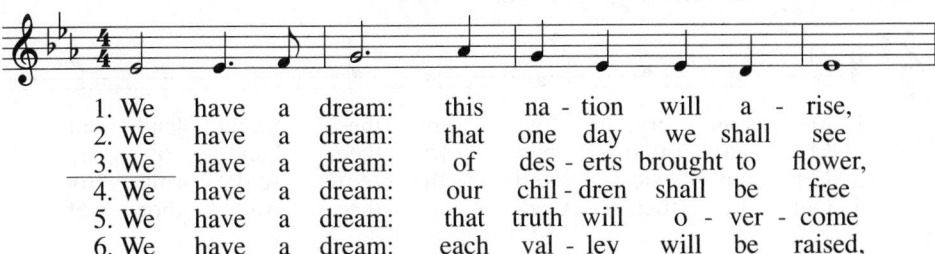

1. We have a dream: this na - tion will a - rise,
2. We have a dream: that one day we shall see
3. We have a dream: of des - erts brought to flower,
4. We have a dream: our chil - dren shall be free
5. We have a dream: that truth will o - ver - come
6. We have a dream: each val - ley will be raised,

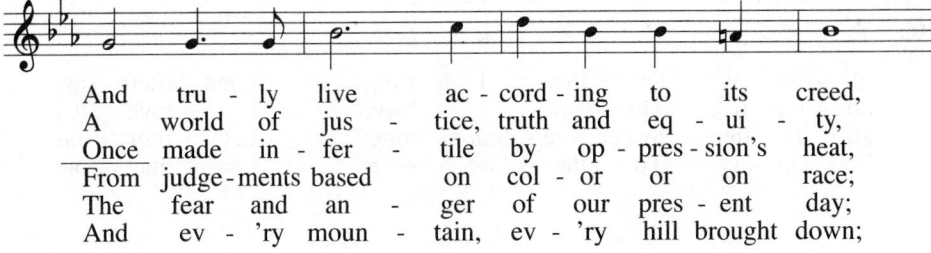

And tru - ly live ac - cord - ing to its creed,
A world of jus - tice, truth and eq - ui - ty,
Once made in - fer - tile by op - pres - sion's heat,
From judge - ments based on col - or or on race;
The fear and an - ger of our pres - ent day;
And ev - 'ry moun - tain, ev - 'ry hill brought down;

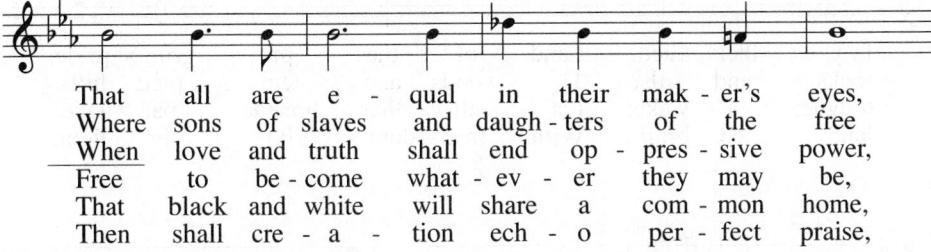

That all are e - qual in their mak - er's eyes,
Where sons of slaves and daugh - ters of the free
When love and truth shall end op - pres - sive power,
Free to be - come what - ev - er they may be,
That black and white will share a com - mon home,
Then shall cre - a - tion ech - o per - fect praise,

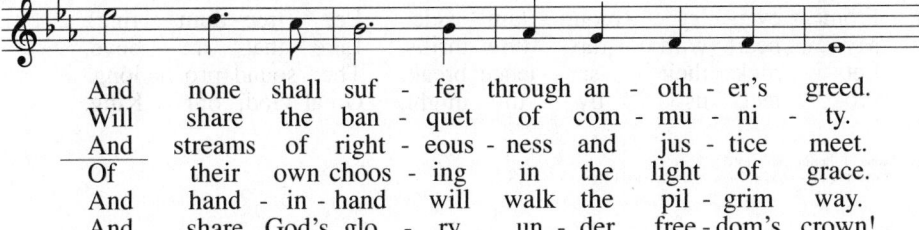

And none shall suf - fer through an - oth - er's greed.
Will share the ban - quet of com - mu - ni - ty.
And streams of right - eous - ness and jus - tice meet.
Of their own choos - ing in the light of grace.
And hand - in - hand will walk the pil - grim way.
And share God's glo - ry un - der free - dom's crown!

Text: Michael Forster, b.1946, © 1997, Kevin Mayhew, Ltd.
Tune: NATIONAL HYMN, 10 10 10 10; George W. Warren, 1828–1902

# 988 My Country, 'Tis of Thee

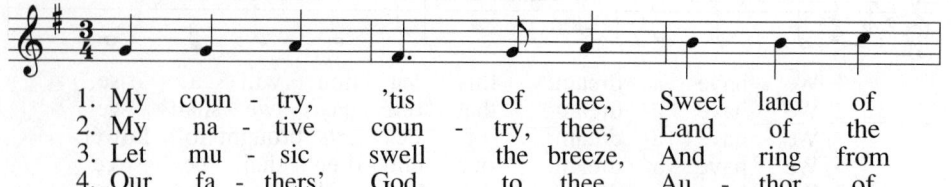

1. My coun - try, 'tis of thee, Sweet land of
2. My na - tive coun - try, thee, Land of the
3. Let mu - sic swell the breeze, And ring from
4. Our fa - thers' God, to thee, Au - thor of

lib - er - ty, Of thee I sing; Land where my
no - ble, free; Thy name I love; I love thy
all the trees Sweet free - dom's song; Let mor - tal
lib - er - ty, To thee we sing; Long may our

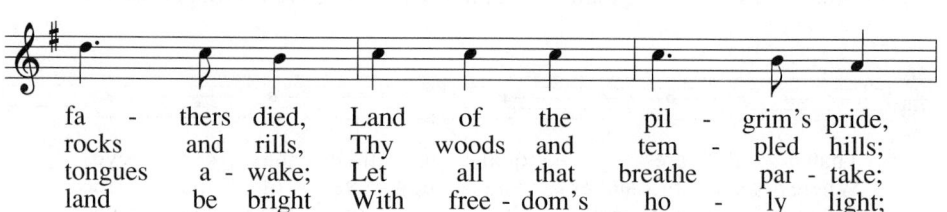

fa - thers died, Land of the pil - grim's pride,
rocks and rills, Thy woods and tem - pled hills;
tongues a - wake; Let all that breathe par - take;
land be bright With free - dom's ho - ly light;

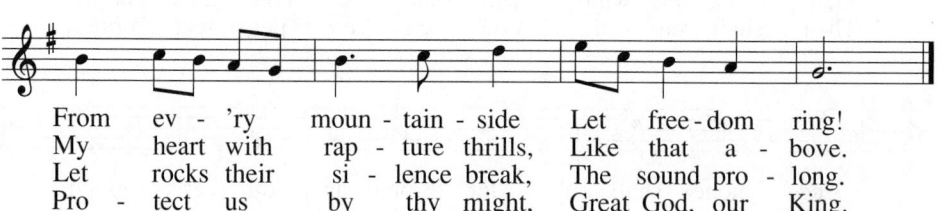

From ev - 'ry moun - tain - side Let free - dom ring!
My heart with rap - ture thrills, Like that a - bove.
Let rocks their si - lence break, The sound pro - long.
Pro - tect us by thy might, Great God, our King.

Text: Samuel F. Smith, 1808–1895
Tune: AMERICA, 66 4 666 4; *Thesaurus Musicus*, 1744

# The God of All Eternity  989

1. The God of all e - ter - ni - ty, Un - bound by
2. What shall we of - fer God to - day— Our dreams of
3. God does not share our doubts and fears, Nor shrinks from
4. Let faith or for - tune rise or fall, Let dreams and
5. God grant that we, in this new year, May show the

space yet al - ways near, Is pres - ent
what we can - not see, Or, with eyes
the un - known or strange: The one who
dread both have their day; Those whom God
world the King - dom's face, And let our

where his peo - ple meet To cel - e -
fas - tened to the past, Our dread of
fash - ioned heav'n and earth Makes all things
loves walk un - a - fraid With Christ their
work and wor - ship thrive As signs of

brate the com - ing year.
what is yet to be?
new and ush - ers change.
guide and Christ their way.
hope and means of grace.

Text: John L. Bell, b.1949, © 1989, Iona Community, GIA Publications, Inc., agent
Tune: O WALY WALY, 8 8 8 8; English traditional; arr. by John L. Bell, b.1949, © 1989, Iona Community, GIA Publications, Inc., agent

# Advent / Christmas

## 990

In various ways and various places the Church has marked the days around the winter solstice (or the summer solstice in the southern hemisphere) in late December and early January. Customs, traditions, and rituals from the world's cultures have quite naturally found a home around the many-faceted celebration of the Word-made-flesh, the manifestation of God-with-us.

The present Roman calendar observes the season of Advent for three to four weeks prior to December 25. This season has a two-fold focus: the second coming of Jesus Christ at the end of human history and the historical incarnation of Jesus two thousand years ago.

Advent is filled with beautiful scripture readings, songs, prayers and gestures. These abound with images of God's promise and human longing, the beauty present in both darkness and light, the earth's sorrows and its fullness, and the goodness and mystery of time.

At Christmas this spirit blossoms in acclamation: the stories of nativity and epiphany, of Mary and of the Innocents, of Jesus baptized and of water become wine. Until well into January the songs and sights and smells of Christmas surround the Church not with sentimental fantasies but with everyday faith in a gracious God. The festivals of the Christmas season bear their own reflection of what is proclaimed on every Sunday of the year and in every baptism: our lives are caught up now in Jesus who was born of the virgin Mary, who suffered, died and has been raised.

The lectionary of Advent/Christmas is the foundation of these winter days. These scripture readings, proclaimed and pondered year after year, turn the Christian and the Church toward that peace and glory we name but do not yet know.

## FIRST SUNDAY OF ADVENT / A 991

**READING I** *Isaiah 2:1–5 / 1*

**RESPONSORIAL PSALM** *Psalm 122:1–2, 3–4ab, 4cd–5, 6–7, 8–9*

Let us go re - joic - ing to the house of the Lord.

I rejoiced when they said to me,
"Let us go to the house of the LORD."
And now our feet are standing
within your gates, O Jerusalem. ℟.

Jerusalem is built as a city
bonded as one together.
It is there that the tribes go up,
the tribes of the LORD. ℟.

For Israel's witness it is
to praise the name of the LORD.
There were set the thrones for judgment,

the thrones of the house of David. ℟.

For the peace of Jerusalem pray,
"May they prosper, those who love
you."
May peace abide in your walls,
and security be in your towers. ℟.

For the sake of my family and friends,
let me say, "Peace upon you."
For the sake of the house of the LORD,
our God,
I will seek good things for you. ℟.

**READING II** *Romans 13:11–14*

**GOSPEL** *Matthew 24:37–44*

## FIRST SUNDAY OF ADVENT / B 992

**READING I** *Isaiah 63:16b-17, 19b; 64:2–7 / 2*

**RESPONSORIAL PSALM** *Psalm 80:2ac and 3b, 15–16, 18–19*

Lord, make us turn to you; let us see your

face and we shall be saved.

O shepherd of Israel, hear us,
enthroned on the cherubim, shine
forth.
Rouse up your might and come
to save us. ℟.

God of hosts, turn again, we implore;
look down from heaven and see.
Visit this vine and protect it,
the vine your right hand has planted,
the son of man you have claimed
for yourself. ℟.

May your hand be on the man at your
   right hand,
      the son of man you have confirmed
         as your own.

And we shall never forsake you again;
   give us life that we may call upon
      your name. ℟.

**READING II**                                          *1 Corinthians 1:3–9*

**GOSPEL**                                               *Mark 13:33–37*

---

## 993   FIRST SUNDAY OF ADVENT / C

**READING I**                                          *Jeremiah 33:14–16 / 3*

**RESPONSORIAL PSALM**                    *Psalm 25:4–5, 8–9, 10 and 14*

To you, O Lord, I  lift my soul, to you  I  lift my soul.

O LORD, make me know your ways.
   Teach me your paths.
Guide me in your truth, and teach me;
   for you are the God of my salvation.
I have hoped in you all day long. ℟.

Good and upright is the LORD;
   he shows the way to sinners.
He guides the humble in right judgment;
   to the humble he teaches his way. ℟.

All the LORD's paths are mercy
   and faithfulness,
      for those who keep his covenant
         and commands.
The LORD's secret is for those
   who fear him;
      to them he reveals his covenant. ℟.

**READING II**                                          *1 Thessalonians 3:12—4:2*

**GOSPEL**                                               *Luke 21:25–28, 34–36*

---

## 994   SECOND SUNDAY OF ADVENT / A

**READING I**                                          *Isaiah 11:1–10 / 4*

**RESPONSORIAL PSALM**                    *Psalm 72:1–2, 7–8, 12–13, 17*

Jus - tice shall flour - ish in his time, and

full - ness of peace for ev - er.

O God, give your judgment to the king,
 to a king's son your justice,
that he may judge your people in justice,
 and your poor in right judgment. ℟.

In his days shall justice flourish,
 and great peace till the moon is no
 more.
He shall rule from sea to sea,
 from the River to the bounds
 of the earth. ℟.

For he shall save the needy when
 they cry,
 the poor, and those who are helpless.
He will have pity on the weak and
 the needy,
 and save the lives of the needy. ℟.

May his name endure forever,
 his name continue like the sun.
Every tribe shall be blest in him,
 all nations shall call him blessed. ℟.

**READING II**                                      *Romans 15:4–9*

**GOSPEL**                                          *Matthew 3:1–12*

---

## SECOND SUNDAY OF ADVENT / B                                  995

**READING I**                                       *Isaiah 40:1–5, 9–11 / 5*

**RESPONSORIAL PSALM**                              *Psalm 85:9ab–10, 11–12, 13–14*

Lord, let us see your kind‑ness, and grant us your sal‑va‑tion.

I will hear what the LORD God speaks;
 he speaks of peace for his people
 and his faithful.
His salvation is near for those who fear him,
 and his glory will dwell in our land. ℟.

Merciful love and faithfulness have met;
 justice and peace have kissed.

Faithfulness shall spring from the earth,
 and justice look down from
 heaven. ℟.

Also the LORD will bestow his bounty,
 and our earth shall yield its increase.
Justice will march before him,
 and guide his steps on the way. ℟.

**READING II**                                      *2 Peter 3:8–14*

**GOSPEL**                                          *Mark 1:1–8*

## 996   SECOND SUNDAY OF ADVENT / C

**READING I**                                                    *Baruch 5:1–9 / 6*

**RESPONSORIAL PSALM**                       *Psalm 126:1–2ab, 2cd–3, 4–5, 6*

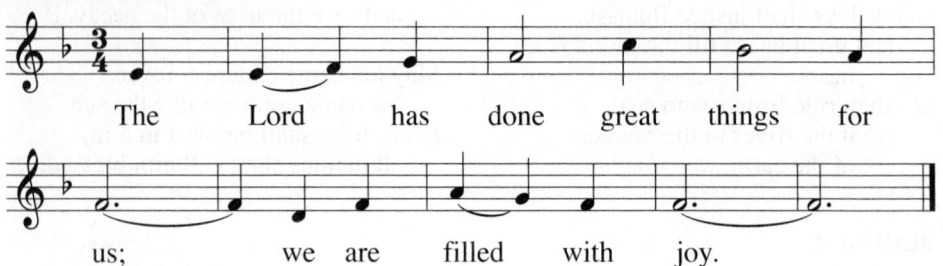

The Lord has done great things for us; we are filled with joy.

When the Lord brought back the
    exiles of Sion,
  we thought we were dreaming.
Then was our mouth filled with
    laughter;
  on our tongues, songs of joy. ℟.

Then the nations themselves said,
  "What great deeds the Lord
    worked for them!"
What great deeds the Lord worked
    for us!
  Indeed, we were glad. ℟.

Bring back our exiles, O Lord,
  as streams in the south.
Those who are sowing in tears
  will sing when they reap. ℟.

They go out, they go out, full of tears,
  bearing seed for the sowing;
they come back, they come back with
    a song,
  bearing their sheaves. ℟.

**READING II**                                              *Philippians 1:4–6, 8–11*

**GOSPEL**                                                          *Luke 3:1–6*

## 997   THIRD SUNDAY OF ADVENT / A

**READING I**                                              *Isaiah 35:1–6a, 10 / 7*

**RESPONSORIAL PSALM**                       *Psalm 146:6c–7, 8–9a, 9bc–10*

*Or: Alleluia.*

Lord, come and save us.

It is the LORD who preserves fidelity
  forever,
    who does justice to those who are
      oppressed.
It is he who gives bread to the hungry,
    the LORD who sets prisoners free. ℟.

The LORD who opens the eyes of the blind,
    the LORD who raises up those who
      are bowed down.

It is the LORD who loves the just,
    the LORD who protects the
      stranger. ℟.

The LORD upholds the orphan and
    the widow,
      but thwarts the path of the wicked.
The LORD will reign forever,
    the God of Sion from age to age. ℟.

**READING II**                                         *James 5:7–10*

**GOSPEL**                                         *Matthew 11:2–11*

## THIRD SUNDAY OF ADVENT / B                          998

**READING I**                                  *Isaiah 61:1–2a, 10–11 / 8*

**RESPONSORIAL PSALM**                    *Luke 1:46–48, 49–50, 53–54*

My   soul   re - joic - es   in   my   God,

my   soul   re - joic - es   in   my   God.

My soul proclaims the greatness of the
  Lord;
    my spirit rejoices in God my Savior,
for he has looked upon his lowly servant.
    From this day all generations will
      call me blessed: ℟.

The Almighty has done great things for
  me,
    and holy is his Name.

He has mercy on those who fear him
  in every generation. ℟.

He has filled the hungry with good
    things,
      and the rich he has sent away empty.
He has come to the help of his servant
    Israel
      for he has remembered his promise
        of mercy. ℟.

**READING II**                                  *1 Thessalonians 5:16–24*

**GOSPEL**                                         *John 1:6–8, 19–28*

## 999 THIRD SUNDAY OF ADVENT / C

**READING I**  *Zephaniah 3:14–18a / 9*

**RESPONSORIAL PSALM**  *Isaiah 12:2–3, 4bcd, 5–6*

Cry out with joy and glad - ness: for a -

mong you is the great and Ho - ly One of Is - ra - el.

God indeed is my savior;
  I am confident and unafraid.
My strength and my courage is the LORD,
  and he has been my savior.
With joy you will draw water
  at the fountain of salvation. ℟.

Give thanks to the LORD, acclaim his
  name;
  among the nations make known his
  deeds,
  proclaim how exalted is his name. ℟.

Sing praise to the LORD for his glorious
  achievement;
  let this be known throughout all the
  earth.
Shout with exultation, O city of Zion,
  for great in your midst
  is the Holy One of Israel! ℟.

**READING II**  *Philippians 4:4–7*

**GOSPEL**  *Luke 3:10–18*

## 1000 FOURTH SUNDAY OF ADVENT / A

**READING I**  *Isaiah 7:10–14 / 10*

**RESPONSORIAL PSALM**  *Psalm 24:1–2, 3–4ab, 5–6*

Let the Lord en - ter; he is king of glo - ry.

The LORD's is the earth and its fullness,
  the world, and those who dwell in it.
It is he who set it on the seas;
  on the rivers he made it firm. ℟.

Who shall climb the mountain of the
  LORD?
  Who shall stand in his holy place?
The clean of hands and pure of heart,
  whose soul is not set on vain
  things. ℟.

Blessings from the LORD shall he receive,
and right reward from the God who
saves him.

Such are the people who seek him,
who seek the face of the God of
Jacob. ℟.

**READING II**                                                    *Romans 1:1–7*

**GOSPEL**                                                    *Matthew 1:18–24*

---

## FOURTH SUNDAY OF ADVENT / B                1001

**READING I**                    *2 Samuel 7:1–5, 8b–12, 14a, 16 / 11*

**RESPONSORIAL PSALM**              *Psalm 89:2–3, 4–5, 27 and 29*

For ev - er I will sing the good - ness of the Lord.

I will sing forever of your mercies,
O LORD;
   through all ages my mouth will
   proclaim your fidelity.
I have declared your mercy is
   established forever;
   your fidelity stands firm as the
   heavens. ℟.

"With my chosen one I have made a
   covenant;
   I have sworn to David my servant:

I will establish your descendants
   forever,
   and set up your throne through all
   ages." ℟.

"He will call out to me, 'You are my
   father,
   my God, the rock of my salvation.'
I will keep my faithful love for him
   always;
   with him my covenant shall last." ℟.

**READING II**                                                    *Romans 16:25–27*

**GOSPEL**                                                    *Luke 1:26–38*

---

## FOURTH SUNDAY OF ADVENT / C                1002

**READING I**                                                    *Micah 5:1–4a / 12*

**RESPONSORIAL PSALM**  *Psalm 80:2ac and 3b, 15–16, 18–19*

Lord, make us turn to you; let us see your

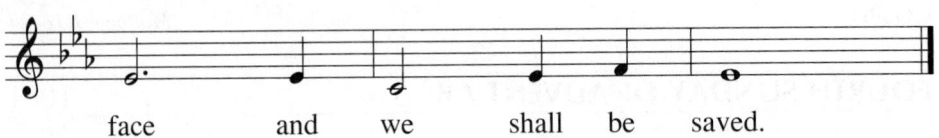

face and we shall be saved.

O shepherd of Israel, hear us,
  enthroned on the cherubim, shine forth.
  Rouse up your might and come to save us. ℟.

God of hosts, turn again, we implore;
  look down from heaven and see.
Visit this vine and protect it,
  the vine your right hand has planted,

the son of man you have claimed
  for yourself. ℟.

May your hand be on the man at your right hand,
  the son of man you have confirmed as your own.
And we shall never forsake you again;
  give us life that we may call upon your name. ℟.

**READING II**  *Hebrews 10:5–10*

**GOSPEL**  *Luke 1:39–45*

---

## 1003   DECEMBER 25: CHRISTMAS—VIGIL MASS / ABC

**READING I**  *Isaiah 62:1–5 / 13*

**RESPONSORIAL PSALM**  *Psalm 89:4–5, 16–17, 27 and 29*

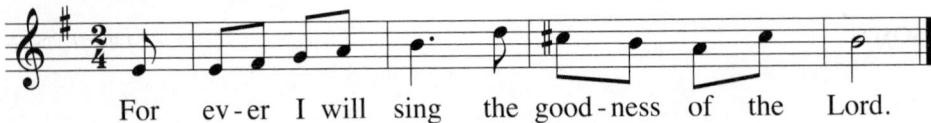

For ev-er I will sing the good-ness of the Lord.

"With my chosen one I have made a covenant;
  I have sworn to David my servant:
I will establish your descendants forever,
  and set up your throne through all ages." ℟.

How blessed the people who know your praise,
  who walk, O Lord, in the light of your face,
who find their joy every day in your name,
  who make your justice their joyful acclaim. ℟.

"He will call out to me, 'You are my father,
    my God, the rock of my salvation.'
I will keep my faithful love for him
always;
    with him my covenant shall last." ℟.

**READING II**                             *Acts 13:16–17, 22–25*

**GOSPEL**                   *Matthew 1:1–25 or 1:18–25*

---

# DEC. 25: CHRISTMAS—MASS DURING THE NIGHT / ABC    1004

**READING I**                        *Isaiah 9:1–6 / 14*

**RESPONSORIAL PSALM**      *Psalm 96:1–2a, 2b–3, 11–12, 13*

To-day, to-day, to-day is born our Sav-ior, Christ the Lord.

O sing a new song to the LORD;
    sing to the LORD, all the earth.
    O sing to the LORD; bless his name. ℟.

Proclaim his salvation day by day.
    Tell among the nations his glory,
    and his wonders among all the
        peoples. ℟.

Let the heavens rejoice and earth be glad;
    let the sea and all within it thunder
        praise.

Let the land and all it bears
    rejoice.
Then will all the trees of the wood
    shout for joy. ℟.

At the presence of the LORD, for he
    comes,
    he comes to judge the earth.
He will judge the world with justice;
    he will govern the peoples with his
        truth. ℟.

**READING II**                               *Titus 2:11–14*

**GOSPEL**                               *Luke 2:1–14*

## 1005   DEC. 25: CHRISTMAS—MASS AT DAWN / ABC

**READING I**                                                         *Isaiah 62:11–12 / 15*

**RESPONSORIAL PSALM**                                    *Psalm 97:1 and 6, 11–12*

A light will shine on us this day:   the Lord   is born for     us.

The LORD is king, let earth rejoice;
   let the many islands be glad.
The skies proclaim his justice;
   all peoples see his glory. ℟.

Light shines forth for the just one,
   and joy for the upright of heart.
Rejoice in the LORD, you just;
   to the memory of his holiness give
   thanks. ℟.

**READING II**                                                              *Titus 3:4–7*

**GOSPEL**                                                                  *Luke 2:15–20*

## 1006   DEC. 25: CHRISTMAS—MASS DURING THE DAY / ABC

**READING I**                                                         *Isaiah 52:7–10 / 16*

**RESPONSORIAL PSALM**                            *Psalm 98:1, 2–3ab, 3cd–4, 5–6*

All the ends of the earth have seen the  sav - ing pow'r of   God.

O sing a new song to the LORD,
   for he has worked wonders.
His right hand and his holy arm
   have brought salvation. ℟.

The LORD has made known his salvation,
   has shown his deliverance to the
   nations.
He has remembered his merciful love
   and his truth for the house of
   Israel. ℟.

All the ends of the earth have seen
   the salvation of our God.
Shout to the LORD, all the earth;
   break forth into joyous song,
   and sing out your praise. ℟.

Sing psalms to the LORD with the harp,
   with the harp and the sound of song.
With trumpets and the sound of the horn,
   raise a shout before the King,
   the LORD. ℟.

**READING II**                                                           *Hebrews 1:1–6*

**GOSPEL**                                               *John 1:1–18 or 1:1–5, 9–14*

## HOLY FAMILY OF JESUS, MARY AND JOSEPH / ABC          1007

**READING I**                                              *Sirach 3:2–7, 12–14 / 17*

**RESPONSORIAL PSALM**                                     *Psalm 128:1–2, 3, 4–5*

Bless-ed are those who fear the Lord and walk in his ways.

Blessed are all who fear the LORD,
  and walk in his ways!
By the labor of your hands you shall eat.
  You will be blessed and prosper. ℟.

Your wife like a fruitful vine
  in the heart of your house;
your children like shoots of the olive
  around your table. ℟.

Indeed thus shall be blessed
  the man who fears the LORD.
May the LORD bless you from Sion.
  May you see Jerusalem prosper
  all the days of your life! ℟.

**READING II**                                            *Colossians 3:12–21 or 3:12–17*

**GOSPEL / A**                                            *Matthew 2:13–15, 19–23*

**GOSPEL / B**                                            *Luke 2:22–40 or 2:22, 39–40*

**GOSPEL / C**                                            *Luke 2:41–52*

## IN YEAR B, THESE READINGS MAY BE USED          1008

**READING I**                                            *Genesis 15:1–6; 21:1–3*

**RESPONSORIAL PSALM**                                   *Psalm 105:1–2, 3–4, 6–7, 8–9*

The Lord re - mem - bers his cov - e - nant for ev - er.

Give thanks to the LORD; proclaim his
  name.
  Make known his deeds among the
  peoples.
O sing to him, sing his praise;
  tell all his wonderful works! ℟.

Glory in his holy name;
  let the hearts that seek the LORD
  rejoice.
Turn to the LORD and his strength;
  constantly seek his face. ℟.

O children of Abraham, his servant,
  O descendants of the Jacob he chose,
he, the LORD, is our God;
  his judgments are in all the earth. ℟.

He remembers his covenant forever:
  the promise he ordained for a
    thousand generations,
  the covenant he made with Abraham,
  the oath he swore to Isaac. ℟.

**READING II**                             *Hebrews 11:8, 11–12, 17–19*

## 1009  IN YEAR C, THESE READINGS MAY BE USED

**READING I**                             *1 Samuel 1:20–22, 24–28*

**RESPONSORIAL PSALM**                *Psalm 84:2–3, 5–6, 9–10*

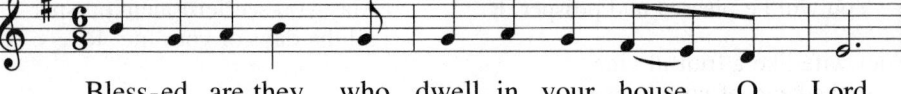

Bless-ed are they who dwell in your house, O Lord.

How lovely is your dwelling place,
  O LORD of hosts.
My soul is longing and yearning
  for the courts of the LORD.
My heart and my flesh cry out
  to the living God. ℟.

Blessed are they who dwell in your house,
  forever singing your praise.

Blessed the people whose strength is in
  you,
  whose heart is set on pilgrim
  ways. ℟.

O LORD God of hosts, hear my prayer;
  give ear, O God of Jacob.
Turn your eyes, O God, our shield;
  look on the face of your anointed. ℟.

**READING II**                             *1 John 3:1–2, 21–24*

## 1010  JAN. 1: SOLEMNITY OF MARY, HOLY MOTHER OF GOD / ABC

**READING I**                             *Numbers 6:22–27 / 18*

**RESPONSORIAL PSALM**               *Psalm 67:2–3, 5, 6 and 8*

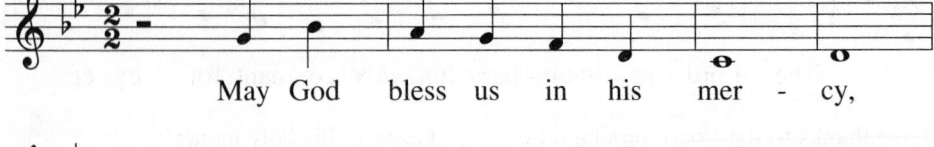

May God bless us in his mer - cy,

may God bless us in his mer - cy.

O God, be gracious and bless us
and let your face shed its light upon us.
So will your ways be known upon earth
and all nations learn your salvation. ℟.

Let the nations be glad and shout for joy,
with uprightness you rule the peoples;
you guide the nations on earth. ℟.

Let the peoples praise you, O God;
let all the peoples praise you.
May God still give us his blessing
that all the ends of the earth may
revere him. ℟.

**READING II**                               *Galatians 4:4–7*

**GOSPEL**                                    *Luke 2:16–21*

## EPIPHANY OF THE LORD / ABC                                    1011

**READING I**                                *Isaiah 60:1–6 / 20*

**RESPONSORIAL PSALM**              *Psalm 72:1–2, 7–8, 10–11, 12–13*

Lord, ev-'ry na-tion on earth will a-dore you.

O God, give your judgment to the king,
to a king's son your justice,
that he may judge your people in justice,
and your poor in right judgment. ℟.

In his days shall justice flourish,
and great peace till the moon is no
more.
He shall rule from sea to sea,
from the River to the bounds of the
earth. ℟.

The kings of Tarshish and the islands
shall pay him tribute.
The kings of Sheba and Seba
shall bring him gifts.
Before him all kings shall fall prostrate,
all nations shall serve him. ℟.

For he shall save the needy when they
cry,
the poor, and those who are helpless.
He will have pity on the weak and the
needy,
and save the lives of the needy. ℟.

**READING II**                               *Ephesians 3:2–3a, 5–6*

**GOSPEL**                                    *Matthew 2:1–12*

## 1012  BAPTISM OF THE LORD / ABC

**READING I**                                                  *Isaiah 42:1–4, 6–7 / 21*

**RESPONSORIAL PSALM**                     *Psalm 29:1a and 2, 3ac–4, 3b and 9b–10*

The Lord will bless his peo-ple with his peace.

Ascribe to the LORD, you heavenly powers,
  ascribe to the LORD glory and strength.
Ascribe to the LORD the glory of his name;
  bow down before the LORD, majestic
    in holiness. ℟.

The voice of the LORD upon the waters,
  the LORD on the immensity of waters;
the voice of the LORD full of power;

the voice of the LORD full of
  splendor. ℟.

The God of glory thunders;
  in his temple they all cry, "Glory!"
The LORD sat enthroned above the
    flood;
  the LORD sits as king forever. ℟.

**READING II**                                                        *Acts 10:34–38*

**GOSPEL / A**                                                     *Matthew 3:13–17*

**GOSPEL / B**                                                        *Mark 1:7–11*

**GOSPEL / C**                                                   *Luke 3:15–16, 21–22*

## 1013  IN YEAR B, THESE READINGS MAY BE USED

**READING I**                                                       *Isaiah 55:1–11*

**RESPONSORIAL PSALM**                               *Isaiah 12:2–3, 4bcd, 5–6*

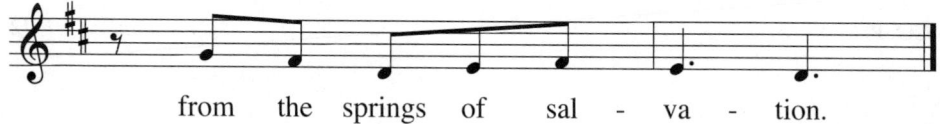

You will draw wa - ter          joy - ful - ly

from the springs of sal - va - tion.

God indeed is my savior;
  I am confident and unafraid.
My strength and my courage is the LORD,
  and he has been my savior.
With joy you will draw water
  at the fountain of salvation. ℟.

Give thanks to the LORD, acclaim his name;
  among the nations make known his
  deeds,

proclaim how exalted is his name. ℟.

Sing praise to the LORD for his glorious
  achievement;
  let this be known throughout all the
  earth.
Shout with exultation, O city of Zion,
  for great in your midst
  is the Holy One of Israel! ℟.

**READING II**                                        *1 John 5:1–9*

# IN YEAR C, THESE READINGS MAY BE USED                    1014

**READING I**                                        *Isaiah 40:1–5, 9–11*

**RESPONSORIAL PSALM**                    *Psalm 104:1b-2, 3–4, 24–25, 27–28, 29–30*

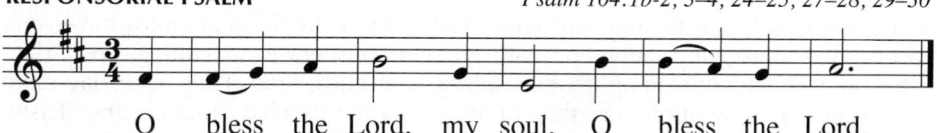

O bless the Lord, my soul, O bless the Lord.

O LORD my God, how great you are,
  clothed in majesty and honor,
wrapped in light as with a robe!
  You stretch out the heavens like a
  tent. ℟.

On the waters you establish your
  dwelling.
  You make the clouds your chariot;
  you ride on the wings of the wind.
You make the winds your messengers,
  flame and fire your servants. ℟.

How many are your works, O LORD!
  In wisdom you have made them all.
  The earth is full of your creatures.
Vast and wide is the span of the sea,

with its creeping things past counting,
living things great and small. ℟.

All of these look to you
  to give them their food in due season.
You give it, they gather it up;
  you open wide your hand, they are
  well filled. ℟.

You take away their breath, they die,
  returning to the dust from which
  they came.
You send forth your spirit, and they
  are created,
  and you renew the face of the
  earth. ℟.

**READING II**                                        *Titus 2:11–14; 3:4–7*

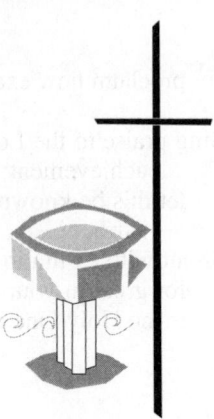

# Lent / Easter

## 1015

On a Wednesday in February or early March the Church enters into prayer and fasting and almsgiving, attending with great seriousness to its calling. Forty days later on a Thursday evening, that season of Lent ends. From Holy Thursday night until Easter Sunday afternoon, the church keeps the Paschal Triduum, the "Easter Three Days." Good Friday and Holy Saturday find Christians fasting, keeping vigil, remembering the passion, death and resurrection of the Lord until, at the great Vigil liturgy, the church celebrates this paschal mystery in baptism, confirmation and eucharist. Then, for the fifty days of Eastertime the church again sings the alleluia and rejoices to bring God's peace to the world.

The origins of Lent are bound up with the final stages in the initiation of those seeking to be baptized. After months or years of learning gradually the Christian way of life, the catechumens were called to spend the last weeks before baptism in fasting and prayer. The whole church stayed by the catechumens in these days. The lenten season was also kept intensely by those doing penance for their sins. Today both catechumens and penitents keep Lent with the whole church. Lent's scriptures, prayers and rites give clarity and strength to the life-long struggle against evil. That struggle is waged with many forms of prayer and fasting and practices of charity.

The origins of the fifty days of Eastertime are even more ancient. This is the springtime rejoicing of people who know their dependence on fields and flocks. It is the rejoicing of Israel remembering the exodus from slavery to freedom. It became the rejoicing of the church in the resurrection of Jesus and the presence of that risen life in the newly baptized. The Eastertime lectionary is filled with a lively peace and the quiet exuberance of those who believe that evil is not finally triumphant. When the fifty days conclude at Pentecost the church knows again how disturbing, how restless, how strong is the Spirit given by Christ.

*For Ash Wednesday, see no. 1194.*

# FIRST SUNDAY OF LENT / A                    1016

**READING I**                                    *Genesis 2:7–9; 3:1–7 / 22*

**RESPONSORIAL PSALM**                *Psalm 51:3–4, 5–6a, 12–13, 14 and 17*

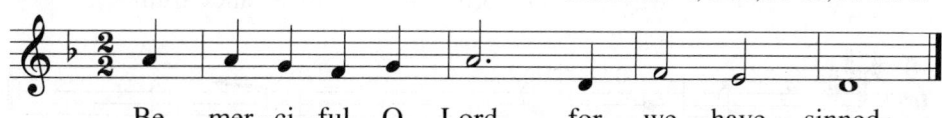

Be mer - ci - ful, O Lord, for we have sinned.

Have mercy on me, O God,
  according to your merciful love;
according to your great compassion,
  blot out my transgressions.
Wash me completely from my iniquity,
  and cleanse me from my sin. ℟.

My transgressions, truly I know them;
  my sin is always before me.
Against you, you alone, have I sinned;
  what is evil in your sight I have
     done. ℟.

Create a pure heart for me, O God;
  renew a steadfast spirit within me.
Do not cast me away from your presence;
  take not your holy spirit from me. ℟.

Restore in me the joy of your salvation;
  sustain in me a willing spirit.
O Lord, open my lips
  and my mouth shall proclaim your
    praise. ℟.

**READING II**                          *Romans 5:12–19 or 5:12, 17–19*

**GOSPEL**                                        *Matthew 4:1–11*

**RITE OF ELECTION**
*At the beginning of Lent, it is the responsibility of the bishop to call those who are judged ready to prepare for the sacraments of initiation at Easter. The bishop is to consult first with the pastors, catechists and others. The rite may take place at the cathedral. If the rite takes place in the parish church, the bishop may designate the pastor to act in his place.*

*   This rite is also called the "Enrollment of Names." Each candidate now gives his/her name, or writes it down. When all have been enrolled, the bishop says: "You have been chosen to be initiated into the sacred mysteries at the Easter Vigil." He then speaks to them and to their sponsors about their lenten preparation for baptism.*

*   The faithful join in prayers of intercession for the elect, as the catechumens are now called. If the eucharist is to be celebrated, the elect are first dismissed.*

# FIRST SUNDAY OF LENT / B                    1017

**READING I**                                    *Genesis 9:8–15 / 23*

**RESPONSORIAL PSALM**  *Psalm 25:4–5ab, 6 and 7bc, 8–9*

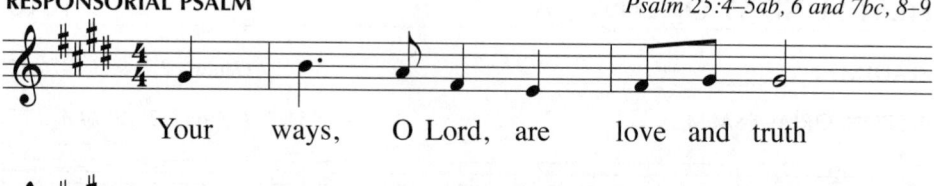

Your ways, O Lord, are love and truth

to those who keep your cov - e - nant.

O LORD, make me know your ways.
Teach me your paths.
Guide me in your truth, and teach me;
for you are the God of my
salvation. ℟.

Remember your compassion, O LORD,
and your merciful love,
for they are from of old.
In your merciful love remember me,

because of your goodness,
O LORD. ℟.

Good and upright is the LORD;
he shows the way to sinners.
He guides the humble in right
judgment;
to the humble he teaches his
way. ℟.

**READING II**  *1 Peter 3:18–22*

**GOSPEL**  *Mark 1:12–15*

**RITE OF ELECTION**
*See no. 1016*

---

## 1018  FIRST SUNDAY OF LENT / C

**READING I**  *Deuteronomy 26:4–10 / 24*

**RESPONSORIAL PSALM**  *Psalm 91:1–2, 10–11, 12–13, 14–15*

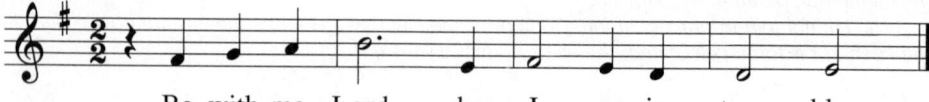

Be with me, Lord, when I am in trou - ble.

He who dwells in the shelter of the
Most High,
and abides in the shade of the
Almighty,
says to the LORD, "My refuge,
my stronghold, my God in whom I
trust!" ℟.

Upon you no evil shall fall,
no plague approach your tent.
For you has he commanded his angels
to keep you in all your ways. ℟.

They shall bear you upon their hands,
  lest you strike your foot against a
    stone.
On the lion and the viper you will tread,
  and trample the young lion and the
    serpent. ℟.

Since he clings to me in love, I will
  free him,
    protect him, for he knows my name.
When he calls on me, I will answer
  him;
I will be with him in distress;
I will deliver him, and give him
  glory. ℟.

**READING II**                                      *Romans 10:8–13*

**GOSPEL**                                          *Luke 4:1–13*

**RITE OF ELECTION**
*See no. 1016*

---

## SECOND SUNDAY OF LENT / A                      1019

**READING I**                                       *Genesis 12:1–4a / 25*

**RESPONSORIAL PSALM**                              *Psalm 33:4–5, 18–19, 20 and 22*

Lord, let your mer-cy be on us, as we place our trust in you.

The word of the LORD is faithful,
  and all his works to be trusted.
The LORD loves justice and right,
  and his merciful love fills the earth. ℟.

Yes, the LORD's eyes are on those who
  fear him,
who hope in his merciful love,

to rescue their souls from death,
  to keep them alive in famine. ℟.

Our soul is waiting for the LORD.
  He is our help and our shield.
May your merciful love be upon us,
  as we hope in you, O LORD. ℟.

**READING II**                                      *2 Timothy 1:8b–10*

**GOSPEL**                                          *Matthew 17:1–9*

---

## SECOND SUNDAY OF LENT / B                      1020

**READING I**                                       *Genesis 22:1–2, 9a, 10–13, 15–18 / 26*

**RESPONSORIAL PSALM**  *Psalm 116:10 and 15, 16–17, 18–19*

I will walk be-fore the Lord, in the land of the liv - ing.

I trusted, even when I said,
    "I am sorely afflicted."
How precious in the eyes of the LORD
    is the death of his faithful. ℟.

Your servant, LORD, your servant am I,
    the son of your handmaid;
    you have loosened my bonds.

A thanksgiving sacrifice I make;
    I will call on the name of the
    LORD. ℟.

My vows to the LORD I will fulfill
    before all his people,
in the courts of the house of the LORD,
    in your midst, O Jerusalem. ℟.

**READING II**  *Romans 8:31b–34*

**GOSPEL**  *Mark 9:2–10*

---

## 1021  SECOND SUNDAY OF LENT / C

**READING I**  *Genesis 15:5–12, 17–18 / 27*

**RESPONSORIAL PSALM**  *Psalm 27:1, 7–8, 9abc, 13–14*

The Lord is my light and my sal - va - tion.

The LORD is my light and my salvation;
    whom shall I fear?
The LORD is the stronghold of my life;
    whom should I dread? ℟.

O LORD, hear my voice when I call;
    have mercy and answer me.
Of you my heart has spoken, "Seek his
    face."
    It is your face, O LORD, that I seek. ℟.

Hide not your face from me.
    Dismiss not your servant in anger;
you have been my help.
    Do not abandon or forsake me. ℟.

I believe I shall see the LORD's goodness
    in the land of the living.
Wait for the LORD; be strong;
    be stouthearted, and wait for the
    LORD! ℟.

**READING II**  *Philippians 3:17—4:1 or 3:20—4:1*

**GOSPEL**  *Luke 9:28b–36*

## THIRD SUNDAY OF LENT / A     1022

**READING I**          *Exodus 17:3–7 / 28*

**RESPONSORIAL PSALM**      *Psalm 95:1–2, 6–7c, 7d–9*

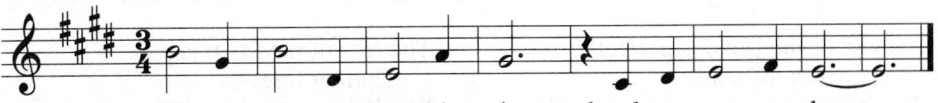

If to - day you hear his voice,  hard-en not your hearts.

Come, let us ring out our joy to the LORD;
 hail the rock who saves us.
Let us come into his presence, giving
  thanks;
 let us hail him with a song of praise. ℟.

O come; let us bow and bend low.
 Let us kneel before the God who
  made us,
for he is our God and we

the people who belong to his pasture,
the flock that is led by his hand. ℟.

O that today you would listen to his
 voice!
"Harden not your hearts as at Meribah,
 as on that day at Massah in the desert
when your forebears put me to the test;
 when they tried me, though they saw
  my work." ℟.

**READING II**         *Romans 5:1–2, 5–8*

**GOSPEL**     *John 4:5–42 or 4:5–15, 19b-26, 39a, 40–42*

**FIRST SCRUTINY**

*During Lent, the elect (those catechumens who have been called to prepare for baptism at Easter) are called to come before the community for exorcisms and prayers. This takes place after the liturgy of the word on the Third, Fourth, and Fifth Sundays of Lent. These rites are intended to purify the hearts and minds of the elect, to strengthen them against temptation, to help them progress in the love of God.*

*  The presider asks the assembly to pray in silence for the elect, then to join in intercessions for them. The presider lays hands on each of the elect and prays that the elect be delivered from the power of evil and become witnesses to the gospel. A song or psalm may be sung, then the elect are dismissed as usual and the faithful continue with the liturgy of the eucharist.*

## THIRD SUNDAY OF LENT / B     1023

**READING I**    *Exodus 20:1–17 or 20:1–3, 7–8, 12–17 / 29*

**RESPONSORIAL PSALM**                                   *Psalm 19:8, 9, 10, 11*

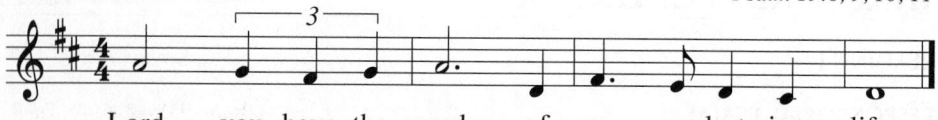

Lord, you have the words of ev-er-last-ing life.

The law of the LORD is perfect;
  it revives the soul.
The decrees of the LORD are steadfast;
  they give wisdom to the simple. ℟.

The precepts of the LORD are right;
  they gladden the heart.
The command of the LORD is clear;
  it gives light to the eyes. ℟.

The fear of the LORD is pure,
  abiding forever.
The judgments of the LORD are true;
  they are, all of them, just. ℟.

They are more to be desired than gold,
  than quantities of gold.
And sweeter are they than honey,
  than honey flowing from the
    comb. ℟.

**READING II**                                          *1 Corinthians 1:22–25*

**GOSPEL**                                                   *John 2:13–25*

**FIRST SCRUTINY**
*See no. 1022*

---

## 1024  THIRD SUNDAY OF LENT / C

**READING I**                                       *Exodus 3:1–8a, 13–15 / 30*

**RESPONSORIAL PSALM**                   *Psalm 103:1–2, 3–4, 6–7, 8 and 11*

The Lord is kind and mer-ci-ful;

the Lord is kind and mer-ci-ful.

Bless the LORD, O my soul,
  and all within me, his holy name.
Bless the LORD, O my soul,
  and never forget all his benefits. ℟.

It is the Lord who forgives all your sins,
  who heals every one of your ills,
who redeems your life from the grave,
  who crowns you with mercy and

compassion. ℟.

The LORD does just deeds,
  gives full justice to all who are
    oppressed.
He made known his ways to Moses,
  and his deeds to the children of
    Israel. ℟.

The LORD is compassionate and gracious,
    slow to anger and rich in mercy.

For as the heavens are high above the earth,
    so strong his mercy for those who fear him. ℟.

**READING II**                                            *1 Corinthians 10:1–6, 10–12*

**GOSPEL**                                                *Luke 13:1–9*

**FIRST SCRUTINY**
*See no. 1022*

---

# FOURTH SUNDAY OF LENT / A              1025

**READING I**                                   *1 Samuel 16:1b, 6–7, 10–13a / 31*

**RESPONSORIAL PSALM**                       *Psalm 23:1–3a, 3b–4, 5, 6*

The Lord is my shep-herd; there is noth-ing I shall want.

The LORD is my shepherd;
    there is nothing I shall want.
Fresh and green are the pastures
    where he gives me repose.
Near restful waters he leads me;
    he revives my soul. ℟.

He guides me along the right path,
    for the sake of his name.
Though I should walk in the valley of
    the shadow of death,
    no evil would I fear, for you are
    with me.

Your crook and your staff will give
    me comfort. ℟.

You have prepared a table before me
    in the sight of my foes.
My head you have anointed with oil;
    my cup is overflowing. ℟.

Surely goodness and mercy shall
    follow me
    all the days of my life.
In the LORD's own house shall I dwell
    for length of days unending. ℟.

**READING II**                                                    *Ephesians 5:8–14*

**GOSPEL**                          *John 9:1–41 or 9:1, 6–9, 13–17, 34–38*

**SECOND SCRUTINY**
*During Lent, the elect (those catechumens who have been called to prepare for baptism at Easter) are called to come before the community for exorcisms and prayers. This takes place after the liturgy of the word on the Third, Fourth, and Fifth Sundays of Lent. These rites are intended to purify the hearts and minds of the elect, to strengthen them against temptation, to help them progress in the love of God.*

    *The presider asks the assembly to pray in silence for the elect, then to join in intercessions for them. The presider lays hands on each of the elect and prays that the elect be delivered from the power of evil and become witnesses to the gospel. A song or psalm may be sung, then the elect are dismissed as usual and the faithful continue with the liturgy of the eucharist.*

## 1026  FOURTH SUNDAY OF LENT / B

**READING I**                                    *2 Chronicles 36:14–16, 19–23 / 32*

**RESPONSORIAL PSALM**                          *Psalm 137:1–2, 3, 4–5, 6*

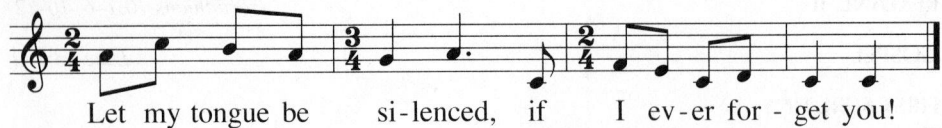

Let my tongue be  si-lenced,  if  I ev-er for - get you!

By the rivers of Babylon
  there we sat and wept,
  remembering Sion;
on the poplars that grew there
  we hung up our harps. ℟.

For it was there that they asked us,
  our captors, for songs,
  our oppressors, for joy.
"Sing to us," they said,
  "one of Sion's songs." ℟.

O how could we sing
  the song of the Lᴏʀᴅ
  on foreign soil?
If I forget you, Jerusalem,
  let my right hand wither! ℟.

O let my tongue
  cleave to my palate
  if I remember you not,
if I prize not Jerusalem
  as the first of my joys! ℟.

**READING II**                                  *Ephesians 2:4–10*

**GOSPEL**                                       *John 3:14–21*

**SECOND SCRUTINY**
*See no. 1025*

## 1027  FOURTH SUNDAY OF LENT / C

**READING I**                                    *Joshua 5:9a, 10–12 / 33*

**RESPONSORIAL PSALM**                          *Psalm 34:2–3, 4–5, 6–7*

Taste  and  see  the  good - ness  of  the  Lord.

I will bless the Lᴏʀᴅ at all times;
  praise of him is always in my mouth.
In the Lᴏʀᴅ my soul shall make its boast;
  the humble shall hear and be glad. ℟.

Glorify the Lᴏʀᴅ with me;
  together let us praise his name.
I sought the Lᴏʀᴅ, and he answered me;

from all my terrors he set me free. ℟.

Look toward him and be radiant;
  let your faces not be abashed.
This lowly one called; the Lᴏʀᴅ heard,
  and rescued him from all his
  distress. ℟.

**READING II** *2 Corinthians 5:17–21*

**GOSPEL** *Luke 15:1–3, 11–32*

**SECOND SCRUTINY**
*See no. 1025*

## FIFTH SUNDAY OF LENT / A 1028

**READING I** *Ezekiel 37:12–14 / 34*

**RESPONSORIAL PSALM** *Psalm 130:1–2, 3–4, 5–6ab and 7a, 7b–8*

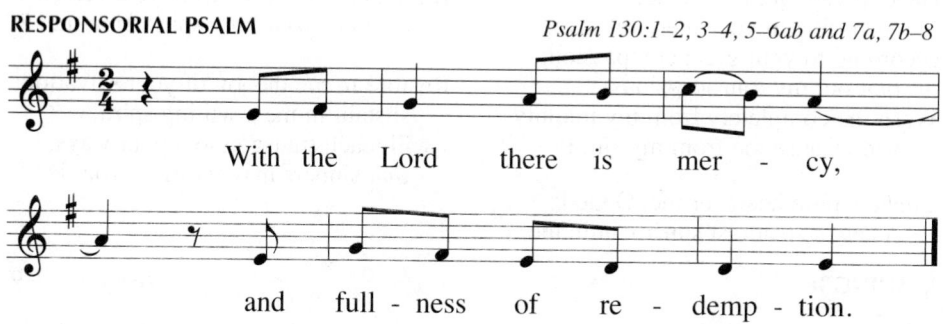

With the Lord there is mer - cy,
and full - ness of re - demp - tion.

Out of the depths I cry to you, O Lord;
  Lord, hear my voice!
O let your ears be attentive
  to the sound of my pleadings. ℟.

If you, O Lord, should mark iniquities,
  Lord, who could stand?
But with you is found forgiveness,
  that you may be revered. ℟.

I long for you, O Lord,
  my soul longs for his word.
My soul hopes in the Lord
  more than watchmen for daybreak.
Let Israel hope for the Lord. ℟.

For with the Lord there is mercy,
  in him is plentiful redemption.
It is he who will redeem Israel
  from all its iniquities. ℟.

**READING II** *Romans 8:8–11*

**GOSPEL** *John 11:1–45 or 11:3–7, 17, 20–27, 33b–45*

**THIRD SCRUTINY**
*During Lent, the elect (those catechumens who have been called to prepare for baptism at Easter) are called to come before the community for exorcisms and prayers. This takes place after the liturgy of the word on the Third, Fourth, and Fifth Sundays of Lent. These rites are intended to purify the hearts and minds of the elect, to strengthen them against temptation, to help them progress in the love of God.*
    *The presider asks the assembly to pray in silence for the elect, then to join in intercessions for them. The presider lays hands on each of the elect and prays that the elect be delivered from the power of evil and become witnesses to the gospel. A song or psalm may be sung, then the elect are dismissed as usual and the faithful continue with the liturgy of the eucharist.*

## 1029  FIFTH SUNDAY OF LENT / B

**READING I**                                   *Jeremiah 31:31–34 / 35*

**RESPONSORIAL PSALM**                          *Psalm 51:3–4, 12–13, 14–15*

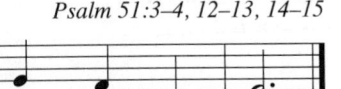

Cre - ate in me, cre - ate in me  a  clean heart, O  God.

Have mercy on me, O God,
　according to your merciful love;
according to your great compassion,
　blot out my transgressions.
Wash me completely from my iniquity,
　and cleanse me from my sin. ℟.

Create a pure heart for me, O God;
　renew a steadfast spirit within me.

Do not cast me away from your presence;
　take not your holy spirit from me. ℟.

Restore in me the joy of your salvation;
　sustain in me a willing spirit.
I will teach transgressors your ways,
　that sinners may return to you. ℟.

**READING II**                                  *Hebrews 5:7–9*

**GOSPEL**                                       *John 12:20–33*

**THIRD SCRUTINY**
*See no. 1028*

## 1030  FIFTH SUNDAY OF LENT / C

**READING I**                                   *Isaiah 43:16–21 / 36*

**RESPONSORIAL PSALM**                          *Psalm 126:1–2ab, 2cd–3, 4–5, 6*

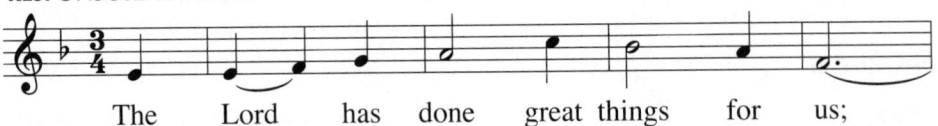

The  Lord  has  done  great things  for  us;

we  are  filled  with  joy.

When the LORD brought back the exiles
　of Sion,
　we thought we were dreaming.
Then was our mouth filled with laughter;
　on our tongues, songs of joy. ℟.

Then the nations themselves said,
　"What great deeds
　the LORD worked for them!"
What great deeds the LORD worked for
　us!
　Indeed, we were glad. ℟.

Bring back our exiles, O LORD,
 as streams in the south.
Those who are sowing in tears
 will sing when they reap. ℟.

They go out, they go out, full of tears,
 bearing seed for the sowing;
they come back, they come back with
 a song,
 bearing their sheaves. ℟.

**READING II**                                              *Philippians 3:8–14*

**GOSPEL**                                                      *John 8:1–11*

**THIRD SCRUTINY**
*See no. 1028*

---

## PALM SUNDAY OF THE PASSION OF THE LORD          1031

Passion or Palm Sunday is the last Sunday in Lent. Its closeness to the end of Lent
has given this liturgy two distinct features: the procession with palms and the gospel
reading of the Lord's passion. The blessing and carrying of palms celebrates Jesus'
entrance into Jerusalem to accomplish his paschal mystery. The reading of the passion comes as a conclusion to all the gospel readings of the lenten Sundays: these
scriptures yearly prepare catechumens and the faithful to approach the celebration
of Christ's death and resurrection. That celebration takes place most especially in
the sacraments of initiation at the Easter Vigil.

## COMMEMORATION OF THE LORD'S
## ENTRANCE INTO JERUSALEM

*This rite may be very simple or may involve the entire assembly in a procession with the blessing of
palms and the gospel reading of Jesus' entrance into Jerusalem. Depending on the local Church,
then, some of the following hymns, psalms and readings will be used.*

**OPENING ANTIPHON**                                              1032
*The following or another appropriate acclamation may be sung.*

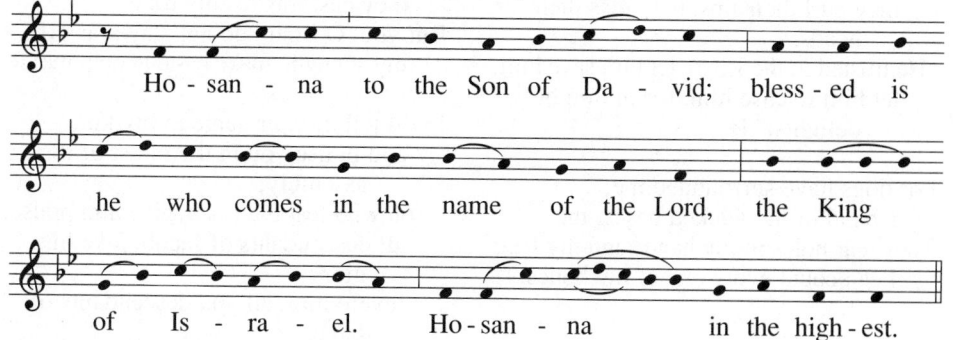

Ho - san - na to the Son of Da - vid; bless - ed is
he who comes in the name of the Lord, the King
of Is - ra - el. Ho - san - na in the high - est.

Text: ICEL, © 2010
Music: ICEL, © 2010; acc. by Richard Proulx, © 1985, 2011, GIA Publications, Inc.

**BLESSING OF BRANCHES**                                          1033
*All hold branches as these are blessed. The branches may be of palm or from a tree that is native
to the area. The green or flowering branches signify the victory of life.*

| | |
|---|---|
| **GOSPEL / A** | *Matthew 21:1–11 / 37* |
| **GOSPEL / B** | *Mark 11:1–10 or John 12:12–16* |
| **GOSPEL / C** | *Luke 19:28–40* |

## 1034 PROCESSION

*All join in the procession or at least in the song. Such a movement of people expresses the experience of Lent: the Church has been called to move on, to go ever further toward the paschal mystery of death and resurrection. Hymn no. 498, or another appropriate song, is sung.*

*This dialogue may be used:*

*Priest, deacon, or other minister:* Let us go forth in peace.

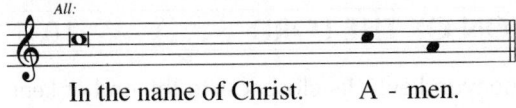

In the name of Christ.     A - men.

*The commemoration of the Lord's entrance into Jerusalem, whether this is done in a simple or solemn manner, concludes with the opening prayer of the Mass.*

---

# 1035  LITURGY OF THE WORD / ABC

| | |
|---|---|
| **READING I** | *Isaiah 50:4–7 / 38* |
| **RESPONSORIAL PSALM** | *Psalm 22:8–9, 17–18a, 19–20, 23–24* |

My God, my God,     why have you a - ban-doned me?

All who see me deride me;
  they curl their lips, they toss their
    heads:
"He trusted in the LORD, let him save him;
  let him release him, for in him he
    delights." ℟.

For dogs have surrounded me;
  a band of the wicked besets me.
They tear holes in my hands and my feet;
  I can count every one of my bones. ℟.

They divide my clothing among them,
  they cast lots for my robe.
But you, O LORD, do not stay afar off;
  my strength, make haste to help me! ℟.

I will tell of your name to my kin,
  and praise you in the midst of the
    assembly;
"You who fear the LORD, give him praise;
  all descendants of Jacob, give him
    glory;
  revere him, all you descendants of
    Israel. ℟.

| | |
|---|---|
| **READING II** | *Philippians 2:6–11* |

## GOSPEL / A

*For short form read only the part in brackets.*

One of the Twelve, who was called Judas Iscariot, went to the chief priests and said, "What are you willing to give me if I hand him over to you?" They paid him thirty pieces of silver, and from that time on he looked for an opportunity to hand him over.

On the first day of the Feast of Unleavened Bread, the disciples approached Jesus and said, "Where do you want us to prepare for you to eat the Passover?" He said, "Go into the city to a certain man and tell him, 'The teacher says, "My appointed time draws near; in your house I shall celebrate the Passover with my disciples."'" The disciples then did as Jesus had ordered, and prepared the Passover.

When it was evening, he reclined at table with the Twelve. And while they were eating, he said, "Amen, I say to you, one of you will betray me." Deeply distressed at this, they began to say to him one after another, "Surely it is not I, Lord?" He said in reply, "He who has dipped his hand into the dish with me is the one who will betray me. The Son of Man indeed goes, as it is written of him, but woe to that man by whom the Son of Man is betrayed. It would be better for that man if he had never been born." Then Judas, his betrayer, said in reply, "Surely it is not I, Rabbi?" He answered, "You have said so."

While they were eating, Jesus took bread, said the blessing, broke it, and giving it to his disciples said, "Take and eat; this is my body." Then he took a cup, gave thanks, and gave it to them, saying, "Drink from it, all of you, for this is my blood of the covenant, which will be shed on behalf of many for the forgiveness of sins. I tell you, from now on I shall not drink this fruit of the vine until the day when I drink it with you new in the kingdom of my Father." Then, after singing a hymn, they went out to the Mount of Olives.

Then Jesus said to them, "This night all of you will have your faith in me shaken, for it is written:

*I will strike the shepherd,*
    *and the sheep of the flock will be dispersed;*
but after I have been raised up, I shall go before you to Galilee." Peter said to him in reply, "Though all may have their faith in you shaken, mine will never be." Jesus said to him, "Amen, I say to you, this very night before the cock crows, you will deny me three times." Peter said to him, "Even though I should have to die with you, I will not deny you." And all the disciples spoke likewise.

Then Jesus came with them to a place called Gethsemane, and he said to his disciples, "Sit here while I go over there and pray." He took along Peter and the two sons of Zebedee, and began to feel sorrow and distress. Then he said to them, "My soul is sorrowful even to death. Remain here and keep watch with me." He advanced a little and fell prostrate in prayer, saying, "My Father, if it is possible, let this cup pass from me; yet, not as I will, but as you will." When he returned to his disciples he found them asleep. He said to Peter, "So you could not keep watch with me for one hour? Watch and pray that you may not undergo the test. The spirit is willing, but the flesh is weak." Withdrawing a second time, he prayed again, "My Father, if it is not possible that this cup pass without my drinking it, your will be done!" Then he returned once more and found them asleep, for they could not keep their eyes open. He left them and withdrew again and prayed a third time, saying the same thing again. Then he returned to his disciples and said to them, "Are you still sleeping and taking your rest? Behold, the hour is at hand when the Son of Man is to be handed over to sinners. Get up, let us go. Look, my betrayer is at hand."

While he was still speaking, Judas, one of the Twelve, arrived, accompanied by a large crowd, with swords and clubs, who had come from the chief priests and the elders of the people. His betrayer had arranged a sign with them, saying, "The man I shall kiss is the one; arrest him." Immediately he went over to Jesus and said, "Hail, Rabbi!" and he kissed him. Jesus answered him, "Friend, do what you have come for." Then stepping forward they laid hands on Jesus and arrested him. And behold, one of those who accompanied Jesus put his hand to his sword, drew it, and struck the high priest's servant, cutting off his ear. Then Jesus said to him, "Put your sword back into its sheath, for all who take the sword will perish by the sword. Do you think that I cannot call upon my Father and he will not provide me at this moment with more than twelve legions of angels? But then how would the Scriptures be fulfilled which say that it must come to pass in this way?" At that hour Jesus said to the crowds, "Have you come out as against a robber, with swords and clubs to seize me? Day after day I sat teaching in the temple area, yet you did not arrest me. But all this has come to pass that the writings of the prophets may be fulfilled." Then all the disciples left him and fled.

Those who had arrested Jesus led him away to Caiaphas the high priest, where the scribes and the elders were assembled. Peter was following him at a distance as far as the high priest's courtyard, and going inside he sat down with the servants to see the outcome. The chief priests and the entire Sanhedrin kept trying to obtain false testimony against Jesus in order to put him to death, but they found none, though many false witnesses came forward. Finally two came forward who stated, "This man said, 'I can destroy the temple of God and within three days rebuild it.'" The high priest rose and addressed him, "Have you no answer? What are these men testifying against you?" But Jesus was silent. Then the high priest said to him, "I order you to tell us under oath before the living God whether you are the Christ, the Son of God." Jesus said to him in reply, "You have said so. But I tell you: From now on you will see

'the Son of Man

seated at the right hand of the Power'

and 'coming on the clouds of heaven.'"

Then the high priest tore his robes and said, "He has blasphemed! What further need have we of witnesses? You have now heard the blasphemy; what is your opinion?" They said in reply, "He deserves to die!" Then they spat in his face and struck him, while some slapped him, saying, "Prophesy for us, Christ: who is it that struck you?"

Now Peter was sitting outside in the courtyard. One of the maids came over to him and said, "You too were with Jesus the Galilean." But he denied it in front of everyone, saying, "I do not know what you are talking about!" As he went out to the gate, another girl saw him and said to those who were there, "This man was with Jesus the Nazorean." Again he denied it with an oath, "I do not know the man!" A little later the bystanders came over and said to Peter, "Surely you too are one of them; even your speech gives you away." At that he began to curse and to swear, "I do not know the man." And immediately a cock crowed. Then Peter remembered the word that Jesus had spoken: "Before the cock crows you will deny me three times." He went out and began to weep bitterly.

When it was morning, all the chief priests and the elders of the people took counsel against Jesus to put him to death. They bound him, led him away, and handed him over to Pilate, the governor.

Then Judas, his betrayer, seeing that Jesus had been condemned, deeply regretted what he had done. He returned the thirty pieces of silver to the chief priests and elders, saying, "I have sinned in betraying innocent blood." They said, "What is that to us? Look to it yourself." Flinging the money into the temple, he departed and went off and hanged himself. The chief priests gathered up the money, but said, "It is not lawful to deposit this in the temple treasury, for it is the price of blood." After consultation, they used it to buy the potter's field as a burial place for foreigners. That is why that field even today is called the Field of Blood. Then was fulfilled what had been said through Jeremiah the prophet, *And they took the thirty pieces of silver, the value of a man with a price on his head, a price set by some of the Israelites, and they paid it out for the potter's field just as the Lord had commanded me.*

Now [Jesus stood before the governor, and he questioned him, "Are you the king of the Jews?" Jesus said, "You say so." And when he was accused by the chief priests and elders, he made no answer. Then Pilate said to him, "Do you not hear how many things they are testifying against you?" But he did not answer him one word, so that the governor was greatly amazed.

Now on the occasion of the feast the governor was accustomed to release to the crowd one prisoner whom they wished. And at that time they had a notorious prisoner called Barabbas. So when they had assembled, Pilate said to them, "Which one do you want me to release to you, Barabbas, or Jesus called Christ?" For he knew that it was out of envy that they had handed him over. While he was still seated on the bench, his wife sent him a message, "Have nothing to do with that righteous man. I suffered much in a dream today because of him." The chief priests and the elders persuaded the crowds to ask for Barabbas but to destroy Jesus. The governor said to them in reply, "Which of the two do you want me to release to you?" They answered, "Barabbas!" Pilate said to them, "Then what shall I do with Jesus called Christ?" They all said, "Let him be crucified!" But he said, "Why? What evil has he done?" They only shouted the louder, "Let him be crucified!" When Pilate saw that he was not succeeding at all, but that a riot was breaking out instead, he took water and washed his hands in the sight of the crowd, saying, "I am innocent of this man's blood. Look to it yourselves." And the whole people said in reply, "His blood be upon us and upon our children." Then he released Barabbas to them, but after he had Jesus scourged, he handed him over to be crucified.

Then the soldiers of the governor took Jesus inside the praetorium and gathered the whole cohort around him. They stripped off his clothes and threw a scarlet military cloak about him. Weaving a crown out of thorns, they placed it on his head, and a reed in his right hand. And kneeling before him, they mocked him, saying, "Hail, King of the Jews!" They spat upon him and took the reed and kept striking him on the head. And when they had mocked him, they stripped him of the cloak, dressed him in his own clothes, and led him off to crucify him.

As they were going out, they met a Cyrenian named Simon; this man they pressed into service to carry his cross.

And when they came to a place called Golgotha—which means Place of the Skull—, they gave Jesus wine to drink mixed with gall. But when he had tasted it, he refused to drink. After they had crucified him, they divided his garments by casting lots; then they sat down and kept watch over him there. And they placed over his head the written charge against him: This is Jesus, the King of the Jews. Two revolutionaries were crucified with him, one on his right and the other on his left. Those passing by reviled him, shaking their heads and saying, "You who would destroy the temple and rebuild it in three days, save yourself, if you are the Son of God, and come down from the cross!" Likewise the chief priests with the scribes and elders mocked him and said, "He saved others; he cannot save himself. So he is the king of Israel! Let him come down from the cross now, and we will believe in him. He trusted in God; let him deliver him now if he wants him. For he said, 'I am the Son of God.'" The revolutionaries who were crucified with him also kept abusing him in the same way.

From noon onward, darkness came over the whole land until three in the afternoon. And about three o'clock Jesus cried out in a loud voice, "*Eli, Eli, lema sabachthani?*" which means, "My God, my God, why have you forsaken me?" Some of the bystanders who heard it said, "This one is calling for Elijah." Immediately one of them ran to get a sponge; he soaked it in wine, and putting it on a reed, gave it to him to drink. But the rest said, "Wait, let us see if Elijah comes to save him." But Jesus cried out again in a loud voice, and gave up his spirit.

*Here all kneel and pause for a short time.*

And behold, the veil of the sanctuary was torn in two from top to bottom. The earth quaked, rocks were split, tombs were opened, and the bodies of many saints who had fallen asleep were raised. And coming forth from their tombs after his resurrection, they entered the holy city and appeared to many. The centurion and the men with him who were keeping watch over Jesus feared greatly when they saw the earthquake and all that was happening, and they said, "Truly, this was the Son of God!"] There were many women there, looking on from a distance, who had followed Jesus from Galilee, ministering to him. Among them were Mary Magdalene and Mary the mother of James and Joseph, and the mother of the sons of Zebedee.

When it was evening, there came a rich man from Arimathea named Joseph, who was himself a disciple of Jesus. He went to Pilate and asked for the body of Jesus; then Pilate ordered it to be handed over. Taking the body, Joseph wrapped it in clean linen and laid it in his new tomb that he had hewn in the rock. Then he rolled a huge stone across the entrance to the tomb and departed. But Mary Magdalene and the other Mary remained sitting there, facing the tomb. The next day, the one following the day of preparation, the chief priests and the Pharisees gathered before Pilate and said, "Sir, we remember that this impostor while still alive said, 'After three days I will be raised up.' Give orders, then, that the grave be secured until the third day, lest his disciples come and steal him and say to the people, 'He has been raised from the dead.' This last imposture would be worse than the first." Pilate said to them, "The guard is yours; go, secure it as best you can." So they went and secured the tomb by fixing a seal to the stone and setting the guard.

## GOSPEL / B

*For short form read only the part in brackets.*

The Passover and the Feast of Unleavened Bread were to take place in two days' time. So the chief priests and the scribes were seeking a way to arrest him by treachery and put him to death. They said, "Not during the festival, for fear that there may be a riot among the people."

When he was in Bethany reclining at table in the house of Simon the leper, a woman came with an alabaster jar of perfumed oil, costly genuine spikenard. She broke the alabaster jar and poured it on his head. There were some who were indignant. "Why has there been this waste of perfumed oil? It could have been sold for more than three hundred days' wages and the money given to the poor." They were infuriated with her. Jesus said, "Let her alone. Why do you make trouble for her? She has done a good thing for me. The poor you will always have with you, and whenever you wish you can do good to them, but you will not always have me. She has done what she could. She has anticipated anointing my body for burial. Amen, I say to you, wherever the gospel is proclaimed to the whole world, what she has done will be told in memory of her."

Then Judas Iscariot, one of the Twelve, went off to the chief priests to hand him over to them. When they heard him they were pleased and promised to pay him money. Then he looked for an opportunity to hand him over.

On the first day of the Feast of Unleavened Bread, when they sacrificed the Passover lamb, his disciples said to him, "Where do you want us to go and prepare for you to eat the Passover?" He sent two of his disciples and said to them, "Go into the city and a man will meet you, carrying a jar of water. Follow him. Wherever he enters, say to the master of the house, 'The Teacher says, "Where is my guest room where I may eat the Passover with my disciples?"' Then he will show you a large upper room furnished and ready. Make the preparations for us there." The disciples then went off, entered the city, and found it just as he had told them; and they prepared the Passover.

When it was evening, he came with the Twelve. And as they reclined at table and were eating, Jesus said, "Amen, I say to you, one of you will betray me, one who is eating with me." They began to be distressed and to say to him, one by one, "Surely it is not I?" He said to them, "One of the Twelve, the one who dips with me into the dish. For the Son of Man indeed goes, as it is written of him, but woe to that man by whom the Son of Man is betrayed. It would be better for that man if he had never been born."

While they were eating, he took bread, said the blessing, broke it, and gave it to them, and said, "Take it; this is my body." Then he took a cup, gave thanks, and gave it to them, and they all drank from it. He said to them, "This is my blood of the covenant, which will be shed for many. Amen, I say to you, I shall not drink again the fruit of the vine until the day when I drink it new in the kingdom of God." Then, after singing a hymn, they went out to the Mount of Olives.

Then Jesus said to them, "All of you will have your faith shaken, for it is written:

*I will strike the shepherd,*
*and the sheep will be dispersed.*

But after I have been raised up, I shall go before you to Galilee." Peter said to him, "Even though all should have their faith shaken, mine will not be." Then Jesus said to him, "Amen, I say to you, this very night before the cock crows twice you will deny me three times." But he vehemently replied, "Even though I should have to die with you, I will not deny you." And they all spoke similarly.

Then they came to a place named Gethsemane, and he said to his disciples, "Sit here while I pray." He took with him Peter, James, and John, and began to be troubled and distressed. Then he said to them, "My soul is sorrowful even to death. Remain here and keep watch." He advanced a little and fell to the ground and prayed that if it were possible the hour might pass by him; he said, "Abba, Father, all things are possible to you. Take this cup away from me, but not what I will but what you will." When he returned he found them asleep. He said to Peter, "Simon, are you asleep? Could you not keep watch for one hour? Watch and pray that you may not undergo the test. The spirit is willing but the flesh is weak." Withdrawing again, he prayed, saying the same thing. Then he returned once more and found them asleep, for they could not keep their eyes open and did not know what to answer him. He returned a third time and said to them, "Are you still sleeping and taking your rest? It is enough. The hour has come. Behold, the Son of Man is to be handed over to sinners. Get up, let us go. See, my betrayer is at hand."

Then, while he was still speaking, Judas, one of the Twelve, arrived, accompanied by a crowd with swords and clubs who had come from the chief priests, the scribes, and the elders. His betrayer had arranged a signal with them, saying, "The man I shall kiss is the one; arrest him and lead him away securely." He came and immediately went over to him and said, "Rabbi." And he kissed him. At this they laid hands on him and arrested him. One of the bystanders drew his sword, struck the high priest's servant, and cut off his ear. Jesus said to them in reply, "Have you come out as against a robber, with swords and clubs, to seize me? Day after day I was with you teaching in the temple area, yet you did not arrest me; but that the Scriptures may be fulfilled." And they all left him and fled. Now a young man followed him wearing nothing but a linen cloth about his body. They seized him, but he left the cloth behind and ran off naked.

They led Jesus away to the high priest, and all the chief priests and the elders and the scribes came together. Peter followed him at a distance into the high priest's courtyard and was seated with the guards, warming himself at the fire. The chief priests and the entire Sanhedrin kept trying to obtain testimony against Jesus in order to put him to death, but they found none. Many gave false witness against him, but their testimony did not agree. Some took the stand and testified falsely against him, alleging, "We heard him say, 'I will destroy this temple made with hands and within three days I will build another not made with hands.'" Even so their testimony did not agree. The high priest rose before the assembly and questioned Jesus, saying, "Have you no answer? What are these men testifying against you?" But he was silent and answered nothing. Again the high priest asked him and said to him, "Are you the Christ, the son of the Blessed One?"

Then Jesus answered, "I am;
and 'you will see the Son of Man
seated at the right hand of the Power
and coming with the clouds of heaven.'"

At that the high priest tore his garments and said, "What further need have we of witnesses? You have heard the blasphemy. What do you think?" They all condemned him as deserving to die. Some began to spit on him. They blindfolded him and struck him and said to him, "Prophesy!" And the guards greeted him with blows.

While Peter was below in the courtyard, one of the high priest's maids came along. Seeing Peter warming himself, she looked intently at him and said, "You too were with the Nazarene, Jesus." But he denied it saying, "I neither know nor understand what you are talking about." So he went out into the outer court. Then the cock crowed. The maid saw him and began again to say to the bystanders, "This man is one of them." Once again he denied it. A little later the bystanders said to Peter once more, "Surely you are one of them; for you too are a Galilean." He began to curse and to swear, "I do not know this man about whom you are talking." And immediately a cock crowed a second time. Then Peter remembered the word that Jesus had said to him, "Before the cock crows twice you will deny me three times." He broke down and wept.

[As soon as morning came, the chief priests with the elders and the scribes, that is, the whole Sanhedrin held a council. They bound Jesus, led him away, and handed him over to Pilate. Pilate questioned him, "Are you the king of the Jews?" He said to him in reply, "You say so." The chief priests accused him of many things. Again Pilate questioned him, "Have you no answer? See how many things they accuse you of." Jesus gave him no further answer, so that Pilate was amazed.

Now on the occasion of the feast he used to release to them one prisoner whom they requested. A man called Barabbas was then in prison along with the rebels who had committed murder in a rebellion. The crowd came forward and began to ask him to do for them as he was accustomed. Pilate answered, "Do you want me to release to you the king of the Jews?" For he knew that it was out of envy that the chief priests had handed him over. But the chief priests stirred up the crowd to have him release Barabbas for them instead. Pilate again said to them in reply, "Then what do you want me to do with the man you call the king of the Jews?" They shouted again, "Crucify him." Pilate said to them, "Why? What evil has he done?" They only shouted the louder, "Crucify him." So Pilate, wishing to satisfy the crowd, released Barabbas to them and, after he had Jesus scourged, handed him over to be crucified.

The soldiers led him away inside the palace, that is, the praetorium, and assembled the whole cohort. They clothed him in purple and, weaving a crown of thorns, placed it on him. They began to salute him with, "Hail, King of the Jews!" and kept striking his head with a reed and spitting upon him. They knelt before him in homage. And when they had mocked him, they stripped him of the purple cloak, dressed him in his own clothes, and led him out to crucify him.

They pressed into service a passer-by, Simon, a Cyrenian, who was coming in from the country, the father of Alexander and Rufus, to carry his cross.

They brought him to the place of Golgotha —which is translated Place of the Skull—. They gave him wine drugged with myrrh, but he did not take it. Then they crucified him and divided his garments by casting lots for them to see what each should take. It was nine o'clock in the morning when they crucified him. The inscription of the charge against him read, "The King of the Jews." With him they crucified two revolutionaries, one on his right and one on his left. Those passing by reviled him, shaking their heads and saying, "Aha! You who would destroy the temple and rebuild it in three days, save yourself by coming down from the cross." Likewise the chief priests, with the scribes, mocked him among themselves and said, "He saved others; he cannot save himself. Let the Christ, the King of Israel, come down now from the cross that we may see and believe." Those who were crucified with him also kept abusing him.

At noon darkness came over the whole land until three in the afternoon. And at three o'clock Jesus cried out in a loud voice, "*Eloi, Eloi, lema sabachthani?*" which is translated, "My God, my God, why have you forsaken me?" Some of the bystanders who heard it said, "Look, he is calling Elijah." One of them ran, soaked a sponge with wine, put it on a reed and gave it to him to drink saying, "Wait, let us see if Elijah comes to take him down." Jesus gave a loud cry and breathed his last.

*Here all kneel and pause for a short time.*

The veil of the sanctuary was torn in two from top to bottom. When the centurion who stood facing him saw how he breathed his last he said, "Truly this man was the Son of God!"] There were also women looking on from a distance. Among them were Mary Magdalene, Mary the mother of the younger James and of Joses, and Salome. These women had followed him when he was in Galilee and ministered to him. There were also many other women who had come up with him to Jerusalem.

When it was already evening, since it was the day of preparation, the day before the sabbath, Joseph of Arimathea, a distinguished member of the council, who was himself awaiting the kingdom of God, came and courageously went to Pilate and asked for the body of Jesus. Pilate was amazed that he was already dead. He summoned the centurion and asked him if Jesus had already died. And when he learned of it from the centurion, he gave the body to Joseph. Having bought a linen cloth, he took him down, wrapped him in the linen cloth, and laid him in a tomb that had been hewn out of the rock. Then he rolled a stone against the entrance to the tomb. Mary Magdalene and Mary the mother of Joses watched where he was laid.

## 1038 GOSPEL / C                          *Luke 22:14—23:56 or 23:1—49*

*For short form read only the part in brackets.*

When the hour came, Jesus took his place at table with the apostles. He said to them, "I have eagerly desired to eat this Passover with you before I suffer, for, I tell you, I shall not eat it again until there is fulfillment in the kingdom of God." Then he took a cup, gave thanks, and said, "Take this and share it among yourselves; for I tell you that from this time on I shall not drink of the fruit of the vine until the kingdom of God comes." Then he took the bread, said the blessing, broke it, and gave it to them, saying, "This is my body, which will be given for you; do this in memory of me." And likewise the cup after they had eaten, saying, "This cup is the new covenant in my blood, which will be shed for you.

"And yet behold, the hand of the one who is to betray me is with me on the table; for the Son of Man indeed goes as it has been determined; but woe to that man by whom he is betrayed." And they began to debate among themselves who among them would do such a deed.

Then an argument broke out among them about which of them should be regarded as the greatest. He said to them, "The kings of the Gentiles lord it over them and those in authority over them are addressed as 'Benefactors'; but among you it shall not be so. Rather, let the greatest among you be as the youngest, and the leader as the servant. For who is greater: the one seated at table or the one who serves? Is it not the one seated at table? I am among you as the one who serves. It is you who have stood by me in my trials; and I confer a kingdom on you, just as my Father has conferred one on me, that you may eat and drink at my table in my kingdom; and you will sit on thrones judging the twelve tribes of Israel.

"Simon, Simon, behold Satan has demanded to sift all of you like wheat, but I have prayed that your own faith may not fail; and once you have turned back, you must strengthen your brothers." He said to him, "Lord, I am prepared to go to prison and to die with you." But he replied, "I tell you, Peter, before the cock crows this day, you will deny three times that you know me."

He said to them, "When I sent you forth without a money bag or a sack or sandals, were you in need of anything?" "No, nothing," they replied. He said to them, "But now one who has a money bag should take it, and likewise a sack, and one who does not have a sword should sell his cloak and buy one. For I tell you that this Scripture must be fulfilled in me, namely, *He was counted among the wicked*; and indeed what is written about me is coming to fulfillment." Then they said, "Lord, look, there are two swords here." But he replied, "It is enough!"

Then going out, he went, as was his custom, to the Mount of Olives, and the disciples followed him. When he arrived at the place he said to them, "Pray that you may not undergo the test." After withdrawing about a stone's throw from them and kneeling, he prayed, saying, "Father, if you are willing, take this cup away from me; still, not my will but yours be done." And to strengthen him an angel from heaven appeared to him. He was in such agony and he prayed so fervently that his sweat became like drops of blood falling on the ground. When he rose from prayer and returned to his disciples, he found them sleeping from grief. He said to them, "Why are you sleeping? Get up and pray that you may not undergo the test."

While he was still speaking, a crowd approached and in front was one of the Twelve, a man named Judas. He went up to Jesus to kiss him. Jesus said to him, "Judas, are you betraying the Son of Man with a kiss?" His disciples realized what was about to happen, and they asked, "Lord, shall we strike with a sword?" And one of them struck the high priest's servant and cut off his right ear. But Jesus said in reply, "Stop, no more of this!" Then he touched the servant's ear and healed him. And Jesus said to the chief priests and temple guards and elders who had come for him, "Have you come out as against a robber, with swords and clubs? Day after day I was with you in the temple area, and you did not seize me; but this is your hour, the time for the power of darkness."

After arresting him they led him away and took him into the house of the high priest; Peter was following at a distance. They lit a fire in the middle of the courtyard and sat around it, and Peter sat down with them. When a maid saw him seated in the light, she looked intently at him and said, "This man too was with him." But he denied it saying, "Woman, I do not know him." A short while later someone else saw him and said, "You too are one of them"; but Peter answered, "My friend, I am not." About an hour later, still another insisted, "Assuredly, this man too was with him, for he also is a Galilean." But Peter said, "My friend, I do not know what you are talking about." Just as he was saying this, the cock crowed, and the Lord turned and looked at Peter; and Peter remembered the word of the Lord, how he had said to him, "Before the cock crows today, you will deny me three times." He went out and began to weep bitterly. The men who held Jesus in custody were ridiculing and beating him. They blindfolded him and questioned him, saying, "Prophesy! Who is it that struck you?" And they reviled him in saying many other things against him.

When day came the council of elders of the people met, both chief priests and scribes, and they brought him before their Sanhedrin. They said, "If you are the Christ, tell us," but he replied to them, "If I tell you, you will not believe, and if I question, you will not respond. But from this time on the Son of Man will be seated at the right hand of the power of God." They all asked, "Are you then the Son of God?" He replied to them, "You say that I am." Then they said, "What further need have we for testimony? We have heard it from his own mouth."

[*Short form begins:* The elders of the people, chief priests and scribes, arose and brought Jesus before Pilate.] Then the whole assembly of them arose and brought him before Pilate. [They brought charges against him, saying, "We found this man misleading our people; he opposes the payment of taxes to Caesar and maintains that he is the Christ, a king." Pilate asked him, "Are you the king of the Jews?" He said to him in reply, "You say so." Pilate then addressed the chief priests and the crowds, "I find this man not guilty." But they were adamant and said, "He is inciting the people with his teaching throughout all Judea, from Galilee where he began even to here."

On hearing this Pilate asked if the man was a Galilean; and upon learning that he was under Herod's jurisdiction, he sent him to Herod who was in Jerusalem at that time. Herod was very glad to see Jesus; he had been wanting to see him for a long time, for he had heard about him and had been hoping to see him perform some sign. He questioned him at length, but he gave him no answer. The chief priests and scribes, meanwhile, stood by accusing him harshly. Herod and his soldiers treated him contemptuously and mocked him, and after clothing him in resplendent garb, he sent him back to Pilate. Herod and Pilate became friends that very day, even though they had been enemies formerly. Pilate then summoned the chief priests, the rulers, and the people and said to them, "You brought this man to me and accused him of inciting the people to revolt. I have conducted my investigation in your presence and have not found this man guilty of the charges you have brought against him, nor did Herod, for he sent him back to us. So no capital crime has been committed by him. Therefore I shall have him flogged and then release him."

But all together they shouted out, "Away with this man! Release Barabbas to us." (Now Barabbas had been imprisoned for a rebellion that had taken place in the city and for murder.) Again Pilate addressed them, still wishing to release Jesus, but they continued their shouting, "Crucify him! Crucify him!" Pilate addressed them a third time, "What evil has this man done? I found him guilty of no capital crime. Therefore I shall have him flogged and then release him." With loud shouts, however, they persisted in calling for his crucifixion, and their voices prevailed. The verdict of Pilate was that their demand should be granted. So he released the man who had been imprisoned for rebellion and murder, for whom they asked, and he handed Jesus over to them to deal with as they wished.

As they led him away they took hold of a certain Simon, a Cyrenian, who was coming in from the country; and after laying the cross on him, they made him carry it behind Jesus. A large crowd of people followed Jesus, including many women who mourned and lamented him. Jesus turned to them and said, "Daughters of Jerusalem, do not weep for me; weep instead for yourselves and for your children for indeed, the days are coming when people will say, 'Blessed are the barren, the wombs that never bore and the breasts that never nursed.' At that time people will say to the mountains, 'Fall upon us!' and to the hills, 'Cover us!' for if these things are done when the wood is green what will happen when it is dry?" Now two others, both criminals, were led away with him to be executed.

When they came to the place called the Skull, they crucified him and the criminals there, one on his right, the other on his left. Then Jesus said, "Father, forgive them, they know not what they do." They divided his garments by casting lots. The people stood by and watched; the rulers, meanwhile, sneered at him and said, "He saved others, let him save himself if he is the chosen one, the Christ of God." Even the soldiers jeered at him. As they approached to offer him wine they called out, "If you are King of the Jews, save yourself." Above him there was an inscription that read, "This is the King of the Jews."

Now one of the criminals hanging there reviled Jesus, saying, "Are you not the Christ? Save yourself and us." The other, however, rebuking him, said in reply, "Have you no fear of God, for you are subject to the same condemnation? And indeed, we have been condemned justly, for the sentence we received corresponds to our crimes, but this man has done nothing criminal." Then he said, "Jesus, remember me when you come into your kingdom." He replied to him, "Amen, I say to you, today you will be with me in Paradise."

It was now about noon and darkness came over the whole land until three in the afternoon because of an eclipse of the sun. Then the veil of the temple was torn down the middle. Jesus cried out in a loud voice, "Father, into your hands I commend my spirit"; and when he had said this he breathed his last.

*Here all kneel and pause for a short time.*

The centurion who witnessed what had happened glorified God and said, "This man was innocent beyond doubt." When all the people who had gathered for this spectacle saw what had happened, they returned home beating their breasts; but all his acquaintances stood at a distance, including the women who had followed him from Galilee and saw these events.]

Now there was a virtuous and righteous man named Joseph who, though he was a member of the council, had not consented to their plan of action. He came from the Jewish town of Arimathea and was awaiting the kingdom of God. He went to Pilate and asked for the body of Jesus. After he had taken the body down, he wrapped it in a linen cloth and laid him in a rock-hewn tomb in which no one had yet been buried. It was the day of preparation, and the sabbath was about to begin. The women who had come from Galilee with him followed behind, and when they had seen the tomb and the way in which his body was laid in it, they returned and prepared spices and perfumed oils. Then they rested on the sabbath according to the commandment.

# Paschal Triduum

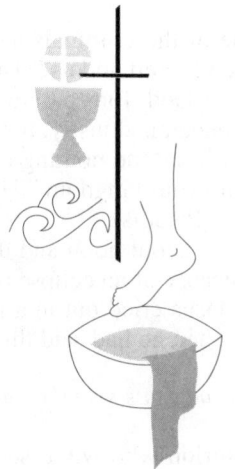

### 1039

"The Easter Triduum of the passion and resurrection of Christ is...the culmination of the entire liturgical year. What Sunday is to the week, the solemnity of Easter is to the liturgical year" (General Norms for the Liturgical Year, #18).

Lent ends quietly on Thursday afternoon. The Church enters the Triduum ("three days"). On Thursday night the Church begins a time of prayer and fasting, a time of keeping watch, that lasts into the great Vigil between Saturday and Sunday. The Church emphasizes that the fasting of Good Friday and, if possible, Holy Saturday is integral to the keeping of these days and the preparation for the sacraments of initiation celebrated at the Vigil. On Thursday night and on Friday afternoon or evening the Church gathers to pray and to remember the many facets of the single mystery.

## 1040   THURSDAY OF THE LORD'S SUPPER: EVENING MASS

On Thursday night Lent has ended and the Church, at this Mass of the Lord's Supper, enters into the Paschal Triduum. From the very first moment the all-embracing experience of these three days is proclaimed: "We should glory in the Cross of our Lord Jesus Christ, in whom is our salvation, life and resurrection, through whom we are saved and delivered." This is the whole of the great Triduum. On Thursday night, the liturgy draws us toward this through Scripture, through the mandatum or washing of feet, which is the direct expression of our service to one another and the world, and through the eucharistic banquet itself.

### LITURGY OF THE WORD / ABC

**READING I** *Exodus 12:1–8, 11–14 / 39*

**RESPONSORIAL PSALM** *Psalm 116:12–13, 15 and 16bc, 17–18*

Our bless-ing-cup is a com-mun-ion with the Blood of Christ.

| | |
|---|---|
| How can I repay the LORD<br>   for all his goodness to me? | The cup of salvation I will raise;<br>   I will call on the name of the LORD. ℟. |

How precious in the eyes of the Lord
   is the death of his faithful.
Your servant am I, the son of your
   handmaid;
   you have loosened my bonds. ℟.

A thanksgiving sacrifice I make;
   I will call on the name of the Lord.
My vows to the Lord I will fulfill
   before all his people. ℟.

**READING II**                                              *I Corinthians 11:23–26*

**GOSPEL**                                                   *John 13:1–15*

## WASHING OF FEET                      1041

*The homily is followed by the washing of feet, the mandatum (from the Latin word for "command": "A new commandment I give to you..."). This is a simple gesture of humble service: the priest, assisted by other ministers, washes the feet of various members of the assembly. Such a gesture, with the song which accompanies it, speaks directly of the way of life Christians seek.*

*The Mass continues with the Prayer of the Faithful.*

## TRANSFER OF THE MOST BLESSED SACRAMENT    1042

*When the communion rite is concluded, the eucharistic bread that remains is solemnly carried from the altar to a specially prepared place of repose. Hail Our Savior's Glorious Body / Pange Lingua, no. 509, or another appropriate selection, accompanies the procession.*
   *The liturgy has no concluding rite, no dismissal. Rather, the Church continues to watch and pray throughout the Triduum.*

---

## GOOD FRIDAY: CELEBRATION OF THE PASSION OF THE LORD   1043

In Good Friday's liturgy of the word and adoration of the cross there is great solemnity as the Church ponders the "mystery of faith": the passion, death and resurrection of our Lord Jesus Christ. Fasting and praying during these days, the catechumens and the baptized assemble on Good Friday in the afternoon or evening for the Passion liturgy, which begins in silence.

## LITURGY OF THE WORD / ABC

**READING I**                                         *Isaiah 52:13—53:12 / 40*

**RESPONSORIAL PSALM**             *Psalm 31:2 and 6, 12–13, 15–16, 17 and 25*

Fa - ther, in - to your hands I com - mend my spir-it.

In you, O Lord, I take refuge.
   Let me never be put to shame.
   In your justice, set me free.
Into your hands I commend my spirit.
   You will redeem me, O Lord,
      O faithful God. ℟.

Because of all my foes

I have become a reproach,
an object of scorn to my neighbors
   and of fear to my friends.
Those who see me in the street
   flee from me.
I am forgotten, like someone dead,
   and have become like a broken
      vessel. ℟.

But as for me, I trust in you, O LORD;
I say, "You are my God.
My lot is in your hands, deliver me
from the hands of my enemies
and those who pursue me. ℟.

"Let your face shine on your servant.
Save me in your merciful love."
Be strong, let your heart take courage,
all who hope in the LORD. ℟.

## READING II

*Hebrews 4:14–16; 5:7–9*

## GOSPEL

*John 18:1 – 19:42*

Jesus went out with his disciples across the Kidron valley to where there was a garden, into which he and his disciples entered. Judas his betrayer also knew the place, because Jesus had often met there with his disciples. So Judas got a band of soldiers and guards from the chief priests and the Pharisees and went there with lanterns, torches, and weapons. Jesus, knowing everything that was going to happen to him, went out and said to them, "Whom are you looking for?" They answered him, "Jesus the Nazorean." He said to them, "I AM." Judas his betrayer was also with them. When he said to them, "I AM," they turned away and fell to the ground. So he again asked them, "Whom are you looking for?" They said, "Jesus the Nazorean." Jesus answered, "I told you that I AM. So if you are looking for me, let these men go." This was to fulfill what he had said, "I have not lost any of those you gave me." Then Simon Peter, who had a sword, drew it, struck the high priest's slave, and cut off his right ear. The slave's name was Malchus. Jesus said to Peter, "Put your sword into its scabbard. Shall I not drink the cup that the Father gave me?"

So the band of soldiers, the tribune, and the Jewish guards seized Jesus, bound him, and brought him to Annas first. He was the father-in-law of Caiaphas, who was high priest that year. It was Caiaphas who had counseled the Jews that it was better that one man should die rather than the people.

Simon Peter and another disciple followed Jesus. Now the other disciple was known to the high priest, and he entered the courtyard of the high priest with Jesus. But Peter stood at the gate outside. So the other disciple, the acquaintance of the high priest, went out and spoke to the gatekeeper and brought Peter in. Then the maid who was the gatekeeper said to Peter, "You are not one of this man's disciples, are you?" He said, "I am not." Now the slaves and the guards were standing around a charcoal fire that they had made, because it was cold, and were warming themselves. Peter was also standing there keeping warm.

The high priest questioned Jesus about his disciples and about his doctrine. Jesus answered him, "I have spoken publicly to the world. I have always taught in a synagogue or in the temple area where all the Jews gather, and in secret I have said nothing. Why ask me? Ask those who heard me what I said to them. They know what I said." When he had said this, one of the temple guards standing there struck Jesus and said, "Is this the way you answer the high priest?" Jesus answered him, "If I have spoken wrongly, testify to the wrong; but if I have spoken rightly, why do you strike me?" Then Annas sent him bound to Caiaphas the high priest.

Now Simon Peter was standing there keeping warm. And they said to him, "You are not one of his disciples, are you?" He denied it and said, "I am not." One of the slaves of the high priest, a relative of the one whose ear Peter had cut off, said, "Didn't I see you in the garden with him?" Again Peter denied it. And immediately the cock crowed.

Then they brought Jesus from Caiaphas to the praetorium. It was morning. And they themselves did not enter the praetorium, in order not to be defiled so that they could eat the Passover. So Pilate came out to them and said, "What charge do you bring against this man?" They answered and said to him, "If he were not a criminal, we would not have handed him over to you." At this, Pilate said to them, "Take him yourselves, and judge him according to your law." The Jews answered him, "We do not have the right to execute anyone," in order that the word of Jesus might be fulfilled that he said indicating the kind of death he would die. So Pilate went back into the praetorium and summoned Jesus and said to him, "Are you the King of the Jews?" Jesus answered, "Do you say this on your own or have others told you about me?" Pilate answered, "I am not a Jew, am I? Your own nation and the chief priests handed you over to me. What have you done?" Jesus answered, "My kingdom does not belong to this world. If my kingdom did belong to this world, my attendants would be fighting to keep me from being handed over to the Jews. But as it is, my kingdom is not here." So Pilate said to him, "Then you are a king?" Jesus answered, "You say I am a king. For this I was born and for this I came into the world, to testify to the truth. Everyone who belongs to the truth listens to my voice." Pilate said to him, "What is truth?"

When he had said this, he again went out to the Jews and said to them, "I find no guilt in him. But you have a custom that I release one prisoner to you at Passover. Do you want me to release to you the King of the Jews?" They cried out again, "Not this one but Barabbas!" Now Barabbas was a revolutionary.

Then Pilate took Jesus and had him scourged. And the soldiers wove a crown out of thorns and placed it on his head, and clothed him in a purple cloak, and they came to him and said, "Hail, King of the Jews!" And they struck him repeatedly. Once more Pilate went out and said to them, "Look, I am bringing him out to you, so that you may know that I find no guilt in him." So Jesus came out, wearing the crown of thorns and the purple cloak. And he said to them, "Behold, the man!" When the chief priests and the guards saw him they cried out, "Crucify him, crucify him!" Pilate said to them, "Take him yourselves and crucify him. I find no guilt in him." The Jews answered, "We have a law, and according to that law he ought to die, because he made himself the Son of God." Now when Pilate heard this statement, he became even more afraid, and went back into the praetorium and said to Jesus, "Where are you from?" Jesus did not answer him. So Pilate said to him, "Do you not speak to me? Do you not know that I have power to release you and I have power to crucify you?" Jesus answered him, "You would have no power over me if it had not been given to you from above. For this reason the one who handed me over to you has the greater sin." Consequently, Pilate tried to release him; but the Jews cried out, "If you release him, you are not a Friend of Caesar. Everyone who makes himself a king opposes Caesar."

When Pilate heard these words he brought Jesus out and seated him on the judge's bench in the place called Stone Pavement, in Hebrew, Gabbatha. It was preparation day for Passover, and it was about noon. And he said to the Jews, "Behold, your king!" They cried out, "Take him away, take him away! Crucify him!" Pilate said to them, "Shall I crucify your king?" The chief priests answered, "We have no king but Caesar." Then he handed him over to them to be crucified.

So they took Jesus, and, carrying the cross himself, he went out to what is called the Place of the Skull, in Hebrew, Golgotha. There they crucified him, and with him two others, one on either side, with Jesus in the middle. Pilate also had an inscription written and put on the cross. It read, "Jesus the Nazorean, the King of the Jews." Now many of the Jews read this inscription, because the place where Jesus was crucified was near the city; and it was written in Hebrew, Latin, and Greek. So the chief priests of the Jews said to Pilate, "Do not write 'The King of the Jews,' but that he said, 'I am the King of the Jews'." Pilate answered, "What I have written, I have written."

When the soldiers had crucified Jesus, they took his clothes and divided them into four shares, a share for each soldier. They also took his tunic, but the tunic was seamless, woven in one piece from the top down. So they said to one another, "Let's not tear it, but cast lots for it to see whose it will be," in order that the passage of Scripture might be fulfilled that says:

> They divided my garments among them,
>     and for my vesture they cast lots.

This is what the soldiers did. Standing by the cross of Jesus were his mother and his mother's sister, Mary the wife of Clopas, and Mary of Magdala. When Jesus saw his mother and the disciple there whom he loved he said to his mother, "Woman, behold, your son." Then he said to the disciple, "Behold, your mother." And from that hour the disciple took her into his home.

After this, aware that everything was now finished, in order that the Scripture might be fulfilled, Jesus said, "I thirst." There was a vessel filled with common wine. So they put a sponge soaked in wine on a sprig of hyssop and put it up to his mouth. When Jesus had taken the wine, he said, "It is finished." And bowing his head, he handed over the spirit.

*Here all kneel and pause for a short time.*

Now since it was preparation day, in order that the bodies might not remain on the cross on the sabbath, for the sabbath day of that week was a solemn one, the Jews asked Pilate that their legs be broken and that they be taken down. So the soldiers came and broke the legs of the first and then of the other one who was crucified with Jesus. But when they came to Jesus and saw that he was already dead, they did not break his legs, but one soldier thrust his lance into his side, and immediately blood and water flowed out. An eyewitness has testified, and his testimony is true; he knows that he is speaking the truth, so that you also may come to believe. For this happened so that the Scripture passage might be fulfilled:

> Not a bone of it will be broken.

And again another passage says:

> They will look upon him whom they have pierced.

After this, Joseph of Arimathea, secretly a disciple of Jesus for fear of the Jews, asked Pilate if he could remove the body of Jesus. And Pilate permitted it. So he came and took his body. Nicodemus, the one who had first come to him at night, also came bringing a mixture of myrrh and aloes weighing about one hundred pounds. They took the body of Jesus and bound it with burial cloths along with the spices, according to the Jewish burial custom. Now in the place where he had been crucified there was a garden, and in the garden a new tomb, in which no one had yet been buried. So they laid Jesus there because of the Jewish preparation day; for the tomb was close by.

**SOLEMN INTERCESSIONS**
*As at Sunday liturgy, the word service concludes with prayers of intercession. Today these prayers take a more solemn form as the Church lifts up to God its own needs and those of the world.*

## ADORATION OF THE HOLY CROSS                    1044
*An ancient liturgical text reads: "See here the true and most revered Tree. Hasten to kiss it and to cry out with faith: You are our help, most revered Cross." For many centuries the Church has solemnly venerated the relic or image of the cross on Good Friday. It is not present as a picture of suffering only but as a symbol of Christ's passover, where "dying he destroyed our death and rising restored our life." It is the glorious, the life-giving cross that the faithful venerate with song, prayer, kneeling and a kiss.*

*As the cross is shown to the assembly, the following is sung.*

*Priest or deacon:* Behold the wood of the Cross,
on which hung the salvation of the world.

Come, let us a - dore.

*As the assembly comes forward to venerate the cross, appropriate chants and hymns may be sung.*

## HOLY COMMUNION                    1045
*This liturgy concludes with a simple communion rite. All recite the Lord's Prayer and receive Holy Communion. There is no concluding rite or dismissal for the Church continues to be at prayer throughout the Triduum.*

## HOLY SATURDAY                    1046

The Church continues to fast and pray and to make ready for this night's great Vigil. Saturday is a day of great quiet and reflection. Catechumens, sponsors and some of the faithful may assemble during the day for prayer, the recitation of the Creed, and for the rite of Ephphetha (opening of ears and mouth).

## EASTER VIGIL IN THE HOLY NIGHT                    1047

The long preparation of the catechumens, the lenten disciplines and fast of the faithful, the vigiling and fasting and prayer that have gone on since Thursday night—all culminate in the great liturgy of this night. On this night the Church assembles to spend much time listening to Scripture, praying psalms, acclaiming the death and resurrection of the Lord. Only then are the catechumens called forward and prayed over, challenged to renounce evil and affirm their faith in God, led to the font and baptized in the blessed water. The newly baptized are then anointed with chrism and the entire assembly joins in intercession and finally in the Eucharist.

# LUCERNARIUM

## BLESSING OF THE FIRE AND PREPARATION OF THE PASCHAL CANDLE
*The night vigil begins with the kindling of new fire and the lighting of the paschal candle.*

## PROCESSION
*The ministers and assembly go in procession to the place where Scripture will be read. The following is sung during the procession.*

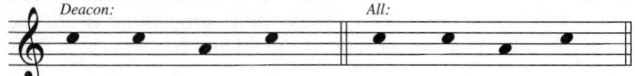

The Light of Christ. Thanks be to God.

## EASTER PROCLAMATION: THE EXSULTET
*In this ancient text the Church gives thanks and praise to God for all that is recalled this night: Adam's fall, the deliverance from Egypt, the passover of Christ, the wedding of earth and heaven, our reconciliation.*

# LITURGY OF THE WORD / ABC
*At the Vigil, the liturgy of the word is an extended time of readings, silence and the singing of psalms. On this night when the faithful know the death and resurrection of the Lord in baptism and eucharist, the Church needs first to hear these scripture readings, which are the foundation of our life together: the creation story, Abraham and Isaac, the dividing of the sea, the poetry of Isaiah and Baruch and Ezekiel, the proclamation of Paul to the Romans and the gospel account of Jesus' resurrection.*

## 1048 READING I
*Genesis 1:1—2:2 or 1:1, 26–31a / 41*

## RESPONSORIAL PSALM
*1. Psalm 104:1–2a, 5–6, 10 and 12, 13–14, 24 and 35c*

Lord, send out your Spir - it, and re - new the face of the earth.

Bless the LORD, O my soul!
O LORD my God, how great you are,
clothed in majesty and honor,
wrapped in light as with a robe! ℟.

You set the earth on its foundation,
immovable from age to age.
You wrapped it with the depths like a
cloak;

the waters stood higher than the
mountains. ℟.

You make springs gush forth in the
valleys;
they flow in between the hills.
There the birds of heaven build their
nests;
from the branches they sing their
song. ℟.

From your dwelling you water the hills;
    by your works the earth has its fill.
You make the grass grow for the cattle
    and plants to serve mankind's need,
    that he may bring forth bread from
      the earth. ℟.

How many are your works, O LORD!
    In wisdom you have made them all.
The earth is full of your creatures.
    Bless the LORD, O my soul. ℟.

*Or:*

**RESPONSORIAL PSALM**                *2. Psalm 33:4–5, 6–7, 12–13, 20 and 22*

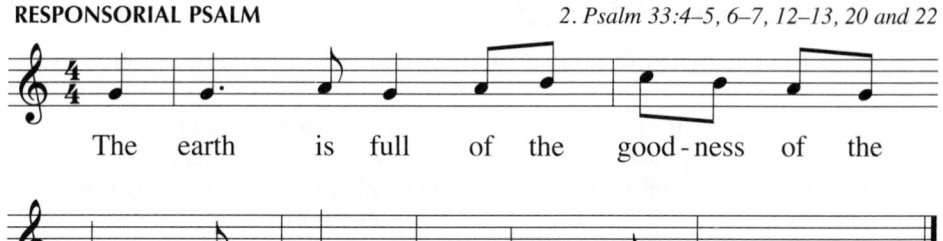

The earth is full of the good-ness of the Lord, the good-ness of the Lord.

The word of the LORD is faithful,
    and all his works to be trusted.
The LORD loves justice and right,
    and his merciful love fills the earth. ℟.

By the word of the LORD the heavens
    were made,
    by the breath of his mouth all their
      host.
As in a flask, he collects the waves of
    the ocean;
    he stores up the depths of the sea. ℟.

Blessed the nation whose God is the
    LORD,
    the people he has chosen as his
      heritage.
From the heavens the Lord looks forth;
    he sees all the children of men. ℟.

Our soul is waiting for the LORD.
    He is our help and our shield.
May your merciful love be upon us,
    as we hope in you, O LORD. ℟.

**READING II**        *Genesis 22:1–18 or 22:1–2, 9a, 10–13, 15–18* 1049

**RESPONSORIAL PSALM**                *Psalm 16:5 and 8, 9–10, 11*

You are my in-her-i-tance, O Lord.

O LORD, it is you who are my portion
    and cup;
    you yourself who secure my lot.
I keep the LORD before me always;
    with him at my right hand, I shall
      not be moved. ℟.

And so, my heart rejoices, my soul is
    glad;
    even my flesh shall rest in hope.
For you will not abandon my soul to
    hell,
    nor let your holy one see
      corruption. ℟.

You will show me the path of life,
  the fullness of joy in your presence,
  at your right hand, bliss forever. ℟.

## 1050  READING III

*Exodus 14:15—15:1*

**RESPONSORIAL PSALM**

*Exodus 15:1–2, 3–4, 5–6, 17–18*

Let us sing to the Lord; he has cov-ered him-self in glo - ry.

I will sing to the LORD, for he is
  gloriously triumphant;
  horse and chariot he has cast into
  the sea.
My strength and my courage is the LORD,
  and he has been my savior.
He is my God, I praise him;
  the God of my father, I extol him. ℟.

The LORD is a warrior,
  LORD is his name!
Pharaoh's chariots and army he hurled
  into the sea;
  the elite of his officers were
  submerged in the Red Sea. ℟.

The flood waters covered them,
  they sank into the depths like a stone.
Your right hand, O LORD, magnificent
  in power,
  your right hand, O LORD, has
  shattered the enemy. ℟.

You brought in the people you redeemed
  and planted them on the mountain
  of your inheritance—
the place where you made your seat, O
  LORD,
  the sanctuary, LORD, which your
  hands established.
The LORD shall reign forever and ever. ℟.

## 1051  READING IV

*Isaiah 54:5–14*

**RESPONSORIAL PSALM**

*Psalm 30:2 and 4, 5–6, 11 and 12a and 13b*

I will praise you, Lord, for you have res-cued me.

I will extol you, LORD, for you have
  raised me up,
  and have not let my enemies rejoice
  over me.
O LORD, you have lifted up my soul
  from the grave,
  restored me to life from those who
  sink into the pit. ℟.

Sing psalms to the LORD, you faithful
  ones;
  give thanks to his holy name.

His anger lasts a moment; his favor
  all through life.
At night come tears, but dawn
  brings joy. ℟.

Hear, O LORD, and have mercy on me;
  be my helper, O LORD.
You have changed my mourning into
  dancing.
O LORD my God, I will thank you
  forever. ℟.

## READING V

*Isaiah 55:1–11* 1052

### RESPONSORIAL PSALM

*Isaiah 12:2–3, 4bcd, 5–6*

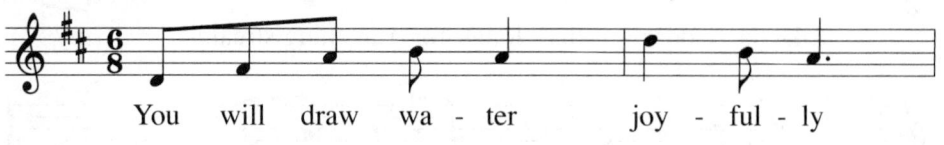

You will draw wa - ter joy - ful - ly

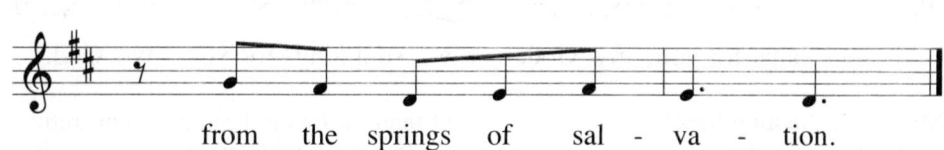

from the springs of sal - va - tion.

God indeed is my savior;
    I am confident and unafraid.
My strength and my courage is the LORD,
    and he has been my savior.
With joy you will draw water
    at the fountain of salvation. ℟.

Give thanks to the LORD, acclaim his
    name;
    among the nations make known his
    deeds,
    proclaim how exalted is his name. ℟.

Sing praise to the LORD for his glorious
    achievement;
    let this be known throughout all the
    earth.
Shout with exultation, O city of Zion,
    for great in your midst
    is the Holy One of Israel! ℟.

## READING VI

*Baruch 3:9–15, 32—4:4* 1053

### RESPONSORIAL PSALM

*Psalm 19:8, 9, 10, 11*

Lord, you have the words of ev - er-last-ing life.

The law of the LORD is perfect;
    it revives the soul.
The decrees of the LORD are steadfast;
    they give wisdom to the simple. ℟.

The precepts of the LORD are right;
    they gladden the heart.
The command of the LORD is clear;
    it gives light to the eyes. ℟.

The fear of the LORD is pure,
    abiding forever.
The judgments of the LORD are true;
    they are, all of them, just. ℟.

They are more to be desired than gold,
    than quantities of gold.
And sweeter are they than honey,
    than honey flowing from the comb. ℟.

## READING VII

*Ezekiel 36:16–17a, 18–28* 1054

**RESPONSORIAL PSALM**            *1. Psalm 42:3, 5bcd; 43:3, 4*

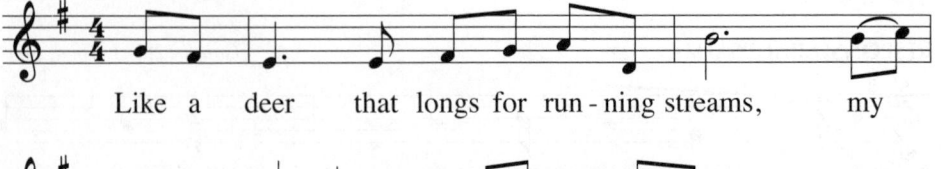

Like a deer that longs for run - ning streams, my

soul longs for you, my God; my soul longs for you, my God.

My soul is thirsting for God,
   the living God;
when can I enter and appear
   before the face of God? ℟.

For I would go to the place
   of your wondrous tent,
   all the way to the house of God,
amid cries of gladness and thanksgiving,
   the throng keeping joyful festival. ℟.

O send forth your light and your truth;
   they will guide me on.
They will bring me to your holy
   mountain,
   to the place where you dwell. ℟.

And I will come to the altar of God,
   to God, my joy and gladness.
To you will I give thanks on the harp,
   O God, my God. ℟.

*Or:*            *2. Isaiah 12:2–3, 4bcd, 5–6*

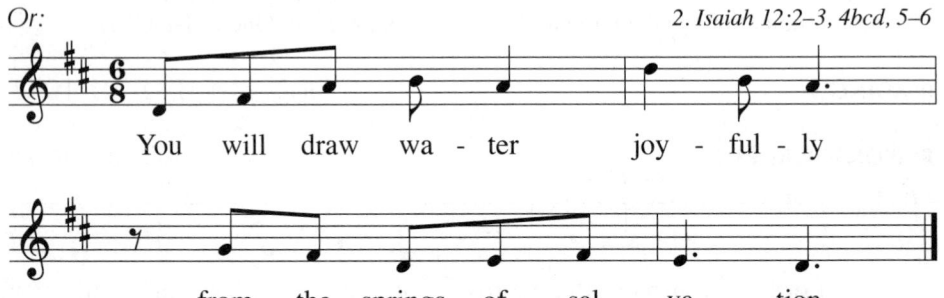

You will draw wa - ter joy - ful - ly

from the springs of sal - va - tion.

God indeed is my savior;
   I am confident and unafraid.
My strength and my courage is the LORD,
   and he has been my savior.
With joy you will draw water
   at the fountain of salvation. ℟.

Give thanks to the LORD, acclaim his
   name;
   among the nations make known his

deeds,
   proclaim how exalted is his name. ℟.

Sing praise to the LORD for his glorious
   achievement;
   let this be known throughout all the
   earth.
Shout with exultation, O city of Zion,
   for great in your midst
   is the Holy One of Israel! ℟.

*Or:*                                                    *3. Psalm 51:12–13, 14–15, 18–19*

Cre - ate in me,   cre - ate in me   a   clean heart,   O   God.

Create a pure heart for me, O God;
  renew a steadfast spirit within me.
Do not cast me away from your
    presence;
  take not your holy spirit from me. ℟.

Restore in me the joy of your salvation;
  sustain in me a willing spirit.
I will teach transgressors your ways,

that sinners may return to you. ℟.

For in sacrifice you take no delight;
  burnt offering from me would not
    please you.
My sacrifice to God, a broken spirit:
  a broken and humbled heart,
  O God, you will not spurn. ℟.

**GLORIA**

**PRAYER**

**EPISTLE**                                              *Romans 6:3–11*  **1055**

**ALLELUIA PSALM**                                       *Psalm 118:1–2, 16–17, 22–23*

Al - le-lu - ia,   al - le-lu - ia,   al - le - lu - ia!

Give praise to the LORD, for he is good;
  his mercy endures forever.
Let the house of Israel say,
  "His mercy endures forever." ℟.

"The LORD's right hand has done mighty
    deeds;
  his right hand is exalted."

I shall not die, I shall live
  and recount the deeds of the
    LORD. ℟.

The stone that the builders rejected
  has become the cornerstone.
By the LORD has this been done,
  a marvel in our eyes. ℟.

**GOSPEL / A**                                           *Matthew 28:1–10*

**GOSPEL / B**                                           *Mark 16:1–7*

**GOSPEL / C**                                           *Luke 24:1–12*

## 1056 BAPTISMAL LITURGY

*After the homily the catechumens are called forward. The assembly chants the litany of the saints, invoking the holy women and men of all centuries. Patron saints of the Church and of the catechumens and the faithful may be included in the litany.*

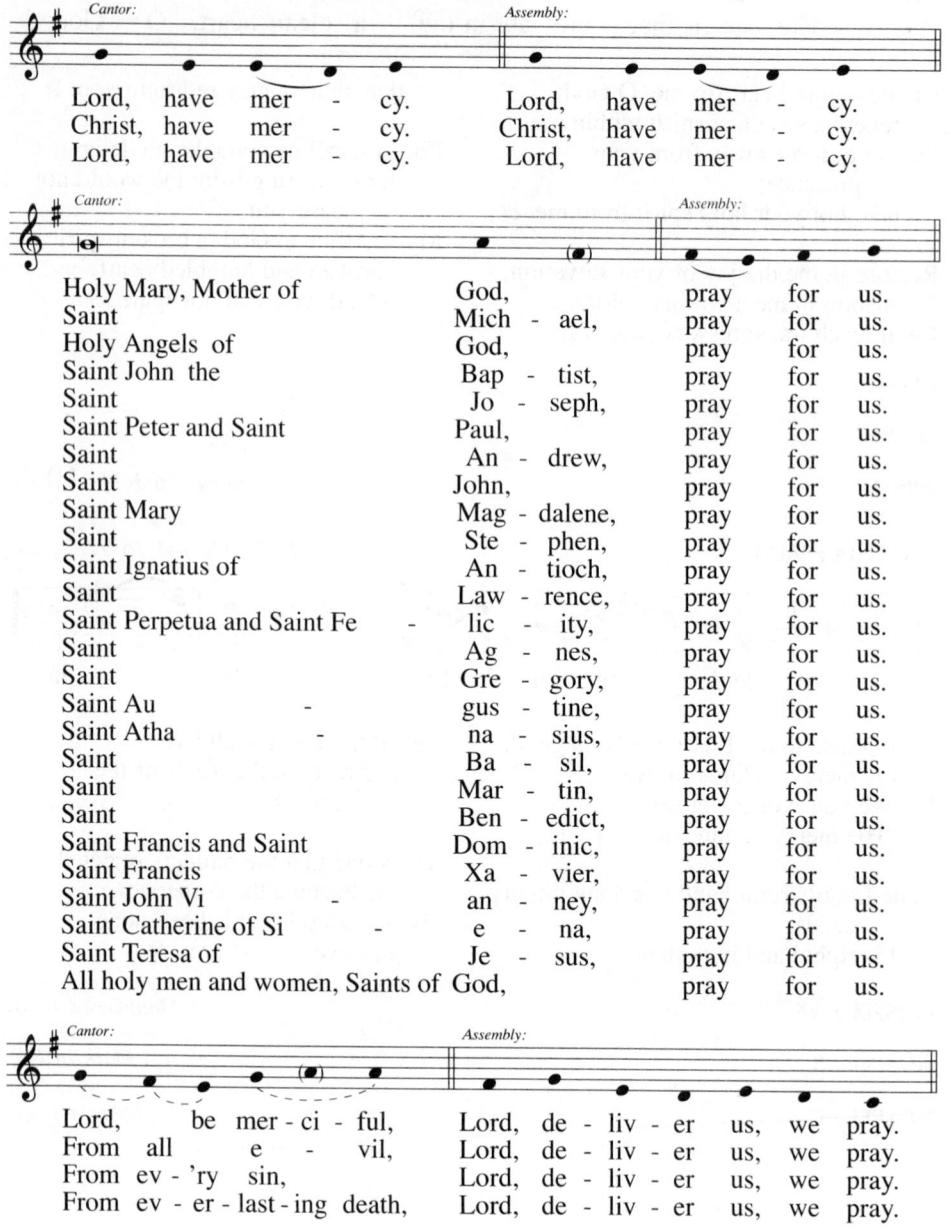

Cantor:

Assembly:

| Lord, have mercy. | Lord, have mercy. |
| Christ, have mercy. | Christ, have mercy. |
| Lord, have mercy. | Lord, have mercy. |

Cantor:

Assembly:

Holy Mary, Mother of God, pray for us.
Saint Mich - ael, pray for us.
Holy Angels of God, pray for us.
Saint John the Bap - tist, pray for us.
Saint Jo - seph, pray for us.
Saint Peter and Saint Paul, pray for us.
Saint An - drew, pray for us.
Saint John, pray for us.
Saint Mary Mag - dalene, pray for us.
Saint Ste - phen, pray for us.
Saint Ignatius of An - tioch, pray for us.
Saint Law - rence, pray for us.
Saint Perpetua and Saint Fe - lic - ity, pray for us.
Saint Ag - nes, pray for us.
Saint Gre - gory, pray for us.
Saint Au - gus - tine, pray for us.
Saint Atha - na - sius, pray for us.
Saint Ba - sil, pray for us.
Saint Mar - tin, pray for us.
Saint Ben - edict, pray for us.
Saint Francis and Saint Dom - inic, pray for us.
Saint Francis Xa - vier, pray for us.
Saint John Vi - an - ney, pray for us.
Saint Catherine of Si - e - na, pray for us.
Saint Teresa of Je - sus, pray for us.
All holy men and women, Saints of God, pray for us.

Cantor:

Assembly:

Lord, be mer - ci - ful, Lord, de - liv - er us, we pray.
From all e - vil, Lord, de - liv - er us, we pray.
From ev - 'ry sin, Lord, de - liv - er us, we pray.
From ev - er - last - ing death, Lord, de - liv - er us, we pray.

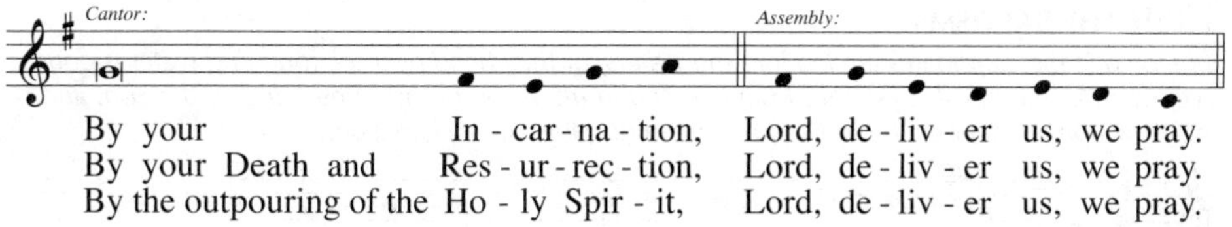

By your In - car - na - tion, Lord, de - liv - er us, we pray.
By your Death and Res - ur - rec - tion, Lord, de - liv - er us, we pray.
By the outpouring of the Ho - ly Spir - it, Lord, de - liv - er us, we pray.

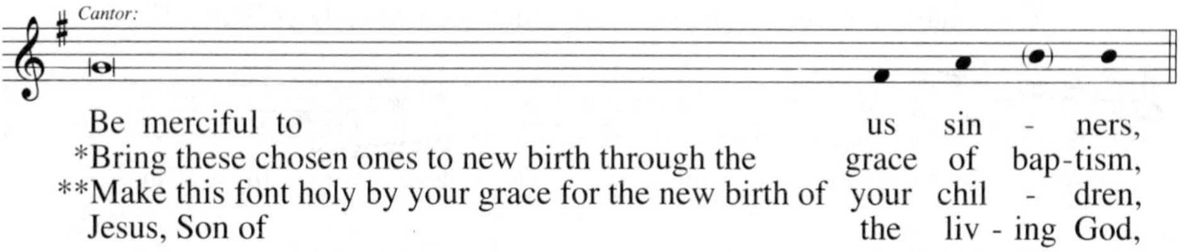

Be merciful to us sin - ners,
*Bring these chosen ones to new birth through the grace of bap-tism,
**Make this font holy by your grace for the new birth of your chil - dren,
Jesus, Son of the liv - ing God,

Lord, we ask you, hear our prayer.
Lord, we ask you, hear our prayer.
Lord, we ask you, hear our prayer.
Lord, we ask you, hear our prayer.

Christ, hear us. Christ, hear us.

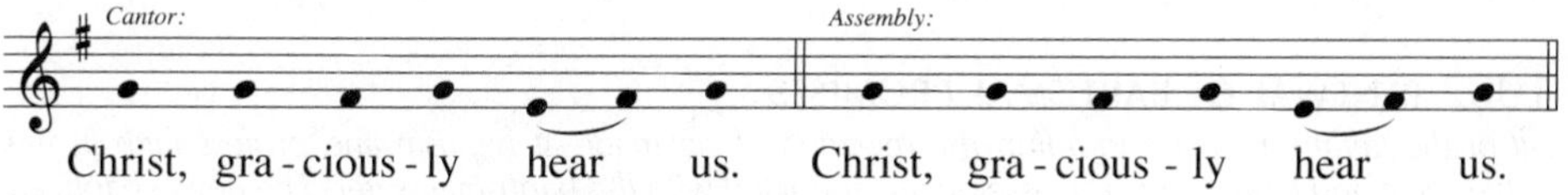

Christ, gra - cious - ly hear us. Christ, gra - cious - ly hear us.

*If there are candidates to be baptized.
**If there are no candidates to be baptized.

Text: *Litany of the Saints, Roman Missal*
Music: *Litany of the Saints, Roman Missal*
© 2010, ICEL

## BLESSING OF WATER
1057

*The priest gives thanks and praise to God over the waters of baptism. This acclamation is sung by all.*

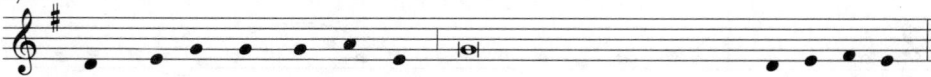

Springs of wa - ter, bless the Lord; praise and exalt him above all for ev - er.

Text: *Roman Missal*
Music: *Roman Missal*
© 2010, ICEL

## RENUNCIATION OF SIN AND PROFESSION OF FAITH
1058

*Each candidate for baptism is asked to reject sin and the ways of evil and to testify to faith in Father, Son and Holy Spirit.*

## 1059 THE BAPTISMS

*One by one the candidates are led into the waters, or they bend over the font, and water is poured over them as the priest says: "N., I baptize you in the name of the Father, and of the Son, and of the Holy Spirit." After each baptism, the assembly sings an acclamation.*

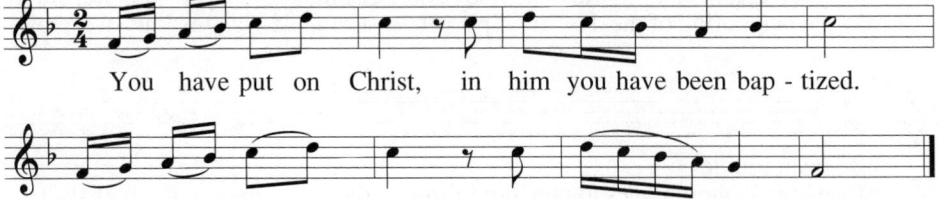

You have put on Christ, in him you have been bap - tized.

Al - le - lú - ia, al - le - lú - ia.

Text: ICEL, © 1969
Music: Howard Hughes, SM, © 1977, ICEL

*Each of the newly baptized is then clothed in a baptismal garment.*

## 1060 RECEPTION INTO FULL COMMUNION

*Those who have been previously baptized are now called forward to profess their faith and to be received into the full communion of the Catholic Church.*

## 1061 CONFIRMATION

*Infants who have been baptized are anointed with chrism. Children and adults are usually confirmed: the priest prays and lays hands on them, then anoints each of the newly baptized with chrism saying: "N., be sealed with the Gift of the Holy Spirit."*

## 1062 RENEWAL OF BAPTISMAL PROMISES

*All of the faithful repeat and affirm the rejection of sin made at baptism and profess faith in the Father, Son and Holy Spirit. The assembly is sprinkled with the baptismal water. The newly baptized then take their places in the assembly and, for the first time, join in the prayer of the faithful, the prayers of intercession.*

# 1063 LITURGY OF THE EUCHARIST

*The gifts and table are prepared and the eucharist is celebrated in the usual way.*

## 1064 CONCLUDING RITE

*The dismissal is sung with "alleluia," and all respond.*

Assembly:

Thanks be to God, al - le - lú - ia, al - le - lú - ia.

# EASTER SUNDAY / ABC

1065

**READING I**                                                          *Acts 10:34a, 37–43 / 42*

**RESPONSORIAL PSALM**                                   *Psalm 118:1–2, 16–17, 22–23*

*Or: Alleluia.*

This is the day the Lord has made;
let us re-joice and be glad.

Give praise to the LORD, for he is good;
   his mercy endures forever.
Let the house of Israel say,
   "His mercy endures forever." ℟.

"The LORD's right hand has done mighty
   deeds;
   his right hand is exalted."

I shall not die, I shall live
   and recount the deeds of the LORD. ℟.

The stone that the builders rejected
   has become the cornerstone.
By the LORD has this been done,
   a marvel in our eyes. ℟.

**READING II**                                                      *Colossians 3:1–4*

*Or:*

**READING II**                                                      *1 Corinthians 5:6b-8*

**SEQUENCE**

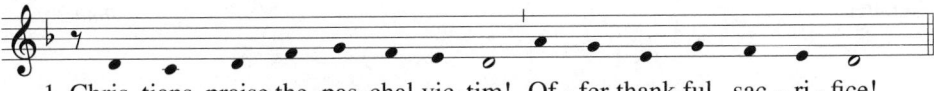

1. Chris-tians, praise the pas-chal vic-tim! Of-fer thank-ful sac-ri-fice!
1. *Ví - cti - mae Pa-schá-li lau-des ím-mo-lent Chri-sti - á - ni.*

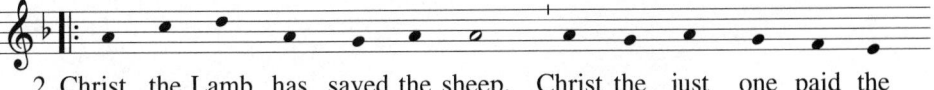

2. Christ the Lamb has saved the sheep, Christ the just one paid the
3. Death and life fought bit-ter-ly for this won-drous vic-to-
2. *A - gnus re - dé - mit ó - ves: Chri-stus ín - no-cens Pá -*
3. *Mors et vi - ta du - él - lo con - fli - xé - re mi - rán -*

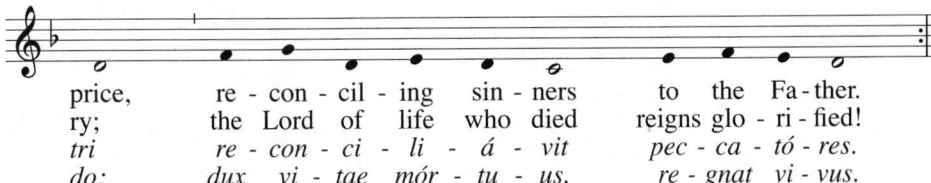

price, re - con - cil - ing sin - ners to the Fa-ther.
ry; the Lord of life who died reigns glo - ri - fied!
*tri re - con - ci - li - á - vit pec - ca - tó - res.*
*do: dux vi - tae mór - tu - us, re - gnat vi - vus.*

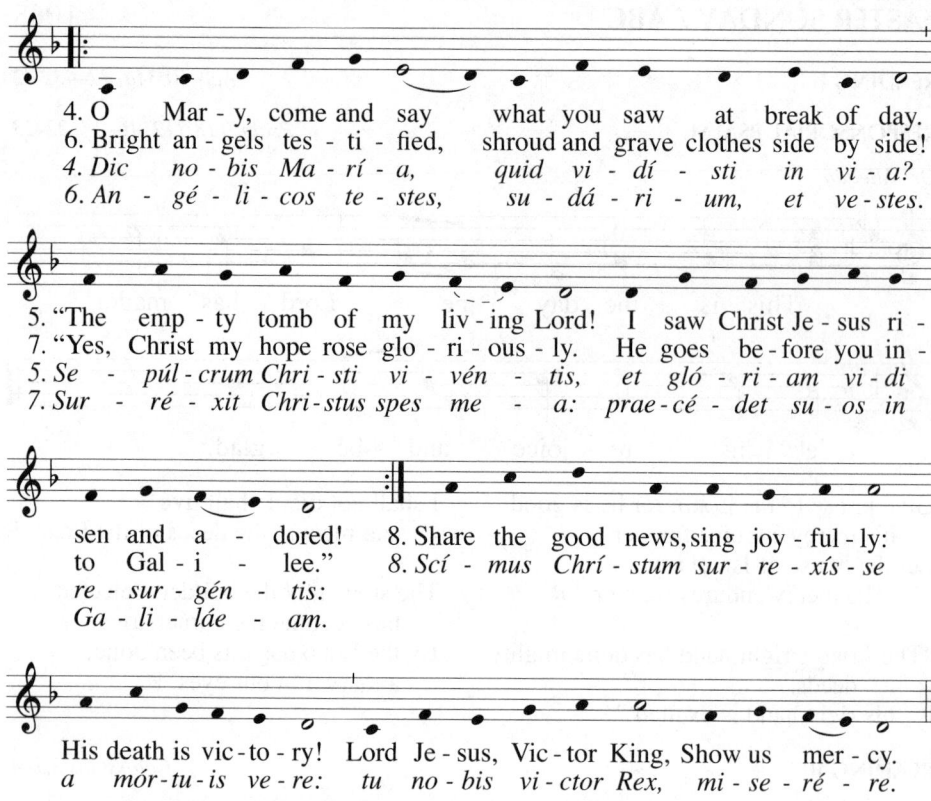

4. O Mar - y, come and say what you saw at break of day.
6. Bright an - gels tes - ti - fied, shroud and grave clothes side by side!
4. *Dic no - bis Ma - rí - a, quid vi - dí - sti in vi - a?*
6. *An - gé - li - cos te - stes, su - dá - ri - um, et ve - stes.*

5. "The emp - ty tomb of my liv - ing Lord! I saw Christ Je - sus ri -
7. "Yes, Christ my hope rose glo - ri - ous - ly. He goes be - fore you in -
5. *Se - púl - crum Chri - sti vi - vén - tis, et gló - ri - am vi - di*
7. *Sur - ré - xit Chri - stus spes me - a: prae - cé - det su - os in*

sen and a - dored! 8. Share the good news, sing joy - ful - ly:
to Gal - i - lee." 8. *Scí - mus Chrí - stum sur - re - xís - se*
*re - sur - gén - tis:*
*Ga - li - láe - am.*

His death is vic - to - ry! Lord Je - sus, Vic - tor King, Show us mer - cy.
*a mór - tu - is ve - re: tu no - bis vi - ctor Rex, mi - se - ré - re.*

Text: Sequence for Easter, ascr. to Wipo of Burgundy, d.1048; tr. by Peter J. Scagnelli, b.1949, © 1983
Tune: Mode I; acc. by Richard Proulx, 1937–2010, © 1975, GIA Publications, Inc.

At an afternoon or evening Mass, another Gospel may be read (see *Lectionary for Mass*).

**GOSPEL** *John 20:1–9*

## SECOND SUNDAY OF EASTER / ABC          1066

**READING I / A**         *Acts 2:42–47 / 43*

**READING I / B**         *Acts 4:32–35 / 44*

**READING I / C**         *Acts 5:12–16 / 45*

**RESPONSORIAL PSALM**         *Psalm 118:2–4, 13–15, 22–24*

*Or: Alleluia.*

Give thanks to the Lord for he is good, his love is ev - er - last - ing.

Let the house of Israel say,
   "His mercy endures forever."
Let the house of Aaron say,
   "His mercy endures forever."
Let those who fear the LORD say,
   "His mercy endures forever." ℟.

I was thrust down, thrust down and falling,
   but the LORD was my helper.
The LORD is my strength and my song;

he was my savior.
There are shouts of joy and salvation
   in the tents of the just. ℟.

The stone that the builders rejected
   has become the cornerstone.
By the LORD has this been done,
   a marvel in our eyes.
This is the day the LORD has made;
   let us rejoice in it and be glad. ℟.

**READING II / A**         *1 Peter 1:3–9*

**READING II / B**         *1 John 5:1–6*

**READING II / C**         *Revelation 1:9–11a, 12–13, 17–19*

**GOSPEL**         *John 20:19–31*

## THIRD SUNDAY OF EASTER / A          1067

**READING I**         *Acts 2:14, 22–33 / 46*

**RESPONSORIAL PSALM**                                   *Psalm 16:1–2a and 5, 7–8, 9–10, 11*

*Or: Alleluia.*

Lord, you will show us the path of life.

Preserve me, O God, for in you I take
    refuge.
  I say to the LORD, "You are my Lord."
O LORD, it is you who are my portion
    and cup;
  you yourself who secure my lot. ℟.

I will bless the LORD who gives me
    counsel,
  who even at night directs my heart.
I keep the LORD before me always;
  with him at my right hand, I shall
    not be moved. ℟.

And so, my heart rejoices, my soul is
    glad;
  even my flesh shall rest in hope.
For you will not abandon my soul to
    hell,
  nor let your holy one see
    corruption. ℟.

You will show me the path of life,
  the fullness of joy in your presence,
  at your right hand, bliss forever. ℟.

**READING II**                                                   *1 Peter 1:17–21*

**GOSPEL**                                                       *Luke 24:13–35*

---

## 1068   THIRD SUNDAY OF EASTER / B

**READING I**                                          *Acts 3:13–15, 17–19 / 47*

**RESPONSORIAL PSALM**                                 *Psalm 4:2, 4, 7b–8a, 9*

*Or: Alleluia.*

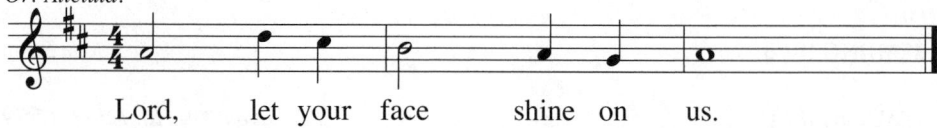

Lord, let your face shine on us.

I called, the God of justice gave me
    answer;
  from anguish you released me,
    have mercy and hear me! ℟.

Know that the LORD works wonders for
    his faithful one;
  the LORD will hear me whenever I
    call him. ℟.

Lift up the light of your face on us,
    O LORD.
  You have put into my heart a
    greater joy. ℟.

In peace I will lie down and fall asleep,
  for you alone, O LORD, make me
    dwell in safety. ℟.

**READING II**                                                   *1 John 2:1–5a*

**GOSPEL**                                                       *Luke 24:35–48*

# THIRD SUNDAY OF EASTER / C                                        1069

**READING I**                                              *Acts 5:27–32, 40b–41 / 48*

**RESPONSORIAL PSALM**                    *Psalm 30:2 and 4, 5–6, 11 and 12a and 13b*

*Or: Alleluia.*

I will praise you, Lord, for you have res-cued me.

I will extol you, LORD, for you have
    raised me up,
  and have not let my enemies rejoice
    over me.
O LORD, you have lifted up my soul
    from the grave,
  restored me to life from those who
    sink into the pit. ℟.

Sing psalms to the LORD, you faithful
    ones;
  give thanks to his holy name.

His anger lasts a moment; his favor all
    through life.
At night come tears, but dawn
    brings joy. ℟.

Hear, O LORD, and have mercy on me;
  be my helper, O LORD.
You have changed my mourning into
    dancing.
O LORD my God, I will thank you
    forever. ℟.

**READING II**                                              *Revelation 5:11–14*

**GOSPEL**                                          *John 21:1–19 or 21:1–14*

# FOURTH SUNDAY OF EASTER / A                                       1070

**READING I**                                              *Acts 2:14a, 36–41 / 49*

**RESPONSORIAL PSALM**                              *Psalm 23:1–3a, 3b–4, 5, 6*

*Or: Alleluia.*

The Lord is my shep-herd; there is noth-ing I shall want.

The LORD is my shepherd;
  there is nothing I shall want.
Fresh and green are the pastures
  where he gives me repose.
Near restful waters he leads me;
  he revives my soul. ℟.

He guides me along the right path,
  for the sake of his name.
Though I should walk in the valley of
    the shadow of death,
  no evil would I fear, for you are
    with me.
Your crook and your staff will give
    me comfort. ℟.

You have prepared a table before me
in the sight of my foes.
My head you have anointed with oil;
my cup is overflowing. ℟.

Surely goodness and mercy shall
follow me
all the days of my life.
In the LORD's own house shall I dwell
for length of days unending. ℟.

**READING II**                                     *1 Peter 2:20b–25*

**GOSPEL**                                          *John 10:1–10*

---

## 1071  FOURTH SUNDAY OF EASTER / B

**READING I**                                      *Acts 4:8–12 / 50*

**RESPONSORIAL PSALM**        *Psalm 118:1 and 8–9, 21–23, 26 and 21 and 29*

*Or: Alleluia.*

The stone re-ject-ed by the build-ers has be-come the cor-ner-stone.

Give praise to the LORD, for he is good;
his mercy endures forever.
It is better to take refuge in the LORD
than to trust in man;
it is better to take refuge in the LORD
than to trust in princes. ℟.

I will thank you, for you have
answered,
and you are my savior.
The stone that the builders rejected
has become the cornerstone.

By the LORD has this been done,
a marvel in our eyes. ℟.

Blest is he who comes in the name of
the LORD.
We bless you from the house of the
LORD.
I will thank you, for you have answered,
and you are my savior.
Give praise to the LORD, for he is good;
his mercy endures forever. ℟.

**READING II**                                     *1 John 3:1–2*

**GOSPEL**                                          *John 10:11–18*

---

## 1072  FOURTH SUNDAY OF EASTER / C

**READING I**                                      *Acts 13:14, 43–52 / 51*

**RESPONSORIAL PSALM**                                         *Psalm 100:1–2, 3, 5*

*Or: Alleluia.*

We are his peo-ple, the sheep of his flock.

Cry out with joy to the LORD, all the earth.
  Serve the LORD with gladness.
  Come before him, singing for joy. ℟.

Know that he, the LORD, is God.
  He made us; we belong to him.

We are his people, the sheep of his flock. ℟.

Indeed, how good is the LORD,
  eternal his merciful love.
  He is faithful from age to age. ℟.

**READING II**                                              *Revelation 7:9, 14b–17*

**GOSPEL**                                                      *John 10:27–30*

---

## FIFTH SUNDAY OF EASTER / A                                      1073

**READING I**                                                 *Acts 6:1–7 / 52*

**RESPONSORIAL PSALM**                               *Psalm 33:1–2, 4–5, 18–19*

*Or: Alleluia.*

Lord, let your mer-cy be on us, as we place our trust in you.

Ring out your joy to the LORD, O you just;
  for praise is fitting for the upright.
Give thanks to the LORD upon the harp;
  with a ten-stringed lute sing him
    songs. ℟.

For the word of the LORD is faithful,
  and all his works to be trusted.
The LORD loves justice and right,

and his merciful love fills the
  earth. ℟.

Yes, the LORD's eyes are on those who
  fear him,
  who hope in his merciful love,
to rescue their souls from death,
  to keep them alive in famine. ℟.

**READING II**                                                  *1 Peter 2:4–9*

**GOSPEL**                                                      *John 14:1–12*

## 1074   FIFTH SUNDAY OF EASTER / B

**READING I**                                                    *Acts 9:26–31 / 53*

**RESPONSORIAL PSALM**                      *Psalm 22:26b–27, 28 and 30, 31–32*

*Or: Alleluia.*

I will praise you, Lord, in the as-sem-bly of your peo-ple.

My vows I will pay before those who
  fear him.
  The poor shall eat and shall have
  their fill.
They shall praise the Lord, those who
  seek him.
  May their hearts live on forever and
  ever! ℟.

All the earth shall remember and return
  to the Lord,
  all families of the nations worship
  before him.

They shall worship him, all the mighty
  of the earth;
  before him shall bow all who go
  down to the dust. ℟.

And my soul shall live for him, my
  descendants serve him.
  They shall tell of the Lord to
  generations yet to come,
declare his saving justice to peoples
  yet unborn:
  "These are the things the Lord
  has done." ℟.

**READING II**                                                  *1 John 3:18–24*

**GOSPEL**                                                      *John 15:1–8*

## 1075   FIFTH SUNDAY OF EASTER / C

**READING I**                                                  *Acts 14:21–27 / 54*

**RESPONSORIAL PSALM**                      *Psalm 145:8–9, 10–11, 12–13ab*

*Or: Alleluia.*

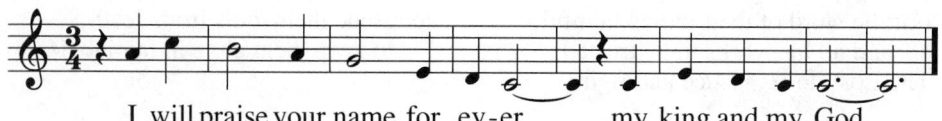

I will praise your name for ev-er, my king and my God.

The Lord is kind and full of compassion,
  slow to anger, abounding in mercy.
How good is the Lord to all,
  compassionate to all his creatures. ℟.

All your works shall thank you, O Lord,
  and all your faithful ones bless you.
They shall speak of the glory of your
  reign,

and declare your mighty deeds. ℟.

To make known your might to the
  children of men,
  and the glorious splendor of your
  reign.
Your kingdom is an everlasting kingdom;
  your rule endures for all
  generations. ℟.

**READING II**                                                    *Revelation 21:1–5a*

**GOSPEL**                                                    *John 13:31–33a, 34–35*

---

## SIXTH SUNDAY OF EASTER / A                                              1076

**READING I**                                                    *Acts 8:5–8, 14–17 / 55*

**RESPONSORIAL PSALM**                          *Psalm 66:1–3a, 4–5, 6–7a, 16 and 20*

*Or: Alleluia.*

Let all the earth cry out to God with joy.

Cry out with joy to God, all the earth;
   O sing to the glory of his name.
O render him glorious praise.
   Say to God, "How awesome your
      deeds! ℟.

"Before you all the earth shall bow
    down,
   shall sing to you, sing to your name!"
Come and see the works of God:
   awesome his deeds among the
    children of men. ℟.

He turned the sea into dry land;
   they passed through the river on foot.
Let our joy, then, be in him;
   he rules forever by his might. ℟.

Come and hear, all who fear God;
   I will tell what he did for my soul.
Blest be God, who did not reject my
    prayer,
   nor withhold from me his merciful
    love. ℟.

**READING II**                                                    *1 Peter 3:15–18*

**GOSPEL**                                                    *John 14:15–21*

---

## SIXTH SUNDAY OF EASTER / B                                              1077

**READING I**                                                    *Acts 10:25–26, 34–35, 44–48 / 56*

**RESPONSORIAL PSALM**                    *Psalm 98:1, 2–3ab, 3cd–4*

*Or: Alleluia.*

The Lord has re-vealed to the na - tions

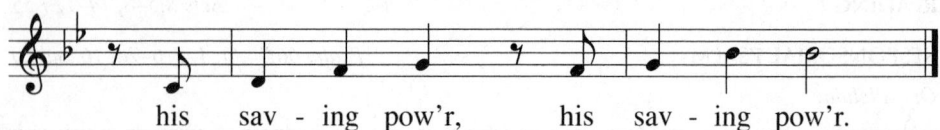

his sav - ing pow'r, his sav - ing pow'r.

O sing a new song to the LORD,
  for he has worked wonders.
His right hand and his holy arm
  have brought salvation. ℟.

The LORD has made known his salvation,
  has shown his deliverance to the
    nations.
He has remembered his merciful love

and his truth for the house of
  Israel. ℟.

All the ends of the earth have seen
  the salvation of our God.
Shout to the LORD, all the earth;
  break forth into joyous song,
  and sing out your praise. ℟.

**READING II**                              *1 John 4:7–10*

**GOSPEL**                                  *John 15:9–17*

---

## 1078  SIXTH SUNDAY OF EASTER / C

**READING I**                           *Acts 15:1–2, 22–29 / 57*

**RESPONSORIAL PSALM**              *Psalm 67:2–3, 5, 6 and 8*

*Or: Alleluia.*

O God, O God, let all the na-tions praise you!

O God, be gracious and bless us
  and let your face shed its light
    upon us.
So will your ways be known upon earth
  and all nations learn your
    salvation. ℟.

Let the nations be glad and shout for joy,
  with uprightness you rule the

peoples;
  you guide the nations on earth. ℟.

Let the peoples praise you, O God;
  let all the peoples praise you.
May God still give us his blessing
  that all the ends of the earth may
  revere him. ℟.

**READING II**                                    *Revelation 21:10–14, 22–23*

**GOSPEL**                                              *John 14:23–29*

---

# ASCENSION OF THE LORD / ABC                                    1079

**READING I**                                              *Acts 1:1–11 / 58*

**RESPONSORIAL PSALM**                              *Psalm 47:2–3, 6–7, 8–9*

*Or: Alleluia.*

God mounts his throne to shouts of joy: a blare of trum-pets for the Lord.

All peoples, clap your hands.
    Cry to God with shouts of joy!
For the LORD, the Most High, is
        awesome,
    the great king over all the earth. ℟.

God goes up with shouts of joy.
    The LORD goes up with trumpet blast.

Sing praise for God; sing praise!
Sing praise to our king; sing
    praise! ℟.

God is king of all the earth.
    Sing praise with all your skill.
God reigns over the nations.
    God sits upon his holy throne. ℟.

**READING II**                                        *Ephesians 1:17–23*

*Or:*

**READING II / B**                          *Ephesians 4:1–13 or 4:1–7, 11–13*

*Or:*

**READING II / C**                             *Hebrews 9:24–28; 10:19–23*

**GOSPEL / A**                                          *Matthew 28:16–20*

**GOSPEL / B**                                              *Mark 16:15–20*

**GOSPEL / C**                                              *Luke 24:46–53*

## 1080 SEVENTH SUNDAY OF EASTER / A

**READING I** *Acts 1:12–14 / 59*

**RESPONSORIAL PSALM** *Psalm 27:1, 4, 7–8a*

*Or: Alleluia.*

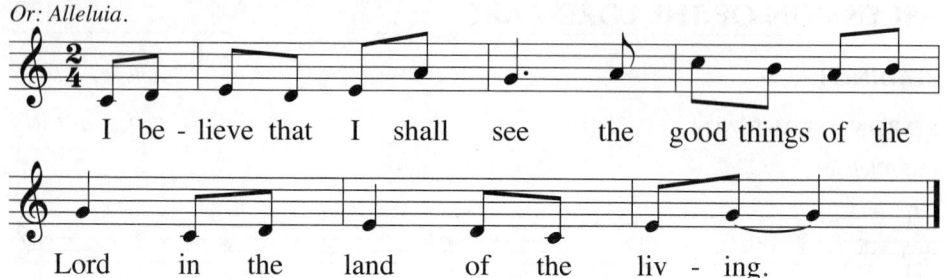

I be - lieve that I shall see the good things of the Lord in the land of the liv - ing.

The LORD is my light and my salvation;
   whom shall I fear?
The LORD is the stronghold of my life;
   whom should I dread? ℟.

There is one thing I ask of the LORD,
   only this do I seek:
to live in the house of the LORD

all the days of my life,
to gaze on the beauty of the LORD,
   to inquire at his temple. ℟.

O LORD, hear my voice when I call;
   have mercy and answer me.
Of you my heart has spoken,
   "Seek his face." ℟.

**READING II** *1 Peter 4:13–16*

**GOSPEL** *John 17:1–11a*

## 1081 SEVENTH SUNDAY OF EASTER / B

**READING I** *Acts 1:15–17, 20a, 20c-26 / 60*

**RESPONSORIAL PSALM** *Psalm 103:1–2, 11–12, 19–20ab*

*Or: Alleluia.*

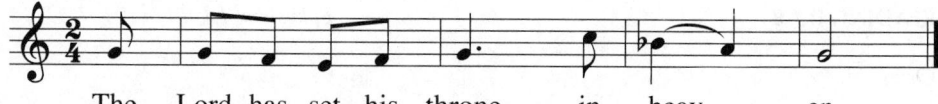

The Lord has set his throne in heav - en.

Bless the LORD, O my soul,
   and all within me, his holy name.
Bless the LORD, O my soul,
   and never forget all his benefits. ℟.

For as the heavens are high above the
      earth,
   so strong his mercy for those who
      fear him.

As far as the east is from the west,
   so far from us does he remove our
      transgressions. ℟.

The LORD has fixed his throne in heaven,
   and his kingdom is ruling over all.
Bless the LORD, all you his angels,
   mighty in power, fulfilling his
      word. ℟.

**READING II** *1 John 4:11–16*

**GOSPEL** *John 17:11b-19*

## SEVENTH SUNDAY OF EASTER / C                                        1082

**READING I**                                                          *Acts 7:55–60 / 61*

**RESPONSORIAL PSALM**                                   *Psalm 97:1 and 2b, 6 and 7c, 9*

*Or: Alleluia.*

The Lord is king, the Lord Most High    o-ver all the earth.

The LORD is king, let earth rejoice;
   let the many islands be glad.
   Justice and right are the foundation
      of his throne. ℟.

The skies proclaim his justice;

all peoples see his glory.
All you angels, worship him. ℟.

For you indeed are the LORD,
   most high above all the earth,
   exalted far above all gods. ℟.

**READING II**                                           *Revelation 22:12–14, 16–17, 20*

**GOSPEL**                                                             *John 17:20–26*

---

## PENTECOST SUNDAY—VIGIL MASS / ABC                                   1083

**READING I**                                                          *Genesis 11:1–9 / 62*
*Or:*

**READING I**                                                          *Exodus 19:3–8a, 16–20b*
*Or:*

**READING I**                                                          *Ezekiel 37:1–14*
*Or:*

**READING I**                                                          *Joel 3:1–5*

**RESPONSORIAL PSALM**                      *Psalm 104:1–2a, 24 and 35c, 27–28, 29bc–30*

*Or: Alleluia.*

Lord, send out your Spir - it, and re - new the face of the earth.

Bless the LORD, O my soul!
   O LORD my God, how great you are,
clothed in majesty and honor,
   wrapped in light as with a robe! ℟.

How many are your works, O LORD!
   In wisdom you have made them all.
The earth is full of your creatures.
   Bless the LORD, O my soul.
      Alleluia! ℟.

All of these look to you
    to give them their food in due season.
You give it, they gather it up;
    you open wide your hand, they are
      well filled. ℟.

You take away their breath, they die,
    returning to the dust from which
      they came.
You send forth your spirit, and they are
    created,
    and you renew the face of the
      earth. ℟.

**READING II**                      *Romans 8:22–27*

**GOSPEL**                           *John 7:37–39*

## 1084  PENTECOST SUNDAY—MASS DURING THE DAY / ABC

**READING I**                       *Acts 2:1–11 / 63*

**RESPONSORIAL PSALM**       *Psalm 104:1ab and 24ac, 29bc–30, 31 and 34*

*Or: Alleluia.*

Lord, send out your Spir - it, and re - new the face of the earth.

Bless the Lord, O my soul!
    O Lord my God, how great you are.
How many are your works, O Lord!
    The earth is full of your creatures. ℟.

You take away their breath, they die,
    returning to the dust from which
      they came.
You send forth your spirit, and they are

    created,
    and you renew the face of the
      earth. ℟.

May the glory of the Lord last forever!
    May the Lord rejoice in his works!
May my thoughts be pleasing to him.
    I will rejoice in the Lord. ℟.

**READING II / ABC**            *1 Corinthians 12:3b–7, 12–13*

*Or:*

**READING II / B**                  *Galatians 5:16–25*

*Or:*

**READING II / C**                     *Romans 8:8–17*

**SEQUENCE**

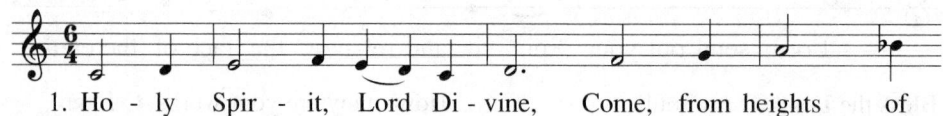

1. Ho - ly Spir - it, Lord Di - vine, Come, from heights of
2. Come, O Fa - ther of the poor, Come, whose treas - ured

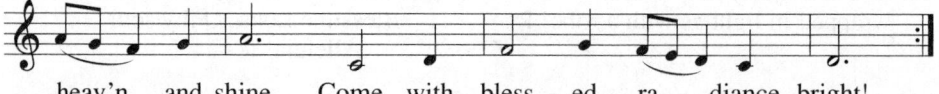

heav'n and shine, Come with bless - ed ra - diance bright!
gifts en - dure, Come, our heart's un - fail - ing light!

3. Of con - sol - ers, wis - est, best, And our soul's most
4. In our la - bor rest most sweet, Pleas - ant cool - ness

wel - come guest, Sweet re - fresh - ment sweet re - pose.
in the heat, Con - so - la - tion in our woes.

5. Light most bless - ed, shine with grace In our heart's most
6. Left with - out your pres - ence here, Life it - self would

se - cret place, Fill your faith - ful through and through.
dis - ap - pear, Noth - ing thrives a - part from you!

7. Cleanse our soil - ed hearts of sin, Ar - id souls re -
8. Bend the stub - born heart and will, Melt the fro - zen,

fresh with - in, Wound - ed lives to health re - store.
warm the chill, Guide the way - ward home once more!

9. On the faith - ful who are true And pro -
10. Give us vir - tue's sure re - ward, Give us

fess their faith in you, In your sev'n - fold gift de - scend!
your sal - va - tion, Lord, Give us joys that nev - er end!

Text: Sequence for Pentecost, 13th. C.; tr. by Peter J. Scagnelli; b.1949, © 1983
Tune: Mode I; acc. by Adriaan Engels, 1906–2003, © Interkerkelijke Stichting voor het Kerklied Den Haag

**GOSPEL / ABC**                                          *John 20:19–23*

*Or:*

**GOSPEL / B**                                      *John 15:26–27; 16:12–15*

*Or:*

**GOSPEL / C**                                        *John 14:15–16, 23b–26*

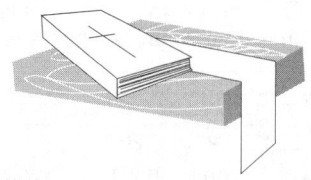

# Ordinary Time

## 1085

When the Church assembles, time is always given to the reading of Scripture. This is the book the Church esteems: the Law and the prophets, the books of wisdom and psalms, the letters and writings of Paul and of the other apostles, the gospels themselves. Throughout the history of the Church the readings from Scripture have been arranged so that the various Sundays have their assigned texts. This book of assigned scripture readings is the lectionary. In the present Roman lectionary the readings are ordered according to a cycle of three years.

Most of each year is called "Ordinary Time" or "Sundays of the Year." These are the weeks between the Christmas season and Lent, and the long period between Pentecost (the conclusion of the Easter season) and Advent (usually the first Sunday in December). On the Sundays of Ordinary Time, the lectionary has us read through the letters of the New Testament and the gospels. In the first year of the cycle, the gospel of Matthew is read from beginning to end; in the second year, Mark; in the third, Luke. Likewise, each Sunday finds the Church picking up the reading of one of the letters of the New Testament roughly where the previous week's reading concluded. At present, the first reading at Sunday Mass in Ordinary Time is chosen from the Hebrew Scriptures; these texts show the richness and the continuity of faith.

Sunday by Sunday, year after year, the Church reads through its book in the weeks of Ordinary Time. Each Christian, each local Church, each generation listens and so finds its own life in God's word.

The Church assembles around Scripture and around the Lord's table on Sunday. This day is called by Christians the Lord's Day. Whether the Church is in Ordinary Time or in the seasons of Advent/Christmas or Lent/Easter, the Lord's Day is kept holy; it is the original feast day. The rhythm of the weekdays and the Sunday is the basic rhythm of life in Christian churches. The practices with which a Church keeps the Lord's Day vary, but always and everywhere Christians assemble on this day so that the Church may listen to God's word. Through the days of the week, the Sunday's scripture readings are to be for reflection and nourishment as they are repeated and pondered in the households of the assembly.

## MOST HOLY TRINITY / A 1086

**READING I** *Exodus 34:4b–6, 8–9 / 164*

**RESPONSORIAL PSALM** *Daniel 3:52, 53, 54, 55*

Glo - ry and praise for ev - er - more.

Blessed are you, O Lord, the God of our fathers,
  praiseworthy and exalted above all forever;
and blessed is your holy and glorious name,
  praiseworthy and exalted above all for all ages. ℟.

Blessed are you in the temple of your holy glory,
  praiseworthy and glorious above all forever. ℟.

Blessed are you on the throne of your kingdom,
  praiseworthy and exalted above all forever. ℟.

Blessed are you who look into the depths from your throne upon the cherubim,
  praiseworthy and exalted above all forever. ℟.

**READING II** *2 Corinthians 13:11–13*

**GOSPEL** *John 3:16–18*

## MOST HOLY TRINITY / B 1087

**READING I** *Deuteronomy 4:32–34, 39–40 / 165*

**RESPONSORIAL PSALM** *Psalm 33:4–5, 6 and 9, 18–19, 20 and 22*

Bless - ed the peo - ple the Lord has cho - sen to be his own.

The word of the LORD is faithful,
  and all his works to be trusted.
The LORD loves justice and right,
  and his merciful love fills the earth. ℟.

By the word of the LORD the heavens were made,
  by the breath of his mouth all their host.
He spoke, and it came to be.
  He commanded; it stood in place. ℟.

Yes, the LORD's eyes are on those who fear him,
  who hope in his merciful love,
to rescue their souls from death,
  to keep them alive in famine. ℟.

Our soul is waiting for the LORD.
  He is our help and our shield.
May your merciful love be upon us,
  as we hope in you, O LORD. ℟.

**READING II**                                                *Romans 8:14–17*

**GOSPEL**                                                   *Matthew 28:16–20*

---

## 1088   MOST HOLY TRINITY / C

**READING I**                                          *Proverbs 8:22–31 / 166*

**RESPONSORIAL PSALM**                          *Psalm 8:4–5, 6–7, 8–9*

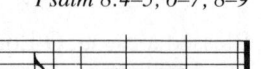

O  Lord, our God, how won-der-ful your name  in  all the earth!

When I see the heavens, the work of
  your fingers,
  the moon and the stars which you
  arranged,
what is man that you should keep him
  in mind,
  the son of man that you care for
  him? ℞.

Yet you have made him little lower
  than the angels;

with glory and honor you crowned
  him,
gave him power over the works of your
  hands:
  you put all things under his feet. ℞.

All of them, sheep and oxen,
  yes, even the cattle of the fields,
birds of the air, and fish of the sea
  that make their way through the
  waters. ℞.

**READING II**                                                 *Romans 5:1–5*

**GOSPEL**                                                      *John 16:12–15*

---

## 1089   MOST HOLY BODY AND BLOOD OF CHRIST / A

**READING I**                         *Deuteronomy 8:2–3, 14b–16a / 167*

**RESPONSORIAL PSALM**                  *Psalm 147:12–13, 14–15, 19–20*

*Or: Alleluia.*

O        praise        the        Lord,        Je - ru - sa - lem.

O Jerusalem, glorify the LORD!
  O Sion, praise your God!
He has strengthened the bars of your
  gates;
  he has blessed your children within
  you. ℞.

He established peace on your borders;
  he gives you your fill of finest
  wheat.
He sends out his word to the earth,
  and swiftly runs his command. ℞.

He reveals his word to Jacob;
to Israel, his decrees and judgments.
He has not dealt thus with other nations;

he has not taught them his
judgments. ℟.

**READING II**                                      *1 Corinthians 10:16–17*

**GOSPEL**                                               *John 6:51–58*

---

## MOST HOLY BODY AND BLOOD OF CHRIST / B          1090

**READING I**                                         *Exodus 24:3–8 / 168*

**RESPONSORIAL PSALM**                *Psalm 116:12–13, 15 and 16bc, 17–18*

*Or: Alleluia.*

I will take the cup of sal-va-tion, and call on the name of the Lord.

How can I repay the LORD
for all his goodness to me?
The cup of salvation I will raise;
I will call on the name of the
LORD. ℟.

Your servant am I,
the son of your handmaid;
you have loosened my bonds. ℟.

A thanksgiving sacrifice I make;
I will call on the name of the LORD.

How precious in the eyes of the LORD
is the death of his faithful.

My vows to the LORD I will fulfill
before all his people. ℟.

**READING II**                                        *Hebrews 9:11–15*

**GOSPEL**                                           *Mark 14:12–16, 22–26*

---

## MOST HOLY BODY AND BLOOD OF CHRIST / C          1091

**READING I**                                       *Genesis 14:18–20 / 169*

**RESPONSORIAL PSALM**                              *Psalm 110:1, 2, 3, 4*

You are a priest for ev-er, in the line of Mel-chi - ze-dek.

The LORD's revelation to my lord:
"Sit at my right hand,
until I make your foes your
footstool." ℟.

The LORD will send from Sion
your scepter of power:
rule in the midst of your foes. ℟.

With you is princely rule
    on the day of your power.
In holy splendor, from the womb before
    the dawn,
I have begotten you. ℟.

The LORD has sworn an oath he
    will not change:
"You are a priest forever,
    in the line of Melchizedek." ℟.

**READING II**                           *1 Corinthians 11:23–26*

**GOSPEL**                                *Luke 9:11b–17*

---

## 1092  MOST SACRED HEART OF JESUS / A

**READING I**                           *Deuteronomy 7:6–11 / 170*

**RESPONSORIAL PSALM**            *Psalm 103:1–2, 3–4, 6–7, 8 and 10*

The Lord's kind - ness   is ev-er - last - ing   to those who fear him.

Bless the LORD, O my soul,
    and all within me, his holy name.
Bless the LORD, O my soul,
    and never forget all his benefits. ℟.

It is the Lord who forgives all your sins,
    who heals every one of your ills,
who redeems your life from the grave,
    who crowns you with mercy and
        compassion. ℟.

The LORD does just deeds,
    gives full justice to all who are

oppressed.
He made known his ways to Moses,
    and his deeds to the children of
        Israel. ℟.

The LORD is compassionate and
    gracious,
slow to anger and rich in mercy.
He does not treat us according to our
    sins,
    nor repay us according to our
        faults. ℟.

**READING II**                                *1 John 4:7–16*

**GOSPEL**                              *Matthew 11:25–30*

---

## 1093  MOST SACRED HEART OF JESUS / B

**READING I**                         *Hosea 11:1, 3–4, 8c–9 / 171*

**RESPONSORIAL PSALM** *Isaiah 12:2–3, 4bcd, 5–6*

You will draw wa - ter joy - ful - ly

from the springs of sal - va - tion.

God indeed is my savior;
 I am confident and unafraid.
My strength and my courage is the LORD,
 and he has been my savior.
With joy you will draw water
 at the fountain of salvation. ℟.

Give thanks to the LORD, acclaim his
 name;
 among the nations make known his
 deeds,
 proclaim how exalted is his name. ℟.

Sing praise to the LORD for his glorious
 achievement;
 let this be known throughout all the
 earth.
Shout with exultation, O city of Zion,
 for great in your midst
 is the Holy One of Israel! ℟.

**READING II** *Ephesians 3:8–12, 14–19*

**GOSPEL** *John 19:31–37*

---

# MOST SACRED HEART OF JESUS / C 1094

**READING I** *Ezekiel 34:11–16 / 172*

**RESPONSORIAL PSALM** *Psalm 23:1–3a, 3b-4, 5, 6*

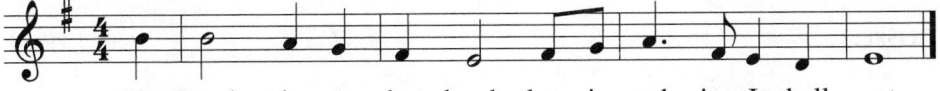

The Lord is my shep-herd; there is noth - ing I shall want.

The LORD is my shepherd;
 there is nothing I shall want.
Fresh and green are the pastures
 where he gives me repose.
Near restful waters he leads me;
 he revives my soul. ℟.

He guides me along the right path,
 for the sake of his name.
Though I should walk in the valley of
 the shadow of death,
 no evil would I fear, for you are
 with me.
Your crook and your staff will give
 me comfort. ℟.

You have prepared a table before me
   in the sight of my foes.
My head you have anointed with oil;
   my cup is overflowing. ℞.

Surely goodness and mercy shall follow
   me
   all the days of my life.
In the LORD's own house shall I dwell
   for length of days unending. ℞.

**READING II**     *Romans 5:5b-11*

**GOSPEL**     *Luke 15:3–7*

---

## 1095   SECOND SUNDAY IN ORDINARY TIME / A

**READING I**     *Isaiah 49:3, 5–6 / 64*

**RESPONSORIAL PSALM**     *Psalm 40:2 and 4ab, 7–8a, 8b–9, 10*

Here am I, Lord; here am I, Lord; I come to do your will.

I waited, I waited for the LORD,
   and he stooped down to me;
     he heard my cry.
He put a new song into my mouth,
   praise of our God. ℞.

You delight not in sacrifice and
       offerings,
   but in an open ear.
You do not ask for holocaust and victim.
   Then I said, "See, I have come." ℞.

In the scroll of the book it stands
   written of me:
   "I delight to do your will, O my
     God;
   your instruction lies deep within
     me." ℞.

Your justice I have proclaimed
   in the great assembly.
My lips I have not sealed;
   you know it, O LORD. ℞.

**READING II**     *1 Corinthians 1:1–3*

**GOSPEL**     *John 1:29–34*

---

## 1096   SECOND SUNDAY IN ORDINARY TIME / B

**READING I**     *1 Samuel 3:3b–10, 19 / 65*

**RESPONSORIAL PSALM**     *Psalm 40:2 and 4ab, 7–8a, 8b–9, 10*

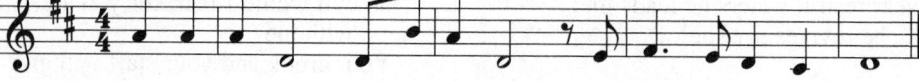

Here am I, Lord; here am I, Lord; I come to do your will.

I waited, I waited for the LORD,
  and he stooped down to me;
    he heard my cry.
He put a new song into my mouth,
  praise of our God. ℟.

You delight not in sacrifice and
    offerings,
  but in an open ear.
You do not ask for holocaust and victim.
  Then I said, "See, I have come." ℟.

In the scroll of the book it stands
    written of me:
  "I delight to do your will, O my God;
  your instruction lies deep within
    me." ℟.

Your justice I have proclaimed
  in the great assembly.
My lips I have not sealed;
  you know it, O LORD. ℟.

**READING II**                                      *1 Corinthians 6:13c–15a, 17–20*

**GOSPEL**                                          *John 1:35–42*

---

## SECOND SUNDAY IN ORDINARY TIME / C                    1097

**READING I**                                       *Isaiah 62:1–5 / 66*

**RESPONSORIAL PSALM**                  *Psalm 96:1–2a, 2b–3, 7–8a, 9–10a and c*

Pro-claim his mar-vel-ous deeds to all the na - tions.

O sing a new song to the LORD;
  sing to the LORD, all the earth.
  O sing to the LORD; bless his name. ℟.

Proclaim his salvation day by day.
  Tell among the nations his glory,
  and his wonders among all the
    peoples. ℟.

Give the LORD, you families of peoples,

give the LORD glory and power;
give the LORD the glory of his
  name. ℟.

Worship the LORD in holy splendor.
  O tremble before him, all the earth.
Say to the nations, "The LORD is king."
  He will judge the peoples in
    fairness. ℟.

**READING II**                                      *1 Corinthians 12:4–11*

**GOSPEL**                                          *John 2:1–11*

---

## THIRD SUNDAY IN ORDINARY TIME / A                     1098

**READING I**                                       *Isaiah 8:23 – 9:3 / 67*

**RESPONSORIAL PSALM**  *Psalm 27:1, 4, 13–14*

The Lord is my light and my sal - va - tion.

The Lord is my light and my salvation;
  whom shall I fear?
The Lord is the stronghold of my life;
  whom should I dread? ℟.

There is one thing I ask of the Lord,
  only this do I seek:
to live in the house of the Lord
  all the days of my life,

to gaze on the beauty of the Lord,
  to inquire at his temple. ℟.

I believe I shall see the Lord's
    goodness
  in the land of the living.
Wait for the Lord; be strong;
  be stouthearted, and wait for the
    Lord! ℟.

**READING II**  *1 Corinthians 1:10–13, 17*

**GOSPEL**  *Matthew 4:12–23 or 4:12–17*

---

## 1099 THIRD SUNDAY IN ORDINARY TIME / B

**READING I**  *Jonah 3:1–5, 10 / 68*

**RESPONSORIAL PSALM**  *Psalm 25:4–5ab, 6 and 7bc, 8–9*

Teach me your ways, O Lord, teach me your ways.

O Lord, make me know your ways.
  Teach me your paths.
Guide me in your truth, and teach me;
  for you are the God of my salvation. ℟.

Remember your compassion, O Lord,
  and your merciful love,
  for they are from of old.

In your merciful love remember me,
  because of your goodness, O
    Lord. ℟.

Good and upright is the Lord;
  he shows the way to sinners.
He guides the humble in right judgment;
  to the humble he teaches his way. ℟.

**READING II**  *1 Corinthians 7:29–31*

**GOSPEL**  *Mark 1:14–20*

## THIRD SUNDAY IN ORDINARY TIME / C 1100

**READING I** *Nehemiah 8:2–4a, 5–6, 8–10 / 69*

**RESPONSORIAL PSALM** *Psalm 19:8, 9, 10, 15*

Your words, O Lord, are Spir - it and life.

The law of the LORD is perfect;
  it revives the soul.
The decrees of the LORD are steadfast;
  they give wisdom to the simple. ℟.

The precepts of the LORD are right;
  they gladden the heart.
The command of the LORD is clear;
  it gives light to the eyes. ℟.

The fear of the LORD is pure,
  abiding forever.
The judgments of the LORD are true;
  they are, all of them, just. ℟.

May the spoken words of my mouth,
  the thoughts of my heart,
win favor in your sight, O LORD,
  my rock and my redeemer! ℟.

**READING II** *1 Corinthians 12:12–30 or 12:12–14, 27*

**GOSPEL** *Luke 1:1–4; 4:14–21*

## FOURTH SUNDAY IN ORDINARY TIME / A 1101

**READING I** *Zephaniah 2:3; 3:12–13 / 70*

**RESPONSORIAL PSALM** *Psalm 146:6c–7, 8–9a, 9bc–10*

*Or: Alleluia.*

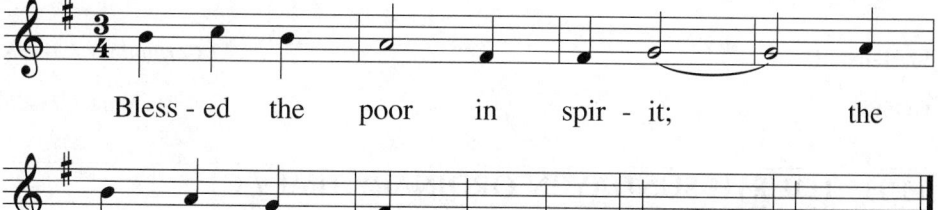

Bless - ed the poor in spir - it; the

king - dom of heav - en is theirs!

It is the LORD who preserves fidelity
  forever,
  who does justice to those who are
  oppressed.
It is he who gives bread to the hungry,
  the LORD who sets prisoners free. ℟.

The LORD who opens the eyes of the
  blind,
  the LORD who raises up those who
  are bowed down.
It is the LORD who loves the just,
  the LORD who protects the stranger. ℟.

The LORD upholds the orphan and the
widow,
but thwarts the path of the wicked.

The LORD will reign forever,
the God of Sion from age to age.
Alleluia. ℟.

**READING II**                                      *1 Corinthians 1:26–31*

**GOSPEL**                                           *Matthew 5:1–12a*

---

## 1102  FOURTH SUNDAY IN ORDINARY TIME / B

**READING I**                                       *Deuteronomy 18:15–20 / 71*

**RESPONSORIAL PSALM**                              *Psalm 95:1–2, 6–7c, 7d–9*

If to - day you hear his voice, hard-en not your hearts.

Come, let us ring out our joy to the
LORD;
hail the rock who saves us.
Let us come into his presence, giving
thanks;
let us hail him with a song of
praise. ℟.

O come; let us bow and bend low.
Let us kneel before the God who
made us,
for he is our God and we

the people who belong to his pasture,
the flock that is led by his
hand. ℟.

O that today you would listen to his
voice!
"Harden not your hearts as at Meribah,
as on that day at Massah in the
desert
when your forebears put me to the test;
when they tried me, though they saw
my work." ℟.

**READING II**                                     *1 Corinthians 7:32–35*

**GOSPEL**                                          *Mark 1:21–28*

---

## 1103  FOURTH SUNDAY IN ORDINARY TIME / C

**READING I**                                       *Jeremiah 1:4–5, 17–19 / 72*

**RESPONSORIAL PSALM**                              *Psalm 71:1–2, 3–4a, 5–6ab, 15ab and 17*

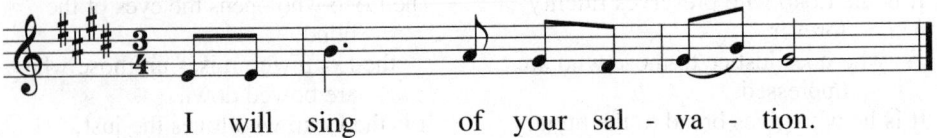

I will sing of your sal - va - tion.

In you, O LORD, I take refuge;
let me never be put to shame.
In your justice, rescue me, free me;
incline your ear to me and save me. ℟.

Be my rock, my constant refuge,
a mighty stronghold to save me,
for you are my rock, my stronghold.
My God, free me from the hand of
the wicked. ℟.

It is you, O Lord, who are my hope,
my trust, O LORD, from my youth.
On you I have leaned from my birth;
from my mother's womb, you have
been my help. ℟.

My mouth will tell of your justice,
and all the day long of your salvation.
O God, you have taught me from my
youth,
and I proclaim your wonders still. ℟.

**READING II**                                    *1 Corinthians 12:31—13:13 or 13:4–13*

**GOSPEL**                                                            *Luke 4:21–30*

---

# FIFTH SUNDAY IN ORDINARY TIME / A                              1104

**READING I**                                                      *Isaiah 58:7–10 / 73*

**RESPONSORIAL PSALM**                              *Psalm 112:4–5, 6–7, 8a and 9*

*Or: Alleluia.*

The just man is a light in dark-ness to the up-right.

A light rises in the darkness for the
upright;
he is generous, merciful, and just.
It goes well for the man who deals
generously and lends,
who conducts his affairs with
justice. ℟.

He will never be moved;
forever shall the just be remembered.

He has no fear of evil news;
with a firm heart, he trusts in the
LORD. ℟.

With a steadfast heart he will not fear.
Openhanded, he gives to the poor;
his justice stands firm forever.
His might shall be exalted in
glory. ℟.

**READING II**                                                    *1 Corinthians 2:1–5*

**GOSPEL**                                                         *Matthew 5:13–16*

## 1105   FIFTH SUNDAY IN ORDINARY TIME / B

**READING I**                                        *Job 7:1–4, 6–7 / 74*

**RESPONSORIAL PSALM**                          *Psalm 147:1–2, 3–4, 5–6*

*Or: Alleluia.*

Praise the Lord, praise the Lord, who heals the bro - ken - heart - ed.

How good to sing psalms to our God;
　how pleasant to chant fitting praise!
The LORD builds up Jerusalem
　and brings back Israel's exiles; ℟.

He heals the brokenhearted;
　he binds up all their wounds.

He counts out the number of the stars;
　he calls each one by its name. ℟.

Our Lord is great and almighty;
　his wisdom can never be measured.
The LORD lifts up the lowly;
　he casts down the wicked to the
　　ground. ℟.

**READING II**                          *1 Corinthians 9:16–19, 22–23*

**GOSPEL**                                          *Mark 1:29–39*

---

## 1106   FIFTH SUNDAY IN ORDINARY TIME / C

**READING I**                            *Isaiah 6:1–2a, 3–8 / 75*

**RESPONSORIAL PSALM**                  *Psalm 138:1–2a, 2b–3, 4–5, 7c–8*

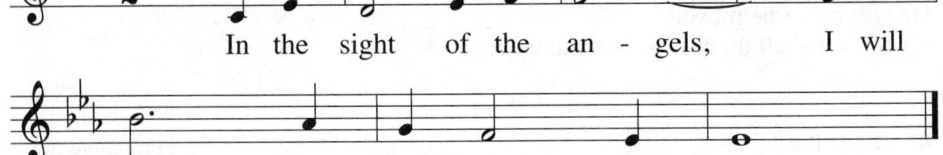

In the sight of the an - gels, I will sing your prais - es, O Lord.

I thank you, LORD, with all my heart;
　you have heard the words of my
　　mouth.
In the presence of the angels I praise you.
　I bow down toward your holy
　　temple. ℟.

I give thanks to your name
　for your merciful love and your
　　faithfulness.
You have exalted your name over all.
On the day I called, you answered me;
　you increased the strength of my
　　soul. ℟.

All earth's kings shall thank you,
O Lord,
when they hear the words of your
mouth.
They shall sing of the ways of the Lord,
"How great is the glory of the
Lord!" ℟.

With your right hand you save me;
the Lord will accomplish this for
me.
O Lord, your merciful love is eternal;
discard not the work of your
hands. ℟.

**READING II**                                      *1 Corinthians 15:1–11 or 15:3–8, 11*

**GOSPEL**                                                              *Luke 5:1–11*

## SIXTH SUNDAY IN ORDINARY TIME / A                      1107

**READING I**                                                  *Sirach 15:15–20 / 76*

**RESPONSORIAL PSALM**                  *Psalm 119:1–2, 4–5, 17–18, 33–34*

Bless - ed are they who fol - low the law of the Lord!

Blessed are those whose way is
blameless,
who walk in the law of the Lord!
Blessed are those who keep his decrees!
With all their hearts they seek him. ℟.

You have laid down your precepts
to be carefully kept.
May my ways be firm
in keeping your statutes. ℟.

Deal bountifully with your servant,
that I may live and keep your word.
Open my eyes, that I may see
the wonders of your law. ℟.

Lord, teach me the way of your
statutes,
and I will keep them to the end.
Grant me insight that I may keep your
law,
and observe it wholeheartedly. ℟.

**READING II**                                              *1 Corinthians 2:6–10*

**GOSPEL**                  *Matthew 5:17–37 or 5:20–22a, 27–28, 33–34a, 37*

## SIXTH SUNDAY IN ORDINARY TIME / B                      1108

**READING I**                                      *Leviticus 13:1–2, 44–46 / 77*

**RESPONSORIAL PSALM**  *Psalm 32:1–2, 5, 11*

I turn to you, O Lord, in time of trou-ble, and you fill me with the joy of sal-va-tion.

Blessed is he whose transgression is
  forgiven,
  whose sin is remitted.
Blessed the man to whom the LORD
  imputes no guilt,
  in whose spirit is no guile. ℟.

To you I have acknowledged my sin;
  my guilt I did not hide.

I said, "I will confess my transgression
  to the LORD."
And you have forgiven the guilt of
  my sin. ℟.

Rejoice in the LORD; exult, you just!
  Ring out your joy, all you upright of
  heart! ℟.

**READING II**  *1 Corinthians 10:31 — 11:1*

**GOSPEL**  *Mark 1:40–45*

---

# 1109  SIXTH SUNDAY IN ORDINARY TIME / C

**READING I**  *Jeremiah 17:5–8 / 78*

**RESPONSORIAL PSALM**  *Psalm 1:1–2, 3, 4 and 6*

Bless-ed are they, bless-ed are they who hope in the Lord.

Blessed indeed is the man
  who follows not the counsel of the
    wicked,
nor stands in the path with sinners,
  nor abides in the company of scorners,
but whose delight is the law of the LORD,
  and who ponders his law day and
    night. ℟.

He is like a tree that is planted
  beside the flowing waters,

that yields its fruit in due season,
and whose leaves shall never fade;
  and all that he does shall prosper. ℟.

Not so are the wicked, not so!
  For they, like winnowed chaff,
  shall be driven away by the wind;
for the LORD knows the way of the just,
  but the way of the wicked will
    perish. ℟.

**READING II**                                           *1 Corinthians 15:12, 16–20*

**GOSPEL**                                               *Luke 6:17, 20–26*

---

## SEVENTH SUNDAY IN ORDINARY TIME / A                    1110

**READING I**                                            *Leviticus 19:1–2, 17–18 / 79*

**RESPONSORIAL PSALM**                                   *Psalm 103:1–2, 3–4, 8 and 10, 12–13*

The Lord is kind and mer-ci-ful; the Lord is kind and mer-ci-ful.

Bless the LORD, O my soul,
  and all within me, his holy name.
Bless the LORD, O my soul,
  and never forget all his benefits. ℟.

It is the Lord who forgives all your sins,
  who heals every one of your ills,
who redeems your life from the grave,
  who crowns you with mercy and
    compassion. ℟.

The LORD is compassionate and gracious,
  slow to anger and rich in mercy.

He does not treat us according to our
  sins,
  nor repay us according to our
    faults. ℟.

As far as the east is from the west,
  so far from us does he remove our
    transgressions.
As a father has compassion on his
  children,
  the LORD's compassion is on those
    who fear him. ℟.

**READING II**                                           *1 Corinthians 3:16–23*

**GOSPEL**                                               *Matthew 5:38–48*

---

## SEVENTH SUNDAY IN ORDINARY TIME / B                    1111

**READING I**                                            *Isaiah 43:18–19, 21–22, 24b–25 / 80*

**RESPONSORIAL PSALM**                                   *Psalm 41:2–3, 4–5, 13–14*

Lord,    heal my    soul,    for    I  have sinned  a - gainst you.

Blessed is he who has concern for the
  poor.
  In time of trouble, the LORD will
    rescue him.

The LORD will guard him, give him life,
  and make him blessed in the land,
  not give him up to the will of his
    foes. ℟.

The LORD will help him on his bed of
    pain;
    you will bring him back from
        sickness to health.
As for me, I said, "LORD, have mercy
    on me;
    heal my soul, for I have sinned

against you." ℟.

In my integrity you have upheld me,
    and have set me in your presence
        forever.
Blest be the LORD, the God of Israel,
    from age to age. Amen. Amen. ℟.

**READING II**                                          *2 Corinthians 1:18–22*

**GOSPEL**                                                      *Mark 2:1–12*

---

## 1112   SEVENTH SUNDAY IN ORDINARY TIME / C

**READING I**                          *1 Samuel 26:2, 7–9, 12–13, 22–23 / 81*

**RESPONSORIAL PSALM**                   *Psalm 103:1–2, 3–4, 8 and 10, 12–13*

The Lord is kind and mer-ci-ful; the Lord is kind and mer-ci-ful.

Bless the LORD, O my soul,
    and all within me, his holy name.
Bless the LORD, O my soul,
    and never forget all his benefits. ℟.

It is the Lord who forgives all your sins,
    who heals every one of your ills,
who redeems your life from the grave,
    who crowns you with mercy and
        compassion. ℟.

The LORD is compassionate and
        gracious,
    slow to anger and rich in mercy.

He does not treat us according to our
        sins,
    nor repay us according to our
        faults. ℟.

As far as the east is from the west,
    so far from us does he remove our
        transgressions.
As a father has compassion on his
        children,
    the LORD's compassion is on those
        who fear him. ℟.

**READING II**                                          *1 Corinthians 15:45–49*

**GOSPEL**                                                      *Luke 6:27–38*

---

## 1113   EIGHTH SUNDAY IN ORDINARY TIME / A

**READING I**                                            *Isaiah 49:14–15 / 82*

**RESPONSORIAL PSALM**  *Psalm 62:2–3, 6–7, 8–9ab*

Rest in God a-lone, rest in God a-lone, my soul.

In God alone is my soul at rest;
  my salvation comes from him.
He alone is my rock, my salvation,
  my fortress; never shall I falter. ℟.

In God alone be at rest, my soul,
  for my hope is from him.
He alone is my rock, my salvation,

my fortress; never shall I falter. ℟.

In God is my salvation and glory,
  my rock of strength;
  in God is my refuge.
Trust him at all times, O people.
  Pour out your hearts before him. ℟.

**READING II**  *1 Corinthians 4:1–5*

**GOSPEL**  *Matthew 6:24–34*

---

# EIGHTH SUNDAY IN ORDINARY TIME / B      1114

**READING I**  *Hosea 2:16b, 17b, 21–22 / 83*

**RESPONSORIAL PSALM**  *Psalm 103:1–2, 3–4, 8 and 10, 12–13*

The Lord is kind and mer-ci-ful; the Lord is kind and mer-ci-ful.

Bless the LORD, O my soul,
  and all within me, his holy name.
Bless the LORD, O my soul,
  and never forget all his benefits. ℟.

It is the Lord who forgives all your sins,
  who heals every one of your ills,
who redeems your life from the grave,
  who crowns you with mercy and
    compassion. ℟.

The LORD is compassionate and
    gracious,
  slow to anger and rich in mercy.

He does not treat us according to our
    sins,
  nor repay us according to our
    faults. ℟.

As far as the east is from the west,
  so far from us does he remove our
    transgressions.
As a father has compassion on his
    children,
  the LORD's compassion is on those
    who fear him. ℟.

**READING II**                                              *2 Corinthians 3:1b–6*

**GOSPEL**                                                       *Mark 2:18–22*

---

## 1115  EIGHTH SUNDAY IN ORDINARY TIME / C

**READING I**                                               *Sirach 27:4–7 / 84*

**RESPONSORIAL PSALM**                          *Psalm 92:2–3, 13–14, 15–16*

Lord, it is good to give thanks to you, to give thanks to you.

It is good to give thanks to the LORD,
  to make music to your name,
    O Most High,
to proclaim your loving mercy in the
    morning,
  and your truth in the watches of
    the night. ℟.

The just will flourish like the palm tree,
  and grow like a Lebanon cedar.

Planted in the house of the LORD,
  they will flourish in the courts of
  our God. ℟.

Still bearing fruit when they are old,
  still full of sap, still green,
to proclaim that the LORD is upright.
  In him, my rock, there is no
  wrong. ℟.

**READING II**                                            *1 Corinthians 15:54–58*

**GOSPEL**                                                       *Luke 6:39–45*

---

## 1116  NINTH SUNDAY IN ORDINARY TIME / A

**READING I**                                   *Deuteronomy 11:18, 26–28, 32 / 85*

**RESPONSORIAL PSALM**                     *Psalm 31:2–3a, 3bc–4, 17 and 25*

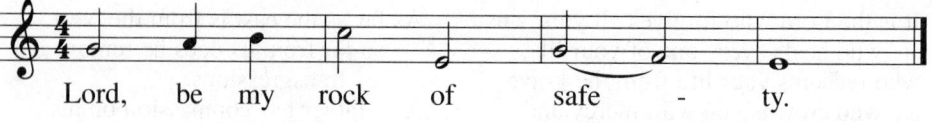

Lord, be my rock of safe - ty.

In you, O LORD, I take refuge.
  Let me never be put to shame.
In your justice, set me free;
    incline your ear to me, and speedily
    rescue me. ℟.

Be a rock of refuge for me,
  a mighty stronghold to save me.

For you are my rock, my stronghold!
  Lead me, guide me, for the sake of
  your name. ℟.

Let your face shine on your servant.
  Save me in your merciful love.
Be strong, let your heart take courage,
  all who hope in the LORD. ℟.

**READING II**                                                      *Romans 3:21–25, 28*

**GOSPEL**                                                           *Matthew 7:21–27*

---

## NINTH SUNDAY IN ORDINARY TIME / B                                  1117

**READING I**                                                 *Deuteronomy 5:12–15 / 86*

**RESPONSORIAL PSALM**                          *Psalm 81:3–4, 5–6ab, 6c–8a, 10–11b*

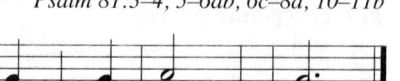

Sing with joy to God!                    Sing to God our help!

Raise a song and sound the timbrel,
   the sweet-sounding harp and the lute;
blow the trumpet at the new moon,
   when the moon is full, on our
      feast. ℟.

For this is a statute in Israel,
   a command of the God of Jacob.
He made it a decree for Joseph,
   when he went out from the land of
      Egypt. ℟.

A voice I did not know said to me:

"I freed your shoulder from the
   burden;
your hands were freed from the
   builder's basket.
You called in distress and I
   delivered you." ℟.

"Let there be no strange god among
   you,
   nor shall you worship a foreign god.
I am the LORD your God,
   who brought you up from the land
   of Egypt." ℟.

**READING II**                                                     *2 Corinthians 4:6–11*

**GOSPEL**                                                  *Mark 2:23–3:6 or 2:23–28*

---

## NINTH SUNDAY IN ORDINARY TIME / C                                  1118

**READING I**                                                      *1 Kings 8:41–43 / 87*

**RESPONSORIAL PSALM**                                              *Psalm 117:1, 2*

*Or: Alleluia.*

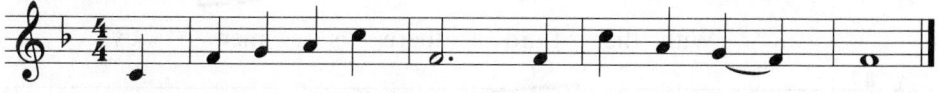

Go out to all the world    and tell the Good    News.

O praise the LORD, all you nations;
   acclaim him, all you peoples! ℟.

For his merciful love has prevailed
   over us;
   and the LORD's faithfulness endures
   forever. ℟.

**READING II**                                                 *Galatians 1:1–2, 6–10*

**GOSPEL**                                                            *Luke 7:1–10*

## 1119   TENTH SUNDAY IN ORDINARY TIME / A

**READING I**                                                    *Hosea 6:3–6 / 88*

**RESPONSORIAL PSALM**                            *Psalm 50:1 and 8, 12–13, 14–15*

To the up-right I will show   the sav-ing pow'r of God.

The God of gods, the LORD,
  has spoken and summoned the earth,
  from the rising of the sun to its
    setting.
"I do not rebuke you for your sacrifices;
  your offerings are always before
    me." ℟.

"Were I hungry, I would not tell you,
  for the world and its fullness is mine.

Do I eat the flesh of bulls,
  or drink the blood of goats?" ℟.

"Give your praise as a sacrifice to God,
  and fulfill your vows to the
    Most High.
Then call on me in the day of distress.
  I will deliver you and you shall
    honor me." ℟.

**READING II**                                                  *Romans 4:18–25*

**GOSPEL**                                                      *Matthew 9:9–13*

## 1120   TENTH SUNDAY IN ORDINARY TIME / B

**READING I**                                                  *Genesis 3:9–15 / 89*

**RESPONSORIAL PSALM**                  *Psalm 130:1–2, 3–4, 5–6ab and 7a, 7b–8*

With   the   Lord     there   is     mer - cy,

and   full - ness   of   re - demp - tion.

Out of the depths I cry to you, O LORD;
    Lord, hear my voice!
O let your ears be attentive
    to the sound of my pleadings. ℟.

If you, O LORD, should mark iniquities,
    Lord, who could stand?
But with you is found forgiveness,
    that you may be revered. ℟.

I long for you, O LORD,
    my soul longs for his word.
My soul hopes in the Lord
    more than watchmen for daybreak. ℟.

Let Israel hope for the LORD.
For with the LORD there is mercy,
    in him is plentiful redemption.
It is he who will redeem Israel
    from all its iniquities. ℟.

**READING II**        *2 Corinthians 4:13—5:1*

**GOSPEL**        *Mark 3:20–35*

## TENTH SUNDAY IN ORDINARY TIME / C      1121

**READING I**        *1 Kings 17:17–24 / 90*

**RESPONSORIAL PSALM**        *Psalm 30:2 and 4, 5–6, 11 and 12a and 13b*

I will praise you, Lord, for you have res-cued me.

I will extol you, LORD, for you have
    raised me up,
    and have not let my enemies rejoice
    over me.
O LORD, you have lifted up my soul
    from the grave,
    restored me to life from those who
    sink into the pit. ℟.

Sing psalms to the LORD, you faithful
    ones;
    give thanks to his holy name.

His anger lasts a moment; his favor all
    through life.
    At night come tears, but dawn
    brings joy. ℟.

Hear, O LORD, and have mercy on me;
    be my helper, O LORD.
You have changed my mourning into
    dancing.
    O LORD my God, I will thank you
    forever. ℟.

**READING II**        *Galatians 1:11–19*

**GOSPEL**        *Luke 7:11–17*

## ELEVENTH SUNDAY IN ORDINARY TIME / A      1122

**READING I**        *Exodus 19:2–6a / 91*

**RESPONSORIAL PSALM**  *Psalm 100:1–2, 3, 5*

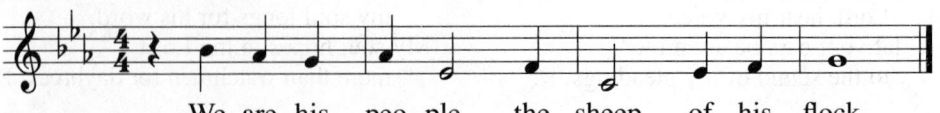

We are his peo-ple, the sheep of his flock.

Cry out with joy to the LORD, all the
   earth.
   Serve the LORD with gladness.
   Come before him, singing for joy. ℟.

Know that he, the LORD, is God.
   He made us; we belong to him.

We are his people, the sheep of his
   flock. ℟.

Indeed, how good is the LORD,
   eternal his merciful love.
   He is faithful from age to age. ℟.

**READING II**  *Romans 5:6–11*

**GOSPEL**  *Matthew 9:36 – 10:8*

---

## 1123 ELEVENTH SUNDAY IN ORDINARY TIME / B

**READING I**  *Ezekiel 17:22–24 / 92*

**RESPONSORIAL PSALM**  *Psalm 92:2–3, 13–14, 15–16*

Lord, it is good to give thanks to you, to give thanks to you.

It is good to give thanks to the LORD,
   to make music to your name,
      O Most High,
   to proclaim your loving mercy in the
         morning,
      and your truth in the watches of the
         night. ℟.

The just will flourish like the palm tree,
   and grow like a Lebanon cedar.

Planted in the house of the LORD,
   they will flourish in the courts of
      our God. ℟.

Still bearing fruit when they are old,
   still full of sap, still green,
   to proclaim that the LORD is upright.
      In him, my rock, there is no
         wrong. ℟.

**READING II**  *2 Corinthians 5:6–10*

**GOSPEL**  *Mark 4:26–34*

## ELEVENTH SUNDAY IN ORDINARY TIME / C          1124

**READING I**                                   *2 Samuel 12:7–10, 13 / 93*

**RESPONSORIAL PSALM**                    *Psalm 32:1–2, 5, 7, 11*

Lord, for - give the wrong I have done.

Blessed is he whose transgression is
   forgiven,
   whose sin is remitted.
Blessed the man to whom the LORD
   imputes no guilt,
   in whose spirit is no guile. ℟.

To you I have acknowledged my sin;
   my guilt I did not hide.
I said, "I will confess my transgression
   to the LORD."

And you have forgiven the guilt of
   my sin. ℟.

You are a hiding place for me;
   you keep me safe from distress;
   you surround me with cries of
    deliverance. ℟.

Rejoice in the LORD; exult, you just!
   Ring out your joy, all you upright of
   heart! ℟.

**READING II**                               *Galatians 2:16, 19–21*

**GOSPEL**                              *Luke 7:36–8:3 or 7:36–50*

## TWELFTH SUNDAY IN ORDINARY TIME / A          1125

**READING I**                              *Jeremiah 20:10–13 / 94*

**RESPONSORIAL PSALM**              *Psalm 69:8–10, 14 and 17, 33–35*

Lord, in your great love, an - swer me.

It is for you that I suffer taunts,
   that shame has covered my face.
To my own kin I have become an
   outcast,
   a stranger to the children of my
    mother.
Zeal for your house consumes me,
   and taunts against you fall on me. ℟.

But I pray to you, O LORD,
   for a time of your favor.
In your great mercy, answer me, O God,
   with your salvation that never fails.
LORD, answer, for your mercy is kind;
   in your great compassion, turn
   toward me. ℟.

The poor when they see it will be glad,
and God-seeking hearts will revive;
for the LORD listens to the needy,
and does not spurn his own in their
chains.

Let the heavens and the earth give him
praise,
the seas and everything that moves
in them. ℟.

**READING II** *Romans 5:12–15*

**GOSPEL** *Matthew 10:26–33*

---

## 1126 TWELFTH SUNDAY IN ORDINARY TIME / B

**READING I** *Job 38:1, 8–11 / 95*

**RESPONSORIAL PSALM** *Psalm 107:23–24, 25–26, 28–29, 30–31*

*Or: Alleluia.*

Give thanks to the Lord, his love is ev-er-last - ing.

Some went down to the sea in ships,
to trade on the mighty waters.
These have seen the deeds of the LORD,
the wonders he does in the deep. ℟.

For he spoke and raised up the
storm-wind,
tossing high the waves of the sea
that surged to heaven and dropped to
the depths.
Their souls melted away in their
distress. ℟.

Then they cried to the LORD in their
need,
and he rescued them from their
distress.
He stilled the storm to a whisper,
and the waves of the sea were
hushed. ℟.

They rejoiced because of the calm,
and he led them to the haven they
desired.
Let them thank the LORD for his mercy,
his wonders for the children of
men. ℟.

**READING II** *2 Corinthians 5:14–17*

**GOSPEL** *Mark 4:35–41*

---

## 1127 TWELFTH SUNDAY IN ORDINARY TIME / C

**READING I** *Zechariah 12:10–11; 13:1 / 96*

**RESPONSORIAL PSALM**  *Psalm 63:2, 3–4, 5–6, 8–9*

My soul is thirst-ing for you, O Lord,

thirst-ing for you my God.

O God, you are my God; at dawn
I seek you;
for you my soul is thirsting.
For you my flesh is pining,
like a dry, weary land without
water. ℟.

I have come before you in the sanctuary,
to behold your strength and your
glory.
Your loving mercy is better than life;
my lips will speak your praise. ℟.

I will bless you all my life;
in your name I will lift up my hands.
My soul shall be filled as with a
banquet;
with joyful lips, my mouth shall
praise you. ℟.

For you have been my strength;
in the shadow of your wings I
rejoice.
My soul clings fast to you;
your right hand upholds me. ℟.

**READING II**  *Galatians 3:26–29*

**GOSPEL**  *Luke 9:18–24*

## THIRTEENTH SUNDAY IN ORDINARY TIME / A  1128

**READING I**  *2 Kings 4:8–11, 14–16a / 97*

**RESPONSORIAL PSALM**  *Psalm 89:2–3, 16–17, 18–19*

For ev-er I will sing the good-ness of the Lord.

I will sing forever of your mercies,
O LORD;
through all ages my mouth will
proclaim your fidelity.
I have declared your mercy is
established forever;
your fidelity stands firm as the
heavens. ℟.

How blessed the people who know your
praise,
who walk, O LORD, in the light of
your face,
who find their joy every day in your
name,
who make your justice their joyful
acclaim. ℟.

For you are the glory of their strength;
    by your favor it is that our might is
        exalted.

Behold, the LORD is our shield;
    he is the Holy One of Israel, our
        king. ℟.

**READING II**                                                  *Romans 6:3–4, 8–11*

**GOSPEL**                                                      *Matthew 10:37–42*

---

## 1129  THIRTEENTH SUNDAY IN ORDINARY TIME / B

**READING I**                                    *Wisdom 1:13–15; 2:23–24 / 98*

**RESPONSORIAL PSALM**          *Psalm 30:2 and 4, 5–6, 11 and 12a and 13b*

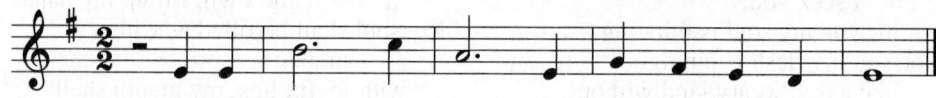

I will praise you, Lord, for you have res-cued me.

I will extol you, LORD, for you have
    raised me up,
    and have not let my enemies rejoice
        over me.
O LORD, you have lifted up my soul
    from the grave,
    restored me to life from those who
        sink into the pit. ℟.

Sing psalms to the LORD, you faithful
    ones;
    give thanks to his holy name.

His anger lasts a moment; his favor all
    through life.
    At night come tears, but dawn
        brings joy. ℟.

Hear, O LORD, and have mercy on me;
    be my helper, O LORD.
You have changed my mourning into
    dancing.
    O LORD my God, I will thank you
        forever. ℟.

**READING II**                                        *2 Corinthians 8:7, 9, 13–15*

**GOSPEL**                                    *Mark 5:21–43 or 5:21–24, 35b-43*

---

## 1130  THIRTEENTH SUNDAY IN ORDINARY TIME / C

**READING I**                                    *1 Kings 19:16b, 19–21 / 99*

**RESPONSORIAL PSALM**          *Psalm 16:1–2a and 5, 7–8, 9–10, 11*

You are my in - her - i - tance, O Lord.

Preserve me, O God, for in you I take
    refuge.
    I say to the LORD, "You are my Lord."

O LORD, it is you who are my portion
    and cup;
    you yourself who secure my lot. ℟.

I will bless the LORD who gives me
counsel,
who even at night directs my heart.
I keep the LORD before me always;
with him at my right hand,
I shall not be moved. ℟.

And so, my heart rejoices, my soul is
glad;

even my flesh shall rest in hope.
For you will not abandon my soul to
hell,
nor let your holy one see
corruption. ℟.

You will show me the path of life,
the fullness of joy in your presence,
at your right hand, bliss forever. ℟.

**READING II**                                   *Galatians 5:1, 13–18*

**GOSPEL**                                        *Luke 9:51–62*

---

## FOURTEENTH SUNDAY IN ORDINARY TIME / A          1131

**READING I**                                     *Zechariah 9:9–10 / 100*

**RESPONSORIAL PSALM**                    *Psalm 145:1–2, 8–9, 10–11, 13cd–14*

*Or: Alleluia.*

I will praise your name for ev-er,    my king and my God.

I will extol you, my God and king,
and bless your name forever and
ever.
I will bless you day after day,
and praise your name forever and
ever. ℟.

The LORD is kind and full of compassion,
slow to anger, abounding in mercy.
How good is the LORD to all,
compassionate to all his creatures. ℟.

All your works shall thank you,
O LORD,
and all your faithful ones bless you.
They shall speak of the glory of your
reign,
and declare your mighty deeds. ℟.

The LORD is faithful in all his words,
and holy in all his deeds.
The LORD supports all who fall,
and raises up all who are bowed
down. ℟.

**READING II**                                   *Romans 8:9, 11–13*

**GOSPEL**                                        *Matthew 11:25–30*

---

## FOURTEENTH SUNDAY IN ORDINARY TIME / B          1132

**READING I**                                     *Ezekiel 2:2–5 / 101*

**RESPONSORIAL PSALM**     *Psalm 123:1–2a, 2bcd, 3–4*

Our eyes are fixed on the Lord, plead-ing for his mer-cy.

To you have I lifted up my eyes,
  you who dwell in the heavens.
Behold, like the eyes of slaves
  on the hand of their lords. ℟.

Like the eyes of a servant
  on the hand of her mistress,
so our eyes are on the LORD our God,

till he show us his mercy. ℟.

Have mercy on us, LORD, have mercy.
  We are filled with contempt.
Indeed, all too full is our soul
  with the scorn of the arrogant,
  the disdain of the proud. ℟.

**READING II**     *2 Corinthians 12:7–10*

**GOSPEL**     *Mark 6:1–6*

---

## 1133  FOURTEENTH SUNDAY IN ORDINARY TIME / C

**READING I**     *Isaiah 66:10–14c / 102*

**RESPONSORIAL PSALM**     *Psalm 66:1–3a, 4–5, 6–7a, 16 and 20*

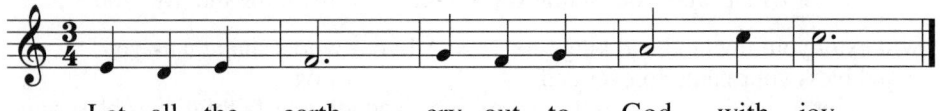

Let all the earth cry out to God with joy.

Cry out with joy to God, all the earth;
  O sing to the glory of his name.
O render him glorious praise.
  Say to God, "How awesome your
  deeds! ℟.

"Before you all the earth shall bow
  down,
  shall sing to you, sing to your name!"
Come and see the works of God:
  awesome his deeds among the
  children of men. ℟.

He turned the sea into dry land;
  they passed through the river on
  foot.
Let our joy, then, be in him;
  he rules forever by his might. ℟.

Come and hear, all who fear God;
  I will tell what he did for my soul.
Blest be God, who did not reject my
  prayer,
  nor withhold from me his merciful
  love. ℟.

**READING II**     *Galatians 6:14–18*

**GOSPEL**     *Luke 10:1–12, 17–20 or 10:1–9*

## FIFTEENTH SUNDAY IN ORDINARY TIME / A 1134

**READING I** *Isaiah 55:10–11 / 103*

**RESPONSORIAL PSALM** *Psalm 65:10abcd, 10e–11, 12–13, 14*

The seed that falls on good ground will

yield a fruit - ful har - vest.

You visit the earth, give it water;
    you fill it with riches.
God's ever-flowing river brims over
    to prepare the grain. ℞.

And thus you provide for the earth:
    you drench its furrows;
you level it, soften it with showers;
    you bless its growth. ℞.

You crown the year with your bounty.
    Abundance flows in your pathways;
in pastures of the desert it flows.
    The hills are girded with joy. ℞.

The meadows clothed with flocks.
    The valleys are decked with wheat.
    They shout for joy; yes, they
        sing! ℞.

**READING II** *Romans 8:18–23*

**GOSPEL** *Matthew 13:1–23 or 13:1–9*

## FIFTEENTH SUNDAY IN ORDINARY TIME / B 1135

**READING I** *Amos 7:12–15 / 104*

**RESPONSORIAL PSALM** *Psalm 85:9ab and 10, 11–12, 13–14*

Lord, let us see your kind - ness, and grant us your sal - va - tion.

I will hear what the LORD God speaks;
    he speaks of peace for his people
        and his faithful.
His salvation is near for those who fear

him,
and his glory will dwell in our
    land. ℞.

Merciful love and faithfulness have met;
   justice and peace have kissed.
Faithfulness shall spring from the earth,
   and justice look down from
      heaven. ℟.

Also the Lord will bestow his bounty,
   and our earth shall yield its increase.
Justice will march before him,
   and guide his steps on the way. ℟.

**READING II**                                      *Ephesians 1:3–14 or 1:3–10*

**GOSPEL**                                          *Mark 6:7–13*

## 1136   FIFTEENTH SUNDAY IN ORDINARY TIME / C

**READING I**                                       *Deuteronomy 30:10–14 / 105*

**RESPONSORIAL PSALM**              *Psalm 69:14 and 17, 30–31, 33–34, 36ab and 37*

Turn to the Lord in your need, and you will live.

I pray to you, O Lord,
   for a time of your favor.
In your great mercy, answer me, O God,
   with your salvation that never fails.
Lord, answer, for your mercy is kind;
   in your great compassion, turn
      toward me. ℟.

As for me in my poverty and pain,
   let your salvation, O God, raise me up.
Then I will praise God's name with a
   song;
   I will glorify him with thanksgiving. ℟.

The poor when they see it will be glad,
   and God-seeking hearts will revive;
for the Lord listens to the needy,
   and does not spurn his own in their
      chains. ℟.

For God will bring salvation to Sion,
   and rebuild the cities of Judah.
The children of his servants shall
   inherit it;
   those who love his name shall dwell
      there. ℟.

*Or:*

**RESPONSORIAL PSALM**                              *Psalm 19:8, 9, 10, 11*

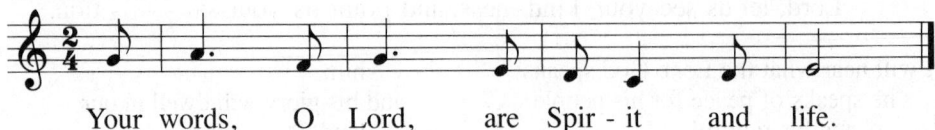

Your words, O Lord, are Spir-it and life.

The law of the Lord is perfect;
   it revives the soul.

The decrees of the Lord are steadfast;
   they give wisdom to the simple. ℟.

The precepts of the LORD are right;
  they gladden the heart.
The command of the LORD is clear;
  it gives light to the eyes. ℟.

The fear of the LORD is pure,
  abiding forever.

The judgments of the LORD are true;
  they are, all of them, just. ℟.

They are more to be desired than gold,
  than quantities of gold.
And sweeter are they than honey,
  than honey flowing from the
    comb. ℟.

**READING II**                                          *Colossians 1:15–20*

**GOSPEL**                                                  *Luke 10:25–37*

---

## SIXTEENTH SUNDAY IN ORDINARY TIME / A                1137

**READING I**                                    *Wisdom 12:13, 16–19 / 106*

**RESPONSORIAL PSALM**                         *Psalm 86:5–6, 9–10, 15–16*

Lord, you are good and for - giv - ing.

O Lord, you are good and forgiving,
  full of mercy to all who call to you.
Give ear, O LORD, to my prayer,
  and attend to my voice in
    supplication. ℟.

All the nations you have made shall come;
  they will bow down before you,
    O Lord,
  and glorify your name,

for you are great and do marvelous
    deeds,
  you who alone are God. ℟.

But you, O God, are compassionate and
    gracious,
  slow to anger, O Lord,
abundant in mercy and fidelity;
  turn and take pity on me.
O give your strength to your servant. ℟.

**READING II**                                          *Romans 8:26–27*

**GOSPEL**                              *Matthew 13:24–43 or 13:24–30*

---

## SIXTEENTH SUNDAY IN ORDINARY TIME / B                1138

**READING I**                                      *Jeremiah 23:1–6 / 107*

**RESPONSORIAL PSALM**                                    *Psalm 23:1–3a, 3b–4, 5, 6*

The Lord is my shep-herd; there is noth-ing I shall want.

The LORD is my shepherd;
  there is nothing I shall want.
Fresh and green are the pastures
  where he gives me repose.
Near restful waters he leads me;
  he revives my soul. ℟.

He guides me along the right path,
  for the sake of his name.
Though I should walk in the valley of
  the shadow of death,
  no evil would I fear, for you are
  with me.

Your crook and your staff will give
  me comfort. ℟.

You have prepared a table before me
  in the sight of my foes.
My head you have anointed with oil;
  my cup is overflowing. ℟.

Surely goodness and mercy shall
  follow me
  all the days of my life.
In the LORD's own house shall I dwell
  for length of days unending. ℟.

**READING II**                                    *Ephesians 2:13–18*

**GOSPEL**                                          *Mark 6:30–34*

---

## 1139  SIXTEENTH SUNDAY IN ORDINARY TIME / C

**READING I**                                    *Genesis 18:1–10a / 108*

**RESPONSORIAL PSALM**                           *Psalm 15:2–3a, 3bc–4ab, 5*

He who does jus-tice will live in the pres-ence of the Lord.

Whoever walks without fault;
  who does what is just,
and speaks the truth from his heart;
  whoever does not slander with his
  tongue. ℟.

Who does no wrong to a neighbor,
  who casts no slur on a friend,
who looks with scorn on the wicked,

but honors those who fear the
  LORD. ℟.

Who lends no money at interest,
  and accepts no bribes against the
  innocent.
Such a one shall never be shaken. ℟.

**READING II**                                    *Colossians 1:24–28*

**GOSPEL**                                          *Luke 10:38–42*

## SEVENTEENTH SUNDAY IN ORDINARY TIME / A 1140

**READING I** *1 Kings 3:5, 7–12 / 109*

**RESPONSORIAL PSALM** *Psalm 119:57 and 72, 76–77, 127–128, 129–130*

Lord, I love your com-mands, I love your com-mands.

I have said, "O LORD, my portion
    is to obey your words."
The law from your mouth means more
        to me
    than large quantities of silver and
        gold. ℟.

Let your merciful love console me
    by your promise to your servant.
Show me compassion, that I may live,
    for your law is my delight. ℟.

That is why I love your commands
    more than finest gold,
why I rule my life by your precepts,
    and hate false ways. ℟.

Your decrees are wonderful indeed;
    therefore my soul obeys them.
The unfolding of your word gives light,
    and understanding to the simple. ℟.

**READING II** *Romans 8:28–30*

**GOSPEL** *Matthew 13:44–52 or 13:44–46*

## SEVENTEENTH SUNDAY IN ORDINARY TIME / B 1141

**READING I** *2 Kings 4:42–44 / 110*

**RESPONSORIAL PSALM** *Psalm 145:10–11, 15–16, 17–18*

The hand of the Lord feeds us; he an-swers all our needs.

All your works shall thank you,
    O LORD,
    and all your faithful ones bless you.
They shall speak of the glory of your
        reign,
    and declare your mighty deeds. ℟.

The eyes of all look to you,
    and you give them their food in

due season.
You open your hand and satisfy
    the desire of every living thing. ℟.

The LORD is just in all his ways,
    and holy in all his deeds.
The LORD is close to all who call him,
    who call on him in truth. ℟.

READING II                                                    *Ephesians 4:1–6*

GOSPEL                                                          *John 6:1–15*

---

## 1142   SEVENTEENTH SUNDAY IN ORDINARY TIME / C

READING I                                               *Genesis 18:20–32 / 111*

RESPONSORIAL PSALM                    *Psalm 138:1–2a, 2bcd–3, 6–7ab, 7c–8*

Lord, on the day I called for help, you an-swered me.

I thank you, Lᴏʀᴅ, with all my heart;
  you have heard the words of my
    mouth.
In the presence of the angels I praise you.
  I bow down toward your holy
    temple. ℞.

I give thanks to your name
  for your merciful love and your
    faithfulness.
  You have exalted your name over all.
On the day I called, you answered me;
  you increased the strength of my
    soul. ℞.

The Lᴏʀᴅ is high, yet he looks on the
  lowly,
  and the haughty he knows from afar.
You give me life though I walk amid
  affliction;
  you stretch out your hand against
    the anger of my foes. ℞.

With your right hand you save me;
  the Lᴏʀᴅ will accomplish this for
    me.
O Lᴏʀᴅ, your merciful love is eternal;
  discard not the work of your
    hands. ℞.

READING II                                              *Colossians 2:12–14*

GOSPEL                                                     *Luke 11:1–13*

---

## 1143   EIGHTEENTH SUNDAY IN ORDINARY TIME / A

READING I                                               *Isaiah 55:1–3 / 112*

RESPONSORIAL PSALM                    *Psalm 145:8–9, 15–16, 17–18*

The hand of the Lord feeds us; he an-swers all our needs.

The Lᴏʀᴅ is kind and full of compassion,
  slow to anger, abounding in mercy.
How good is the Lᴏʀᴅ to all,
  compassionate to all his creatures. ℞.

The eyes of all look to you,
  and you give them their food in due
    season.
You open your hand and satisfy
  the desire of every living thing. ℞.

The Lord is just in all his ways,
    and holy in all his deeds.

The Lord is close to all who call him,
    who call on him in truth. ℟.

**READING II**　　　　　　　　　　　　　　　　　　*Romans 8:35, 37–39*

**GOSPEL**　　　　　　　　　　　　　　　　　　　*Matthew 14:13–21*

---

## EIGHTEENTH SUNDAY IN ORDINARY TIME / B　　　1144

**READING I**　　　　　　　　　　　　　　　*Exodus 16:2–4, 12–15 / 113*

**RESPONSORIAL PSALM**　　　　　　*Psalm 78:3 and 4bc, 23–24, 25 and 54*

The Lord gave them bread from heav - en.

The things we have heard and
    understood,
      the things our fathers have told us,
      we will tell to the next generation:
The glories of the Lord and his might,
    and the marvelous deeds he has
      done. ℟.

He commanded the clouds above,

and opened the gates of heaven.
He rained down manna to eat,
    and gave them bread from heaven. ℟.

Man ate the bread of angels.
    He sent them abundance of food.
So he brought them to his holy land,
    to the mountain his right hand
      had won. ℟.

**READING II**　　　　　　　　　　　　　　　　*Ephesians 4:17, 20–24*

**GOSPEL**　　　　　　　　　　　　　　　　　　　*John 6:24–35*

---

## EIGHTEENTH SUNDAY IN ORDINARY TIME / C　　　1145

**READING I**　　　　　　　　　　　　*Ecclesiastes 1:2; 2:21–23 / 114*

**RESPONSORIAL PSALM**　　　　　*Psalm 90:3–4, 5–6, 12–13, 14 and 17*

If to-day you hear his voice, hard-en not your hearts.

You turn man back to dust,
    and say, "Return, O children of men."
To your eyes a thousand years
    are like yesterday, come and gone,
    or like a watch in the night. ℟.

You sweep them away like a dream,
    like grass which is fresh in the
      morning.
In the morning it sprouts and is fresh;
    by evening it withers and fades. ℟.

Then teach us to number our days,
   that we may gain wisdom of heart.
Turn back, O Lord! How long?
   Show pity to your servants. ℟.

At dawn, fill us with your merciful love;
   we shall exult and rejoice all our

days.
Let the favor of the Lord our God be
   upon us;
give success to the work of our
   hands.
O give success to the work of our
   hands. ℟.

**READING II**                                   *Colossians 3:1–5, 9–11*

**GOSPEL**                                           *Luke 12:13–21*

---

## 1146  NINETEENTH SUNDAY IN ORDINARY TIME / A

**READING I**                                   *1 Kings 19:9a, 11–13a / 115*

**RESPONSORIAL PSALM**                        *Psalm 85:9ab–10, 11–12, 13–14*

Lord, let us see your kind-ness, and grant us your sal - va - tion.

I will hear what the Lord God speaks;
   he speaks of peace for his people
      and his faithful.
His salvation is near for those who fear
   him,
   and his glory will dwell in our land. ℟.

Merciful love and faithfulness have met;
   justice and peace have kissed.

Faithfulness shall spring from the earth,
   and justice look down from
      heaven. ℟.

Also the Lord will bestow his bounty,
   and our earth shall yield its increase.
Justice will march before him,
   and guide his steps on the way. ℟.

**READING II**                                   *Romans 9:1–5*

**GOSPEL**                                           *Matthew 14:22–33*

---

## 1147  NINETEENTH SUNDAY IN ORDINARY TIME / B

**READING I**                                   *1 Kings 19:4–8 / 116*

**RESPONSORIAL PSALM**                        *Psalm 34:2–3, 4–5, 6–7, 8–9*

Taste   and   see   the   good - ness   of   the   Lord.

I will bless the LORD at all times;
  praise of him is always in my mouth.
In the LORD my soul shall make its boast;
  the humble shall hear and be glad. ℟.

Glorify the LORD with me;
  together let us praise his name.
I sought the LORD, and he answered me;
  from all my terrors he set me free. ℟.

Look toward him and be radiant;

let your faces not be abashed.
This lowly one called; the LORD heard,
  and rescued him from all his
  distress. ℟.

The angel of the LORD is encamped
  around those who fear him,
  to rescue them.
Taste and see that the LORD is good.
  Blessed the man who seeks refuge
  in him. ℟.

**READING II**                                              *Ephesians 4:30—5:2*

**GOSPEL**                                                      *John 6:41–51*

---

## NINETEENTH SUNDAY IN ORDINARY TIME / C                     1148

**READING I**                                              *Wisdom 18:6–9 / 117*

**RESPONSORIAL PSALM**                      *Psalm 33:1 and 12, 18–19, 20 and 22*

Bless-ed the peo-ple the Lord has cho - sen to  be his  own.

Ring out your joy to the LORD, O you
  just;
  for praise is fitting for the upright.
Blessed the nation whose God is
    the LORD,
  the people he has chosen as his
  heritage. ℟.

Yes, the LORD's eyes are on those
  who fear him,

who hope in his merciful love,
to rescue their souls from death,
  to keep them alive in famine. ℟.

Our soul is waiting for the LORD.
  He is our help and our shield.
May your merciful love be upon us,
  as we hope in you, O LORD. ℟.

**READING II**                              *Hebrews 11:1–2, 8–19 or 11:1–2, 8–12*

**GOSPEL**                                      *Luke 12:32–48 or 12:35–40*

## 1149  TWENTIETH SUNDAY IN ORDINARY TIME / A

**READING I**                                             *Isaiah 56:1, 6–7 / 118*

**RESPONSORIAL PSALM**                          *Psalm 67:2–3, 5, 6 and 8*

O God, O God, let all the na-tions praise you!

O God, be gracious and bless us
  and let your face shed its light upon us.
So will your ways be known upon earth
  and all nations learn your salvation. ℟.

Let the nations be glad and shout for joy,
  with uprightness you rule the peoples;

you guide the nations on earth. ℟.

Let the peoples praise you, O God;
  let all the peoples praise you.
May God still give us his blessing
  that all the ends of the earth may
  revere him. ℟.

**READING II**                                      *Romans 11:13–15, 29–32*

**GOSPEL**                                              *Matthew 15:21–28*

---

## 1150  TWENTIETH SUNDAY IN ORDINARY TIME / B

**READING I**                                          *Proverbs 9:1–6 / 119*

**RESPONSORIAL PSALM**                        *Psalm 34:2–3, 4–5, 6–7*

Taste and see the good - ness of the Lord.

I will bless the LORD at all times;
  praise of him is always in my mouth.
In the LORD my soul shall make its boast;
  the humble shall hear and be glad. ℟.

Glorify the LORD with me;
  together let us praise his name.
I sought the LORD, and he answered me;

from all my terrors he set me free. ℟.

Look toward him and be radiant;
  let your faces not be abashed.
This lowly one called; the LORD heard,
  and rescued him from all his
  distress. ℟.

**READING II**                                         *Ephesians 5:15–20*

**GOSPEL**                                                  *John 6:51–58*

# TWENTIETH SUNDAY IN ORDINARY TIME / C                    1151

**READING I**                                             *Jeremiah 38:4–6, 8–10 / 120*

**RESPONSORIAL PSALM**                                    *Psalm 40:2, 3, 4, 18*

Lord, come to my aid, Lord, come to my aid!

I waited, I waited for the LORD,
  and he stooped down to me;
he heard my cry. ℟.

He drew me from the deadly pit,
  from the miry clay.
He set my feet upon a rock,
  made my footsteps firm. ℟.

He put a new song into my mouth,
  praise of our God.
Many shall see and fear
  and shall trust in the LORD. ℟.

Wretched and poor though I am,
  the Lord is mindful of me.
You are my rescuer, my help;
  O my God, do not delay. ℟.

**READING II**                                            *Hebrews 12:1–4*

**GOSPEL**                                                *Luke 12:49–53*

---

# TWENTY-FIRST SUNDAY IN ORDINARY TIME / A               1152

**READING I**                                             *Isaiah 22:19–23 / 121*

**RESPONSORIAL PSALM**                                    *Psalm 138:1–2a, 2bc and 3, 6 and 8bc*

Lord, your love is e-ter-nal; do not for-sake the work of your hands.

I thank you, LORD, with all my heart;
  you have heard the words of my
    mouth.
In the presence of the angels I praise you.
  I bow down toward your holy
    temple. ℟.

I give thanks to your name
  for your merciful love and your
    faithfulness.

On the day I called, you answered me;
  you increased the strength of my
    soul. ℟.

The LORD is high, yet he looks on the
    lowly,
  and the haughty he knows from afar.
O LORD, your merciful love is eternal;
  discard not the work of your
    hands. ℟.

**READING II**                                            *Romans 11:33–36*

**GOSPEL**                                                *Matthew 16:13–20*

## 1153  TWENTY-FIRST SUNDAY IN ORDINARY TIME / B

**READING I**                                                   *Joshua 24:1–2a, 15–17, 18b / 122*

**RESPONSORIAL PSALM**                                *Psalm 34:2–3, 16–17, 18–19, 20–21*

Taste and see the good-ness of the Lord.

I will bless the LORD at all times;
    praise of him is always in my mouth.
In the LORD my soul shall make its boast;
    the humble shall hear and be glad. ℟.

The LORD turns his eyes to the just,
    and his ears are open to their cry.
The LORD turns his face against the
    wicked
    to destroy their remembrance from
    the earth. ℟.

When the just cry out, the LORD hears,

and rescues them in all their distress.
The LORD is close to the
    brokenhearted;
    those whose spirit is crushed he will
    save. ℟.

Many are the trials of the just man,
    but from them all the LORD will
    rescue him.
He will keep guard over all his bones;
    not one of his bones shall be
    broken. ℟.

**READING II**                            *Ephesians 5:21–32 or 5:2a, 25–32*

**GOSPEL**                                     *John 6:60–69*

## 1154  TWENTY-FIRST SUNDAY IN ORDINARY TIME / C

**READING I**                                        *Isaiah 66:18–21 / 123*

**RESPONSORIAL PSALM**                                   *Psalm 117:1, 2*

*Or: Alleluia.*

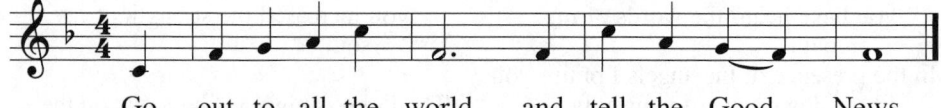

Go out to all the world and tell the Good News.

O praise the LORD, all you nations;
    acclaim him, all you peoples! ℟.

For his merciful love has prevailed
    over us;
    and the LORD's faithfulness
    endures forever. ℟.

**READING II**                                  *Hebrews 12:5–7, 11–13*

**GOSPEL**                                     *Luke 13:22–30*

## TWENTY-SECOND SUNDAY IN ORDINARY TIME / A          1155

**READING I**                                                    *Jeremiah 20:7–9 / 124*

**RESPONSORIAL PSALM**                                    *Psalm 63:2, 3–4, 5–6, 8–9*

My soul is thirst-ing  for you, O Lord, thirst-ing  for you  my God.

O God, you are my God; at dawn I
　　seek you;
　　for you my soul is thirsting.
For you my flesh is pining,
　　like a dry, weary land without
　　water. ℟.

I have come before you in the sanctuary,
　　to behold your strength and your
　　glory.
Your loving mercy is better than life;
　　my lips will speak your praise. ℟.

I will bless you all my life;
　　in your name I will lift up my hands.
My soul shall be filled as with a
　　banquet;
　　with joyful lips, my mouth shall
　　praise you. ℟.

For you have been my strength;
　　in the shadow of your wings I
　　rejoice.
My soul clings fast to you;
　　your right hand upholds me. ℟.

**READING II**                                                      *Romans 12:1–2*

**GOSPEL**                                                         *Matthew 16:21–27*

---

## TWENTY-SECOND SUNDAY IN ORDINARY TIME / B          1156

**READING I**                                             *Deuteronomy 4:1–2, 6–8 / 125*

**RESPONSORIAL PSALM**                                    *Psalm 15:2–3a, 3bc–4ab, 5*

One who does jus-tice  will live in the   pres-ence of the      Lord.

Whoever walks without fault;
　　who does what is just,
and speaks the truth from his heart;
　　whoever does not slander with his
　　tongue. ℟.

Who does no wrong to a neighbor,
　　who casts no slur on a friend,

who looks with scorn on the wicked,
　　but honors those who fear the
　　LORD. ℟.

Who lends no money at interest,
　　and accepts no bribes against the
　　innocent.
Such a one shall never be shaken. ℟.

**READING II**                                             *James 1:17–18, 21b-22, 27*

**GOSPEL**                                                 *Mark 7:1–8, 14–15, 21–23*

## 1157 TWENTY-SECOND SUNDAY IN ORDINARY TIME / C

**READING I** *Sirach 3:17–18, 20, 28–29 / 126*

**RESPONSORIAL PSALM** *Psalm 68:4–5ac, 6–7ab, 10–11*

God, in your good-ness, you have made a home for the poor.

The just shall rejoice at the presence
of God;
they shall exult with glad rejoicing.
O sing to God; make music to his name.
The LORD is his name. ℟.

Father of orphans, defender of widows:
such is God in his holy place.
God gives the desolate a home to dwell in;
he leads the prisoners forth into

prosperity. ℟.

You poured down, O God, a generous
rain;
when your people languished, you
restored their inheritance.
It was there that your flock began to
dwell.
In your goodness, O God, you
provided for the poor. ℟.

**READING II** *Hebrews 12:18–19, 22–24a*

**GOSPEL** *Luke 14:1, 7–14*

## 1158 TWENTY-THIRD SUNDAY IN ORDINARY TIME / A

**READING I** *Ezekiel 33:7–9 / 127*

**RESPONSORIAL PSALM** *Psalm 95:1–2, 6–7c, 7d–9*

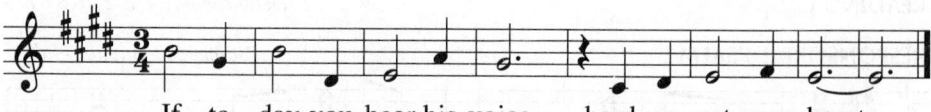

If to-day you hear his voice, hard-en not your hearts.

Come, let us ring out our joy to the LORD;
hail the rock who saves us.
Let us come into his presence, giving
thanks;
let us hail him with a song of praise. ℟.

O come; let us bow and bend low.
Let us kneel before the God who
made us,
for he is our God and we
the people who belong to his pasture,

the flock that is led by his hand. ℟.

O that today you would listen to his
voice!
"Harden not your hearts as at
Meribah,
as on that day at Massah in the
desert
when your forebears put me to the test;
when they tried me, though they saw
my work." ℟.

**READING II**                                                    *Romans 13:8–10*

**GOSPEL**                                                        *Matthew 18:15–20*

---

## TWENTY-THIRD SUNDAY IN ORDINARY TIME / B          1159

**READING I**                                                    *Isaiah 35:4–7a / 128*

**RESPONSORIAL PSALM**                              *Psalm 146:6c–7, 8–9a, 9bc–10*

*Or: Alleluia.*

Praise the Lord, my soul! Praise the Lord!

It is the LORD who preserves fidelity
 forever,
 who does justice to those who are
 oppressed.
It is he who gives bread to the hungry,
 the LORD who sets prisoners free. ℟.

The LORD who opens the eyes of the
 blind,
 the LORD who raises up those who

are bowed down.
It is the LORD who loves the just,
 the LORD who protects the stranger. ℟.

The LORD upholds the orphan and the
 widow,
 but thwarts the path of the wicked.
The LORD will reign forever,
 the God of Sion from age to age.
 Alleluia. ℟.

**READING II**                                                    *James 2:1–5*

**GOSPEL**                                                        *Mark 7:31–37*

---

## TWENTY-THIRD SUNDAY IN ORDINARY TIME / C          1160

**READING I**                                                    *Wisdom 9:13–18b / 129*

**RESPONSORIAL PSALM**                          *Psalm 90:3–4, 5–6, 12–13, 14 and 17*

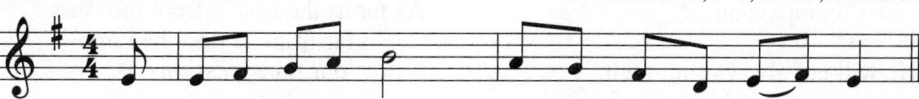

In ev-'ry age, O Lord, you have been our ref - uge.

You turn man back to dust,
 and say, "Return, O children of men."
To your eyes a thousand years
 are like yesterday, come and gone,
 or like a watch in the night. ℟.

You sweep them away like a dream,
 like grass which is fresh in the
 morning.
In the morning it sprouts and is fresh;
 by evening it withers and fades. ℟.

Then teach us to number our days,
that we may gain wisdom of heart.
Turn back, O Lord! How long?
Show pity to your servants. ℟.

At dawn, fill us with your merciful love;
we shall exult and rejoice all our days.

Let the favor of the Lord our God be
upon us;
give success to the work of our
hands.
O give success to the work of our
hands. ℟.

**READING II** *Philemon 9–10, 12–17*

**GOSPEL** *Luke 14:25–33*

---

## 1161 TWENTY-FOURTH SUNDAY IN ORDINARY TIME / A

**READING I** *Sirach 27:30—28:7 / 130*

**RESPONSORIAL PSALM** *Psalm 103:1–2, 3–4, 9–10, 11–12*

The Lord is kind and mer - ci - ful,

slow to an - ger, and rich in com - pas - sion.

Bless the Lord, O my soul,
and all within me, his holy name.
Bless the Lord, O my soul,
and never forget all his benefits. ℟.

It is the Lord who forgives all your sins,
who heals every one of your ills,
who redeems your life from the grave,
who crowns you with mercy and
compassion. ℟.

He will not always find fault;
nor persist in his anger forever.

He does not treat us according to our
sins,
nor repay us according to our
faults. ℟.

For as the heavens are high above the
earth,
so strong his mercy for those who
fear him.
As far as the east is from the west,
so far from us does he remove
our transgressions. ℟.

**READING II** *Romans 14:7–9*

**GOSPEL** *Matthew 18:21–35*

## TWENTY-FOURTH SUNDAY IN ORDINARY TIME / B      1162

**READING I** *Isaiah 50:5–9a / 131*

**RESPONSORIAL PSALM** *Psalm 116:1–2, 3–4, 5–6, 8–9*

*Or: Alleluia.*

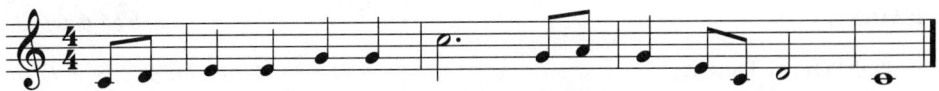

I will walk be-fore the Lord, in the land of the liv - ing.

I love the LORD, for he has heard
   my voice, my appeal;
for he has turned his ear to me
   whenever I call. ℟.

They surrounded me, the snares of death;
   the anguish of the grave has found me;
   anguish and sorrow I found.
I called on the name of the LORD:
   "Deliver my soul, O LORD!" ℟.

How gracious is the LORD, and just;
   our God has compassion.
The LORD protects the simple;
   I was brought low, and he saved
   me. ℟.

He has kept my soul from death,
   my eyes from tears, and my feet
   from stumbling.
I will walk in the presence of the LORD
   in the land of the living. ℟.

**READING II** *James 2:14–18*

**GOSPEL** *Mark 8:27–35*

## TWENTY-FOURTH SUNDAY IN ORDINARY TIME / C      1163

**READING I** *Exodus 32:7–11, 13–14 / 132*

**RESPONSORIAL PSALM** *Psalm 51:3–4, 12–13, 17 and 19*

I will rise and go to my fa - ther.

Have mercy on me, O God,
   according to your merciful love;
according to your great compassion,
   blot out my transgressions.
Wash me completely from my iniquity,
   and cleanse me from my sin. ℟.

Create a pure heart for me, O God;
   renew a steadfast spirit within me.
Do not cast me away from your

presence;
   take not your holy spirit from me. ℟.

O Lord, open my lips
   and my mouth shall proclaim your
   praise.
My sacrifice to God, a broken spirit:
   a broken and humbled heart,
   O God, you will not spurn. ℟.

**READING II**                                          *1 Timothy 1:12–17*

**GOSPEL**                                       *Luke 15:1–32 or 15:1–10*

## 1164   TWENTY-FIFTH SUNDAY IN ORDINARY TIME / A

**READING I**                                          *Isaiah 55:6–9 / 133*

**RESPONSORIAL PSALM**             *Psalm 145:2–3, 8–9, 17–18*

The   Lord   is near   to   all who call on him.

I will bless you day after day,
  and praise your name forever and
    ever.
The LORD is great and highly to be
    praised;
  his greatness cannot be measured. ℟.

The LORD is kind and full of compassion,
  slow to anger, abounding in mercy.

How good is the LORD to all,
  compassionate to all his creatures. ℟.

The LORD is just in all his ways,
  and holy in all his deeds.
The LORD is close to all who call him,
  who call on him in truth. ℟.

**READING II**                                  *Philippians 1:20c-24, 27a*

**GOSPEL**                                            *Matthew 20:1–16a*

## 1165   TWENTY-FIFTH SUNDAY IN ORDINARY TIME / B

**READING I**                              *Wisdom 2:12, 17–20 / 134*

**RESPONSORIAL PSALM**             *Psalm 54:3–4, 5, 6 and 8*

The   Lord   up-holds   my   life.

O God, save me by your name;
  by your power, defend my cause.
O God, hear my prayer;
  give ear to the words of my mouth. ℟.

For the proud have risen against me,
  and the ruthless seek my life.
  They have no regard for God. ℟.

See, I have God for my help.
  The Lord sustains my soul.
I will sacrifice to you with willing
    heart,
  and praise your name, for it is
    good. ℟.

**READING II** *James 3:16—4:3*

**GOSPEL** *Mark 9:30–37*

---

## TWENTY-FIFTH SUNDAY IN ORDINARY TIME / C 1166

**READING I** *Amos 8:4–7 / 135*

**RESPONSORIAL PSALM** *Psalm 113:1–2, 4–6, 7–8*

*Or: Alleluia.*

Praise the Lord, praise the Lord, who lifts up the poor.

Praise, O servants of the LORD,
 praise the name of the LORD!
May the name of the LORD be blest
 both now and forevermore! ℞.

High above all nations is the LORD,
 above the heavens his glory.
Who is like the LORD, our God,
 who dwells on high,

who lowers himself to look down
 upon heaven and earth? ℞.

From the dust he lifts up the lowly,
 from the ash heap he raises the
 poor,
to set them in the company of princes,
 yes, with the princes of his
 people. ℞.

**READING II** *1 Timothy 2:1–8*

**GOSPEL** *Luke 16:1–13 or 16:10–13*

---

## TWENTY-SIXTH SUNDAY IN ORDINARY TIME / A 1167

**READING I** *Ezekiel 18:25–28 / 136*

**RESPONSORIAL PSALM** *Psalm 25:4–5ab, 6–7, 8–9*

Re - mem - ber your mer-cies, O Lord.

O LORD, make me know your ways.
 Teach me your paths.
Guide me in your truth, and teach me;
 for you are the God of my salvation. ℞.

Remember your compassion, O LORD,
 and your merciful love,

for they are from of old.
Do not remember the sins of my youth,
 nor my transgressions.
In your merciful love remember me,
 because of your goodness,
 O LORD. ℞.

Good and upright is the LORD;
  he shows the way to sinners.
He guides the humble in right judgment;
to the humble he teaches his
  way. ℟.

**READING II**                    *Philippians 2:1–11 or 2:1–5*

**GOSPEL**                         *Matthew 21:28–32*

---

## 1168  TWENTY-SIXTH SUNDAY IN ORDINARY TIME / B

**READING I**                      *Numbers 11:25–29 / 137*

**RESPONSORIAL PSALM**             *Psalm 19:8, 10, 12–13, 14*

The pre-cepts of the Lord give joy to the heart.

The law of the LORD is perfect;
  it revives the soul.
The decrees of the LORD are steadfast;
  they give wisdom to the simple. ℟.

The fear of the LORD is pure,
  abiding forever.
The judgments of the LORD are true;
  they are, all of them, just. ℟.

So in them your servant finds
  instruction;
  great reward is in their keeping.
But who can detect their own errors?
  From hidden faults acquit me. ℟.

From presumption restrain your servant;
  may it not rule me.
Then shall I be blameless,
  clean from grave sin. ℟.

**READING II**                    *James 5:1–6*

**GOSPEL**                         *Mark 9:38–43, 45, 47–48*

---

## 1169  TWENTY-SIXTH SUNDAY IN ORDINARY TIME / C

**READING I**                      *Amos 6:1a, 4–7 / 138*

**RESPONSORIAL PSALM**             *Psalm 146:6c–7, 8–9a, 9bc–10*

*Or: Alleluia.*

Praise the Lord, my soul! Praise the Lord!

It is the LORD who preserves
    fidelity forever,
  who does justice to those who are
    oppressed.
It is he who gives bread to the hungry,
  the LORD who sets prisoners free. ℞.

The LORD who opens the eyes of the blind,
  the LORD who raises up those who
    are bowed down.

It is the LORD who loves the just,
  the LORD who protects the
    stranger. ℞.

The LORD upholds the orphan and the
  widow,
  but thwarts the path of the wicked.
The LORD will reign forever,
  the God of Sion from age to age.
  Alleluia. ℞.

**READING II**                                        *1 Timothy 6:11–16*

**GOSPEL**                                                *Luke 16:19–31*

## TWENTY-SEVENTH SUNDAY IN ORDINARY TIME / A  1170

**READING I**                                            *Isaiah 5:1–7 / 139*

**RESPONSORIAL PSALM**     *Psalm 80:9 and 12, 13–14, 15–16, 19–20*

The vine-yard of the Lord is the house of Is-ra-el.

You brought a vine out of Egypt;
  you drove out the nations and
    planted it.
It stretched out its branches to the sea;
  to the River it stretched out its
    shoots. ℞.

Then why have you broken down its
  walls?
  It is plucked by all who pass by the
    way.
It is ravaged by the boar of the forest,
  devoured by the beasts of the field. ℞.

God of hosts, turn again, we implore;
  look down from heaven and see.
Visit this vine and protect it,
  the vine your right hand has planted,
  the son of man you have claimed
    for yourself. ℞.

And we shall never forsake you again;
  give us life that we may call upon
    your name.
O LORD God of hosts, bring us back;
  let your face shine forth, and we
    shall be saved. ℞.

**READING II**                                        *Philippians 4:6–9*

**GOSPEL**                                            *Matthew 21:33–43*

## 1171 TWENTY-SEVENTH SUNDAY IN ORDINARY TIME / B

**READING I**                                    *Genesis 2:18–24 / 140*

**RESPONSORIAL PSALM**                    *Psalm 128:1–2, 3, 4–5, 6*

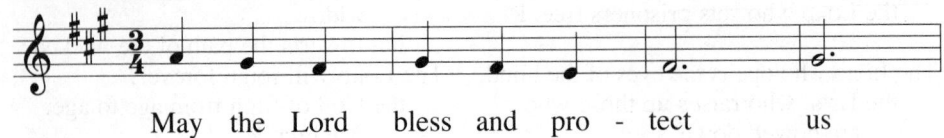

May the Lord bless and pro - tect us all the days of our lives.

Blessed are all who fear the LORD,
   and walk in his ways!
By the labor of your hands you shall eat.
   You will be blessed and prosper. ℟.

Your wife like a fruitful vine
   in the heart of your house;
your children like shoots of the olive
   around your table. ℟.

Indeed thus shall be blessed
   the man who fears the LORD.
May the LORD bless you from Sion.
   May you see Jerusalem prosper
   all the days of your life! ℟.

May you see your children's children.
   On Israel, peace! ℟.

**READING II**                                    *Hebrews 2:9–11*

**GOSPEL**                                *Mark 10:2–16 or 10:2–12*

## 1172 TWENTY-SEVENTH SUNDAY IN ORDINARY TIME / C

**READING I**                        *Habakkuk 1:2–3; 2:2–4 / 141*

**RESPONSORIAL PSALM**                    *Psalm 95:1–2, 6–7c, 7d–9*

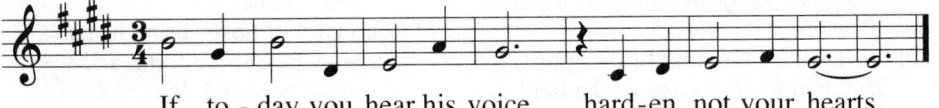

If to - day you hear his voice, hard-en not your hearts.

Come, let us ring out our joy to the LORD;
   hail the rock who saves us.
Let us come into his presence, giving
     thanks;
   let us hail him with a song of
     praise. ℟.

O come; let us bow and bend low.
   Let us kneel before the God who
     made us,
for he is our God and we
   the people who belong to his
     pasture,
   the flock that is led by his hand. ℟.

O that today you would listen to his
    voice!
  "Harden not your hearts as at
    Meribah,
  as on that day at Massah in the

desert
when your forebears put me to the test;
  when they tried me, though they
    saw my work." ℟.

**READING II** *2 Timothy 1:6–8, 13–14*

**GOSPEL** *Luke 17:5–10*

---

## TWENTY-EIGHTH SUNDAY IN ORDINARY TIME / A     1173

**READING I** *Isaiah 25:6–10a / 142*

**RESPONSORIAL PSALM** *Psalm 23:1–3a, 3b–4, 5, 6*

I shall live in the house of the Lord     all the days of my life.

The LORD is my shepherd;
  there is nothing I shall want.
Fresh and green are the pastures
  where he gives me repose.
Near restful waters he leads me;
  he revives my soul. ℟.

He guides me along the right path,
  for the sake of his name.
Though I should walk in the valley of
  the shadow of death,
  no evil would I fear, for you are
  with me.

Your crook and your staff will give
  me comfort. ℟.

You have prepared a table before me
  in the sight of my foes.
My head you have anointed with oil;
  my cup is overflowing. ℟.

Surely goodness and mercy shall
  follow me
  all the days of my life.
In the LORD's own house shall I dwell
  for length of days unending. ℟.

**READING II** *Philippians 4:12–14, 19–20*

**GOSPEL** *Matthew 22:1–14 or 22:1–10*

---

## TWENTY-EIGHTH SUNDAY IN ORDINARY TIME / B     1174

**READING I** *Wisdom 7:7–11 / 143*

**RESPONSORIAL PSALM**  *Psalm 90:12–13, 14–15, 16–17*

Fill us with your love, O Lord, and we will sing for joy!

Teach us to number our days,
    that we may gain wisdom of heart.
Turn back, O LORD! How long?
    Show pity to your servants. ℟.

At dawn, fill us with your merciful love;
    we shall exult and rejoice all our days.
Give us joy for the days of our affliction,
    for the years when we looked upon
        evil. ℟.

Let your deed be seen by your servants,
    and your glorious power by their
        children.
Let the favor of the Lord our God be
    upon us;
    give success to the work of our
        hands.
O give success to the work of our
    hands. ℟.

**READING II**  *Hebrews 4:12–13*

**GOSPEL**  *Mark 10:17–30 or 10:17–27*

---

## 1175 TWENTY-EIGHTH SUNDAY IN ORDINARY TIME / C

**READING I**  *2 Kings 5:14–17 / 144*

**RESPONSORIAL PSALM**  *Psalm 98:1, 2–3ab, 3cd–4*

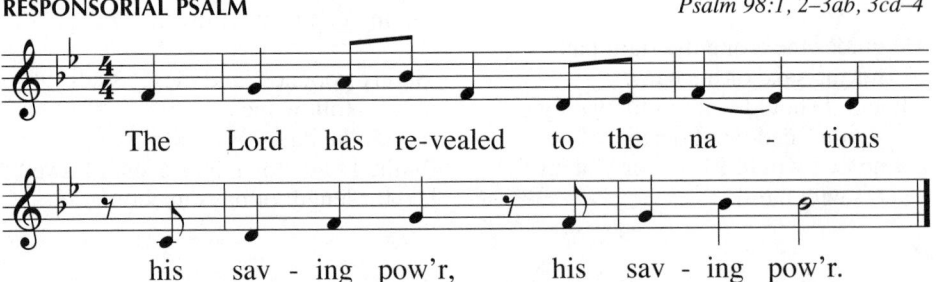

The Lord has re-vealed to the na - tions his sav - ing pow'r, his sav - ing pow'r.

O sing a new song to the LORD,
    for he has worked wonders.
His right hand and his holy arm
    have brought salvation. ℟.

The LORD has made known his salvation,
    has shown his deliverance to the
        nations.

He has remembered his merciful love
    and his truth for the house of Israel. ℟.

All the ends of the earth have seen
    the salvation of our God.
Shout to the LORD, all the earth;
    break forth into joyous song,
    and sing out your praise. ℟.

**READING II**  *2 Timothy 2:8–13*

**GOSPEL**  *Luke 17:11–19*

## TWENTY-NINTH SUNDAY IN ORDINARY TIME / A  1176

**READING I**  *Isaiah 45:1, 4–6 / 145*

**RESPONSORIAL PSALM**  *Psalm 96:1 and 3, 4–5, 7–8, 9–10a and c*

Give the Lord glo - ry and hon - or.

O sing a new song to the LORD;
  sing to the LORD, all the earth.
Tell among the nations his glory,
  and his wonders among all the
  peoples. ℟.

For the LORD is great and highly to be
  praised,
  to be feared above all gods.
For the gods of the nations are naught.
  It was the LORD who made the
  heavens. ℟.

Give the LORD, you families of peoples,
  give the LORD glory and power;
give the LORD the glory of his name.
  Bring an offering and enter his
  courts. ℟.

Worship the LORD in holy splendor.
  O tremble before him, all the earth.
Say to the nations, "The LORD is king."
  He will judge the peoples in
  fairness. ℟.

**READING II**  *1 Thessalonians 1:1–5b*

**GOSPEL**  *Matthew 22:15–21*

## TWENTY-NINTH SUNDAY IN ORDINARY TIME / B  1177

**READING I**  *Isaiah 53:10–11 / 146*

**RESPONSORIAL PSALM**  *Psalm 33:4–5, 18–19, 20 and 22*

Lord, let your mer-cy be on us, as we place our trust in you.

The word of the LORD is faithful,
  and all his works to be trusted.
The LORD loves justice and right,
  and his merciful love fills the earth. ℟.

Yes, the LORD's eyes are on those who
  fear him,
  who hope in his merciful love,

to rescue their souls from death,
  to keep them alive in famine. ℟.

Our soul is waiting for the LORD.
  He is our help and our shield.
May your merciful love be upon us,
  as we hope in you, O LORD. ℟.

**READING II**  *Hebrews 4:14–16*

**GOSPEL**  *Mark 10:35–45 or 10:42–45*

## 1178 TWENTY-NINTH SUNDAY IN ORDINARY TIME / C

**READING I**                                    *Exodus 17:8–13 / 147*

**RESPONSORIAL PSALM**                    *Psalm 121:1–2, 3–4, 5–6, 7–8*

Our help is from the Lord, who made heav-en    and earth.

I lift up my eyes to the mountains;
   from where shall come my help?
My help shall come from the LORD,
   who made heaven and earth. ℟.

He will keep your foot from stumbling.
   Your guard will never slumber.
No, he sleeps not nor slumbers,
   Israel's guard. ℟.

The LORD your guard, the LORD

    your shade
   at your right hand.
By day the sun shall not smite you,
   nor the moon in the night. ℟.

The LORD will guard you from evil;
   he will guard your soul.
The LORD will guard your going and
   coming,
    both now and forever. ℟.

**READING II**                                  *2 Timothy 3:14—4:2*

**GOSPEL**                                        *Luke 18:1–8*

## 1179 THIRTIETH SUNDAY IN ORDINARY TIME / A

**READING I**                                    *Exodus 22:20–26 / 148*

**RESPONSORIAL PSALM**            *Psalm 18:2–3a, 3bc–4, 47 and 51ab*

I   love you, Lord,    my strength,    my strength.

I love you, LORD, my strength;
   O LORD, my rock, my fortress,
    my savior. ℟.

My God, my rock where I take refuge;
   my shield, my saving strength, my
    stronghold.
I cry out, "Praised be the LORD!"
   and see, I am saved from my foes. ℟.

The LORD lives, and blest be my Rock!
   May the God of my salvation be
    exalted.
The LORD gives great victories to his
   king,
   and shows merciful love for his
    anointed. ℟.

**READING II**                                  *1 Thessalonians 1:5c–10*

**GOSPEL**                                        *Matthew 22:34–40*

## THIRTIETH SUNDAY IN ORDINARY TIME / B          1180

**READING I**                                          *Jeremiah 31:7–9 / 149*

**RESPONSORIAL PSALM**                        *Psalm 126:1–2ab, 2cd–3, 4–5, 6*

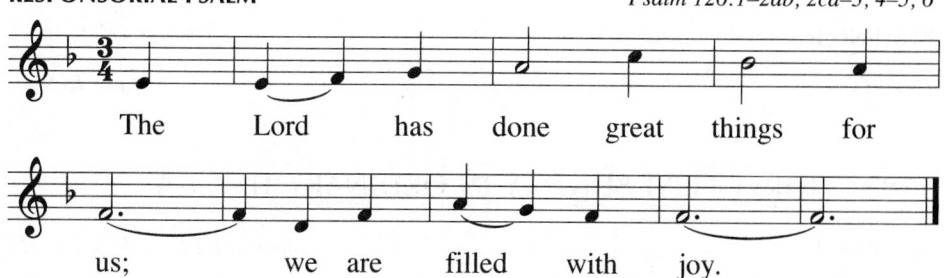

The Lord has done great things for us; we are filled with joy.

When the LORD brought back the
  exiles of Sion,
 we thought we were dreaming.
Then was our mouth filled with laughter;
 on our tongues, songs of joy. ℟.

Then the nations themselves said,
  "What great deeds
 the LORD worked for them!"
What great deeds the LORD worked for us!
 Indeed, we were glad. ℟.

Bring back our exiles, O LORD,
 as streams in the south.
Those who are sowing in tears
 will sing when they reap. ℟.

They go out, they go out, full of tears,
 bearing seed for the sowing;
they come back, they come back with
  a song,
 bearing their sheaves. ℟.

**READING II**                                          *Hebrews 5:1–6*

**GOSPEL**                                              *Mark 10:46–52*

## THIRTIETH SUNDAY IN ORDINARY TIME / C          1181

**READING I**                                          *Sirach 35:12–14, 16–18 / 150*

**RESPONSORIAL PSALM**                        *Psalm 34:2–3, 17–18, 19 and 23*

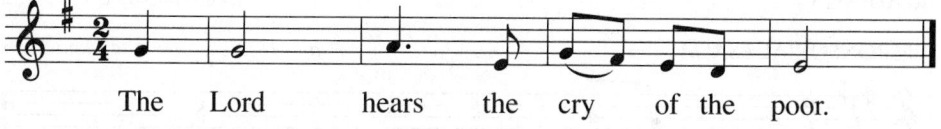

The Lord hears the cry of the poor.

I will bless the LORD at all times;
 praise of him is always in my mouth.
In the LORD my soul shall make its boast;
 the humble shall hear and be glad. ℟.

The LORD turns his face against the

wicked
 to destroy their remembrance from
  the earth.
When the just cry out, the LORD hears,
 and rescues them in all their
  distress. ℟.

The LORD is close to the brokenhearted;
  those whose spirit is crushed he will
    save.
The LORD ransoms the souls of his
servants.
All who trust in him shall not be
  condemned. ℞.

**READING II**                    *2 Timothy 4:6–8, 16–18*

**GOSPEL**                           *Luke 18:9–14*

---

## 1182   THIRTY-FIRST SUNDAY IN ORDINARY TIME / A

**READING I**                 *Malachi 1:14b-2:2b, 8–10 / 151*

**RESPONSORIAL PSALM**              *Psalm 131:1, 2, 3*

In you, O Lord, I have found my peace.

O LORD, my heart is not proud,
  nor haughty my eyes.
I have not gone after things too great,
  nor marvels beyond me. ℞.

Truly, I have set my soul
  in tranquility and silence.

As a weaned child on its mother,
  as a weaned child is my soul within
    me. ℞.

O Israel, wait for the LORD,
  both now and forever. ℞.

**READING II**              *1 Thessalonians 2:7b-9, 13*

**GOSPEL**                         *Matthew 23:1–12*

---

## 1183   THIRTY-FIRST SUNDAY IN ORDINARY TIME / B

**READING I**               *Deuteronomy 6:2–6 / 152*

**RESPONSORIAL PSALM**        *Psalm 18:2–3a, 3bc–4, 47 and 51ab*

I love you, Lord, my strength, my strength.

I love you, LORD, my strength;
  O LORD, my rock, my fortress,
    my savior. ℞.

My God, my rock where I take refuge;

my shield, my saving strength, my
  stronghold.
I cry out, "Praised be the LORD!"
  and see, I am saved from my foes. ℞.

The LORD lives, and blest be my Rock!
  May the God of my salvation be
    exalted.
The LORD gives great victories to his
king,
  and shows merciful love for his
    anointed. ℟.

**READING II**                                          *Hebrews 7:23–28*

**GOSPEL**                                               *Mark 12:28b–34*

## THIRTY-FIRST SUNDAY IN ORDINARY TIME / C      1184

**READING I**                                      *Wisdom 11:22—12:2 / 153*

**RESPONSORIAL PSALM**          *Psalm 145:1–2, 8–9, 10–11, 13cd–14*

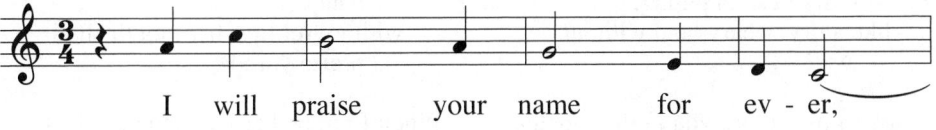

I will praise your name for ev - er,

my king and my God.

I will extol you, my God and king,
  and bless your name forever and
    ever.
I will bless you day after day,
  and praise your name forever and
    ever. ℟.

The LORD is kind and full of
    compassion,
  slow to anger, abounding in mercy.
How good is the LORD to all,
  compassionate to all his creatures. ℟.

All your works shall thank you, O
    LORD,
  and all your faithful ones bless you.
They shall speak of the glory of your
    reign,
  and declare your mighty deeds. ℟.

The LORD is faithful in all his words,
  and holy in all his deeds.
The LORD supports all who fall,
  and raises up all who are bowed
    down. ℟.

**READING II**                                  *2 Thessalonians 1:11—2:2*

**GOSPEL**                                              *Luke 19:1–10*

## THIRTY-SECOND SUNDAY IN ORDINARY TIME / A      1185

**READING I**                                      *Wisdom 6:12–16 / 154*

**RESPONSORIAL PSALM**                                    *Psalm 63:2, 3–4, 5–6, 7–8*

My soul is thirst-ing for you, O Lord,

thirst-ing for you my God.

O God, you are my God; at dawn I seek
    you;
    for you my soul is thirsting.
For you my flesh is pining,
    like a dry, weary land without
    water. ℟.

I have come before you in the sanctuary,
    to behold your strength and your
    glory.
Your loving mercy is better than life;
    my lips will speak your praise. ℟.

I will bless you all my life;
    in your name I will lift up my hands.
My soul shall be filled as with a
    banquet;
    with joyful lips, my mouth shall
    praise you. ℟.

When I remember you upon my bed,
    I muse on you through the watches
    of the night.
For you have been my strength;
    in the shadow of your wings I
    rejoice. ℟.

**READING II**                            *1 Thessalonians 4:13–18 or 4:13–14*

**GOSPEL**                                             *Matthew 25:1–13*

---

## 1186 THIRTY-SECOND SUNDAY IN ORDINARY TIME / B

**READING I**                                          *1 Kings 17:10–16 / 155*

**RESPONSORIAL PSALM**                          *Psalm 146:6c–7, 8–9a, 9bc–10*

*Or: Alleluia.*

Praise the Lord, my soul! Praise the Lord!

It is the Lord who preserves
    fidelity forever,
    who does justice to those who are
    oppressed.
It is he who gives bread to the hungry,
    the Lord who sets prisoners free. ℟.

The Lord who opens the eyes of the
    blind,
    the Lord who raises up those who
    are bowed down.
It is the Lord who loves the just,
    the Lord who protects the
    stranger. ℟.

The LORD upholds the orphan and the widow,
   but thwarts the path of the wicked.

The LORD will reign forever,
   the God of Sion from age to age.
   Alleluia. ℟.

**READING II**                               *Hebrews 9:24–28*

**GOSPEL**                          *Mark 12:38–44 or 12:41–44*

---

## THIRTY-SECOND SUNDAY IN ORDINARY TIME / C     1187

**READING I**                      *2 Maccabees 7:1–2, 9–14 / 156*

**RESPONSORIAL PSALM**          *Psalm 17:1, 5–6, 8b and 15*

Lord, when your glo-ry ap-pears, my joy will be full.

O LORD, hear a cause that is just;
   pay heed to my cry.
Turn your ear to my prayer:
   no deceit is on my lips. ℟.

I kept my steps firmly in your paths.
   My feet have never faltered.
To you I call; for you will surely heed
     me, O God.
   Turn your ear to me; hear my
     words. ℟.

Guard me as the apple of your eye.
Hide me in the shadow of your
   wings.
As for me, in justice I shall behold your
   face;
   when I awake I shall be filled with
     the vision of your presence. ℟.

**READING II**                    *2 Thessalonians 2:16—3:5*

**GOSPEL**             *Luke 20:27–38 or 20:27, 34–38*

---

## THIRTY-THIRD SUNDAY IN ORDINARY TIME / A     1188

**READING I**                    *Proverbs 31:10–13, 19–20, 30–31 / 157*

**RESPONSORIAL PSALM** *Psalm 128:1–2, 3, 4–5*

Bless - ed are those who fear the Lord.

Blessed are all who fear the LORD,
  and walk in his ways!
By the labor of your hands you shall eat.
  You will be blessed and prosper. ℟.

Your wife like a fruitful vine
  in the heart of your house;
your children like shoots of the olive

around your table. ℟.

Indeed thus shall be blessed
  the man who fears the LORD.
May the LORD bless you from Sion.
  May you see Jerusalem prosper
  all the days of your life! ℟.

**READING II** *1 Thessalonians 5:1–6*

**GOSPEL** *Matthew 25:14–30 or 25:14–15, 19–21*

---

## 1189 THIRTY-THIRD SUNDAY IN ORDINARY TIME / B

**READING I** *Daniel 12:1–3 / 158*

**RESPONSORIAL PSALM** *Psalm 16:5 and 8, 9–10, 11*

You are my in - her - i - tance, O Lord.

O LORD, it is you who are my portion
  and cup;
  you yourself who secure my lot.
I keep the LORD before me always;
  with him at my right hand, I shall
    not be moved. ℟.

And so, my heart rejoices, my soul is
  glad;
  even my flesh shall rest in hope.

For you will not abandon my soul to
  hell,
  nor let your holy one see
    corruption. ℟.

You will show me the path of life,
  the fullness of joy in your presence,
  at your right hand, bliss forever. ℟.

**READING II** *Hebrews 10:11–14, 18*

**GOSPEL** *Mark 13:24–32*

## THIRTY-THIRD SUNDAY IN ORDINARY TIME / C — 1190

**READING I** — *Malachi 3:19–20a / 159*

**RESPONSORIAL PSALM** — *Psalm 98:5–6, 7–9a, 9bc*

The Lord comes to rule the earth with jus - tice.

Sing psalms to the LORD with the harp,
  with the harp and the sound of song.
With trumpets and the sound of the horn,
  raise a shout before the King,
    the LORD. ℟.

Let the sea and all within it thunder;
  the world, and those who dwell in it.

Let the rivers clap their hands,
  and the hills ring out their joy
  at the presence of the LORD, for he
    comes. ℟.

He comes to judge the earth.
  He will judge the world with justice,
  and the peoples with fairness. ℟.

**READING II** — *2 Thessalonians 3:7–12*

**GOSPEL** — *Luke 21:5–19*

---

## OUR LORD JESUS CHRIST, KING OF THE UNIVERSE / A — 1191

**READING I** — *Ezekiel 34:11–12, 15–17 / 160*

**RESPONSORIAL PSALM** — *Psalm 23:1–2a, 2b–3, 5–6*

The Lord is my shep-herd; there is noth - ing I shall want.

The LORD is my shepherd;
  there is nothing I shall want.
Fresh and green are the pastures
  where he gives me repose. ℟.

Near restful waters he leads me;
  he revives my soul.
He guides me along the right path,
  for the sake of his name. ℟.

You have prepared a table before me
  in the sight of my foes.
My head you have anointed with oil;
  my cup is overflowing. ℟.

Surely goodness and mercy shall
  follow me
  all the days of my life.
In the LORD's own house shall I dwell
  for length of days unending. ℟.

**READING II** — *1 Corinthians 15:20–26, 28*

**GOSPEL** — *Matthew 25:31–46*

## 1192  OUR LORD JESUS CHRIST, KING OF THE UNIVERSE / B

**READING I**                                          *Daniel 7:13–14 / 161*

**RESPONSORIAL PSALM**                        *Psalm 93:1ab, 1c–2, 5*

The Lord is king; he is robed in maj-es-ty.

The LORD is king, with majesty enrobed.
  The LORD has robed himself with
    might;
  he has girded himself with power. ℟.

The world you made firm, not to be
    moved;

your throne has stood firm from of
    old.
  From all eternity, O LORD, you are. ℟.

Truly your decrees are to be trusted.
  Holiness is fitting to your house,
  O LORD, until the end of time. ℟.

**READING II**                                       *Revelation 1:5–8*

**GOSPEL**                                            *John 18:33b-37*


## 1193  OUR LORD JESUS CHRIST, KING OF THE UNIVERSE / C

**READING I**                                        *2 Samuel 5:1–3 / 162*

**RESPONSORIAL PSALM**              *Psalm 122:1–2, 3–4ab, 4cd–5*

Let us go re - joic - ing to the house of the Lord.

I rejoiced when they said to me,
  "Let us go to the house of the LORD."
And now our feet are standing
  within your gates, O Jerusalem. ℟.

Jerusalem is built as a city
  bonded as one together.
It is there that the tribes go up,

the tribes of the LORD. ℟.

For Israel's witness it is
  to praise the name of the LORD.
There were set the thrones for
    judgment,
  the thrones of the house of
    David. ℟.

**READING II**                                       *Colossians 1:12–20*

**GOSPEL**                                            *Luke 23:35–43*

# Other Feasts and Celebrations

## ASH WEDNESDAY 1194

**READING I** *Joel 2:12–18 / 219*

**RESPONSORIAL PSALM** *Psalm 51:3–4, 5–6a, 12–13, 14 and 17*

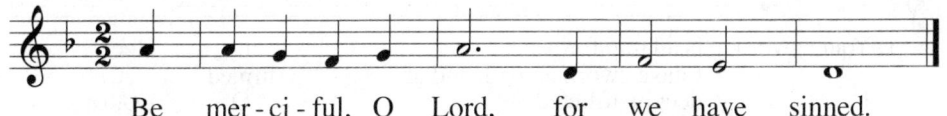

Be mer - ci - ful, O Lord, for we have sinned.

Have mercy on me, O God,
   according to your merciful love;
according to your great compassion,
   blot out my transgressions.
Wash me completely from my iniquity,
   and cleanse me from my sin. ℟.

My transgressions, truly I know them;
   my sin is always before me.
Against you, you alone, have I sinned;
   what is evil in your sight I have
     done. ℟.

Create a pure heart for me, O God;
   renew a steadfast spirit within me.
Do not cast me away from your
     presence;
   take not your holy spirit from me. ℟.

Restore in me the joy of your salvation;
   sustain in me a willing spirit.
O Lord, open my lips
   and my mouth shall proclaim your
     praise. ℟.

**READING II** *2 Corinthians 5:20—6:2*

**GOSPEL** *Matthew 6:1–6, 16–18*

## 1195   FEBRUARY 2: PRESENTATION OF THE LORD

Forty days after the celebration of Christmas, this feast tells of how Mary and Joseph brought the child to the Temple. There the aged Simeon took the baby in his arms and proclaimed that Jesus would be "a light to the Gentiles, the glory of Israel." These words have been sung for centuries on February 2 as Christians have blessed and carried lighted candles in procession.

### BLESSING OF CANDLES AND PROCESSION

*As the candles are lighted, this antiphon (with optional verses) may be sung:*

Antiphon

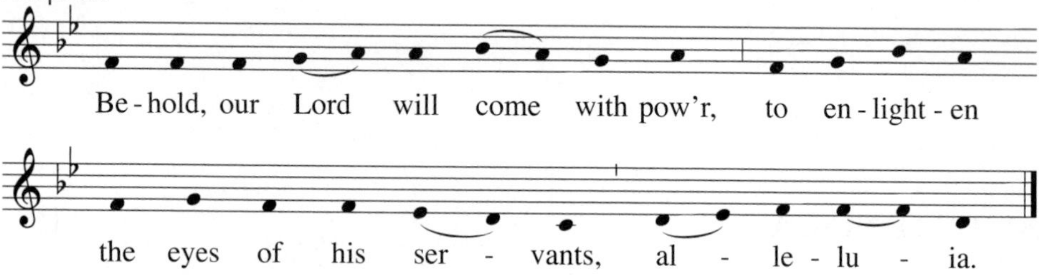

Be - hold, our Lord will come with pow'r, to en - light - en

the eyes of his ser - vants, al - le - lu - ia.

Psalm 119:105–108, 111–112

1. Your word is a lamp for my feet,
   I have sworn an oath and af - firmed it,
2. I am deeply afflicted, O LORD;
   Accept, LORD, my freely offered hom - age,
3. Your de - crees are my heritage for ev - er,
   I incline my heart to carry out your stat - utes

**D.C.**

and a light for my path.
to obey your last judg - ments. ℟.
by your word, give me life.
and teach me your de - crees. ℟.
the joy of my heart.
for - ev - er, to the end. ℟.

Text: Psalm 119:105–108, 111–112, *The Revised Grail Psalms*, © 2010, Conception Abbey and The Grail, admin. by GIA Publications, Inc.; antiphon, ICEL, © 2010
Music: Chant Mode VIII; acc. by Richard Proulx, © 1985, GIA Publications, Inc.; antiphon, ICEL, © 2010

*When the candles have been blessed, the priest sings:*

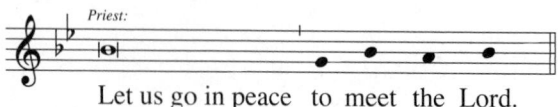

Priest:

Let us go in peace to meet the Lord.

*Or:*

Let us go forth in peace. In the name of Christ. A - men.

*During the procession, the following may be sung:*  **1196**

Antiphon

A light for rev - e - la - tion to the Gen - tiles

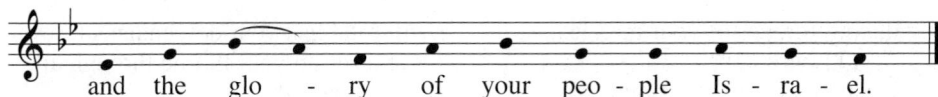

and the glo - ry of your peo - ple Is - ra - el.

Canticle, Luke 2:29–32

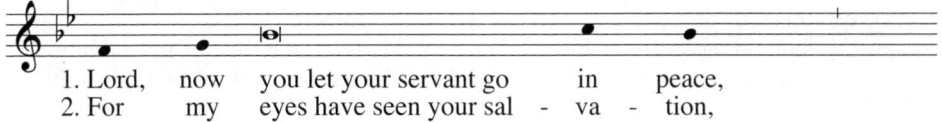

1. Lord, now you let your servant go in peace,
2. For my eyes have seen your sal - va - tion,

**D.C.**

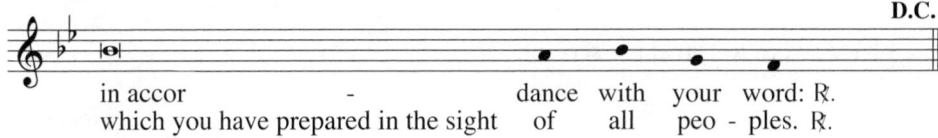

in accor - dance with your word: ℟.
which you have prepared in the sight of all peo - ples. ℟.

Text: Luke 2:29–32, trans. ICEL, © 2010
Music: Chant Mode VIII; acc. by Richard Proulx, © 1985, GIA Publications, Inc.; antiphon, ICEL, © 2010

**READING I**  *Malachi 3:1–4 / 524*

**RESPONSORIAL PSALM**  *Psalm 24:7, 8, 9, 10*

Who is this king of glo-ry? It is the Lord!

O gates, lift high your heads;
  grow higher, ancient doors.
  Let him enter, the king of glory! ℟.

Who is this king of glory?
  The LORD, the mighty, the valiant;
  the LORD, the valiant in war. ℟.

O gates, lift high your heads;
  grow higher, ancient doors.
  Let him enter, the king of glory! ℟.

Who is this king of glory?
  He, the LORD of hosts,
  he is the king of glory. ℟.

**READING II**                                                   *Hebrews 2:14–18*

**GOSPEL**                                            *Luke 2:22–40 or 2:22–32*

---

## 1197   MARCH 19: JOSEPH, HUSBAND OF MARY

**READING I**                                *2 Samuel 7:4–5a, 12–14a, 16 / 543*

**RESPONSORIAL PSALM**                          *Psalm 89:2–3, 4–5, 27 and 29*

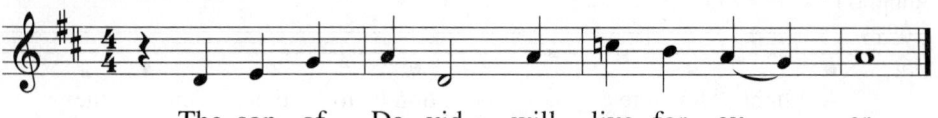

The son of Da - vid will live for ev - er.

I will sing forever of your mercies,
O LORD;
  through all ages my mouth will
  proclaim your fidelity.
I have declared your mercy is
  established forever;
  your fidelity stands firm as the
  heavens. ℟.

"With my chosen one I have made a
  covenant;
  I have sworn to David my servant:

I will establish your descendants forever,
  and set up your throne through all
  ages." ℟.

"He will call out to me, 'You are my
  father,
  my God, the rock of my salvation.'
I will keep my faithful love for him
  always;
  with him my covenant shall last." ℟.

**READING II**                                          *Romans 4:13, 16–18, 22*

**GOSPEL**                                         *Matthew 1:16, 18–21, 24a*

*Or:*

**GOSPEL**                                                    *Luke 2:41–51a*

---

## 1198   MARCH 25: ANNUNCIATION OF THE LORD

**READING I**                                  *Isaiah 7:10–14; 8:10 / 545*

**RESPONSORIAL PSALM**                          *Psalm 40:7–8a, 8b–9, 10, 11*

Here am I, Lord; here am I, Lord;    I come to do your will.

You delight not in sacrifice and offerings,
  but in an open ear.
You do not ask for holocaust and victim.
  Then I said, "See, I have come." ℟.

In the scroll of the book it stands
    written of me:
  "I delight to do your will, O my God;
  your instruction lies deep within
    me." ℟.

Your justice I have proclaimed

in the great assembly.
My lips I have not sealed;
  you know it, O LORD. ℟.

Your saving help I have not hidden in
    my heart;
  of your faithfulness and salvation I
    have spoken.
I made no secret of your merciful love
  and your faithfulness to the great
    assembly. ℟.

**READING II**                                  *Hebrews 10:4–10*

**GOSPEL**                                        *Luke 1:26–38*

---

# JUNE 24: NATIVITY OF ST. JOHN THE BAPTIST—VIGIL MASS   1199

**READING I**                                  *Jeremiah 1:4–10 / 586*

**RESPONSORIAL PSALM**          *Psalm 71:1–2, 3–4a, 5–6ab, 15ab and 17*

Since my moth-er's womb,     you have been my strength.

In you, O LORD, I take refuge;
  let me never be put to shame.
In your justice, rescue me, free me;
  incline your ear to me and save me. ℟.

Be my rock, my constant refuge,
  a mighty stronghold to save me,
for you are my rock, my stronghold.
  My God, free me from the hand
    of the wicked. ℟.

It is you, O Lord, who are my hope,
  my trust, O LORD, from my youth.
On you I have leaned from my birth;
  from my mother's womb, you have
    been my help. ℟.

My mouth will tell of your justice,
  and all the day long of your salvation.
O God, you have taught me from my
    youth,
  and I proclaim your wonders still. ℟.

**READING II**                                  *1 Peter 1:8–12*

**GOSPEL**                                        *Luke 1:5–17*

---

# JUNE 24: NATIVITY OF ST. JOHN THE BAPTIST–MASS DURING THE DAY   1200

**READING I**                                  *Isaiah 49:1–6 / 587*

**RESPONSORIAL PSALM**  *Psalm 139:1–3, 13–14ab, 14c–15*

I praise you, O Lord, for I am won-der-ful-ly made.

O Lord, you search me and you know me.
  You yourself know my resting and
    my rising;
  you discern my thoughts from afar.
You mark when I walk or lie down;
  you know all my ways through and
    through. ℟.

For it was you who formed my inmost
    being,
  knit me together in my mother's
    womb.
I thank you who wonderfully made me;
  how wonderful are your works,
  which my soul knows well! ℟.

My frame was not hidden from you,
  when I was being fashioned in
    secret
  and molded in the depths of the
    earth. ℟.

**READING II**  *Acts 13:22–26*

**GOSPEL**  *Luke 1:57–66, 80*

---

## 1201   JUNE 29: STS. PETER & PAUL, APOSTLES—VIGIL MASS

**READING I**  *Acts 3:1–10 / 590*

**RESPONSORIAL PSALM**  *Psalm 19:2–3, 4–5*

Their mes - sage goes out through all the earth.

The heavens declare the glory of God,
  and the firmament proclaims the
    work of his hands.
Day unto day conveys the message,
  and night unto night imparts the
    knowledge. ℟.

No speech, no word, whose voice goes
    unheeded;
  their sound goes forth through all
    the earth,
  their message to the utmost bounds
    of the world. ℟.

**READING II**  *Galatians 1:11–20*

**GOSPEL**  *John 21:15–19*

## JUNE 29: STS. PETER & PAUL, APOSTLES–MASS DURING THE DAY 1202

**READING I**                                                                    *Acts 12:1–11 / 591*

**RESPONSORIAL PSALM**                                      *Psalm 34:2–3, 4–5, 6–7, 8–9*

The an-gel of the Lord will res-cue those who fear him.

I will bless the LORD at all times;
   praise of him is always in my mouth.
In the LORD my soul shall make its boast;
   the humble shall hear and be glad. ℟.

Glorify the LORD with me;
   together let us praise his name.
I sought the LORD, and he answered me;
   from all my terrors he set me free. ℟.

Look toward him and be radiant;

let your faces not be abashed.
This lowly one called; the LORD heard,
   and rescued him from all his
     distress. ℟.

The angel of the LORD is encamped
   around those who fear him,
     to rescue them.
Taste and see that the LORD is good.
   Blessed the man who seeks refuge
     in him. ℟.

**READING II**                                                          *2 Timothy 4:6–8, 17–18*

**GOSPEL**                                                                    *Matthew 16:13–19*

## JULY 4: INDEPENDENCE DAY                                                  1203

**RESPONSORIAL PSALM**                          *Psalm 85:9ab and 10, 11–12, 13–14*

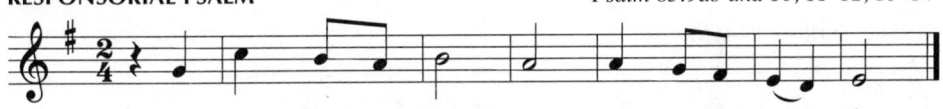

The Lord speaks of peace, peace, peace to his peo - ple.

I will hear what the LORD God speaks;
   he speaks of peace for his people
     and his faithful.
His salvation is near for those who
     fear him,
   and his glory will dwell in our
     land. ℟.

Merciful love and faithfulness have met;
   justice and peace have kissed.

Faithfulness shall spring from the earth,
   and justice look down from
     heaven. ℟.

Also the LORD will bestow his bounty,
   and our earth shall yield its increase.
Justice will march before him,
   and guide his steps on the way. ℟.

## 1204 AUGUST 6: TRANSFIGURATION OF THE LORD

**READING I** *Daniel 7:9–10, 13–14 / 614*

**RESPONSORIAL PSALM** *Psalm 97:1–2, 5–6, 9*

The Lord is king, the Lord Most High o-ver all the earth.

The LORD is king, let earth rejoice;
    let the many islands be glad.
Cloud and darkness surround him;
    justice and right are the foundation
        of his throne. ℟.

The mountains melt like wax
    before the face of the LORD,

before the face of the Lord of all the
    earth.
The skies proclaim his justice;
    all peoples see his glory. ℟.

For you indeed are the LORD,
    most high above all the earth,
    exalted far above all gods. ℟.

**READING II** *2 Peter 1:16–19*

**GOSPEL / A** *Matthew 17:1–9*

**GOSPEL / B** *Mark 9:2–10*

**GOSPEL / C** *Luke 9:28b-36*

## 1205 AUGUST 15: ASSUMPTION OF MARY—VIGIL MASS

**READING I** *1 Chronicles 15:3–4, 15–16; 16:1–2 / 621*

**RESPONSORIAL PSALM** *Psalm 132:6–7, 9–10, 13–14*

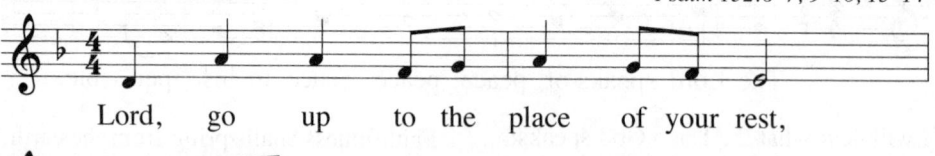

Lord, go up to the place of your rest,

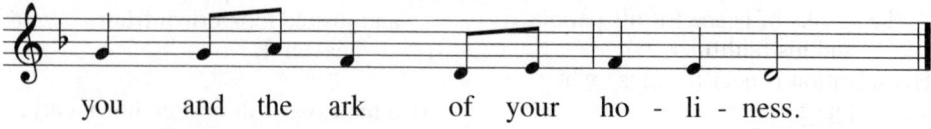

you and the ark of your ho - li - ness.

At Ephrata we heard of it;
    we found it in the plains of Yearim.
"Let us go to the place of his dwelling;
    let us bow down at his footstool." ℟.

Your priests shall be clothed with justice;
    your faithful shall ring out their joy.
For the sake of David your servant,

do not reject your anointed. ℟.

For the LORD has chosen Sion;
    he has desired it for his dwelling:
"This is my resting place from age to
    age;
    here have I chosen to dwell." ℟.

**READING II**                                                   *1 Corinthians 15:54b–57*

**GOSPEL**                                                       *Luke 11:27–28*

---

## AUGUST 15: ASSUMPTION OF MARY—MASS DURING THE DAY 1206

**READING I**                                       *Revelation 11:19a; 12:1–6a, 10ab / 622*

**RESPONSORIAL PSALM**                               *Psalm 45:10, 11, 12ab, 16*

The queen stands at your right hand,   ar-rayed in gold.

The daughters of kings are those whom
  you favor.
On your right stands the queen in
  gold of Óphir. ℟.

Listen, O daughter; pay heed and give ear:
  forget your own people and your
  father's house. ℟.

So will the king desire your beauty.
He is your lord, pay homage to
  him. ℟.

They are escorted amid gladness and
  joy;
they pass within the palace of the
  king. ℟.

**READING II**                                                   *1 Corinthians 15:20–27*

**GOSPEL**                                                       *Luke 1:39–56*

---

## FIRST MONDAY IN SEPTEMBER: LABOR DAY                    1207

**RESPONSORIAL PSALM**                         *Psalm 90:2, 3–4, 12–13, 14 and 16*

Lord, give suc-cess to the work of our hands, to the work of our hands.

Before the mountains were born,
  or the earth or the world were
    brought forth,
  you are God, from age to age. ℟.

You turn man back to dust,
  and say, "Return, O children of men."
To your eyes a thousand years
  are like yesterday, come and gone,
  or like a watch in the night. ℟.

Then teach us to number our days,
  that we may gain wisdom of heart.
Turn back, O Lord! How long?
  Show pity to your servants. ℟.

At dawn, fill us with your merciful love;
  we shall exult and rejoice all our
    days.
Let your deed be seen by your servants,
  and your glorious power by their
    children. ℟.

## 1208 SEPTEMBER 14: EXALTATION OF THE HOLY CROSS

**READING I** *Numbers 21:4b–9 / 638*

**RESPONSORIAL PSALM** *Psalm 78:1–2, 34–35, 36–37, 38*

Do not for - get the works of the Lord!

Give ear, my people, to my teaching;
   incline your ear to the words of my
      mouth.
I will open my mouth in a parable
   and utter hidden lessons of the
      past. ℞.

When he slew them, then they sought
      him,
   repented and earnestly sought God.
They would remember that God was
      their rock,
   God the Most High their redeemer. ℞.

Yet they deceived him with their mouths;
   they lied to him with their tongues.
For their hearts were not steadfast
      toward him;
   they were not faithful to his
      covenant. ℞.

Yet he who is full of compassion
   forgave them their sin and spared
      them.
So often he held back his anger,
   and did not stir up all his rage. ℞.

**READING II** *Philippians 2:6–11*

**GOSPEL** *John 3:13–17*

## 1209 NOVEMBER 1: ALL SAINTS

**READING I** *Revelation 7:2–4, 9–14 / 667*

**RESPONSORIAL PSALM** *Psalm 24:1–2, 3–4ab, 5–6*

Lord, this is the peo - ple that longs to see your face.

The LORD's is the earth and its fullness,
   the world, and those who dwell in it.
It is he who set it on the seas;
   on the rivers he made it firm. ℞.

Who shall climb the mountain of the
      LORD?
   Who shall stand in his holy place?
The clean of hands and pure of heart,

whose soul is not set on vain
   things. ℞.

Blessings from the LORD shall he receive,
   and right reward from the God who
      saves him.
Such are the people who seek him,
   who seek the face of the God of
      Jacob. ℞.

**READING II** *1 John 3:1–3*

**GOSPEL** *Matthew 5:1–12a*

## NOVEMBER 2: ALL SOULS' DAY 1210

**RESPONSORIAL PSALM** *Psalm 23:1–3a, 3b–4, 5, 6 / 668*

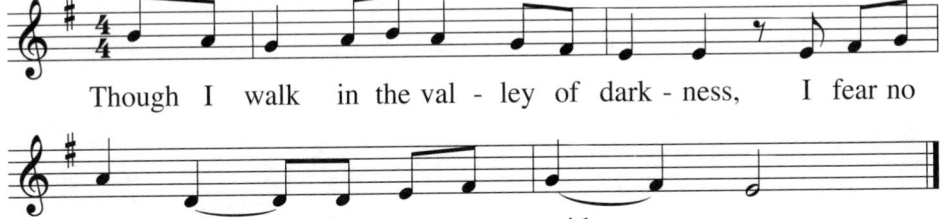

The Lord is my shep-herd; there is noth-ing I shall want.

*or:*

Though I walk in the val-ley of dark-ness, I fear no

e - vil, for you are with me.

The LORD is my shepherd;
    there is nothing I shall want.
Fresh and green are the pastures
    where he gives me repose.
Near restful waters he leads me;
    he revives my soul. ℟.

He guides me along the right path,
    for the sake of his name.
Though I should walk in the valley of
    the shadow of death,
    no evil would I fear, for you are
    with me.

Your crook and your staff will give
    me comfort. ℟.

You have prepared a table before me
    in the sight of my foes.
My head you have anointed with oil;
    my cup is overflowing. ℟.

Surely goodness and mercy shall follow
    me
    all the days of my life.
In the LORD's own house shall I dwell
    for length of days unending. ℟.

*Or:*

**RESPONSORIAL PSALM** *Psalm 25:6–7bc, 17–18, 20–21*

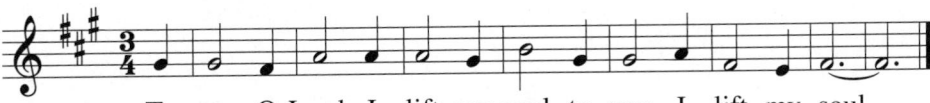

To you, O Lord, I lift my soul, to you I lift my soul.

*or:*

No one who waits for you, O Lord, will ev-er be put to shame.

Remember your compassion, O LORD,
    and your merciful love,
    for they are from of old.

In your merciful love remember me,
    because of your goodness,
    O LORD. ℟.

Relieve the anguish of my heart,
  and set me free from my distress.
See my lowliness and suffering,
  and take away all my sins. ℟.

Preserve my life and rescue me.
  Let me not be put to shame,
  for in you I trust.
May integrity and virtue protect me,
  for I have hoped in you, O LORD. ℟.

*Or:*

**RESPONSORIAL PSALM**　　　　　　　　　*Psalm 27:1, 4, 7 and 8b and 9a, 13–14*

The Lord is my light and my sal - va - tion.

*or:*

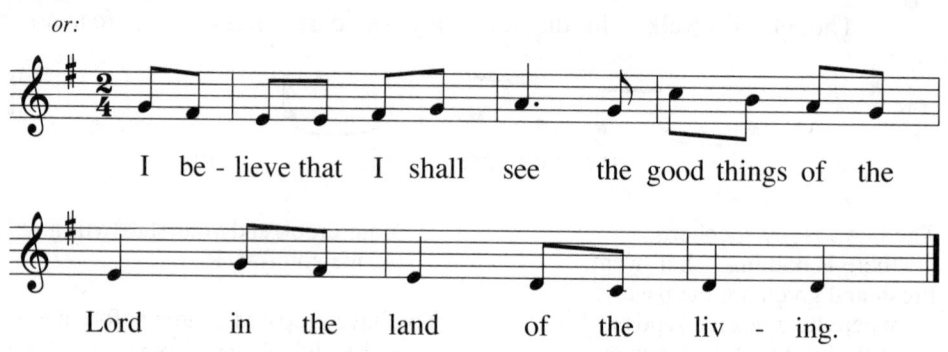

I be - lieve that I shall see the good things of the

Lord in the land of the liv - ing.

The LORD is my light and my salvation;
  whom shall I fear?
The LORD is the stronghold of my life;
  whom should I dread? ℟.

There is one thing I ask of the LORD,
  only this do I seek:
to live in the house of the LORD
  all the days of my life,
to gaze on the beauty of the LORD,
  to inquire at his temple. ℟.

O LORD, hear my voice when I call;
  have mercy and answer me.
It is your face, O LORD, that I seek;
  hide not your face from me. ℟.

I believe I shall see the LORD's
    goodness
  in the land of the living.
Wait for the LORD; be strong;
  be stouthearted, and wait for the
    LORD! ℟.

## 1211　NOVEMBER 9: DEDICATION OF THE LATERAN BASILICA

**READING I**　　　　　　　　　　　　　*Ezekiel 47:1–2, 8–9, 12 / 671*

**RESPONSORIAL PSALM** *Psalm 46:2–3, 5–6, 8–9*

The wa-ters of the riv - er glad-den the cit - y of God,

the ho - ly dwell-ing of the Most High.

God is for us a refuge and strength,
  an ever-present help in time of
    distress:
so we shall not fear though the earth
    should rock,
  though the mountains quake to the
    heart of the sea. ℞.

The waters of a river give joy to God's
    city,
  the holy place, the dwelling of the
    Most High.
God is within, it cannot be shaken;
  God will help it at the dawning of
    the day. ℞.

The LORD of hosts is with us:
  the God of Jacob is our stronghold.
Come and behold the works of the
    LORD,
  the awesome deeds he has done on
    the earth. ℞.

**READING II** *1 Corinthians 3:9c-11, 16–17*

**GOSPEL** *John 2:13–22*

---

# THANKSGIVING DAY 1212

**RESPONSORIAL PSALM** *1 Chronicles 29:10bc, 11, 12*

O God, O God, let all the na-tions praise you!

"Blessed may you be, O LORD,
  God of Israel our father,
  from eternity to eternity." ℞.

"Yours, O LORD, are grandeur and power,
  majesty, splendor, and glory.
For all in heaven and on earth is yours;
  yours, O LORD, is the sovereignty;
  you are exalted as head over all." ℞.

"Riches and honor are from you,
  and you have dominion over all.
In your hand are power and might;
  it is yours to give grandeur and
    strength to all." ℞.

## 1213   DECEMBER 8: IMMACULATE CONCEPTION

**READING I**                                                    *Genesis 3:9–15, 20 / 689*

**RESPONSORIAL PSALM**                                  *Psalm 98:1, 2–3ab, 3cd–4*

Sing    to    the    Lord    a    new    song,

for    he    has    done    mar - vel - ous    deeds.

O sing a new song to the LORD,
  for he has worked wonders.
His right hand and his holy arm
  have brought salvation. ℟.

The LORD has made known his salvation,
  has shown his deliverance to the
    nations.

He has remembered his merciful love
  and his truth for the house of Israel. ℟.

All the ends of the earth have seen
  the salvation of our God.
Shout to the LORD, all the earth;
  break forth into joyous song,
  and sing out your praise. ℟.

**READING II**                                               *Ephesians 1:3–6, 11–12*

**GOSPEL**                                                         *Luke 1:26–38*

**3** © 1987, GIA Publications, Inc.

**4** Text: © 1963, 1986, The Grail, GIA Publications, Inc., agent; refrain trans. © 1974, ICEL. Music: © 1985, 1996, OCP. 5536 NE Hassalo, Portland, OR 97213. All rights reserved. Used with permission.

**7** Music: © 1986, GIA Publications, Inc.

**8** Acc.: © 1975, 1993, GIA Publications, Inc.

**9** Music: © 1979, GIA Publications, Inc.

**13** Text: © William G. Storey. Acc.: © 1975, GIA Publications, Inc.

**14** Text: © 2010, Conception Abbey and The Grail, admin. by GIA Publications, Inc. Music: © 1979, GIA Publications, Inc.

**17** Music: © 1979, GIA Publications, Inc.

**18** Acc.: © 1975, 1993, GIA Publications, Inc.

**19** Music: © 1979, GIA Publications, Inc.

**23** Text: Verses, © 2010, Conception Abbey and The Grail, admin. by GIA Publications, Inc., refrain, © 1979, GIA Publications, Inc. Music: © 1979, GIA Publications, Inc.

**24** Text tr.: © Peter Scagnelli. Music adapt.: © 1982, GIA Publications, Inc.

**25** Text: © 1974, ICEL. Music adapt.: © 1986, GIA Publications, Inc.

**26** Text: © 1974, ICEL. Music adapt.: © 1986, GIA Publications, Inc.

**28** Text: © 1989, GIA Publications, Inc., refrain trans. © 1969, ICEL. Music: © 1989, GIA Publications, Inc.

**29** Text: © 1993, GIA Publications, Inc.; refrain trans., © 1969, ICEL. Music: © 1993, GIA Publications, Inc.

**30** Text: © 1988, GIA Publications, Inc.; refrain III trans. © 1969, ICEL. Music: © 1988, 1994, GIA Publications, Inc.

**31** Text: © 1983, GIA Publications, Inc.; refrain trans. © 1969, ICEL. Music: © 1983, GIA Publications, Inc.

**32** Text: © 2010, Conception Abbey and The Grail, admin. by GIA Publications, Inc. English refrain trans. © 1969, ICEL; Spanish refrain trans., © admin. by Obra Nacional de la Buena Prensa. Music: © 2003, GIA Publications, Inc.

**33** Text: © 1983, GIA Publications, Inc.; refrain trans. © 1969, ICEL. Music: © 1983, GIA Publications, Inc.

**34** Antiphons: © 1963, The Grail, GIA Publications, Inc., agent. Psalm tone: © 1975, GIA Publications, Inc. Gelineau Tone: © 1963, The Grail, GIA Publications, Inc., agent. Verses text: © 2010, Conception Abbey and The Grail, admin. by GIA Publications, Inc.

**35** © 1986, GIA Publications, Inc.

**36** Text: © 2010, Conception Abbey and The Grail, admin. by GIA Publications, Inc.; refrain trans. © 1969, ICEL; Spanish refrain © 1970, 1972, Conferencia Episcopal Española. Music: © 1994, 1998, 2004, GIA Publications, Inc.

**37** Text: © 1993, GIA Publications, Inc.; refrain I trans. © 1969, ICEL. Music: © 1993, GIA Publications, Inc.

**38** Text: © 1985, GIA Publications, Inc.; refrain trans. © 1969, ICEL. Music: © 1985, GIA Publications, Inc.

**39** Text: © 1982, GIA Publications, Inc.; refrain trans. © 1969, ICEL. Music: © 1982, GIA Publications, Inc.

**40** Text: © 2000, GIA Publications, Inc.; refrain trans. © 1969, ICEL. Music: © 2000, GIA Publications, Inc.

**41** © 1983, GIA Publications, Inc.

**42** Text: Verses, © 1963, The Grail, GIA Publications, Inc., agent; refrain. Music: © 1985, Paul Inwood. Published by OCP. 5536 NE Hassalo, Portland, OR 97213. All rights reserved. Used with permission.

**43** Text: © 2010, Conception Abbey and The Grail, admin. by GIA Publications, Inc.; refrain trans. © 1969, ICEL; Spanish refrain © 1970, 1972, Conferencia Episcopal Española. Music: © 1994, 1998, 2004, GIA Publications, Inc.

**44** Text: © 1987, 2011, GIA Publications, Inc.; refrain trans. © 1969, ICEL. Music: © 1987, 1994, GIA Publications, Inc.

**45** Text: © 1980, GIA Publications, Inc.; refrain trans. © 1969, ICEL. Music: © 1980, GIA Publications, Inc.

**46** Text: © 2010, Conception Abbey and The Grail, admin. by GIA Publications, Inc.; refrain trans. © 1969, ICEL. Music: © 1995, GIA Publications, Inc.

**47** © 1978, 1991, John B. Foley, SJ, and OCP. 5536 NE Hassalo, Portland, OR 97213. All rights reserved. Used with permission.

**48** © 2004, GIA Publications, Inc.

**49** Verse text and Music: © 1971, 1991, North American Liturgy Resources. Published by OCP. 5536 NE Hassalo, Portland, OR 97213. All rights reserved. Used with permission. Refrain trans.: © 1969, ICEL

**50** © 1983, GIA Publications, Inc.

**51** Text: © 1983, GIA Publications, Inc.; refrain trans. © 1969, ICEL. Music: © 1983, GIA Publications, Inc.

**52** Text: © 1963, 1993, The Grail, GIA Publications, Inc., agent; refrain trans. © 1969, ICEL. Music: © 1998, GIA Publications, Inc.

**53** Antiphon 1 text and music: © 1963, 1993, The Grail, GIA Publications, Inc., agent; Antiphons 2–4: text, © 1969, 1981, ICEL. Antiphons 2, 3 music: © 1975, GIA Publications, Inc. Antiphon 5 music: © 1979, 1995, GIA Publications, Inc. Psalm tone music: © Gethsemani Abbey. Verses text: © 2010, Conception Abbey and The Grail, admin. by GIA Publications, Inc. Verses music: © 1963, 1993, The Grail, GIA Publications, Inc., agent

**54** Text: verses 2, 4 adapt., © 2004, GIA Publications, Inc. Verses 1, 3 tr., © 1970, Conferencia Episcopal Española. Refrain tr. © 1969, ICEL. Music: © 2005, GIA Publications, Inc.

**55** Text: Verse adapt., © 1970, Confraternity of Christian Doctrine, Washington, DC. Refrain text and music: © 1987, GIA Publications, Inc.

**56** Antiphon 1 text: © 1969, 1981, ICEL. Antiphon 1 music: © 1975, GIA Publications, Inc. Antiphon 2: © 1979, GIA Publications, Inc. Psalm tone: © 1994, 1998, GIA Publications, Inc. Verses text: © 2010, Conception Abbey and The Grail, admin. by GIA Publications, Inc. Verses music: © 1963, The Grail, GIA Publications, Inc., agent

**57** Verses text and Music: © 1997, 1998, Steve Angrisano. Published by OCP. 5536 NE Hassalo, Portland, OR 97213. All rights reserved. Used with permission. Refrain trans. and Alt. refrain trans. © 1974, ICEL.

**58** © 1982, GIA Publications, Inc.

**59** © 1982, GIA Publications, Inc.

**60** © 1987, 1994, GIA Publications, Inc.

**61** Antiphon: © 1963, The Grail, GIA Publications, Inc., agent. Psalm tone: © Gethsemani Abbey. Verses text: © 2010, Conception Abbey and The Grail, admin. by GIA Publications, Inc. Verses music: © 1963, 1993, The Grail, GIA Publications, Inc., agent

**62** Text: © 1983, GIA Publications, Inc.; refrain trans. © 1969, ICEL. Music: © 1983, GIA Publications, Inc.

# Acknowledgments/*continued*

**63** Antiphon text: © 1974, ICEL. Antiphon music: © 1986, GIA Publications, Inc. Psalm tone: © Gethsemani Abbey. Verses text: © 2010, Conception Abbey and The Grail, admin. by GIA Publications, Inc. Verses music: © 1963, 1993, The Grail, GIA Publications, Inc., agent

**64** Verses text: © 1963, 1993, The Grail, GIA Publications, Inc., agent. Alt text: © 1988, 1993, GIA Publications, Inc., refrain trans. © 1969, ICEL. Music: © 1988, 1994, GIA Publications, Inc.

**65** © 1980, GIA Publications, Inc.

**66** © 1983, 1994, GIA Publications, Inc.

**67** Text: © 1989, GIA Publications, Inc., refrain trans. © 1969, ICEL. Music: © 1989, 1994, GIA Publications, Inc.

**68** Verses tr.: © 1970, Confraternity of Christian Doctrine, Washington, D.C.; refrain tr. © 1969, ICEL. Music: © 1976, GIA Publications, Inc.

**69** Text: © 2010, Conception Abbey and The Grail, admin. by GIA Publications, Inc.; refrain trans. © 1969, ICEL. Spanish tr., © 1970, 1972, Conferencia Episcopal Española. Music: © 1995, 2004, GIA Publications, Inc.

**70** © 1983, 1994 GIA Publications, Inc.

**71** © 1983, GIA Publications, Inc.

**72** © 1993, GIA Publications, Inc.

**73** Antiphon text: © 1963, 1993, The Grail, GIA Publications, Inc., agent. Antiphon music: © 1986, GIA Publications, Inc. Psalm tone: © 1994, 1998, GIA Publications, Inc. Verses text: © 2010, Conception Abbey and The Grail, admin. by GIA Publications, Inc. Verses music: © 1963, 1993, The Grail, GIA Publications, Inc., agent

**74** Text: © 2010, Conception Abbey and The Grail, admin. by GIA Publications, Inc. Spanish tr., © 1970, 1972, Conferencia Episcopal Española. Music: © 2010, GIA Publications, Inc.

**75** Text: © 1983, GIA Publications, Inc.; refrain trans. © 1969, ICEL. Music: © 1983, GIA Publications, Inc.

**76** Text: © 1985, GIA Publications, Inc.; refrain trans. © 1969, ICEL. Music: © 1985, GIA Publications, Inc.

**77** Antiphon text: © 1969, 1981, ICEL. Antiphon music: © 1975, GIA Publications, Inc. Psalm tone: © 1994, 1998, GIA Publications, Inc. Verses text: © 2010, Conception Abbey and The Grail, admin. by GIA Publications, Inc. Verses music: © 1963, 1993, The Grail, GIA Publications, Inc., agent

**78** © 1983, GIA Publications, Inc.

**79** Text: © 2003, GIA Publications, Inc.; Spanish refrain trans. © 1970, Conferencia Episcopal Española. Music: © 2003, GIA Publications, Inc.

**80** Text: © 1987, GIA Publications, Inc.; refrain II trans. © 1969, ICEL. Music: © 1987, GIA Publications, Inc.

**81** Text: © 1983, GIA Publications, Inc,; refrain trans. © 1969, ICEL. Music: © 1983, GIA Publications, Inc.

**82** Text: Verses, © Confraternity of Christian Doctrine, Washington D.C.; refrain trans. © 1969, ICEL. Music: © 1981, 1982, Jan Michael Joncas Trust. Published by OCP. 5536 NE Hassalo, Portland, OR 97213. All rights reserved. Used with permission.

**83** Text: © 1963, 1993, The Grail, GIA Publications, Inc., agent; refrain: © 1979, GIA Publications, Inc. Music: © 1979, GIA Publications, Inc.

**84** Text: © 1987, GIA Publications, Inc.; refrain trans. © 1969, ICEL. Music: © 1987, GIA Publications, Inc

**85** Text: © 1981, 1997, GIA Publications, Inc., refrain trans. © 1969, ICEL. Music: © 1981, 1997, GIA Publications, Inc.

**86** © 1987, 1993, GIA Publications, Inc.

**87** Text: © 1983, GIA Publications, Inc.; refrain trans. © 1969, ICEL. Music: © 1983, GIA Publications, Inc.

**88** © 2008, GIA Publications, Inc.

**89** Text: © 1985, GIA Publications, Inc.; refrain trans. © 1969, ICEL. Music: © 1985, GIA Publications, Inc.

**90** © 1987, GIA Publications, Inc.

**91** © 1989, GIA Publications, Inc.

**92** © 1983, GIA Publications, Inc.

**93** Text: © 1963, 1993, The Grail, GIA Publications, Inc., agent. Music: © 1990, GIA Publications, Inc.

**94** © 1964, World Library Publications, Franklin Park, IL wlpmusic.com 800-566-6150 All rights reserved. Used by permission.

**95** © 1992, GIA Publications, Inc.

**96** © 1997, GIA Publications, Inc.

**97** © 1988, 1994, GIA Publications, Inc.

**98** Text: © 2003, GIA Publications, Inc.; English refrain tr. © 1969, ICEL. Music: © 2003, GIA Publications, Inc.

**99** Text: © 1970, Confraternity of Christian Doctrine, Inc. Music: © 2002, World Library Publications, Franklin Park, IL wlpmusic.com 800-566-6150 All rights reserved. Used by permission.

**100** Text: © 2004, GIA Publications, Inc. Music: © 1979, 1988, GIA Publications, Inc.

**101** © 1980, GIA Publications, Inc.

**102** © 1989, GIA Publications, Inc.

**103** Text: © 1992, GIA Publications, Inc. Harm.: © 1987, GIA Publications, Inc.

**104** Text: © 1995, GIA Publications, Inc. Music: © 2003, GIA Publications, Inc.

**105** © 2010, GIA Publications, Inc.

**115** Text: © 1985, ICEL. Music: © 1991, MorningStar Music Publishers

**119** Text: Refrain © 1969, ICEL; Verses © 2010, Conception Abbey and The Grail, admin. by GIA Publications, Inc. Music: Refrain © 1984, Anthony E. Jackson; Verses © The Antilles Episcopal Conference

**139** Text tr.: © 1969, James Quinn, SJ, Selah Publishing Co., Inc., North American agent. www.selahpub.com.

**143** Verses text: © 2010, Conception Abbey and The Grail, admin. by GIA Publications, Inc.

**150** Verses text: © 2010, Conception Abbey and The Grail, admin. by GIA Publications, Inc.

**156** Verses text: © 2010, Conception Abbey and The Grail, admin. by GIA Publications, Inc.

**329** Music: arr. © 1990, Iona Community, GIA Publications, Inc., agent

**331** Music: © 1984, Les Presses de Taizé, GIA Publications, Inc., agent

**332** Music: © 1998, Les Presses de Taizé, GIA Publications, Inc., agent

**334** © 1985, Fintan O'Carroll and Christopher Walker. Published by OCP. 5536 NE Hassalo, Portland, OR 97213. All rights reserved. Used with permission.

**335** Music: © 1998, Les Presses de Taizé, GIA Publications, Inc., agent

**345** Music: © 1998, Les Presses de Taizé, GIA Publications, Inc., agent

**346** Music: © 1998, Les Presses de Taizé, GIA Publications, Inc., agent

**348** Music: © 1980, Les Presses de Taizé, GIA Publications, Inc., agent

**352** Music: © 1994, World Library Publications, Franklin Park, IL wlpmusic.com 800-566-6150 All rights reserved. Used by permission.

**353** Music: © 2001, World Library Publications, Franklin Park, IL wlpmusic.com 800-566-6150 All rights reserved. Used by permission.

**354** © 2004, Rufino Zaragoza, OFM. Published by OCP. 5536 NE Hassalo, Portland, OR 97213. All rights reserved. Used with permission.

**367** Music adapt.: © 1980, The Church Pension Fund. Acc. © 1986, and Choral Arr. © 2004, GIA Publications, Inc.

**381** Music: © 1970, 1987, 2010, World Library Publications, Franklin Park, IL wlpmusic.com 800-566-6150 All rights reserved. Used by permission.

# Acknowledgments/*continued*

# Acknowledgments/*continued*

# Acknowledgments/*continued*

# Acknowledgments/*continued*

**751** © 1977, Universal Music—Brentwood Benson Publishing. All Rights Reserved. Used By Permission.

**752** © 2003, 2011, Les Presses de Taizé, GIA Publications, Inc., agent

**753** © 1986, North American Liturgy Resources. Published by OCP. 5536 NE Hassalo, Portland, OR 97213. All rights reserved. Used with permission.

**754** Text: © 1996, The Pilgrim Press, from *Circle of Care*. Tune: © 2007, GIA Publications, Inc.

**755** © 2002, JL Zwane Memorial Congregation

**756** Text: Spanish Vss. 2-4, © 1983, Abingdon Press. English tr.: © 2004, Abingdon Press (Administered by The Copyright Company, Nashville, TN) All Rights Reserved. International Copyright Secured. Used By Permission. Arr.: © 2004, GIA Publications, Inc.

**758** © 2000, World Library Publications, Franklin Park, IL wlpmusic.com 800-566-6150 All rights reserved. Used by permission.

**759** © 2009, GIA Publications, Inc.

**760** © 2003, World Library Publications, Franklin Park, IL wlpmusic.com 800-566-6150 All rights reserved. Used by permission.

**761** © 1990, Bernadette Farrell. Published by OCP. 5536 NE Hassalo, Portland, OR 97213. All rights reserved. Used with permission.

**762** © 2007, GIA Publications, Inc.

**763** Arr.: © 1998, Iona Community, GIA Publications, Inc., agent.

**764** Text: © 1988, Oxford University Press. Reproduced by permission. All rights reserved.

**765** Text: © 1972, and Harm. © 1983, Hope Publishing Co., Carol Stream, IL 60188. All rights reserved. Used by permission.

**766** © 1981, Daniel L. Schutte and OCP. 5536 NE Hassalo, Portland, OR 97213. All rights reserved. Used with permission.

**767** Text: © 2005, GIA Publications, Inc. Tune: © 2007, GIA Publications, Inc.

**768** © 1993, Howard S. Olson

**769** Text: © 1964, Abingdon Press. (Administered by The Copyright Company, Nashville, TN) All Rights Reserved. International Copyright Secured. Used By Permission.

**770** © 2003, GIA Publications, Inc.

**771** © 2011, GIA Publications, Inc.

**772** © 2003, GIA Publications, Inc.

**773** © 1981, Damean Music. Distributed by GIA Publications, Inc.

**774** Text: © 1992, GIA Publications, Inc. Tune: © 2002, GIA Publications, Inc.

**775** © 1997, 1998, Steve Agrisano and Thomas N. Tomaszek. Published by OCP. 5536 NE Hassalo, Portland, OR 97213. All rights reserved. Used with permission.

**776** © 1984, Utryck, Walton Music Corp., agent

**777** © 1981, OCP. 5536 NE Hassalo, Portland, OR 97213. All rights reserved. Used with permission.

**778** © 1978, OCP. 5536 NE Hassalo, Portland, OR 97213. All rights reserved. Used with permission.

**779** © 2007, GIA Publications, Inc.

**780** Harm. © Estate of Wendell Whalum

**781** Text and Tune: © 1979, Cesáreo Gabaráin. Sole U.S. Agent: OCP. English text: © 1982, Willard Francis Jabusch. Administered by OCP, 5536 NE Hassalo, Portland, OR 97213. All rights reserved. Used with permission.

**782** © 1981, Daniel L. Schutte and OCP. 5536 NE Hassalo, Portland, OR 97213. All rights reserved. Used with permission.

**783** © 1983, Bernadette Farrell. Published by OCP. 5536 NE Hassalo, Portland, OR 97213. All rights reserved. Used with permission.

**784** © 1983, GIA Publications, Inc.

**785** © 1983, GIA Publications, Inc.

**786** Refrain text and music, and verses arr.: © 2005, GIA Publications, Inc. Verses text and melody, © 1963, 1993, The Grail, GIA Publications, Inc., agent. Tr., © 2010, GIA Publications, Inc.

**787** © 2001, GIA Publications, Inc.

**788** Text: © Herbert O'Driscoll. Tune: © 1998, GIA Publications, Inc.

**789** © 2003, GIA Publications, Inc.

**790** Text and arr.: © 1987, Iona Community, GIA Publications, Inc., agent

**791** Text: © 2004, Iona Community, GIA Publications, Inc., agent. Arr.: © 2007, GIA Publications, Inc.

**792** © 1988, GIA Publications, Inc.

**793** © 1986, GIA Publications, Inc.

**794** © 1993, GIA Publications, Inc.

**795** © 1995, Iona Community, GIA Publications, Inc., agent

**796** Text and Harm.: © 1963, Stainer & Bell, Ltd. (Admin. Hope Publishing Co., Carol Stream, IL 60188). All rights reserved. Used by permission.

**797** Text: © 1991, GIA Publications, Inc.

**798** Text: © 1986, GIA Publications, Inc. Tune: © 1970, GIA Publications, Inc.

**799** Text: © 1991, GIA Publications, Inc. Tune: © 2003, GIA Publications, Inc.

**800** © 1997, GIA Publications, Inc.

**802** © 1997, Tom Booth. Published by OCP. 5536 NE Hassalo, Portland, OR 97213. All rights reserved. Used with permission.

**803** Text: © 1968, Hope Publishing Co., Carol Stream, IL 60188. All rights reserved. Used by permission.

**804** Text: © 1983, and Music © 1995, Hope Publishing Co., Carol Stream, IL 60188. All rights reserved. Used by permission.

**805** Text: © 1992, Hope Publishing Co., Carol Stream, IL 60188. All rights reserved. Used by permission. Tune: © 2007, GIA Publications, Inc.

**806** © 1985, GIA Publications, Inc.

**807** © 1988, GIA Publications, Inc.

**808** Text: © 1994, GIA Publications, Inc.

**809** © 1992, 1994, GIA Publications, Inc.

**810** © 1991, GIA Publications, Inc.

**811** Text: © 1992, GIA Publications, Inc. Tune: © 1994, GIA Publications, Inc.

**812** Text: © 1998, Hope Publishing Co., Carol Stream, IL 60188. All rights reserved. Used by permission. Tune: © 2001, GIA Publications, Inc.

**813** Text: "Baptism By Fire" from *Incendiary Fellowship*, © 1967, David Elton Trueblood. Reprinted by permission.

**814** © 1984, Utryck, Walton Music Corp., agent

**815** Text: © 1997, GIA Publications, Inc. Tune: © 1984, GIA Publications, Inc.

**816** © 2001, GIA Publications, Inc.

**817** Harm.: © 1981 by Abingdon Press (Administered by The Copyright Company, Nashville, TN) All Rights Reserved. International Copyright Secured. Used By Permission.

**818** Arr.: © 1991, Iona Community, GIA Publications, Inc., agent

**819** Acc.: © 1993, GIA Publications, Inc.

**820** © 1998, Christine Carson and Iona Community, GIA Publications, Inc., agent

**821** © 1987, GIA Publications, Inc

**822** Acc.: © 1994, GIA Publications, Inc.

**823** © 2002, GIA Publications, Inc.

**824** Text: © 1989, Hope Publishing Co., Carol Stream, IL 60188. All rights reserved. Used by permission. Harm.: © The Trustees of Downside Abbey, Bath BA3 4RH, UK

# Acknowledgments/*continued*

# Acknowledgments/*continued*

# Scripture Passages Related to Hymns/*continued*

# Scripture Passages Related to Hymns/*continued*

**HOSEA**

| | | |
|---|---|---|
| 2:16 | Hosea | 484 |
| 2:21 | Hosea | 484 |
| 3:3 | Hosea | 484 |
| 6:1 | Hosea | 484 |
| 6:3 | Mine Eyes Have Seen the Glory | 985 |
| 14:2 | Deep Within | 486 |
| 21: | Hosea | 484 |

**JOEL**

| | | |
|---|---|---|
| 2: | The Trumpet in the Morning | 864 |
| 2:1 | Return to the Lord | 471 |
| 2:12 | Deep Within | 486 |
| 2:12 | Hosea | 484 |
| 2:12 | Return to God / Volvamos Hoy a Nuestro Dios | 478 |
| 2:12–14 | Let Justice Roll Like a River | 810 |
| 2:12–18 | Again We Keep This Solemn Fast | 487 |
| 2:12–18 | Merciful God | 489 |
| 2:12–18 | Remember You Are Dust | 469 |
| 2:12–18 | Return to the Lord | 471 |
| 2:17 | Parce Dómine | 473 |
| 2:26 | Return to the Lord | 471 |
| 3:1 | Sing a New Church | 743 |
| 3:1 | Song over the Waters | 661 |

**AMOS**

| | | |
|---|---|---|
| 5:21–24 | Let Justice Roll Like a River | 810 |
| 8:4 | Let Justice Roll Like a River | 810 |

**MICAH**

| | | |
|---|---|---|
| 4:3–4 | Let Justice Roll Like a River | 810 |
| 5:2 | O Little Town of Bethlehem | 446 |
| 6:8 | Let Justice Roll Like a River | 810 |
| 6:8 | Lord, Today | 464 |
| 6:8 | We Are Called | 807 |
| 7:18 | Love Divine, All Loves Excelling | 641 |

**HABAKKUK**

| | | |
|---|---|---|
| 2:20 | Let All Mortal Flesh Keep Silence | 619 |

**HAGGAI**

| | | |
|---|---|---|
| 2:7 | Angels, from the Realms of Glory | 438 |
| 2:7 | Come, O Long-Expected Jesus | 403 |
| 2:7 | O Come, O Come, Emmanuel | 395 |

**MALACHI**

| | | |
|---|---|---|
| 3:1 | Love Divine, All Loves Excelling | 641 |
| 3:1 | On Jordan's Bank | 418 |
| 4:2 | Hark! The Herald Angels Sing | 424 |

**MATTHEW**

| | | |
|---|---|---|
| 1:18–24 | God of Adam, God of Joseph | 982 |
| 1:23 | Praise We the Lord This Day | 875 |
| 2: | Night of Silence | 442 |
| 2:1–2 | O Little Town of Bethlehem | 446 |
| 2:1–11 | Good Christian Friends, Rejoice | 440 |
| 2:1–11 | The Virgin Mary Had a Baby Boy | 454 |
| 2:1–12 | Angels, from the Realms of Glory | 438 |
| 2:1–12 | As with Gladness Men of Old | 465 |
| 2:1–12 | Songs of Thankfulness and Praise | 459 |
| 2:1–12 | The First Nowell | 460 |
| 2:1–12 | We Three Kings of Orient Are | 463 |
| 2:2 | Star-Child | 449 |
| 2:2–10 | What Star Is This | 461 |
| 2:10–11 | O Come, All Ye Faithful / Venid, Fieles Todos / Adéste Fidéles | 439 |

| | | |
|---|---|---|
| 2:11 | What Child Is This | 466 |
| 2:12–18 | Mary, First among Believers | 893 |
| 2:13–23 | God of Adam, God of Joseph | 982 |
| 3:3 | On Jordan's Bank | 418 |
| 3:13–17 | Songs of Thankfulness and Praise | 459 |
| 3:13–17 | When John Baptized by Jordan's River | 467 |
| 4:1–2 | Forty Days and Forty Nights | 483 |
| 4:1–2 | The Glory of These Forty Days | 481 |
| 4:1–11 | Lord, Who throughout These Forty Days | 479 |
| 4:1–11 | Tree of Life | 475 |
| 4:4 | Shepherd of Souls | 910 |
| 4:12–23 | Two Fishermen | 798 |
| 4:16 | Child of Mercy | 431 |
| 4:16 | Comfort, Comfort, O My People | 413 |
| 4:18–22 | Lord, When You Came / Pescador de Hombres | 781 |
| 4:24 | The King of Glory | 572 |
| 5:1–6 | Jerusalem, My Destiny | 492 |
| 5:3 | O Breathe on Me, O Breath of God | 902 |
| 5:3–11 | We Are the Light of the World | 592 |
| 5:3–12 | Blest Are They / Benditos los Pobres | 735 |
| 5:6 | Called by Christ | 767 |
| 5:6 | We Are Called | 807 |
| 5:13–14 | Gather Us In | 848 |
| 5:13–16 | Bring Forth the Kingdom | 734 |
| 5:13–16 | Go Make a Difference | 775 |
| 5:14 | We Are Called | 807 |
| 5:14–16 | As a Fire Is Meant for Burning | 744 |
| 5:14–16 | This Little Light of Mine | 591 |
| 5:14–16 | We Are the Light of the World | 592 |
| 5:21–24 | Forgive Our Sins | 965 |
| 5:38–48 | Lord of All Nations, Grant Me Grace | 703 |
| 6:1–6 | Again We Keep This Solemn Fast | 487 |
| 6:9–13 | This Is My Song | 986 |
| 6:9–15 | Forgive Our Sins | 965 |
| 6:16–18 | Again We Keep This Solemn Fast | 487 |
| 6:25–34 | Lord of All Hopefulness | 663 |
| 6:25–34 | Peace, Be Not Anxious | 830 |
| 6:25–34 | Praise and Thanksgiving | 861 |
| 6:33 | Seek Ye First | 658 |
| 6:33 | Wait for the Lord | 406 |
| 7:7 | Seek Ye First | 658 |
| 7:7 | Wait for the Lord | 406 |
| 7:15–29 | Deliver Us, O Lord of Truth | 750 |
| 7:24 | How Can I Keep from Singing? | 685 |
| 7:24–27 | Called by Christ | 767 |
| 9:1–2 | I Danced in the Morning | 796 |
| 9:9–13 | For the Faithful Who Have Answered | 883 |
| 9:11–13 | The Master Came to Bring Good News | 964 |
| 10:34 | God, Whose Purpose Is to Kindle | 813 |
| 10:34 | You, Lord, Are Both Lamb and Shepherd | 628 |
| 10:37–39 | The Summons | 790 |
| 10:37–42 | Take Up Your Cross | 801 |
| 11:23–30 | Rest Now in Me | 711 |
| 11:25–30 | I Heard the Voice of Jesus Say | 724 |
| 11:28 | Come to Me | 720 |
| 11:28 | Come to Us | 842 |
| 11:28 | Like a Shepherd | 402 |
| 11:28–30 | Come to Me | 731 |
| 11:28–30 | Come to Me, O Weary Traveler | 727 |
| 11:28–30 | Come to the Water | 584 |

# Scripture Passages Related to Hymns/*continued*

# Scripture Passages Related to Hymns/*continued*

| | |
|---|---|
| 13:13–14 | Pan de Vida 920 |
| 13:14–15 | Where Two or Three Are Gathered 907 |
| 13:34–35 | Where Two or Three Are Gathered 907 |
| 13:35 | Holy Spirit, Come to Us 547 |
| 13:35 | They'll Know We Are Christians 835 |
| 14: | There Are Many Rooms 867 |
| 14:1–3 | Do Not Let Your Hearts Be Troubled 869 |
| 14:1–3 | Peace, Be Not Anxious 830 |
| 14:1–12 | I Know That My Redeemer Lives 527 |
| 14:6 | I Receive the Living God 916 |
| 14:6 | Jesus Christ, Yesterday, Today, and Forever / Jesucristo Ayer 847 |
| 14:6–7 | Do Not Let Your Hearts Be Troubled 869 |
| 14:10–14 | Do Not Let Your Hearts Be Troubled 869 |
| 14:15–21 | Come Down, O Love Divine 556 |
| 14:18 | Alleluia! Sing to Jesus! 949 |
| 14:23–27 | Unless a Grain of Wheat 783 |
| 14:24–26 | Come, Holy Ghost 559 |
| 14:24–26 | Veni Creátor Spíritus 558 |
| 14:25–27 | Peace, Be Not Anxious 830 |
| 14:27 | Dona Nobis Pacem 822 |
| 14:27 | Healing River of the Spirit 665 |
| 14:27 | I Receive the Living God 916 |
| 14:27 | Let There Be Peace on Earth 829 |
| 14:27 | Make Me a Channel of Your Peace 828 |
| 14:27 | Take and Eat 950 |
| 14:27 | World Peace Prayer 827 |
| 14:27 | You Are Mine / Contigo Estoy 721 |
| 15: | Lord of All Nations, Grant Me Grace 703 |
| 15:4 | I Danced in the Morning 796 |
| 15:4 | Now We Remain 785 |
| 15:4–5 | Unless a Grain of Wheat 783 |
| 15:4–5 | We Have Been Told 784 |
| 15:5 | Alleluia! Give the Glory 844 |
| 15:5 | I Receive the Living God 916 |
| 15:5–14 | I Will Be the Vine 872 |
| 15:7–8 | Unless a Grain of Wheat 783 |
| 15:9 | I Receive the Living God 916 |
| 15:9 | Let Us Be Bread 946 |
| 15:9–17 | No Greater Love 701 |
| 15:9–17 | The Master Came to Bring Good News 964 |
| 15:12–13 | Holy Spirit, Come to Us 547 |
| 15:12–14 | Song of the Lord's Command 506 |
| 15:14 | Let Us Be Bread 946 |
| 15:14–15 | Christ Is Risen! Shout Hosanna! 521 |
| 15:15 | Stand Up, Friends! 565 |
| 15:16 | Song of the Lord's Command 506 |
| 15:17 | We Are Called 807 |
| 16:13 | Come Now, Almighty King 562 |
| 17:20–26 | Lord, Who at Your First Eucharist 914 |
| 17:20–23 | For the Healing of the Nations 803 |
| 17:21–23 | Christ Is the King! 571 |
| 17:21–23 | O God of Every Nation 825 |
| 19: | O Sacred Head Surrounded 512 |
| 19: | What Wondrous Love Is This 642 |
| 19:25 | At the Cross Her Station Keeping 488 |
| 19:25 | Immaculate Mary 886 |
| 19:25–27 | O Sanctíssima / O Most Holy One 895 |
| 19:25b–27 | Mary, First among Believers 893 |
| 19:34 | Were You There 511 |
| 19:36–42 | I Danced in the Morning 796 |
| 20: | O Sons and Daughters 532 |
| 20: | That Easter Day with Joy Was Bright 542 |
| 20:19–23 | Christ Has Risen 530 |
| 20:22 | O Breathe on Me, O Breath of God 902 |
| 20:27–29 | We Walk by Faith 680 |
| 21:15–17 | Heart of a Shepherd / El Corazón de un Buen Pastor 786 |

## ACTS

| | |
|---|---|
| 1:1–11 | A Hymn of Glory Let Us Sing! 545 |
| 1:8 | Come Down, O Love Divine 556 |
| 1:8 | Come, Holy Ghost 559 |
| 1:8 | O Holy Spirit, by Whose Breath 551 |
| 1:8 | Veni Creátor Spíritus 558 |
| 1:9 | Alleluia! Sing to Jesus! 949 |
| 1:9–11 | Hail the Day That Sees Him Rise 543 |
| 2: | O Spirit All-Embracing 553 |
| 2:1–2 | Song over the Waters 661 |
| 2:1–11 | Diverse in Culture, Nation, Race 833 |
| 2:1–11 | Veni Sancte Spíritus 482 |
| 2:3 | God, Whose Purpose Is to Kindle 813 |
| 2:24 | Christ the Lord Is Risen Today 523 |
| 3:6 | The Love of the Lord 792 |
| 4:11 | The Church's One Foundation 742 |
| 10:37 | On Jordan's Bank 418 |
| 17:28 | Jesus, the Lord 491 |

## ROMANS

| | |
|---|---|
| 5:2–11 | Amazing Grace 645 |
| 6:1–4 | Baptized in Water 903 |
| 6:3–11 | I Know That My Redeemer Lives 527 |
| 6:5–8 | This Is a Day of New Beginnings 522 |
| 8:11–19 | Neither Death nor Life 647 |
| 8:14–17 | In Christ There Is No East or West 832 |
| 8:15 | All Things New 541 |
| 8:18–23 | On Holy Ground 809 |
| 8:18–39 | There's a Wideness in God's Mercy 644 |
| 8:22–25 | Neither Death nor Life 647 |
| 8:28–35 | Neither Death nor Life 647 |
| 8:35, 38 | Shall Tribulation or Distress 649 |
| 8:38 | Neither Death nor Life 647 |
| 8:38–39 | God Will Wipe the Tears 715 |
| 8:39 | Nothing Can Ever 697 |
| 11:33–35 | There's a Wideness in God's Mercy 644 |
| 11:33–36 | All Glory Is Yours 605 |
| 12:15 | The Servant Song 751 |
| 14:7–8 | Resucitó 535 |
| 14:8 | Pues Si Vivimos / When We Are Living 756 |
| 14:17 | The Kingdom of God 736 |

## 1 CORINTHIANS

| | |
|---|---|
| 1:18 | Lift High the Cross 881 |
| 2:9–10 | Eye Has Not Seen 728 |
| 3:11 | Christ Is Made the Sure Foundation 745 |
| 3:11 | The Church's One Foundation 742 |
| 3:13–15 | Come, You Thankful People, Come 634 |
| 5:6–8 | Steal Away to Jesus 868 |
| 9:24–26 | Guide My Feet 780 |
| 10:16 | Take and Eat, This Is My Body 908 |
| 10:16–17 | One Bread, One Body 932 |
| 10:16–17 | You Satisfy the Hungry Heart 940 |
| 11:23–26 | I Come with Joy 919 |
| 11:23–26 | Life-Giving Bread, Saving Cup 926 |
| 11:23–26 | Now We Remain 785 |
| 11:23–26 | Song of the Lord's Supper 508 |
| 11:24 | Take and Eat this Bread 928 |

# Scripture Passages Related to Hymns/*continued*

# Scripture Passages Related to Hymns/*continued*

# Liturgical Index/*continued*

# Liturgical Index/*continued*

# Liturgical Index/*continued*

# Liturgical Index/*continued*

# Liturgical Index/*continued*

# Topical Index 1217

# Topical Index/*continued*

# Topical Index/*continued*

# Topical Index/*continued*

# Topical Index/*continued*

# Topical Index/*continued*

# Topical Index/*continued*

# Topical Index/*continued*

# Topical Index/*continued*

# Topical Index/*continued*

# Topical Index/*continued*

# Topical Index/*continued*

# Topical Index/*continued*

# Topical Index/*continued*

# Topical Index/*continued*

# Topical Index/*continued*

# Topical Index/*continued*

# Topical Index/*continued*

# Topical Index/*continued*

# Topical Index/*continued*

# Topical Index/*continued*

# Topical Index/*continued*

# Topical Index/*continued*

885 For All the Saints Who've Shown Your Love
883 For the Faithful Who Have Answered
567 Holy, Holy, Holy! Lord God Almighty!
694 How Firm a Foundation
603 I Will Sing a Song of Love
870 Jerusalem, My Happy Home
1056 Litany of the Saints
914 Lord, Who at Your First Eucharist
893 Mary, First among Believers
875 Praise We the Lord This Day
37 Psalm 24: We Long to See Your Face
873 Shall We Gather at the River
457 Sing of Mary, Pure and Lowly
539 Sing with All the Saints in Glory / Canten con Gloriosos Fieles
163 Song of Farewell
742 The Church's One Foundation
710 The Clouds' Veil
878 Transform Us
696 Ubi Cáritas
898 Wade in the Water
882 Ye Watchers and Ye Holy Ones

## SALVATION
621 Ad Te Jesu Christe
541 All Things New
645 Amazing Grace
536 At the Lamb's High Feast We Sing
903 Baptized in Water
514 Behold the Wood
620 Bless the Lord
431 Child of Mercy
523 Christ the Lord Is Risen Today
403 Come, O Long-Expected Jesus
533 Come, You Faithful, Raise the Strain
396 Comfort, My People
574 Crown Him with Many Crowns
976 Dwellers in the Holy City
537 Easter Alleluia
941 Eat This Bread
462 Epiphany Carol
95 Exodus 15: Song at the Sea
96 Exodus 15: Song of Moses
580 For God So Loved the World
606 Glory and Praise to Our God
501 Glory in the Cross
440 Good Christian Friends, Rejoice
494 Hold Us in Your Mercy: Penitential Litany
796 I Danced in the Morning
718 I Have Been Anointed
972 I Know That My Redeemer Lives (Haas)
973 I Know That My Redeemer Lives (Hughes)
639 In the Lord I'll Be Ever Thankful
97 Isaiah 12: With Joy You Shall Draw Water
98 Isaiah 12: You Will Draw Water Joyfully / Sacarán Aguas con Alegría
540 Jesus Christ Is Risen Today
847 Jesus Christ, Yesterday, Today and for Ever / Jesucristo Ayer
437 Joy to the World
646 Keep in Mind

619 Let All Mortal Flesh Keep Silence
624 Lift Up Your Hearts
602 Lord, I Lift Your Name on High
479 Lord, Who throughout These Forty Days
641 Love Divine, All Loves Excelling
102 Luke 1:46–55: Holy Is Your Name
103 Luke 1:68–79: Now Bless the God of Israel
892 Magnificat
394 May We Be One
489 Merciful God
876 No Wind at the Window
785 Now We Remain
917 O Taste and See
975 Peace Be with Those
597 Praise Our God and Savior
616 Praise to the Lord, the Almighty
400 Prepare the Way of the Lord
41 Psalm 27: The Lord Is My Light (Haas)
121 Psalm 27: The Lord Is My Light (Jackson)
42 Psalm 30: I Will Praise You, Lord
43 Psalm 31: Father, into Your Hands / Padre, a Tus Manos
45 Psalm 34: Taste and See
59 Psalm 66: Let All the Earth
150 Psalm 71: My God, My God
60 Psalm 72: Every Nation on Earth
62 Psalm 85: Lord, Let Us See Your Kindness
64 Psalm 89: For Ever I Will Sing
67 Psalm 96: Proclaim to All the Nations
68 Psalm 96: Today Is Born Our Savior
69 Psalm 96: Today Is Born Our Savior / Hoy Nos Ha Nacido un Salvador
70 Psalm 98: All the Ends of the Earth
72 Psalm 103: The Lord Is Kind and Merciful
74 Psalm 103: The Lord Is Kind and Merciful / El Señor Es Compasivo
78 Psalm 116: Our Blessing-Cup
79 Psalm 116: Our Blessing-Cup / El Cáliz que Bendecimos
80 Psalm 116: The Name of God
81 Psalm 118: Let Us Rejoice
90 Psalm 136: Love Is Never Ending
91 Psalm 138: The Fragrance of Christ
93 Psalm 146: I Will Praise the Lord
478 Return to God / Volvamos Hoy a Nuestro Dios
471 Return to the Lord
421 Savior of the Nations, Come
1084 Sequence for Pentecost
873 Shall We Gather at the River
607 Sing a New Song
627 Sing a New Song to the Lord
434 Sing Alleluia
600 Sing Praise to God
519 Sing to the Mountains

459 Songs of Thankfulness and Praise
555 Spirit Blowing through Creation
899 Sweet Refreshment
928 Take and Eat This Bread
787 Take Up Your Cross
572 The King of Glory
736 The Kingdom of God
690 The Lord Is My Light
644 There's a Wideness in God's Mercy
573 To Jesus Christ, Our Sovereign King
854 We Arise
517 We Walk His Way / Ewe, Thina
642 What Wondrous Love Is This
467 When John Baptized by Jordan's River
404 When the King Shall Come Again
583 Wisdom, My Road

**SALVATION HISTORY** *See Salvation*

**SECOND COMING**
912 Amén. El Cuerpo de Cristo
399 Awake to the Day
634 Come, You Thankful People, Come
396 Comfort, My People
574 Crown Him with Many Crowns
884 For All the Saints
814 Freedom Is Coming
715 God Will Wipe the Tears
772 How Can We Be Silent
578 How Great Thou Art
945 I Am the Bread of Life / Yo Soy el Pan de Vida
972 I Know That My Redeemer Lives (Haas)
973 I Know That My Redeemer Lives (Hughes)
593 I Want to Walk as a Child of the Light
639 In the Lord I'll Be Ever Thankful
909 Jesus, Hope of the World
810 Let Justice Roll Like a River
641 Love Divine, All Loves Excelling
397 Maranatha, Lord Messiah
985 Mine Eyes Have Seen the Glory
415 My Soul in Stillness Waits / En el Silencio Te Aguardo
647 Neither Death nor Life
825 O God of Every Nation
863 O Holy City, Seen of John
862 On That Day
455 Once in Royal David's City
975 Peace Be with Those
409 People, Look East
400 Prepare the Way of the Lord
84 Psalm 122: Let Us Go Rejoicing
713 Quietly, Peacefully
568 Rejoice, the Lord Is King!
607 Sing a New Song
865 Soon and Very Soon
742 The Church's One Foundation
572 The King of Glory
414 The King Shall Come When Morning Dawns
921 The Living Bread of God
864 The Trumpet in the Morning
867 There Are Many Rooms
520 This Is the Feast of Victory

# Topical Index/*continued*

# Topical Index/*continued*

# Topical Index/*continued*

# Topical Index/*continued*

# Topical Index/*continued*

Index of Composers, Authors and Sources/*continued*

# Index of Composers, Authors and Sources/*continued*

**SM (SHORT METER - 66 86)**
504 SOUTHWELL
875 877 SWABIA

**CM (COMMON METER - 86 86)**
437 ANTIOCH
706 CHRISTIAN LOVE
965 DETROIT
750 870 919 LAND OF REST
738 832 McKEE
414 MORNING SONG
645 NEW BRITAIN
680 815 SHANTI
910 ST. AGNES
688 ST. ANNE
902 ST. COLUMBA
474 479 ST. FLAVIAN

**CMD (COMMON METER DOUBLED)**
433 CAROL
102 808 FOREST GREEN
724 KINGSFOLD
984 MATERNA
673 MOSHIER
458 THE FLIGHT OF THE EARLS

**LM (LONG METER - 88 88)**
953 ARLINGTON
703 BEATUS VIR
420 CONDITOR ALME SIDERUM
874 DICKSON
137 DUGUET
527 DUKE STREET
481 801 ERHALT UNS HERR
13 JESU DULCIS MEMORIA
765 885 966 989 O WALY WALY
487 853 OLD HUNDREDTH
563 PROSPECT
461 542 PUER NOBIS
833 TALLIS' CANON
22 TE LUCIS ANTE TERMINUM
551 558 VENI CREATOR SPIRITUS
418 WINCHESTER NEW

**LM WITH ALLELUIAS**
545 610 882 LASST UNS ERFREUEN
531 STUEMPFLE

**LM WITH REFRAIN**
677 ST. CATHERINE
395 VENI EMMANUEL

**LMD (LONG METER DOUBLED)**
16 MAGNIFICAT
894 DUKTA

**5 5 5 4 D**
856 ANDREA
855 861 BUNESSAN
857 EVENING HYMN

**66 4 666 4**
988 AMERICA
562 ITALIAN HYMN

**7 6 7 6 D**
742 797 AURELIA

769 ELLACOMBE
404 533 GAUDEAMUS PARITER
512 668 707 825 956 PASSION CHORALE
498 ST. THEODULPH

**7 6 7 6 WITH REFRAIN**
729 BALM IN GILEAD
428 GO TELL IT ON THE MOUNTAIN
566 GOTT VATER SEI GEPRIESEN

**7 7 7 7 WITH REFRAIN**
430 GLORIA
916 LIVING GOD
577 SING OUT

**77 77 WITH ALLELUIAS**
540 EASTER HYMN
523 543 LLANFAIR

**77 77 D**
459 536 SALZBURG
634 ST. GEORGE'S WINDSOR

**8 7 8 7**
727 DUNSTAN
712 824 ST. COLUMBA
851 STUTTGART

**8 7 8 7 WITH REFRAIN**
788 COME AND JOURNEY
709 COMFORT
982 983 FARRELL
466 GREENSLEEVES
873 HANSON PLACE
685 HOW CAN I KEEP FROM SINGING
573 964 ICH GLAUB AN GOTT

**8 7 8 7 8 7**
613 LAUDA ANIMA
104 PEACETIME
619 628 878 PICARDY
438 REGENT SQUARE
774 ROSEMARY
139 745 803 976 ST. THOMAS

**8 7 8 7 D**
544 843 ABBOT'S LEIGH
462 665 744 859 BEACH SPRING
813 EBENEZER
839 852 HOLY MANNA
521 HOSANNA
641 949 969 HYFRYDOL
539 614 HYMN TO JOY
644 764 IN BABILONE
403 JEFFERSON
443 JOYOUS LIGHT
811 LA GRANGE
625 743 NETTLETON
457 883 893 PLEADING SAVIOR
530 TRANSFORMATION
631 WE GIVE YOU THANKS

**888 WITH ALLELUIAS**
571 GELOBT SEI GOTT
532 O FILII ET FILIAE
525 VICTORY

# Metrical Index of Tunes/*continued*

A light will shine on us this day: the Lord is born for us.  1005

A sacrifice you accept, O God, is a humble spirit.  53

All the ends of the earth have seen the power of God.  70

All the ends of the earth have seen the saving power of God.  1006

Alleluia, alleluia, alleluia!  81 94 1055

As morning breaks I look to you, O Lord, to be my strength this day.  4

As morning breaks I look to you; be my strength this day.  57

Be merciful, O Lord, for we have sinned.  51 52 53 1016 1194

Be with me, Lord, when I am in trouble, be with me, Lord, I pray.  65

Be with me, Lord, when I am in trouble.  1018

Blessed are they, blessed are they who hope in the Lord.  1109

Blessed are they who dwell in your house, O Lord.  1009

Blessed are they who follow the law of the Lord!  1107

Blessed are those who fear the Lord.  1188

Blessed are those who fear the Lord and walk in his ways.  1007

Blessed be the Lord, for he has come to his people and set them free.  6

Blessed the people the Lord has chosen to be his own.  1087 1148

Blessed the poor in spirit; the kingdom of heaven is theirs!  1101

Blest are those who love you, happy those who follow you, blest are those who seek you, O God.  86

Create a clean heart, a clean heart in me, O God.  53

Create a clean heart in me, O God.  52

Create in me a clean heart, O God.  1029 1054

Cry out with joy and gladness, for the Lord is in your midst, the holy one of Israel.  97

Cry out with joy and gladness: for among you is the great and Holy One of Israel.  999

Day and night I cry to you, my God.  63

Dichoso el pueblo que el Señor se escogió como heredad.  44

Do not forget the works of the Lord!  1208

El cáliz que bendecimos es la comunión de la sangre de Cristo.  79

El Señor es compasivo y misericordioso.  74

El Señor es mi pastor, nada me falta.  36

Emptied and humbled, obedient to death, Christ embraced the cross. Jesus Christ is Lord!  105

Every nation on earth will adore you, Lord.  60

Father, into your hands I commend my spirit.  43 1043

Fill us with your love, O Lord, and we will sing for joy!  1174

For ever I will sing the goodness of the Lord.  64 1001 1003 1128

Give thanks to the Lord, for he is good, his love is everlasting.  1066

Give thanks to the Lord, his love is everlasting.  1126

Give the Lord glory and honor.  67 1176

Glory and praise for evermore.  1086

Go out to all the world and tell the Good News.  1118 1154

God is praised and exalted above all forever.  99

God mounts his throne to shouts of joy: a blare of trumpets for the Lord.  1079

God mounts his throne to shouts of joy, O sing your praises to the Lord!  50

God, in your goodness, you have made a home for the poor.  1157

Happy are the people the Lord has chosen, chosen to be his own.  44

Have mercy, Lord, cleanse me from all my sins.  53

He who does justice will live in the presence of the Lord.  1139

Here I am, here I am, I come to do your will.  48

Here I am, Lord, here I am. I come to do your will.  49

Here am I, Lord; here am I, Lord; I come to do your will.  1095 1096 1198

How lovely is your dwelling place, O Lord of hosts.  61

Hoy nos ha nacido un Salvador: el mesías, el Señor.  69

I believe that I shall see the good things of the Lord in the land of the living.  1080 1210

I love you, Lord, my strength, my strength.  1179 1183

I praise you, O Lord, for I am wonderfully made.  1200

I shall live in the house of the Lord all the days of my life.  1173

I turn to you, O Lord, in time of trouble, and you fill me with the joy of salvation.  1108

I will bless the Lord at all times.  46

I will praise the Lord all my days, make music to my God while I live.  93

I will praise you, Lord, for you have rescued me.  1051 1069 1121 1129

I will praise you, Lord, in the assembly of your people.  1074

I will praise you, Lord, you have rescued me, I will praise you, Lord, for your mercy.  42

I will praise your name for ever, my king and my God.  92 1075 1131 1184

I will rise and go to my father.  53 1163

I will sing, I will sing to the God who sets me free! Pharaoh's army and his chariots God cast into the sea!  96

I will sing of your salvation.  1103

I will take the cup of life, I will call God's name all my days.  80

I will take the cup of salvation, and call on the name of the Lord.  1090

I will walk before the Lord, in the land of the living.  1020 1162

If today you hear his voice, harden not your hearts.  66 1022 1102 1145 1158 1172

# Psalm Refrains Set to Music/*continued*

In every age, O Lord, you have been our refuge. 1160

In his days justice will flourish; in his days fullness of peace forevermore. 60

In the land of the living, I will walk with God all my days. 80

In the morning I will sing, will sing glad songs of praise to you. 56

In the presence of the angels, O Lord, may we praise your name. 91

In the sight of the angels, I will sing your praises, O Lord. 1106

In the silent hours of night, bless the Lord. 23

In you, O Lord, I have found my peace. 89 1182

Justice shall flourish in his time, and fullness of peace for ever. 994

Keep me safe, O God, I take refuge in you. 30

Keep me safe, O God: you are my hope; you are my hope, O God. 29

La misericordia de nuestro Dios llena la tierra. 44

Let all the earth cry out in joy to the Lord! 59

Let all the earth cry out to God with joy. 1076 1133

Let my tongue be silenced, if I ever forget you! 1026

Let the Lord enter; he is king of glory. 1000

Let us go rejoicing to the house of the Lord. 84 85 991 1193

Let us sing to the Lord who is covered in wondrous glory. 95

Let us sing to the Lord; he has covered himself in glory. 1050

Let your mercy be on us, O God, as we place our trust in you. 44

Like a deer that longs for running streams, my soul longs for you, my God. 1054

Lord, be my rock of safety. 1116

Lord, come and save us. 997

Lord, come to my aid, Lord, come to my aid! 1151

Lord, every nation on earth will adore you. 1011

Lord, forgive the wrong I have done. 1123

Lord, give success to the work of our hands, to the work of our hands. 1207

Lord, go up to the place of your rest, you and the ark of your holiness. 1205

Lord, heal my soul for I have sinned against you. 1111

Lord, I love your commands. 1140

Lord, in your great love, answer me. 1125

Lord, it is good to give thanks to you. 1115 1123

Lord, let us see your kindness. 62

Lord, let us see your kindness, and grant us your salvation. 995 1135 1146

Lord, let your face shine on us. 1068

Lord, let your mercy be on us, as we place our trust in you. 1019 1073 1177

Lord, make us turn to you; let us see your face and we shall be saved. 992 1002

Lord, may our prayer rise like incense in your sight, may this place be filled with the fragrance of Christ. 91

Lord, on the day that I called for help, you answered me. 91 1142

Lord, send out your Spirit, and renew the face of the earth. 76 77 1048 1083 1084

Lord, this is the people that longs to see your face. 1209

Lord, when your glory appears, my joy will be full. 1187

Lord, you are good and forgiving. 1137

Lord, you have the words of everlasting life. Tú tienes, Señor, palabras de vida eterna. 32

Lord, you have the words of everlasting life. 31 1023 1053

Lord, you will show us the path of life. 1067

Lord, your love is eternal; do not forsake the work of your hands. 1152

May God bless us in his mercy, may God bless us in his mercy. 1010

May the Lord bless and protect us all the days of our lives. 1171

May the Lord bless us, may the Lord protect us, all the days, all the days of our life. 86

Misericordia, Señor, hemos pecado. Be merciful, O Lord, for we have sinned. 54

My God, my God, come quickly to help me. 150

My God, my God, why have you abandoned me? 33 1035

My prayers rise like incense, my hands like an evening offering. 14

My shepherd is the Lord, nothing indeed shall I want. 34

My soul, give thanks to the Lord, and bless God's Holy Name. 73

My soul is thirsting for you, O Lord, thirsting for you my God. 55 56 57 1127 1155 1185

My soul rejoices in my God, my soul rejoices in my God. 998

O bless the Lord, my soul, O bless the Lord. 1014

O God, I seek you, my soul thirsts for you, your love is finer than life. 58

O God, O God, let all the nations praise you! 1078 1149 1212

O God, this is the people that longs to see your face. 37

O Lord, our God, how wonderful your name in all the earth! 1088

O praise the Lord, Jerusalem. 1089

One who does justice will live in the presence of the Lord. 1156

Open wide your gates; let the King of Glory in! 37

Our blessing-cup is a communion with the Blood of Christ. 78 79 80 1040

Our eyes are fixed on the Lord, pleading for his mercy. 1132

Our help comes from the Lord, the maker of heaven and earth. 83

Our help is from the Lord, who made heaven and earth. 1178

Out of the depths I cry to you, O Lord. 88

Padre, a tus manos encomiendo mi espíritu. 43

Praise the Lord, my soul! Praise the Lord! 1159 1169 1186

Praise the Lord, praise the Lord, who heals the broken-hearted.  1105

Praise the Lord, praise the Lord, who lifts up the poor.  1166

Proclaim his marvelous deeds to all the nations.  1097

Proclaim the greatness of God; rejoice in God, my Savior!  101

Proclaim to all the nations the marvelous deeds of the Lord!  67

Remember your mercies, O Lord.  38 1167

Rest in God alone, rest in God alone, my soul.  1113

Sacarán aguas con alegría de las fuentes de salvación.  98

Señor, que tu misericordia venga sobre nosotros.  44

Shepherd me, O God, beyond my wants, beyond my fears, from death into life.  35

Since my mother's womb, you have been my strength.  1199

Sing to the Lord a new song, for God has done wonderful deeds.  70

Sing to the Lord a new song, for he has done marvelous deeds.  1213

Sing with joy to God! Sing to God our help!  1117

Taste and see the goodness of the Lord.  45 46 156 1027 1147 1150 1153

Teach me your ways, O Lord, teach me your ways.  38 1099

The Almighty has done great things for me, and holy is his Name.  16

The angel of the Lord will rescue those who fear him.  1202

The earth is full of the goodness of the Lord, the goodness of the Lord.  44 1048

The hand of the Lord feeds us; he answers all our needs.  1141 1143

The just man is a light in darkness to the upright.  1104

The Lord comes to rule the earth with justice.  1190

The Lord comes to the earth to rule the earth with justice.  70

The Lord gave them bread from heaven.  1144

The Lord has done great things for us; we are filled with joy.  996 1030 1180

The Lord has revealed to the nations his saving power, his saving power.  1077 1175

The Lord has set his throne in heaven.  1081

The Lord hears the cry of the poor.  46 1181

The Lord hears the cry of the poor. Blessed be the Lord.  47

The Lord is kind and merciful, slow to anger and rich in compassion.  72 74 1161

The Lord is kind and merciful, the Lord is kind and merciful.  75 1024 1110 1112 1114

The Lord is king; he is robed in majesty.  1192

The Lord is king, the Lord Most High over all the earth.  1082 1204

The Lord Is My Light and my salvation.  121 1021 1098 1210

The Lord Is My Light and my salvation, of whom should I be afraid, of whom should I be afraid?  41

The Lord is my shepherd; nothing shall I fear.  36

The Lord is my shepherd, nothing shall I want: he leads me by safe paths, nothing shall I fear.  34

The Lord is my shepherd; there is nothing I shall want.  36 1025 1070 1094 1138 1191 1210

The Lord is near to all who call on him.  1164

The Lord remembers his covenant for ever.  1008

The Lord speaks of peace, peace, peace to his people.  1203

The Lord upholds my life.  1165

The Lord will bless his people with his peace.  1012

The Lord's kindness is everlasting to those who fear him.  1092

The precepts of the Lord give joy to the heart.  1168

The queen stands at your right hand, arrayed in gold.  1206

The seed that falls on good ground will yield a fruitful harvest.  1134

The son of David will live for ever.  1197

The stone rejected by the builders has become the cornerstone.  1071

The vineyard of the Lord is the house of Israel.  1170

The waters of the river gladden the city of God, the holy dwelling of the Most High.  1211

Their message goes out through all the earth.  1201

They who do justice will live in the presence of God!  28

This is the day the Lord has made; let us rejoice and be glad.  81 82 1065

Though I walk in the valley of darkness, I fear no evil, for you are with me.  1210

To the upright I will show the saving power of God.  1119

To you, O Lord, I lift my soul, to you I lift my soul.  39 40 993

Today is born our Savior, Christ the Lord.  68 69 1004

Turn to the Lord in your need, and you will live.  1136

We are God's people, the flock of the Lord.  71

We are his people, the sheep of his flock.  1072 1122

Who is this king of glory? It is the Lord!  1196

With joy you shall draw water from the springs of endless life; With joy you shall draw water from the living well of God.  97

With the Lord there is mercy and fullness of redemption.  87 143 1027 1120

You are a priest for ever, in the line of Melchizedek.  1091

You are my inheritance, O Lord.  30 1049 1130 1189

You will draw water joyfully from the springs of salvation.  98 1013 1052 1054 1093

You will show me the path of life, you, my hope and my shelter.  30

Your ways, O Lord, are love and truth to those who keep your covenant.  1017

Your words, O Lord, are Spirit and life.  1100 1136

# 1223 Index of Settings with Foreign Languages

# Index of Settings with Foreign Languages/*continued*

# Index of First Lines and Common Titles/*continued*

# Index of First Lines and Common Titles/*continued*

# Index of First Lines and Common Titles/*continued*

# Index of First Lines and Common Titles/*continued*

# Index of First Lines and Common Titles/*continued*

# Index of First Lines and Common Titles/*continued*

# Index of First Lines and Common Titles/*continued*

# Index of First Lines and Common Titles/*continued*

# Index of First Lines and Common Titles/*continued*